ANNUAL REVIEW OF PHYSIOLOGY

EDITORIAL COMMITTEE (1986)

ANNUAL REVIEW OF PHYSIOLOGY

VOLUME 48, 1986

ROBERT M. BERNE, *Editor*

University of Virginia Medical School

JOSEPH F. HOFFMAN, *Associate Editor*

Yale University School of Medicine

ANNUAL REVIEWS INC.   4139 EL CAMINO WAY   PALO ALTO, CALIFORNIA 94306

A̲R̲ ANNUAL REVIEWS INC.
    Palo Alto, California, USA

International Standard Serial Number: 0066–4278
International Standard Book Number: 0–8243–0348-2
Library of Congress Catalog Card Number: 39-15404

Typesetting by Kachina Typesetting Inc., Tempe, Arizona; John Olson, President
Typesetting coordinator, Janis Hoffman

PRINTED AND BOUND IN THE UNITED STATES OF AMERICA

Annual Review of Physiology
Volume 48, 1986

CONTENTS

viii   CONTENTS   *(continued)*

OTHER REVIEWS OF INTEREST TO PHYSIOLOGISTS

From the *Annual Review of Biochemistry,* Volume 55 (1986):

From the *Annual Review of Medicine,* Volume 37 (1986):

From the *Annual Review of Neuroscience,* Volume 9 (1986):

ANNUAL REVIEWS INC. is a nonprofit scientific publisher established to promote the advancement of the sciences. Beginning in 1932 with the *Annual Review of Biochemistry,* the Company has pursued as its principal function the publication of high quality, reasonably priced *Annual Review* volumes. The volumes are organized by Editors and Editorial Committees who invite qualified authors to contribute critical articles reviewing significant developments within each major discipline. The Editor-in-Chief invites those interested in serving as future Editorial Committee members to communicate directly with him. Annual Reviews Inc. is administered by a Board of Directors, whose members serve without compensation.

ANNUAL REVIEWS OF
Anthropology
Astronomy and Astrophysics
Biochemistry
Biophysics and Biophysical Chemistry
Cell Biology
Earth and Planetary Sciences
Ecology and Systematics
Energy
Entomology
Fluid Mechanics
Genetics
Immunology
Materials Science

Medicine
Microbiology
Neuroscience
Nuclear and Particle Science
Nutrition
Pharmacology and Toxicology
Physical Chemistry
Physiology
Phytopathology
Plant Physiology
Psychology
Public Health
Sociology

SPECIAL PUBLICATIONS
Annual Reviews Reprints:
Cell Membranes, 1975–1977
Cell Membranes, 1978–1980
Immunology, 1977–1979

Excitement and Fascination of Science, Vols. 1 and 2

History of Entomology

Intelligence and Affectivity, by Jean Piaget

Telescopes for the 1980s

For the convenience of readers, a detachable order form/envelope is bound into the back of this volume.

C. Ladd Prosser

Ann. Rev. Physiol. 1986. 48:001–06

THE MAKING OF A COMPARATIVE PHYSIOLOGIST

C. Ladd Prosser

Professor Emeritus, Department of Physiology and Biophysics, University of Illinois, 407 South Goodwin Avenue, Urbana, Illinois 61801

I spent my youth in Avon, a small town twenty miles south of Rochester, New York. There was frequent electric train service to the city, and opportunity to hike along the Genesee River and up and down the hills leading to western Finger Lakes and their outlets. My interest in nature was stimulated by weekly hikes with my father. Fossils were abundant in the slate and shale lining the many gullies. I started collecting insects with two pals with Blatchley's *Coleoptera*, and plants with Gray's *Botany* in the seventh grade. I majored in biology at the University of Rochester where a turning point in my career was a course in Physiological Psychology in which the text was Herrick's *Neurological Basis of Behavior*. During this course I decided that the neural basis of behavior could better be studied with invertebrates than with mammals. I went to The Johns Hopkins University for graduate study, and wrote a thesis on the physiology of the nervous system of earthworms. The summer after my first year there was spent as a research assistant to S. O. Mast at the Mount Desert Biological Station. My first published paper was on amoeboid movement (1). During that summer (1930) I was out at every low tide becoming acquainted with invertebrate animals.

Hopkins was a stimulating place; visitors to H. S. Jennings (protozoan genetics) and to S. O. Mast (protozoan physiology) included the geneticist T. H. Morgan from Columbia, cytologist C. E. McClung from the University of Pennsylvania, and general physiologists Newton Harvey of Princeton and L. V. Heilbrunn from the University of Pennsylvania. The summer of 1931 I spent taking the physiology course at the Marine Biological Laboratory in Woods Hole, where I learned much from the neurophysiologist Phillip Bard, respiration physiologists Lawrence Irving and A. C. Redfield, kineticist Leonor Michaelis, and membrane transport experts Merkel Jacobs and Rudolph Höber. It became evident to me that study of anatomy and ethophysiology of in-

1

0066-4278/86/0315-0001$02.00

vertebrate nervous systems had limitations, and that electrophysiological techniques were more likely to be useful in elucidating the neural basis of behavior.

I finished my PhD in the depth of the depression; there were no National Institute of Health (NIH) fellowships and the National Science Foundation (NSF) did not exist. Phillip Bard at Harvard Medical School helped me to obtain a Harvard postdoctoral fellowship (requiring celibacy) to study in the laboratory of Hallowell Davis. These were days before Tektronix or Hewlett-Packard: a row of relay racks housed separate power supplies, vertical amplifiers, sweep circuits, and stimulators, all to serve one five-inch oscilloscope. My first recording had been at Woods Hole with a string galvanometer. From Davis I learned the basic techniques of electrical recording and some of the physiology of hearing. The Harvard Medical School Physiology Department was an intellectually stimulating place, and afternoon tea provided an opportunity to become acquainted with Professor W. B. Cannon, Arturo Rosenblueth, Phillip Bard, Magnus Gregorsen, John Edsall, and others. I participated in the physiology laboratory for medical students, and Hal Davis encouraged me to test my ideas on invertebrate nervous systems. I recorded extracellularly from crayfish central nervous systems, and everything I observed was new. I produced four papers on crayfish nervous systems during my first year. The most significant discovery was that an isolated nervous system could produce rhythmic electrical activity in single units (2). This discovery dealt a blow to the behaviorist dictum that all patterned behavior must be initiated by sensory input. Another find was a light-sensitive ganglion in the crayfish abdomen (3). I frequently visited the Harvard Biological Laboratories, and there continued my zoological interests in discussions with G. H. Parker, B. F. Skinner, W. J. Crozier, and with collaboration with John Welsh.

After a year and a half at Harvard Medical School I went to England to work with Professor E. D. Adrian, who had recently published on electrical activity in insect nervous systems. I learned not only from him but from Joseph Barcroft, Brian Matthews, William Rushton, and others. On the day of my arrival Professor Adrian took me to meet Professor Barcroft who was up to his elbows in a bathtub of warm Locke solution in which rested an anesthetized sheep from which Barcroft was removing the fetus with circulation intact. It was apparent that everyone in a British laboratory, including the Professor, enjoyed research. I attended a course of lectures on neurophysiology by Adrian, who did not seem to enjoy student contacts. His laboratory had been occupied previously by Keith Lucas, and much of Lucas' equipment—rheotomes, induction coils, a maze of overhead wires—remained. In Adrian's laboratory we used Matthews oscillographs, magnetic devices that followed fast potential changes such as nerve spikes. Shortly before I arrived in England, the German neurologist Berger had announced that rhythmic electrical waves could be recorded from outside the skull of humans. I was a subject in Adrian's confirmation of what became known as alpha waves. During my stay at Cambridge I mapped sensory fields of segmental nerves of earthworms (4).

A high spot for me as a young American physiologist in England was attendance at the monthly meetings of the Physiological Society. Dale and Feldberg had recently presented evidence for acetylcholine as a transmitter in sympathetic ganglia; Eccles maintained that transmission was electrical, and the debates were memorable. Dale's training in British debate gave him an advantage over Eccles. The best assay for acetylcholine in a perfusate was contraction of a leech muscle, and I well remember Dale's account of the contraction of this muscle to demonstrate the presence of acetylcholine in the sweat from a sock fresh off the tennis court.

I asked Eccles if I might spend a few weeks with him and in early May I rode my bicycle from Cambridge to Oxford and worked as Eccles' associate on cat sympathetic ganglia. I heard Sherrington, the most famous of Oxford physiologists, give his last lecture to the medical students, and watched him demonstrate the motor cortex of a monkey. Sherrington impressed me as a thoughtful, modest man. Eccles had many interesting stories about Oxford neurophysiologists, especially the wealthy American John Fulton. John Z. Young had recently discovered the giant fiber system in squid. I biked back to Cambridge after a useful stay at Oxford. During the spring break I travelled to the Continent, where I visited several laboratories, including that of Monnier in the Sorbonne. At that time, Lapique's idea of isochronism between nerve and muscle was under attack by William Rushton. I had long talks with the Dutch neuroanatomist Ariens-Kappers and the German comparative neurophysiologist Hans Bethe.

On returning to America in August 1934, I found that academic positions were virtually nonexistent. I was fortunate to obtain a research appointment with Hudson Hoagland at Clark University. I was then married to Hazel Blanchard who was to be my most valuable supporter and strictest critic. We had met at the MBL in the summer of 1932, and she had then spent a year studying in von Frisch's Institute of Zoology in Munich before our marriage.

At Clark I observed the political astuteness of Hudson Hoagland. The most cited of my publications was with the psychologist Walter Hunter on extinction and dishabituation in spinal rats (5). Meanwhile, I continued on crayfish nervous systems and had some teaching experience. Each summer was spent at the MBL on the staff in Physiology. I learned much from Harry Grundfest, Kenneth (Kacy) Cole, and Otto Loewi. On the recommendation of the zoologist G. H. Parker of Harvard I was offered a post at the University of Illinois, where I arrived in 1939 on the day Hitler invaded Poland. The dean of the Graduate School, R. D. Carmichael, was very supportive. My job was to give a zoology course to agriculture students, and (at my insistence) I initiated courses in comparative and cellular physiology. Then came World War II. I spent one year on a chemical warfare project developing a test with freshwater fish for war gas contamination of water supplies. In the summer of 1943, I was asked by Kacy Cole and Howard Curtis to join them at the Metallurgical Laboratory of the Manhattan Project. This was a very responsible job; I directed the internal workings of a laboratory of some 150 biologists and chemists. This was a very exciting period because all of us who knew what was going on realized that success in the war depended on achievement of the atomic bomb. Near the end of the war, after the Alamogordo test, I joined a group of scientists who signed a petition to President Truman urging that the bomb be demonstrated on an uninhabited South Pacific island rather than on a city. I learned much about radiation biology, but after the war the opportunity to return to Illinois seemed to me better than to remain with the Atomic Energy Commission (AEC). The University of Illinois was expanding in all fields.

While in Chicago I wrote a review on invertebrate nervous systems for Ralph Gerard, editor of *Physiological Reviews* (6). At about that time I concluded that the speed of animal movement is limited more by muscles than by nervous systems. On returning to the MBL in the summers of 1947–1949 I concentrated on invertebrate nonstriated muscles, and collaborated with Howard Curtis (7). During the winters I worked with mammalian smooth muscle, and have continued to do so with a current interest in rhythmicity. In 1977 I wrote a chapter for the *Handbook of Physiology* on the evolution of smooth muscle in which I indicated there was no linear evolution but great diversity. That review (8) led to several symposia and a new functional classification of muscle. Transverse alignment of thick and thin filaments has evolved many times in wide-fibered muscle, and these have T-tubules for signal coupling over the hundred micron distance between cell membrane and contractile filaments. In narrow-fibered muscles, oval, ribbon-shaped or cylindrical coupling between membrane and filaments is direct over distances of a few microns.

Meanwhile, I investigated biochemical mechanisms of acclimation of fishes to cold and warm environments. Acclimatory responses include selective protein synthesis and change in saturation of membrane phospholipids, which affect membrane fluidity. Most recently, we have found acclimatory reorganization in cultured cells much as in intact fishes. Sequential alterations in central nervous functions bring about resistance adaptations (9).

While at Clark and in my first two years at Illinois, I developed a plan for a book on comparative physiology which would emphasize evolutionary and ecological applications of physiology. The idea of such a book appealed to the W. B. Saunders editor, and the first edition of *Comparative Animal Physiology* appeared in 1951. I had several collaborators and the book set the tone for comparative physiology for many years. A second edition came out in 1961 and a third edition in 1973 (10). I enjoyed treating adaptations of animals to various environments. Comparative physiology differs from other kinds of physiology in that the comparative approach uses the kind of organism as an experimental variable, and it emphasizes the long evolutionary history leading to life in diverse environments.

Early in the fifties I served on one of the first NSF panels, which included environmental, developmental, regulatory, molecular, and systematic biologists. This was the beginning for me of two decades of service on Washington committees. These included panels at the Office of Naval Research (ONR), several at NSF, NASA, and NIH. During this period I was active in several societies: Society of General Physiology (President 1958–59), American Society of Zoologists (President 1961), A.A.A.S. and American Physiological Society (President 1969–70); and in the mid-seventies the National Academy of Sciences (Chairman, Physiology Section 1977). Experience on these committees and councils was both rewarding and frustrating. In APS the education program was implemented; my effort to sectionalize the society was voted down by the membership, but adopted ten years later.

I was the Department Chairman of Physiology and Biophysics at Illinois from 1960 to 1969. For several years as we expanded the Department toward biophysics I learned much from my colleagues, especially Bernard (Bud) Abbott (muscle) and Robert Emerson (photosynthesis). A memorable semester was when Otto Warburg spent four months in the photosynthesis laboratory. Several of us designed a degree in physico-chemical biology, but this was soon replaced by the magical word "biophysics." During several summers I participated in training programs at Woods Hole, one with Steve Kuffler on neurophysiology, and a later one with Bud Abbott on comparative physiology. During this period I jealously protected my afternoons for research, and regularly took sabbatical leaves. The most notable were in Munich and Naples, and at Monash in Australia. I have worked at some ten marine laboratories, visited others, and made three cruises on the research vessel Alpha Helix.

Official retirement in 1975 freed me for research, editing, and writing. As I contemplate my fifty years as a comparative physiologist I note that despite the Depression the thirties were golden years for training, and I was fortunate to have constructive contact with many leaders in physiology. My early discoveries with invertebrate nervous systems, later ones on diverse nonstriated muscles, and more recent findings on the biochemical and neural mechanisms of temperature adaptations of fishes have kept my interests centered in laboratory research. Writing reviews and an advanced text (three editions) provided an opportunity to contribute to the theory of comparative physiology. Frequently, physiological generalizations are discovered better in the library than in the laboratory. My research could not have been accomplished without the forty doctoral and dozen postdoctoral students whose research I have directed. Contact with colleagues and administrative duties have been rewarding, but the greatest satisfaction has come from discovering new facts and functional relationships.

Literature Cited

1. Mast, S. O., Prosser, C. L. 1932. Effect of temperature, salts, and hydrogen-ion concentration on rupture of the phasmagel sheet, rate of locomotion, and gel/sol. ratio in *Amoeba proteus*. *JCCP* 1:333–54

2. Prosser, C. L. 1934. Action potentials in the nervous system of the crayfish. I. Spontaneous impulses. *J. Cell. Comp. Physiol.* 4:185–209

3. Prosser, C. L. 1934. II. Responses to illumination of the eye and caudal ganglion. *J. Cell. Comp. Physiol.* 4:363–77

4. Prosser, C. L. 1935. Impulses in the segmental nerves of earthworm. *J. Exp. Biol.* 12:95–104

5. Prosser, C. L., Hunter, W. S. 1936. The extinction of startle responses and spinal reflexes in the white rat. *Am. J. Physiol.* 117:609–18

6. Prosser, C. L. 1946. The physiology of nervous systems of invertebrate animals. *Physiol. Rev.* 26:337–82

7. Prosser, C. L., Curtis, H. J., Travis, D. M. 1951. Action potentials from some invertebrate non-striated muscles. *J. Cell. Comp. Physiol.* 38:299–320

8. Prosser, C. L. 1980. Evolution and diversity of nonstriated muscles. *Handbook of Physiology—The Cardiovascular System*, Vol. 2, Ch. 21, pp. 635–70. Bethesda, Md: Amer. Physiol. Soc.

9. Prosser, C. L., Nelson, D. O. 1981. The role of nervous systems in temperature adaptation of poikilotherms. *Ann. Rev. Physiol.* 43:281–300.

10. Prosser, C. L., ed. 1973. *Comparative Animal Physiology*. Philadelphia: Saunders. 1011 pp. 3rd ed.

RENAL AND ELECTROLYTE PHYSIOLOGY

RENAL CELL INTEGRITY AND REPAIR AFTER ISCHEMIC INJURY

Introduction, Carl W. Gottschalk, *Section Editor*

This year's Section on Renal and Electrolyte Physiology reflects the increased interest and research into the biochemical aspects of renal function. Each review concerns essential biochemical mechanisms basic to cell function and/or tubular transport.

Soltoff examines the dependence of several important renal functions on ATP and the interrelations between these functions and ATP production in the kidney. Since Na,K-ATPase plays a cardinal role in performing the work of the kidney, much of Soltoff's review is directed towards aspects of metabolic support of the renal sodium pump. Specific questions considered include: (*a*) what are the relative contributions to ATP synthesis from the heterogenous segments of the nephron; (*b*) how is the utilization of ATP apportioned among the various endergonic functions of the renal cell; (*c*) what is the quantitative dependence of the endergonic functions on ATP; (*d*) how is ATP compartmentalized within the renal cell; and (*e*) is there a common pool of ATP to support the diverse energy-requiring functions.

Jones considers renal metabolism during normoxia, hypoxia, and ischemic injury. He differentiates two general conditions in which there is an insufficient supply of oxygen to kidney cells. Simple hypoxia, in which there is anoxia but blood flow is unchanged, and stagnant hypoxia, in which blood flow is compromised and ischemia is the limiting condition. Renal ischemia is of major clinical interest because of its role in acute renal failure, whereas pathological

7

changes related to simple hypoxia have not been clearly defined. Jones discusses the response of the O_2-dependent enzymes to lack of oxygen, heterogeneity of subcellular oxygenation resulting from clusters of mitochrondria, and protection against ischemic injury by several diverse mechanisms.

Troyer, Schwertz, Kreisberg, and Venkatachalam consider inositol phospholipid (phosphoinositide) metabolism in the kidney. Although they are minor membrane lipids that comprise less than 5% of the total mass of cells, phosphoinositides function as a second messenger system. They are analogous in this regard to cyclic AMP. The authors first consider general aspects of phosphoinositide metabolism and how the products of stimulated phosphoinositide metabolism are related to transduction of extracellular signals across the plasma membrane. They then consider renal phosphoinositide metabolism. The study of renal phosphoinositides is relatively new, and less is known about phosphoinositide metabolism in the kidney than in other organs. However, Troyer et al point out that the complex physiological functions of the kidney and its responsiveness to a variety of hormones make this a promising area for future investigation.

Ann. Rev. Physiol. 1986. 48:9–31

ATP AND THE REGULATION OF RENAL CELL FUNCTION

Stephen P. Soltoff

Department of Physiology, Tufts University School of Medicine, Boston, Massachusetts 02111

INTRODUCTION

The importance of adenosine 5'-triphosphate (ATP) as the main provider of chemical energy in the cell is basic to cellular physiology, and the involvement of ATP in maintaining various cellular processes has been investigated in many diverse contexts since Lipmann (61) postulated the wide-ranging biological importance of the ATP-ADP couple. This article is an examination of the specific dependence of several important renal functions on ATP, and on the interrelationship between these functions and ATP production in the kidney. Due to the cardinal role that the Na,K-ATPase plays in performing the work of the kidney, much of this review is directed toward aspects involving the metabolic support of the renal sodium pump. Other transport and metabolic processes performed by the kidney also require ATP, and several of these will also be discussed, as will several effects of extracellular ATP.

Under steady-state conditions, the consumption of ATP by endergonic processes in the renal cell is matched by the production of ATP, resulting in the maintenance of a constant concentration of ATP within the cell. About 95% of the ATP in the kidney is supplied by oxidative metabolism (22, 63), and thus the renal mitochondria play an integral role in maintaining the energy-requiring processes of the kidney. From the renal rate of oxygen consumption (QO_2), which varies between 3 and 6 μmol O_2/min·g kidney for rat, dog, and rabbit (22, 89), and the assumption that 6 moles of ATP are produced by the mitochondria for every mole of O_2 consumed, it can be calculated that the ATP turnover in the kidney is 18–36 μmol ATP/min·g kidney. In this review several questions related to this synthesis will be considered, including: (*a*) what are the relative contributions to ATP synthesis from the heterogeneous segments of the

9

0066-4278/86/0315-0009$02.00

nephron; (b) how is the utilization of ATP apportioned among the various endergonic functions of the renal cell; (c) what is the quantitative dependence of the endergonic functions on ATP; (d) how is ATP compartmentalized within the renal cell; and (e) is there a common pool of ATP to support the diverse energy-requiring functions. The complete answers to these questions are not yet known, but the search for their answers involves areas of renal research that are presently being intensely investigated. Additional information concerning related aspects of renal transport and metabolism may be found in several recent reviews (22, 35, 56, 78).

UTILIZATION OF ATP BY THE RENAL CELL

Dependence of Sodium Transport on Oxidative Metabolism: The interrelationship between the Na,K-ATPase and the mitochondria

The maintenance of intracellular ion gradients is dependent on cellular metabolism in both glycolytic and aerobic tissues. In mammalian red blood cells (which lack mitochondria), active ion transport was demonstrated to be closely correlated with glycolysis (40, 62). In epithelia, the interrelationship between oxidative metabolism and active ion transport has been well established. In 1956, Zerahn (104) reported that there was a linear relationship between active sodium transport and the rate of oxygen consumption (QO_2) in frog skin, and presciently calculated that three sodium ions were transported for every ATP produced by oxidative phosphorylation. Similar calculations were later applied to determine the stoichiometry of the sodium pump, which was as yet undiscovered when Zerahn performed his studies. A linear relationship was subsequently observed by others using renal tissue (65, 89, 90), and provided information regarding the stoichiometry and mechanism of coupling between oxidative phosphorylation and active sodium transport (for review see 63).

The Na,K-ATPase, the biochemical equivalent of the sodium pump, is now perceived to play the central role in directing the ion transport activity of the kidney (52, 53). It directs the transepithelial transport of sodium and potassium across the cell, as well as the secondary active transport of other solutes, through its establishment of a sodium gradient across the membrane. The Na,K-ATPase is localized in the basolateral membrane of the renal cell, and the transport of three sodium ions and two potassium ions in opposite directions across the membrane is coupled to the hydrolysis of one molecule of ATP (52, 53).

Several groups have measured the heterogeneity of Na,K-ATPase activity along the nephron. The absolute rates of activity determined in the different studies vary, but the characterizations of the relative distribution are generally similar (32, 55). When normalized to tubule length, the activity is highest in the distal convoluted tubule, thick ascending limb of Henle's loop, and the proximal convoluted tubule (see Figure 1). The lowest activity was measured in the thin limb, and intermediate levels of activity were present in the collecting duct and proximal straight tubule. Moreover, there is a direct relationship between

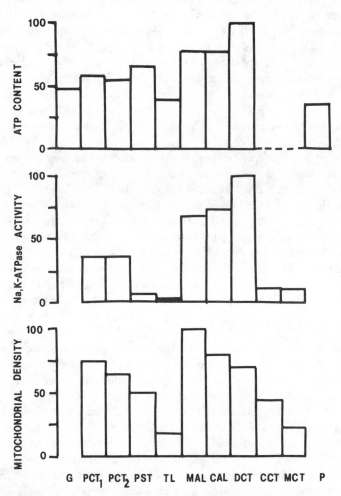

Figure 1 Comparison of several parameters measured in the rat nephron. All values are normalized to the highest values in the nephron, as follows: ATP content, 16.8 mmol/kg dry wt (12); Na,K-ATPase, 6679 pmol/mm·hr (55); mitochondrial density, 44% mitochondrial volume as a percentage of cytosolic volume (73). Abbreviations: G, glomerulus; PCT, proximal convoluted tubule (1 = early, 2 = late); PST, proximal straight tubule; TL, thin limb; MAL, medullary thick ascending limb; CAL, cortical thick ascending limb; DCT, distal convoluted tubule; CCT, cortical collecting tubule; MCT, medullary collecting tubule; P, papilla.

net sodium reabsorption and Na,K-ATPase activity for the various segments of the nephron (32).

The parallel alterations observed between the QO_2 and sodium transport suggest that the rate of ATP production by the mitochondria is tightly coupled to the rate of ATP consumption by the active transport mechanism, the sodium pump. Whittam and coworkers postulated that an obligatory coupling exists between the Na,K-ATPase activity and the rate of mitochondrial oxygen consumption, such that the former serves as the pacemaker for cellular respiration (6, 100). ATP and the products of its hydrolysis, ADP and inorganic phosphate (P_i), were postulated to be the cytosolic mediators between the transport enzyme in the basolateral membrane and the ATP synthesis machinery in the mitochondria. The precise mechanism by which cellular metabolism is regulated (e.g. the ATP/ADP or ATP/ADP·P_i ratios, the ADP concentration) continues to be debated (see 25, 88). Inhibition and stimulation of sodium pump activity was accompanied by an increase and decrease, respectively, in the ATP/ADP ratio in a suspension of rabbit proximal tubules (4). In rabbit proximal tubules it was also observed that the QO_2 and active transport (ouabain-sensitive ^{42}K uptake) varied in parallel between 15 and 37°C, producing similar molar ratios of potassium transported per O_2 consumed. This suggests that (at least in this preparation) the link between oxidative metabolism and ion transport remains tightly coupled within this temperature range (86). However, low temperatures (15°C) produced an increase in the K^+/O_2 ratio in renal cortical slices of rabbit and other species (101). The differences between the two studies may be due to methodological differences or to diffusional limitations of ions and oxygen, which can affect slice preparations.

Other Ion-Sensitive ATPases

In addition to the Na,K-ATPase, other ion-sensitive ATPases have been associated with several compartments of the kidney. However, the parallel relationship between ion transport activity and ATP hydrolysis that is found for the Na,K-ATPase has not yet been established for these ATPases.

Calcium reabsorption occurs in several portions of the nephron. Although the majority of the reabsorption is believed to be passive, there is also evidence for active calcium reabsorption (44, 70). In the proximal convoluted tubule, the net calcium flux rate was 7% of the net sodium flux (28). Several transport systems have been implicated in transepithelial calcium transport, and in the maintenance of intracellular calcium homeostasis, including Na^+-Ca^{2+} exchange and a Ca-ATPase (28, 44, 64, 102). Ca-ATPases of both high and low calcium affinity have been found in the kidney. A low affinity Ca-ATPase that was localized in the basolateral plasma membrane was reported by Kinne-Saffran & Kinne (58). The distribution of a low affinity Ca-ATPase along the rabbit nephron was described by Katz & Doucet (54). The enzyme was maximally stimulated by 5 mM calcium ($K_m \approx 1$ mM) or 1–4 mM magnesium, and ATP concentrations of 2–7.5 mM were required for maximal activity. The activity was composed of a mitochondrial component and a plasma membrane component, which was distributed along the nephron in a different pattern from the Na,K-ATPase. The total low-affinity Ca-ATPase in each segment was generally between 20 and 50% of the Na,K-ATPase activity.

A high affinity Ca-ATPase (K_m for calcium = 0.1–0.2 μM) was identified in purified basolateral membrane vesicles from rat renal cortex, and the activity was about 5% as large as the Na,K-ATPase activity (33). High affinity Ca-ATPase activity was found in all segments of the rabbit nephron (23). The activity was generally less than 10% of the Na,K-ATPase, required about 6 mM ATP for maximal activity, and (unlike the low affinity enzyme) had an absolute requirement for magnesium. Presumably the enzyme with high calcium affinity is involved in transepithelial calcium transport, since it is activated by physiological concentrations of calcium. The calcium transport capacity of the high-affinity Ca-ATPase was reported to be four- to fivefold larger than the Na^+-Ca^{2+} exchange mechanism in basolateral membrane vesicles (44). Moreover, it was estimated that this Ca-ATPase could quantitatively account for most of the unidirectional transepithelial calcium fluxes measured in the different nephron segments (23).

Mg-ATPase activity is present in all segments of the nephron, except perhaps the thin limb of Henle's loop (32, 55). In the proximal convoluted tubule, medullary thick ascending limb, and distal convoluted tubule, the three segments of the rabbit nephron which have the highest Na,K-ATPase activity, the Mg-ATPase activity is 50–80% of the Na,K-ATPase activity; and in other segments the Mg-ATPase activity is larger than the Na,K-ATPase (55). These proportions may vary with different species, but the Mg-ATPase makes up a substantial portion of the total ATPase activity along the rat, rabbit, and mouse nephron (32, 55). In a brush border preparation from rabbit kidney cortex, two populations of Mg-ATPase could be distinguished: one associated with the luminal membrane and one originating from mitochondrial membranes (14, 59). Bicarbonate was reported to stimulate the Mg-ATPase activity of the brush border enzyme (59). A Mg-ATPase purified from sheep kidney medulla was activated by a variety of divalent and trivalent cations (30), and displayed a biphasic affinity for ATP (31). It is not clear whether any of these Mg-ATPases is an ion pump. The bicarbonate-stimulated Mg-ATPase in the proximal luminal membrane may function as a H^+ pump, since ATP hydrolysis and H^+ secretion were observed in brush border vesicles prepared from rat kidney cortex (57). However, a similar Mg-ATPase activity associated with red cell membranes was shown to have no ion pumping activity (27).

It is difficult to estimate the degree to which ATPases other than the Na,K-ATPase contribute to the ATP turnover of the cell. Although various kinetic parameters of these enzymes are known, our lack of knowledge about the function of the ATPases and measurements of their activity in intact cells makes it difficult to quantitate the specific energetic demand that they make on the renal cell.

Other ATP-Dependent Cellular Processes

In addition to ion transport, there are many cellular processes that require energy and are supported by oxidative metabolism. Recent studies suggest that between 40–50% of the renal QO_2 is utilized for the support of basal metabolism (41, 79). This proportion was estimated by inhibiting transepithelial sodium transport, and thus this value may also include the metabolic support of transport systems other than the sodium pump. Far less is known in quantitative terms about the support of basal processes than about the support of sodium transport. Other endergonic processes include the synthesis and interconversions of substrates; phosphorylation reactions (e.g. protein kinases), which use ATP; fatty acid metabolism; protein synthesis and degradation; and the energy required for the maintenance of the structural aspects of renal cells.

The Role of ATP in Ischemic Damage

Alterations in the adenine nucleotide pool, particularly ATP, and the subsequent cellular damages that occur during ischemia have been characterized by many investigators in renal and other tissue. After one minute of ischemia, whole kidney ATP content was decreased by 70%, ADP levels were reduced by 13%, and AMP and inorganic phosphate levels were increased by 77 and 270%, respectively (45). With longer durations (10 min), ATP (measured by ^{31}P-NMR) decreased to less than 10% of the control level (80). Ischemia is accompanied by the loss of ion transport functions, as well as structural damage to membranes, which is characterized in the early stages of ischemia by the loss of brush border in the proximal convoluted tubule (49, 81, 96). Although alterations in the cellular content of ATP are associated with the alterations in structure and function, it is still uncertain whether ATP depletion plays the causal role in cell injury (see 97). During extended ischemic episodes there is a decrease in the pool of adenine nucleotides. The duration of ATP depletion and the loss of additional components of the adenine nucleotide pool may determine the reversibility of cellular damage. Impermeant nucleotides may be converted to permeant nucleosides, and the loss of purine precursors of ATP may prevent the return to normal ATP levels at the conclusion of the ischemic period. Post-ischemic infusions of ATP-$MgCl_2$ produced faster recovery of ATP levels in ischemic rat kidneys (80), and also enhanced the recovery of tubular function and histology (2, 81). Siegel et al (80) attributed the accelerated recovery of the ATP content to accelerated synthesis of nucleotide precursors in the renal cell, and not to the direct entry of infused ATP into the cell. The controversy over whether or not ATP can cross the renal plasma membrane is noted in the next section. Although maintenance of high levels of ATP is doubtlessly necessary for cellular integrity, cellular damage following the diminishment of ATP may involve numerous events, including alterations in pH, calcium, membrane protein phosphorylation, and membrane phospholipase activity (26, 48), thus a single cause for cell damage is difficult to establish. At the level of the Na,K-ATPase, apart from the effect that a decrease in ATP has on the activity of the sodium pump, a decrease in the intracellular pH and/or an increase in inorganic phosphate during ischemia would further decrease the activity of the Na,K-ATPase due to the pH dependence of the inhibitory effect of inorganic phosphate (46).

The effects of an insufficient energy supply on the structural integrity of the kidney were demonstrated by Brezis et al (10). The development of hypoxic lesions in the medullary thick ascending limb (mTAL) in the isolated rat kidney was more extensive when polyene antibiotics, which increase the ionic permeability of membranes and thereby stimulate ion transport activity, were added to the perfusion medium. The addition of ouabain prior to the antibiotics blocked the damage entirely, demonstrating that the damage was promoted by the stimulated transport activity rather than the membrane alterations produced by the antibiotics. Thus, the cellular damage appeared to be correlated with the demand for oxygen (and ATP), which is insufficiently met in this preparation under normal conditions, and this demand was intensified when the transport activity was increased. These results demonstrate the contribution of ATP to maintaining the structural integrity of the cell, and the susceptibility of the mTAL to cell death when the availability of oxygen is insufficient.

Effects of Extracellular ATP

In addition to the various biological processes that are regulated by intracellular ATP, extracellular ATP has been reported to promote many diverse effects, including alterations of carbohydrate metabolism, ionic permeability, cell volume, tissue adenine nucleotide content, and renal circulation. In seemingly contradictory reports, ATP was observed to dilate renal blood vessels of dogs (43), as well as to increase renal vascular resistance in rats (98). The vasodilatory action of ATP is similar to the well-known vasodilatory activity of adenosine in cardiac circulation (5). This might be expected, since ATP added to rat cortical slices was found to be metabolized to adenosine (19), as well as to ADP and AMP (19, 77, 98). ATP added to perfused rabbit kidneys stimulated the biosynthesis and release of prostaglandins (68), which may also affect renal circulation.

The addition of ATP to the basolateral bathing solution of cultured Madin-Darby canine kidney (MDCK) cells was reported to stimulate chloride secretion, which was inhibited by furosemide (84). In rabbit cortical tubules suspended in 2.5 mM calcium, the addition of 4 mM ATP increased the tissue calcium content by about 200%; and in tubules suspended in low ($<$ 0.1 mM) calcium, ATP produced large increases in tissue water, sodium, and calcium (77). These effects were attributed to alterations in the physical properties of the tubule membrane and/or changes in membrane permeability. ATP has also been observed to promote alterations in ion fluxes and to increase the nucleotide permeability of the plasma membrane of various nonrenal cultured cells (for example see 99).

In rat kidney cortical slices and in isolated perfused rat kidneys, the addition of 2.5–5 mM ATP had the following effects on metabolism (98): (*a*) gluconeogenesis from lactate was inhibited; (*b*) the rate of glucose uptake from the medium was increased; (*c*) the cellular content of ATP, ADP, and AMP was increased; and (*d*) there was no significant effect on QO_2. The effects on carbohydrate metabolism were attributed to the increased level of intracellular AMP, which has an allosteric regulatory effect on glycolytic and gluconeogenic enzymes. In rabbit cortical slices, ATP concentrations larger than 1 mM were reported to inhibit QO_2, reduce glucose oxidation, and increase acetate oxidation (67). Also, 5 mM extracellular ATP was reported to increase the ATP content of rat and rabbit cortical slices (67, 74). The effects of the post-ischemic addition of ATP on the cellular ATP content were noted above.

Although ATP crosses the mitochondrial membrane, a transport event mediated by the adenine nucleotide translocase and which occurs in exchange for ADP, the passage of ATP across the plasma membrane is not unequivocally accepted. Data in support of and contrary to this possibility have been reported (for reviews see 11 and 18). Radiolabeled ATP, ADP, and AMP appeared to be taken up and concentrated in rat cortical slices, and their uptake was inhibited by probenecid (67). This suggested that adenine nucleotides may be taken up by the organic anion transport system, which is localized in the basolateral membrane of the proximal tubule. However, it should be pointed out that kidney slices have collapsed lumens, thus restricting luminal entry, as well as restricting ion transport in general. At concentrations below 3 mM, the uptake of ATP from the luminal medium of rabbit ileum displayed saturation uptake kinetics, which suggests that cellular entry occurred through a carrier-mediated system (39). The uptake of adenosine by the ileum was also nonlinear, and the entry of ATP and adenosine appeared to be mutually inhibitory, which suggests a common carrier for both compounds (39). In renal tissue the uptake of ATP was found to be a saturable process ($K_{0.5}$ = 0.3 mM) in brush border membrane vesicles prepared from rabbit proximal tubules (24); a saturable adenosine transport system was found in both luminal and basolateral membrane vesicles isolated from rat renal cortex (92).

It is apparent that multiple events can be promoted by extracellular ATP. The cellular mechanisms by which these effects are manifested are not all recognized. Since extracellular ATP is extensively metabolized (19, 77, 98), it is possible that, at least in some instances, a metabolite of ATP may account for some of the actions attributed to ATP. Additional studies will be necessary to clarify whether ATP is in fact the moiety directly responsible for these effects.

ATP SYNTHESIS IN THE KIDNEY

Heterogeneity of Mitochondrial Energy Production in the Kidney

As might be expected on the basis of the differences in the transport activity along the nephron, the distribution of mitochondria also varies. As measured by stereoscopic analysis (73), the density of mitochondrial volume (mitochondrial volume per unit volume of cytoplasm) decreases from 33% to 22% along the proximal tubule (see Figure 1). Along the distal portion of the nephron it decreases from 44%, its highest level (found in the medullary thick ascending limb), to 31% in the distal convoluted tubule. The density in the thin limbs is only 6–8%, and the collecting tubule has about 20 and 10% in the cortical and medullary segments, respectively. Since aerobic metabolism supplies the majority of the energy for renal work, it is appropriate that the greatest proportion of mitochondria are present in the segments of the kidney in which active transport is expected to require the greatest support. Moreover, the distribution of the surface density (membrane area per unit volume of cyto-plasm) of the mitochondrial inner membrane, which makes up the cristae responsible for the production of ATP by oxidative phosphorylation, is quite similar to that of the mitochondrial density and the basolateral membrane surface density (membrane area per unit volume of cytoplasm) (73). Using the amount of mitochondrial cristae membrane surface and calculating the number of membrane respiratory chain units and their consumption of O_2, Pfaller (71) estimated an upper limit for the rate of ATP formation in the different segments of the nephron. Proximal segments synthesized 14.2 μmol ATP/min, the thick limb and distal segments together produced 5.9 μmol/min, and the contribution from the remaining portions of the nephron was less than 1 μmol/min. The sum for the entire kidney was 21.0 μmol/min, which compares favorably with the rate of 18–36 μmol/min estimated from the rates of oxygen consumption of the kidney (see Introduction).

Distribution of ATP in Different Segments of the Nephron

In several studies the intracellular concentration of ATP in kidney cells was estimated to be about 2 mM (20, 50, 93). Many estimates of the quantitation of ATP in the kidney suffered from complications caused by the rapid depletion of ATP during sampling procedures and problems inherent in various prepara-tions, e.g. anoxic cores present in tissues slices due to diffusional limitations of oxygen (see 63). Measurements of the relative distribution of ATP in various regions of the nephron were also complicated by an averaging effect from samples that contained multiple types of segments. In one study, the rat renal medulla was found to contain about 28% less ATP than the cortex (12); however, another study found that the ATP content was uniformly distributed in rat cortical and medullary slices (69). The ATP content in slices of rat renal papilla was reported to be about 75% of that found in either cortical or medullary slices (83). Burch et al (13) employed fluorometric assay techniques on microdissected segments obtained from quick-frozen rat kidney, and noted a variation in the distribution of ATP (see Figure 1). The ATP content was lowest in the papilla ($\cong 6.1$ mmol/kg dry wt) and the thin limb (6.7), and highest in the distal convoluted tubule (16.8) and thick ascending limb (13.0). Intermediate levels (9.3–11.4) were found in the proximal portions. It should be noted that a different relative distribution would be obtained if the ATP values were normalized to tubule length, the unit in which ion flux and ATPase activities are frequently presented, since the ratio of dry weight/tubule length can vary up to threefold for different nephron segments (95). Also, the range of values reported for the ATP content of rabbit proximal tubules in suspension is similar to that of the rabbit medullary thick ascending limb (see Table 1), and did not display the segmental differences depicted in Figure 1. This may be due to differences between the two species (rat vs. rabbit), or to the fact that different types of preparations were used (rapid freezing and microdissection vs. tubule suspension).

Compartmentation of ATP Within the Renal Cell

Since most of the cellular ATP is made in the mitochondria and is transported to the cytoplasm by the adenine nucleotide translocase in exchange for ADP, adenine nucleotides are found in both the mitochondrial and extramitochondrial (cytosolic) compartments. Digitonin, a detergent which selectively permeabilizes cholesterol-containing membranes (e.g. the plasma membrane), was employed to separate the mitochondrial and cytosolic compartments in liver cells (1). The metabolites in the two compartments were separated by centrifuging digitonin-treated cells through an oil layer, since the aqueous cytosolic compartment remained above the oil. In a recent report by Pfaller et al (72), the digitonin fractionation procedure was modified for renal tissue, and was combined with quantitative morphological analysis in order to determine the absolute concentrations of ATP in both compartments of rat proximal tubules. The ATP concentrations were 4.33 mM in the cytosolic compartment and 2.62 mM in the mitochondrial space, and the distribution of the total cellular ATP content was 70% and 30%, respectively. Similar distributions of ATP content were observed using the digitonin procedure for isolated hepatocytes (1). The added dimension of the morphometric analysis provides an increased opportunity for understanding regulatory aspects of cellular processes. It would be of great interest to obtain additional information regarding the distribution of ADP, AMP, and other metabolites within the intracellular compartment, as well as whether cytosolic adenine nucleotide concentrations vary greatly in different renal segments.

ALTERATIONS IN THE PRODUCTION OF ATP

Under steady-state conditions, the rate of ATP production is equal to the rate of ATP utilization, and the ATP concentration remains constant. In considering the degree to which a cell can support ATP-dependent functions, not only is the absolute concentration of ATP of interest, but the rate of ATP production is of prime importance. Three ways that the renal cell has been observed to respond to alterations in the demand for ATP are discussed below. One response, an increase in the rate of ATP production, was observed when the rate of active transport was increased. Another response, an increase in the rate of glycolysis or substrate level phosphorylation, was reported to supply ATP when oxidative metabolism was reduced by hypoxia or mitochondrial inhibitors. A third response was an alteration in the way in which the relative distribution of ATP utilization is shifted from one endergonic process to another without necessarily altering the net consumption of ATP, and involved the competition for a constant pool of ATP.

Mitochondrial Respiratory Reserve

In the kidney and various other aerobic tissues the stimulation of sodium transport results in the stimulation of oxygen consumption, and the inhibition of transport reduces the QO_2. The role that ATP and ADP play in linking the Na,K-ATPase activity to mitochondrial oxidative metabolism is outlined above. Two questions of interest concerning the bioenergetics of the renal cell are, (a) what is the maximal rate of ATP production, and (b) what proportion of this capacity is utilized to meet the normal requirements of cellular functions. In the segments of the kidney that normally depend on oxidative metabolism, these questions can best be viewed in the context of the classical mitochondrial respiratory states (16). In state 3, the phosphorylating activity of the mitochondria is maximal, and is measured by the QO_2 of mitochondria exposed to a saturating concentration of ADP. In state 4 the mitochondria perform nonphosphorylating respiration. Using a suspension of rabbit proximal tubules, Harris et al (41) observed that the normal rate of tubular respiration in the presence of NADH-linked substrates and fats was about 60% of the state 3 rate. When the Na,K-ATPase activity of the tubules was increased by increasing the intracellular sodium concentration by the addition of a cationophore (nystatin), the QO_2 increased to the full state 3 rate. Under this condition, the Na,K-

ATPase activity was limited by the rate of ATP production, and the ATP content was reduced. In the presence of ouabain the QO_2 declined to a level of about 30% of the state 3 rate. Thus, under normal conditions about 30% $(60-30 = 30)$ of the maximal capacity for ATP production was utilized to support the Na,K-ATPase, and about an equivalent amount was used for basal metabolic processes and nonphosphorylating respiration. Therefore, the proximal tubule has the reserve capacity to meet the energetic requirements created by a large increase in sodium transport and, presumably, by the stimulation of other ATP-dependent processes. These results depended on there being no limitation in the delivery of oxygen or metabolic substrates to the mitochondria. Exposure of the proximal tubule to short chain fatty acids enhanced the delivery of reducing equivalents to the mitochondria when the sodium pump was stimulated (41).

Estimates of the maximal rate of ATP production from empirical measurements of the QO_2 of the rabbit proximal tubule and the medullary thick ascending limb are shown in Table 1, along with several other related parameters. In the presence of butyrate, a short chain fatty acid, the nystatin-stimulated QO_2 was much larger for mTAL than for proximal tubules. Thus, the maximal rates of ATP production (calculated assuming a P:O of 3) were about 275 and 630 nmol ATP/mg protein·min for the proximal and medullary segments, respectively, under conditions in which the availability of metabolic substrates was not limiting. In the presence of glucose as the sole metabolic substrate the energy available for the support of the mTAL was also much greater than that for the proximal tubule, due to the relative distribution of glycolytic enzymes in the two segments (78, 95). The normal turnover of the ATP pool can be calculated from the QO_2 and the ATP content of the tubules. For the proximal tubule a QO_2 of 25 nmol O_2/mg protein·min represents the production (and consumption) of 150 nmol ATP/mg protein·min. Thus, if the ATP content is 8 nmol/mg protein, the ATP content completely turns over once every 3.2 seconds. A similar turnover can be calculated for the ATP pool of the mTAL. This suggests that if the synthesis of ATP is completely inhibited, the ATP content of these cells will be depleted within several seconds. This assumes several conditions, as follows: (a) the endergonic work functions continue at their normal rate until the ATP is completely gone, and (b) all the ATP is produced by oxidative phosphorylation. The first assumption is probably not true. In a situation in which the ATP production is completely inhibited, the sodium pump activity would diminish as the ATP content was reduced (see below), thus lengthening the time that it would take for the cytosolic ATP to be completely consumed. In fact, when FCCP (carbonylcyanide-p-trifluoromethoxyphenylhdyrazone), which uncouples mitochondrial oxidative phosphorylation, was added to a suspension of rabbit proximal tubules, the ATP content decreased only 50% within about 18 seconds (S. P. Soltoff & L. J.

Table 1 Bioenergetic parameters of rabbit proximal tubules and medullary thick ascending limb tubules in suspension

Tubule type	Substrate*	QO_2 (nmol O_2/mg prot·min)			Maximum rate of ATP synthesis** (nmol/mg prot·min)	ATP content (nmol/mg prot)	Na,K-ATPase (nmol P_i/mg prot·min)	References
		Normal	Nystatin	Ouabain				
Proximal	G, L, A, B	26	46	12	276	6.4–8.8	277	37, 41, 86
	G	16	22	10	132			
mTAL	G, B	35	105	19	630	6.2–8.1	578	15, M. E. Chamberlin and L. J. Mandel, in press.
	G	30	65	16	390			

*G, glucose; L, lactate; A, alanine; B, butyrate
**Calculated from the nystatin-stimulated QO_2, assuming $ATP/O_2 = 6$

Mandel, unpublished observations). Aspects of the second consideration are discussed below.

Energetic Contributions of Nonoxidative ATP Production

The glycolytic enzymes of the kidney are largely distributed along the latter portion of the nephron, and the proximal tubule has relatively low rates of glycolytic activity (78, 95). When lactate production was measured in isolated segments of the rat nephron, proximal tubules did not produce any measurable lactate (3). However, measurable amounts were produced by all distal segments, and production was increased when oxidative metabolism was inhibited by antimycin A (3). Therefore, when aerobic metabolism is restricted, anaerobic glycolysis may contribute substantially to the production of ATP in these segments. During the first 30 seconds of ischemia the production of lactate was much larger in the medulla than in the cortex, and the ATP levels in the rat kidney declined much more rapidly (65–75%) in cortical slices than in medullary slices (19–33%) (69). Similarly, after one minute of ischemia, the ATP content was only slightly reduced in rat renal papilla, but the ATP in the cortex declined to about one-third the control level (50). Apparently, glycolysis was able to buffer the rate of ATP decline in the medullary and papillary tissue. Gronow & Cohen (34) reported that the reduction in the fractional reabsorption of sodium in rat kidneys perfused with hypoxic solutions was lessened when glucose or α-ketoglutarate was added to the substrate-free perfusion medium. This suggests that ATP produced by anaerobic glycolysis and by the anaerobic mitochondrial oxidation of α-ketoglutarate to succinate (22) may partially support renal function when oxidative metabolism is limited. However, Wittner et al (103) reported that although glucose could support transepithelial transport (measured by the short circuit current) in perfused segments of rabbit cortical thick ascending limb, it was unable to do so when oxidative metabolism was inhibited by cyanide. Thus, glycolysis does not appear to be sufficient to maintain active NaC1 reabsorption in this segment.

Competition Between Cellular Processes for ATP

The linear relationship between the rate of oxygen consumption and transepithelial transport in the kidney suggests that basal metabolism is invariant, and that the energetic support is varied in proportion to the work of transport. The extrapolation of such experiments to the point of zero transport activity has been used to identify the energetic cost of basal metabolism. This has given rise to the view that basal metabolism is very low, between 3–18% of the normal metabolic rate of the kidney (22). However, other studies suggest that the energetic demand of basal processes is as much as 50% of the total demand for ATP (41, 79). Thus, a point of interest is whether there may be a common cytosolic pool of ATP for the various endergonic activities in the cell, and whether there is competition for ATP between the transport and nontransport functions.

One paradigm that has been widely examined in this regard is the relationship between gluconeogenesis, an ATP-dependent process (depending on the metabolic substrate), and sodium transport in the proximal tubule. Gluconeogenesis is primarily localized in the proximal tubule, as evidenced by the fact that the activity of its key regulatory enzymes is much greater in this segment than in any other segment (78, 95). In perfused rat kidneys, no alterations in the QO_2 were observed when sodium transport was increased by increasing the perfusion pressure, and a decrease in gluconeogenesis was noted (82). The energy saved by the reduction of glucose formation appeared to be applied toward the sodium transport activity, such that no changes in oxidative metabolism occurred. Similarly, in cortical tubules isolated from rat kidney, ouabain was found to stimulate gluconeogenesis, which suggests that the energy saved from the reduction in transport was available to support glucose production (29). The conclusion from these and other experiments is that these two ATP-dependent processes compete for ATP, and that the inhibition or stimulation of one process produces the converse effect in the other. Other studies also suggest that basal metabolism is not a fixed quantity, and that large increases in transport activity can be energetically paid by borrowing from basal metabolism. Thus, when the activity of the sodium pump of the proximal tubule was doubled by the addition of nystatin, the gluconeogenic rate was greatly inhibited (36); and when potassium was added to tubules suspended in potassium-free media, it was suggested from estimations of the K^+/O_2 stoichiometry that a substantial portion of the basal QO_2 was directed to support the stimulated activity of the sodium pump (87).

The simplicity of the interaction between transport and gluconeogenesis is in conflict with several findings reported in rabbit proximal tubules (36), as follows: (a) the stimulation of gluconeogenesis, up to 200%, by the addition of various substrates did not alter the rate of fluid reabsorption (J_v); (b) under some conditions, a decrease in gluconeogenesis was produced by concentrations of ouabain that were sufficient to inhibit the sodium pump; and (c) the inhibition of gluconeogenesis by 3-mercaptopicolinate produced a reduction in J_v. The differences in observations reported in the literature may be due to the availability of substrates in various preparations. Under normal conditions, in which the renal (proximal) tubule possesses sufficient capacity for ATP synthesis, the energy required for gluconeogenesis is at most 5% of the total energetic demand, and the renal cell appears to be able to supply sufficient energy for both ATP-dependent processes (36). However, under conditions in which ATP production may be insufficient, due to a substrate limitation or to nonphysiological increases in the rate of sodium transport, an inverse relationship may develop between transport and other ATP-dependent processes.

In the perfused rat kidney, substrates (glycine, inositol) used by the kidney for ATP-consuming biosynthetic work did not maintain tissue potassium levels as well as substrates that entered the glycolytic pathway or the tricarboxylic acid cycle, in which they could be used to produce ATP (21). Therefore, in this preparation, which is substrate-limited, there appears to be competition for ATP between biosynthesis and cellular activities which maintain the potassium content (i.e. the Na,K-ATPase or processes responsible for maintaining the membrane permeability to potassium).

Quantitative Relationship Between Active Transport and ATP

Although the linear dependence of net sodium reabsorption on the rate of oxygen consumption suggests that active sodium transport is supported by ATP, quantitative studies have provided equivocal results. In amphibian urinary bladder (38), mammalian whole kidney (91, 94), and mammalian kidney slices (66), alterations in sodium transport were not correlated with alterations of adenine nucleotide levels, which suggests that ATP did not play a role in the link between cell metabolism and transport (for review see 56). However, in a recent study it was demonstrated that concentrations of rotenone and antimycin A that maximally inhibited oxidative phosphorylation in a suspension of rabbit proximal tubules also completely inhibited net fluid reabsorption in isolated perfused proximal tubules (37). The reasons for the conflicting results may have to do with methodological limitations (e.g. diffusional limitations of substrates and oxygen) of different preparations and with sampling problems due to the rapid turnover of ATP (56, 63).

On the other hand, the role of ATP (actually, the Mg-ATP complex) as the energetic substrate for the Na,K-ATPase has been well established, although several other nucleotides may also support the hydrolytic activity of the enzyme (85). In studies of renal tissue performed using purified enzyme or homogenized material, the $K_{0.5}$ for ATP ranged between 0.22 and 0.8 mM (7, 17, 51, 60, 76). In actuality, a biphasic dependence on ATP has been demonstrated, and the 'high-affinity' site has a $K_{0.5}$ in the micromolar range (see 75). Studies performed using intact preparations are few in number. One question that may be asked is the extent (if any) to which ATP can be reduced without there being a reduction in transport activity. Since the $K_{0.5}$ for the Na,K-ATPase appears to be well below the ATP concentration in the renal cell, it would appear that in intact cells the sodium pump is saturated with ATP and that its activity would not be limited. However, it was reported that a concentration of rotenone sufficient to inhibit the QO_2 and ATP content of the rabbit proximal tubule by 30–40% also inhibited transepithelial transport (J_v) by the same amount, thus suggesting a parallel relationship among these processes (37).

In a recent study, the dependence of the sodium pump activity on the ATP concentration was investigated using a suspension of rabbit proximal tubules

(87). In these experiments the intracellular sodium and extracellular potassium sites of the sodium pump were saturated, and the cellular content of ATP was varied using rotenone. A linear and nonsaturating dependence of the sodium pump activity on ATP was measured up to about 3.5 mM ATP, the estimated normal ATP concentration. This suggested that under the conditions of the experiment, the ATP concentration was rate limiting, and that alterations in the cellular ATP concentration should produce corresponding changes in sodium transport activity. However, the Na,K-ATPase hydrolytic activity of broken membranes of the tubule suspension displayed saturation kinetics, and had a $K_{0.5}$ value of 0.4 mM. The differences between the results obtained using broken membrane fragments and intact tubules may have been due to differences between the constituents of the ATPase hydrolytic assay medium and the intracellular milieu of the proximal tubule, including ADP, P_i, magnesium, and other cellular factors known to alter Na,K-ATPase activity. In a different study, a linear dependence of rubidium (potassium) transport on the ATP content was observed using HeLa cells, a nonepithelial preparation, and there was no difference in the linear relationship whether the ATP was produced by aerobic glycolysis or oxidative phosphorylation (47). These results, along with those in the kidney, suggest that at least under some conditions transport activity may be directly dependent on the concentration of ATP.

It must be acknowledged that the situation in the kidney may be much more complicated than is suggested from these several examples, and multiple factors probably play critical roles in determining the transport activity. In a study of the phosphate dependence of transepithelial transport, Brazy et al (9) reported that the removal of inorganic phosphate from the intraluminal fluid reduced J_v from 1.0 nl·mm^{-1}·min^{-1} to zero in the perfused proximal tubule. However, the QO_2 and ATP content of tubules suspended in P_i-free media were reduced by only 30–40%. The addition of various substrates to P_i-free media restored ATP and J_v in a disparate manner: Short chain fatty acids (butyrate, valerate) restored the ATP content to about 75% of the control (P_i present) level, but did not alter J_v, whereas tricarboxylic acid cycle intermediates (succinate, malate, citrate) restored about 85–90% of the ATP, accompanied by a partial return of J_v. Results such as these demonstrate that the relationship between ATP and transepithelial transport may not be a simple one, and may depend on a variety of complicated and as yet unknown factors.

Alterations in the substrate mixture may play a role in altering renal function only when the normal physiological state is disrupted, for example, when sodium transport is greatly stimulated or in preparations which are substrate-limited. Under such conditions, metabolic substrates may increase the degree to which ATP synthesis is increased. Thus, in the rabbit proximal tubule, short chain fatty acids were found to support the stimulated activity of the sodium pump to a better degree than glucose or a combination of glucose, lactate, and alanine. In the presence of fatty acids the ATP content was maintained closer to normal levels during sodium pump–stimulated conditions (41, 42). In contrast, the addition of short chain fatty acids to the perfusion solution of isolated perfused proximal tubules did not alter J_v, and altered the ATP content of proximal tubules in suspension to only a minor extent (36).

Relative Dependence of Luminal Transport Systems on ATP

Although transepithelial sodium reabsorption varies in linear fashion with oxidative metabolism, the same cannot be said for solutes whose entry across the luminal membrane is coupled to the entry of sodium. The entry of glucose, amino acids, and other solutes across the luminal membrane of the proximal tubule and other epithelia occurs by a secondary active process, and depends on the sodium electrochemical potential difference that is created by the activity of the sodium pump in the basolateral membrane. Several reports have indicated that the sensitivity of phosphate and glucose transport to reductions in oxidative metabolism and ATP is different than that of sodium transport (J_v) in the rabbit proximal tubule. Partial inhibition of oxidative phosphorylation by arsenate, which uncouples the mitochondria, inhibited J_v by 47%, reduced the lumen-to-bath phosphate flux by 57%, but reduced the lumen-to-bath glucose flux by only 14% (8). Similarly, a concentration of rotenone that reduced the QO_2 and ATP content by about 35% reduced J_v by 40%, the phosphate flux by 90%, and glucose flux by 24% (37). The differences may be due to the relative dependence of sodium, glucose, and phosphate on alterations in the chemical and electrical gradients across the luminal membrane, and to alterations in intracellular cofactors caused by metabolic inhibition (8, 37). Such studies demonstrate that different transport systems may be regulated by multiple factors in addition to their (primary or secondary) dependence on the activity of the sodium pump.

CONCLUSIONS

ATP is of central importance to a myriad of cellular activities. This review focused on several important processes in which ATP is known to be involved in renal cells, including aspects of cell metabolism and ion transport. Although the absolute concentration of ATP within the cell may be of foremost importance to the regulation of processes such as kinase reactions, which require ATP but do not make large demands on the ATP supply, the rate of ATP production is also of primary importance to those renal processes that greatly contribute to the rapid turnover of the ATP pool, especially active sodium reabsorption. Under normal conditions the renal segments that perform the majority of active ion transport utilize only a portion of their capacity to generate ATP, and the energetic demands of submaximal stimulations of endergonic activity can be met by the reserve capacity of the mitochondria to produce ATP. When the rate of ATP consumption is greatly increased, as when ion transport activity is maximized, or under conditions in which there is a limitation in the availability of metabolic substrates or oxygen, the capacity of the renal cell to generate ATP becomes rate limiting, and ion transport and other ATP-consuming processes are diminished.

The relative compartmentation of ATP and other cellular metabolites between the cytosol and the mitochondria has not been widely studied in the kidney, but this subject has recently received an increasing amount of attention. In addition, there may be a functional compartmentation of adenine nucleotides, oxygen, and other metabolites within the cytosol, and thus there may be unique microenvironments within the renal cell (see article by Dean Jones in this volume). Such possibilities await resolution by more advanced analytical techniques.

ACKNOWLEDGMENT

The author wishes to thank Drs. L. C. Cantley, M. E. Chamberlin, L. H. English, and L. J. Mandel for critically reading the manuscript. This work was supported in part by the Machu Picchu Research Foundation and by NIH GM 26199.

Literature Cited

1. Akerboom, T. P. M., Bookelman, H., Zuurendonk, P. F., Van der Meer, R., Tager, J. M. 1978. Intramitochondrial and extramitochondrial concentrations of adenine nucleotides and inorganic phosphate in isolated hepatocytes from fasted rats. *Eur. J. Biochem.* 84:413–20

2. Andrews, P. M., Coffey, A. K. 1983. Protection of kidneys from acute renal failure resulting from normothermic ischemia. *Lab. Invest.* 49:87–98

3. Bagnasco, S., Good, D., Balaban, R., Burg, M. 1985. Lactate production in isolated segments of the rat nephron. *Am. J. Physiol.* 248:F522–26

4. Balaban, R. S., Mandel, L. J., Soltoff, S. P., Storey, J. M. 1980. Coupling of active ion transport and aerobic respiratory rate in isolated renal tubules. *Proc. Natl. Acad. Sci. USA* 77:447–51

5. Berne, R. M. 1963. Cardiac nucleotides in hypoxia: possible role in regulation of coronary blood flow. *Am. J. Physiol.* 204:317–22

6. Blond, D. M., Whittam, R. 1964. The regulation of kidney respiration by sodium and potassium ions. *Biochem. J.* 92:158–67

7. Braughler, J. M., Corder, C. N. 1977. Purification of the $(Na^+ + K^+)$-adenosine triphosphatase from human renal tissue. *Biochim. Biophys. Acta* 481:313–27

8. Brazy, P. C., Balaban, R. S., Gullans, S. R., Mandel, L. J., Dennis, V. W. 1980. Inhibition of metabolism: relative effects of arsenate on sodium, phosphate and glucose transport by the rabbit proximal tubule. *J. Clin. Invest.* 66:1211–21

9. Brazy, P. C., Mandel, L. J., Gullans, S. R., Soltoff, S. P. 1984. Interactions between phosphate and oxidative metabolism in proximal renal tubules. *Am. J. Physiol.* 247:F575–81

10. Brezis, M., Rosen, S., Silva, P., Spokes, K., Epstein, F. 1984. Polyene toxicity in renal medulla: injury mediated by transport activity. *Science* 224:66–68

11. Buhl, M. R. 1982. Purine metabolism in ischaemic kidney tissue. *Dan. Med. Bull.* 29:1–31

12. Burch, H. B., Choi, S., Dence, C. N., Alvey, T. R., Cole, B. R., Lowry, O. H. 1980. Metabolic effects of large fructose loads in different parts of the rat nephron. *J. Biol. Chem.* 255:8239–44

13. Burch, H. B., Lowry, O. H., Meinhardt, L., Max, P. Jr., Chyu, K.-J. 1970. Effect of fructose, dihydroxyacetone, glycerol, and glucose on metabolites and related compounds in liver and kidney. *J. Biol. Chem.* 245:2092–2102

14. Busse, D., Pohl, B., Bartel, H., Buschmann, F. 1980. The Mg^{2+}-dependent adenosine triphosphatase activity in the brush border of the rabbit kidney cortex. *Arch. Biochem. Biophys.* 201:147–59

15. Chamberlin, M. E., LeFurgey, A., Mandel, L. J. 1984. Suspension of medullary thick ascending limb tubules from the rabbit kidney. *Am. J. Physiol.* 247:F955–64

16. Chance, B., Williams, G. R. 1956. The respiratory chain and oxidative phosphorylation. *Adv. Enzymol.* 17:65–134

17. Charney, A. N., Silva, P., Epstein, F. H. 1975. An *in vitro* inhibitor of Na-K-ATPase presented in an adenosinetriphosphate preparation. *J. Appl. Physiol.* 39:156–58

18. Chaudry, I. H. 1982. Does ATP cross the cell plasma membrane? *Yale J. Biol. Med.* 55:1–10

19. Chaudry, I. H., Sayeed, M. M., Baue, A. E. 1976. Uptake of ATP by liver and kidney in vitro. *Can. J. Physiol. Pharmacol.* 54:742–49

20. Cohen, J. J., Barac-Nieto, M. 1973. Renal metabolism of substrates in relation to renal function. In *Handbook of Physiology. Renal Physiology*, ed. J. Orloff, R. W. Berliner, pp. 909–1001. Washington, DC: Physiol. Soc.

21. Cohen, J. J., Black, A. J. 1982. Substrate-selective maintenance of tissue K^+ in perfused rat kidney. *Am. J. Physiol.* 242:F360–69

22. Cohen, J. J., Kamm, D. E. 1981. Renal metabolism: relation to renal function. In *The Kidney*, ed. B. M. Brenner, F. C. Rector, pp. 144–248. Philadelphia: Saunders. 2nd ed.

23. Doucet, A., Katz, A. I. 1982. High-affinity Ca-Mg-ATPase along the rabbit nephron. *Am. J. Physiol.* 242:F346–52

24. Elgavish, A., Elgavish, G. A. 1985. Evidence for the presence of an ATP transport system in brush-border membrane vesicles isolated from the kidney cortex. *Biochim. Biophys. Acta* 812:595–99

25. Erecinska, M., Wilson, D. F. 1982. Regulation of cellular energy metabolism. *J. Membr. Biol.* 70:1–14

26. Farber, J. L. 1982. Biology of disease: membrane injury and calcium homeostasis in the pathogenesis of coagulative necrosis. *Lab. Invest.* 47:114–23

27. Forgac, M., Cantley, L. 1984. The plasma membrane (Mg^{2+})-dependent adenosine triphosphatase from the human erythrocyte is not an ion pump. *J. Membr. Biol.* 80:185–90

28. Friedman, P. A., Figueiredo, J. F., Maack, T., Windhager, E. E. 1981. Sodium-calcium interactions in the renal proximal convoluted tubule of the rabbit. *Am. J. Physiol.* 240:F558–68

29. Friedrichs, D., Schoner, W. 1973. Stimulation of renal gluconeogenesis by inhibition of the sodium pump. *Biochim. Biophys. Acta* 304:142–60

30. Gantzer, M. L., Grisham, C. M. 1979. Characterization of Mg^{2+}-ATPase from sheep kidney medulla: purification. *Arch. Biochem. Biophys.* 198:263–67

31. Gantzer, M. L., Grisham, C. M. 1979. Characterization of Mg^{2+}-ATPase from sheep kidney medulla: magnetic resonance and kinetic studies. *Arch. Biochem. Biophys.* 198:268–79

32. Garg, L. C., Knepper, M. A., Burg, M. B. 1981. Mineralocorticoid effects on Na-K-ATPase in individual nephron segments. *Am. J. Physiol.* 240:F536–44

33. Gmaj, P., Murer, H., Carafoli, E. 1982. Localization and properties of a high-affinity ($Ca^{2+} + Mg^{2+}$)-ATPase in isolated kidney cortex plasma membranes. *FEBS Lett.* 144:226–30

34. Gronow, G. H. J., Cohen, J. J. 1984. Substrate support for renal functions during hypoxia in the perfused rat kidney. *Am. J. Physiol.* 247:F618–31

35. Guder, W. G., Ross, B. D. 1984. Enzyme distribution along the nephron. *Kidney Int.* 26:101–11

36. Gullans, S. R., Brazy, P. C., Dennis, V. W., Mandel, L. J. 1984. Interactions between gluconeogenesis and sodium transport in rabbit proximal tubule. *Am. J. Physiol.* 246:F859–69

37. Gullans, S. R., Brazy, P. C., Soltoff, S. P., Dennis, V. W., Mandel, L. J. 1982. Metabolic inhibitors: effects on metabolism and transport in the proximal tubule. *Am. J. Physiol.* 243:F133–40

38. Handler, J. S., Preston, A. S., Orloff, J. 1972. Effect of ADH, aldosterone, ouabain, and amiloride on toad bladder epithelial cells. *Am. J. Physiol.* 222:1071–1074

39. Harms, V., Stirling, C. E. 1977. Transport of purine nucleotides and nucleosides by in vitro rabbit ileum. *Am. J. Physiol.* 233:E47–55

40. Harris, E. J. 1941. The influence of metabolism of human erythrocytes on their potassium content. *J. Biol. Chem.* 141:579–95

41. Harris, S. I., Balaban, R. S., Barrett, L., Mandel, L. J. 1981. Mitochondrial respiratory capacity and Na$^+$- and K$^+$-dependent adenosine triphosphatase-mediated ion transport in the intact renal cell. *J. Biol. Chem.* 256:10319–28
42. Harris, S. I., Patton, L., Barrett, L., Mandel, L. J. 1982. (Na$^+$, K$^+$)-ATPase kinetics within the intact renal cell. *J. Biol. Chem.* 257:6996–7002
43. Hashimoto, K., Kumakura, S. 1965. The pharmacological features of the coronary, renal, mesenteric and femoral arteries. *Jpn. J. Physiol.* 15:540–51
44. van Heeswijk, M. P. E., Geertsen, J. A. M., van Os, C. H. 1984. Kinetic properties of the ATP-dependent Ca^{2+} pump and the Na$^+$/Ca^{2+} exchange system in basolateral membranes from rat kidney cortex. *J. Membr. Biol.* 79:19–31
45. Hems, D. A., Brosnan, J. T. 1970. Effects of ischaemia on content of metabolites in rat liver and kidney *in vivo. Biochem. J.* 120:105–11
46. Huang, W.-H., Askari, A. 1984. Regulation of (Na$^+$+K$^+$)-ATPase by inorganic phosphate: pH dependence and physiological implications. *Biochem. Biophys. Res. Commun.* 123:438–43
47. Ikehara, T., Yamaguchi, H., Hosokawa, K., Sakai, T., Miyamoto, H. 1984. Rb$^+$ influx in response to changes in energy generation: effect of the regulation of the ATP content of HeLa cells. *J. Cell. Physiol.* 119:273–82
48. Jennings, R. B., Reimer, K. A. 1981. Lethal myocardial ischemic injury. *Am. J. Pathol.* 102:241–55
49. Johnston, P. A., Rennke, H., Levinsky, N. G. 1984. Recovery of proximal tubular function from ischemic injury. *Am. J. Physiol.* 246:F159–66
50. Jones, N. F., Welt, L. G. 1967. Adenosinetriphosphate in rat renal papilla: effects of vasopressin and of ischemia. *Am. J. Physiol.* 212:939–44
51. Jørgensen, P. L. 1968. Regulation of the (Na$^+$ + K$^+$)-activated hydrolyzing enzyme system in rat kidney. I. The effect of adrenalectomy and the supply of sodium on the enzyme system. *Biochim. Biophys. Acta* 151:212–24
52. Jørgensen, P. L. 1980. Sodium and potassium ion pump in kidney tubules. *Physiol. Rev.* 60:864–917
53. Katz, A. I. 1982. Renal Na-K-ATPase: its role in tubular sodium and potassium transport. *Am. J. Physiol.* 242:F207–19
54. Katz, A. I., Doucet, A. 1980. Calcium-activated adenosine triphosphatase along the rabbit nephron. *Int. J. Biochem.* 12:125–29
55. Katz, A. I., Doucet, A., Morel, F. 1979. Na-K-ATPase activity along the rabbit, rat, and mouse nephron. *Am. J. Physiol.* 237:F114–20
56. Kinne, R. 1979. Metabolic correlates of tubular transport. In *Membrane Transport in Biology*, ed. G. Giebisch, D. C. Tosteson, H. H. Ussing, 4B:529–62 Berlin: Springer-Verlag
57. Kinne-Saffran, E., Beauwens, R., Kinne, R. 1982. An ATP-driven proton pump in brush-border membranes from rat renal cortex. *J. Membr. Biol.* 64:67–78
58. Kinne-Saffran, E., Kinne, R. 1974. Localization of a calcium-stimulated ATPase in the basal-lateral plasma membrane of the proximal tubule of the rat kidney cortex. *J. Membr. Biol.* 17:263–74
59. Kinne-Saffran, E., Kinne, R. 1979. Further evidence for the existence of an intrinsic bicarbonate-stimulated Mg^{2+}-ATPase in brush border membranes isolated from rat kidney cortex. *J. Membr. Biol.* 49:235–51
60. Kinsolving, C. R., Post, L., Beaver, D. L. 1963. Sodium plus potassium transport adenosine triphosphatase activity in kidney. *J. Cell. Comp. Physiol.* 62:85–93
61. Lipmann, F. 1941. Metabolic generation and utilization of phosphate bond energy. *Adv. Enzymol.* 1:99–165
62. Maizels, M. 1951. Factors in the active transport of cations. *J. Physiol.* 112:59–83
63. Mandel, L. J., Balaban, R. S. 1981. Stoichiometry and coupling of active transport to oxidative metabolism in epithelial tissues. *Am. J. Physiol.* 240:F357–71
64. Mandel, L. J., Murphy, E. 1984. Regulation of cytosolic free calcium in rabbit proximal renal tubules. *J. Biol. Chem.* 259:11188–96
65. Mathisen, Ø., Montclair, T., Kiil, F. 1980. Oxygen requirements of bicarbonate-dependent sodium reabsorption in the dog kidney. *Am. J. Physiol.* 238:F175–80
66. Maxild, J. 1973. Energy requirements for active transport of p-aminohippurate in renal cortical slices. *Arch. Int. Physiol. Biochim.* 81:501–21
67. Maxild, J. 1978. Effects of externally added ATP and related compounds on active transport of *p*-aminohippurate and metabolism in cortical slices of the rabbit kidney. *Arch. Int. Physiol. Biochim.* 86:509–30
68. Needleman, P., Minkes, M. S., Doug-

las, J. R. Jr. 1974. Stimulation of prostaglandin biosynthesis by adenine nucleotides. Profile of prostaglandin release by perfused organs. *Circ. Res.* 34:455–60

69. Needleman, P., Passonneau, J. V., Lowry, O. H. 1968. Distribution of glucose and related metabolites in rat kidney. *Am. J. Physiol.* 215:655–59

70. Ng, R. C. K., Peraino, R. A., Suki, W. N. 1982. Divalent cation transport in isolated tubules. *Kidney Int.* 22:492–97

71. Pfaller, W. 1982. Structure function correlation on rat kidney. *Adv. Anat. Embryol. Cell Biol.* 70:1–106

72. Pfaller, W., Guder, W. G., Gstraunthaler, G., Kotanko, P., Jehart, I., Purschel, S. 1984. Compartmentation of ATP within renal proximal tubular cells. *Biochim. Biophys. Acta* 805:152–57

73. Pfaller, W., Rittinger, M. 1980. Quantitative morphology of the rat kidney. *Int. J. Biochem.* 12:17–22

74. Rea, C., Segal, S. 1972. ATP content of rat kidney cortex slices: relation to α-aminoisobutyric acid uptake. *Kidney Int.* 2:101–6

75. Robinson, J. D., Flashner, M. S. 1979. The $(Na^+ + K^+)$-activated ATPase. Enzymatic and transport properties. *Biochim. Biophys. Acta* 549:145–76

76. Rodriguez, H. J., Hogan, W. C., Hellman, R. N., Klahr, S. 1980. Mechanism of activation of renal Na^+-K^+-ATPase in the rat: effects of potassium loading. *Am. J. Physiol.* 238:F315–23

77. Rorive, G., Kleinzeller, A. 1972. The effect of ATP and Ca^{2+} on the cell volume in isolated kidney tubules. *Biochim. Biophys. Acta* 274:226–39

78. Ross, B. D., Guder, W. G. 1982. Heterogeneity and compartmentation in the kidney. In *Metabolic Compartmentation*, ed. H. Sies, pp. 363–409. London: Academic

79. Sejersted, O., Mathisen, O., Kiil, F. 1977. Oxygen requirement of renal Na,K-ATPase dependent sodium reabsorption. *Am. J. Physiol.* 232:F152–58

80. Siegel, N. J., Avison, M. J., Reilly, H. F., Alger, J. R., Shulman, R. G. 1983. Enhanced recovery of renal ATP with postischemic infusion of ATP-MgCl$_2$ determined by ^{31}P-NMR. *Am. J. Physiol.* 245:F530–34

81. Siegel, N. J., Glazier, W. B., Chaudry, I. H., Gaudio, K. M., Lytton, B., et al. 1980. Enhanced recovery from acute renal failure by the postischemic infusion of adenine nucleotides and magnesium chloride in rats. *Kidney Int.* 17:338–49

82. Silva, P., Hallac, R., Spokes, K., Epstein, F. H. 1982. Relationship among gluconeogenesis, QO$_2$, and Na^+ transport in the perfused rat kidney. *Am. J. Physiol.* 242:F508–13

83. Simmonnet, H., Gauthier, C., Pellet, M. 1980. Effect of acidosis, alkalosis and monofluoroacetate administration on citrate and ATP content of rat renal medulla and papilla. *Arch. Int. Physiol. Biochim.* 88:69–74

84. Simmons, N. L. 1981. Stimulation of Cl^- secretion by exogenous ATP in cultured MDCK epithelial monolayers. *Biochim. Biophys. Acta* 646:231–41

85. Skou, J. C. 1974. Effect of ATP on the intermediary steps of the reaction of the $(Na^+ + K^+)$-dependent enzyme system. II. Effect of a variation in the ATP/Mg^{2+} ratio. *Biochim. Biophys. Acta* 439:246–57

86. Soltoff, S. P., Mandel, L. J. 1984. Active ion transport in the renal proximal tubule. I. Transport and metabolic studies. *J. Gen. Physiol.* 84:601–22

87. Soltoff, S. P., Mandel, L. J. 1984. Active ion transport in the renal proximal tubule. III. The ATP dependence of the Na pump. *J. Gen. Physiol.* 84:643–62

88. Tager, J. M., Wanders, R. J. A., Groen, A. K., Kunz, W., Bohnensack, R., et al. 1983. Control of mitochondrial respiration. *FEBS Lett.* 151:1–9

89. Thurau, K. 1961. Renal Na reabsorption and O$_2$ uptake in dogs during hypoxia and hydrochlorthiazide infusion. *Proc. Soc. Exp. Biol. Med.* 106:714–17

90. Torelli, G., Mella, E., Faelli, A., Costantini, S. 1966. Energy requirements for sodium reabsorption in the in vivo rabbit kidney. *Am. J. Physiol.* 211:576–80

91. Trimble, M. E., Bowman, R. H. 1973. Renal Na^+ and K^+ transport: effects of glucose, palmitate, and α-bromopalmitate. *Am. J. Physiol.* 225:1057–1062

92. Trimble, M. E., Coulson, R. 1984. Adenosine transport in perfused rat kidney and renal cortical membrane vesicles. *Am. J. Physiol.* 246:F794–F803

93. Urbaitis, B. K., Kessler, R. H. 1969. Concentration of adenine nucleotide compounds in renal cortex and medulla. *Nephron* 6:217–34

94. Urbaitis, B. K., Kessler, R. H. 1971. Actions of inhibitor compounds on adenine nucleotides of renal cortex and sodium excretion. *Am. J. Physiol.* 220:116–23

95. Vanderwalle, A., Wirthensohn, G., Heidrich, H.-G., Guder, W. G. 1981. Distribution of hexokinase and phos-

phoenolpyruvate carboxykinase along the rabbit nephron. *Am. J. Physiol.* 240:F492–F500

96. Venkatachalam, M. A., Bernard, D. B., Donohue, J. F., Levinsky, N. G. 1978. Ischemic damage and repair in the rat proximal tubule: differences among the S_1, S_2, and S_3 segments. *Kidney Int.* 14:31–49

97. Venkatachalam, M. A., Kreisberg, J. I., Stein, J. H., Lifschitz, M. D. 1983. Salvage of ischemic cells by impermeant solute and adenosinetriphosphate. *Lab. Invest.* 49:1–3

98. Weidemann, M. J., Hems, D. A., Krebs, H. A. 1969. Effects of added adenine nucleotides on renal carbohydrate metabolism. *Biochem. J.* 115:1–10

99. Weisman, G. A., De, B. K., Friedberg, I., Pritchard, R. S., Heppel, L. A. 1984. Cellular responses to external ATP which precede an increase in nucleotide permeability in transformed cells. *J. Cell. Physiol.* 119:211–19

100. Whittam, R. 1961. Active cation transport as a pace-maker of respiration. *Nature* 191:603–4

101. Willis, J. S. 1968. Cold resistance of kidney cells of mammalian hibernators: cation transport vs. respiration. *Am. J. Physiol.* 214:923–28

102. Windhager, E. E., Taylor, A. 1983. Regulatory role of intracellular calcium ions in epithelial Na transport. *Ann. Rev. Physiol.* 45:519–32

103. Wittner, M., Weidtke, C., Schlatter, E., di Stefano, A., Greger, R. 1984. Substrate utilization in the isolated perfused cortical thick ascending limb of rabbit nephron. *Pflügers Arch.* 402:52–62

104. Zerahn, K. 1956. Oxygen consumption and active sodium transport in the isolated and short-circuited frog skin. *Acta Physiol. Scand.* 36:300–18

Ann. Rev. Physiol. 1986 48:33–50
Copyright © 1986 by Annual Reviews, Inc. All rights reserved

RENAL METABOLISM DURING NORMOXIA, HYPOXIA, AND ISCHEMIC INJURY

Dean P. Jones

Department of Biochemistry, Emory University School of Medicine, Atlanta, Georgia 30322

INTRODUCTION

Substantial advances have recently been made in developing methods for the study of hypoxic and ischemic metabolism, in conceptualizing the metabolic responses of cells to oxygen deficiency, and in effectively altering metabolism to protect cells from irreversible injury. The large number of diverse studies precludes a comprehensive treatment, and therefore only some of the major developments will be surveyed here. I have attempted to summarize recent advances and to bring into focus critical issues concerning hypoxic and ischemic metabolism.

Definition of Hypoxic and Ischemic Models

Two general conditions occur in which there is insufficient O_2 supply to kidney cells. A *simple hypoxia,* in which there is a decrease in O_2 supply without a loss of blood flow, occurs with decreased ambient pO_2 (mountain sickness, anesthesia accidents), with interrupted gas exchange in the lung (obstructive lung diseases), and with diminished O_2 carrying capacity of blood (anemias). A *stagnant hypoxia,* in which there is an insufficient blood flow and hence interruption in supply and removal of many components, occurs with peripheral vascular obstruction (arteriosclerosis, thrombosis), and with insufficient cardiac output or blood volume loss (heart failure, shock). The limiting condition of simple hypoxia is a simple *anoxia,* the condition in which no oxygen is present but blood flow is continued. The limiting condition of stagnant hypoxia is *ischemia,* the condition in which blood flow is stopped. While renal

33

0066-4278/86/0315-0033$02.00

pathologies related to simple hypoxia have not been clearly defined, renal ischemia is of major clinical interest because of its role in acute renal failure (12).

Anoxia is an important component of ischemia, but loss of blood flow creates a distinctly different condition than seen with simple hypoxia. Simple hypoxia can be readily studied with isolated tubules, cells, and subcellular fractions by varying O_2 concentration (63), but analogous study of cellular metabolism in intact kidney is limited by tissue oxygen gradients and autoregulation of blood flow. Stagnant hypoxia, on the other hand, has been studied almost exclusively in intact kidneys because the incubation medium in disrupted preparations offers a large reservoir of nutrients and prevents rapid accumulation of high concentrations of intermediates and products. An important methodological advance is the use of preparations of isolated cells and tubules (6, 93) to test the efficacy of various treatments intended to ameliorate anoxic injury (45). In principle, this approach can be used to recreate the ischemic environment *in vitro* by suitable additions of lactate, adjustment of pH, etc. This will allow systematic analyses of the metabolism of the ischemic state and investigation of the relationship of these changes to those found in simple hypoxia, as previously studied in perfused kidney (46). Such studies are critical for understanding the basis of irreversible injury and the mechanisms involved in tissue preservation. Obviously, some cell types have a remarkable capability to preserve viability and to recover normal function following relatively long anoxic periods. An understanding of this capability will serve as a guide to improve tissue preservation.

The Anoxic "Steady State"

Within seconds following ischemia, pyridine nucleotides become reduced (7, 33), ATP concentration falls, lactic acid accumulates, and tissue pH decreases (see for instance Reference 121). While these rapidly occurring bioenergetic changes have previously been considered as primary events leading ultimately to cell death, renal cells survive 25–60 min without irreversible injury (42, 45, 121). Given the relatively common occurrence of hypoxia (in terms of evolution), mechanisms at the cellular level would appear to have evolved to protect against such acute injury. Numerous mechanisms for organismic acclimitization to hypoxia are known, e.g. increases in erythropoiesis, respiration, cardiac output, and vasodilation (53, 97, 118). Similarly, at the cellular level, stimulated glycolysis provides ATP under conditions of restricted mitochondrial function. Given the highly regulated nature of metabolism and ion transport, initial changes in function of many enzymes and transport systems during hypoxia and ischemia may be protective in nature. Hence, there is no a priori reason to presume a given alteration in metabolism or transport is deleterious.

This concept is illustrated in Figure 1. In simple anoxia or hypoxia the

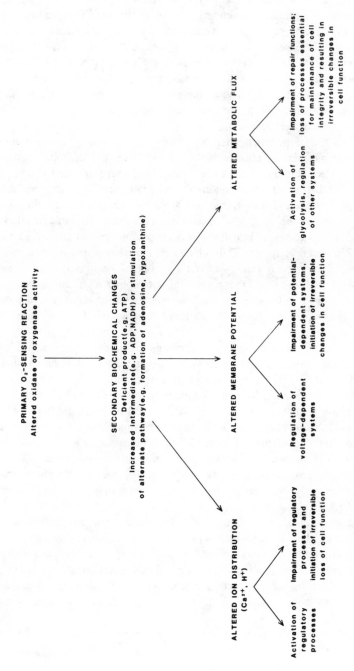

Figure 1   Parallel relationship of regulatory and pathological changes to primary O_2-sensing reactions.

primary signal for a biochemical or physiological response to decreased O_2 tension involves a primary O_2-sensing process, presumably through the function of an O_2-dependent enzyme[1]. Altered activity results in decreased product formation and increased concentrations of intermediates. Either of these types of changes (e.g. deficient ATP or increased levels of a "messenger") can be important in metabolic perturbations such as altered ion distribution, membrane potential, or metabolic flux. These changes may have multiple effects; they may aid in acclimatization to the new condition or, conversely, may lead to irreversible loss of cell function.

Recent studies of the biochemical alterations of lipids during renal ischemia provide examples of these potentially dichotomous roles of metabolic changes. Matthys et al (84) found that irreversible ischemic damage (60 min ischemia in rats) correlated with persistent abnormalities of phosphatidylcholine metabolism and persistent elevations of free fatty acids, lysophosphatidylcholine, and diacylglycerol. On the other hand, even after a reversible ischemic insult (15 min ischemia), phosphatidylinositol was decreased and phosphatidic acid was elevated 2 hr post reperfusion. Thus, changes in these lipids are associated with a response to nonlethal injury. Given the role of phosphoinositides and phosphatidic acid as second messengers, it is tempting to speculate that the prolonged changes in these components are related to the regulation of post-ischemic metabolism or repair processes rather than involvement in a pathological sequence.

Smith et al (109) studied changes in mitochondrial lipids of rat kidney during ischemia. Free fatty acids were increased at 30 min while total phospholipid fatty acids decreased steadily. The proportion of cardiolipin in the total phospholipid was decreased at 300 min, but the proportion of phosphatidylcholine and phosphatidylethanolamine did not change until the irreversible phase of injury. Thus, changes in cardiolipin precede irreversible injury. Smith et al postulated that degradation of cardiolipin by phospholipase A_2 results in irreversible loss of mitochondrial function and thereby contributes to the irreversible phase of ischemic injury. Alternatively, since the decline in cardiolipin is relatively slow ($< 25\%$ in 1 hr), this change may be a manifestation of control mechanisms of anoxia.

A close parallel between regulatory processes and potential pathological sequences can also be seen in arachidonate metabolism during ischemia. Morrison et al (89) described increased prostaglandin biosynthesis and arachidonate release as functional markers of renal cell injury. They presented a potential mechanism for propagation of renal injury that entails an increase in phospholipid hydrolysis. The consequent increase in free polyunsaturated fatty

---

[1]In principle, an O_2-binding protein that signals a response by an allosteric mechanism may also occur, but none are known.

acids provides substrates for synthesis of regulatory prostanoids by the cyclooxygenase and lipoxygenase pathways, as well as providing substrates for the generation of toxic species.

Thus, during hypoxia or ischemia, regulatory changes may be coincident with or precede changes that contribute to pathological processes. It follows that since these biochemical changes occur rapidly relative to irreversible changes, cells can exist in a nonlethal anoxic condition that is distinct from either aerobic or irreversibly injured anoxic/ischemic cells. During this time cell processes may be controlled to give a metabolic state that approximates a quiescent or dormant steady state, thereby preserving the functional integrity of the cells. Transition to this state would appear to be fully reversible, and survival appears limited by the efficiency of the control mechanisms and modulation by exogenous effectors.

As an example of this possibility, one can consider that if irreversible cell injury is a consequence of collapse of plasma membrane ion gradients, a rapid, controlled decrease in ion permeability will protect cells. Use of exogenous inhibitors of ion flux could thereby protect cells, and stimulation of ion flux would be expected to decrease survival. Brezis et al (12, 13) recently found that transport activity is a determining factor of anoxic cell death in the thick ascending limb of Henle's loop in rat. The severe lesions found following 90 min hypoxic perfusion could be attenuated or abolished by inhibiting resorptive transport with ouabain or furosemide. Similarly, halting glomerular filtration with a hyperoncotic medium or maintaining kidneys under warm ischemia prevented the severe lesions seen during anoxic perfusion. Thus, under these conditions a decrease in ion flux appears to limit cell damage from anoxia.

Endogenous mechanisms for inhibiting ion flux during hypoxia could also function to protect against injury. Recent studies of Johnston et al (59) show that brief ischemia results in significant alterations in proximal tubular reabsorption of sodium and glucose, which correlates with a substantial loss of brush border. Two to four hours after restoration of flow, transport of either sodium or glucose is significantly reduced even though cell morphology has returned to normal. Thus, experiments are needed to address whether such loss of transport activity is part of a regulated response that has evolved to protect cells from ischemic injury.

METABOLIC HYPOXIA VERSUS BIOENERGETIC HYPOXIA

Theories of Hypoxic and Ischemic Injury

The early recognition of rapid and quantitatively large changes in cellular energetics (49, 113) and of the dependence of numerous cell functions upon ATP concentrations (81) led to a generalized conceptualization of hypoxic and ischemic injury as due largely to failed oxidative phosphorylation and cell death due to ATP depletion (see Reference 120). However, Trifillis et al (116) concluded that the absolute concentration of ATP is not a reliable criterion of cell viability in the ischemic rat model, but that the ability to resynthesize ATP may be determinant in the reversibility of the lesion. Others have considered the possibility that increased acid production substantially lowers pH, altering enzyme function and potentially activating lytic enzymes of lysosomes (124, 127). In opposition to the applicability of this model to kidney, Penttila & Trump (104) found that acidosis protects rat kidney cortex against anoxic injury.

Another proposal to explain anoxic and ischemic injury is that alterations in cellular energetics and membrane permeability lead to cytoplasmic and mitochondrial loading of Ca^{2+}, with consequent irreversible loss of cell functions (129). While considerable uncertainty remains about the relative contribution of organelles and the mechanistic details of the role of Ca^{2+} in toxicity, recent studies document that the Ca^{2+} channel blocker, verapamil, provides significant protection against renal ischemic injury (see below). Thus, abnormal Ca^{2+} balance appears to contribute to the pathological sequelae of renal ischemic injury.

Recent evidence suggests that irreversible injury following ischemia may also be a consequence of oxidative injury during reoxygenation (102). Under ischemic conditions ATP is degraded to AMP and subsequently to hypoxanthine. Upon reoxygenation, hypoxanthine and xanthine are oxidized with rapid enzymatic generation of H_2O_2 and O_2^-. These reactive forms of oxygen initiate oxidative injury, presumably through formation of hydroxyl radicals (35). Cellular injury by this process results in altered enzyme and transport functions (60), altered Ca^{2+} homeostasis (58), altered membrane permeability (86), broken DNA strands (117), and tumor promotion (17).

A common feature of the above explanations is that the function of a large number of macromolecules is altered by a "key" component, i.e. by ATP concentration, pH, Ca^{2+} concentration, or oxidative injury. Thus, change in a single entity causes massive disruption of metabolism. While these explanations offer simple working hypotheses, they do not provide a molecular explanation for the irreversible step(s) in injury. The implication is that numerous individual reactions contribute to the irreversible injury, and therefore the most appropriate means for protection is to supplement ATP, adjust pH, block Ca^{2+} entry, or inhibit oxidative processes. However, if the altered ATP, pH, or Ca^{2+} is also functioning in regulation of the response to anoxia, then exogenous control of this parameter may have multiple effects, negative as well as positive.

The alternative to the concept of massive disruption of metabolism is the possibility that irreversible injury results from the failure of a single (or small number of) enzymatic, transport, or regulatory steps. Thus, although a large number of metabolic changes occur, only a small number of these are critical in injury. If this possibility is correct, then identification of these steps and control of their function could provide the basis for more specific and efficient protection. Ultimately, an understanding of the molecular details of hypoxic and ischemic injury will require definition of these irreversible steps.

Molecular Oxygen Sensors and the Metabolic Response to Hypoxia

Because distinction between the irreversible steps and regulatory steps is essential, study of the two processes are inexorably linked (see Figure 1). Hence, it is appropriate to examine the effects of hypoxia and anoxia on the function of the primary biochemical sensors of oxygen, namely the enzymes that depend upon oxygen for normal function. In earlier studies of the O_2 dependence of oxidases and oxygenases, these enzymes were found to have distinct apparent Km_{O_2} values, and to function independently in cells with regard to their O_2 dependences (63, 65, 66). Thus, one can distinguish between altered bioenergetic functions due to insufficient O_2 supply to mitochondrial cytochrome oxidase ("bioenergetic hypoxia") and altered metabolic functions due to insufficient O_2 supply to other enzymes that require molecular O_2 as substrate ("metabolic hypoxia").

Although cytochrome oxidase accounts for most of the O_2 consumption, at least 30 other enzymes functioning in a wide variety of processes are present in kidney cells (Table 1). The apparent Km_{O_2} values for many of these enzymes are considerably higher than the Km for mitochondrial cytochrome oxidase, and therefore, O_2-dependent function of these enzymes may provide sensitive indicators of cellular oxygenation. For example, many biological amines and pharmacologic agents containing amines are oxidized by O_2-dependent reactions. The Km_{O_2} values for monoamine oxidase, diamine oxidase, and indoleamine dioxygenase range from 30 to 300 torr (8, 52, 62). Thus, the activities of each of these is expected to be O_2-dependent under physiological conditions. Similarly, the plasma membrane thiol oxidase has a Km_{O_2} of about 70 torr (94). Although the function of this enzyme is unknown, it is present in the basolateral plasma membrane, and could function in modulating the thiol-disulfide status of peptide hormones or hormone receptors (77). Other oxidases and oxygenases are involved in prostaglandin and thromboxane metabolism, steriod hormone metabolism, vitamin D_3 synthesis, amino acid metabolism, carnitine synthesis, etc (see Table 1). Very little is known about the potential contribution of functional changes in these reactions to regulatory and pathological processes during simple or stagnant hypoxia.

The causal relationship of biochemical changes to these primary O_2 sensors is particularly important since erythropoietin production, blood flow auto-

Table I Renal oxidases and oxygenases

Oxidase or oxygenase	Reference	Oxidase or oxygenase	Reference
Cytochrome oxidase	93	Inositol oxidase	20, 21
Cytochrome P-450 (drug monoxygenases)	67, 95	Phenylalanine 4-hydroxylase	68, 69
Cytochrome P-450 (fatty acid ω-hydroxylase)	67	Protocollagen prolyl hydroxylase	37, 112
25-Hydroxycholecalciferol 1α-hydroxylase	41	Xanthine oxidase	106
Arachidonate cyclooxygenase	25	Monamine oxidase	82
12-Lipoxygenase	111	D-Amino acid oxidase	87
15-Lipoxygenase	111	L-α-Hydroxy acid oxidase (L-amino acid oxidase)	24, 90
p-Hydroxyphenylpyruvate oxidase	30	Glycolate oxidase	105
γ-Butyrobetaine hydroxylase	28	D-Aspartate oxidase	26
ε-Alkyllysinase	73	N-Methylamino acid oxidase (demethylase)	88
Homogentisate oxidase	82	Indoleamine dioxygenase	51
3-Hydroxyanthranilate 3, 4-dioxygenase	92	Urate oxidase	80
4-Methylsterol oxidase	16, 40	Thiol oxidase	77
Squalene epoxidase	16, 107	Diamine oxidase	74

regulation, and numerous other responses to hypoxia are likely to involve such reactions. Fisher & coworkers (31, 32) reviewed the control of erythropoietin production in kidney; although considerable knowledge is available concerning this regulatory process, the primary O_2 sensor is not known. The regulatory scheme they proposed involves Ca^{2+}-dependent activation of phospholipase, stimulated synthesis of prostaglandins, activation of adenylate cyclase and guanylate cyclase, labilization of lysosomes, and release and activation of hydrolases (31). While such a complex scheme may be correct, it must be emphasized that erythropoietin is produced continuously by normoxic kidneys, and stimulation of production does not appear to require a pathological process. Because this regulation is a normal physiological process, it would appear that greater specificity would be required than afforded by generalized Ca^{2+}-dependent activation, cyclic nucleotide metabolism, or lysosomal activation. Since erythropoietin is not stored in tissues (57), regulation may involve control of transcriptional or translational processes (22, 47). Alternatively, Fyhrquist et al (36) have proposed that de novo synthesis of erythropoietin does not occur in kidney; instead, they conclude erythropoietin is produced by renal activation of plasma angiotensinogen. If this is correct, regulation of renal production would appear to occur through regulation of angiotensinogen supply or regulation of activation. In either case, the question concerning the primary O_2 sensor is an important one because acclimitization involves multiple metabolic changes; it is not known whether these changes occur in concert (i.e. one primary sensor) or independently (i.e. multiple O_2 sensors).

The primary oxygen sensors involved in blood flow autoregulation also remain unknown. While mechanisms resulting from altered cytochrome oxidase function in mitochondria, such as adenosine release (96, 110), or stimulated thromboxane A_2 or prostanoids release (2, 31), can be envisaged, cytochrome oxidase is known to have a very low Km_{O_2} (18, 19). Since blood flow autoregulation occurs at relatively high O_2 partial pressures (72), one could infer that other oxidases or oxygenases with higher Km_{O_2} values may be more likely to function as primary O_2 sensors. However, recent evidence, as described below, indicates that the effective Km_{O_2} for cytochrome oxidase is markedly increased in cells in which mitochondria are present in high densities in specific regions. Thus, there is no basis at present to rule out either of the oxidases or oxygenases as possible sensors.

CELLULAR OXYGEN SUPPLY AND MITOCHONDRIAL FUNCTION

Intracellular O_2 Gradients

In early studies using a platinum O_2 microelectrode to study oxygen supply in blood-perfused rat kidney, Leichtweiss et al. (79) found that most cortical pO_2

measurements were in the range of 20–40 torr when arterial pO_2 was 80–100 torr. The critical pO_2 for O_2 consumption was between 6 and 28 torr. Thus, tissue pO_2 values are considerably below the arterial pO_2 value, and O_2 consumption is sensitive to arterial O_2 concentration at tissue concentrations considerably higher than that needed for maximal function of isolated mitochondria (about 1 torr; 19). Subsequent microelectrode studies have confirmed the difference between arterial and tissue values (91). Similarly, studies of the fluorescence of pyridine nucleotides and absorbance of mitochondrial cytochromes have shown that the critical pO_2 is relatively high in perfused kidneys (7, 29, 33). The results from these various approaches have been explained by extensive shunting (79), and interpreted to mean that substantial portions of the kidney exist on the brink of anoxia despite high arterial and venous pO_2 (7, 29).

The understanding of subcellular oxygen supply has been enhanced by the recognition that the critical pO_2 in isolated tubules and kidney cells is in the range of 10–17 torr (6, 125) and, from studies of liver cells, that the distribution of mitochondria in clusters markedly increases the apparent Km_{O_2} (61). Early studies of Sjöstrand and Rhodin (108) showed that mitochondria are present at high densities on the basal side of proximal tubule cells. This distribution is variable in the different cell types [48; also shown schematically in Figure 2 of Bulger & Dobyan's review of renal morphology (14)], and appears likely to be responsible for both the heterogeneity of oxygen tension measurements as well as the relatively high critical pO_2 values in certain regions of the kidney.

Because mitochondria consume most of the O_2 used by cells, they have a relatively high O_2 consumption rate per volume. Under conditions where mitochondria are tightly packed together, this creates a region with a very high O_2 consumption rate (61). A cluster of six to ten mitochondria in an electron micrograph may have a radius of 2 μm and be part of a three dimensional array of 50 mitochondria in the cell or in adjacent cells. Modeling of oxygen gradients in such clusters indicates that very steep gradients occur under oxygen-limiting conditions. Thus, the previously documented high density of mitochondria in the basolateral region of both proximal and distal tubule cells could result in O_2 diffusion gradients within the cells and thereby account for the high Km_{O_2} for respiration seen in isolated tubules and perfused kidney. Moreover, the differences in distribution and content of mitochondria could markedly affect the sensitivity of different cell types to hypoxia.

Regulation of Mitochondrial Function

While considerable research has focused upon changes in mitochondrial function as potentially critical in the pathological consequences of ischemia, an additional issue that warrants consideration is the concept that mitochondrial function changes rapidly during hypoxia and ischemia due to metabolic regulation. Various aspects of mitochondrial respiration are known to be highly regulated. Multiple control mechanisms are known for pyruvate oxidation by pyruvate dehydrogenase and the citric acid cycle (128). The function of the F_1ATPase in ATP synthesis is regulated by an endogenous inhibitor, the binding of which is modulated by Ca^{2+} (54, 130). The exchange of ATP and ADP by the adenine nucleotide translocase is modulated by fatty acyl-CoA esters (99). The K^+/H^+ antiporter is controlled by a voltage-dependent gating mechanism (10). The $Ca^{2+}/2H^+$ antiporter is regulated by the redox status of mitochondrial pyridine nucleotides (9, 78). Thus, numerous mechanisms are available to control mitochondrial function during anoxia. While these functions have been studied in extrarenal tissues, it is likely that many of these features also occur in kidney.

The possibility that mitochondrial function is controlled during anoxia is further suggested by studies of the proton motive force during anoxia. Even though ATP production by mitochondria essentially stops, the mitochondrial membrane potential ($\Delta\psi$), as measured by triphenylmethyl phosphonium ion (TPMP) distribution, and the mitochondrial pH gradient (ΔpH), as measured by 5,5-dimethyloxazolidine-2,4-dione (DMO) distribution, are largely preserved during 30 min anoxia (3, 4). Preservation of these entities is essential to maintain distribution of ATP, ADP, inorganic phosphate, pyruvate, tricarboxylate and dicarboxylate substrates of the Krebs cycle, and Ca^{2+} (75), and thus to allow facile recovery upon return to normoxia. Early changes in metabolic function of mitochondria during hypoxia or ischemia may therefore reflect activation of control processes to preserve these ion distributions. Since irreversible injury during ischemia is more closely associated with the ability of mitochondria to recover ATP production than with ATP concentration (116), the irreversible step in injury may be the result of the inability of control processes to preserve a viable anoxic steady state.

PROTECTION AGAINST ISCHEMIC INJURY

In spite of the continued uncertainty about the irreversible steps of hypoxia and ischemia, considerable progress has been made in protecting and salvaging cells from ischemic injury. One successful approach has been to use isotonic or hypertonic solutions containing impermeant solutes such as mannitol or polyethylene glycol. Such treatments counteract the cellular swelling that constricts capillary lumina and impairs blood flow (see Reference 120 for discussion). A mildly beneficial effect has also been observed by infusing prostacyclin, a prostaglandin with vasodilator and platelet antiaggregating properties (55).

More dramatic protection against ischemic injury has been found with either pretreatment or posttreatment with ATP-$MgCl_2$ (5, 39, 114). The mechanism of this protection is not clear, but one view is that the protective effect is due to the amelioration of ischemic depletion of cellular energy stores (120). This interpretation is compatable with metabolic studies that show that the kidney can better maintain tubular functions during severe hypoxia if substrates are available to provide ATP anaerobically (46). However, utilization of exogenous ATP for such purposes would require direct uptake. Recent studies of Elgavish & Elgavish (27) provide evidence for uptake of intact ATP by renal brush-border membrane vesicles. While extracellular $ATP-MgCl_2$ increases tissue adenine nucleotide content following ischemia (38), the relative contributions of direct uptake, as opposed to breakdown, uptake of free bases, and resynthesis of ATP, needs to be further studied. Another alternative is that $ATP-MgCl_2$ improves microcirculation and decreases cell swelling (23). However, other potent vasodilators (phenoxybenzamine, dopamine) do not produce a significant recovery of functional parameters, and therefore this is not likely to provide a complete explanation (114).

An alternate means to protect against postischemic renal injury has been to use the Ca^{2+} channel blocker, verapamil. Regulation of proximal tubule cell calcium has been studied in detail (83), and marked changes, especially in the mitochondrial pool, have been described during anoxia (129). Infusion of verapamil before ischemia gave partial but significant protection against 100 min ischemia in rats (43) and against 30 min ischemia in guinea pigs (126). Infusion in dogs after 50 min renal ischemia also provided marked protection (122). Thus, as found in other tissues, blocking Ca^{2+} entry significantly protects physiological functions against ischemic injury. However, additional verification and clarification of the mechanism of this effect are necessary since others have not observed the protection by verapamil (11), and Freundenrich et al (34) concluded that changes in the cytosolic Ca^{2+} during anoxia are probably related to mitochondrial release rather than to altered plasma membrane transport.

An additional approach is based upon the recognition that free radical–mediated oxidative injury can occur upon reoxygenation of ischemic tissues (85, 100). Earlier studies described increases in free radicals following cardiac ischemia (1), and also allopurinol protection against renal ischemia (50, 115, 119). These isolated observations were clarified by studies of Granger, McCord and coworkers, who provided evidence for a scheme in which hypoxanthine and xanthine accumulate during hypoxia from the degradation of ATP, and xanthine dehydrogenase is converted to xanthine oxidase (102, 106). Upon reoxygenation, conditions are appropriate for rapid generation of superoxide ion and H_2O_2, resulting in oxidative injury. Protection from injury is obtained by addition of soybean trypsin inhibitor to inhibit the proteolytic conversion of xanthine dehydrogenase to xanthine oxidase, by addition of allopurinol to inhibit xanthine oxidase, or by addition of superoxide dismutase to detoxify superoxide anion (44, 101, 106). The possibility that oxygen radicals are important in renal ischemic injury is supported by the allopurinol studies mentioned above, and by studies showing protection by superoxide dismutase and by the hydroxyl radical scavenger, dimethylthiourea (98). In addition, other radical scavengers (mannitol, chlorpromazine, dimethylsulfoxide) also protect against ischemic renal injury (56, 70, 71, 103). Thus, available evidence supports the concept that oxygen radicals are an important component in the pathology of ischemic renal failure.

Radical-induced injury could also be responsible for other features of ischemic injury, such as DNA damage, and other means of protection may be found based upon this causative mechanism. Warnick & Lazarus (123) found that nicotinic acid administration prior to ischemia minimized DNA damage. They interpreted this effect in terms of the supply of nicotinic acid as a precursor for NAD^+, which is used in poly (ADPribose) synthetase-dependent DNA repair. Earlier studies (15) showing that nicotinic acid protects against anoxic death in vitro in rats suggest that nicotinic acid may protect by other mechanisms as well. Thus, nicotinic acid may also be useful to enhance tissue resistance to hypoxic and ischemic injury. The recent finding that intact glutathione (GSH) can be transported into renal epithelial cells by a Na^+-dependent electrogenic system (76) suggests that GSH may also be used to enhance renal resistance to ischemic injury. Studies with intestinal epithelial cells, which contain a similar GSH uptake system, show that these cells are protected from t-butylhydroperoxide- or menadione-induced injury by incubation with GSH (64). Thus, administration of GSH could provide additional substrate for intracellular reduction of toxic peroxides and mediate against post-ischemic oxidative injury.

SUMMARY AND CONCLUSIONS

The reversible period of hypoxia and ischemia is a consequence of the function of numerous regulatory mechanisms which convert cells to a quiescent state. Thus, early changes in metabolism reflect regulatory events rather than pathological events. O_2-dependent enzymes (oxidases and oxygenases) are the primary sensors for physiological responses to hypoxia, and failure of their functions are ultimately responsible for hypoxic and ischemic cell injury. At least 30 of these enzymes are known to occur in kidney, but only cytochrome oxidase has been extensively studied with regard to the above processes. Heterogeneity of subcellular oxygenation occurs as a result of the existance of clusters of mitochondria in the basolateral regions of proximal and distal tubule cells. This creates regions with very high O_2 consumption rates, and results in diffusion limitations in O_2 supply. Finally, dramatic progress has been made in protecting against ischemic injury through use of nonpermeant solutes to reduce cell swelling, addition of ATP-MgCl$_2$ to stimulate recovery of cellular adenylates upon reoxygenation, use of a Ca^{2+} uptake blocker to prevent cellular loading of Ca^{2+}, and addition of compounds to inhibit superoxide and H$_2$O$_2$ production or scavenge reactive O$_2$ species. While the mechanistic details and complete description of metabolic effects are not yet available, the ability to alter cellular metabolism and delay or prevent irreversible injury marks a very important advance in renal physiology.

Literature Cited

1. Akiyama, K. 1969. Studies on myocardial metabolism in the ischemic heart II. Studies by the electron spin resonance method. *Jpn. Circ. J.* 33:165–70
2. Anderson, C. B., Tannenbaum, J. S., Sicard, G. A., Etheredge, E. E. 1984. Renal thromboxane synthesis in excised kidney distal to renovascular lesions. *J. Am. Med. Assoc.* 251:3118–20
3. Andersson, B. S., Jones, D. P. 1984. Effect of hypoxia on membrane potentials and ΔH$^+$ in isolated hepatocytes. *Fed. Proc.* 43:2001
4. Andersson, B. S., Jones, D. P. 1985. Use of digitonin fractionation to determine mitochondrial transmembrane ion distribution in cells during anoxia. *Anal. Biochem.* 146:164–72
5. Andrews, P. M., Coffey, A. K. 1983. Protection of kidneys from acute renal failure resulting from normothermic ischemia. *Lab. Invest.* 49:87–98
6. Balaban, R. S., Soltoff, S. P., Storey, J. M., Mandel, L. J. 1980. Improved renal cortical tubule suspension: Spectrophotometric study of O$_2$ delivery. *Am. J. Physiol.* 238:F50–F59
7. Balaban, R. S., Sylvia, A. L. 1981. Spectrophotometric monitoring of O$_2$ delivery to the exposed rat kidney. *Am. J. Physiol.* 241:F257–62
8. Bardsley, W. G., Crabbe, M. J. C., Shindler, J. S. 1973. Kinetics of the diamine oxidase reaction. *Biochem. J.* 131:459–69
9. Bellomo, G., Martino, A., Richelmi, P., Moore, G. A., Jewell, S. A., Orrenius, S. 1984. Pyridine-nucleotide oxidation, Ca^{2+} cycling and membrane damage during tert-butyl hydroperoxide metabolism by rat-liver mitochondria. *Eur. J. Biochem.* 140:1–6
10. Bernardi, P., Azzone, G. F. 1983. Electroneutral H$^+$-K$^+$ exchange in liver mitochondria. Regulation by membrane potential. *Biochim. Biophys. Acta* 724:212–23
11. Bock, A., Bertschin, S., Brunner, F. P.,

Thiel, G. 1984. Verapamil does not protect from acute ischemic renal failure in rats. *Kidney Int.* 25:988
12. Brezis, M., Rosen, S., Silva, P., Epstein, F. H. 1984. Renal ischemia: A new perspective. *Kidney Int.* 26:375–83
13. Brezis, M., Rosen, S., Spokes, K., Silva, P., Epstein, F. H. 1984. Transport-dependent anoxic cell injury in the isolated perfused rat kidney. *Am. J. Pathol.* 116:327–41
14. Bulger, R. E., Dobyan, D. C. 1982. Recent advances in renal morphology. *Ann. Rev. Physiol.* 44:147–49
15. Calder, R. M. 1948. Effect of nicotinic acid on anoxia in rats. *Proc. Soc. Exp. Biol. Med.* 68:642–46
16. Carreau, J. P., Lapous, D., Raulin, J. 1982. Cholesterol synthesis in the liver, kidneys and brain after injection of uniformly 14C-labeled oleic or linoleic acid to developing rats. *Ann. Nutr. Metab.* 26:217–26
17. Cerutti, P. A. 1985. Prooxidant states and tumor promotion. *Science* 227:375–81
18. Chance, B. 1957. Cellular oxygen requirements. *Fed. Proc.* 16:671–80
19. Chance, B. 1976. Pyridine nucleotide as an indicator of the oxygen requirements for energy-linked functions of mitochondria. *Circ. Res.* (Suppl. I) 38:I31–I38
20. Charalampous, F. C. 1959. Biochemical studies on inositol. V. Purification and properties of the enzyme that cleaves inositol to D-glucuronic acid. *J. Biol. Chem.* 234:220–29
21. Charalampous, F. C. 1960. Biochemical studies on inositol. VI. Mechanism of cleavage of inositol to D-glucuronic acid *J. Biol. Chem.* 235:1286–91
22. Clark, B. F. C., Petersen, H. U., eds. 1984. *Gene Expression. The Translational Step and its Control. Alfred Benzon Symp. 19th* p. 127 Copenhagen: Munksgaard. 527 pp.
23. Clemens, M. G., McDonagh, P. H., Chaudry, I. H., Baue, A. E. 1983. He-

patic microvascular protection from ischemia with ATP-MgCl₂. *Microvasc. Res.* 3:228–29

24. Cromartie, T. H., Walsh, C. T. 1975. Rat kidney L-α hydroxy acid oxidase: Isolation of enzyme with one flavin coenzyme per two subunits. *Biochemistry* 14:2588–96

25. Currie, M. G., Needleman, P. 1984. Renal arachidonic acid metabolism. *Ann. Rev. Physiol.* 46:327–41

26. Dixon, M., Kenworthy, P. 1967. D-Aspartate oxidase of kidney. *Biochem. Biophys. Acta* 146:54–76

27. Elgavish, A., Elgavish, G. A. 1985. Evidence for the presence of an ATP transport system in brush-border membrane vesicles isolated from the kidney cortex. *Biochim. Biophys. Acta* 812:595–99

28. England, S., Carnicero, H. H. 1978. γ-Butyrobetaine hydroxylation to carnitine in mammalian kidney. *Arch. Biochem. Biophys.* 190:361–64

29. Epstein, F. H., Balaban, R. S., Ross, B. D. 1982. Redox state of cytochrome aa₃ in isolated perfused rat kidney. *Am. J. Physiol.* 243:F356–63

30. Fellman, J. H., Fujita, T. S., Roth, E. S., 1972. Assay, properties and tissue distribution of p-hydroxyphenylpyruvate hydroxylase. *Biochim. Biophys. Acta* 284:90–100

31. Fisher, J. W. 1983. Control of erythropoietin production. *Proc. Soc. Exp. Biol. Med.* 173:289–305

32. Fisher, J. W., Nelson, P. K., Beckman, B., Burdowski, A. 1983. Kidney control of erythropoietin production. In *Renal Endocrinology*, ed. M. J. Dunn, pp. 142–80. Baltimore: Williams & Wilkins

33. Franke, H., Barlow, C. H., Chance, B. 1976. Oxygen delivery in perfused rat kidney: NADH fluorescence and renal functional state. *Am. J. Physiol.* 231: 1082–89

34. Freundenrich, C. C., Snowdowne, K. W., Borle, A. B. 1984. The effect of anoxia on cytosolic free calcium in kidney cells. *Fed. Proc.* 43:769

35. Fridovich, I. 1978. The biology of oxygen radicals. *Science* 201:875–80

36. Fyhrquist, F., Rosenlof, K., Grönhagen-Riska, C., Horling, L., Tikkanen, I. 1984. Is renin substrate an erythropoietin precursor? *Nature* 308:649–52

37. Gallup, P. M., Paz, M. A. 1975. Post-translational protein modifications, with special attention to collagen and elastin. *Physiol. Rev.* 55:418–87

38. Garvin, P. J., Jellinek, M. J., Morgan, R., Codd, J. E. 1981. Renal cortical levels of adenosine triphosphate. Restoration after prolonged ischemia by in situ perfusion of ATP-MgCl₂. *Arch. Surg.* 116:221–24

39. Gaudio, K. M., Ardito, T. A., Reilly, H. F., Kashgarian, M., Siegel, N. J. 1983. Accelerated cellular recovery after an ischemic renal injury. *Am. J. Pathol.* 112:338–46

40. Gaylor, J. L., Miyake, Y., Yamano, T. 1975. Stoichiometry of 4-methyl sterol oxidase of rat liver microsomes. *J. Biol. Chem.* 250:7159–67

41. Ghazarian, J. G., Jefcoate, C. R., Knutson, J. C., Orme-Johnson, W. H., DeLuca, H. F. 1974. Mitochondrial cytochrome P₄₅₀. A component of chick kidney 25-hyroxycholecalciferol-1-hydroxylase. *J. Biol. Chem.* 249:3026–33

42. Glaumann, B., Glaumann, H., Berezesky, I. K., Trump, B. F. 1975. Studies on the pathogenesis of ischemic cell injury. *Virchows Arch. B* 19:281–302

43. Goldfarb, D., Iaina, A., Serban, I., Gavendo, S., Kapuler, S., Eliahou, H. E. 1983. Beneficial effect of verapamil in ischemic acute renal failure in the rat. *Proc. Soc. Exp. Med. Biol.* 172:389–92

44. Granger, D. N., Rutili, G., McCord, J. M. 1981. Superoxide radicals in feline intestinal ischemia. *Gastroenterology* 81:22–29

45. Gronow, G., Meya, F., Weiss, C. 1984. Studies on the ability of kidney cells to recover after periods of anoxia. *Adv. Exp. Med. Biol.* 169:589–95

46. Gronow, G. H. J., Cohen, J. J. 1984. Substrate support for renal functions during hypoxia in the perfused rat kidney. *Am. J. Physiol.* 247:F618–31

47. Grunberg-Manago, M., Safer, B., eds. 1982. *Interaction of Translational and Transcriptional Controls in the Regulation of Gene Expression. Developments in Biochemistry*, Vol. 24. New York: Elsevier. 524 pp.

48. Guder, W. G., Ross, B. P. 1984. Enzyme distribution along the nephron. *Kidney Int.* 26:101–11

49. Gurdjian, E. S., Webster, J. E., Stone, W. E. 1949. Cerebral constituents in relation to blood gases. *Am. J. Physiol.* 156:149–57

50. Hansson, R., Gustafsson, B., Jonsson, O., Lundström, S., Pettersson, S., et al. 1982. Effect of xanthine oxidase inhibition on renal circulation after ischemia. *Transplant Proc.* 14:51–58

51. Hayaishi, O. 1976. Properties and function of indoleamine 2,3-dixoygenase. *J. Biochem.* 79:13p–21p

52. Hirata, F., Ohnishi, T., Hayaishi, O. 1977. Indoleamine 2,3-dioxygenase. Characterization and properties of en-

zyme·O_2 complex. *J. Biol. Chem.* 252:4637–42

53. Hochachka, P. W. 1980. Integrating aerobic and anaerobic glycolysis. In *Living Without Oxygen* Ch. 6, 79–99. Cambridge, Mass.: Harvard Univ. Press. 181 pp.

54. Husain, I., Jackson, P. J., Harris, D. A. 1985. Interaction between F_1 ATPase and its naturally occurring inhibitor protein. Studies using a specific anti-inhibitor antibody. *Biochim. Biophys. Acta* 767: 64–74

55. Isenberg, G., Racelis, D., Oh, J., Schanzer, H. 1982. Prevention of ischemic renal damage with prostacyclin. *Mt. Sinai J. Med. NY* 49:415–17

56. Jablonski, P., Howden, B., Leslie, E., Rae, D., Birrell, C. et al. 1983. Recovery of renal function after warm ischemia. *Transplantation* 35:535–39

57. Jelkmann, W. 1982. Temporal pattern of erythropoietin titers in kidney tissue during hypoxic hypoxia. *Pflugers Arch.* 393:88–91

58. Jewell, S., Bellomo, G., Thor, H., Orrenius, S. 1982. Bleb formation in hepatocytes during drug metabolism is caused by disturbances in thiol and calcium homeostasis. *Science* 217:1257–59

59. Johnston, P. A., Rennke, H., Levinsky, N. G. 1984. Recovery of proximal tubular function from ischemic injury. *Am. J. Physiol.* 246:F159–66

60. Jones, D. P. 1985. The role of oxygen concentration in oxidative stress: Hypoxic and hyperoxic models. In *Oxidative Stress*, ed. H. Sies, pp. 151–95. London: Academic

61. Jones, D. P. 1984. Effect of mitochondrial clustering on O_2 supply in hepatocytes. *Am. J. Physiol.* 247:C83–C89

62. Jones, D. P. 1984. Benzylamine metabolism at low O_2 concentrations: Relative sensitivities of monoamine oxidase, aldehyde dehydrogenase and hippurate synthesis to hypoxia. *Biochem. Pharmacol.* 33:413–17

63. Jones, D. P., Aw, T. Y., Kennedy, F. G. 1983. Isolated hepatocytes as a model for the study of cellular hypoxia. In *Isolation, Characterization and Use of Hepatocytes*, ed. R. A. Harris, N. W. Cornell, pp. 323–32. New York: Elsevier.

64. Jones, D. P., Lash, L. H. 1985. Glutathione uptake by rat intestinal epithelial cells protects against oxidative injury. *13th Int. Congr. Biochem., Amsterdam*

65. Jones, D. P., Mason, H. S. 1978. Metabolic hypoxia: Accumulation of tyrosine metabolites in hepatocytes at low pO_2. *Biochem. Biophys. Res. Commun.* 80:477–83

66. Jones, D. P., Mason, H. S. 1978. Gradients of O_2 concentration in hepatocytes. *J. Biol. Chem.* 253:4874–80

67. Jones, D. P., Orrenius, S., Jakobson, S. W. 1980. Cytochrome P-450-linked monooxygenase systems in the kidney. In *Extrahepatic Metabolism of Drugs and Other Foreign Compounds*, ed. T. E. Gram, pp. 123–58. Jamaica, N.Y: Spectrum

68. Kaufman, S. 1976. On the nature of an intermediate that is formed during the enzymatic conversion of phenylalanine to tyrosine. In *Iron and Copper Proteins*, ed. K. T. Yasunobu, H. F. Mower, O. Hayaishi, pp. 91–102. New York: Plenum

69. Kaufman, S., Fisher, D. B., 1970. Purification and some physical properties of phenylalanine hydroxylase from rat liver. *J. Biol. Chem.* 245:4745–50

70. Kedar, I., Cohen, J., Jacob, E. T., Ravid, M. 1981. Alleviation of experimental ischemic acute renal failure by dimethyl sulfoxide. *Nephron* 29:55–58

71. Kedar, I., Jacob, E. T., Bar-Natan, N., Ravid, M. 1983. Dimethyl sulfoxide in acute ischemia of the kidney. *Ann. NY Acad. Sci.* 411:131–34

72. Kessler, M., Lang, H., Sinagowitz, E., Rink, R., Höper, J. 1973. Homeostasis of oxygen supply in liver and kidney. In *Oxygen Transport to Tissue*, Part A, ed. D. F. Bruley, H. I. Bicher, pp. 351–59. New York: Plenum

73. Kim, S., Benoiton, L., Paik, W. K. 1964. ε-Alkyllysinase: Purification and properties of the enzyme. *J. Biol. Chem.* 239:3790–96

74. Kitao, T., Hattori, K. 1982. Purification of pig kidney diamine oxidase (histaminase) and in vivo effects on passive cutaneous anaphylaxis and histamine induced bronchoconstriction of guineapigs. *Experientia* 38:906–7

75. LaNoue, K., Schoolwerth, A. 1979. Metabolite transport in mitochondria. *Ann. Rev. Biochem.* 48:871–922

76. Lash, L. H., Jones, D. P. 1984. Renal glutathione transport: Characteristics of the sodium dependent system in the basal-lateral membrane. *J. Biol. Chem.* 259:14508–14

77. Lash, L. H., Jones, D. P., Orrenius, S. 1984. The renal thiol (glutathione) oxidase. Subcellular localization and properties. *Biochem. Biophys. Acta* 779:191–200

78. Lehninger, A. L., Vercesi, A., Bababun-

mi, E. A. 1978. Regulation of Ca^{2+} release from mitochondria by the oxidation-reduction state of pyridine nucleotides. *Proc. Natl. Acad. Sci. USA* 75:1690–94

79. Leichtweiss, H.-P., Lübbers, D. W., Weiss, C., Baumgärtl, H., Reschke, W. 1969. The oxygen supply of the rat kidney: Measurement of the intra-renal pO_2. *Pflugers Arch.* 309:328–49

80. Leone, E. 1955. Uricase. *Methods Enzymol.* 2:485–89

81. Lipmann, F. 1941. Metabolic generation and utilization of phosphate bond energy. *Adv. Enzymol.* 1:99–162

82. Mahler, H. R., Cordes, E. H. 1966. *Biological Chemistry*. New York: Harper & Row. 872 pp.

83. Mandel, L. J., Murphy, E. 1984. Regulation of cytosolic free calcium in rabbit proximal renal tubules. *J. Biol. Chem.* 259:11188–96

84. Matthys, E., Patel, Y., Kreisberg, J., Stewart, J. H., Venkatachalam, M. 1984. Lipid alterations by renal ischemia: Pathogenic factor in membrane damage. *Kidney Int.* 26:153–61

85. McCord, J. M. 1983. The superoxide free radical: Its biochemistry and pathophysiology. *Surgery* 94:412–14

86. Mead, J. F. 1976. Free radical mechanisms of lipid damage and consequences for cell membranes. In *Free Radicals in Biology*, Vol. 1, ed. W. A. Pryor, pp. 51–68. New York: Academic

87. Miyake, Y., Aki, K., Hashimoto, S., Yamano, T. 1965. Crystallization and some properties of D-amino acid oxidase apoenzyme. *Biochem. Biophys. Acta* 105:86–99

88. Moritani, M., Tung, T.-C., Fujii, S., Mito, H., Izumiya, N., et al. 1954. Specificity of rabbit kidney demethylase. *J. Biol. Chem.* 209:485–92

89. Morrison, A. R., Pascoe, N., Tank, N., Kennerly, D. 1984. Biochemical alterations of membrane lipids associated with renal injury. *Fed. Proc.* 43:2811–14

90. Nakano, M., Danowski, T. S. 1966. Crystalline mammalian L-amino acid oxidase from rat kidney mitochondria. *J. Biol. Chem.* 241:2075–83

91. Nelimarkka, O., Niinikoski, J. 1984. Oxygen and carbon dioxide tensions in the canine kidney during arterial occlusion and hemorraghic hypotension. *Surg. Gynecol. Obstet.* 158:27–32

92. Ogasawara, N., Gander, J. E., Henderson, L. M. 1966. Purification and properties of 3-hydroxyanthranilate oxygenase from beef kidney. *J. Biol. Chem.* 241: 613–19

93. Ormstad, K., Jones, D. P., Orrenius, S. 1981. Preparation and characteristics of isolated kidney cells. *Methods Enzymol.* 77:137–46

94. Ormstad, K., Låstbom, T., Orrenius, S. 1981. Characteristics of renal glutathione oxidase activity. *FEBS Lett.* 130:239–43

95. Orrenius, S., Ellin, Å., Jakobsson, S. V., Thor, H., Cinti, D. L., et al. 1973. The cytochrome P-450-containing monooxygenase system of rat kidney cortex microsomes. *Drug Metab. Dispos.* 1: 350–57

96. Osborn, J. L., Hoversten, L. G., DiBona, G. F. 1983. Impaired blood flow autoregulation in nonfiltering kidneys: Effects of theophylline administration (41744). *Proc. Soc. Exp. Biol. Med.* 174:328–35

97. Ou, L. C., Silverstein, J., Edwards, B. R. 1984. Renal function in rats chronically exposed to high altitude. *Am. J. Physiol.* 247:F45–F49

98. Paller, M. S., Hoidal, J. R., Ferris, T. F. 1984. Oxygen free radicals in ischemic acute renal failure in the rat. *J. Clin. Invest.* 74:1156–64

99. Pande, S. V., Goswami, T., Parvin, R. 1984. Protective role of adenine nucleotide translocase in O_2-deficient hearts. *Am. J. Physiol.* 247:H25–H34

100. Parks, D. A., Bulkley, G. B., Granger, D. N. 1983. Role of oxygen free radicals in shock, ischemia, and organ preservation. *Surgery* 94:428–32

101. Parks, D. A., Bulkley, G. B., Granger, D. N., Hamilton, S. R., McCord, J. M. 1982. Ischemic injury in the cat small intestine: Role of superoxide radicals. *Gastroenterology* 82:9–15

102. Parks, D. A., Granger, D. N. 1983. Oxygen-derived radicals and ischemia-induced tissue injury. In *Oxy Radicals and their Scavenger Systems*, Vol. 2, ed. R. A. Greenwald, G. Cohen, pp. 135–44. Amsterdam: Elsevier.

103. Pavlock, G. S., Southard, J. H., Lutz, M. F., Belzer, J. P., Belzer, F. O. 1981. Effects of mannitol and chlorpromazine pretreatments of rabbits on kidney mitochondria following *in vivo* ischemia and reflow. *Life Sci.* 29:2667–72

104. Penttila, A., Trump, B. F. 1974. Extracellular acidosis protects Ehrlich ascites tumor cells and rat renal cortex against anoxic injury. *Science* 185:277–78

105. Robinson, J. C., Keay, L., Molinari, R., Sizer, I. W. 1962. L-α-hydroxy acid oxidases of hog renal cortex. *J. Biol. Chem.* 237:2001–10

106. Roy, R. S., McCord, J. M. 1983. Super-

oxide and ischemia: Conversion of xanthine dehydrogenase to xanthine oxidase. See Ref. 102, pp. 145–53.

107. Saat, Y. A., Bloch, K. E. 1976. Effect of a supernatant protein on microsomal squalene epoxidase and 2,3-oxidosqualene-lanosterol cyclase. *J. Biol. Chem.* 251:5155–60

108. Sjöstrand, F. S., Rhodin, J. 1953. The ultrastructure of the proximal convoluted tubules of the mouse kidney as revealed by high resolution electron microscopy. *Exp. Cell Res.* 4:426–56

109. Smith, M. W., Collan, Y., Kahng, M. W., Trump, B. F. 1980. Changes in mitochondrial lipids of rat kidney during ischemia. *Biochim. Biophys. Acta* 618:192–201

110. Spielman, W. S., Thompson, C. I. 1982. A proposed role for adenosine in the regulation of renal hemodynamics and renin release. *Am. J. Physiol.* 242:F423–35

111. Sraer, J., Rigaud, M., Bens, M., Rabinovitch, H., Ardaillou, R. 1983. Metabolism of arachidonic acid via the lipoxygenase pathway in human and murine glomeruli. *J. Biol. Chem.* 258:4325–30

112. Stassen, F. L. H., Cardinale, G. J., McGee, J. O'D., Udenfriend, S. 1974. Prolyl hydroxylase and an immunologically related protein in mammalian tissues. *Arch. Biochem. Biophys.* 160:340–45

113. Stone, W. E., Marshall, C., Nims, L. F. 1941. Chemical changes in the brain produced by injury and anoxia. *Am. J. Physiol.* 132:770–75

114. Sumpio, B. E., Chaudry, I. H., Clemens, M. G., Baue, A. E. 1984. Accelerated functional recovery of isolated rat kidney with ATP-MgCl$_2$ after warm ischemia. *Am. J. Physiol.* 247:R1047–53

115. Toledo-Pereyra, L. H., Simmons, R. L., Najarian, J. S. 1974. Effect of allopurinol on the preservation of ischemic kidneys perfused with plasma or plasma substitutes. *Ann. Surg.* 180:780–82

116. Trifillis, A. L., Kahng, M. W., Cowley, R. A., Trump, B. F. 1984. Metabolic studies of postischemic acute renal failure in the rat. *Exp. Mol. Pathol.* 40:155–68

117. Ts'o, P. O. P., Caspary, W. J., Lorentzen, R. J. 1977. The involvement of free radicals in chemical carcinogenesis. In *Free Radicals in Biology*, Vol. 3, ed. W. A. Pryor, pp. 251–303. New York: Academic

118. van Liere, E. J., Stickney, J. 1963. *Hypoxia*. New York: Plenum. 381 pp.

119. Vasko, K. A., DeWall, R. A., Riley, A. M. 1972. Effect of allopurinol in renal ischemia. *Surgery* 71:787–90

120. Venkatachalam, M. A., Kreisberg, J. I., Stein, J. H., Lifschitz, M. D. 1983. Salvage of ischemic cells by impermeant solute and adenosinetriphosphate. *Lab. Invest.* 49:1–3

121. Vogt, M. T., Farber, E. 1968. On the molecular pathology of ischemic renal cell death. *Am. J. Path.* 53:1–24

122. Wait, R. B., White, G., Davis, J. H. 1983. Beneficial effects of verapamil on postischemic renal failure. *Surgery* 94:276–81

123. Warnick, C. T., Lazarus, H. M. 1983. Protection from DNA damage during an ischemic cell injury. *Biochem. Biophys. Res. Commun.* 113:996–1003

124. Wattiaux, R., Wattiaux-DeConinck, S. 1984. Effects of ischemia on lysosomes. *Int. Rev. Exp. Pathol.* 26:85–106

125. Weiss, C. 1968: Critical oxygen tension and rate of respiration of isolated kidney cells. In *Oxygen Transport in Blood and Tissues*, ed. D. W. Lubbers, U. G. Luft, G. Thews, E. Witzlab, pp. 227–37. Stuttgart, Germany: Georg Thieme

126. Widener, L. L., Mela-Riker, L. M. 1984. Verapamil pretreatment preserves mitochondrial function and tissue magnesium in the ischemic kidney. *Circ. Shock* 13:27–37

127. Wildenthal, K. 1978. Lysosomal alterations in ischemic myocardium: Result or cause of myocellular damage? *J. Mol. Cell. Cardiol.* 10:595–603

128. Williamson, J. R., Cooper, R. H. 1980. Regulation of the citric acid cycle in mammalian system. *FEBS Lett.* 117:K73–K85

129. Wilson, D. R., Arnold, P. E., Burke, T. J., Schrier, R. W. 1984. Mitochondrial calcium accumulation and respiration in ischemic acute renal failure in the rat. *Kidney Int.* 25:519–26

130. Yamada, E. W., Shiffman, F. H., Hazel, N. J. 1980. Ca^{2+}-regulated release of an ATPase inhibitor protein from submitochondrial particles derived from skeletal muscles of the rat. *J. Biol. Chem.* 255:267–73

Ann. Rev. Physiol. 1986. 48:51–71

INOSITOL PHOSPHOLIPID METABOLISM IN THE KIDNEY

D. A. Troyer, D. W. Schwertz, J. I. Kreisberg, and M. A. Venkatachalam

Departments of Pathology and Medicine, The University of Texas Health Science Center at San Antonio, 7703 Floyd Curl Drive, San Antonio, Texas 78284

INTRODUCTION

The ability of cells to respond to external stimuli involves the transduction of messages across the plasma membrane. Mechanisms for the control of cell growth, differentiation, and metabolism are all linked to external signals. Although some stimuli, such as steroid hormones, actually enter cells and bind to internal receptors, other agents interact with plasma membrane receptors and generate a second messenger. Cyclic AMP is one example of a widely studied second messenger system. A second signalling pathway has been proposed which utilizes inositol phospholipids (phosphoinositides) as part of a transducing system. After considering the general aspects of phosphoinositide metabolism, this review will describe what is currently known about renal phosphoinositide metabolism. It will be apparent that the data on renal phosphoinositide metabolism derived from different studies is difficult to fit into a single hypothesis. Perhaps this should not be surprising in view of the structural and functional heterogeneity within the kidney itself.

The phosphoinositides are minor membrane lipids comprising less than 5% of the total lipid mass of cells. Although small in amount, these lipids, which include phosphatidylinositol (PtdIns), phosphatidylinositol 4-phosphate [PtdIns(4)P], and phosphatidylinositol 4,5-bisphosphate [PtdIns(4,5)P$_2$], display greater metabolic activity than other, more abundant phospholipids. The phosphoinositides are formed from a glycerol backbone linked to the six-carbon cyclitol, inositol, by a phosphodiester bond (Figure 1). The remaining two bonds of the glycerol backbone are esterified to fatty acids, usually a saturated fatty acid at the 1 position and arachidonic acid at the 2 position. This basic

51

0066-4278/86/0315-0051$02.00

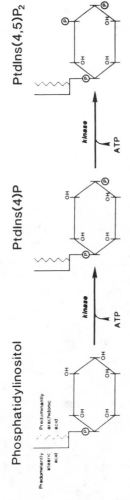

Figure 1   Conversion of PtdIns to the polyphosphoinositides by kinase enzymes and ATP.

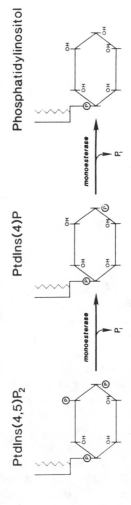

Figure 2   Removal of phosphates from the polyphosphoinositides by the action of phosphomonoesterases.

molecule is PtdIns, the most abundant of the phosphoinositides. Phosphorylation of PtdIns at the 4 and 5 hydroxyl groups of inositol by kinase enzymes and ATP produces PtdIns(4)P and PtdIns(4,5)P$_2$ (Figure 1). These latter two phospholipids, also referred to as polyphosphoinositides, were discovered by Folch (31) and have been shown to participate in stimulated phosphoinositide metabolism (1, 27). Thus, when stimulated phosphoinositide metabolism is considered today, it involves PtdIns, PtdIns(4)P, and PtdIns(4,5)P$_2$. In addition to the phosphorylation reactions depicted in Figure 1, phosphomonoesterases can remove phosphate groups from the inositol ring to convert PtdIns(4,5)P$_2$ to PtdIns(4)P and subsequently PtdIns (Figure 2).

These phosphorylation/dephosphorylation reactions may be important in maintaining a small but relatively constant pool of PtdIns(4,5)P$_2$ as a substrate for hydrolysis by an agonist-stimulated phosphodiesterase, phospholipase C. The products of phospholipase C attack on the phosphoinositides are the focus of much interest as potential second messengers.

The action of phospholipase C on phosphoinositides produces 1,2-diacylglycerol (diglyceride) and one or more water-soluble inositol phosphates (Figure 3). Both diglyceride and the water-soluble products of phospholipase C action can be reincorporated into PtdIns. For diglyceride, this is accomplished by the sequential action of three enzymes. First, diglyceride kinase catalyzes the addition of a γ-phosphate group from ATP to form phosphatidic acid. Second, a transferase enzyme produces CDP-diglyceride from CTP and phosphatidic acid. Third, another transferase enzyme (also referred to as PtdIns synthase) incorporates inositol in the terminal step of PtdIns resynthesis. This enzyme has a high K_m for inositol, and therefore requires high levels of the sugar for optimum function. The incorporation of inositol into PtdIns at this step also allows for potential recycling of the water-soluble inositol phosphates because they can be converted to free inositol by the action of phosphatases (Figure 2).

It is currently believed that a number of cellular stimuli lead to the breakdown of polyphosphoinositides via a phospholipase C, and that the hydrolytic products, inositol trisphosphate (InsP$_3$) and diglyceride, are effectors of postreceptor events that are necessary for stimulus-response coupling. In this respect these breakdown products are considered important "second messengers." For example, diglyceride activates a phospholipid- and calcium-dependent protein kinase C. Diglyceride increases the affinity of this enzyme for calcium, and apparently activates the enzyme without a net increase in cytosolic calcium levels (65). The cellular functions of protein kinase C are poorly understood, but it phosphorylates seryl and threonyl residues of endogenous proteins in most tissues (65). Phospholipase C activation (measured as diglyceride and phosphatidic acid production) and shape change in platelets are correlated with phosphorylation of a protein with an approximate molecular weight of 40,000.

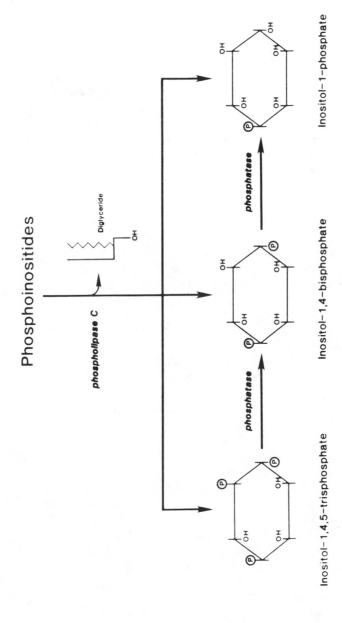

Figure 3   The products of the action of phospholipase C on phosphoinositides and dephosphorylation of the inositol phosphates by phosphatase enzymes are shown. It is not known whether one phospholipase acts on all three phosphoinositides or if there is a specific phospholipase for each phosphoinositide.

This protein has been shown to be a substrate for protein kinase C *in vitro* (65). It is possible, therefore, that diglyceride formed by agonist-stimulated phospholipase C stimulates protein kinase C. The role of protein kinase C in cell surface signal transduction is the topic of intense study, and the reader is referred to a recent review (65) for further information.

A second product of phospholipase C action in cells is $InsP_3$ (7). Increased hydrolysis of $PtdIns(4,5)P_2$ leads to increased levels of $InsP_3$. It should be noted that the amount of $InsP_3$ may also be controlled by its rate of conversion to $InsP_2$ by the action of a phosphatase. This idea is supported by work describing a phosphatase with specificity for the 5-phosphate group of $InsP_3$ (19b, 50b, 81b). While it is usually assumed that $InsP_3$ has phosphates attached at the 1, 4, and 5 positions, an isomer with the phosphate groups at the 1, 3, and 4 positions has been described (50a). Berridge has recently proposed that $InsP_3$ serves as a second messenger by increasing cytosolic calcium (7). Numerous studies have demonstrated the formation of $InsP_3$ following agonist-receptor interaction in a variety of cell types. The role of $InsP_3$ as a calcium-mobilizing second messenger has been studied using cells made permeable in various ways (11), or by injection of $InsP_3$ into intact oocytes (91). These studies indicate that micromolar quantities of $InsP_3$ release large amounts of calcium from an ATP-dependent pool, thought to be the endoplasmic reticulum (7).

Prostaglandins are generated concomitantly with phospholipase C activation and increased cytosolic calcium in many cell types. One rate-limiting step in prostaglandin production is thought to be the release of arachidonic acid from the 2 position of the glycerol backbone of phospholipids by the action of a phospholipase A_2. This step is now the subject of much investigation, and it appears that several lipids are used as substrate for phospholipase A_2. This topic was reviewed recently by Lapetina (56), and the reader is referred there for further information. However, the possible links between phospholipase C action on phosphoinositides and prostaglandin production should be noted. First, mobilization of cellular calcium is an effective means for activation of phospholipase A_2 (56). Second, products of phospholipase C action, such as diglyceride and phosphatidic acid, may serve as substrates for phospholipase A_2 or diglyceride lipase (56).

It is apparent, then, that the products of stimulated phosphoinositide metabolism are somehow related to transduction of extracellular signals across the plasma membrane. Hormonal agonists that evoke this response include α-adrenergic, muscarinic, and cholinergic hormones, and peptides such as vasopressin and angiotensin II. Additional factors known to stimulate phosphoinositide metabolism include mitogens, growth factors, electrical stimulation, and platelet activating factor, among others. This is a bewildering array of stimulatory agents, and it seems likely that phosphoinositide metabolism plays some role in regulating cellular functions in virtually all cell types.

There are exceptions to the general outline given above for stimulated phosphoinositide metabolism. Studies of PTH action in renal brush border membranes and of ACTH on adrenal cortical cells provide indirect evidence that synthesis (rather than catabolism) of phosphoinositides predominates (29, 47). It is not clear how these observations fit the calcium mobilization scheme proposed by Berridge. Another pattern of stimulated phosphoinositide metabolism has been described by Cockroft (18). This author suggests that phospholipase D rather than phospholipase C plays a central role in neutrophil phosphoinositide metabolism. Phospholipase D cleaves the phosphodiester bond between phosphatidic acid and the inositol moiety of phosphoinositides. For example, PtdIns(4,5)P_2 may be broken down by phospholipase D to phosphatidic acid and inositol bisphosphate, rather than diglyceride and InsP$_3$ as seen following phospholipase C action.

Further exceptions to the patterns of phosphoinositide metabolism outlined previously have been shown. Rabbit platelets stimulated for 10 sec with a concentration of thrombin that causes maximal aggregation and partial release of granule contents showed no change in the amount of PtdIns(4,5)P_2 (89), rather than the expected decrease. In addition, there was an increase in the mass of PtdIns(4)P_1, PtdIns, and phosphatidic acid. Therefore, these studies suggest that early events in stimulated platelets do not necessarily include net breakdown of phosphoinositides. Increased amounts of PtdIns(4,5)P_2 and PtdIns(4)P are also seen within 15 sec of fertilization in sea urchin eggs (86). It was suggested that this increase might promote early fusion of membranes following fertilization.

Nevertheless, a growing body of data suggests that stimulated phosphoinositide metabolism is linked to cellular calcium mobilization and to the activation of protein kinase C. Durell et al (27) initially suggested that increased phosphoinositide metabolism, first observed by Hokin & Hokin (42), is linked to a receptor-mediated phenomenon. Subsequently, Michell proposed that phosphoinositide metabolism is stimulated as a mechanism for receptor-mediated mobilization of calcium (63). This hypothesis was recently expanded by Berridge to include the generation of a calcium-mobilizing second messenger, InsP$_3$. This water-soluble product of increased phosphoinositide catabolism is thought to promote calcium mobilization from intracellular stores (7). Finally, with the discovery of a calcium-phospholipid-dependent protein kinase, Nishizuka has provided an additional arm for the interaction of phosphoinositide metabolism with cell signalling events (65).

RENAL PHOSPHOINOSITIDE METABOLISM

1. Enzymology and General Aspects

The study of renal phosphoinositide metabolism is relatively new. In comparison to other cells and organs, such as platelets or brain, less is known about phosphoinositide metabolism in the kidney. However, the complex physiological functions of the kidney and its responsiveness to a variety of hormones make this a promising area of investigation.

Plasma membranes are enriched in polyphosphoinositides, and organs with extensive membranous structures, such as brain and kidney, would be expected to contain large amounts of these lipids (26). This has been verified by measurements of polyphosphoinositides in various organs (41). As expected, renal PtdIns is present in much larger amounts than PtdIns(4)P and PtdIns(4,5)P$_2$. Most measurements have apparently underestimated tissue levels of polyphosphoinositides, and the preferred techniques have been recently outlined (26).

Several of the enzymes involved in phosphoinositide metabolism have been described in the kidney. Lee & Huggins described a PtdIns(4,5)P$_2$ phosphomonoesterase in the endoplasmic reticulum from homogenates derived from rat kidney cortex (57). On the other hand, Cooper & Hawthorne have described both PtdIns(4,5)P$_2$ and PtdIns(4)P phosphomonoesterases from the Golgi fraction of rat kidney cortex (20).

The kinase enzyme that converts PtdIns(4)P to PtdIns(4,5)P$_2$ was described in plasma membrane fractions of kidney cortex by Tou et al (84). Cooper & Hawthorne identified separate enzymes converting PtdIns to PtdIns(4)P and PtdIns(4)P to PtdIns(4,5)P$_2$, and localized them to the microsomal and Golgi fractions, respectively (21). They were unable to detect significantly greater activity of either enzyme in brush border membranes compared to homogenates of renal cortex. The recent studies of Hruska et al definitively established the presence of diglyceride kinase, PtdIns kinase, and PtdIns(4)P kinase in renal brush border membrane vesicles (BBMV) (47).

Phospholipase C–mediated hydrolysis of PtdIns in rat cortical and medullary slices has been reported (81a). A PtdIns-specific phospholipase C has also been found in purified brush border membranes (74). The activity was substantially lower in other kidney cortex cell membranes and cytosol compared to the brush border membrane. The activity of this enzyme against PtdIns(4)P and PtdIns(4,5)P$_2$ was not tested. The location of this phospholipase C is important to any hypothesis that attempts to link mobilization of cellular calcium to agonist-receptor interaction at the plasma membrane. More specifically, the hypothesis of Berridge, which proposes generation of a second messenger at the plasma membrane would require a link between the occupied receptor and the phospholipase C, which suggests a close association between the phospholipase and the plasma membrane.

Tou et al identified a cytosolic phosphodiesterase in the kidney that hydrolyzes both PtdIns(4,5)P$_2$ and PtdIns(4)P (83). The enzyme does not attack other phospholipids, including PtdIns. Downes & Michell found evidence for the presence of polyphosphoinositide phosphodiesterase(s) in erythrocyte ghosts (25). This enzyme was activated by calcium and attacked PtdIns(4,5)P$_2$ and

PtdIns(4)P with equal facility. Similarly, a phosphodiesterase active against both PtdIns(4)P and PtdIns(4,5)P$_2$ has been shown in rat liver plasma membranes (77). This suggests that, at least in some cells, PtdIns(4,5)P$_2$ phosphodiesterase can be found in the plasma membrane. A microsomal PtdIns(4,5)P$_2$ phosphodiesterase that did not attack PtdIns was described in smooth muscle cells (2). Finally, Wilson et al describe a cytosolic phospholipase C from sheep seminal vesicles that hydrolyzes PtdIns and the polyphosphoinositides (93). These authors suggested that a single phospholipase C could account for agonist-induced hydrolysis of all three phosphoinositides. In this context, it is of interest that the phospholipase C in the renal cortex has its highest activity in the brush border membrane fraction (74). Unfortunately, it has not been determined whether the enzyme is active against PtdIns(4) and PtdIns(4,5)P$_2$ in addition to PtdIns. This is one of very few studies indicating the presence of a plasma membrane–bound phosphodiesterase acting on PtdIns. Receptor-mediated breakdown of PtdIns in isolated rat liver plasma membranes has been shown following vasopressin treatment in the presence of deoxycholate (90) or after treatment with norepinephrine (in the presence of cytosol) (37). These studies both suggest that agonist-mediated PtdIns breakdown can occur at the plasma membrane, but they do not provide definitive evidence that the relevant phospholipase is associated with the plasma membrane.

2. Effects of Parathyroid Hormone (PTH)

Known renal effects of PTH include the following: PTH increases renal phosphate excretion and decreases calcium excretion. The sites of PTH-induced calcium reabsorption include the thick ascending limb of Henle and the distal tubule (17). In the proximal tubule, where there is reabsorption of sodium and calcium in part through a paracellular pathway, PTH decreases calcium reabsorption in parallel with a decrease in sodium reabsorption (17).

Recent studies suggest that calcium binding to the proximal tubule brush border may be promoted by increased levels of phosphoinositides and phosphatidic acid (47, 51, 80). Results from two laboratories now indicate that PTH increases the mass of PtdIns, PtdIns(4)P, PtdIns(4,5)P$_2$, and phosphatidic acid in the renal cortex after PTH administration in vivo, and in isolated renal cortical tubules after PTH treatment in vitro (9, 29, 30, 62). This PTH-induced increase in the levels of phosphoinositides is similar to the ACTH-induced response in adrenal cortical cells described by Farese (29). It should be noted that this agonist-induced increase in phosphoinositides is the opposite of that usually seen in other cell types. Nearly all other studies of agonist-stimulated phosphoinositide metabolism show a decline in phosphoinositides (7).

The proximal tubular brush border membrane lacks both the calcium-magnesium ATPase and the sodium/calcium exchanger found in other renal tubular membranes (47). As a consequence, the movement of calcium across the proximal tubular brush border membrane, the cellular entry step for transcellular resorption is passive, occurs by diffusion, and follows a steep electrochemical gradient. Having noted that PTH causes an increase in cortical tubular acidic phospholipids, Hruska et al initiated studies on brush border membrane vesicles (BBMV) to examine the effects of increased phosphorylation of acidic phospholipids on calcium binding by the BBMV. Increased phosphorylation of the phosphoinositides took place in the presence of ATP, presumably by the action of kinases on PtdIns, PtdIns(4)P, and diglyceride (see Introduction). Increases in phosphatidic acid and the polyphosphoinositides were seen, and this was accompanied by increased $^{45}Ca^{++}$ content of the BBMV (47). The increased calcium uptake consisted of calcium bound to the membranes, and this binding first involved the external face of the membranes and, subsequently, the internal face. Since gentamicin is known to bind to acidic phospholipids, it was added to the incubation medium to determine if calcium binding to vesicles could be prevented. This completely inhibited the ATP-stimulated increase in membrane binding of calcium, but had no effect on basal calcium uptake in BBMV incubated without ATP, nor on ^{32}P uptake by BBMV incubated with ATP. These results suggest that increases of the acidic phospholipids are associated with an increase in membrane-bound calcium. This relationship between increased levels of acidic phospholipids and membrane-bound calcium in vitro was confirmed by other studies on BBMV from animals that had been treated with PTH in vivo. Thus, PtdIns and phosphatidic acid were increased and $^{45}Ca^{++}$ binding was augmented in BBMV isolated from dogs given PTH prior to nephrectomy (51). Gentamicin also inhibited the uptake of $^{45}Ca^{++}$ by these vesicles. Although PtdIns(4)P and PtdIns(4,5)P$_2$ were not increased, it is possible that these labile lipids were lost during the isolation procedure. These studies indicate that PTH increases the binding of calcium to the BBMV, probably by increasing the membrane content of acidic phospholipids, which avidly bind calcium.

The possible role of phosphatidic acid in BBMV calcium binding has been emphasized by Somermeyer et al (80). They found that exposure of BBMV to 250 μM exogenous phosphatidic acid doubled their content of phosphatidic acid and increased the binding of calcium. The same concentrations of PtdIns or phosphatidylcholine had no effect on calcium uptake. These authors also confirmed the finding of Hruska et al that increased phosphorylation of acidic phospholipids leads to increased calcium binding to BBMV. Finally, Hruska et al found that BBMV exhibit a voltage-dependent uptake of calcium that is independent of binding and represents a diffusive permeability to calcium. When PTH was administered to dogs prior to nephrectomy and BBMV preparation, this voltage-dependent uptake of calcium was inhibited (46). Taken together, these observations indicate that increased levels of polyphosphoinositides and phosphatidic acid are associated with increased binding of calcium to

BBMV. Furthermore, when administered to dogs prior to nephrectomy, PTH causes an increase in these same phospholipids and an increase in BBMV calcium binding. These findings seem to contradict the known physiological actions of PTH, i.e. decreased rather than increased net transepithelial calcium transport (17). These observations might perhaps be explained by hypothesizing that increases of acidic phospholipids promote calcium *binding* but inhibit calcium *diffusion* across the brush border membrane. This might account for the decrease in transcellular movement of calcium in the proximal nephron caused by PTH. An additional consideration is that decreased permeability of the paracellular pathway could diminish calcium movement as well. However, other inhibitory effects of PTH on active Na^+ transport, through inhibition of apical Na^+ entry via the Na^+/H^+ antiport, may also account for the effects of PTH on fluid, Na^+, and calcium transport in the proximal nephron.

The effects of PTH on proximal tubule basolateral membrane vesicles have also been studied. In contrast to BBMV, these vesicles possess a sodium-dependent calcium exchanger. PTH stimulated sodium-dependent calcium efflux when given to dogs prior to preparation of basolateral membrane vesicles (48). In addition, PTH stimulated both phosphorylation and dephosphorylation of phosphoinositides in basolateral membrane vesicles treated in vitro (45). The basolateral membrane vesicles are apparently rendered more permeable to calcium by PTH, whereas BBMV became less permeable to calcium in spite of the increased binding of calcium. The possible physiological relevance of these findings remains unknown.

3. Renal Metabolism and Transport of Inositol

The kidney plays a major role in regulating inositol excretion and metabolism (43). Regulation of inositol metabolism involves both transport and catabolism by the kidney. About 95% of filtered inositol was reabsorbed in the isolated perfused dog kidney (64). Very little inositol is present in normal urine, but patients with glycosuria have marked inosituria, and this observation led to the suggestion that glucose may interfere with an inositol transporter mechanism in the kidney (22). The existence of such a transporter had been suggested by Hauser's studies demonstrating a sodium- and energy-dependent uptake of inositol in kidney slices (40). Studies of BBMV inositol uptake confirmed the existence of a sodium-dependent inositol transporter (36). Elevated glucose was shown to interfere with inositol uptake, but elevated inositol levels did not interfere with glucose transport. This was interpreted to mean that the inositol transporter in BBMV was separate from that responsible for bulk transport of D-glucose, but that glucose can compete with inositol for its transporter. The finding that glucose interfered with BBMV inositol uptake suggests an explanation for how hyperglycemia and glycosuria produce inosituria in patients with diabetes. These observations taken together suggest that under normal conditions inositol is not excreted by the kidney, but that pathologic states such as diabetes and glycosuria may lead to abnormal renal inositol excretion.

The amount of free inositol present in the whole kidney is among the higher levels seen in various organs, but the highest levels are seen in the pituitary gland, seminal vesicles, thyroid, and brain (23). The concentration of free intracellular inositol in these tissues is 300–500 times the mean plasma concentration of 29 μM (15, 23). Peripheral nerve also has high levels of free inositol, and declines in these levels are associated with decreased nerve conduction velocity (see below). The whole kidney contains 70–100 times the plasma concentration of inositol, but there is a striking concentration of inositol in the outer medulla (19a). This is not the location where one would predict the highest levels of free renal inositol if it were actively transported by the proximal tubule. The concentration of free inositol in cellular water of the outer medulla may be more than one thousand–fold that in plasma water (19a). The significance of the extremely high intracellular free inositol levels of the outer medulla is not known. Although portions of the kidney maintain extremely high inositol levels, very little free inositol appears in the urine. Since so little inositol is excreted in the urine, other mechanisms for eliminating inositol must exist. One possible mechanism is catabolism, or breakdown.

Studies of the fate of radiolabelled inositol injected into rats indicate that the kidney is the only organ that significantly catabolizes inositol (44). Nephrectomized rats are unable to convert labelled inositol into labelled respiratory CO_2. Cortex, medulla, and isolated tubules demonstrated similar catabolic rates for inositol (44). Metabolic studies indicate that about 1% of net renal inositol elimination is accounted for by urinary excretion (15). These studies also confirmed that inositol is catabolized to D-glucose, D-glucuronolactone, or completely oxidized to carbon dioxide and water. Inositol oxygenase has been isolated from hog kidneys and partially characterized (68). It is this enzyme that converts inositol to D-glucuronate, and thus it is responsible for the first step in the catabolism of inositol. As noted, catabolism is thought to occur exclusively in the kidney. A product of inositol catabolism, D-xylulose 5-phosphate, enters the pentosephosphate cycle (68). One point of possible interest is that myoinositol oxygenase activity is decreased in streptozotocin diabetic rats (92).

In contrast to inositol catabolism, which occurs only in the kidney, inositol synthesis occurs in several organs. De novo inositol synthesis has been identified in brain, kidney, liver, and testis. Inositol is produced by the action of inositol-1-phosphate synthase, an NAD-dependent enzyme that converts D-glucose-6-phosphate to L-inositol-1-phosphate. Free myoinositol results from dephosphorylation of L-inositol-1-phosphate by a phosphatase enzyme (28). The studies of Sherman et al indicate that the optical isomers D- and L-inositol-1-phosphate coexist in brain and kidney (78). The L-isomer is derived from de novo synthesis, whereas the D-isomer is the result of phosphoinositide breakdown. Renal de novo synthesis of inositol-1-phosphate is approximately four-fold greater than the production of inositol-1-phosphate from phosphoinositide metabolism (78). The opposite situation exists in the brain, in which the amount of inositol-1-phosphate derived from phosphoinositide catabolism is estimated to be sevenfold greater than that due to de novo synthesis (78). In humans, de novo inositol synthesis by one kidney is approximately 2 grams per day, an amount well in excess of the normal dietary intake of about 1 gram per day (43). It is not clear what contribution various organs make toward the total amount synthesized.

The control of inositol-1-phosphate synthase activity is important. The activity is higher in the testes than any other organ; this activity is diminished in diabetic rats (92). Possible hormonal control of the enzyme is suggested by recent studies of liver and testis (38). Hypophysectomy led to a decline in inositol-1-phosphate synthase activity in testis and liver, though the kidney was apparently unaffected. Thyroxine restored hepatic inositol-1-phosphate synthase activity, while gonadotropins restored activity in the testis. These findings suggest that the hormonal milieu may control inositol-1-phosphate synthase activity in some organs, but its control in the kidney remains poorly understood.

4. Altered Inositol Levels in Disease States

Dietary deficiencies of inositol are lipotropic in several species, and in spite of endogenous inositol production and its synthesis by intestinal flora, inositol deficiency states have been induced (43, 55). Concomitant physiological stress, such as pregnancy or lactation, in experimental animals will lead to deficiency states that would not otherwise be evident (12). The nutritional aspects of inositol have been recently reviewed by Holub (43), and only a few issues relevant to the kidney and diabetes will be introduced here.

The inosituria of diabetes was mentioned previously, and recent studies indicate that peripheral nerve demonstrates a deficiency of inositol in diabetes. This is seen in both experimental animals (16, 32, 66) and in human (60) diabetes. Experimental diabetic neuropathy is reversed, and inositol content restored, by dietary inositol supplementation (35). This correction occurred despite persistent hyperglycemia and elevated nerve sorbitol and fructose concentrations (32). More recent studies on diabetic nerves suggest that diminished sodium-potassium ATPase activity is linked to the peripheral neuropathy (34). This finding is of special interest because of the known activation of this enzyme (sodium-potassium ATPase) in the kidney by lipids, including PtdIns (58). It is tempting to speculate that high intracellular free-inositol levels maintain appropriate levels of PtdIns in the membrane environment of the ATPase. CDP-diacylglycerol inositol transferase (phosphatidylinositol synthase), which converts CDP-diacylglycerol and inositol to PtdIns, has a high

K_m (1.5 mM) for inositol (79). Thus, it is possible that high intracellular levels of free inositol are necessary to maintain appropriate levels of PtdIns. Small declines in inositol levels have an acute and substantial effect in reducing endoneurial O_2 consumption, and this effect may relate to the decline in activity of CDP-diacylglycerol inositol transferase (79). Furthermore, diabetes reduces the activity of this enzyme, and also of the enzyme inositol-1-phosphate synthase, which provides for de novo synthesis of inositol from glucose-6-phosphate (92). Although diabetes reduces the activity of these enzymes, it is likely that the major effect of diabetes is to reduce inositol transport into tissues as glucose competes with inositol for the transporter (33). Reduced cellular free-inositol levels would in turn reduce cellular PtdIns levels due to the sensitivity of CDP-diglyceride inositol transferase to small declines in inositol. These findings concerning inositol deficiency in peripheral nerve may be important in considering the significance of studies showing decreased inositol levels in glomeruli of diabetic rats (8). These studies showed that the experimental drug sorbinil reversed the decline of glomerular inositol in diabetic animals. It is possible, therefore, that tissues other than peripheral nerve, including the kidney, may be adversely affected by diabetes-related inositol deficiency.

In contrast to diabetic patients who show inositol deficiency, chronic renal failure leads to increased plasma levels of inositol. Plasma inositol levels 10–15 times greater than normal have been demonstrated in patients with untreated chronic renal failure (15). Although inositol is only one of many substances increased in the plasma of patients with chronic renal failure, some evidence suggests a correlation between plasma inositol levels and decreased nerve conduction velocity (14, 69). It may be important to recall that the kidney alone metabolizes inositol to glucuronic acid (see above). Thus, it has been suggested that chronic renal failure may interfere with inositol catabolism (15).

5. Studies of Phosphoinositide Metabolism in Cultured Mesangial Cells

The mesangial cell is the contractile cell of the glomerular mesangium. In culture, these cells contract when exposed to angiotensin II, vasopressin, or prostaglandin E_2 (PGE$_2$) (3, 54, 88). Vasopressin and bradykinin also cause increased prostaglandin production in mesangial cells (87). Contraction caused by angiotensin II or vasopressin is dependent upon extracellular calcium, whereas that caused by PGE$_2$ is not. Other studies have shown that there is a class of hormones which evoke calcium-dependent smooth muscle cell contraction and stimulate phosphoinositide metabolism (82). Stimulation of prostaglandin production has also been linked to accelerated phosphoinositide metabolism (59). Recent studies indicate that vasopressin stimulates phosphoinositide metabolism in mesangial cells (67, 85). The pattern of this stimulated metabolism is similar to that described as a "classical" phosphoinositide effect—the agonist leads to increased breakdown of phosphoinositides. Our studies are directed toward understanding how phosphoinositide metabolism in mesangial cells may relate to contraction, calcium mobilization, and prostaglandin production.

Following 30 min exposure of cultured mesangial cells to 10 nM vasopressin, the mass of diglyceride and phosphatidic acid increased, while PtdIns decreased. Increased uptake of ^{32}P into PtdIns(4)P and PtdIns(4,5)P$_2$ could be demonstrated at 45 sec. Within 5–10 min the content of PtdIns(4,5)P$_2$ decreased and the formation of inositol phosphates, including InsP$_3$, increased (85). These studies indicate that vasopressin leads to activation of a phospholipase C enzyme, since increased formation of InsP$_3$ is indicative of cleavage of the phosphodiester bond of PtdIns(P)$_2$. Bonventre et al, using Quin 2 as an intracellular probe of cytosolic calcium levels, have shown that increases in cytosolic calcium occur rapidly in mesangial cells following treatment with vasopressin and angiotensin II (10), even if extracellular calcium is made unavailable by chelation with EGTA (J. Bonventre, personal communication). This observation, combined with the studies showing increased InsP$_3$ levels, is consistent with the concept that agonist-stimulated phospholipase C activation promotes calcium mobilization via InsP$_3$ from intracellular stores.

The possible role of extracellular calcium in mesangial cell phosphoinositide metabolism was studied in view of the dependence of vasopressin-induced contraction on extracellular calcium (3). It was found that depletion of calcium from the incubation medium was insufficient to reduce vasopressin-stimulated PtdIns breakdown, and that chelation of calcium ions with EGTA was necessary to achieve inhibition (85). This might mean that membrane-associated calcium is important for the action of phospholipase C. However, because contraction of mesangial cells is totally inhibited by simple deletion of calcium from the incubation medium (in the absence of EGTA), the relationships among hormone-stimulated calcium mobilization from intracellular stores, extracellular calcium, phosphoinositide turnover, and contraction still remain obscure.

Although our biochemical findings are compatible with the notion that agonist-stimulated phosphoinositide metabolism occurs mainly as a result of PtdIns(4,5)P$_2$ hydrolysis, they do not exclude the possibility that PtdIns and PtdIns(4)P are also broken down by a phospholipase C. Thus, a decline in the mass of PtdIns could be accounted for either by its utilization to produce more PtdIns(4)P and PtdIns(4,5)P$_2$ or by direct hydrolysis to form diglyceride.

Vasopressin-stimulated PGE$_2$ production was also studied over time. Vasopressin treatment led to rapid formation of PGE$_2$, and other prostaglandins, which plateaued in 30 min. Using an experimental protocol of repeated exchanges of experimental and control medium, we found that new PGE$_2$ synthesis fell rapidly after the first 30 min of vasopressin treatment. In contrast, vasopressin continued to stimulate ^{32}P incorporation into PtdIns and phosphatidic acid at an undiminished rate (85). These observations suggested that stimulated phosphoinositide metabolism and prostaglandin production are independently regulated.

Additional studies indicate that angiotensin II (70), A23187 (72), and platelet activating factor (73) also stimulate prostaglandin production in mesangial cells. The possible effects of these agents on stimulated phosphoinositide metabolism in mesangial cells have not been studied. PGE$_2$ has been shown to cause contraction of mesangial cells at a concentration of 2×10^{-9} M. This concentration of PGE$_2$ does not alter phosphoinositide metabolism (D. Troyer, unpublished observations), which suggests that PGE$_2$ may bypass the agonist-receptor interaction step that leads to stimulated phosphoinositide metabolism. Further studies may clarify this issue.

6. Effects of Aminoglycosides on Renal Phosphoinositides

Nephrotoxicity is one of the major limiting factors in the use of aminoglycoside antibiotics for the treatment of infection due to gram-negative bacteria. The mechanism of aminoglycoside-induced renal proximal tubule cell injury remains poorly understood. Recent studies indicate a role for the accumulation of lipids in the pathology of aminoglycoside nephrotoxicity. For example, morphological studies have documented the accumulation of phospholipid membrane inclusions in proximal tubule lysosomes (myeloid bodies) in rats (53) and humans (24, 49). Biochemical studies indicate increased renal cortical levels of phosphatidic acid and PtdIns in rats treated with gentamicin (52). Similar findings were seen in gentamicin-treated LLC-PK$_1$ cells, which resemble proximal tubular epithelial cells (76). These studies showed accumulation of phosphatidylcholine and PtdIns in a time- and dose-dependent manner. Increases in Ptd(4)P and PtdIns(4,5)P$_2$ were also seen. This phospholipidosis could be due either to increased de novo synthesis of phospholipid or decreased breakdown of phospholipids.

Several studies suggest that phospholipase inhibition may play an important role in this phospholipidosis. As noted above, a PtdIns-specific phospholipase C has been described in BBMV isolated from rat kidney (74). Its activity in BBMV was far in excess of what could be obtained in other fractions, including the cytosol. Further studies have shown a marked inhibition of this BBMV-associated phospholipase C by gentamicin and other aminoglycosides (75). Other investigators have shown inhibition of lysosomal sphingomyelinase and phospholipases A$_1$ and A$_2$ (13) by aminoglycosides. These findings support the hypothesis that aminoglycoside-induced phospholipidosis is due to decreased phospholipid degradation. Phosphatidic acid and the phosphoinositides, which are increased in experimental aminoglycoside nephrotoxicity, may play an important role in agonist-stimulated events, and these lipid alterations may interfere with cellular functions.

A second area of interest in studies of aminoglycoside nephrotoxicity has been the role of calcium. It has been shown that dietary calcium loading ameliorates experimental gentamicin nephrotoxicity in rats (6). It has been proposed that this could be the result of displacement of gentamicin from binding sites by calcium (49). In this connection, increased levels of calcium had no effect on gentamicin inhibition of brush border membrane PtdIns-specific phospholipase C activity in vitro (75). Further, elevated calcium had no effect on gentamicin-induced increases of PtdIns and phosphatidylcholine in LLC-PK$_1$ cells (76). Gentamicin-treated LLC-PK$_1$ cells did bind more calcium (76) (possibly due to increased levels of polyphosphoinositides). In spite of this, calcium transport into and through the LLC-PK$_1$ monolayer was markedly inhibited by gentamicin. The considerations outlined earlier, that increased membrane content of acidic phospholipids may promote increased calcium binding, but inhibit diffusion across BBMV (see above) may be applicable in this regard.

7. Renal Phosphoinositide Metabolism and Prostaglandin Production: Other Studies

Treatment of cortical tubules (type not further specified) with angiotensin II and phenylephrine caused increased ^{32}P uptake into PtdIns (94). Vasopressin was without effect. In cultured MDCK cells, epinephrine caused increased incorporation of ^{3}H inositol into PtdIns (61). Epinephrine also caused increased prostaglandin production in these cells. Arachidonic acid release and prostaglandin production have been studied in renal medullary slices stimulated with A23187 (5). Finally, Ausiello & Zusman have studied the role of calcium in prostaglandin production by cultured renal-medullary interstitial cells (4).

SUMMARY AND CONCLUSION

The unique features of renal phosphoinositide metabolism include an increase in tissue phosphoinositide levels induced by PTH (9, 29, 30, 62). The significance of this finding remains unclear. Another unusual finding is the localization of phospholipase C activity in a BBMV preparation (74). As suggested in the review, the transducing mechanism involving cleavage of phosphoinositides by a phospholipase C would be expected to include a close association between phospholipase C and the plasma membrane. However, few attempts to localize phospholipase C activity in the plasma membrane have succeeded.

The kidney also plays an unusual role in inositol metabolism in that it is the only organ that significantly catabolizes inositol. The kidneys also synthesize inositol (15, 43). There is an enormous concentration of inositol in the outer medulla (19). This coexistence of significant inositol synthesis, breakdown, and the presence of extremely high amounts of free inositol is an intriguing but unexplained phenomenon.

The substantial rate of endogenous renal inositol synthesis does not, however, preclude inositol deficiency states. There is a deficiency of inositol in diabetic peripheral nerve and in glomeruli isolated from diabetic rats (8, 16, 32, 66). Such deficiencies may arise from a disturbance in the balance of synthesis, breakdown, and excretion of inositol, and particularly from the competition of glucose with the inositol transporter in the proximal tubule.

Future studies of renal phosphoinositide metabolism need to address both basic cell biological questions and broader physiological or functional questions. The more basic issues include the question of which phosphoinositide is being attacked by agonist-stimulated phospholipase C. That is, are all the events explained by hydrolysis of PtdIns(4,5)P_2, or are the other phosphoinositides hydrolyzed as well? Also, it would appear that stimulated phosphoinositide metabolism occurs quite early following receptor occupation, but there is still no way of selectively blocking stimulated phosphoinositide metabolism to see if it is a necessary first step in a cascade of events leading to cell response. Thus, the relationship of stimulated phosphoinositide metabolism to cell functions remains incompletely understood. At least two cellular functional or biochemical changes associated with stimulated phosphoinositide metabolism in the kidney have been identified, prostaglandin production and mesangial cell contraction. The regulation of prostaglandin production and its relationship to stimulated phosphoinositide metabolism are subjects of continuing study. The topic was recently reviewed by Hassid (39). It is not clear that stimulated phosphoinositide metabolism is a necessary event for prostaglandin metabolism, but it is certainly permissive, possibly by mobilizing calcium for phospholipase A_2 action.

Other topics for study include diabetes-induced alterations in renal phosphoinositide metabolism. The finding of diminished glomerular inositol levels in streptozotocin diabetic rats should provide a stimulus for further in vitro and in vivo studies of phosphoinositide metabolism in diabetes. Altered phosphoinositide metabolism may, in conjunction with other features of diabetes, lead to cellular abnormalities that contribute to the renal pathology of diabetes.

The possible implications for cellular regulation by phospholipid-dependent protein kinase C in the kidney have received little attention to date. It has recently been suggested that protein kinase C may be involved in the action of vasopressin on the toad urinary bladder (71).

In summary, numerous areas of phosphoinositide metabolism in the kidney deserve further study. The filtration and transport functions of the kidney make this a particularly interesting organ since a variety of hormones modulate these activities. We hope this review will stimulate interest in the area.

ACKNOWLEDGMENT

We wish to thank Dr. Keith Hruska for critical review of the manuscript. We also thank Sharon Cloer for typing the manuscript. The authors' work presented in this review was supported by grants from the American Heart Association (Texas Affiliate G-614), the Pharmaceutical Manufacturers Association, and the National Institutes of Health (AM 29787 and AM 17387).

Literature Cited

1. Abdel-Latif, A. A., Akhtar, R. A., Hawthorne, J. N. 1977. Acetylcholine increases the breakdown of triphosphoinositide of rabbit iris muscle prelabelled with (^{32}P) phosphate. *Biochem. J.* 162:61–73
2. Akhtar, R., Abdel-Latif, A. A. 1978. Studies on the properties of triphosphoinositide phosphomonoesterase and phosphodiesterase of rabbit iris smooth muscle. *Biochim. Biophys. Acta* 527: 159–70
3. Ausiello, D. A., Kreisberg, J. I., Roy, C., Karnovsky, M. J. 1980. Contraction of cultured rat glomerular cells of apparent mesangial origin after stimulation with angiotensin II and arginine vasopressin. *J. Clin. Invest.* 65:754–60
4. Ausiello, D. A., Zusman, R. M. 1984. The role of calcium in the stimulation of prostaglandin synthesis by vasopressin in rabbit renal-medullary interstitial cells in tissue culture. *Biochem. J.* 220:139–45
5. Benabe, J. E., Spry, L. A., Morrison, A. R. 1982. Effects of angiotensin II on phosphatidylinositol and polyphosphoinositide turnover in rat kidney. *J. Biol. Chem.* 257:7430–34
6. Bennett, W. M., Elliott, W. C., Houghton, D. C., Gilbert, D. N., DeFehr, J., McCarron, D. A. 1982. Reduction of gentamicin nephrotoxicity in rats by dietary calcium loading. *Antimicrob. Agents Chemother.* 22:508–12
7. Berridge, M. J., Irvine, R. F. 1984. Inositol trisphosphate, a novel second messenger in cellular signal transduction. *Nature* 312:315–21
8. Beyer-Mears, A., Ku, L., Cohen, M. P. 1984. Glomerular polyol accumulation in diabetes and its prevention by oral sorbinil. *Diabetes* 33:604–7
9. Bidot-Lopez, P., Farese, R. V., Sabir, M. A. 1981. Parathyroid hormone and adenosine-3',5'-monophosphate acutely increase phospholipids of the phosphatidate-polyphosphoinositide pathway in rabbit kidney cortex tubules *in vitro* by a

cycloheximide-sensitive process. *Endocrinology* 108:2078–81
10. Bonventre, J. V., Cheung, J. Y., Skorecki, K., Kreisberg, J. I., Ausiello, D. A. 1984. Vasopressin and angiotensin II increase cytosolic free Ca^{++} levels in glomerular mesangial cells. *Kidney Int.* 27(#73):323 (Abstr.)
11. Burgess, G. M., Godfrey, P. P., McKinney, J. S., Berridge, M. J., Irvine, R. F., Putney, J. W. 1984. The second messenger linking receptor activation to internal Ca release in liver. *Nature* 309:63–66
12. Burton, L. E., Wells, W. W. 1976. Myoinositol metabolism during lactation and development in the rat. The prevention of lactation-induced fatty liver by dietary myo-inositol. *J. Nutr.* 106:1617–28
13. Carlier, M. B., Laurent, G., Claes, P. J., Vanderhaeghe, H. J., Tulkens, P. M. 1983. Inhibition of lysosomal phospholipases by aminoglycoside antibiotics: *In vitro* comparative studies. *Antimicrob. Agents Chemother.* 23:440–49
14. Clements, R. S., DeJesus, P. V., Winegrad, A. I. 1973. Raised plasma myoinositol levels in uraemia and experimental neuropathy. *Lancet* 1:1137–41
15. Clements, R. S., Diethelm, A. G. 1979. The metabolism of myo-inositol by the human kidney. *J. Lab. Clin. Med.* 93: 210–19
16. Clements, R. S. Jr., Stockard, C. R. 1980. Abnormal sciatic nerve *myo*-inositol metabolism in the streptozotocin-diabetic rat. *Diabetes* 29:227–35
17. Coburn, J. W., Slatopolsky, E. 1981. Vitamin D, parathyroid hormone and renal osteodystrophy. In *The Kidney*, ed. B. Brenner, F. Rector, 43:2233–35. Philadelphia: Saunders
18. Cockroft, S. 1984. Ca^{++}-dependent conversion of phosphatidylinositol to phosphatidate in neutrophils stimulated with fMet-Leu-Phe or ionophore A23187. *Biochim. Biophys. Acta* 795:37–46
19a. Cohen, M. A., Hruska, K. A., Daughaday, W. H. 1982. Free myo-inositol in

canine kidneys: Selective concentration in the renal medulla. *Proc. Soc. Exp. Biol. Med.* 169:380–85

19b. Connolly, T. M., Bross, T. E., Majerus, P. W. 1985. Isolation of a phosphomonoesterase from human platelets that specifically hydrolyzes the 5-phosphate of inositol 1,4,5,-trisphosphate. *J. Biol. Chem.* 260:7868–74

20. Cooper, P. H., Hawthorne, J. N. 1975. Phosphomonoesterase hydrolysis of polyphosphoinositides in rat kidney. *Biochem. J.* 150:537–51

21. Cooper, P. H., Hawthorne, J. N. 1976. Phosphatidylinositol kinase and diphosphoinositide kinase of rat kidney cortex. *Biochem. J.* 160:97–105

22. Daughaday, W. H., Larner, J., Houghton, E. 1954. The renal excretion of inositol by normal and diabetic rats. *J. Clin. Invest.* 33:1075–80

23. Dawson, R. M. C., Freinkel, N. 1961. The distribution of free mesoinositol in mammalian tissues, including some observations on the lactating rat. *Biochem. J.* 78:606–10

24. DeBroe, M. E., Paulus, G. J., Venpooten, G. A., Roels, F., Buyssens, N., et al. 1984. Early effects of gentamicin, tobramycin, and amikacin on the human kidney. *Kidney Int.* 25:643–52

25. Downes, C. P., Michell, R. H. 1981. The polyphosphoinositide phosphodiesterase of erythrocyte membranes. *Biochem. J.* 198:133–40

26. Downes, P., Michell, R. H. 1982. Phosphatidylinositol 4-phosphate and phosphatidylinositol 4,5-bisphosphate: Lipids in search of a function. *Cell Calcium* 3:467–502

27. Durell, J., Garland, J. T., Friedel, R. O. 1969. Acetylcholine action: Biochemical aspects. *Science* 165:862–66

28. Eisenberg, F. Jr. 1967. D-Myoinositol 1-phosphate as product of cyclization of glucose 6-phosphate and substrate for a specific phosphatase in rat testis. *J. Biol. Chem.* 242:1375–82

29. Farese, R. V. 1983. Phosphoinositide metabolism and hormone action. *Endocrine Rev.* 4:78–95

30. Farese, R. V., Bidot-Lopez, P., Sabir, A., Smith, J., Schinbeckler, B., Larson, R. 1980. Parathyroid hormone acutely increases polyphosphoinositides of the rabbit kidney cortex by a cycloheximide-sensitive process. *J. Clin. Invest.* 65:1523–26

31. Folch, J. 1949. Brain diphosphoinositide, a new phosphatide having inositol metadiphosphate as a constituent. *J. Biol. Chem.* 177:505–19

32. Greene, D. A., DeJesus, P. V. Jr., Winegrad, A. I. 1975. Effects of insulin and dietary myoinositol on impaired peripheral motor nerve conduction velocity in acute streptozotocin diabetes. *J. Clin. Invest.* 55:1326–36

33. Greene, D. A., Lattimer, S. A. 1982. Sodium- and energy-dependent uptake of *myo*-inositol by rabbit peripheral nerve. *J. Clin. Invest.* 70:1009–18

34. Greene, D. A., Lattimer, S. A. 1983. Impaired rat sciatic nerve sodium-potassium adenosine triphosphatase in acute streptozocin diabetes and its correction by dietary *myo*-inositol supplementation. *J. Clin. Invest.* 72:1058–63

35. Greene, D. A., Lewis, R. A., Lattimer, S. A., Brown, M. J. 1982. Selective effects of *myo*-inositol administration on sciatic and tibial motor nerve conduction parameters in the streptozotocin-diabetic rat. *Diabetes* 31:573–78

36. Hammerman, M. R., Sacktor, B., Daughaday, W. H. 1980. Myo-inositol transport in renal brush border vesicles and its inhibition by D-glucose. *Am. J. Physiol.* 239:F113–20

37. Harrington, C. A., Eichberg, J. 1983. Norepinephrine causes alpha 1-adrenergic receptor-mediated decrease of phosphatidylinositol in isolated rat liver plasma membranes supplemented with cytosol. *J. Biol. Chem.* 258:2087–90

38. Hasegawa, R., Eisenberg, F. Jr. 1981. Selective hormonal control of *myo*-inositol biosynthesis in reproductive organs and liver of the male rat. *Proc. Natl. Acad. Sci. USA* 78:4863–66

39. Hassid, A. 1982. Regulation of prostaglandin biosynthesis in cultured cells. *Am. J. Physiol.* 243:C205–11

40. Hauser, G. 1965. Energy- and sodium-dependent uptake of inositol by kidney cortex slices. *Biochem. Biophys. Res. Comm.* 19:696–701

41. Hawthorne, J. N., White, D. A. 1975. Myo-inositol lipids. *Vitam. Horm.* 33:529–73

42. Hokin, M. R., Hokin, L. E. 1953. Enzyme secretion and the incorporation of ^{32}P into phospholipids of pancreas slices. *J. Biol. Chem.* 203:967–77

43. Holub, B. J. 1982. The nutritional significance, metabolism, and function of myo-inositol and phosphatidylinositol in health and disease. *Adv. Nutr. Res.* 4:107–41

44. Howard, C. F. Jr., Anderson, L. 1967. Metabolism of myo-inositol in animals. II. Complete catabolism of myo-inositol ^{14}C by rat kidney slices. *Arch. Biochem. Biophys.* 118:332–39

45. Hruska, K. A., Esbrit, P. 1983. Cyclic nucleotide independent stimulation of phospholipid phosphorylation and turnover by parathyroid hormone in basolateral membranes of renal tubular cells in vitro. Clin. Res. 31:502A (Abstr.)

46. Hruska, K., Khalifa, S., Mills, S. 1983. Voltage dependent calcium uptake in renal tubular brush border membrane vesicles. Fed. Proc. 42(#5826):1286 (Abstr.)

47. Hruska, K. A., Mills, S. C., Khalifa, S., Hammerman, M. R. 1983. Phosphorylation of renal brush-border membrane vesicles. J. Biol. Chem. 258:2501–7

48. Hruska, K. A., Mills, S., Scoble, J. 1984. Calcium transport in renal basolateral membrane vesicles: Effects of parathyroid hormone. Kidney Int. 25(#20):144 (Abstr.)

49. Humes, D. H., Weinberg, J. M., Knauss, J. C. 1982. Clinical and pathophysiologic aspects of aminoglycoside nephrotoxicity. Am. J. Kidney Dis. 2:5–29

50a. Irvine, R. F., Letcher, A. J., Lander, D. J., Downes, C. P. 1984. Inositol trisphosphates in carbachol-stimulated rat parotid glands. Biochem. J. 223:237–43

50b. Joseph, S. K., Williams, R. J. 1985. Subcellular localization and some properties of the enzymes hydrolyzing inositol polyphosphates in rat liver. FEBS Lett. 180:150–54

51. Khalifa, S., Mills, S., Hruska, K. A. 1983. Stimulation of calcium uptake by parathyroid hormone in renal brush-border membrane vesicles. J. Biol. Chem. 258:14400–6

52. Knauss, T. C., Weinberg, J. M., Humes, H. D. 1983. Alterations in renal cortical phospholipid content induced by gentamicin: Time course, specificity and subcellular localization. Am. J. Physiol. 244:F535-F546

53. Kosek, J. C., Mazze, R. I., Cousins, M. J. 1974. Nephrotoxicity of gentamicin. Lab. Invest. 30:48–57

54. Kreisberg, J. I. 1985. Contractile properties of cultured glomerular mesangial cells. Am. J. Phys. In press

55. Kuksis, A., Mookerjea, S. 1978. Inositol. Nutr. Rev. 36:233–38

56. Lapetina, E. G. 1984. Phospholipases. In Ann. Rep. Med. Chem. 19:213–21

57. Lee, T. C., Huggins, C. G. 1968. Triphosphoinositide phosphomonoesterase in rat kidney cortex. Arch. Biochem. Biophys. 126:214–20

58. Mandersloot, J. G., Roelofsen, B., DeGier, J. 1978. Phosphatidylinositol as the endogenous activator of the $(Na + K+)$-ATPase in microsomes of rabbit kidney. Biochim. Biophys. Acta 508:478–85

59. Marshall, P. J., Boatman, D. E., Hokin, L. E. 1981. Direct demonstration of the formation of prostaglandin E_2 due to phosphatidylinositol breakdown associated with stimulation of enzyme secretion in the pancreas. J. Biol. Chem. 256:844–47

60. Mayhew, J. A., Gillon, K. R. W., Hawthorne, J. N. 1983. Free and lipid inositol, sorbitol and sugars in sciatic nerve obtained post-mortem from diabetic patients and control subjects. Diabetologia 24:13–15

61. Meier, K. E., Snavely, M. D., Brown, S. L., Brown, J. H., Insel, P. A. 1983. Alpha 1- and beta 2-adrenergic receptor expression in the Madin-Darby canine kidney epithelial cell line. J. Cell Biol. 97:405–15

62. Meltzer, V., Weinreb, S., Bellorin-Font, E., Hruska, K. A. 1982. Parathyroid hormone stimulation of renal phosphoinositide metabolism is a cyclic nucleotide-independent effect. Biochim. Biophys. Acta 712:258–67

63. Michell, R. H. 1975. Inositol phospholipids and cell surface receptor function. Biochim. Biophys. Acta 415:81–147

64. Molitoris, B. A., Hruska, K. A., Fishman, N., Daughaday, W. H. 1979. Effects of glucose and parathyroid hormone on the renal handling of myoinositol by isolated perfused dog kidneys. J. Clin. Invest. 63:1110–18

65. Nishizuka, Y. 1984. The role of protein kinase C in cell surface signal transduction and tumor promotion. Nature 308:693–98

66. Palmano, K. P., Whiting, P. H., Hawthorne, J. N. 1977. Free and lipid myoinositol in tissues from rats with acute and less severe streptozotocin-induced diabetes. Biochem. J. 167:229–35

67. Pfeilschifter, J., Kurtz, A., Bauer, C. 1984. Activation of phospholipase C and prostaglandin synthesis by [arginine]vasopressin in cultures. Biochem. J. 223:855–59

68. Reddy, C. C., Swan, J. S., Hamilton, G. A. 1981. Myo-inositol oxygenase from hog kidney. J. Biol. Chem. 256:8510–18

69. Reznek, R. H., Salway, J. G., Thomas, P. K. 1977. Plasma-myoinositol concentrations in uremic neuropathy. Lancet 1:675–76

70. Scharschmidt, L. A., Dunn, M. J. 1983. Prostaglandin synthesis by rat glomerular mesangial cells in culture: Effects of angiotensin II and arginine vasopressin. J. Clin. Invest. 71:1756–64

71. Schlondorff, D., Levine, S. D. 1985. Protein kinase C inhibits vasopressin stimulated water flow in toad urinary

bladder. *Kidney Int.* 27(#73):334 (Abstr.)

72. Schlondorff, D., Perez, J., Satriano, J. A. 1985. Differential stimulation of PGE$_2$ synthesis in mesangial cells by angiotensin and A23187. *Am. J. Physiol.* 248:C119–26

73. Schlondorff, D., Satriano, J. A., Hagege, J., Perez, J., Baud, L. 1984. Effect of platelet-activating factor and serum-treated zymosan on prostaglandin E$_2$ synthesis, arachidonic acid release, and contraction of cultured rat mesangial cells. *J. Clin. Invest.* 73:1227–31

74. Schwertz, D. W., Kreisberg, J. I., Venkatachalam, M. A. 1983. Characterization of rat kidney proximal tubule brush border membrane-associated phosphatidylinositol phosphodiesterase. *Arch. Biochem. Biophys.* 224:555–67

75. Schwertz, D. W., Kreisberg, J. I., Venkatachalam, M. A. 1984. Effects of aminoglycosides on proximal tubule brush border membrane phosphatidylinositolspecific phospholipase C. *J. Pharmacol. Exp. Ther.* 231:48–55

76. Schwertz, D. W., Kreisberg, J. I., Venkatachalam, M. A. 1985. Gentamicininduced alterations in pig kidney epithelial cells (LLC-PK$_1$) cells in culture. *J. Pharmacol. Exp. Therapeut.* In press

77. Seyfred, M. A., Wells, W. W. 1984. Subcellular site and mechanism of vasopressin-stimulated hydrolysis of phosphoinositides in rat hepatocytes, *J. Biol. Chem.* 259:7666–72

78. Sherman, W. R., Munsell, L. Y., Gish, B. G., Honchar, M. P. 1985. Effects of systemically administered lithium on phosphoinositide metabolism in rat brain, kidney and testis. *J. Neurochem.* 44:798–807

79. Simmons, D. A., Winegrad, A. I., Martin, D. B. 1982. Significance of tissue *myo*-inositol concentrations in metabolic regulation in nerve. *Science* 217:848–50

80. Somermeyer, M. G., Knauss, T. C., Weinberg, J. M., Humes, H. D. 1983. Characterization of Ca^{++} transport in rat renal brush-border membranes and its modulation by phosphatidic acid. *Biochem. J.* 214:37–46

81a. Speziale, N. B., Speziale, E. H. S., Terragno, A., Terragno, N. A. 1982. Phospholipase C activity in rat kidney. Effect of deoxycholate on phosphatidylinositol turnover. *Biochim. Biophys. Acta* 712:65–70

81b. Storey, D. J., Shears, S. B., Kirk, C. J., Michell, R. H. 1984. Stepwise enzymatic dephosphorylation of inositol 1,4,5-trisphosphate to inositol in liver. *Nature* 312:374–76

82. Takenawa, T. 1982. Inositol phospholipids in stimulated smooth muscles. *Cell Calcium* 3:359–68

83. Tou, J. S., Hurst, M. W., Baricos, W. H., Huggins, C. G. 1973. The hydrolysis of triphosphoinositide by a phosphodiesterase in rat kidney cortex. *Arch. Biochem. Biophys.* 154:593–600

84. Tou, J. S., Hurst, M. W., Huggins, C. G., Foor, W. E. 1970. Biosynthesis of triphosphoinositide in rat kidney cortex. *Arch. Biochem. Biophys.* 140:492–502

85. Troyer, D. A., Kreisberg, J. I., Schwertz, D. W., Venkatachalam, M. A. 1985. The effects of vasopressin on phosphoinositide and prostaglandin production in cultured mesangial cells. *Am. J. Phys.* 249:F139–47

86. Turner, P. R., Sheetz, M. P., Jaffe, L. A. 1984. Fertilization increases the polyphosphoinositide content of sea urchin eggs. *Nature* 310:414–15

87. Uglesity, A., Kreisberg, J. I., Levine, L. 1983. Stimulation of arachidonic acid metabolism in rat kidney mesangial cells by bradykinin, antidiuretic hormone, and their analogues. *Prostaglandins Leukotrienes Med.* 10:83–93

88. Venkatachalam, M. A., Kreisberg, J. I. 1985. Agonist induced isotonic contraction of cultured mesangial cells after multiple passages. *Am. J. Physiol.* 249:C48–C55

89. Vickers, J. D.. Kiniough-Rathbone, R. L., Mustard, J. F. 1984. Changes in platelet phosphoinositides during the first minute after stimulation of washed rabbit platelets with thrombin. *Biochem. J.* 219:25–31

90. Wallace, M. A., Randazzo, P., Li, S., Fain, J. N. 1982. Direct stimulation of phosphatidylinositol degradation by addition of vasopressin to purified rat liver plasma membranes. *Endocrinology* 111:341–43

91. Whitaker, M., Irvine, R. F. 1984. Inositol 1,4,5-trisphosphate microinjection activates sea urchin eggs. *Nature* 312:636–39

92. Whiting, P. H., Palmano, K. P., Hawthorne, J. N. 1979. Enzymes of myoinositol and inositol lipid metabolism in rats with streptozotocin-induced diabetes. *Biochem. J.* 179:549–53

93. Wilson, D. B., Bross, T. E., Hofman, S., Majerus, P. W. 1984. Hydrolysis of polyphosphoinositides by purified sheep seminal vesicle phospholipase C enzymes. *J. Biol. Chem.* 259:11718–24

94. Wirthensohn, G., Lefrank, S., Guder, W. G. 1984. Phospholipid metabolism in rat kidney cortical tubules. II. Effects of hormones on ^{32}P incorporation. *Biochim. Biophys. Acta* 795:401–10

GASTROINTESTINAL PHYSIOLOGY

RECEPTOR IDENTIFICATION AND CELL ACTIVATION MECHANISMS

Introduction, John G. Forte, *Section Editor*

The gastrointestinal system is finely regulated to serve the physiological function of alimentation. This frequently involves radical changes in tissue activity from basal metabolic stasis to maximal transport function. In this volume the section on Gastrointestinal Physiology is devoted to a review of the identification of specific receptors and their coupling to cytosolic activation events that express a given transport function.

Receptor signalling mechanisms in salivary glands include (*a*) those involving cyclic adenosine-3',5'-monophosphate (cyclic AMP), which primarily regulate enzyme secretion; and (*b*) those involving inositol triphosphate (IP$_3$), via changes in intracellular Ca^{2+}, which regulate ion and water secretion. Dr. Putney reviews these pathways for salivary cell activation with particular emphasis on the relationship between receptors, Ca^{2+} mobilization, and the role of inositol lipids.

Drs. Soll and Sanders review research that has characterized receptors on gastric parietal cells and other cells isolated from fundic mucosa. They propose an interaction of neurocrine, endocrine, and paracrine transmitters that may finely regulate HCl secretion.

Identification of receptors that activate pancreatic enzyme secretion is the subject of the chapter by Drs. Gardner and Jensen. Pancreatic enzyme receptors are divided into two general categories: those that cause mobilization of cell Ca^{2+}, and those that increase cellular cyclic AMP levels. While these receptor classes are functionally independent in the initial stages leading to enzyme output, the authors suggest that the cytosolic activation pathways may converge at the final steps. Such a convergence might explain potentiation of enzyme secretion.

Hepatocyte receptors are concerned with recognition and catabolism of circulating plasma lipoproteins. Dr. Havel's review deals with identification and localization of receptors involved with metabolism of various classes of lipoproteins. He also reviews recent work concerning receptor-mediated endocytosis in hepatocytes. Interrelationships between regulation of specific lipoprotein receptor activity and plasma lipoprotein levels are discussed.

As with many other activities of the digestive tract, it is now clear that intestinal absorption and secretion are modulated by receptor-mediated activation processes through cytosolic levels of Ca^{2+} and cyclic AMP. Drs. Donowitz and Welsh review evidence demonstrating the role of these cellular activation pathways in membrane transport processes associated with the flow of salt and water across mammalian small intestine and colon.

Ann. Rev. Physiol. 1986. 48:75–88

IDENTIFICATION OF CELLULAR ACTIVATION MECHANISMS ASSOCIATED WITH SALIVARY SECRETION

J. W. Putney, Jr.

Division of Cellular Pharmacology, Medical College of Virginia, Richmond, Virginia 23298-0001

INTRODUCTION

Over the past thirty years, the salivary glands have continued to prove useful models for understanding receptor and cellular signalling mechanisms in the gastrointestinal (GI) tract and elsewhere. This can be attributed largely to the relative anatomical simplicity of the glands, rapid and easily quantitated responses to agonists, and a lack of electrical excitability. This last attribute, lack of electrical excitability, implies that the events linking receptor occupation to the expression of an appropriate cellular response, secretion, likely involve a sequence of simple biochemical and ionic changes, without the complex kinetics of excitation phenomena and propagated signals.

There appear to be two basic stimulus-response coupling pathways involved in salivary secretion. One involves cyclic adenosine $3',5'$-monophosphate (cyclic AMP), and is primarily involved with enzyme secretion; the other has been termed the Ca^{2+}-pathway, and it regulates ion and water flux, and to some degree enzyme secretion. As discussed later, however, recent findings suggest that the term "Ca^{2+}-pathway" may be something of a misnomer. There has been rapid advancement in our understanding of the Ca^{2+}-pathway in recent years; this review therefore emphasizes recent findings on the relationship between receptors, Ca^{2+}-mobilization, and the role of the inositol lipids. Previous reviews dealt in greater detail with the cyclic AMP pathway (14), and other specific aspects of this topic (9, 11, 34, 36, 42–44, 52).

75

0066-4278/86/0315-0075$02.00

THE CYCLIC AMP PATHWAY

The work of Schramm, Selinger, and others provided evidence that in the rat parotid gland, β-adrenoceptor activation stimulates the exocytotic discharge of α-amylase by a mechanism involving cyclic AMP as a messenger (60). Briefly, the findings of this group and others were as follows: (a) amylase secretion can be efficiently activated by butyrated derivatives of cyclic AMP (7); (b) adenylate cyclase is present in parotid membranes (59); (c) β-adrenoceptor agonists cause an increase in parotid content of cyclic AMP (51); and (d) inhibitors of cyclic AMP phosphodiesterase potentiate amylase secretion (7).

The mechanism by which cyclic AMP regulates secretion is unknown. Some cellular Ca seems necessary for the effect, and β-agonists stimulate efflux of ^{45}Ca (48, 63). Accordingly, it has been suggested that cyclic AMP, either directly or through phosphorylation, might release intracellular Ca (48). Recently, it has become possible to directly monitor changes in ionized cytosolic Ca^{2+} with the fluorescent indicator quin-2 (68). With this technique, Aub found that the basal cytosolic $[Ca^{2+}]$ in dispersed parotid cells was about 200 nM (2). Methacholine, a muscarinic-cholinergic stimulus, increased $[Ca^{2+}]_i$ three- to fivefold. Isoproterenol, however, at a concentration (1 μM) adequate to give maximal amylase release, did not cause any change in the level of cytosolic ionized Ca^{2+}. This finding argues against any mobilization of cellular Ca^{2+} in the cyclic AMP pathway, and would favor the concerted model, as described by Butcher & Putney (14), in which Ca^{2+} and cyclic AMP are seen as parallel but potentially interacting regulators of exocytosis.

By comparison with other systems, it seems a reasonable working hypothesis that the cyclic AMP pathway regulates secretion through phosphorylation of specific proteins mediated by cyclic AMP-dependent protein kinase. A number of laboratories have demonstrated protein phosphorylation in salivary glands following β-adrenoceptor activation (6, 24, 50, 64), but evidence implicating one or any in regulation of exocytosis has been difficult to obtain. A major difficulty is that the precise molecular events involved in the process of exocytosis, which could function as control points, are not at all understood (52).

Recent reports on studies using toxins specific for the cAMP system further substantiate the notion that activation of adenylate cyclase can serve to provide a sufficient signal for enzyme secretion. Spearman et al (64) found that cholera toxin, which activates adenylate cyclase by ADP-ribosylation of the stimulatory guanine nucleotide-dependent regulatory protein, stimulated parotid enzyme secretion and produced a pattern of protein phosphorylation similar to that for isoproterenol. Watson & Dowd (70) examined the effects on parotid gland function of forskolin, an agent that also bypasses the receptor in activating adenylate cyclase, but whose precise mode of action is less certain. As for cholera toxin, forskolin reproduced the effects of β-adrenoceptor agonists in increasing cellular cyclic AMP, protein kinase activity, and amylase secretion (70).

THE CALCIUM PATHWAY

Stimulus Permeability Coupling

Evidence for a role of calcium in regulation of salivary secretion was first presented by Douglas & Poisner (17), who reported that Ca ions were necessary for maintenance and stimulation of secretion by perfused salivary glands. In the intact gland, the secretion of ions and water is a manifestation of the epithelial function of the gland and is believed to reflect receptor-regulated monovalent ion permeabilities and transports at the cellular level (34, 42, 58). That these ion fluxes could be studied with in vitro preparations was first demonstrated by Schneyer & Schneyer (57), and was later studied in greater detail by Schramm, Selinger and coworkers (5, 60, 61). The latter investigators found that activation of α-adrenoceptors and muscarinic-cholinergic receptors, but not β-adrenoceptors, resulted in a net efflux of K^+ from parotid gland slices (5). Subsequently, they demonstrated that extracellular Ca^{2+} was required for this effect (61), and that a Ca^{2+} ionophore, A-23187, could also activate K^+ efflux (62). Later experiments suggested a similar mechanism was operable for a substance P receptor (54). Activation of these receptors has been shown to increase both the uptake and efflux of cellular ^{45}Ca (14). Accordingly, a strong case was established for involvement of a Ca^{2+} signalling mechanism in the process of stimulus-permeability coupling in the salivary glands and a variety of other systems (14, 42).

Putney and collaborators (29, 40, 41) investigated the kinetics of the K^+ flux response in the parotid gland slices by using tracer quantities of $^{86}Rb^+$. The increased, unidirectional $^{86}Rb^+$ efflux that occurred with cholinergic stimuli appeared biphasic: an initial rapid, transient increase occurred, which was followed by a less pronounced, more sustained response. In experiments carried out with media lacking Ca^{2+}, the initial transient phase persisted, but the second, sustained phase was abolished. Based on these and other observations it was suggested that the initial, transient phase of the response was due to the release of Ca^{2+}, from an internal pool, and the sustained phase was mediated by receptor-activated Ca^{2+} entry across the plasma membrane (41, 42). Further, experiments involving serial addition of agonists, and agonists applied in combination, suggested that the three separate receptors (muscarinic, α-adrenergic, substance P) regulate a common cellular pool of Ca, and a common Ca entry pathway (29, 41).

An interesting characteristic of the receptor-regulated Ca^{2+} pool in the parotid gland is its apparent requirement for extracellular Ca^{2+} for replenishment. This was best illustrated by the ^{86}Rb$^+$ efflux experiments of Aub et al (3). When a cholinergic stimulus was applied to parotid gland slices in the absence of extracellular Ca, a characteristic transient response occurred; however, when the stimulus was removed, and substance P applied, no response was obtained. This result implied that a small pool of Ca had been discharged by the cholinergic stimulus, which could not be replenished for release by substance P in the absence of extracellular Ca. Measurements of net ^{45}Ca fluxes in parotid cells indicate that the quantity of Ca released under these conditions is only about 10% of the exchangeable Ca, and probably a much smaller fraction of total Ca. To reload the receptor-regulated pool, the cells must be returned to a Ca^{2+}-containing medium (mM quantities) for about 2 min (3). During this reloading process there is a rapid influx in Ca ($>$ .5 nmol/mg protein per min) (37). However, no increased ^{86}Rb efflux is observed, which indicates there is no increase in ionized [Ca^{2+}] in the subplasmalemmal space (3, 37). Taken together these observations all indicate that during refilling the receptor-regulated pool communicates directly with the extracellular space in some unknown manner. This pathway appears to be rectified to some degree, since the pool is quite stable in low Ca^{2+} media (3, 40). This finding shows that appreciable Ca^{2+} flux from the pool to the extracellular space (i.e. the reverse reaction) does not occur.

Phosphoinositides

Hokin & Hokin (21) first demonstrated an enhanced turnover of phosphatidylinositol (PI) and its precursor phosphatidic acid (PA) (measured as ^{32}P incorporation from inorganic phosphate), which is associated with cholinergic activation of exocrine pancreas. Later, Hokin & Sherwin (20) found that a similar phenomenon occurred in the salivary glands. Initially, it was thought that this reaction might be directly involved in the secretory process, but this idea was soon discounted when it was shown that Ca ommission blocked pancreatic secretion due to acetylcholine, but not the PI turnover (19). Subsequently it was shown that for the parotid gland, β-adrenoceptor activation, which is the most efficient pathway for induction of enzyme secretion, did not induce PI turnover (33). However, activation of those receptors associated with Ca^{2+} mobilization (muscarinic, α-adrenergic, substance P) caused a substantial effect (33, 72).

Based on his findings with the parotid gland system, as well as the published results of others, Michell suggested in 1975 (31) that turnover of inositol lipids might in some manner serve to couple receptor activation to cellular Ca mobilization. He based this primarily on three points of circumstantial evidence (31): (a) the PI effect was almost invariably associated with Ca-mobilizing receptors, and never, for example, with receptors linked to adenylate cyclase; (b) the PI effect was relatively resistant to Ca depletion; (c) the PI effect was not activated by Ca ionophores. These observations suggested to Michell that the PI effect was not a consequence of cellular Ca mobilization, and thus might precede Ca mobilization in the stimulus-response coupling pathway (31).

Weiss & Putney (72) investigated the actions of receptors in regulating PI turnover in dispersed parotid acinar cells. Methacholine (a muscarinic-cholinergic agonist), epinephrine (with propranolol, an α-agonist) and substance P each substantially increased cellular PI labelling (by $^{32}PO_4$ added to the incubation medium). The maximum effects for the three agonists differed markedly, however; the rank order was methacholine > epinephrine > substance P, in proportions of about $1:0.4:0.25$. One possible explanation for these variations is that they reflect the relative numbers of the three kinds of receptors present. This suggestion is essentially ruled out by the results of experiments with the agonists applied in combination. Methacholine and epinephrine, as well as methacholine and substance P, when applied in combination gave responses intermediate between the responses obtained with each agonist alone, i.e. epinephrine caused a partial inhibition of the response to methacholine. When epinephrine and substance P were applied in combination, the response obtained was no greater than that with epinephrine alone (72). These results indicate that, as previously shown for Ca^{2+} mobilization, the three receptors regulate a common step (probably a phospholipase C, see below) in the PI turnover pathway. In addition, this evidence indicates that the differences in maximum response were not due to differences in receptor number, but more likely reflected differences in the efficiency with which the different activated receptors could in turn activate the appropriate PI metabolizing enzyme(s).

Pathways of the Phosphoinositide Effect

In those studies in which chemical determination of PI and PA have been made (instead of, or in addition to, radiochemical labelling measurements), receptor activation has almost invariably been found to cause a fall in PI levels and an increase in PA (31). Accordingly, it was suggested that the initial reaction involved in the PI effect is likely to be the breakdown of PI to diacylglycerol (DG) and inositol phosphate by a PI-specific phosphodiesterase or phospholipase C (31).

In addition to phosphatidylinositol, most cell types are capable of synthesizing phosphorylated derivatives of PI, the polyphosphoinositides (31). Specific kinases add monoester phosphates, first to position 4 on the inositol ring to form phosphatidylinositol 4-phosphate (PIP), and then to position 5 to form phosphatidylinositol 4,5-bisphosphate (PIP_2). Specific phosphomonoesterases also exist that sequentially remove the position 5 and then position 4 phosphates. These monoester phosphates turn over rapidly through a futile cycle, which is fueled by, and depends upon, a constant level of ATP. Abdel-Latif and his collaborators (1) first demonstrated an agonist-mediated decline in polyphosphoinositides in iris smooth muscle. Michell's group observed a similar phenomenon in vasopressin-stimulated hepatocytes and suggested that the initial reaction involved in receptor-regulated PI turnover might be the phosphodiesteratic (phospholipase C) breakdown of PIP_2, PIP, or both, rather than PI as originally thought (27).

Similar studies of parotid acinar cells also disclosed a rapid, Ca^{2+}-independent fall in radiolabelled PIP_2 following muscarinic, α-adrenergic, or peptidergic (substance P) receptor stimulation (71). When techniques were developed for labelling (with ^{3}H-inositol), extracting, and separating ^{3}H-inositol phosphates (10), it was possible to carry out kinetic studies to determine the primary substrates involved in phosphoinositide turnover in the parotid gland. Studies carried out independently by Downes & Wusteman (18) and by Aub & Putney (4) reached similar conclusions. These investigators prelabelled the inositol lipids of parotid cells by incubating with ^{3}H-inositol, and examined the rates of formation of ^{3}H-labelled inositol monophosphate (IP), inositol bisphosphate (IP_2), and inositol trisphosphate (IP_3). They found that in the initial seconds following receptor activation IP_3 and IP_2 levels increased faster than IP (4, 18). Further, when turnover of the inositol phosphates was analyzed under quasi-steady-state conditions, IP_2 breakdown could quantitatively account for IP formation. However, IP_3 breakdown could only account for about one half of the rate of appearance of IP_2. Thus it appeared that in intact cells no direct degradation of PI occurred, but that both PIP_2 and PIP were hydrolyzed to diacylglycerol (DG) and their respective inositol phosphates (4, 18).

An assumption in the original analysis by both groups was that IP_3 behaves as a kinetically homogeneous pool. However, if there were a small pool of IP_3 with a relatively rapid turnover rate, this could account for the extra IP_2 formation that Downes & Wusteman (18) and Aub & Putney (4) attributed to PIP hydrolysis. Recent evidence suggests that just such a pool of IP_3 exists. Irvine et al (23) found that the $[^3H]IP_3$ formed in stimulated parotid cells is actually a mixture of two isomers, $(1,3,4)IP_3$ and $(1,4,5)IP_3$. The $(1,4,5)IP_3$ is quantitatively the minor fraction, but its turnover rate may be much faster than $(1,3,4)IP_3$ (23). Thus, the direct breakdown of PIP is now less certain, and it is possible that the PI cycle is initiated by a single enzymatic reaction, the phosphodiesteratic breakdown of PIP_2.

Inositol Lipids and Intracellular Ca-Release

Berridge (8) first suggested that the mechanism by which phosphoinositide hydrolysis couples receptor activation to Ca mobilization could involve the soluble inositol phosphates acting as second messengers to release Ca^{2+} from some intracellular pool. This idea was tested independently in two laboratories (13, 67), utilizing inositol 1,4,5-trisphosphate [(1,4,5)IP$_3$] prepared from human erythrocytes. The first reported biological effects of (1,4,5)IP$_3$ were described by Streb et al (67) in studies with permeable pancreatic acini. By a mechanism apparently quite similar to that for the salivary gland, the pancreas responds to muscarinic-cholinergic stimuli with a biphasic mobilization of Ca^{2+} (internal release followed by influx), and a rapid breakdown of polyphosphoinositides (45). When the plasma membranes of isolated acini were made permeable by a low Ca^{2+} technique, the intracellular organelles of the permeable acini (in the presence of ATP) sequestered Ca^{2+}, and reduced the [Ca^{2+}] of the medium to around 400 nM, as determined by a Ca^{2+} electrode (67). When (1,4,5)IP$_3$ was added, the medium [Ca^{2+}] increased rapidly, which indicates that some of the sequestered Ca^{2+} was released (67). The concentration of (1,4,5)IP$_3$ that produced half of the maximum effect was about 0.4 μM. The uptake of Ca^{2+} and its subsequent release were inhibited by vanadate but not by mitochondrial poisons. These observations indicate that the IP$_3$-sensitive Ca^{2+} pool is probably a component of the endoplasmic reticulum (ER) (67). Essentially similar results were obtained by Burgess et al (13) who used guinea pig hepatocytes made permeable with saponin and measured ^{45}Ca^{2+} exchange of the permeable cells. Again, (1,4,5)IP$_3$ caused release of Ca^{2+} from an internal pool, apparently a component of the ER (13). These results were confirmed for the rat hepatocyte by Joseph et al (25). Subsequently a number of investigators confirmed this ability of (1,4,5)IP$_3$ to release internal Ca^{2+} in a variety of systems (11).

Recently, this observation was confirmed for the rat parotid salivary gland (2). In these experiments, parotid cells were made permeable with saponin and suspended in a medium containing the fluorescent Ca indicator, quin-2, so that the [Ca^{2+}] surrounding the permeable cells could be monitored spectrophotometrically. In the presence of oligomycin (to eliminate mitochondrial Ca^{2+} uptake) and ATP the permeable parotid cells lowered the medium [Ca^{2+}] to about 200 nM, which is similar to the value for resting cytosolic [Ca^{2+}] in the parotid gland as determined with the quin-2 technique (2). The addition of (1,4,5)IP$_3$ caused a rapid increase in quin-2 fluorescence, indicating release of Ca^{2+} from a nonmitochondrial pool. As shown previously in other systems, (2,4,5)IP$_3$ and (4,5)IP$_2$ had some activity in releasing Ca^{2+}, while (1,4)IP$_2$, (1)IP, and inositol had no effect. These results, taken with those described above, suggest that in the parotid salivary gland (and presumably other salivary glands) receptor occupation leads to the phosphodiesteratic breakdown of PIP$_2$ liberating (1,4,5)IP$_3$. The (1,4,5)IP$_3$ then signals the release of sequestered Ca^{2+} from a component of the ER, which results in a transient elevation in cytosolic Ca^{2+}, and a transient increase in K$^+$ flux that is independent of extracellular Ca^{2+}.

Calcium Entry

The molecular mechanisms involved in receptor regulation of Ca^+ entry are much less well understood. Some recent hypotheses are that: (a) PA, formed during the PI cycle, may function like a Ca^{2+} carrier, or ionophore (49, 55, 56); (b) inhibition of the Ca pump, due to a decrease in membrane PIP_2, could result in a net increase in cytosolic $[Ca^{2+}]$ (9) (c) Ca may enter through the Ca^{2+}-activated monovalent cation channels, opened as a result of intracellular Ca^{2+} release (35).

The idea that PA could act as a Ca ionophore was first suggested by Tyson et al (69), but it was Salmon & Honeyman (55, 56) who first associated this idea with receptor-regulated PI turnover. Evidence that PA may be important in salivary glands was obtained by examining the sensitivity of receptor-regulated Ca entry to various cationic inhibitors of Ca flux (49). These substances inhibited receptor-regulated Ca entry in parotid salivary gland in the following order of potency: $La^{3+} > Tm^{3+} >$ neomycin $> Co^{2+} > Ni^{2+} > Ca^{2+}$ (potency as an agonist measured) $>> Mg^{2+}$. These same substances inhibited ^{45}Ca binding to PA in the rank order: $La^{3+} > Tm^{3+} >$ neomycin $> Co^{2+} > Ni^{2+} > Ca^{2+} >> Mg^{2+}$. This correlation, together with the general finding that cellular PA is increased when the PI cycle is activated, provides circumstantial evidence for the idea that PA may mediate trans-plasmalemmal Ca^{2+} entry. However, direct experimental evidence for or against this idea has been difficult to obtain. Much of the debate has dealt with whether or not PA can be shown to have Ca-transporting or "ionophoretic" properties in artificial systems (22); however, as argued previously (47), the relevance of such model systems to the in vivo situation is not clear. It would be much more useful to examine the Ca permeability of plasma membrane vesicles whose PA content has been elevated by receptor activation in vivo, but no such studies have as yet been described.

Plasma membrane vesicles isolated from cells whose PI cycle has been activated show diminished ATP-dependent Ca^{2+}-transport activity (39). There is some evidence that this could be a direct consequence of the fall in PIP_2 levels (9), and it has been suggested that net Ca entry might result from a decreased active extrusion of Ca rather than an increase in membrane permeability to Ca^{2+} (9). Two general observations militate rather strongly against such an hypothesis: (a) When unidirectional ^{45}Ca flux measurements have been made with cells or tissues that show a PI turnover, receptor activation almost invariably results in an increase in unidirectional influx without a decrease in unidirectional efflux [for example (30); for others, see reviews (42, 52, 53)]. (b) In neutrophils, receptor activation increases Ca entry, but the net effect on PIP_2 levels is an increase (after 30 sec) rather than a decrease, i.e. breakdown and release of IP_3 is stimulated, but resynthesis by phosphorylation of PI is stimulated to an even greater extent (16).

As discussed above, intracellular release of Ca^{2+} transiently opens monovalent cation channels in the exocrine glands (34, 42). If Ca^{2+} could also flow through these channels, then Ca^{2+} could enter from the outside, maintain the channels in an open state, and thus result in a sustained, Ca^{2+}-dependent phase of the response (35). The major problem with this model is that it does not allow for sustained control of the response by receptor activation, i.e. it is a "runaway" feed-forward system. Addition of atropine to parotid slices during the sustained phase of the response abruptly blocks the increased $^{86}Rb^+$ flux, which indicates continued receptor control (37). Furthermore, the sustained and transient phases of the responses can be dissociated temporally. If a transient response is elicited in the absence of extracellular Ca^{2+}, and cytosolic Ca is allowed to return to basal levels, then the addition of extracellular Ca^{2+} causes an abrupt increase in $^{86}Rb^+$ flux. This result shows that receptor activation maintains the Ca^{2+} entry mechanism in an "open" state at a time when cytosolic Ca^{2+} has returned to basal levels (41). Thus, it seems likely that activation of Ca entry is a process independent of changes in cytosolic $[Ca^{2+}]$, and is somehow under direct receptor control.

Some years back (41), it was suggested that in the parotid gland Ca release and Ca entry were tightly linked processes, with the receptor-regulated Ca pool simply serving as a binding site in the Ca channel, i.e. an intermediate step between extracellular Ca and the cytosol, or a holding pool. The major flaw in this model is probably the conception of the Ca^{2+} pool as a binding site. Present evidence suggests that the IP_3-sensitive pool is an ATP-dependent vesicular pool. Its persistence in preparations whose plasma membranes have been treated with detergents (saponin, digitonin) suggests that the pool is distinct from the plasma membrane. Furthermore, subcellular fractionation studies indicate that this IP_3-sensitive Ca pool (in exocrine pancreas) copurifies with rough ER and not with plasma membrane (66). However, an overwhelming body of circumstantial evidence still favors a close functional association between the pool and the plasma membrane. The most obvious points in this regard are: (a) In intact cells the pool depends almost entirely on extracellular Ca^{2+} to maintain or restore its Ca content; refilling of the pool from the extracellular space occurs rapidly and without an apparent elevation in cytosolic Ca^{2+} (33, 37). (b) The putative signal for release of Ca^{2+} from the pool, IP_3, is believed to be formed from PIP_2 at the plasma membrane (9, 11), and recently it was shown that the enzyme that degrades IP_3 (a 5-phosphomonoesterase) is primarily located in the plasma membrane (65). Thus, since the pool is able to obtain Ca from the extracellular space so rapidly, it is possible that sustained Ca^{2+} entry to the cytosol could simply reflect the rapid refilling of a pool that is open to the cytosol due to the action of IP_3. Indeed, the recent kinetic model proposed by Mauger et al (30) for Ca^{2+} influx in hepatocytes is consistent with this idea, if their "Ca-X" is designated the

Ca^{2+} pool, and the variable k_2 is the rate increased by IP_3. The appeal of this idea is that both phases of Ca mobilization can be explained by the action of a single messenger substance, IP_3. The major problem is that complex assumptions are necessary concerning the nature of the communication of the pool with the extracellular space, with no specific morphological data to support them.

Finally, the possibility must be considered that receptor activation regulates plasma membrane permeability to Ca by a mechanism that does not involve the inositol lipids at all. Indeed, there are certainly examples of ion channels directly regulated by receptors, the most thoroughly understood being the nicotinic-cholinergic receptor. However, the system seems a bit more complicated for the salivary glands, since receptor-activated Ca entry depends upon metabolic energy, presumably in the form of ATP (38). This finding is consistent with the PA hypothesis as well as the capacitative model because ATP is necessary for PA as well as sustained IP_3 production (9, 18, 38). However, it could also reflect other regulatory roles of ATP in maintaining receptor coupling, GTP levels, etc. Obviously, the elucidation of the molecular mechanism(s) controlling Ca entry in the salivary glands and other receptor-regulated systems represents a difficult challenge for future research.

C Kinase in Salivary Glands

As discussed above, protein phosphorylation may play a role in mediating responses of the cAMP pathway. Recent evidence suggests that phosphorylation could be important for the Ca^{2+} pathway as well, especially for the enzyme secretion that results from activation of this receptor class. It is relatively clear that cAMP does not mediate enzyme secretion by the Ca-mobilizing receptors (muscarinic, α_1-adrenergic, and substance P) (28). Because the response appears Ca-dependent, and can be mimicked by Ca ionophores, it was thought that for these receptors an increase in cytosolic $[Ca^{2+}]$ served as the signal for enzyme secretion as well as for the activation of K^+ flux (14).

More recently, Nishizuka and coworkers have described a protein kinase, designated as C kinase, that requires Ca^{2+} and phospholipid in vitro, and is activated by diacylglycerol (DG) (26; for review see 32). It has been suggested that diacylglycerol, formed from inositol lipid breakdown, activates this enzyme, which would function in concert with Ca^{2+} mobilization to regulate cellular responses such as secretion (32). In intact cells the C kinase appears to be relatively Ca-independent. Thus Ca-mobilizing receptors may activate two pathways: one involving Ca mobilization, and a second due to DG activation of C kinase (9, 32).

The possible role of C kinase in specific response pathways can be most easily examined by using the tumor-promoting drugs, the phorbol esters. These compounds are potent activators of C kinase, and probably act as analogs of DG to bind to the same regulatory site (15, 32). In the salivary glands the phorbol ester 4-β-phorbol dibutyrate (PDBu) induces protein secretion, and the response is Ca^{2+}-independent (46). Cyclic AMP does not seem to be involved since PDBu-induced secretion is not potentiated by inhibitors of cyclic AMP phosphodiesterase. Submaximal doses of PDBu and the Ca^{2+} ionophore, ionomycin, are more than additive in inducing protein secretion when used in combination. This synergism between phorbol ester and Ca ionophore has been demonstrated in a wide variety of systems (9, 32, 46), and is consistent with the idea that receptor-activated secretion results from the combined effects of two parallel receptor-regulated pathways: DG formation leading to C kinase activation, and IP_3 release leading to Ca^{2+} mobilization. For this reason the term *Ca^{2+}-mobilizing receptor* (or pathway) appears an inadequate descriptor for this class of receptor, and it is suggested that the term *phosphoinositide-linked receptor* may more accurately reflect the molecular mechanisms that underlie signalling for these receptors. However, it should be emphasized that such nomenclature is simply a convenient means of summarizing our current understanding of what may be a considerably more complex mechanism [see for example the hypothesis of Bodner et al (12)].

Interestingly, in the parotid gland, phorbol esters do not affect basal $^{86}Rb^+$ efflux or $^{86}Rb^+$ efflux activated by receptor activation or by Ca^{2+} ionophores (46). The term *stimulus-permeability coupling* was originally proposed (42) to call attention to the similarity between this phenomenon and stimulus-secretion coupling. In the parotid gland, however, the phorbol ester studies partially dissociate these mechanisms. The activation of K^+ channels appears simply to reflect changes in cytosolic Ca^{2+}, while enzyme secretion apparently involves a more complex pathway that includes Ca mobilization acting in concert with C kinase–mediated phosphorylations.

SUMMARY

In recent years, our understanding of receptor-signalling mechanisms in the salivary glands has advanced considerably. Two receptor pathways exist, one involving cAMP, which primarily regulates enzyme secretion, and another involving the hydrolysis of PIP_2, which regulates Ca^{2+} mobilization and, subsequently, monovalent ion fluxes probably important in ion and water secretion in the intact gland. Mobilization of Ca^{2+} results from both the release of internal Ca^{2+}, and from Ca^{2+} entry from the extracellular space. The signal for Ca^{2+} release appears to be $(1,4,5)IP_3$, one of the water soluble products of PIP_2 hydrolysis. The mechanism controlling Ca entry is not understood, but speculation abounds. Hydrolysis of PIP_2 also produces DG, which has a messenger role in activating a specific protein kinase, the C kinase. The C kinase interacts with Ca^{2+} mobilization in some as yet uncharacterized way in regulating enzyme secretion.

ACKNOWLEDGMENT

Work from the author's laboratory cited in this review was supported by a grant from the NIH, No. DE-05764.

Literature Cited

1. Abdel-Latif, A. A., Akhtar, R. A., Hawthorne, J. N. 1977. Acetylcholine increases the breakdown of triphosphoinositide of rabbit iris muscle prelabeled with [^{32}P]phosphate. *Biochem. J.* 162:61–73

2. Aub, D. L. 1985. *Role of inositol phosphates in stimulus-response coupling.* PhD thesis. Virginia Commonwealth Univ. Richmond.

3. Aub, D. L., McKinney, J. S., Putney, J. W. Jr. 1982. Nature of the receptor-regulated calcium pool in the rat parotid gland. *J. Physiol.* 331:557–65

4. Aub, D. L., Putney, J. W. Jr. 1984. Metabolism of inositol phosphates in parotid cells: Implications for the pathways of the phosphoinositide effect and for the possible messenger role of inositol trisphosphate. *Life Sci.* 34:1347–55

5. Batzri, S., Selinger, Z., Schramm, M., Robinovitch, M. R. 1973. Potassium release mediated by the epinephrine α-receptor in rat parotid slices. Properties and relation to enzyme secretion. *J. Biol. Chem.* 248:361–68

6. Baum, B. J., Freiberg, J. M., Ito, H., Roth, G. S., Filburn, C. R. 1981. β-adrenergic regulation of protein phosphorylation and its relationship to exocrine secretion in dispersed rat parotid gland acinar cells. *J. Biol. Chem.* 256:9731–36

7. Bdolah, A., Schramm, M. 1965. The function of 3′, 5′-cyclic AMP in enzyme secretion. *Biochem. Biophys. Res. Commun.* 18:452–54

8. Berridge, M. J. 1983. Rapid accumulation of inositol trisphosphate reveals that agonists hydrolyse polyphosphoinositides instead of phosphatidylinositol. *Biochem. J.* 212:849–58

9. Berridge, M. J. 1984. Inositol trisphosphate and diacylglycerol as second messengers. *Biochem. J.* 220:345–60

10. Berridge, M. J., Dawson, R. M. C., Downes, C. P., Heslop, J. P., Irvine, R. F. 1983. Changes in the levels of inositol phosphates following agonist-dependent hydrolysis of membrane phosphoinositides. *Biochem. J.* 212:473–82

11. Berridge, M. J., Irvine, R. F. 1984. Inositol trisphosphate, a novel second messenger in cellular signal transduction. *Nature* 312:315–21

12. Bodner, L., Hooper, M. T., Gee, M., Ito, H., Roth, G. S., Baum, B. J. 1983. Multiple transduction mechanisms are likely involved in calcium-mediated exocrine secretory events in rat parotid cells. *J. Biol. Chem.* 258:2774–77

13. Burgess, G. M., Godfrey, P. P., McKinney, J. S., Berridge, M. J., Irvine, R. F., Putney, J. W. Jr. 1984. The second messenger linking receptor activation to internal Ca release in liver. *Nature* 309:63–66

14. Butcher, F. R., Putney, J. W. Jr. 1980. Regulation of parotid gland function by cyclic nucleotides and calcium. In *Advances in Cyclic Nucleotide Research*, ed. P. Greengard, G. A. Robison, Vol. 13, pp. 215–49. New York: Raven

15. Castagna, M., Takai, Y., Kaibuchi, K., Sano, K., Kikkawa, U., Nishizuka, Y. 1982. Direct activation of calcium-activated, phospholipid-dependent protein kinase by tumor-promoting phorbol esters. *J. Biol. Chem.* 257:7847–51

16. Dougherty, R. W., Godfrey, P. P., Hoyle, P. C., Putney, J. W. Jr., Freer, R. J. 1984. Secretagogue-induced phosphoinositide metabolism in human leucocytes. *Biochem. J.* 222:307–14

17. Douglas, W. W., Poisner, A. M. 1963. The influence of calcium on the secretory response of the submaxillary gland to acetylcholine or to noradrenaline. *J. Physiol.* 165:528–41

18. Downes, C. P., Wusteman, M. M. 1983. Breakdown of polyphosphoinositides and not phosphatidylinositol accounts for muscarinic agonist-stimulated inositol phospholipid metabolism in rat parotid glands. *Biochem. J.* 216:633–40

19. Hokin, L. E. 1966. Effects of calcium omission on acetylcholine-stimulated amylase secretion and phospholipid synthesis in pigeon pancreas slices. *Biochim. Biophys. Acta* 115:219–21

20. Hokin, L. E., Sherwin, A. L. 1957. Protein secretion and phosphate turnover in the phospholipids in salivary glands *in vitro*. *J. Physiol.* 135:18–29

21. Hokin, M. R., Hokin, L. E. 1954. Effects of acetylcholine on phospholipids in the pancreas. *J. Biol. Chem.* 209:549–58

22. Holmes, R. P., Yoss, N. L. 1983. Failure of phosphatidic acid to translocate Ca^{2+}

across phosphatidylcholine membranes. *Nature* 305:637–38

23. Irvine, R. F., Letcher, A. J., Lander, D. J., Downes, C. P. 1984. Inositol trisphosphates in carbachol-stimulated rat parotid glands. *Biochem. J.* 223:237–43

24. Jahn, R., Söling, H. D. 1983. Phosphorylation of the ribosomal protein S6 in response to secretagogues in the guinea pig exocrine pancreas, parotid and lacrimal gland. *FEBS Lett.* 153:71–76

25. Joseph, S. K., Thomas, A. P., Williams, R. F., Irvine, R. F., Williamson, J. R. 1984. myo-Inositol 1,4,5-trisphosphate. A second messenger for the hormonal mobilization of intracellular Ca^{2+} in liver. *J. Biol. Chem.* 259:3077–81

26. Kawahara, Y., Takai, Y., Minakuchi, R., Sano, K., Nishizuka, Y. 1980. Phospholipid turnover as a possible transmembrane signal for protein phosphorylation during human platelet activation by thrombin. *Biochem. Biophys. Res. Commun.* 97:309–17

27. Kirk, C. F., Creba, J. A., Downes, C. P., Michell, R. H. 1981. Hormone-stimulated metabolism of inositol lipids and its relationship to hepatic receptor function. *Biochem. Soc. Trans.* 9:377–79

28. Leslie, B. A., Putney, J. W. Jr., Sherman, J. M. 1976. α-Adrenergic, β-adrenergic and cholinergic mechanisms for amylase secretion by rat parotid gland *in vitro*. *J. Physiol.* 260:351–70

29. Marier, S. H., Putney, J. W. Jr., Van De Walle, C. M. 1978. Control of calcium channels by membrane receptors in the rat parotid gland. *J. Physiol.* 279:141–51

30. Mauger, J.-P., Poggioli, J., Guesdon, F., Claret, M. 1984. Noradrenaline, vasopressin and angiotensin increase Ca^{2+} influx by opening a common pool of Ca^{2+} channels in isolated rat liver cells. *Biochem. J.* 221:121–27

31. Michell, R. H. 1975. Inositol phospholipids and cell surface receptor function. *Biochim. Biophys. Acta* 415:81–147

32. Nishizuka, Y. 1984. Turnover of inositol phospholipids and signal transduction. *Science* 225:1365–70

33. Oron, Y., Lowe, M., Selinger, Z. 1973. Involvement of the α-adrenergic receptor in the phospholipid effect in rat parotid. *FEBS Lett.* 34:198–200

34. Petersen, O. H. 1980. The electrophysiology of gland cells *Monogr. Physiol. Soc.* 36:1–253

35. Petersen, O. H., Maruyama, Y. 1983. What is the mechanism of the calcium influx to pancreatic acinar cells evoked by secretagogues? *Pflüg. Arch.* 396:82–84

36. Petersen, O. H., Maruyama, Y. 1984. Calcium-activated potassium channels and their role in secretion. *Nature* 307:693–96

37. Poggioli, J., Putney, J. W. Jr. 1982. Net calcium fluxes in rat parotid acinar cells. Evidence for a hormone-sensitive calcium pool in or near the plasma membrane. *Pflüg. Arch.* 392:239–43

38. Poggioli, J., Weiss, S. J., McKinney, J. S., Putney, J. W. Jr. 1983. Actions of antimycin A on receptor-activated calcium mobilization and phosphoinositide metabolism in rat parotid gland. *Mol. Pharmacol.* 23:71–77

39. Prpić, V., Green, K. C., Blackmore, P. F., Exton, J. H. 1984. Vasopressin-, angiotensin II-, and α_1-adrenergic-induced inhibition of Ca^{2+} transport by rat liver plasma membrane vesicles. *J. Biol. Chem.* 259:1382–85

40. Putney, J. W. Jr. 1976. Biphasic modulation of potassium release in rat parotid gland by carbachol and phenylephrine. *J. Pharmacol. Exp. Ther.* 198:375–84

41. Putney, J. W. Jr. 1977. Muscarinic, α-adrenergic and peptide receptors regulate the same calcium influx sites in the parotid gland. *J. Physiol.* 268:139–49

42. Putney, J. W. Jr. 1978. Stimulus-permeability coupling: Role of calcium in the receptor regulation of membrane permeability. *Pharmacol. Rev.* 30:209–45

43. Putney, J. W. Jr. 1982. Inositol lipids and cell stimulation in mammalian salivary gland. *Cell Calcium* 3:369–383

44. Putney, J. W. Jr. 1983. Activation by calcium of membrane channels for potassium in exocrine gland cells. *Cell Calcium* 4:439–50

45. Putney, J. W. Jr., Burgess, G. M., Halenda, S. P., McKinney, J. S., Rubin, R. P. 1983. Effects of secretagogues on $[^{32}P]$phosphatidylinositol 4,5-bisphosphate metabolism in the exocrine pancreas. *Biochem. J.* 212:483–88

46. Putney, J. W. Jr., McKinney, J. S., Aub, D. L., Leslie, B. A. 1984. Phorbol ester-induced protein secretion in rat parotid gland. Relationship to the role of inositol lipid breakdown and protein kinase C activation in stimulus-secretion coupling. *Mol. Pharmacol.* 26:261–66

47. Putney, J. W. Jr., Poggioli, J., Weiss, S. J. 1981. Receptor regulation of calcium release and calcium permeability in parotid gland cells. *Philos. Trans. R. Soc. London Ser. B.* 296:37–45

48. Putney, J. W. Jr., Weiss, S. J., Leslie, B. A., Marier, S. H. 1977. Is calcium the final mediator of exocytosis in the rat parotid gland? *J. Pharmacol. Exp. Ther.* 203:144–45

49. Putney, J. W. Jr., Weiss, S. J., Van De Walle, C. M., Haddas, R. A. 1980. Is phosphatidic acid a calcium ionophore under neurohumoral control? *Nature* 284:345–47

50. Quissel, D. O., Deisher, L. M., Barzen, K. A. 1983. Role of protein phosphorylation in regulating rat submandibular mucin secretion. *Am. J. Physiol.* 245:G44–G53

51. Rasmussen, H., Tenenhouse, A. 1968. Cyclic adenosine monophosphate, Ca^{++} and membranes. *Proc. Natl. Acad. Sci. USA* 59:1364–70

52. Rubin, R. P. 1982. *Calcium and Cellular Secretion*. New York: Plenum. 276 pp.

53. Rubin, R. P., Weiss, G. B., Putney, J. W. Jr., eds. 1985. *Calcium in Biological Systems*. New York: Plenum. 737 pp.

54. Rudich, L., Butcher, F. R. 1976. Effect of substance P and eledoisin on K^+ efflux, amylase release and cyclic nucleotide levels in slices of rat parotid gland. *Biochim. Biophys. Acta.* 444:704–11

55. Salmon, D. M., Honeyman, T. W. 1979. Increased phosphatidate accumulation during single contractions of isolated smooth muscle cells. *Biochem. Soc. Trans.* 7:986–88

56. Salmon, D. M., Honeyman, T. W. 1980. Proposed mechanism of cholinergic action in smooth muscle. *Nature* 284:344–45

57. Schneyer, L. H., Schneyer, C. A. 1964. Effects of pilocarpine on exchange of K^{42} in slices of submaxillary gland. *Proc. Soc. Exp. Biol. Med.* 116:813–17

58. Schneyer, L. H., Young, J. A., Schneyer, C. A. 1972. Salivary secretion of electrolytes. *Physiol. Rev.* 52:720–77

59. Schramm, M., Naim, E. 1970. Adenyl cyclase of rat parotid: Activation by fluoride and norepinephrine. *J. Biol. Chem.* 245:3225–31

60. Schramm, M., Selinger, Z. 1975. The functions of cyclic AMP and calcium as alternative second messengers in parotid gland and pancreas. *J. Cyclic Nucleotide Res.* 1:181–92

61. Selinger, Z., Batzri, S., Eimerl, S., Schramm, M. 1973. Calcium and energy requirements for K^+ release mediated by

62. Selinger, Z., Eimerl, S., Schramm, M. 1974. A calcium ionophore simulating the action of epinephrine on the α-adrenergic receptor. *Proc. Natl. Acad. Sci. USA* 71:128–31

63. Selinger, Z., Naim, E. 1970. The effect of calcium on amylase secretion by rat parotid slices. *Biochim. Biophys. Acta* 203:335–37

64. Spearman, T. N., Durham, J. P., Butcher, F. R. 1983. Cyclic AMP in the regulation of exocytosis in the rat parotid gland. Evidence obtained with cholera toxin. *Biochim. Biophys. Acta* 759:117–24

65. Storey, D. J., Shears, S. B., Kirk, C. J., Michell, R. H. 1984. Stepwise enzymatic dephosphorylation of inositol 1,4,5-trisphosphate to inositol in liver. *Nature* 312:374–76

66. Streb, H., Bayerdörffer, E., Haase, W., Irvine, R. F., Schulz, I. 1984. Effect of inositol-1,4,5-trisphosphate on isolated subcellular fractions of rat pancreas. *J. Membr. Biol.* 81:241–53

67. Streb, H., Irvine, R. F., Berridge, M. J., Schulz, I. 1983. Release of Ca^{2+} from a nonmitochondrial intracellular store in pancreatic acinar cells by inositol 1,4,5-trisphosphate. *Nature* 306:67–68

68. Tsien, R. Y., Pozzan, T., Rink, T. J. 1982. Calcium homeostasis in intact lymphocytes: Cytoplasmic free calcium monitored with a new, intracellularly trapped fluorescent indicator. *J. Cell Biol.* 94:325–34

69. Tyson, C. A., Zande, H. V., Green, D. E. 1976. Phospholipids as ionophores. *J. Biol. Chem.* 251:1326–32

70. Watson, E. L., Dowd, F. J. 1983. Forskolin: Effects on mouse parotid gland function. *Biochem. Biophys. Res. Commun.* 111:21–27

71. Weiss, S. J., McKinney, J. S., Putney, J. W. Jr. 1982. Receptor mediated net breakdown of phosphatidylinositol-4,5-bisphosphate in parotid acinar cells. *Biochem. J.* 206:555–60

72. Weiss, S. J., Putney, J. W. Jr. 1981. The relationship of phosphatidylinositol turnover to receptors and calcium channels in rat parotid acinar cells. *Biochem. J.* 194:463–68

Ann. Rev. Physiol. 1986. 48:89–101

CHARACTERIZATION OF RECEPTORS REGULATING SECRETORY FUNCTION IN THE FUNDIC MUCOSA[1]

Martin J. Sanders and Andrew H. Soll

Center for Ulcer Research and Education, Medical and Research Services, Veterans Administration Wadsworth Hospital Center, Los Angeles, California 90073; University of California at Los Angeles, School of Medicine, Los Angeles, California

INTRODUCTION

In vivo, the regulation of acid secretion is complex, with the chemical signals mediating regulation delivered by three major routes: neurocrine (neurotransmitters released from postganglionic nerves innervating the fundic mucosa); endocrine (hormones, such as gastrin, delivered by blood); and paracrine (transmitters diffusing from local tissue stores across the intercellular compartment). Each of these pathways is physiologically important to the regulation of acid secretion (1, 2). The paracrine pathway has been the most difficult to evaluate, and the physiological importance of histamine in the regulation of acid secretion was hotly debated (3, 4) until the H_2 receptor antagonists were introduced (5) and found to inhibit acid secretion stimulated by all physiologic modalities.

The complexity of the regulation of acid secretion also results from an interdependence that exists among the regulatory pathways. This interdependence is clearly evident in the ability of specific histamine H_2 and muscarinic receptor antagonists to each inhibit basal secretion and the acid secretory response to gastrin, histamine, and vagal/cholinergic stimulation. Although the release of gastrin with a protein meal appears to largely account for the acid secretory response (6), both H_2 receptor antagonists and anti-

---

89

cholinergic agents inhibit this phase, which indicates a role for both neurocrine (acetylcholine) and paracrine (histamine) pathways.

The mechanisms underlying the interdependence among the pathways regulating acid secretion remain controversial. This controversy centers on whether acetylcholine and gastrin act on the fundic histamine cell to induce histamine release as the final mediator of acid secretion (3), or whether histamine, gastrin, and acetylcholine each act directly on the parietal cell, with the interdependency among their effects reflecting interactions at the level of the parietal cell itself (7). Attempts to resolve this controversy have focused on localization of the receptors mediating the actions of histamine, cholinergic agents, and gastrin. Such studies are difficult in intact mucosa, in part because of cellular heterogeneity and the presence of acetylcholine and histamine in the mucosa itself. Dispersion of mucosal cells allows study of parietal and other cell types free from the influence of local transmitters. This review will focus on studies of isolated canine mucosal cells; the early phase of this work found a direct action of histamine, gastrin, and acetylcholine on the parietal cell (8). More recent work has indicated that gastrin and muscarinic receptors are present on other regulatory cells as well (9–11). This review provides an overview of selected topics (see 12–15 for more comprehensive reviews).

DISPERSION AND IDENTIFICATION OF FUNDIC MUCOSAL CELLS

Cells are dispersed from the fundic mucosa using enzyme treatment. A variety of approaches have been developed for different species. Rabbit gastric glands have been prepared with crude collagenase (16), canine mucosal cells dispersed with sequential treatment with crude collagenase and EDTA (8), and rat (17) and amphibian (18) mucosal cells dispersed with pronase. Several procedures have been used to enrich the component cell types of the mucosa, including velocity separation at unit gravity or in an elutriator rotor and density separation, using either step or linear gradients (15).

The methods used to identify specific cell types are critical to cell separation. Staining slides prepared using a cytocentrifuge with periodic acid-Schiff allows identification of parietal cells, chief cells, and mucous cells (9). Mast cells are identified with toluidine blue staining (19). Endocrine cells, containing peptides such as somatostatin or glucagon, are identified with immunohistochemical methods. Two markers of endocrine-like cells have been useful in studies of canine mucosal cells: Serotonin measured by radioenzymatic assay or immunohistochemistry and DOPA-decarboxylase activity detected by radioenzymatic assay (10, 11, 20).

ASSAYS OF CELL FUNCTION

With dispersion, parietal cells lose their polar orientation and therefore acid secretion can only be indirectly assessed. With stimulation, isolated parietal cells undergo a morphologic transformation similar to that observed in vivo (15, 16); tubulovesicles, which fill the cytoplasm in the basal state, transform into secretory canaliculi. Both oxygen consumption and glucose oxidation provide an index of the overall degree of cell activation, since the secretion of acid is a highly energy-dependent process. Weak bases, such as ^{14}C-aminopyrine (AP), accumulate by pH partition in the acid spaces of the stimulated parietal cell, therefore providing evidence for the secretion of H^+ by isolated parietal cells (21, 22). Using fluorescent microscopy, another weak base, acridine orange, has been shown to accumulate within canaliculi of stimulated rabbit gastric glands (21).

Function in the other cell types can often be measured more directly. For example, mast cell and chief cell function is monitored by measuring the release of histamine and pepsinogen, respectively. Release of endocrine cell products, such as somatostatin, are determined by radioimmunoassay (10).

STUDIES OF PARIETAL CELL RECEPTOR SPECIFICITY

Several lines of evidence indicate that the *canine* parietal cell has specific receptors for histamine, cholinergic agents, and gastrin (8). Histamine and carbachol stimulate oxygen consumption, AP accumulation, and glucose oxidation by isolated canine parietal cells (8, 15, 22, 23). Histamine and cholinergic agents stimulate parietal cell function in rabbit gastric glands (16, 24), and the function of parietal cells dispersed from the rat (17, 25), guinea pig (26), and frog (18).

Receptors for Histamine

Several studies lead to the firm conclusion that histamine action on dispersed parietal cells is mediated by an H_2 receptor. H_2 blockers competitively inhibit histamine stimulation of oxygen consumption and AP accumulation by rabbit gastric glands (24, 27) and isolated canine, guinea pig, and rat parietal cells (8, 22, 25, 28). The dissociation constant determined for cimetidine is about 1 μM, and is thus similar to the K_d found for H_2 receptors in atrium and uterus. Anticholinergic agents do not inhibit histamine stimulation.

Direct study of histamine receptors using radiolabelled ligands has been difficult (29). In studies with guinea pig parietal cells the identified binding sites had a specificity different from H_2 receptors (28, 30). Histamine receptor studies are complicated by the purity of the parietal cell population, interaction with sites other than the H_2 receptor (such as histamine methyltransferase), rapid degradation of histamine by parietal cells (20), and histamine uptake (24).

Cholinergic Receptors

Anticholinergic agents inhibit carbachol action on oxygen consumption and AP accumulation (8, 17, 22, 26, 27). Atropine inhibition of carbachol-stimulated AP accumulation was surmountable, and was characterized by a dissociation constant of 1 nM (22), a value similiar to that found for atropine in other tissues. Direct studies of muscarinic cholinergic receptors using (^3H)-quinuclidinyl benzilate (QNB) indicated a typical muscarinic receptor in a preparation of enriched rat parietal cells (17). In this study the contribution of the nonparietal cells to the QNB binding was not established. Culp (31) examined the distribution of QNB binding sites on canine fundic mucosal cells separated by elutriation. QNB receptors were found in all of the fractions studied, with the highest apparent density of receptors on chief cells rather than on parietal cells.

Gastrin Response and Gastrin Receptors

Considerable disagreement remains regarding the localization of gastrin receptors within the fundic mucosa. With isolated canine parietal cells, gastrin produced a small but definite increase in both oxygen consumption (8) and AP accumulation (22). These responses were not blocked by either H_2 antagonists or anticholinergic agents. This gastrin effect occurred in fractions enriched by elutriation in parietal cells, but depleted in histamine cells, thus making it unlikely that in these studies gastrin action was mediated by histamine release. Proglumide, an agent shown to selectively block pancreatic acinar cell cholecystokinin (CCK) receptors (32), inhibits gastrin, but not histamine or cholinergic, stimulation of canine parietal cells (9).

The effect of gastrin on parietal cells from species other than dog are controversial. Gastrin has at most a small and variable direct effect on rabbit parietal cells (33). However, in the presence of isobutylmethylxanthine (IBMX), gastrin stimulated AP accumulation, and this effect was markedly inhibited by cimetidine (33, 34). Gastrin actions on rabbit gastric glands are complex; gastrin also induces release of histamine from this preparation (35).

Evidence for the existence of specific gastrin receptors on canine parietal cells comes from studies using ^{125}I-[Leu^{15}]-G17 (gastrin-17) (9). Johnson & coworkers (36) had previously shown preservation of biological activity of this iodinated, leucine-substituted G17. Susceptibility of the methionine in the 15 position to oxidative damage limits the usefulness of native G17. In fractions containing 50–70% parietal cells, 2 fmol of the ^{125}I[Leu^{15}]-G17 tracer was bound per 10^6 cells. Most studies were done with a 20 pM tracer concentration; under these conditions 90% of the binding was specific. Using the elutriator rotor, ^{125}I-[Leu^{15}]-G17 binding was found to correlate with the distribution of parietal cells. This indicates that parietal cells accounted for the majority of the G17 binding to canine fundic mucosal cells. This finding was confirmed in studies in which step density gradients were performed on the elutriator-enriched parietal cell fraction. With these step gradients, enrichment of the parietal cell and of the chief cell content in excess of 85% was achieved (9). ^{125}I-[Leu^{15}]-G17 binding correlated positively with the parietal cell content of the fractions and negatively with the chief cell content. These data leave little question that the parietal cell has a specific gastrin receptor, whereas a gastrin receptor was not detected on canine chief cells. However, in the elutriator separation there was indication of G17 binding to one or more additional cell types that eluted in a small cell fraction, as discussed below. A major advantage of this sequential velocity and density separation is that small cells, which include endocrine cells and mast cells, are removed before density gradient separation. Without this initial size separation the small, light cells will contaminate the density-separated parietal cell fractions.

Gastrin binding was found to correlate with gastrin stimulation of parietal cell function (9). Proglumide inhibited G17 binding, and the inhibition of binding was proportional to inhibition of G17 stimulation of parietal cell function. The octapeptide of cholecystokinin (CCK8) inhibited ^{125}I-[Leu^{15}]-G17 binding and stimulated parietal cell function with a potency similar to that found for the G17 (9).

POTENTIATING INTERACTIONS BETWEEN SECRETAGOGUES

As discussed above, anticholinergic agents and H$_2$ histamine antagonists were found to be specific for the actions on the isolated parietal cell function of acetylcholine and carbachol, respectively. These findings are thus at odds with the in vivo observations that these inhibitors block all forms of acid secretion. This apparent contradiction may reflect the existence of potentiating interactions among secretagogues at the parietal cell itself. In studies of canine parietal cells, potentiating interactions were found between histamine and both gastrin and carbachol (23, 37). Interactions between cholinergic agents and histamine (38), and possibly between gastrin and histamine (33), have been found in rabbit gastric glands. In the presence of these potentiating interactions, the actions of cimetidine and atropine display an apparent nonspecificity reminiscent of that found in vivo (23, 37, 38). Taken together the above studies indicate that receptors for acetylcholine and gastrin, as well as histamine, are present on the parietal cells. However, recent evidence also indicates that receptors for gastrin and acetylcholine exist on other cells in the fundic mucosa that may serve a regulatory function.

RECEPTORS ON OTHER CANINE FUNDIC MUCOSAL CELLS

The hypothesis underlying the following discussion is that interactions among the neurocrine, paracrine, and hormonal pathways regulating acid secretion occur by mechanisms in addition to potentiating interactions at the parietal cell. Evidence for the presence of acetylcholine and gastrin receptors on fundic endocrine/paracrine cells will be considered.

Gastrin Receptors on Paracrine Cells

In the studies of ^{125}I-[Leu^{15}]-gastrin binding to canine fundic mucosal cells separated by elutriation, specific G17 binding was found in cells from the small cell fraction, in addition to parietal cells (9, 11). These small cell fractions contain a variety of cell types, including mast cells (19) and cells containing somatostatin, glucagon, and serotonin (11, 20). We have used a linear density gradient to further separate these various cell types. When the binding of ^{125}I-[Leu^{15}]-G17 to density gradient fractions was performed, a discrete distribution of G17 receptor sites was found in fractions of intermediate density (11). G17 binding was negatively correlated with the distribution of mast cells, but positively correlated the distribution of somatostatin-like immunoreactivity (SLI).

Evidence for gastrin receptors on fundic SLI cells was directly sought by studying mucosal cells cultured for 48 hr (10). SLI cells in this preparation have a low basal release, but show five- to one hundred–fold increases in SLI release in response to stimulation. The chemical transmitters that have thus far been shown to stimulate SLI release are epinephrine, acting as a β receptor, cyclic AMP analogues, and gastrin. Furthermore, these canine somatostatin cells in short-term culture demonstrate remarkable potentiation of the secretory response when exposed to combinations of gastrin with either epinephrine or dibutyryl cyclic AMP (dbcAMP). These data suggest that gastrin, in addition to acting at a stimulatory receptor on the parietal cell, may also activate an inhibitory pathway mediated by the release of somatostatin. In contrast to the canine parietal cell receptor for gastrin that shows equal affinity for CCK8 and G17, CCK8 was more effective and more potent that G17 in stimulating SLI release (39).

Cholinergic Receptors on Other Cells

As noted previously, muscarinic ligands, such an ^{3}H-QNB, bind to all of the elutriator-separated canine fundic mucosal cell fractions (31). This finding is expected since cholinergic agents stimulate pepsinogen, bicarbonate, and mucus secretion, presumably by direct action at muscarinic receptors on chief and mucous cells. A major question is whether muscarinic receptors are present on cell types that may release paracrine or endocrine modulators of the acid secretory response. Treatment of SLI cells with carbachol attenuated stimulation of SLI release by epinephrine, dbcAMP, and gastrin (40). This carbachol effect is blocked by nanomolar concentrations of atropine; the apparent dissociation constant was 0.4 nM (40), a value typical of muscarinic receptors. These findings indicate that cholinergic agents directly inhibit the release of somatostatin and, by blocking release of a paracrine inhibitor, further enhance the acid secretory response.

REGULATION OF HISTAMINE RELEASE FROM FUNDIC MUCOSAL STORES

The regulation of histamine formation and release from fundic mucosal stores is poorly understood. One major reason for the confusion is that the cellular stores of fundic mucosal histamine vary among species. In the rat, histamine is stored in endocrine-like cells (41), and gastrin stimulates the formation of histamine by inducing the activity of histidine decarboxylase (42, 43). Despite considerable evidence suggesting that gastrin interacts with the rat fundic histamine cell, it remains to be established that gastrin induction of histamine release actually mediates gastrin stimulation of acid secretion (4, 44). Gastrin has been demonstrated to cause histamine release from rabbit gastric glands (35) and from amphibian fundic mucosa (45, 46). However, the cells storing histamine in these species remain poorly characterized, and a causal relationship between induction of histamine release and stimulation of the acid secretory response has not been firmly established.

In man and dog mast cells appear to fully account for the fundic mucosal histamine stores, and there are no data to indicate histamine storage in endocrine-like cells (19, 47, 48). The factors regulating fundic mucosal histamine release remain poorly characterized. Stimulation of acid secretion by pentagastrin has been reported to induce the release of histamine from dog and human gastric mucosa. Following pentagastrin in vivo, Man & coworkers (49, 50) found a decrease in the histamine content of the fundic mucosa, and a rise in serum and gastric juice histamine. Cimetidine failed to inhibit pentagastrin-induced histamine release into blood or gastric juice (50), which suggests that the histamine release did not result from a washout concomitant with the acid secretory response. However, cimetidine in these studies was given 1 hr after secretion had been initiated by pentagastrin. In addition, cimetidine was found to increase serum histamine in gastrectomized patients (50). Therefore the stomach may not be the only source of histamine, and cimetidine may influence histamine release by actions independent of inhibition of acid secretion. Furthermore, histamine analogues themselves cause apparent histamine release (51, 52), making it difficult to draw causal relationships between the effects of pentagastrin on histamine release and acid secretion. Multiple mechanisms are involved in the effects of secretagogues on histamine output during stimulation of acid secretion, and caution must be exercised in interpreting apparent effect as a reflection of action at specific receptors on fundic histamine cells, or as a reflection of a causal relationship.

We have studied canine fundic mucosal mast cells, in an attempt to determine the factors regulating histamine formation and release. We have studied histamine release in cells placed in suspension culture overnight (A. H. Soll, M. Toomey, and M. Beaven, unpublished studies). These mast cells demonstrate stimulation of histamine release by the calcium ionophore A23187 and concanavalin A, but they did not respond to treatment with gastrin or cholinomimetics, alone or in combination. These latter negative findings thus agree with the apparent absence of muscarinic and gastrin receptors in the radioligand binding studies noted above. However, negative conclusions must be interpreted with caution. Furthermore, conclusions arrived at in one species may not hold for another species, especially if the fundic cells storing histamine are different.

RECEPTORS FOR OTHER CHEMOTRANSMITTERS

Many other agents may profoundly influence the regulation of secretory function in the fundic mucosa, but only limited knowledge is available regarding possible sites and mechanisms of action.

RECEPTORS FOR SOMATOSTATIN

Somatostatin is a potent inhibitor of acid secretion, yet the mechanisms accounting for this effect remain uncertain. One component of the antisecretory effect of somatostatin reflects inhibition of gastrin release (53, 54). However, somatostatin inhibits the acid secretory response to pentagastrin and cholinergic stimuli. This finding supports the conclusion that somatostatin has a direct action on the fundic mucosa. Somatostatin inhibits histamine-stimulated AP accumulation by parietal cells isolated from rabbit, rat, and guinea pig (26, 55–57), and by rabbit gastric glands (56). These data are somewhat contrary to the anticipated result in vivo, since in the rat and dog somatostatin is a poor inhibitor of the response to exogenous histamine. Somatostatin also inhibits the response of rabbit gastric glands to gastrin plus the phosphodiesterase inhibitor IBMX, but does not block the small response of isolated rabbit parietal cells to gastrin (56). These findings appear to reflect in part an additional component of somatostatin action on rabbit gastric glands; somatostatin blocks pentagastrin stimulation of histamine release from cellular stores within the gastric gland (58). Definitive studies on somatostatin effects on parietal cell function in other species have not yet been reported.

β-ADRENERGIC RECEPTORS

In vivo studies with β-adrenergic regulation of acid secretion have yielded conflicting results, but several reports indicate that β blockers can enhance acid secretion, which suggests an endogenous inhibitory β-adrenergic tone. Exogenous β-adrenergic agonists inhibit acid secretion (59, 60). However, closed arterial infusion into chambered canine gastric mucosa was found to increase acid secretion (61). β-adrenergic agonists have been found to stimulate AP accumulation by rat parietal cells (62). β-adrenergic stimulation of cyclic AMP production also occurred in parietal cell–depleted fractions (63). Species differences again confound study of adrenergic modulators in that β-adrenergic agonists were not found to enhance AP accumulation into canine parietal cells (A. H. Soll, unpublished observations). However, two other sites of action of β-adrenergic agonists have been identified in the canine fundic mucosa. Canine fundic somatostatin cells have a β-adrenergic receptor that stimulates somatostatin secretion (10, 40). Furthermore, β-adrenergic agents potently inhibit histamine release from canine fundic mucosal mast cells (A. H. Soll, M. Toomey, F. Shanahan, unpublished observations).

EPIDERMAL GROWTH FACTOR

In addition to its mitogenic properties, epidermal growth factor (EGF, urogastrone) displays potent inhibition of acid secretion and antiulcer effects. EGF in relatively high concentrations has been shown to directly inhibit the response of isolated canine parietal cells and rabbit gastric glands to histamine (64–66). EGF receptors have been found in guinea pig gastric mucosa (67), and direct binding studies with canine parietal cells have indicated moderately high affinity binding sites for [^{125}I]-EGF, with binding correlating with inhibition of parietal cell function. EGF, however, has binding sites on other, if not all, mucosal cells, and several other actions have been identified in studies with canine fundic cells. For example, EGF stimulates prostaglandin (PG) production, and stimulation of PGE_2 by EGF appears to be accounted for at least in part by fundic macrophages (Chen, Thomas, Sanders, Soll, manuscript in preparation). Thus EGF has many binding sites and potential effects in the fundic mucosa; which of these effects are of physiological importance in modulating secretory function or mucosal resistance to injury remains to be determined.

SUMMARY

A model for a present view of the major pathways and receptors mediating function in the canine fundic mucosa is depicted in Figure 1.
Gastrin has direct actions on the parietal cell and on the somatostatin cell; action

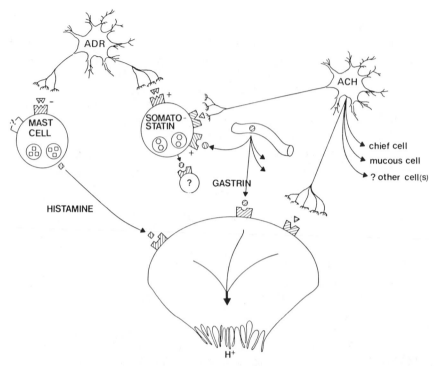

Figure 1   Fundic mucosal regulatory pathways based on the present view of the receptors and pathways regulating acid secretory function in the canine fundic mucosa. Histamine, gastrin, and acetylcholine act in parallel on specific receptors on the parietal cell, with their actions amplified by potentiating interactions. Gastrin, delivered by blood, also acts directly on receptors on the somatostatin cell to activate an inhibitory pathway. Gastrin receptors are probably also present on the stem cell, and possibly on other cell types. Histamine is delivered from mast cells located in the lamina propria. Acetylcholine is delivered by postganglionic nerves to muscarinic receptors on parietal cells, but also to muscarinic receptors on the somatostatin cell. These muscarinic receptors on SLI cells attenuate somatostatin release, and thus dampen the inhibitory pathway mediated by somatostatin. Receptors for adrenergic input also are found on the mast cell and somatostatin cell, with epinephrine producing potent inhibition of histamine release and stimulating the secretion of somatostatin.

on the parietal cell, but not somatostatin cell, is potentiated by histamine. In contrast, gastrin action on the somatostatin cell is potentiated by β-adrenergic agonists. The potency of H_2 blockers against gastrin may reflect blockage by these inhibitors of the stimulatory (parietal cell), but not the inhibitory (somatostatin cell), component of gastrin action, thus shifting the balance of gastrin effects toward the inhibitory side. The profound effects of H_2 antagonists on gastrin action may also reflect an effect mediated by histamine release, but this possibility awaits direct confirmation. Cholinergic pathways also have at least dual sites of action: stimulation of the parietal cell, and blockage of the release of the inhibitory transmitter somatostatin. Anticholinergic agents may therefore have a dual acid inhibitory effect by reducing direct parietal cell stimulation and enhancing somatostatin release. There is little doubt that this model will rapidly evolve, but the concept that the pathways mediating acid secretion both converge in parallel at the parietal cell, and act in series to cause the release of paracrine transmitters, is attractive and likely to persist.

ACKNOWLEDGMENT

This work was supported in part by NIAMDD grants AM 19984, AM 17328, AM 30444, and by the Medical Research Service of the Veterans Administration. AHS is a recipient of a Medical Investigatorship, V. A. Wadsworth Hospital Center.

Literature Cited

1. Grossman, M. I. 1981. Regulation of gastric acid secretion. In *Physiology of the Gastrointestinal Tract*, ed. L. R. Johnson, pp. 659–71. New York: Raven
2. Feldman, M. 1983. Gastric secretion. In *Gastrointestinal Diseases*, ed. M. Sleisenger, J. S. Fordtran, pp. 541–58. Philadelphia: Saunders. 3rd Ed.
3. Code, C. F. 1965. Histamine and gastric secretion: A later look, 1955–1965. *Fed. Proc.* 24:1311–21
4. Johnson, L. R. 1971. Control of gastric secretion: No room for histamine. *Gastroenterology* 61:106–18
5. Black, J. W., Duncan, W. A. M., Durant, C. J., Ganellin, C. R., Parsons, M. E. 1972. Definition and antagonism of histamine H₂-receptors. *Nature* 236: 385–90
6. Feldman, M., Walsh, J. H., Wong, H. C., Richardson, C. T. 1978. Role of gastrin heptadecapeptide in the acid secretory response to amino acids in man. *J. Clin. Invest.* 61:308–13
7. Grossman, M. I., Konturek, S. J. 1974. Inhibition of acid secretion in dog by metiamide, a histamine antagonist acting on H₂ receptors. *Gastroenterology* 66: 517–21
8. Soll, A. H. 1978. The actions of secretatagogues on oxygen uptake by isolated mammalian parietal cells. *J. Clin. Invest.* 61:370–80
9. Soll, A. H., Amirian, D. A., Thomas, L. P., Reedy, T. J., Elashoff, J. D. 1984. Gastrin receptors on isolated canine parietal cells. *J. Clin. Invest.* 73:1434–47
10. Soll, A. H., Yamada, T., Park, J., Thomas, L. P. 1984. Release of somatostatin-like immunoreactivity from canine

fundic mucosal cells in primary culture. *Am. J. Physiol.* 247:G567–73
11. Soll, A. H., Amirian, D. A., Thomas, L. P., Park, J. J., Beaven, M. A., Yamada, T. 1984. Gastrin receptors on nonparietal cells isolated from canine fundic mucosa. *Am. J. Physiol.* 247:G715–23
12. Berglindh, T. 1984. The mammalian gastric parietal cell in vitro. *Ann. Rev. Physiol.* 46:377–92
13. Soll, A. H., Berglindh, T. 1985. Physiology of isolated gastric glands and cells: Receptors and effectors regulating secretion. In *Physiology of Gastrointestinal Tract*, ed. L. R. Johnson. New York: Raven
14. Sachs, G., Berglindh, T. 1981. Physiology of the parietal cell. In *Physiology of the Gastrointestinal Tract*, ed. L. R. Johnson, Ch. 19, pp. 567–602. New York: Raven
15. Soll, A. H. 1981. Physiology of isolated canine parietal cells: Receptors and effectors regulating function. In *Physiology of the Digestive Tract*, ed. L. R. Johnson, pp. 673–91. New York: Raven
16. Berglindh, T., Helander, H. F., Obrink, K. J. 1976. Effects of secretagogues on oxygen consumption, aminopyrine accumulation and morphology in isolated gastric glands. *Acta Physiol. Scand.* 97:401–14
17. Ecknauer, R., Dial, E., Thompson, W. J., Johnson, L. R., Rosenfeld, G. C. 1981. Isolated rat gastric parietal cells: Cholinergic response and pharmacology. *Life. Sci.* 28:609–21
18. Michelangeli, F. 1978. Acid secretion and intracellular pH in isolated oxyntic cells. *J. Membrane. Biol.* 38:31–50

19. Soll, A. H., Lewin, K., Beaven, M. A. 1979. Isolation of histamine containing cells from canine fundic mucosa. *Gastroenterology* 77:1283–90

20. Beaven, M. A., Soll, A. H., Lewin, K. J. 1982. Histamine synthesis by intact mast cells from canine fundic mucosa and liver. *Gastroenterology* 82:254–62

21. Berglindh, T., Dibona, D. R., Ito, S., Sachs, G. 1980. Probes of parietal cell function. *Am. J. Physiol.* 238:G165–76

22. Soll, A. H. 1980. Secretagogue stimulation of ^{14}C-aminopyrine accumulation by isolated canine parietal cells. *Am. J. Physiol.* 238:G366–75

23. Soll, A. H. 1978. The interaction of histamine with gastrin and carbamylcholine on oxygen uptake by isolated mammalian parietal cells. *J. Clin. Invest.* 61:381–89

24. Chew, C. S., Hersey, S. J., Sachs, G., Berglindh, T. 1980. Histamine responsiveness of isolated gastric glands. *Am. J. Physiol.* 238:G312–20

25. Dial, E., Thompson, W. J., Rosenfeld, G. C. 1981. Isolated parietal cells: Histamine response and pharmacology. *J. Pharmacol. Exp. Ther.* 219:585–90

26. Batzri, S., Dyer, J. 1981. Aminopyrine uptake by guinea pig gastric mucosal cells mediation by cyclic amp and interaction among secretagogues. *Biochim. Biophys. Acta* 675:416–26

27. Berglindh, T. 1977. Effects of common inhibitors of gastric acid secretion on secretagogue-induced respiration and aminopyrine accumulation in isolated gastric glands. *Biochim. Biophys. Acta* 464:217–33

28. Batzri, S., Harmon, J. W., Dyer, J., Thompson, W. F. 1982. Interaction of histamine with gastric mucosal cells effect of histamine H$_2$ antagonists on binding and biological response. *Molecular Pharmacology* 22:41–47

29. Bertaccini, G., Coruzzi, G. 1981. Evidence for and against heterogeneity in the histamine H$_2$-receptor population. *Pharmacology* 23:1–13

30. Batzri, S., Harmon, J. W., Thompson, W. F. 1982. Interaction of histamine with gastric mucosal cells effect of histamine agonists on binding and biological response. *Mol. Pharmacol.* 22:33–40

31. Culp, D. J., Wolosin, J. M., Soll, A. H., Forte, J. G. 1983. Muscarinic receptors and guanylate cyclase in mammalian gastric glandular cells. *Am. J. Physiol.* 245:G641–46

32. Hahne, W. F., Jensen, R. T., Lamp, G. F., Gardner, J. D. 1981. Proglumide and benzotript: Members of a different class of cholecystokinin receptor antagonists. *Proc. Natl. Acad. Sci. USA* 10:6304–8

33. Chew, C. S., Hersey, S. J. 1982. Gastrin stimulation of isolated gastric glands. *Am. J. Physiol.* 242:G504–12

34. Berglindh, T., Sachs, G., Takeguchi, N. 1980. Ca$^+$-dependent secretagogue stimulation in isolated rabbit gastric glands. *Am. J. Physiol.* 239:G90–94

35. Berqvist, E., Waller, M., Hammar, L., Obrink, K. J. 1980. Histamine as the secretory mediator in isolated gastric glands. In *Hydrogen Ion Transport in Epithelia*, ed. I. Shulz, G. Sachs, J. G. Forte, K. J. Ullrich, pp. 429–37. Amsterdam: Elsevier/North-Holland Biomed.

36. Takeuchi, K., Speir, G. R., Johnson, L. R. 1979. Mucosal gastrin receptor. I. Assay standardization and fulfillment of receptor criteria. *Am. J. Physiol.* 237:E284–94

37. Soll, A. H. 1982. Potentiating interactions of gastric stimulants on ^{14}C-aminopyrine accumulation by isolated canine parietal cells. *Gastroenterology* 83:216–23

38. Berglindh, T. 1977. Potentiation by carbachol and aminophylline of histamine- and dbcAMP-induced parietal cells activity in isolated gastric glands. *Acta. Physiol. Scand.* 99:75–84

39. Soll, A. H., Amirian, D. A., Park, J., Elashoff, J. D., Yamada, T. 1985. Cholecystokinin potently releases somatostatin from fundic mucosal cell in short-term culture. *Am. J. Physiol.* 248:G569–73

40. Yamada, T., Soll, A. H., Park, J., Elashoff, J. 1984. Autonomic regulation of somatostatin release: Studies with primary cultures of canine fundic mucosal cells. *Am. J. Physiol.* 247:G567–73

41. Soll, A. H., Lewin, K. J., Beaven, M. A. 1981. Isolation of histamine-containing cells from rat gastric mucosa: Biochemical and morphologic differences from mast cells. *Gastroenterology* 80:717–27

42. Kahlson, G., Rosengren, E. 1968. New approaches to the physiology of histamine. *Physiol. Rev.* 48:155–96

43. Hakanson, R., Liedberg, G. 1970. The role of endogenous gastrin in the activation of gastric histidine decarboxylase in the rat. Effect of antrectomy and vagal denervation. *Eur. J. Pharmacol.* 12:94–103

44. Hakanson, R., Liedberg, G., Owman, C. H., Sundler, F. 1973. The cellular localization of gastric histamine and its implications for the concept of histamine as a physiological stimulant of gastric acid secretion. In *Histamine: Mechanisms regulating the biogenic amine levels in tissues with special regard to*

histamine, ed. C. Maslinski, pp. 209–22. Stroudsbury, Penn.: Dowden, Hutchinson, and Ross

45. Rangachari, P. K. 1975. Histamine release by gastric stimulants. *Nature* 253: 53–55

46. Ekblad, E. B. M. 1985. Histamine—The sole mediator of pentagastrin stimulated acid secretion. *Acta Physiol. Scand.* In press

47. Hakanson, R., Lilja, B., Owman, C. H. 1969. Cellular localization of the histamine and monoamines in the gastric mucosa of man. *Histochemie* 18:74–86

48. Lorenz, W., Schauer, A., Heitland, S. T., Calvoer, R., Werle, E. 1969. Biochemical and histochemical studies on the distribution of histamine in the digestive tract of man, dog and other mammals. *Naunyn-Schmiedebergs Arch. Pharmakol.* 265:81–100

49. Man, W. K., Saunders, J. H., Ingoldby, C., Spencer, J. 1981. Effect of pentagastrin on histamine output from the stomach in patients with duodenal ulcer. *Gut* 22: 916–22

50. Man, W. K., Ingoldby, C. J. H., Spencer, J. 1984. Is pentagastrin-stimulated secretion mediated by histamine? *Gut* 25:965–70

51. Lorenz, W., Troidl, H., Barth, H., Rohde, H., Schulz, S. et al. 1976. Stimulus-secretion coupling in the human and canine stomach: role of histamine. In *Stimulus-Secretion Coupling in the Gastrointestinal Tract,* ed. R. M. Case, H. Goebell, pp. 177–91. Lancaster, England: MTP

52. Peden, N. R., Boyd, E. J. S., Callachan, H., Shepherd, D. M., Wormsley, K. G. 1982. The effects of impromidine and pentagastrin on gastric output of histamine, acid and pepsin in man. *Hepato-Gastroenterol.* 29:30–34

53. Walsh, J. H. 1983. Gastrointestinal peptide hormones. In *Gastrointestinal Disease,* ed. M. H. Sleisenger, J. S. Fordtran. Philadelphia: Saunders

54. Wolfe, M. M., Reel, G. M., McGuigan, J. E. 1983. Inhibition of gastrin release by secretin is mediated by somatostatin in cultured rat antral mucosa. *J. Clin. Invest.* 72:1586–93

55. Batzri, S. 1981. Direct action of somatostatin on dispersed mucosal cells form guinea pig stomach. *Biochim. Biophys. Acta.* 677:521–24

56. Chew, C. S. 1983. Inhibitory action of somatostatin on isolated gastric glands

and parietal cells. *Am. J. Physiol.* 245: G221–29

57. Schepp, W., Ruoff, H. J. 1984. Adenylate cyclase and H^+ production of isolated rat parietal cells in response to glucagon and histamine. *Eur. J. Pharmacol.* 98:9–18

58. Obrink, K. J., Bergqvist, E., Nylander, O. 1984. Mode of action by some acid secretion inhibitors on the stimulating mechanism in gastric epithelial cells. In *Hydrogen Ion Transport in Epithelia,* ed. J. G. Forte, D. G. Warnock, F. C. Rector, pp. 343–51. New York: Wiley

59. Hovendal, C. P., Gottrup, F., Bech, K., Andersen, D. 1981. Effect of Isoprenaline on pentagastrin-stimulated gastric acid secretion in dogs with gastric fistula. *Scand. J. Gastroent.* 16:535–40

60. Gottrup, F. 1981. Effect of a beta$_2$-sympathomimetic on urecholine-stimulated gastric acid secretion in dogs. *Scand. J. Gastroent.* 16:213–18

61. Simons, M. A., Moody, F. G. 1982. Effects of beta-adrenergic agents on canine gastric acid secretion. *Surg. Gastroenterol.* 1:35–44

62. Rosenfeld, R. C. 1984. Isolated parietal cells: Adrenergic response and pharmacology. *J. Pharmacol. Exp. Ther.* 229:763–67

63. Ruoff, J. H., Becker, M. 1982. Histamine-sensitive adenylate cyclase in human gastric mucosa: Cellular localization and interaction by PGE$_2$, somatostatin and secretin. *Agents Actions* 12:174–75

64. Konturek, S. J., Cieszkowski, M., Jaworek, J., Konturek, J., Brzozowski, T., Gregory, H. 1984. Effects of epidermal growth factor on gastrointestinal secretions. *Am. J. Physiol.* 246: G580–86

65. Chen, M. C., Amirian, D. A., Soll, A. H. 1984. Epidermal growth factor (EGF) binding and inhibitory effect on acid secretion on isolated parietal cells. *Fed. Proc.* 43:4608 (Abstr.)

66. Reichstein, B. J., Okamoto, C., Forte, J. G. 1984. Inhibition of acid secretion by epidermal growth factor (EGF) in isolated gastric glands is secretatogue specific. *Fed. Proc.* 43:4607 (Abstr.)

67. Forgue-Lafitte, M. E., Kobari, L., Gespach, C., Chamblier, M. C., Rosselin, G. 1984. Characterization and repartition of epidermal growth factor-urogastrone receptors in gastric glands isolated from young adult guinea pigs. *Biochim. Biophys. Acta* 798:192–98

Ann. Rev. Physiol. 1986. 48:103–17

RECEPTORS AND CELL ACTIVATION ASSOCIATED WITH PANCREATIC ENZYME SECRETION[1]

Jerry D. Gardner and Robert T. Jensen

Digestive Diseases Branch, National Institute of Arthritis, Diabetes, and Digestive and Kidney Diseases, National Institutes of Health, Bethesda, Maryland 20205

INTRODUCTION

The various secretagogues that act on pancreatic acinar cells stimulate enzyme secretion by activating one of two functionally distint processes (14). One process involves binding of the secretagogue to its receptrs, increased turnover of phosphatidylinositol, mobilization of cellular calcium, activation of phospholipid-dependent, calcium-sensitive protein kinase, phosphorylation of one or more cellular proteins and, after a series of presently undefined steps, stimulation of enzyme secretion. The other process involves binding of the secretagogue to its receptors, activation of adenylate cyclase, increased cellular cyclic AMP, activation of cyclic AMP-dependent protein kinase, phosphorylation of one or more cellular proteins and, after a series of presently undefined steps, stimulation of enzyme secretion. The initial steps in these two pathways are functionally distinct. Secretagogues that cause mobilization of cellulai calcium do not increase cellular cyclic AMP and secretagogues that increase cellular cyclic AMP do not cause mobilization of cellular calcium. At some presently undefined later step these two processes are functionally coupled. The result of this coupling is potentiation of enzyme secretion when both processes are activated simultaneously by combining a secretagogue that mobilizes cellular calcium with a secretagogue that increases cellular cyclic AMP.

[1]The US Government has the right to retain a nonexclusive, royalty-free license in and to any copyright covering this paper.

RECEPTORS FOR SECRETAGOGUES THAT CAUSE MOBILIZATION OF CELLULAR CALCIUM

Receptors for Cholecystokinin (CCK) and Structurally Related Peptides

CCK (27, 47–49) and its C-terminal octapeptide (CCK-8) (37, 41) can be acylated with the ^{125}I-labeled compound described by Bolton & Hunter (5). CCK labeled with iodinated Bolton-Hunter reagent has been used successfully to detect CCK receptors on pancreatic acinar cells (27, 37, 47–49). In particular, there is a close correlation between the abilities of CCK and structurally related peptides to inhibit binding of ^{125}I-CCK and their ability to alter enzyme secretion from pancreatic acinar cells.

One unusual feature shared by all CCK-related peptides is that their dose-response curves for inhibition of binding of ^{125}I-CCK are broad—the maximally effective concentration of a given peptide is at least one thousand times greater than its threshold concentration (27). Two hypotheses have been proposed to account for the broad dose-inhibition curves for binding of ^{125}I-CCK. One hypothesis, developed by Williams and his collaborators (48), proposes that acinar cells possess two distinct classes of receptors: one class with a low capacity and a high affinity for CCK, and another class with a high capacity and a low affinity for CCK. The major problem with this hypothesis is that it does not account for the biological actions of CCK on pancreactic acinar cells (for example, see References 8 and 9). Another hypothesis, developed by Gardner and coworkers (8, 9), proposes that pancreatic acinar cell CCK receptors each have two classes of binding sites for CCK and that occupation of one binding site influences the affinity of the other binding site for CCK. The major problem with this hypothesis is that it does not account for the broad dose-inhibition curve in a quantitative manner. Thus, at the present time there is no hypothesis that adequately describes the binding of ^{125}I-CCK as well as the biologic actions of CCK on pancreatic acinar cells.

Although the dose-response curve for the action of CCK on amylase secretion is broad and has a biphasic contour, the range of concentrations over which CCK binds to its receptors is the same as that over which the secretagogue produces changes in amylase secretion. Occupation of up to 40% of the receptors by CCK causes progressive stimulation of amylase secretion, and occupation of the remaining 60% causes a progressive reduction in stimulated amylase secretion. Occupation of up to 75% of the receptors by CCK causes a progressive increase in calcium outflux, and occupation of the remaining 25% causes no futher change in calcium outflux.Thus, pancreatic acinar cells possess spare receptors for CCK in terms of the secretagogue-induced changes in calcium outflux, but not in terms of the changes in amylase secretion.

In addition to causing mobilization of cellular calcium and stimulating enzyme secretion, relatively low degrees of receptor occupation by CCK also cause other changes in acinar cell function. CCK causes depolarization and a reduction in surface membrane resistance of pancreatic acinar cells (39, 40). The dose-response curves for these electrical changes are the same as the dose-response curve for CCK-induced changes in calcium outflux. CCK also increases cellular cyclic GMP (for review see Reference 14), and the dose-response curve for changes in cyclic GMP corresponds to the dose-response curve for CCK-induced changes in calcium outflux. Thus, occupation of up to 75% of the CCK receptors by CCK causes electrical changes in the acinar cell plasma membrane, mobilization of cellular calcium, and increased cellular cyclic GMP. CCK also causes increased turnover of phosphatidylinositol (36); however, the dose-response curve for this effect is not sufficiently character-ized to allow comparison to the dose-response curve for receptor occupation by CCK. High degrees of receptor occupation by CCK (i.e. occupation of 50–100% of the receptors by CCK) cause activation of adenylate cyclase (14), increased cellular cyclic AMP (18), inhibition of amino acid uptake (20), increased uptake of glucose (31), desensitization of CCK-stimulated enzyme secretion (1, 52), and CCK-induced residual stimulation of enzyme secretion (8, 9). The basis for the different effects of low and high degrees of CCK receptor occupation is not clear.

In addition to CCK there are two other naturally occurring peptides that interact with the CCK receptor on pancreatic acinar cells. Gastrin occurs naturally in several different chemical forms (53) and shares a common C-terminal pentapeptide-amide sequence with CCK. Caerulein, a decapeptide originally isolated from the skin of *Hyla caerulea,* shares seven of its eight C-terminal amino acids with CCK-8 (2). The apparent affinity of gastrin for CCK receptors on pancreatic acinar cells is approximately one thousand times less than that of CCK, whereas the apparent affinity of caerulein for CCK receptors is approximately ten times greater than that of CCK.

Structure-function studies of various fragments and analogues of CCK indi-cate that C-terminal fragments as small as the dipeptide-amide are capable of interacting with the CCK receptor on pancreatic acinar cells (25, 28). In general, the following is true of the relation between receptor occupation and the accompanying change in cellular function: The unsulfated C-terminal heptapeptide amide of CCK (des[SO_3H]CCK-7) is the smallest C-terminal fragment of CCK with the full spectrum of biologic activity of CCK. Adding a sulfate ester to the tyrosine residue of des [SO_3H]CCK-7 increases the apparent affinity of the peptide by approximately one thousand–fold. Adding an N-terminal aspartyl residue to CCK-7, thereby producing CCK-8, causes a three-to tenfold increase in the apparent affinity of the peptide for the CCK receptors. Extending the N-terminus of CCK-8 either does not change, or reduces by as much as tenfold, the apparent affinity of the peptide for CCK receptors. CCK-6, CCK-5, and CCK-4 interact with CCK receptors but do not reproduce the full spectrum of the dose-response curve for stimulation of enzyme secretion. In particular, CCK-6, CCK-5, and CCK-4 cause the same maximal stimulation of enzyme secretion as CCK-7 or longer peptides, but at supramaximal concentrations they do not cause the same decrement in the dose-response curve. Moreover, CCK-6, CCK-5, and CCK-4 inhibit the downstroke of the dose-response curve for enzyme secretion caused by supramaximal concentrations of CCK-7 or longer peptides. CCK-3 and CCK-2 interact with CCK receptors on pancreatic acinar cells, but do not possess agonist activity.

Since 1979 three classes of CCK receptor antagonists have been described: (*1*) derivatives of cyclic nucleotides, (*2*) derivatives of amino acids, and (*3*) partial sequences of the C-terminal region of CCK (for review see Reference 15). The ability of these various agents to antagonize the actions of CCK has in every instance been first described in dispersed acini prepared from guinea pig pancreas. These antagonists share several common features. Each antagonist inhibits CCK-stimulated amylase secretion and CCK-stimulated outflux of calcium, and the dose-response curves for those inhibitory actions correlate closely with the dose-response curve for the ability of the antagonist to inhibit binding of ^{125}I-CCK to its cell surface receptors on pancreatic acinar cells. The antagonist-induced inhibition of the action of CCK is fully and rapidly reversible, is competitive in nature, and is specific for those secretagogues that interact with the CCK receptor. In pancreatic acini that have been first incubated with relatively high concentrations of CCK and then washed, there is significant residual stimulation of enzyme secretion (8), and this CCK-induced residual stimulation of enzyme secretion can be reversed immediately by adding a CCK receptor antagonist (9, 15). Of the three classes of CCK receptor antagonists, a partial sequence of the C-terminal region of CCK is the most potent antagonist, dibutyryl cyclic GMP is the next most potent antagonist, and derivatives of amino acids are the least potent antagonists (15).

As mentioned previously, high degrees of occupation of the CCK receptor (i.e. occupation of 50–100% of the receptors) cause desensitization of enzyme secretion. In particular, first incubating pancreatic acini with CCK reduces the subsequent response to a maximally effective concentration of CCK by as much as 75% (1). CCK-induced desensitization of enzyme secretion is temperature-dependent and reversible, and the rate of onset and of reversal depend on the concentration of CCK (1). CCK-induced desensitization is proportional to occupation of CCK receptors by various analogues of CCK, and therefore is clearly related to CCK receptor occupation (1, 52). On the other hand, CCK-induced desensitization is not "receptor specific" (1). That is, first incubating pancreatic acini with CCK reduces the subsequent response to all secretagogues that cause mobilization of cellular calcium (i.e. CCK, carbachol, bombesin, physalaemin, or A23187), but does not alter the stimulation of enzyme secretion caused by secretagogues whose actions are mediated by cyclic AMP (i.e. vasoactive intestinal peptide, secretin, or 8Br-cyclic AMP).

High degrees of receptor occupation by CCK cause residual stimulation of enzyme secretion (8, 52). In particular, when pancreatic acini are first incubated with relatively high concentrations of CCK and then washed and reincubated, there is significant stimulation of amylase secretion during the second incubation. In contrast to CCK-induced desensitization, which is abolished by reducing the temperature of the first incubation to 4°C, CCK-induced residual stimulation occurs even when the temperature of the first incubation is reduced to 4°C (1, 8). CCK-induced residual stimulation is proportional to occupation of CCK receptors by various fragments and analogues of CCK (52) and can be reversed immediately by adding a CCK receptor antagonist to the second incubation (9, 15).

Electron microscopic and autoradiographic techniques have been used to localize CCK receptors to the basolateral plasma membrane of pancreatic acinar cells (44, 54). After binding to the CCK receptor, some of the receptor-bound CCK is internalized and degraded (54). ^{125}I-CCK binds to partially purified plasma membranes prepared from pancreatic acinar cells (44–46, 50); however, in contrast to results obtained with intact cells, plasma membranes have only one class of CCK binding sites with a relatively low affinity for CCK (44, 46). Because intact cells appear to possess two classes of CCK binding sites (two independent classes of receptors or one class of receptors with two interacting binding sites), isolated plasma membrane preparations appear to retain only one of these two classes of binding sites. More work is obviously needed to relate the characteristics of binding of CCK to isolated plasma membranes to those of binding of CCK to intact pancreatic acinar cells. Studies performed by covalently cross-linking ^{125}I-CCK to its binding sites on plasma membranes from pancreatic acinar cells indicate that the minimal structure of the CCK receptor is a protein having a M_r of 70,000–80,000 (44–46, 50). This protein appears to exist both in free form and joined by disulfide bonds to a protein having a M_r of 40,000–55,000 (44–46, 50).

Receptors for Bombesin and Structurally Related Peptides

An analogue of bombesin, [Tyr^4]bombesin, has been synthesized, radiolabeled with ^{125}I, and used successfully to identify receptors for bombesin and structurally related peptides on pancreatic acinar cells (29). In particular, there is a close correlation between the abilities of bombesin and structurally related peptides to inhibit binding of ^{125}I-[Tyr^4]bombesin and their abilities to alter enzyme secretion from pancreatic acinar cells.

Although the dose-response curve for bombesin-stimulated amylase secretion has a biphasic contour, the range of concentrations over which bombesin binds to its receptors is the same as that over which the secretagogue produces changes in amylase secretion. Occupation of up to approximately 50% of the receptors by bombesin causes progressive stimulation of amylase secretion, and occupation of the remaining 50% causes a small reduction (approximately

10%) in stimulated amylase secretion. Occupation of up to 75% of the receptors by bombesin causes a maximal increase in calcium outflux, and occupation of the remaining 25% causes no further change in calcium outflux. Thus, as occurs with CCK receptors, pancreatic acinar cells possess spare receptors for bombesin in terms of the secretagogue-induced changes in calcium outflux but not in terms of the changes in amylase secretion.

Like CCK, bombesin causes depolarization of pancreatic acinar cells as a result of a reduction in plasma membrane resistance (39), and the dose-response curves for these electrical changes are the same as the dose-response curve for bombesin-induced changes in calcium outflux. Bombesin also increases cellular cyclic GMP (34, 51), and the dose-response curve for bombesin-induced changes in cyclic GMP is superimposable on the curve for bombesin-induced changes in calcium outflux. The current thinking is that it is the secretagogue-induced mobilization of cellular calcium that actually causes the electrical changes and the increase in cyclic GMP in pancreatic acinar cells. Unlike CCK, high degrees of receptor occupation by bombesin or structurally related peptides do not cause activation of adenylate cyclase or increased cellular cyclic AMP. To our knowledge bombesin has not been tested for an effect on transport of amino acids or sugars.

As is the case with CCK, the intrinsic biologic activity of bombesin and structurally related peptides is a property of the C-terminal portion of the molecule, and the C-terminal nonapeptide of bombesin has the same potency and efficacy as does the native tetradecapeptide (11–13). Shorter C-terminal fragments of bombesin still possess full intrinisic biologic activity, but their potencies are less than that of native bombesin. The region of the bombesin molecule that possesses intrinsic biologic activity also determines the affinity of the peptide for its receptors, i.e. the variation in potency among various fragments and analogues of bombesin reflects variation in their receptor affinities. The relative potencies with which bombesin and three naturally occurring, structurally related peptides inhibit binding of ^{125}I-[Tyr^4]bombesin to pancreatic acini are bombesin > ranatensin = alytesin > litorin. These relative potencies for inhibiting binding of the iodinated peptide are the same as those for causing mobilization of cellular calcium and those for stimulating enzyme secretion (23, 29, 51).

Of the fragments and analogues of bombesin that have been tested, none has been found to occupy the bombesin receptor and not cause a full biologic response. Thus, there are no bombesin-related peptides that function as a bombesin receptor antagonist. However, a peptide originally described as a substance P receptor antagonist, [D-Arg^1, D-Pro^2, D-Trp^{7,9}, Leu^{11}]substance P, also functions as a fully competitive bombesin receptor antagonist (24). This peptide, but not substance P itself, inhibits binding of ^{125}I-[Tyr^4]bombesin to its receptors on pancreatic acinar cells, and inhibits competitively the stimulation of enzyme secretion caused by bombesin and structurally related peptides (23, 29, 51).

Bombesin and structurally related peptides, like CCK, also cause desensitization of pancreatic enzyme secretion (33). In particular, first incubating pancreatic acini with bombesin reduces the subsequent response to a maximally effective concentration of bombesin by as much as 80% (33, 38). Desensitization is reversible, and both the onset of the process and its reversal are time and temperature dependent. Neither the desensitization process nor the resensitization process appears to depend on protein synthesis, because neither process is inhibited by cycloheximide, an inhibitor of protein synthesis. Unlike CCK-induced desensitization, bombesin-induced desensitization is specific for those peptides that interact with the bombesin receptor. First incubating pancreatic acini with bombesin or a structurally related peptide does not alter the subsequent stimulation of enzyme secretion caused by CCK, carbachol, or A23187. Studies relating bombesin binding to bombesin-induced desensitization indicate that bombesin-induced desensitization results from a cycling of the bombesin receptor between active and inactive states (38). The initial step in the action of bombesin on pancreatic acinar cells is irreversible binding of bombesin to its receptor. The ligand-receptor complex is then converted to a state in which the receptor is inactive, perhaps as a result of internalization of the bombesin receptor. Bombesin then dissociates from its inactive receptor and the receptor is recycled to an active state.

In contrast to CCK, bombesin causes only a small degree of residual stimulation of pancreatic enzyme secretion (33, 38). This finding indicates that active bombesin-receptor complexes are rapidly inactivated when bombesin is removed from the incubation medium (38).

No studies have been performed to localize receptors for bombesin or structurally related peptides on pancreatic acinar cells; however, most investigators assume that bombesin receptors are located on the basolateral plasma membrane. Moreover, the plasma membrane receptors for bombesin have not been solubilized and characterized after covalently coupling bombesin or a structurally related peptide to the bombesin receptor using appropriate cross-linking agents.

Receptors for Muscarinic Cholinergic Agents

Two radiolabeled muscarinic cholinergic antagonists, [^{3}H]quinuclidinyl benzilate ([^{3}H]QNB) and [^{3}H]N-methyl scopolamine ([^{3}H]NMS), have been used to identify muscarinic cholinergic receptors on pancreatic acinar cells (3, 10, 32, 35).

Studies of the abilities of various agonists and antagonists to inhibit binding of labeled antagonist to pancreatic acini or their plasma membranes show that binding inhibition curves are monophasic with antagonists and biphasic with agonists (3, 10, 32, 35). Two hypotheses have been proposed to account for these differences. One hypothesis proposes two different *states* of the muscarinic cholinergic receptor that occur when the receptor is occupied by agonist but not when the receptors are occupied by antagonist. The other hypothesis proposes that there are two different *populations* of muscarinic cholinergic receptors. One population has a relatively high affinity for agonists and the other has a relatively low affinity for agonists. Both populations are viewed as having the same affinity for a given antagonist. Additional studies will be required to determine which, if either, of these hypotheses is correct.

The relation between binding of carbachol to muscarinic cholinergic receptors on pancreatic acinar cells and the accompanying carbachol-induced changes in acinar cell function is similar to that for binding of CCK-8 and the accompanying CCK-8-induced changes in acinar cell function. Although the dose-response curve for the action of carbachol on amylase secretion is broad and has a biphasic contour, the range of concentrations over which carbachol binds to its receptors is the same as that over which the secretagogue produces changes in amylase secretion. Occupation of up to approximately 50% of the receptors by carbachol causes progressive stimulation of amylase secretion, and occupation of the remaining 50% causes a progressive reduction in stimulated amylase secretion. Occupation of up to 75% of the receptors by carbachol causes a progressive increase in calcium outflux, and occupation of the remaining 25% causes no further change in calcium outflux. Thus, pancreatic acinar cells possess spare receptors for carbachol in terms of the secretagogue-induced changes in calcium outflux, but not in terms of the changes in amylase secretion. One group of investigators has concluded that pancreatic acinar cells possess spare receptors for muscarinic cholinergic agonists in terms of their abilities to stimulate amylase secretion (10). This conclusion is erroneous because these investigators considered only the upstroke of the dose-response curve for amylase secretion, not the full spectrum of the curve.

Occupation of muscarinic cholinergic receptors by agonists causes depolarization of pancreatic acinar cells, reduction in plasma membrane resistance (39), and increased cellular cyclic GMP (7). As with CCK and bombesin, the electrical changes and the increase in cellular cyclic GMP are believed to be mediated by agonist-induced mobilization of cellular calcium. Unlike CCK, high degrees of receptor occupation by muscarinic cholinergic agonists do not cause activation of adenylate cyclase. To our knowledge cholinergic agonists have not been tested for an effect on transport of amino acids or sugars.

Although they have not been studied extensively, muscarinic cholinergic agonists such as carbachol do cause desensitization of enzyme secretion from pancreatic acini (1). In the one study performed to date (1), carbachol caused desensitization of enzyme secretion to stimulation by carbachol as well as by CCK. These findings suggest that the pattern of carbachol-induced desensitization is probably similar to that of CCK. That is, first incubating pancreatic acinar cells with carbachol will reduce the subsequent response to all those secretagogues that cause mobilization of cellular calcium, but will not reduce the response to those secretagogues whose action is mediated by cyclic AMP.

Unlike CCK and bombesin, muscarinic cholinergic agonists do not cause residual stimulation of amylase secretion. This lack of ability to induce residual stimulation indicates that cholinergic agonists dissociate more rapidly from their receptors than CCK and bombesin.

No studies have been performed to localize receptors for muscarinic cholinergic agonists on pancreatic acinar cells; however, most investigators assume that these receptors, like those for CCK, are located on the basolateral plasma membrane. However, the plasma membrane receptors for muscarinic cholinergic agents have not been isolated and characterized.

Receptors for Physalaemin and Structurally Related Peptides

^{125}I-physalaemin has been used successfully to identify receptors for physalaemin and structurally related peptides on pancreatic acinar cells (22). In particular, there is a close correlation between the abilities of physalaemin and structurally related peptides to inhibit binding of ^{125}I-physalaemin and their abilities to alter enzyme secretion from pancreatic acinar cells. Recently (26), substance P was radiolabeled with ^{125}I using the radioiodinated acylating agent described by Bolton & Hunter (5). Results obtained with ^{125}I-substance P are essentially the same as those obtained with ^{125}I-physalaemin (26).

The dose-response curve for physalaemin-stimulated amylase secretion is the same as that for the physalaemin-induced increase in calcium outflux. Occupation of approximately 50% of the receptors by physalaemin causes maximal stimulation of amylase release and calcium outflux, and occupation of the remaining receptors causes no further change in these functions. Thus, as occurs with secretagogues whose actions are mediated by CCK, bombesin, or muscarinic cholinergic receptors, pancreatic acinar cells possess spare receptors for physalaemin in terms of the secretagogue-induced changes in calcium outflux. In contrast to results with receptors for CCK, bombesin, or muscarinic cholinergic agents, there is also spareness at the receptor level in terms of the ability of physalaemin to stimulate amylase secretion.

Physalaemin and structurally related peptides increase cyclic GMP in pancreatic acinar cells (34, 51), presumably by virtue of the ability of physalaemin and related peptides to cause mobilization of cellular calcium. The dose-response curve for the physalaemin-induced increase in cellular cyclic GMP is the same as that for physalaemin-induced mobilization of cellular calcium. To our knowledge neither physalaemin nor structurally related peptides have been tested for effects on the electrical properties of pancreatic acinar cells; however, because of their abilities to cause mobilization of cellular calcium, it is likely that physalaemin-related peptides will depolarize pancreatic acinar cells by reducing the plasma membrane resistance. Unlike CCK, physalaemin does not activate adenylate cyclase in pancreatic acinar cells. Physalaemin and structurally related peptides have not been tested for effects on transport of amino acids or sugars in pancreatic acinar cells.

As occurs with CCK-related peptides and with bombesin-related peptides, the intrinsic biologic activity of physalaemin and structurally related peptides is a property of the C-terminal portion of the molecule. The smallest C-terminal fragment of physalaemin that has been examined and found to retain biologic activity is the pentapeptide. Eledoisin is approximately 50% more effective than physalaemin and substance P in stimulating amylase secretion from pancreatic acinar cells (51). The relative potencies with which physalaemin and three naturally occurring, structurally related peptides inhibit binding of ^{125}I-physalaemin to pancreatic acini are physalaemin > substance P > eledoisin > kassinin. These relative potencies for inhibiting binding of the iodinated peptide are the same as those for causing mobilization of cellular calcium and stimulation of enzyme secretion (13, 22, 51).

Recently, three analogues of substance P were synthesized and found to competitively antagonize the actions of physalaemin and structurally related peptides on pancreatic acinar cells, [D-Pro^2, D-Trp^{7,9}]substance P, [D-Pro^2, D-Phe^7, D-Trp^9]substance P, and [D-Arg^1, D-Pro^2, D-Trp^{7,9}, Leu^{11}]substance P (26). These antagonists share several common features. Each antagonist inhibits the stimulation of amylase secretion and calcium outflux caused by physalaemin and structurally related peptides, and the dose-response curves for these inhibitory actions correlate closely with the dose-response curve for the ability of the antagonist to inhibit binding of ^{125}I-physalaemin to its cell surface receptors on pancreatic acini. The antagonist-induced inhibition of the action of physalaemin is fully and rapidly reversible, is competitive in nature, and is specific for those secretagogues that interact with the physalaemin receptors.

Unlike CCK, bombesin, or muscarinic cholinergic agents, physalaemin and structurally related peptides do not cause desensitization of pancreatic acinar cells. The basis for this lack of desensitization is not clear, but may be related to the fact that the efficacy of physalaemin and structurally related peptides is only 30–40% of that of CCK, bombesin, or muscarinic cholinergic agonists (51).

Unlike CCK and bombesin, neither physalaemin nor any of its structurally related peptides cause residual stimulation of enzyme secretion from pancreatic acinar cells. This lack of ability to induce residual stimulation suggests that physalaemin and structurally related peptides dissociate more rapidly from their receptors than do CCK and bombesin, or that the ligand-receptor complex is rapidly inactivated.

No studies have been performed to localize receptors for physalaemin and structurally related peptides on pancreatic acinar cells; however, most investigators assume that receptors for physalaemin, like those for CCK, are located on the basolateral plasma membrane of pancreatic acinar cells. Plasma membrane receptors for physalaemin have not been isolated and characterized.

RECEPTORS FOR SECRETAGOGUES THAT INCREASE CELLULAR CYCLIC AMP

Receptors for Vasoactive Intestinal Peptide (VIP) and Secretin

Measurement of binding of ^{125}I-VIP to acinar cells from guinea pig pancreas indicates that these cells have two functionally distinct classes of receptors each of which interact with VIP and secretin (for review see References 14 and 23). One class has a high affinity for VIP and a low affinity for secretin; the other class has a high affinity for secretin and a low affinity for VIP. Measurement of binding of ^{125}I-secretin to acinar cells from guinea pig pancreas detects only the sites with a high affinity for secretin, because there are few sites that have a high affinity for VIP, and they have a low affinity for secretin, and therefore do not bind significant amounts of ^{125}I-secretin (21). There is a close correlation between occupation of the VIP-preferring receptors and the secretin-preferring receptors by VIP, secretin, or a structurally related peptide, and the accompanying increase in cellular cyclic AMP (14, 42).

In contrast to those peptides that produce mobilization of calcium from pancreatic acinar cells and have their intrinsic biologic activities in the C-terminal portion of the molecule, in VIP and secretin the intrinsic biologic activity resides in the N-terminal portion of the molecule (6, 43). For example, secretin-1-14 has an efficacy that is equal to that of native secretin, whereas secretin-5-27 and secretin-14-27 have efficacies that are less than 2% that of native secretin (6, 17, 43). Another feature that distinguishes VIP and secretin from those peptides that cause mobilization of cellular calcium is that, to date, no fragment of VIP or secretin has been found to be as potent as the native molecule. For example, although secretin-1-14 has the same efficacy as native secretin, the apparent affinity of secretin-1-14 for secretin-preferring receptors on pancreatic acinar cells is approximately one thousand times less than the affinity of native secretin for these same receptors (23).

Occupation of the VIP-preferring receptors by VIP, secretin, peptide histidine isoleucine (PHI) or Gila monster venom causes a significant increase in cellular cyclic AMP and an accompanying increase in enzyme secretion (21, 23, 30, 42). The dose-response curve for VIP binding to receptors is the same as the dose-response curve for the action of VIP on cellular cyclic AMP. Both the dose-response curve for VIP binding and that for the VIP-induced increase in cellular cyclic AMP are to the right of the dose-response curve for VIP-stimulated amylase secretion. These findings indicate that there are no spare VIP-preferring receptors in terms of the increase in cellular cyclic AMP, but that there is "spare mediator" in the sense that relatively small increases in cellular cyclic AMP are sufficent to produce maximal stimulation of amylase secretion.

Occupation of the secretin-preferring receptors by secretin, VIP, PHI, or Gila monster venom (21, 23, 30, 42) causes a pronounced increase in cellular cyclic AMP without an accompanying increase in enzyme secretion. These findings indicate that in acinar cells from guinea pig pancreas cyclic AMP is compartmentalized, and only the cyclic AMP that is produced in response to occupation of the VIP-preferring receptors is in the appropriate compartment to cause stimulation of enzyme secretion (16). Measurements of binding of [^{3}H]ouabain suggest that the increase in cellular cyclic AMP that occurs in response to occupation of secretin-preferring receptors may be responsible for stimulation of fluid and electrolyte secretion from pancreatic acinar cells (19). The dose-response curve for binding of secretin is to the right of that for the secretin-induced increase in cellular cyclic AMP. Thus, there are spare secretin-preferring receptors with respect to the increase in cellular cyclic AMP, and occupation of only a fraction of the secretin-preferring receptors is sufficient to produce a maximal increase in cellular cyclic AMP.

VIP, secretin, PHI, and Gila monster venom each interact with VIP-preferring receptors and with secretin-preferring receptors on acinar cells from guinea pig pancreas. VIP, PHI, and Gila monster venom have higher affinities for the VIP-preferring receptors than for the secretin-preferring receptors, whereas secretin has a higher affinity for secretin-preferring receptors than for VIP-preferring receptors.

The foregoing discussion pertains to results obtained using acinar cells from guinea pig pancreas. A much different pattern occurs with acinar cells from rat pancreas, in which four classes of receptors are required to account for the actions of VIP and secretin (4). One class has a high affinity for VIP and does not interact with secretin, and occupation of this class of receptors causes increased cellular cyclic AMP and stimulation of amylase secretion. A second class has a low affinity for VIP and for secretin, and occupation of these receptors does not cause changes in cyclic AMP or amylase secretion. A third class of receptors has a high affinity for secretin and does not interact with VIP, and occupation of these receptors causes increased cellular cyclic AMP and stimulation of amylase secretion. A fourth class of receptors has a low affinity for secretin and does not interact with VIP, and occupation of these receptors causes stimulation of amylase secretion by a mechanism not mediated by cyclic AMP. Not only do rat acinar cells differ from guinea pig acinar cells in terms of the number and type of receptors that interact with VIP and secretin, but in rat acinar cells all of the cellular cyclic AMP appears to be coupled to stimulation of enzyme secretion. In addition, rat acinar cells possess a mechanism for secretin-induced stimulation of enzyme secretion that is not mediated by cyclic AMP. In every other system studied to date, occupation of secretin receptors by secretin causes activation of adenylate cyclase and increased cyclic AMP.

C-terminal fragments of secretin, such as secretin-5–27, secretin-9-27, and secretin-14–27, function as specific, competitive antagonists of the interaction of secretagogues with VIP-preferring receptors and with secretin-preferring receptors on acinar cells from guinea pig pancreas. The antagonist-induced inhibition is fully and rapidly reversible, and is specific for those secretagogues that interact with VIP-preferring and secretin-preferring receptors. Studies of secretin-5–27 have also provided insight into the role of the N-terminal tetrapeptide of secretin in influencing the apparent affinity of secretin for VIP-preferring receptors and secretin-preferring receptors on acinar cells from guinea pig pancreas. Deleting the N-terminal tetrapeptide from secretin does not alter the apparent affinity of the peptide for VIP-preferring receptors, but causes a one thousand–fold decrease in the apparent affinity of the peptide for secretin-preferring receptors (for review see Reference 23).

VIP and secretin, like other agents that increase cyclic AMP in pancreatic acinar cells, do not cause changes in the electrical properties of the acinar cell plasma membrane. This lack of effect presumably reflects the inability of these agents to cause mobilization of cellular calcium. In addition, neither VIP nor secretin cause desensitization of amylase secretion from acinar cells prepared from guinea pig pancreas.

VIP and secretin cause a modest degree of residual stimulation of enzyme secretion. However, this residual stimulation does not reflect persistent occupation of the receptors by the secretagogues, but instead, persistent elevation of the intracellular mediator, cyclic AMP. As the secretagogue-induced increase in cellular cyclic AMP is dissipated there is a corresponding decrease in residual stimulation of enzyme secretion.

No studies have been performed to localize receptors for VIP, secretin, or structurally related peptides on pancreatic acinar cells, and there are no reports of attempts to isolate and characterize receptors for VIP and secretin from pancreatic acinar cells.

ACKNOWLEDGMENT

We thank Mary O'Shaughnessy for preparing this manuscript for publication.

Literature Cited

1. Abdelmoumene, S., Gardner, J. D. 1980. *Am. J. Physiol* 239:G272–79
2. Anastasi, A., Erspamer, V., Endean, R. 1968. *Arch. Biochem. Biophys.* 125:57–68
3. Appert, H. E., Chiu, T. H., Budd, G. C., Leonardi, A. J., Howard, J. M. 1981. *Cell Tissue Res.* 220:673–84
4. Bissonnette, B. M., Collen, M. J., Adachi, H., Jensen, R. T., Gardner, J. D. 1984. *Am. J. Physiol.* 246:G710–17
5. Bolton, A. E., Hunter, W. M. 1973. *Biochem. J.* 133:529–39
6. Christophe, J.-P., Conlon, T. P., Gardner, J. D. 1976. *J. Biol. Chem.* 251:4629–34
7. Christophe, J.-P., Frandsen, E. K., Conlon, T. P., Krishna, G., Gardner, J. D. 1976. *J. Biol. Chem.* 251:4640–45
8. Collins, S. M., Abdelmoumene, S., Jensen, R. T., Gardner, J. D. 1981. *Am. J. Physiol.* 240:G459–65
9. Collins, S. M., Abdelmoumene, S., Jensen, R. T., Gardner, J. D. 1981. *Am. J. Physiol.* 240:G466–71
10. Dehaye, J.-P., Winand, J., Poloczek, P., Christophe, J. 1984. *J. Biol. Chem.* 259:294–300
11. Deschodt-Lanckman, M., Robberecht, P., De Neef, P., Lammens, M., Christophe, J. 1976. *J. Clin. Invest.* 58:891–98
12. Erspamer, V., Melchiorri, P. 1976. *Pure Appl. Chem.* 35:463–94
13. Erspamer, V., Melchiorri, P. 1975. *Gastrointestine Hormones*, pp. 575–89. Austin: Univ. Texas Press
14. Gardner, J. D., Jensen, R. T. 1981. *Physiology of the Gastrointestinal Tract.* Vol. 2, pp. 831–71. New York: Raven
15. Gardner, J. D., Jensen, R. T. 1984. *Am. J. Physiol.* 246:G471–76
16. Gardner, J. D., Korman, L., Walker, M., Sutliff, V. E. 1982. *Am. J. Physiol.* 242:G547–51
17. Gardner, J. D., Rottman, A. J., Natarajan, S., Bodanszky, M. 1979. *Biochim. Biophys. Acta* 583:491–503
18. Gardner, J. D., Sutliff, V. E., Walker, M. D., Jensen, R. T. 1983. *Am. J. Physiol.* 245:G676–80
19. Hootman, S. R., Ernst, S. A., Williams, J. A. 1983. *Am. J. Physiol.* 245:G339–46
20. Iwamoto, Y., Williams, J. A. 1980. *Am. J. Physiol.* 238:G440–44
21. Jensen, R. T., Charlton, C. G., Adachi, H., Jones, S. W., O'Donohue, T. L., et al. 1983. *Am. J. Physiol.* 245:G186–95
22. Jensen, R. T., Gardner, J. D. 1979. *Proc. Natl. Acad. Sci. USA* 76:5679–83
23. Jensen, R. T., Gardner, J. D. 1981. *Fed. Proc.* 40:2486–96
24. Jensen, R. T., Jones, S. W., Folkers, K., Gardner, J. D. 1984. *Nature* 309:61–63
25. Jensen, R. T., Jones, S. W., Gardner, J. D. 1983. *Biochim. Biophys. Acta* 757:250–58
26. Jensen, R. T., Jones, S. W., Lu, Y.-A. Xu, J.-C., Folkers, K., et al. 1984. *Biochim. Biophys. Acta* 804:181–91
27. Jensen, R. T., Lemp, G. F., Gardner, J. D. 1980. *Proc. Natl. Acad. Sci. USA* 77:2079–83
28. Jensen, R. T., Lemp, G. F., Gardner, J. D. 1982. *J. Biol. Chem.* 257:5554–59
29. Jensen, R. T., Moody, T., Pert, C., Rivier, J. E., Gardner, J. D. 1978. *Proc. Natl. Acad. Sci. USA* 75:6139–43
30. Jensen, R. T., Tatemoto, K., Mutt, V., Lemp, G. F., Gardner, J. D. 1981. *Am. J. Physiol.* 241:G498–G502
31. Korc, M., Williams, J. A., Goldfine, I. D. 1979. *J. Biol. Chem.* 254:7624–29
32. Larose, L., Dumont, Y., Asselin, J., Morisset, J., Poirier, G. G. 1976. *Eur. J. Pharmacol.* 76:247–54
33. Lee, P. C., Jensen, R. T., Gardner, J. D. 1980. *Am. J. Physiol.* 238:G213–18
34. May, R. J., Conlon, T. P., Erspamer, V., Gardner, J. D. 1978. *Am. J. Physiol.* 235:E112–18
35. McArthur, K. E., Jensen, R. T., Gardner, J. D., 1983. *Biochim. Biophys. Acta* 762:373–77
36. Michell, R. H. 1975. *Biochim. Biophys. Acta* 415:81–147
37. Miller, L. H., Rosenzweig, S. A., Jamieson, J. D. 1981. *J. Biol. Chem.* 256:12417–23
38. Pandol, S. J., Jensen, R. T., Gardner, J. D. 1984. *J. Biol. Chem.* 257:12024–29
39. Peterson, O. H. 1976. *Physiol. Rev.* 56:537–77
40. Peterson, O. H. 1981. *Physiology of the Gastrointestinal Tract*, pp. 749–72. New York: Raven.
41. Praissman, M., Martinez, P. A., Saladino, C. F., Berkowitz, J. M., Steggles, A. W., et al. 1983. *J. Neurochem.* 40:1406–13
42. Raufman, J.-P., Jensen, R. T., Sutliff, V. E., Pisano, J. J., Gardner, J. D. 1982. *Am. J. Physiol.* 242:G470–74
43. Robberecht, P., Conlon, T. P., Gardner, J. D. 1976. *J. Biol. Chem.* 251:4635–39
44. Rosenzweig, S. A., Miller, L. J., Jamieson, J. D. 1983. *J. Cell Biol.* 96:1288–97
45. Sakamoto, C., Goldfine, I. D., Wil-

liams, J. A. 1983. *J. Biol. Chem.* 258:12707–11
46. Sakemoto, C., Williams, J. A., Wong, K. Y., Goldfine, I. D. 1983. *FEBS Lett.* 151:63–66
47. Sankaran, H., Deveney, C. W., Goldfine, I. D., Williams, J. A. 1979. *J. Biol. Chem.* 254:9349–51
48. Sankaran, H., Goldfine, I. D., Bailey, H., Licko, V., Williams, J. A. 1982. *Am. J. Physiol.* 242:G250–57
49. Sankaran, H., Goldfine, I. D., Deveney, C. W., Wong, K-Y., Williams, J. A. 1980. *J. Biol. Chem.* 255:1849–53

50. Svoboda, M., Lambert, M., Furnelle, J., Christophe, J. 1982. *Regul. Pept.* 4:163–72
51. Uhlemann, E. R., Rottman, A. J., Gardner, J. D. 1979. *Am. J. Physiol.* 236:E571–76
52. Villanueva, M. L., Collins, S. M., Jensen, R. T., Gardner, J. D. 1982. *Am. J. Physiol.* 242:G416–22
53. Walsh, J. H. 1978. *Gastrointestinal Disease,* Ch. 6, pp. 107–57
54. Williams, J. A., Sankaran, H., Roach, E., Goldfine, I. D. 1982. *Am. J. Physiol.* 243:G291–96

Ann. Rev. Physiol. 1986. 48:119–34

FUNCTIONAL ACTIVITIES OF HEPATIC LIPOPROTEIN RECEPTORS

Richard J. Havel

Cardiovascular Research Institute and the Department of Medicine, University of California, San Francisco, California 94143–0130

INTRODUCTION

The liver is now recognized as the major site of the terminal catabolism of those lipoproteins that contain apolipoprotein B [chylomicrons, very low density lipoproteins (VLDL), and low density lipoproteins (LDL)]. The uptake of these particles takes place primarily, via coated pit regions of the plasma membrane, by the classical pathway of receptor-mediated endocytosis, which has been identified in many cells. In addition, the liver is an important site of the catabolism of high density lipoprotein (HDL) components, but the mechanism of uptake in this case seems to differ from the classical pathway, and the receptor dependency of the interaction of HDL with liver cells is less clearly defined. Finally, the liver can remove certain lipoproteins, whose protein moieties have been covalently modified via a "scavenger" receptor, that mediates the endocytosis of these particles. As the liver is the site of synthesis of VLDL and also of a portion of HDL, it is evident that this organ has a central role in lipoprotein metabolism. In this chapter I review the evidence for the contribution of receptor-mediated processes to the catabolism of lipoproteins in mammalian blood plasma and describe the specific receptors involved. I also provide some recent information about the intracellular pathway of receptor-mediated endocytosis in hepatocytes. Finally, I discuss the regulation of the activity of the hepatic LDL receptor and its relationship to the control of plasma lipoprotein levels in mammals, including humans.

119

0066-4278/86/0315-0119$02.00

CONTRIBUTION OF RECEPTOR-MEDIATED PROCESSES TO THE CATABOLISM OF SPECIFIC LIPOPROTEIN CLASSES

Chylomicrons and Their Remnants

Chylomicrons are triglyceride-rich particles secreted by the mucosal cells of the small intestine (38). They are transported via the lymphatic system into the blood. As with the other major plasma lipoproteins, chylomicrons are composed of a monolayer of amphiphilic lipids and proteins, which surround a core of mainly nonpolar lipids. The major nonpolar lipids of chylomicrons are triglycerides and cholesteryl esters, which are synthesized in the mucosal cells from absorbed fatty acids, monoglycerides, and cholesterol. Most of the chylomicron surface is composed of phospholipids and the remainder of cholesterol (some of which is also dissolved in the core) and apoproteins. The major apoproteins of newly secreted ("nascent") chylomicrons are apo A-I, apo A-II, and apo A-IV (all of which are found in plasma HDL), and a specific B apoprotein (B-48) (58). After secretion, C apoproteins and apo E are transferred to chylomicrons from HDL, and the A apoproteins and some phospholipids are transferred from the chylomicron surface to HDL (55).

Chylomicrons are secreted from the mucosal cells at all times, but both their number and size increase during active absorption of dietary fat. The small chylomicrons that can be obtained from mesenteric lymph of fasting rats are readily taken up by perfused livers, whereas large chylomicrons secreted during absorption of dietary fat are not (131). As described below, chylomicron remnants are taken up almost entirely into hepatocytes. Therefore, the failure of uptake of large chylomicrons whose diameter exceeds 1000 Å can be ascribed to their inability to pass through the sieve plates of the endothelial cells that line hepatic sinusoids. Chylomicrons of smaller diameter evidently can pass through the pores of the sieve plates.

The uptake of small chylomicrons from liver perfusates is inhibited by C apoproteins (131). As described below, apo E seems to be the ligand for receptor-dependent uptake of chylomicron remnants into hepatocytes. However, the inhibitory effect of addition of C apoproteins does not depend upon displacement of apo E from the particle surface, and it has been proposed that the C apoproteins produce an altered conformation of apo E in which the recognition site is obscured (133). In any event, the acquisition of C apoproteins by small chylomicrons may prevent premature uptake of the particles by the liver. Normally, most chylomicron triglycerides are removed in capillaries of extrahepatic tissues by the action of lipoprotein lipase. This first lipolytic step is accompanied by modifications of the chylomicron surface in which C apoproteins and phospholipids are returned to HDL, leaving a smaller particle, called a chylomicron remnant, in which the major apoproteins are apo E and apo B-48 (133). The remnant particles, which recirculate in the blood, are rapidly removed in the liver by a saturable process (20, 95). Several lines of evidence indicate that apo E on the remnants is recognized by an hepatic receptor: (*a*) Addition of apo E to small chylomicrons obtained from mesenteric lymph of estradiol-treated rats (in which few E or C apoproteins are available in HDL for transfer to the particle surface) substantially increases the rate of particle uptake into perfused livers (132). (*b*) The kinetics of uptake of a class of HDL particles that contain only apo E closely resembles that of chylomicrons, and the apo E–containing HDL compete for remnant uptake (96). (*c*) The removal of chylomicrons from the blood of humans who have mutant forms of apo E that bind poorly to lipoprotein receptors is very greatly impaired (105). In spite of these findings, some observations suggest that apo E may not be essential for the uptake of chylomicrons or their remnants: (*a*) The small chylomicrons from estradiol-treated rats, which contain little or no apo E, are still taken up into perfused livers (132). (*b*) Depletion of phospholipids from chylomicrons by treatment with phospholipase A_2 promotes uptake of the particles into perfused livers (12, 13). (*c*) Hepatic uptake of phospholipid-stabilized triglyceride emulsions may be independent of added apoproteins, yet it is inhibited by addition of C apoproteins (93). Whether these observations with unusual particles are relevant to normal chylomicron metabolism is uncertain.

VLDL, VLDL Remnants, and LDL

The initial step in the metabolism of VLDL is analogous to that of chylomicrons: hydrolysis of component triglycerides by lipoprotein lipase in extrahepatic tissues. Like small chylomicrons, VLDL from perfusates of isolated rat livers (whose diameter range from 300–800 Å), are taken up into these livers and, as with small chylomicrons, this uptake is inhibited by addition of C apoproteins (131). Thus, the proposition that the normal acquisition of C apoproteins from HDL prevents the premature uptake of VLDL by the liver (38) is also tenable. By further analogy with chylomicron metabolism, VLDL remnants in the rat are rapidly taken up by the liver.

Newly secreted hepatic VLDL of rats contain little A apoproteins but do contain some apo E and C apoproteins, which are synthesized by the liver (26, 77). They also contain a protein resembling apo B-48 of chylomicrons, but in addition contain a B apoprotein of larger molecular weight (apo B-100) (24, 68, 124, 136). Presumably, the two forms of hepatic apo B exist on distinct particles; particles that contain B-48 seem to be removed from the blood of intact rats more rapidly than those that contain B-100 (104). Furthermore, the latter are converted to a greater extent to lipoproteins of higher density, including LDL, which are removed much more slowly from the blood (104). The rat seems to be unique with respect to secretion of apo B-48 from the liver.

In other species, the liver secretes mainly or exclusively VLDL particles that contain apo B-100 (35, 50, 56). In these species, the conversion of VLDL remnants to LDL varies, as described below; however, in most species most hepatic VLDL return to the liver as VLDL remnants (41). That this process is receptor-dependent is supported by two major observations: First, uptake of VLDL remnants is impaired in Watanabe heriditary hyperlipidemic (WHHL) rabbits, which virtually lack one hepatic receptor, the LDL receptor (60). Second, removal from the blood of large VLDL (~450 Å in diameter) is greatly impaired (106) in humans with mutant forms of apo E that bind poorly to lipoprotein receptors, including the LDL receptor.

Whereas removal of chylomicron remnants and those VLDL remnants that are not converted to LDL is rapid and occurs almost exclusively in the liver, LDL are removed more slowly and to a significant extent by extrahepatic tissues (5, 108). However, studies in which LDL have been labeled with substituents that are poorly metabolized and tend to remain within lysosomes after endocytosis indicate that the liver is also a major site of removal of LDL from the blood (5, 108). Other evidence indicates that much of the hepatic uptake of LDL is mediated by receptors that recognize apo B-100, the sole B apoprotein of LDL. Thus, LDL in which lysyl or arginyl residues of apo B-100 have been largely modified (for example by methylation of lysyl residues) are removed more slowly by perfused livers than unmodified LDL (17). Such modifications are known to prevent binding of LDL to receptors. However, such covalently modified LDL are removed from the blood at an appreciable, albeit slower, rate (36), and other evidence indicates that the liver possesses mechanisms for uptake of LDL that are independent of the LDL receptor (87, 103). Therefore, at least two different processes contribute to the hepatic uptake of LDL.

HDL

Some HDL particles that contain one or more molecules of apo E can be taken up into the liver via the receptors that recognize chylomicron remnants or VLDL remnants (18, 76, 88, 125). However, most HDL contain mainly A apoproteins (principally apo A-I) and not apo E, and recent studies have shown that such HDL are taken up primarily by the liver (32, 109, 126). However, this uptake does not seem to represent only a simple endocytic process. The uptake of the major core lipid components of HDL (cholesteryl esters) or of a poorly metabolized analogue of cholesteryl ester, cholesteryl linoleyl ether, by the liver occurs to a greater extent than that of the major surface component, apo A-I (32, 109, 126).

Acetylated LDL and Its Congeners

LDL in which lysyl residues are covalently modified by reagents that increase the net negative charge of the protein bind to a receptor identified on macrophages (15) and endothelial cells (7). This "scavenger receptor" seems to mediate uptake by the classical endocytic pathway (15). When modified LDL, such as acetyl LDL, are labeled in the protein moiety and injected intravenously into rats, they are rapidly removed from the blood and the labeled protein is found almost entirely in the liver (10, 79, 86). Thus, if LDL are similarly modified within the blood, they are likely to be cleared by the liver within minutes.

CELLULAR SITES OF HEPATIC UPTAKE OF SPECIFIC CLASSES OF LIPOPROTEINS

Two general methods have been used to identify the cells that take up and degrade lipoproteins that have been injected intravenously or added to perfusates of isolated livers. The first relies on the localization of markers of lipoproteins in sections of livers at the light or electron microscopic levels. The second utilizes cell separation methods to localize the markers.

For the first method ^{125}I or ^{3}H autoradiography has been employed. At short intervals after intravenous injection, hepatic parenchymal cells are the primary site of localization of ^{3}H-cholesterol-labeled and ^{125}I-labeled chylomicrons (57, 111), and ^{125}I-labeled VLDL, LDL, and HDL (16, 57, 88, 89, 110). As described below, the intracellular localization of autoradiographic grains after injection of labeled chylomicrons, VLDL, and LDL is consistent with processing by the classical pathway of receptor-mediated endocytosis.

Variable results have been reported for the second method, in which the association of injected lipoproteins with cells separated from the liver is determined. Thus, cholesteryl esters and retinyl esters of chylomicrons have been found mainly in parenchymal cells (11, 81), but a substantial fraction of protein-labeled chylomicron remnants was associated with nonparenchymal cells (34, 71), mainly Kupffer cells (71). Nonparenchymal cells have also been found to contain a substantial fraction of ^{125}I- or ^{3}H-cholesteryl ester labeled VLDL, LDL, and HDL injected into rats (119, 127). By contrast, poorly metabolized markers attached covalently to LDL are associated almost entirely with hepatocytes after intravenous injection into rabbits (87). ^{125}I-labeled acetyl LDL is associated mainly with hepatic endothelial cells a few minutes after intravenous injection into rats (11, 79).

The second method may present certain problems related to redistribution of label during the process of cell isolation (43). From the combined evidence currently available, it appears that all of the major classes of normal lipoproteins are taken up by hepatocytes, whereas those lipoproteins that are recognized by the scavenger receptor are taken up by nonparenchymal cells, particularly the sinusoidal endothelium.

SPECIFIC CLASSES OF RECEPTORS: Evidence for Their Existence and Functional Activities

LDL Receptor

LDL receptors have been identified in membrane preparations from liver homogenates of several species (43, 65, 67, 134). They have been identified by their binding specificity, requirement for calcium ion, sensitivity to pronase digestion (61, 65, 67, 134), and by Western blotting to ligands containing apo B-100 or apo E (21). They have also been identified on hepatocytes (6, 85) and on hepatocyte tumor cell lines from humans (Hep G-2 cells) (37, 137) and rats (H-35 cells) (114). It has been difficult to identify LDL receptors on freshly prepared hepatocytes, even when they are prepared from estradiol-treated rats, which express a large number of LDL receptors in vivo and in membrane preparations (J. Belcher & R. J. Havel, unpublished data). Presumably, conditions for expression of the receptor on the cell surface are not met in such preparations. The expression of LDL receptors in membrane preparations from normal and estradiol-treated rats (67, 134) and variously treated dogs (3, 65) and rabbits (17, 19, 61, 113) is well correlated with the capacity of the livers of these animals to take up LDL in vivo.

Chylomicron Remnant Receptor

Rat hepatocytes bind and degrade chylomicron remnants more than chylomicrons (27, 28), but the nature of the binding site has not been established. A class of binding sites that appears to recognize apo E has been identified on H-35 rat hepatoma cells (114). Membrane preparations from adult foxhounds, which virtually lack the capacity to bind LDL that contain only apo B-100, retain appreciable capacity to bind HDL_c (a lipoprotein obtained from cholesterol-fed dogs that contains only apo E) (54). By contrast, membrane preparations from young foxhounds bind LDL as well. It has been suggested that the apo E–binding site may represent the chylomicron remnant receptor (54). Recently, this receptor has been partially purified and shown to be distinct from the LDL receptor, as determined by its apparent molecular weight in SDS-polyacrylamide gels (53). Such activity has not always been found in membrane preparations. For example, little or no high affinity binding of chylomicron remnants and only a small amount of binding of HDL_c has been found in membrane preparations from livers of WHHL rabbits (which virtually lack functional LDL receptors), although livers of these animals take up chylomicron remnants normally in vivo (62).

Scavenger Receptor

Acetyl LDL binds specifically to endothelial cells and to a lesser extent to Kupffer cells from rat liver (79). Binding is closely coupled to degradation, and it can be concluded that these cells express the scavenger receptor. These properties are well correlated with the capacity of these cells to take up chemically modified LDL in vivo.

Lipoprotein Binding Site

Parenchymal and nonparenchymal cells of the liver (6, 83, 118) and hepatoma cells (114), like many other isolated cells, possess a saturable "lipoprotein binding site" of broad specificity. Binding to this site on rat hepatocytes is incompletely coupled to degradation of the protein moiety of lipoproteins, including HDL that do not contain apo E (82). The uptake of a poorly metabolized analogue of cholesteryl ester, the major core component of HDL (cholesteryl linoleyl ether), by the rat hepatocytes is more rapid than that of the major surface component, apo A-I (31, 70). Whatever the mechanism of uptake, this site could mediate the catabolism of HDL components by the liver in vivo.

THE INTRACELLULAR PATHWAY OF LIPOPROTEIN CATABOLISM IN HEPTOCYTES AND ITS RELATIONSHIP TO RECEPTOR RECYCLING

Steps in the Pathway

Lipoproteins that are taken up into hepatocytes by the chylomicron remnant receptor or the LDL receptor seem to be processed by the classical pathway of receptor-dependent endocytosis, identified in hepatocytes and other cells for the uptake of a variety of macromolecules (14, 92). Because lipoproteins can be visualized within organelles by electron microscopy, certain steps of the pathway have become more evident by the study of endocytosis of lipoproteins. Furthermore, the presence of large numbers of lipoproteins within endocytic compartments has recently made it possible to separate these organelles and to identify some of their characteristics.

Lipoproteins are taken up into rat hepatocytes via coated pits, as originally described for the uptake of LDL into cultured fibroblasts (16, 36). Current evidence suggests that lipoproteins and other proteins, such as asialoglycoproteins, may be bound first to sites on the microvilli of the sinusoidal face of the cell and migrate with the receptor to the coated pits (92). The coat material, clathrin, rapidly separates from the primary endosome after it is formed. The endosomes appear to fuse with one another or with pre-existing vesicular compartments near the sinusoidal surface within five minutes of the endocytic event (16, 128). During the next ten minutes the larger endosomes migrate to the biliary canalicular pole of the cell, near the Golgi apparatus. In this region the lipoproteins are seen mainly in multivesicular bodies (MVBs). These are large vesicles of 0.3–0.5 μm in diameter that contain several smaller vesicles, about 0.08 μm in diameter, together with a large number of other lipoproteins, most of which are between 0.02 and 0.08 μm in diameter, i.e. the size of chylomicron or VLDL remnants (16, 49, 57). During the next 15–45 min these structures take on the appearance of secondary lysosomes. In chloroquine-treated rats MVBs become larger and their conversion to secondary lysosomes, accompanied by degradation of lipoprotein components, is delayed (49).

In cultured fibroblasts LDL receptors return to the cell surface within a few minutes of the endocytic event (14). The same phenomenon has been shown for other hepatocyte receptors (92), and it seems likely that LDL receptors recycle in a similar manner in this cell. The endosomal compartments are acidic (117), owing to an ATP-driven proton pump in their membranes (29, 112). The reduced pH is thought to dissociate LDL and other ligands from their receptors before the receptors return to the cell surface (14, 92). The asialoglycoprotein receptor separates from vesicles containing its ligands in a compartment named "CURL" (compartment of uncoupling of receptor and ligand) located near the sinusoidal face of the cell (30). The site of uncoupling of lipoprotein receptors in hepatoyctes has not been identified.

Isolation and Characterization of Lipoprotein-Filled Endocytic Organelles

MVBs containing endocytosed lipoproteins have been isolated from livers of estradiol-treated rats (48). Their low density (1.035 g/ml) facilitates separation from other organelles by flotation in density gradients. However, MVBs can be contaminated by secretory vesicles of the Golgi apparatus, which contain nascent VLDL. Likewise, secretory vesicle–rich fractions of the Golgi apparatus may be contaminated by MVBs. By application of appropriate methods, however, the two lipoprotein-filled vesicular structures can be largely separated (48; R. L. Hamilton, J. Belcher, R. J. Havel, unpublished data). The properties of the lipoproteins that can be recovered from MVBs after rupturing the membrane of the organelle are consistent with those expected for remnants of VLDL or chylomicrons (48).

Evidence has been obtained that the interior of MVBs, like that of other endocytic structures, is acidic. MVBs contain an ATP-driven proton pump (120), the properties of which closely resemble those of coated vesicles isolated from rat livers (121).

The lipoproteins isolated from MVBs are largely undergraded, which is consistent with the low activity of lysosomal hydrolases in this organelle (47, 48). However, the conversion of MVBs to secondary lysosomes involves the acquisition of hydrolases, delivered to the organelle within primary lysosomes, which are thought to originate in the nearby Golgi apparatus (47).

ROLE OF RECEPTORS IN THE REGULATION OF PLASMA LIPOPROTEIN LEVELS

Animal Models: Dietary, Hormonal, Genetic, and Pharmacological Influences

THE ESTRADIOL-TREATED RAT   Administration of pharmacological amounts of 17-α-ethinyl estradiol (5 mg/kg daily for 5 days) increases the number of LDL receptors in rat hepatocytes ten- to twentyfold (67, 134). Treated animals develop a profound hypolipidemia, which encompasses all of the major classes of lipoproteins; LDL may virtually disappear from the blood (18). The reduction of lipoprotein levels is accompanied by increased rates of clearance from the blood into the liver (18, 46). Synthesis of VLDL in the liver remains largely intact, although treated animals eat less than the controls. The VLDL contain increased amounts of cholesteryl esters. In perfused livers from estradiol-treated rats the uptake of HDL that contain little or no apo E is not increased (unlike that of LDL and HDL that contain apo E), but HDL are removed from the blood more rapidly in vivo and HDL cholesterol and apo A-I levels are drastically reduced (18). It has been proposed that, in vivo, HDL particles may transiently acquire a molecule of apo E and then be taken up by hepatic LDL receptors (18). The mechanism by which estradiol increases the number of hepatic LDL receptors is unknown.

DIETARY MODIFICATIONS IN RABBITS AND OTHER SPECIES   In rabbits the activity of LDL receptors in liver membrane preparations falls to low levels during a fast of several days duration, owing to a reduction of receptor-mediated catabolism (113). Levels of intermediate density lipoproteins (IDL) are also increased, but VLDL levels remain unchanged. Rabbits fed diets in which casein is the sole protein source also have greatly increased LDL levels and a much reduced capacity of hepatic membranes to bind lipoproteins containing apo B and apo E (17, 19). Biliary excretion of bile acids and cholesterol is reduced in casein-fed (52) as well as fasted (63) rabbits. The resulting retention of cholesterol in the liver could account for the observed reduction of hepatic LDL receptors.

Diets containing 0.1–2% cholesterol increase serum cholesterol levels in rabbits. These animals accumulate large numbers of cholesteryl ester–enriched VLDL in their blood, which contain substantial amounts of apo E (97) as well as apo B-100 (J.-L. Vigne, R. J. Havel, unpublished observations). These lipoproteins, called beta-VLDL, are derived mainly from cholesterol-enriched VLDL secreted from the liver (116; J.-L. Vigne, R. J. Havel, unpublished observations), which is engorged with cholesteryl esters. The binding of beta-VLDL to hepatic membranes is substantially reduced, presumably due to a reduction in the activity of LDL receptors (66). The hyperlipidemia in cholesterol-fed rabbits is thought to result both from increased secretion of cholesterol-enriched VLDL and from reduced activity of hepatic LDL receptors (66). Both of these phenomena may reflect the failure of the animals to excrete effectively the chylomicron-derived cholesterol in the bile or to convert it to bile acids (22). In none of these rabbit models of reduced (presumably down-regulated) LDL receptors do appreciable amounts of chylomicron remnants accumulate in the blood (116; J.-L. Vigne, R. J. Havel, unpublished data). This suggests that the chylomicron receptor, unlike the LDL receptor, is influenced little by accumulation of cholesterol in hepatocytes.

The reason for the susceptibility of the rabbit to hypercholesterolemia, produced by varied nutritional stimuli, may be linked to the inability of the liver to increase appropriately the formation of bile acids or the excretion of cholesterol into the bile. In dogs and rats, addition of cholesterol to ordinary diets fails to induce marked hypercholesterolemia unless the animals are rendered hypothyroid (1, 84). Reduced thyroid function impairs the formation of bile acids (1, 22), so in these and other species the reduction of hepatic LDL receptors may be linked to the ability of the animal to mount this response to cholesterol loading.

Infusion of chylomicron-rich lymph reduces the activity of LDL receptors in membrane preparations from dog livers by 50% or more in as little as 2 hr (3). Intravenous infusion of bile acids has a similar effect (3). These observations suggest that, as in cultured cells, hepatic LDL receptors turn over rapidly.

PHARMACOLOGICAL INFLUENCES   In dogs and casein-fed rabbits, cholestyr-amine, a bile acid–binding resin that increases the conversion of cholesterol to bile acids in the liver, reduces the level of LDL and increases the activity of LDL receptors in hepatic membrane preparations (19, 65, 99). Administration of competitive inhibitors of hydroxymethylglutaryl-CoA reductase to dogs (65) or rabbits (17) has similar effects. In dogs, administration of resin and reductase inhibitor together has an additive effect (65). Evidently, the reductase inhibitor blocks the compensatory increase in hepatic cholesterol biosynthesis that normally accompanies administration of the resin. It thereby further depletes hepatic cholesterol, and the number of receptors consequently increases to a greater extent than with resin alone. In the rat, neither cholestyramine (64) nor a reductase inhibitor (25) alters LDL levels. The liver of the rat normally has an unusually high rate of cholesterol synthesis. When reductase inhibitor is given, the synthesis of reductase protein increases manyfold. The smooth endoplasmic reticulum proliferates and assumes a crystalloidal appearance, related to the large increase in enzyme content (98). This response has not been observed in other animals, but a similar alteration occurs in a line of Chinese hamster ovary cells exposed to reductase inhibitor (2).

THE WHHL RABBIT   Rabbits later found to be homozygous for a mutation of the LDL receptor were discovered by Watanabe in 1973 (129). The mutation in this animal results in production of a receptor protein that seems to undergo glycosylation very slowly (91). Consequently, little receptor reaches the cell surface. No receptors can be detected in membrane preparations from livers of WHHL homozygotes. Levels of apo B-100 in VLDL, IDL, and LDL are increased 2.5-, 10-, and 20-fold, respectively (45). Lipoprotein cholesterol levels are increased even more as these particles become relatively more enriched with cholesteryl esters and cholesterol (45). The metabolism of chylomicrons is unimpaired in WHHL homozygotes, which indicates that they have intact chylomicron remnant receptors (62). However, the metabolism of VLDL and LDL is impaired and the rate of production of LDL is increased severalfold (9, 60). The augmented production of LDL is not the result of increased secretion of VLDL from the liver, nor of particles of higher density that contain apo B-100 (50), rather a larger than normal fraction of VLDL appears to be converted to LDL owing to reduced hepatic uptake of VLDL remnants via the LDL receptor (60). Cholesteryl esters do not accumulate in the livers of these animals (50), which is consistent with the primary defect in the uptake of VLDL remnants and LDL. However, the newly secreted VLDL are enriched in cholesteryl esters (50). This enrichment may reflect the continuing influx of cholesterol-enriched LDL, which have been shown to be taken up mainly by hepatocytes in these animals (87). Partial ilial bypass (122, 123), administration of cholestyramine (123), or compactin (130) reduces plasma cholesterol levels appreciably in WHHL homozygotes. This could reflect stimulation of the synthesis of the dysfunctional receptors, as in normal rabbits. However, partial ileal bypass reduces LDL synthesis and has no effect on its rate of removal from the blood in the homozygote (107).

Humans with Genetic Hyperlipoproteinemias

FAMILIAL HYPERCHOLESTEROLEMIA   In humans homozygous for mutations of the LDL receptor (homozygous familial hypercholesterolemia), levels of IDL and LDL are usually increased (42, 75, 102), as are concentrations of apo B-100 and apo E (42). It therefore seems likely that the metabolic defect resembles that of WHHL homozygotes. However, in human homozygotes a large fraction of LDL is thought to be produced by a mechanism that does not involve the catabolism of VLDL (100–102). Whether this conclusion, which is based upon isotope kinetic analyses of removal of radioiodinated VLDL, IDL, and LDL from the blood, correctly identifies a difference in lipoprotein metabolism in the two species is unclear.

As in rabbits and dogs, cholestyramine (44) and reductase inhibitors (73) each can reduce levels of LDL by about one-third in humans with heterozygous familial hypercholesterolemia or with other forms of primary hypercholesterolemia (138). When combined, the effects of the drugs are additive (74). When administered with colestipol (another bile acid-binding resin) nicotinic acid also has an additive effect (59). The hypolipidemic effects of resin and reductase inhibitor are presumably caused by an increase in the number of hepatic LDL receptors. The mechanism of the effect of nicotinic acid is less certain, but it is thought to reduce production of VLDL by the liver (69). In those humans with familial hypercholesterolemia who are homozygous for null mutations and hence have no LDL receptors on their cells, these drugs would be expected to be ineffective unless they reduced lipoprotein synthesis. However, in those homozygotes who have one or two mutations that yield a small number of functional receptors on cell surfaces, the drugs may have some beneficial effect (33). The importance of the activity of hepatic LDL receptors for lipoprotein catabolism in humans has recently been dramatically demonstrated in a child with homozygous familial hypercholesterolemia who received a liver transplant. LDL cholesterol levels fell rapidly from 1000 mg/dl to 200 mg/dl, and the rate of removal of ^{125}I-labeled LDL from the blood increased into the low normal range (8).

FAMILIAL DYSBETALIPOPROTEINEMIA   Several point mutations of apo E have been identified that affect properties of the binding of lipoproteins to lipoprotein receptors (90). Each of these produces the phenotypic disorder called familial dysbetalipoproteinemia or type III hyperlipoproteinemia. Affected individuals have defective catabolism of chylomicron remnants and VLDL remnants (39, 105), consistent with the function of these proteins as ligands for hepatic chylomicron remnant receptors and LDL receptors, respectively. However, in contrast to homozygous familial hypercholesterolemia, impairment of the hepatic uptake of VLDL remnants does not increase conversion to LDL; rather, the level of VLDL remnants is high and that of LDL is low (39). The basis for the defect in conversion is unclear, but it has been reported that the beta VLDL in these patients are not readily converted to LDL by lipolytic enzymes unless the mutant protein is replaced by a normal form of apo E (23). Interestingly, the phenotypic abnormality may be as severe in patients with mutations associated with only a moderate decrease in binding affinity for receptors (as measured with isolated preparations of apo E complexed with phosphatidyl choline) as in those with a severe decrease in binding affinity (R. J. Havel, J. P. Kane, unpublished observations). With at least one of the former mutations this lack of difference also applies to the metabolism of the apo B components of intravenously injected chylomicrons and VLDL (105).

As the mutant proteins in familial dysbetalipoproteinemia do retain some capacity to bind to LDL receptors, measures that increase hepatic LDL receptor number should reduce the level of remnant particles.

Speculations about Dietary Regulation in Humans

The clear effect of dietary cholesterol on hepatic LDL receptors in rabbits and other animals, as related to the capacity of the liver to form bile acids, suggests that the hypercholesterolemic action of dietary cholesterol in humans, which mainly involves LDL (4, 72, 78), is mediated by reduction in the activity of LDL receptors (40). The effect in humans is variable and has also been coupled with the extent to which cholesterol synthesis is inhibited (78, 80).

The effect of other dietary components upon hepatic LDL receptors is less clear. The efficiency of removal of LDL from the blood may be increased when diets rich in polyunsaturated fatty acids are fed (94). Some evidence indicates that the lipid composition of LDL may influence its interaction with LDL receptors (115, 135). Therefore, changes in the fatty acid composition of LDL produced by alterations in the quality of dietary fat could affect the functional properties of hepatic LDL receptors. Even more speculatively, the affinity of the LDL receptor on the membrane surface for ligands, or its rate of recycling, could be influenced by the composition of the plasma membrane of the cell. Effective study of the regulation of hepatic LDL receptors in humans may require the development of methods to measure LDL receptor activity noninvasively (51).

Literature Cited

1. Abell, L. L., Mosbach, E. H., Kendall, F. E. 1956. *J. Biol. Chem.* 220:527–36
2. Anderson, R. G., Orci, L., Brown, M. S., Garcia-Segura, L. M., Goldstein, J. L. 1983. *J. Cell. Sci.* 63:1–20
3. Angelin, B., Ravida, C. A., Innerarity, T. L., Mahley, R. 1983. *J. Clin. Invest.* 71:816–31
4. Applebaum-Bowden, D., Hazzard, W. R., Cain, J., Cheung, M. C., Kushwaha, R. S., Albers, J. J. 1979. *Atherosclerosis* 33:385–96
5. Attie, A. D., Pittman, R. C., Steinberg, D. 1982. *Hepatology* 2:269–81
6. Bachorik, P. S., Franklin, F. A., Virgil, D. G., Kwiterovich, P. V. Jr. 1982. *Biochemistry* 21:5675–84
7. Baker, D. P., van Lenten, B. J., Fogelman, A. M., Edwards, P. A., Kean, C., Berliner, J. 1984. *Arteriosclerosis* 4: 248–55
8. Bilheimer, D. W., Goldstein, J. L., Grundy, S. M., Starzl, T. E., Brown, M. S. 1985. *N. Engl. J. Med.* In press
9. Bilheimer, D. W., Watanabe, Y., Kita, T. 1982. *Proc. Natl. Acad. Sci. USA* 79:3305–9
10. Blomhoff, R., Drevon, C. A., Eskild, W., Helgerud, P., Norum, K. F., Berg, T. 1984. *J. Biol. Chem.* 259:8898–8903
11. Blomhoff, R., Helgerud, P., Rasmussen, M., Berg, T., Norum, D. R. 1982. *Proc. Natl. Acad. Sci. USA* 79:7326–30
12. Borensztajn, J., Kotlar, T. J. 1981. *Biochem. J.* 200:547–53
13. Borensztajn, J., Kotlar, T. J., McNeil, B. J. 1980. *Biochem. J.* 192:845–51
14. Brown, M. S., Anderson, R. G. W., Goldstein, J. L. 1983. *Cell* 32:663–67
15. Brown, M. S., Goldstein, J. L. 1983. *Ann. Rev. Biochem.* 52:223
16. Chao, Y.-S., Jones, A. L., Hradek, G. T., Windler, E. E. T., Havel, R. J. 1981. *Proc. Natl. Acad. Sci. USA* 78:597–601
17. Chao, Y.-S., Kroon, P. A., Yamin, T. T., Thompson, G. M., Alberts, A. W. 1983. *Biochim. Biophys. Acta* 754:134–41
18. Chao, Y.-S., Windler, E., Chen, G. C., Havel, R. J. 1979. *J. Biol. Chem.* 254:11360–66
19. Chao, Y.-S., Yamin, T.-T., Alberts, A. W. 1982. *J. Biol. Chem.* 257:3623–27
20. Cooper, A. D., Yu, P. Y. S. 1978. *J. Lipid Res.* 19:635–43
21. Daniel, T. O., Schneider, W. J., Goldstein, J. L., Brown, M. S. 1983. *J. Biol. Chem.* 258:4606–11
22. Dietschy, J. M., Wilson, J. D. 1970. *N.*

Engl. J. Med. 288:1128–38, 1179–83, 1241–49

23. Ehnholm, C., Mahley, R. W., Chappell, D. A., Weisgraber, K. H., Ludwig, E., Witztum, J. L. 1984. *Proc. Natl. Acad. Sci. USA* 81:5566–70

24. Elovson, J., Huang, Y. O., Baker, N., Kannan, R. 1981. *Biochemistry* 78:157–66

25. Endo, A., Tsujita, Y., Koroda, M., Tanzawa, K. 1979. *Biochim. Biophys. Acta* 575:266–76

26. Felker, T. E., Fainaru, M., Hamilton, R. L., Havel, R. J. 1977. *J. Lipid Res.* 18:465–73

27. Florén, C. H., Nilsson, A. 1977. *Biochem. J.* 168:483–94

28. Florén, C. H., Nilsson, A. 1978. *Biochem. J.* 174:827–38

29. Galloway, D. J., Dean, G. E., March, M., Rudneck, G., Millman, L. 1983. *Proc. Natl. Acad. Sci. USA* 80:3334–38

30. Geuze, H. J., Slot, J. W., Strous, J. A. M., Lodish, H. F., Schwartz, A. L. 1983. *Cell* 32:277–87

31. Glass, C., Pittman, R. C., Civen, M., Steinberg, D. 1985. *J. Biol. Chem.* 260:744–50

32. Glass, C. R., Pittman, R. C., Weinstein, D. B., Steinberg, D. 1983. *Proc. Natl. Acad. Sci. USA* 80:5435–39

33. Goldstein, J. L., Brown, M. S. 1982. *Med. Clin. North Am.* 66:335–62

34. Groot, P. H. E., van Berkel, T. J. C., van Tol, A. 1981. *Metabolism* 30:792–97

35. Guo, L. S. S., Hamilton, R. L., Ostwald, R., Havel, R. J. 1982. *J. Lipid Res.* 23:543–55

36. Handley, D. A., Arbeeny, C. M., Eder, H. A., Chien, S. 1981. *J. Cell Biol.* 90:778–87

37. Havekes, L., van Hensbergh, V., Kempen, H. J. 1983. *Biochem. J.* 214:951–58

38. Havel, R. J. 1980. *Ann. NY Acad. Sci.* 348:16–27

39. Havel, R. J. 1982. *Med. Clin. North Am.* 66:441–54

40. Havel, R. J. 1983. *Prog. Biochem. Pharmacol.* 19:111–22

41. Havel, R. J. 1984. *J. Lipid Res.* 25:1570–76

42. Havel, R. J. 1985. *Arteriosclerosis* In press

43. Havel, R. J. 1985. *Methods Enzymol.* In press

44. Havel, R. J., Kane, J. P. 1973. *Ann. Rev. Pharmacol.* 13:287–308

45. Havel, R. J., Kita, T., Kotite, L., Kane, J. P., Hamilton, R. L., et al. 1982. *Arteriosclerosis* 2:467–74

46. Hay, R. V., Pottinger, L. A., Reingold, A. L., Getz, G. S., Wissler, R. W. 1971.

Biochem. Biophys. Res. Commun. 44:1471–77

47. Hornick, C. A., Hamilton, R. L., Jost-Vu, E., Spaziani, E., Enders, G. H., Havel, R. J. 1984. *J. Cell Biol.* 99:118a

48. Hornick, C. A., Hamilton, R. L., Spaziani, E., Enders, G. H., Havel, R. J. 1985. *J. Cell Biol.* 100:1558–69

49. Hornick, C. A., Jones, A. L., Renaud, G., Hradek, G., Havel, R. J. 1984. *Am. J. Physiol.* 256:G187–94

50. Hornick, C. A., Kita, T., Hamilton, R. L., Kane, J. P., Havel, R. J. 1983. *Proc. Natl. Acad. Sci. USA* 80:6096–6100

51. Huettinger, M., Schneider, W. J., Ho, Y. K., Goldstein, J. L., Brown, M. S. 1984. *J. Clin. Invest.* 74:1017–26

52. Huff, M. W., Carroll, K. K. 1980. *J. Lipid Res.* 21:546–48

53. Hui, D. Y., Brecht, W., Lorenz, T., Friedman, G., Innerarity, T. L., Mahley, R. W. 1984. *Circulation* 70:II–311

54. Hui, D. Y., Innerarity, T. L., Mahley, R. W. 1981. *J. Biol. Chem.* 256:5646–55

55. Imaizumi, K., Fainaru, M., Havel, R. J. 1978. *J. Lipid Res.* 19:712–22

56. Johnson, F. L., St. Clair, R. W., Rudel, L. L. 1983. *J. Clin. Invest.* 72:221–36

57. Jones, A. L., Hradek, G. T., Hornick, C., Renaud, G., Windler, E. E. T., Havel, R. J. 1984. *J. Lipid Res.* 25:1151–58

58. Kane, J. P., Hardman, D. A., Paulus, H. E. 1980. *Proc. Natl. Acad. Sci. USA* 77:2465–69

59. Kane, J. P., Malloy, M. J., Tun, P., Phillips, N. R., Freedman, D. D., et al. 1981. *N. Engl. J. Med.* 304:251–58

60. Kita, T., Brown, M. S., Bilheimer, D. W., Goldstein, J. L. 1982. *Proc. Natl. Acad. Sci. USA* 79:5693–97

61. Kita, T., Brown, M. S., Watanabe, Y., Goldstein, J. L. 1981. *Proc. Natl. Acad. Sci. USA* 78:2268–72

62. Kita, T., Goldstein, J. L., Brown, M. S., Watanabe, Y., Hornick, C. A., Havel, R. J. 1982. *Proc. Natl. Acad. Sci. USA* 79:3623–27

63. Klauda, H. C., Zilversmit, D. B. 1975. *J. Lipid Res.* 16:258–63

64. Koelz, H. R., Sherrill, B. D., Turley, S. D., Dietschy, J. M. 1982. *J. Biol. Chem.* 257:8061–72

65. Kovanen, P. T., Bilheimer, D. W., Goldstein, J. L., Jaramillo, J. J., Brown, M. S. 1981. *Proc. Natl. Acad. Sci. USA* 78:1194–98

66. Kovanen, P. T., Brown, M. S., Basu, S. K., Bilheimer, D. W., Goldstein, J. L. 1981. *Proc. Natl. Acad. Sci. USA* 78:1396–1400

67. Kovanen, P. T., Brown, M. S., Gold-

stein, J. L. 1979. *J. Biol. Chem.* 254: 11360–66
68. Krishnaiah, K. V., Walker, L. F., Borensztajn, J., Schonfeld, G., Getz, G. 1980. *Proc. Natl. Acad. Sci. USA* 77: 3806–10
69. Langer, T., Levy, R. I. *Metabolic Effects of Nicotinic Acid and its Derivatives*, pp. 641–47. Bern: Huber
70. Leitersdorf, E., Stein, O., Eisenberg, S., Stein, Y. 1984. *Biochim. Biophys. Acta* 796:72–82
71. Lippiello, P. M., Dijkstra, J., van Galen, M., Scherphof, G., Waite, B. M. 1981. *J. Biol. Chem.* 256:7454–60
72. Lui, D. S., Connor, W. E. 1980. *J. Lipid Res.* 21:1042–52
73. Mabuchi, H., Haba, T., Tatami, R., Miyamoto, S., Sakai, Y., et al. 1981. *N. Engl. J. Med.* 305:478–82
74. Mabuchi, H., Sakai, T., Sakai, Y., Yoshimura, A., Watanabe, A., et al. 1983. *N. Engl. J. Med.* 308:609–13
75. Mabuchi, H., Tatami, R., Veda, K., Haba, T., Kametami, T., et al. 1979. *Atherosclerosis* 32:435–44
76. Mahley, R. W., Innerarity, T. L., Weisgraber, K. H., Oh, S. Y. 1979. *J. Clin. Invest.* 64:743–50
77. Marsh, J. B. 1976. *J. Lipid Res.* 17:85–90
78. Mistry, P., Miller, N. E., Laker, M., Hazzard, W. R., Lewis, B. 1981. *J. Clin. Invest.* 67:493–502
79. Nagelkerke, J. F., Barto, K. S., van Berkel, T. J. C. 1983. *J. Biol. Chem.* 258:12221–27
80. Nestel, P. J., Poyser, A. 1976. *Metabolism* 25:1591–99
81. Nilsson, A., Zilversmit, D. B. 1971. *Biochim. Biophys. Acta* 248:137–42
82. Ose, L., Røken, L., Norum, K. R., Berg, T. 1980. *Exp. Cell. Res.* 130:127–35
83. Ose, L., Røken, L., Norum, K. R., Drevon, C. A., Berg, T. 1981. *Scand. J. Chem. Lab. Invest.* 41:63–73
84. Page, I. H., Brown, H. B. 1952. *Circulation* 6:681–87
85. Pangburn, S. H., Newton, R. S., Chang, C.-M., Weinstein, D. M., Steinberg, D. 1981. *J. Biol. Chem.* 256:3340–47
86. Pitas, R. E., Boyles, J., Mahley, R. W., Bissell, D. M. 1985. *J. Cell Biol.* 100:103–17
87. Pittman, R. C., Carew, T. E., Attie, A. D., Witztum, J. L., Watanabe, Y., Steinberg, D. 1982. *J. Biol. Chem.* 257:7994–8000
88. Quarfordt, S., Hawkes, J., Jones, R. S., Shelburne, F. 1980. *J. Biol. Chem.* 255:2934–37

89. Rachmilowitz, D., Stein, O., Roheim, P. S., Stein, Y. 1972. *Biochim. Biophys. Acta* 270:414–25
90. Rall, S. C. Jr., Weisgraber, K. H., Innerarity, T. L., Mahley, R. W. 1984. In *Latent Dyslipoproteinemias and Atherosclerosis*, pp. 157–63. New York: Raven
91. Schneider, W. J., Brown, M. S., Goldstein, J. L. 1983. *Mol. Biol. Med.* 1:355–67
92. Schwartz, A. L. 1984. *CRC Crit. Rev. Biochem.* 16:207–33
93. Shelburne, F., Hawkes, J., Meyers, W., Quarfordt, S. 1980. *J. Clin. Invest.* 65:652–58
94. Shepherd, J., Packard, C. J., Grundy, S. M., Yashurun, D., Gotto, A. M. Jr., Taunton, O. W. 1980. *J. Lipid Res.* 21:91–99
95. Sherrill, B. C., Dietschy, J. M. 1978. *J. Biol. Chem.* 253:1859–67
96. Sherrill, B. C., Innerarity, T. L., Mahley, R. W. 1980. *J. Biol. Chem.* 255:1804–7
97. Shore, V. G., Shore, B., Hart, R. G. 1974. *Biochemistry* 13:1579–85
98. Singer, I. I., Kawka, D. W., Kazazis, D. M., Alberts, A. W., Chen, J. S., et al. 1984. *Proc. Natl. Acad. Sci. USA* 81:5556–60
99. Slater, H. R., Packard, C. J., Bicker, S., Shepherd, J. 1980. *J. Biol. Chem.* 255: 10210–13
100. Soutar, A. K., Myant, N. B., Thompson, G. R. 1977. *Atherosclerosis* 28:247–56
101. Soutar, A. K., Myant, N. B., Thompson, G. R. 1979. *Atherosclerosis* 32:315–25
102. Soutar, A. K., Myant, N. B., Thompson, G. R. 1982. *Atherosclerosis* 43:217–31
103. Spady, D. K., Bilheimer, D. W., Dietschy, J. M. 1983. *Proc. Natl. Acad. Sci.* 80:3499–3503
104. Sparks, C. E., Marsh, J. B. 1981. *J. Lipid Res.* 22:519–27
105. Stalenhoef, A. F. H., Malloy, M. J., Kane, J. P., Havel, R. J. 1984. *Circulation* 70:II–119
106. Stalenhoef, A. F. H., Malloy, M. J., Kane, J. P., Havel, R. J. 1984. *Proc. Natl. Acad. Sci. USA* 81:1839–43
107. Stalenhoef, A. E. H., van Niekerk, J. L. M., Demacker, P. H. M., van't Laar, A. 1984. *J. Lipid Res.* 25:1350–57
108. Stange, E. F., Dietschy, J. M. 1984. *J. Lipid Res.* 25:703–13
109. Stein, Y., Dabach, Y., Hollander, G., Halperin, G., Stein, O. 1983. *Biochim. Biophys. Acta* 752:98–105
110. Stein, O., Rachmilowitz, D., Sanger, S., Eisenberg, S., Stein, Y. 1974. *Biochim. Biophys. Acta* 360:205–16

111. Stein, O., Stein, Y., Goodman, D. S., Fidge, N. 1969. *J. Cell. Biol.* 43:410–31
112. Stone, D. K., Xie, X.-S., Racker, E. 1983. *J. Biol. Chem.* 258:4059–62
113. Stoudemire, J. B., Renaud, G., Shames, D. M., Havel, R. J. 1984. *J. Lipid Res.* 25:33–39
114. Tamai, T., Patsch, W., Lock, D., Schonfeld, G. 1983. *J. Lipid Res.* 24:1568–77
115. Thompson, G. R., Jadhav, A., Nava, M., Gotto, A. M. Jr. 1976. *Eur. J. Clin. Invest.* 6:241–48
116. Thompson, K. H., Zilversmit, D. B. 1983. *J. Nutr.* 113:2002–10
117. Tycko, B., Keith, C. H., Maxfield, F. R. 1983. *J. Cell Biol.* 97:1762–76
118. van Berkel, T. J. C., Kruijt, J. K., van Gent, T., van Tol, A. 1980. *Biochem. Biophys. Res. Commun.* 92:1002–8
119. van Berkel, T. J. C., van Tol, A. 1979. *Biochem. Biophys. Res. Commun.* 89: 1097–1101
120. Van Dyke, R. W., Hornick, C. A., Belcher, J., Scharschmidt, B. F., Havel, R. J. 1984. *J. Cell Biol.* 99:380a
121. Van Dyke, R. W., Steer, C. J., Scharschmidt, B. F. 1984. *Proc. Natl. Acad. Sci. USA* 81:3108–12
122. van Niekerk, J. L. M., Demacker, P. N. M., Hendriks, T., de Boer, H. H. M. 1983. *Atherosclerosis* 48:243–52
123. van Niekerk, J. L., Hendriks, M. T., de Boer, H. H. M. 1984. *Eur. Surg. Res.* 16:282–87
124. van't Hooft, F. M., Hardman, D. A.,

Kane, J. P., Havel, R. J. 1982. *Proc. Natl. Acad. Sci. USA* 79:179–182
125. van't Hooft, F., Havel, R. J. 1982. *J. Biol. Chem.* 257:10996–11001
126. van't Hooft, F. M., van Gent, T., van Tol, A. 1981. *Biochem. J.* 196:877–85
127. van Tol, A., van Berkel, T. J. C. 1980. *Biochim. Biophys. Acta* 619:156–66
128. Wall, D. A., Wilson, G., Hubbard, A. L. 1980. *Cell* 21:79–93
129. Watanabe, Y. 1980. *Atherosclerosis* 36:261–68
130. Watanabe, Y., Ito, T., Saeki, M., Korada, M., Tanama, K., et al. 1981. *Atherosclerosis* 38:27–31
131. Windler, E., Chao, Y.-S., Havel, R. J. 1980. *J. Biol. Chem.* 255:5475–80
132. Windler, E., Chao, Y.-S., Havel, R. J. 1980. *J. Biol. Chem.* 255:8303–7
133. Windler, E., Havel, R. J. 1985. *J. Lipid Res.* 26:556–65
134. Windler, E. E. T., Kovanen, P. T., Chao, Y.-S., Brown, M. S., Havel, R. J., Goldstein, J. L. 1980. *J. Biol. Chem.* 255:10464–71
135. Witztum, J. C., Young, S. G., Etain, R. L., Carew, T. E., Fisher, M. 1985. *J. Lipid Res.* 26:92–103
136. Wu, A. L., Windmueller, G. 1981. *J. Biol. Chem.* 256:3615–18
137. Wu, G. Y., Wu, C. H., Rifici, V. A., Stockert, R. J. 1984. *Hepatology* 4: 1190–94
138. Yamamoto, A., Sudo, M., Endo, A. 1980. *Atherosclerosis* 35:259–66

Ann. Rev. Physiol. 1986. 48:135–50

Ca²⁺ AND CYCLIC AMP IN REGULATION OF INTESTINAL Na, K, and Cl TRANSPORT

Mark Donowitz

Departments of Medicine and Physiology, Tufts University School of Medicine; New England Medical Center, Boston, Massachusetts 02111

Michael J. Welsh

Department of Medicine, University of Iowa College of Medicine, Iowa City, Iowa 52242

INTRODUCTION

This review is an update of the current understanding of how Ca^{2+} and cAMP regulate mammalian small intestinal and colonic electrolyte transport. We review the transport processes present in plasma membranes of absorptive and secretory epithelial cells and the way these processes are affected by Ca^{2+} and cAMP.

Studies of intestinal electrolyte transport are complicated by several factors, including the presence, and often simultaneous function, of both absorptive and secretory processes, and by the presence of multiple cell types. A cultured cell line that retains the electrolyte transport properties of the intact tissue would greatly simplify investigation. However, to date neither a transporting small intestinal nor an intestinal absorptive cell line has been developed. A Cl-secreting human colonic epithelial cell line, named T-84, has been reported (13–17), but these studies must be interpreted with the realization that such cells do not represent the normal colon, but a cancer cell line.

It is generally believed that electrolyte absorption and secretion are carried out by two separate epithelial cell types (38). The absorptive cells are thought to be present only on the villus of small intestine and on the surface of the colon, while the secretory cells are mostly present in the crypts.

135

0066-4278/86/0315-0135$02.00

CELLULAR MECHANISMS OF ION TRANSPORT

Absorptive Processes

A common feature of intestinal absorptive cells is that the basolateral membrane contains the Na,K-ATPase (the Na pump) and has a parallel K permeability (38, 47, 51). These maintain low cellular Na and high cellular K concentrations, and a negative cell voltage. A large electrochemical gradient for Na entry across the apical membrane is thus formed, which is used for "secondary active" absorption of a variety of ions and nonelectrolytes. Apical transport proteins have a segmental distribution throughout the intestine; it is not certain whether one cell type contains many absorptive processes, or whether there are several absorptive cell types, each containing a few transport processes.

In the jejunum Na entry occurs by: (*a*) Na/H exchange (50); (*b*) Na-substrate cotransport, including Na-glucose or galactose, multiple Na-amino acid cotransport, and an unknown number of Na-dipeptide tripeptide cotransporters (81); and (*c*) Na and PO_4 and Na and SO_4 cotransport. Na/H exchange, first demonstrated in small intestinal brush border vesicles by Murer in 1976 (70), has been identified in multiple mammalian intestines, including human jejunum (4, 42). In rabbit jejunal brush border vesicles the Na/H exchanger has a K_m for Na of 5 mM (50). In jejunum active Cl absorption does not occur; there is no evidence of direct linking of Na and Cl transport, and no Cl/HCO_3 or Cl/OH exchanger (50).

In mammalian ileum, Na and Cl transport are linked[1], and the Na-substrate mechanisms are less prominent. Turnberg and Fordtran first suggested that Na and Cl absorption and HCO_3 secretion in human ileum in vivo was explained by Na/H and Cl/HCO_3 exchangers operating in parallel (87). Nellans et al (72, 73) also suggested a linkage of Na and Cl transport in in vitro rabbit ileum. Insight into this linkage has come from studies by several groups using brush border membrane vesicles from mammalian small intestine. Liedtke & Hopfer suggested the linkage of Na and Cl transport was indirect (62, 63), and this now appears to be via the linkage of parallel brush border Na/H and Cl/HCO_3 exchangers (36, 37, 57–59). There is no coupling of Na and Cl in the presence of a high intravesicular buffer, which would prevent changes in pH as part of the function of the individual exchangers, but coupling is seen with low intravesicular buffer. This suggests that the linking could be via changes in intravesicular (cellular) pH. How pH links the exchangers is not proven. However, it is likely that carbonic anhydrase, which is present in brush border membranes, is involved, especially since the carbonic anhydrase inhibitor acetazolamide inhibits linked NaCl transport both in intact ileum and in brush border vesicles (58, 74).

---

[1]The term "linked" refers to any mechanism of cotransport without specifying the molecular mechanism or stoichiometry.

Another Na and Cl linked transport process (a NaKCl$_2$ cotransporter) is present in the apical membrane of flounder intestine, although it has not yet been identified in absorptive cells in mammalian intestine (71). Direct linking of Na and Cl transport by a single cotransport process in intestine has not been found.

A basolateral membrane K conductance is probably opened with increased electrogenic Na absorption. It appears to function to maintain absorptive cell electronegativity. To date this has been most clearly identified in necturus intestine with stimulated Na absorption (51, 82).

Active K absorption and secretion occur in the rabbit and rat descending colon, but apparently not in rabbit ileum, whereas K secretion occurs in rabbit proximal colon (43, 46, 68, 69, 82, 85, 92; and P. Smith, personal communication). The absorptive process may be energized by an apical membrane K,H-ATPase (43). K secretion is an energy-requiring process dependent on the basolateral membrane Na,K-ATPase, with an inducible apical membrane K permeability. The process is ouabain-inhibitable and is blocked by mucosal barium. It is not known whether K secretory and absorptive processes are present in the same epithelial cell, are located in absorptive or secretory cells, or occur in surface or crypt cells.

Secretory Processes

The crypt is the major site of Cl secretion (38, 91). Rat and rabbit descending colonic crypts contain predominantly two cell populations, goblet cells and "immature columnar cells." The columnar cells have a large number of membrane-bound vesicles in the supranuclear area (56, 84); this number has been reported to decrease following stimulation of secretion with PGE$_2$. While this could indicate the involvement of membrane recycling in Cl secretion, neither the contents of the vesicles are known, nor whether or not they are involved in K, Cl, or macromolecular secretion. It is probable that the crypt Cl secretion is modified by villus absorption of the secreted fluid, particularly by the Cl/HCO$_3$ exchanger present in the apical membrane of villus epithelial cells. This may explain why stool HCO$_3$ loss is so prominent in diarrheal diseases (38).

The current model for Cl secretion consists of a two-step process involving neutral Cl entry at the basolateral membrane and conductive exit at the apical membrane (45). A negative intracellular potential and low intracellular Na activity are established by the Na,K-ATPase and the basolateral K permeability, as in the absorptive cell. Cl entry at the basolateral membrane appears to result from the coupling to Na and K (NaKCl$_2$). This cellular mechanism of Cl secretion appears to apply to a wide variety of Cl-secreting epithelia, including T-84 cells (13), MDCK cells, a renal cell line (69), canine trachea (89), cornea (7), and dogfish rectal gland (35). This model is supported by the finding that intestinal Cl secretion is (7, 35, 38, 45, 69, 77, 91): (*a*) dependent on serosal Na; (*b*) inhibited by serosal ouabain; (*c*) electrically conductive [secretagogues increase transepithelial conductance and the short-circuit current (Isc)]; and (d) inhibited by serosal addition of loop diuretics, such as low concentrations of bumetanide. [Loop diuretics appear to inhibit a basolateral $NaKCl_2$ cotransport process that was first identified in avain red blood cells (76, 78). This process has not been identified in normal mammalian small or large intestinal secretory cells, but appears to be present in T-84 cells.] And finally, (e) stimulation of Cl secretion is associated with appearance of a basolateral membrane K conductance.

A rate limiting step for intestinal Cl secretion is believed to be the apical membrane Cl permeability (46). The only direct evidence is that the first response to addition of PGE in colonic crypts is a depolarization of the cell and a decrease in the relative resistance of the apical membrane (91). Indirect evidence includes: (a) in T-84 cells, vasoactive intestinal peptide (VIP) (acting through cAMP) stimulated Cl secretion and apical membrane Cl permeability (13); and (b) N-phenyl-anthranilic acid inhibited Cl secretion in T-84 cells and rabbit colon (13). The latter compound is thought to decrease apical membrane Cl permeability (53), although its precise mechanism of action, which may include toxicity, is not yet certain.

However, the apical Cl permeability may not always be rate limiting: in T-84 cells, net Cl secretion was stimulated with carbachol. The earliest change detected was an increased basolateral membrane K permeability, although electrophysiologic studies of the apical membrane were not done (16).

REGULATION OF ELECTROLYTE TRANSPORT BY INTRACELLULAR MEDIATORS

Intracellular mediators proposed to directly affect intestinal electrolyte transport include intracellular Na, pH, cAMP, cGMP, and cytosolic free Ca^{2+} (38, 77). Metabolites of arachidonic acid by the cyclooxygenase and lipoxygenase pathways, including prostaglandins, are additional intracellular regulators of intestinal transport. In this review we concentrate on cAMP and Ca^{2+}.

Ca^{2+} and Intestinal Transport

Intracellular Ca^{2+} is a major regulator of mammalian electrolyte transport. It is involved directly or indirectly in regulation of active Na and Cl transport in the small intestine, and in colonic Na, K, and Cl transport in some species (19, 33). The first suggestion that Ca^{2+} might regulate ion transport was based on artificial means of elevating cellular Ca^{2+}. Bolton & Field reported that Ca^{2+} ionophore increased rabbit ileal Isc and decreased NaCl absorption (3), as did high external Ca^{2+} (10 mM) (19, 20). In rabbit colon, A23187 caused Cl secretion (44), and was later shown to increase K secretion (19). In rat colon, high external Ca^{2+} decreased Na and Cl transport (93). In all tissues the ionophore effect was of a lower magnitude and was more variable than that of cAMP. Further support for the role of Ca^{2+} came from the identification of a series of neurohumoral substances normally present in the intestinal mucosa that alter intestinal electrolyte transport by mechanisms that appear to involve changes in intracellular Ca^{2+} (19, 33).

Ca^{2+} EFFECTS ON PLASMA MEMBRANE ION TRANSPORT PRO-CESSES   Three transport processes are affected by altering intracellular Ca^{2+}: linked Na and Cl absorption, Cl secretion, and K secretion.

Ca^{2+} regulation of Na and Cl absorption   In rat colon and rabbit ileum increasing cellular Ca^{2+} decreased neutral NaCl absorption, but did not alter Na-glucose or Na–amino acid absorption (3, 19, 33, 93). Elevating external Ca^{2+} inhibited ileal NaCl absorption in intact tissue and in brush border vesicles; the effect on Na transport was Cl dependent, and vice versa (36). Conversely, in rabbit ileum when cellular Ca^{2+} is lowered by decreasing the external Ca^{2+} to approximately 50 μM, linked NaCl absorption is stimulated (20). Whether Ca^{2+} primarily affects the Na/H or Cl/HCO$_3$ exchanger is not known. Of course, this does not ensure that in intact tissue Ca^{2+} acts only on the brush border; other intracellular organelles, which are excluded from the vesicle studies, could be involved in the intact tissue. Another potential problem is that altering intravesicular Ca^{2+} may produce nonspecific effects. For example, an increase in vesicle Ca^{2+} concentration may decrease the vesicle's ability to maintain Na gradients. Increasing intravesicular Ca^{2+} decreased Na-dependent glucose and amino acid uptake in intestinal brush border vesicles (40).

Ca^{2+} regulation of Cl secretion   The cellular mechanisms by which Ca^{2+} regulates secretory cells are not certain. Increasing cellular Ca^{2+} with A23187 stimulated Cl secretion in rabbit ileum and colon and in T-84 cells (38, 79). While this effect was thought to result only from a direct effect of Ca^{2+}, more recent evidence suggests that at least some of the response is mediated by an increase in prostaglandin production (65, 83). In fact, there has been no clear demonstration that Ca^{2+} can cause a direct change in intestinal apical membrane Cl permeability, although this may occur. The most convincing demonstration of an effect of Ca^{2+} on secretory cells is an increase in the basolateral membrane K permeability. In T-84 cells low doses of Ca^{2+} ionophore or agents that increase cellular Ca^{2+} (carbachol) did not cause transepithelial Cl secretion but did increase the rate of K efflux from the cell into the serosal solution (16). These studies are consistent with recent direct evidence for Ca^{2+} activation of basolateral K channels in another Cl-secreting epithelium, canine trachea (90). There is currently no conclusive evidence regarding the effect of Ca^{2+} on the basolateral Cl entry step (NaKCl$_2$ cotransport) or the Na exit step (the Na,K-ATPase). However, all these must increase to remain in steady state once Cl secretion is initiated. Whether each is regulated separately or by some common mediator is unknown. The only reasonably established fact concerning the role of Ca^{2+} in Cl secretion is that Ca^{2+} activates the basolateral K conductance. Other effects of Ca^{2+} may be secondary to effects on other second messengers. The apical Cl conductance and basolateral K conductance must change in parallel for effective net secretion. This is evidenced by the observation that blocking the basolateral K conductance with Ba inhibited Cl secretion in T-84 cells (13, 17). Ca^{2+} may be the signal that regulates the basolateral K conductance, but future work must define how changes in Cl conductance are coupled to changes in the K conductance.

Ca^{2+} regulation of K transport   In rabbit descending colon the Ca^{2+} ionophore A23187 increased net K secretion (67, 68).

CELLULAR Ca^{2+} HANDLING AND REGULATION OF ION TRANSPORT The specific aspects of Ca^{2+} handling that are involved in regulation of basal transport (in the interprandial state and in the absence of added stimulators of absorption or secretion) and stimulated active intestinal transport of Na, Cl, and K are being defined (19, 33). Those activities identified as involved in regulation of active rabbit ileal Na and Cl transport include entry of Ca^{2+} across the plasma membrane (5, 6, 9, 20, 21, 24, 26, 28–30, 52), mobilization of calcium from intracellular stores (25, 27), and Ca^{2+} binding to calmodulin (34).

Plasma membrane Ca^{2+} entry   Plasma membrane Ca^{2+} entry regulates basal active NaCl absorption and some stimulated secretion in rabbit ileum. Lowering external Ca^{2+} to 50 μM stimulated linked NaCl absorption (20), as did all major classes of Ca^{2+} channel blockers: verapamil (including L-verapamil, which is presumed to act only on Ca^{2+} channels), nifedipine, diltiazem, and Cd (20, 26, 29). The Ca^{2+} entry process involved in regulation of electrolyte transport is on the serosal surface, since serosal but not mucosal verapamil stimulated absorption and decreased uptake of ^{45}Ca^{2+} from the serosal and not the mucosal surface. These results are probably explained by a basolateral membrane Ca^{2+} channel that regulates cell Ca^{2+}, and thereby basal NaCl transport. However, it is also possible that Ca^{2+} channel blockers and changes in external Ca^{2+} modify the epithelial cell neurohumoral environment. In fact, changes in ileal transport caused by electric field stimulation were decreased by verapamil and low external Ca^{2+} (54). It is not known whether Ca^{2+} entry across the brush border is involved in regulation of ileal NaCl transport, and if not, what separates this pool of absorbed Ca^{2+} from that which regulates NaCl transport.

Only rat distal descending colon has been found to respond similarly, with stimulation of Na and Cl absorption, to the lowering of external Ca^{2+} or verapamil (5, 6). No effect on basal transport was seen in rabbit descending colon or rat small intestine with these stimuli (93). In contrast, mucosal Ca^{2+} entry regulates NaCl absorption in the upper descending rat colon. Lowering mucosal Ca^{2+} to 5 μM reversibly stimulated active Na and Cl absorption (29, 32). Whether a brush border Ca^{2+} channel or modification of neurohumoral release by mucosal Ca^{2+} explains these results is not known.

There are many potential causes of the tissue-to-tissue variation in the effects of Ca^{2+} on basal electrolyte transport. One possibility is that the extent to which endogenous neurohumoral substances regulate NaCl cotransport in the basal state may vary.

We suggest that several neurohumoral substances (including serotonin, carbachol, substance P, and neurotensin) normally present in the intestinal mucosa affect ileal electrolyte transport by increasing Ca^{2+} entry across the ileal basolateral membrane (19, 21, 24, 28, 31, 33). All these substances decrease active Na and Cl absorption and/or induce Cl secretion, and these effects are decreased by removing serosal Ca^{2+} or by serosal verapamil. They also all increase the rate of $^{45}Ca^{2+}$ entry across the ileal basolateral membrane (21, 28), and significantly increase the calcium content. In contrast, dopamine has the opposite effect. It increases ileal Na and Cl absorption (24), decreases the rate of basolateral membrane $^{45}Ca^{2+}$ entry, and decreases ileal calcium content. These data suggest that some neurohumoral substances act, at least partially (see calcium stores below), by changing basolateral membrane Ca^{2+} entry, and that the change in transport probably results from a change in intracellular free Ca^{2+}.

Confirmation of a role for neurohumoral substances in regulation of plasma membrane Ca^{2+} entry requires showing that they change epithelial cell free Ca^{2+}, and that they affect transport in intestinal cell lines that are free of nonepithelial cells. Free Ca^{2+} has not been measured in normal viable mammalian intestinal cells, however, in isolated small intestinal cells from the chicken cytosol free Ca^{2+} is increased by the calcium ionophore A23187, substance P, and carbachol (9), and in T-84 cells, carbachol raised cytosol free Ca^{2+} (16).

Intracellular calcium stores   Intracellular calcium stores appear to be involved in regulation of basal and at least some stimulated electrolyte transport. This conclusion is based on the study of dantrolene and TMB-8 [8-(N,N-diethylaminoloctyl 3,4,5-trimethoxybenzoate)], which trap Ca^{2+} within intracellular stores in muscle systems (25, 27) and caused similar changes in Ca^{2+} handling in rabbit ileum. Dantrolene or TMB-8 on the ileal serosal surface significantly increased Na and Cl absorption, but did not alter other aspects of active intestinal ion transport, including glucose-dependent Na absorption.

cAMP- and Ca^{2+}-dependent electrolyte transport showed different responses to these drugs. TMB-8 totally inhibited the effects of carbachol but did not inhibit those of serotonin and cAMP. These results suggest that carbachol mobilizes Ca^{2+} from cellular stores and that the response to serotonin and cAMP does not require Ca^{2+} mobilization, or that TMB-8 and dantrolene affect different intracellular calcium stores than are altered by serotonin and cAMP.

Ca^{2+}-calmodulin (CaM)   The Ca^{2+}-CaM complex is involved in regulation of basal NaCl absorption in rabbit ileum and K secretion in rabbit descending colon, but does not appear to be involved in stimulated Cl secretion in either. Studies of Ca^{2+}-CaM regulation of intestinal transport have relied on Ca^{2+}-CaM-inhibiting drugs (34, 55, 64, 81). In rabbit and rat small intestine high concentrations of the phenothiazines, trifluoperazine (TFP) and chlorpromazine, inhibited Ca^{2+}- and cAMP-induced secretion (55, 64, 81). However, these studies were done before it was suggested that if the concentration of a Ca^{2+}-CaM antagonist needed to inhibit an effect is ten times greater than the IC_{50} (the concentration needed to cause a 50% inhibition of a process) seen in other systems, then the effect is likely independent of the Ca^{2+}-CaM antagonist properties (88). Also, drugs that are Ca^{2+}-CaM antagonists are very hydrophobic, and hydrophobic controls must be used (88). Consequently, drugs called the naphthalenesulfonamides were used to probe the role of Ca^{2+}-CaM in basal transport. These are drug pairs that are structurally identical except for a single chlorine atom, and which have similar hydrophobicity but different potencies as Ca^{2+}-CaM antagonists (86). The more potent Ca^{2+}-CaM antagonist, but not the hydrophobic control, stimulated ileal linked NaCl absorption, but not glucose-dependent Na absorption (34). Ten micromolar TFP (Ic_{50} in nonintestinal tissues is 10 μM) caused similar effects (34).

Of the many cell sites at which Ca^{2+}-CaM could stimulate Na and Cl absorption, only an effect on the brush border has been suggested. Adding CaM to ileal brush border vesicles lowered the Ca^{2+} concentration needed to inhibit NaCl uptake, and 10 μM TFP blocked the Ca^{2+}-induced decrease in NaCl uptake (36). In rat small intestine and rabbit descending colon even high concentrations of TFP had no effect on basal Na and Cl transport (52, 67, 83). In colon, TFP decreased basal K secretion and the Ca^{2+} ionophore-induced increase in K secretion (65). Thus both basal and stimulated colonic K secretion act through the Ca^{2+}-CaM complex.

In contrast to the effect on absorption, Ca^{2+}-stimulated Cl secretion in ileum and colon do not appear to involve the Ca^{2+}-CaM complex. The naphthalenesulfanomides did not attenuate the ileal secretory response to either increased Ca^{2+} (A23187 and serotonin) or cAMP (theophylline and 8-Br-cAMP) (34). Similarly, TFP did not affect the Ca^{2+}- ionophore-stimulated colonic Cl secretion (67).

How Ca^{2+}-CaM regulates NaCl absorption is uncertain, but there are suggestions that Ca^{2+}-CaM-induced phosphorylation may regulate ileal apical membrane Na and Cl uptake. The Ca^{2+}-CaM complex regulates many functions by either directly activating proteins or by regulating phosphorylation/dephosphorylation (8). In ileal brush border vesicles Ca^{2+}-CaM caused a concentration-dependent inhibition of Na uptake in the presence of Cl; the concentration of Ca^{2+} that caused a 50% effect was approximately 0.5 μM (36). Also, Ca^{2+}-CaM increased phosphorylation of five ileal microvillus membrane proteins, with the Ca^{2+} concentration causing a 50% effect between 0.3 and 0.8 μM (23). Thus phosphorylation and inhibition of NaCl transport related to Ca^{2+}-CaM occured at very similar Ca^{2+} concentrations, probably close to that present in epithelial cell cytosol during physiologic function.

Further evidence that Ca^{2+}-CaM effects may be by protein phosphorylation comes from studies with the phenothiazine, promethazine. Promethazine stimulates active NaCl absorption in rabbit ileum with a 50% effect at approximately 9 μM (34), a concentration far lower than that at which it acts as a conventional Ca^{2+}-CaM antagonist. Promethazine also causes a dose-dependent inhibition of Ca^{2+}-CaM-induced microvillus membrane phosphorylation, with a 50% inhibition at approximately 8 μM (11). The similarity in the dose of promethazine that stimulates NaCl absorption and inhibits Ca^{2+}-CaM-dependent phosphorylation suggests that promethazine may act by inhibiting a Ca^{2+}-CaM protein kinase, and that this protein kinase may be involved in regulation of Na and Cl absorption. However, the brush border studies showing Ca^{2+} inhibition of NaCl absorption almost certainly did not contain ATP, which indicates that the Ca^{2+} effect can occur without increased phosphorylation (36). Thus the mechanism by which Ca^{2+} regulates the linked Na and Cl transport in rabbit ileal epithelial cells needs further clarification.

Ca^{2+} exit across the plasma membrane   Ca^{2+}-ATPase and Na/Ca^{2+} exchange appear to be present only in the basolateral membrane, at least in the rat small intestinal epithelial cell. Although CaM and vitamin D stimulate Ca^{2+}-ATPase activity in the small intestinal basolateral membrane (48, 49, 75), a comprehensive picture of their regulation in intestine is not available. Moreover, as yet undefined are the relative contributions of the intestinal plasma membrane Ca^{2+}-ATPase and Na/Ca^{2+} exchange processes to regulation of cytosol free Ca^{2+}, active Na and Cl transport, and transcellular Ca^{2+} transport.

Many other aspects of cellular Ca^{2+} handling are as yet poorly explored in regulation of intestinal ion transport. For instance, the only aspect of intestinal plasma membrane phosphatidylinositol (PI) turnover reported is that protein kinase C alters electrolyte transport in rabbit ileum and rat colon (10, 22, 41). Studies have not used the PI breakdown product diacygylcerol (2), but rather phorbol esters, which are thought to bind and activate protein kinase C. Phorbol esters increased the anion-dependent Isc in rabbit and chicken intestine, and inhibited NaCl absorption and stimulated Cl secretion in rat colon (22). These results, plus the fact that in colon the phorbol effects were synergistic with that of the Ca^{2+} ionophore, suggest a role for PI turnover and C kinase in regulation of electrolyte transport. Also, recently it has been suggested that part—perhaps a majority—of the effects of Ca^{2+} on intestinal transport are mediated by initiation of arachidonic acid metabolism. The Ca^{2+} ionophore A23187 increases ileal prostaglandin release (12), and the effects of the ionophore, and of neurohumoral secretagogues that act through Ca^{2+}, are inhibited by interfering with arachidonic acid metabolism (65). In rabbit colon the ionophore increased PGE_2 release, and indomethacin prevented the ionophore-induced Cl secretion. In contrast, the effect of the ionophore on colonic K secretion was not dependent on arachidonic acid metabolism (67, 83). These data are too preliminary to be specific about which aspects of Ca^{2+}-induced changes in intestinal transport involve arachidonic acid as an intermediate, to compare the role in different intestinal segments, or to identify the membrane source of the arachidonic acid.

Cyclic AMP and Intestinal Transport

Increases in intestinal cAMP alter active Na, Cl, and K transport. Agents that increase intestinal cAMP content include cholera toxin, heat labile *Escherichia coli* enterotoxin, VIP, secretin, PGE_2, bile salts, ATP, ADP, AMP, and adenosine (18, 38, 60, 65, 77). An increase in intestinal cAMP inhibits linked Na and Cl absorption, and increases Cl and K secretion, the latter only in colon (38, 67, 77). The magnitude of the Cl secretory process induced by agents acting through cAMP is greater than that caused by agents acting through Ca^{2+}, although the effects on NaCl are similar (3, 38, 77). This is also true in T-84 cells, which shows that these differences occur at the level of the epithelial cells.

cAMP EFFECTS ON PLASMA MEMBRANE ION TRANSPORT PROCESS   In colonic crypt cells PGE (which increases cAMP levels) depolarized the cell, decreased the relative resistance of the apical membrane, decreased transepithelial resistance, and stimulated Cl secretion (91). These changes indicate an increase in apical membrane Cl permeability. In T-84 cells VIP and cAMP also increased electrogenic Cl secretion (13, 15, 17). These results are consistent with observations in tracheal epithelium in which cAMP increased the apical Cl conductance (90).

In addition to an effect on the apical Cl conductance, cAMP may regulate two basolateral membrane transport processes. In T-84 cells VIP stimulated Cl uptake. The uptake was Na and K dependent, and was inhibited by bumetanide, which suggests stimulation of the $NaKCl_2$ cotransporter. Cyclic AMP may also regulate the basolateral K conductance. In rabbit colonic crypts PGE induced acute changes that suggested an increase in apical Cl permeability; the cell then repolarized and the membrane resistance ratio increased, which suggests an increase in basolateral K permeability (91). Moreover, in T-84 cells an increase in cAMP increased basolateral K efflux from the cells even when Cl secretion was inhibited with ouabain and bumetanide (13, 15, 17). At present it is unclear whether the increase in basolateral K permeability results from a cAMP-induced change in cell Ca^{2+}, a direct effect of cAMP, or the presence of more than one type of basolateral K channel, some regulated by Ca^{2+} and some by cAMP.

Increasing cAMP did not change K absorption in rabbit descending colon, but cAMP and PGE$_2$ increased K secretion. This was not altered by indomethacin but was inhibited by TFP, which suggests that the Ca^{2+}-CaM complex is involved (67, 82, 83, 86).

Interactions of cAMP and Ca^{2+} Systems in Intestinal Transport

There is very limited information concerning the interactions of the Ca^{2+} and cAMP systems in intestinal transport. This is due to the lack of measurements of free Ca^{2+} in intestinal cytosol and uncertainty about whether multiple pools of intracellular cAMP are involved in regulation of intestinal electrolyte transport. There are hints that some of the effects of Ca^{2+} are mediated through cAMP and vice versa, but none of the studies allow clear conclusions. For example, we have already reviewed the evidence that Ca^{2+} ionophore A23187 activates arachidonic acid metabolism, increases prostaglandin production, and increases intestinal cAMP content, although the latter has been shown only for rat colon (12). Part of rat small intestinal adenylate cyclase is also dependent on the Ca^{2+}-CaM complex (1, 61). However, A23187 did not diminish the subsequent response to cAMP in rabbit ileum and rabbit colon, as would be expected if both agents acted through similar pathways (31; Braaten & Donowitz, unpublished observations). Moreover, agents that alter electrolyte transport by Ca^{2+}-dependent mechanisms (carbachol, serotonin, substance P, neurotensin, and ionophore A23187) have not been found to alter cAMP levels in intestinal mucosa (3, 21, 38, 80). Thus the functional significance of potential Ca^{2+} effects on cAMP remain uncertain.

Whether cAMP appears to act on active electrolyte transport through Ca^{2+} in small intestine varies according to species. The strongest evidence that Ca^{2+} is not involved comes from rabbit ileum, while the suggestion that it may be involved is based on studies in rat small intestine. In rabbit ileum the transport effects of cAMP were not altered by inhibiting extracellular Ca^{2+} entry (by decreasing serosal Ca^{2+}, verapamil) or by trapping Ca^{2+} within intracellular stores (TMB-8, dantrolene) (3, 19, 20, 25, 27, 33). In addition, Ca^{2+}-CaM antagonists failed to alter cAMP-stimulated changes in transport (34). Lastly, chloroquine added to the mucosal surface of rabbit ileum inhibited the Ca^{2+} effects on transport but did not alter those caused by cAMP (39). These results are not consistent with involvement of Ca^{2+} in cAMP effects. Nevertheless, cAMP did increase $^{45}Ca^{2+}$ efflux from rabbit ileum, which suggests an effect on Ca^{2+} handling (21). However, it is not known whether cAMP altered changes in ileal intracellular cytosolic free Ca^{2+}, or which aspects of cellular Ca^{2+} handling were affected.

In contrast, in rat small intestine cAMP effects on transport were altered by changes in Ca^{2+} handling (50). Specifically, decreasing serosal Ca^{2+}, verapamil, and TMB-8 all inhibited the effects of cAMP on active electrolyte transport in rat small intestine. Consequently, no general conclusions can yet be made as to whether Ca^{2+} is involved in the intestinal effects of cAMP.

The interactions of Ca^{2+} and cAMP vary depending on the tissue. The best evidence for additivity of the effects of cAMP and Ca^{2+} has been obtained in the Cl-secreting T-84 cell line (13, 15, 17), in which the Cl secretory response to VIP and the Ca^{2+} ionophore A23187 were synergistic.

In contrast, in rabbit ileum increased cAMP and Ca^{2+} have overlapping, nonadditive effects on active Na and Cl transport (31). Addition of maximal and half-maximal concentrations of theophylline and several neurohumoral agents that increase intracellular Ca^{2+} did not alter Na and Cl transport significantly more than theophylline alone.

The mechanistic interpretation of studies demonstrating the presence or absence of cAMP and Ca^{2+} additive or synergistic effects is difficult. It is particularly difficult in intestine which has multiple cell types and in which other neurohumoral mediators may be altered by secretagogues. However, probing these interactions will be crucial to the understanding of second messenger regulation of intestinal electrolyte transport.

ACKNOWLEDGMENT

We thank Drs. E. B. Chang, K. Dharmsathaphorn, M. Field, R. D. McCabe, D. W. Powell, and P. Smith for allowing us access to manuscripts in press. This work was supported in part by NIH Grants R01 AM26535, R01 AM20859, and P30 AM39428, the Center for Gastroenterology Research on Absorptive and Secretory Processes. M. Donowitz is supported by NIH RCDA 1K04-00588. M. J. Welsh is an Established Investigator of the American Heart Association.

Literature Cited

1. Amiranoff, B. M., Laburthe, M. C., Rouyer-Yer-Fessard, C. M., Demaille, J. G., Rosselin, G. E. 1983. Calmodulin stimulation of adenylate cyclase of intestinal epithelium. *Eur. J. Biochem.* 130:33–37

2. Berridge, M. J. 1982. A novel cellular signalling system based on the integration of phospholipid and calcium metabolism. In *Calcium and Cell Functions*, ed. W. Y. Cheung, 3:1–36. New York: Academic

3. Bolton, J. E., Field, M. 1977. Ca ionophore-stimulated ion secretion in rabbit ileal mucosa: relation to actions of cyclic AMP and carbamylcholine. *J. Membr. Biol.* 35:159–74

4. Booth, I., Murer, H., Stange, G., Fenton, T. R., Milla, P. J. 1985. Defective jejunal brush border Na/H exchange: a cause of congenital secretory diarrhea. *Lancet* I:1066–69

5. Bridges, R. J., Nell, G., Rummel, W. 1983. Influence of vasopressin and cal-

cium on electrolyte transport across isolated colonic mucosa of the rat. *J. Physiol.* 338:463–75

6. Bridges, R. J., Rummel, W. 1984. Vasopressin-stimulated Na transport in colon. In *Intestinal Absorption and Secretion*, ed. E. Skadhauge, K. Heintze, pp. 265–72. Lancaster: MTP

7. Candia, O. A., Schoen, H. L. 1978. Selective effects of bumetanide on chloride transport in bullfrog cornea. *Am. J. Physiol.* 234:F297–F305

8. Carafoli, E. 1984. Plasma membrane Ca^{2+} transport and Ca^{2+} handling by intracellular stores: an integrated picture with emphasis on regulation. In *Mechanisms of Intestinal Electrolyte Transport and Regulation of Calcium*, ed. M. Donowitz, G. W. G. Sharp, pp. 121–34. New York: Liss

9. Chang, E. B., Brown, D. R., Wang, N. S., Field, M. 1984. Loperamide selectively inhibits peptide-induced Cl secretion and calcium entry in the gut. *Gastroenterology* 81:1044 (Abstr.)

10. Chang, E. B., Wang, N. S., Rao, M. C. 1985. Role of protein C-kinase in intestinal anion secretion. *Gastroenterology* 88:1345 (Abstr.)

11. Cohen, M. E., Sharp, G. W. G., Donowitz, M. 1985. Promethazine stimulates NaCl absorption and inhibits Ca^{2+}-calmodulin-dependent phosphorylation in rabbit ileum at the same low concentration, suggesting a role for phosphorylation in NaCl transport. *Fed. Proc.* 44:1744 (Abstr.)

12. Craven, P. A., DeRubertis, F. R. 1983. Patterns of prostaglandin synthesis and degradation in isolated superficial and proliferative colonic epithelial cells compared to residual colon. *Prostaglandins* 26:583–604

13. Dharmsathaphorn, K., Mandel, K. G., Masui, H., McRoberts, J. A. 1985. Vasoactive intestinal polypeptide-induced secretion by a colonic epithelial cell line: direct participation of a basolaterally located NaKCl co-transport system. *J. Clin. Invest.* 75:462–71

14. Dharmsathaphorn, K., Mandel, K. G., McRoberts, J. A., Tisdale, L. D., Masui, H. 1984. A human colonic tumor cell line that maintains vectoral electrolyte transport. *Am. J. Physiol.* 246:G204–8

15. Dharmsathaphorn, K., Pandol, S. 1985. Basis for syngerism between cAMP and Ca^{2+} mediated Cl reaction in human colonic cell lines. *Gastroenterology* 88:1364 (Abstr.)

16. Dharmsathaphorn, K., Pandol, S., McRoberts, J. A. 1985. Cl secretion induced by carbachol in a human colonic epithelial cell line: studies of the mechanism of action. *Gastroenterology* 88:1364 (Abstr.)

17. Dharmasthaphorn, K., Weymer, A., McRoberts, J. A. 1985. Chloride secretion induced by prostaglandin E (PGE) and participation of NaKCl cotransport, Cl channels, and K channels. *Gastroenterology* 88:1364 (Abstr.)

18. Dobbins, J. W., Laurenson, J. P., Forrest, J. N. Jr. 1984. Adenosine and adenosine analogues stimulate adenosine cyclic 3',5'-monophosphate-dependent chloride secretion in the mammalian ileum. *J. Clin. Invest.* 74:929–35

19. Donowitz, M. 1983. Ca^{2+} in the control of active Na and Cl transport: involvement in neurohumoral action. *Am. J. Physiol.* 245:G165–77

20. Donowitz, M., Asarkof, N. 1982. Calcium dependence of basal electrolyte transport in rabbit ileum. *Am. J. Physiol.* 243:G28–G35

21. Donowitz, M., Asarkof, N., Pike, G. 1980. Serotonin-induced changes in rabbit ileal active electrolyte transport are calcium dependent and associated with increased ileal calcium uptake. *J. Clin. Invest.* 66:341–52

22. Donowitz, M., Cheng, H., Sharp, G. W. G. 1985. Role of protein kinase C in regulation of rat colonic active NaCl transport. *Gastroenterology* 88:1367 (Abstr.)

23. Donowitz, M., Cohen, M. E., Gudewich, R., Taylor, L., Sharp, G. W. G. 1984. Ca^{2+} calmodulin-, cyclic AMP- and cyclic GMP-induced phosphorylation of proteins in purified microvillus membranes of rabbit ileum. *Biochem. J.* 219:573–81

24. Donowitz, M., Cusolito, S., Battisti, L., Fogel, R., Sharp, G. W. G. 1982. Dopamine stimulation of active Na and Cl absorption in rabbit ileum: interaction with α2-adrenergic and specific dopamine receptors. *J. Clin. Invest.* 69:1008–16

25. Donowitz, M., Cusolito, S., Battisti, L., Sharp, G. W. G. 1983. Dantrolene and basal ileal Na and Cl transport: involvement of calcium stores. *Am. J. Physiol.* 245:G780–85

26. Donowitz, M., Cusolito, S., Battisti, L., Wicks, J., Sharp, G. W. G. 1984. Role of basolateral membrane Ca^{2+} entry in regulation of Na and Cl transport in rabbit ileum. In *Intestinal Absorption and Secretion*, ed. E. Skadhauge, K. Heintze, pp. 409–18. Lancaster: MTP

27. Donowitz, M., Cusolito, S., Sharp, G. W. G. 1985. Effects of the calcium antagonist TMB-8 on active Na and Cl transport in rabbit ileum. *Am. J. Physiol.* In press

28. Donowitz, M., Fogel, R., Battisti, L., Asarkof, N. 1982. The neurohumoral secretagogues carbachol, substance P and neurotensin increase Ca^{2+} influx and calcium content in rabbit ileum: Mechanisms of action? *Life Sci.* 31:1929–37

29. Donowitz, M., Levin, S., Powers, G., Elta, G., Cohen, P., Cheng, H. 1985. Ca^{2+} channel blockers stimulate ileal and colonic water absorption. *Gastroenterology*. In press

30. Donowitz, M., Madara, J. L. 1982. Effect of extracellular calcium depletion on epithelial structure and function in rabbit ileum: A model for selective crypt or villus epithelial cell damage and suggestion of secretion by villus epithelial cells. *Gastroenterology* 83:1231–43

31. Donowitz, M., Tai, Y. H., Asarkof, N. 1980. Effect of serotonin on active electrolyte transport in rabbit ileum and gallbladder. *Am. J. Physiol.* 239:G463–72

32. Donowitz, M., Wicks, J., Battisti, L. 1984. Senokot inhibits active Na and Cl transport in rat descending colon by a Ca^{2+} dependent mechanism. *Gastroenterology* 87:503–12

33. Donowitz, M., Wicks, J., Cusolito, S., Sharp, G. W. G. 1984. Cytosol free Ca^{2+} in the regulation of active intestinal Na and Cl transport. In *Mechanisms of Intestinal Electrolyte Transport and Regulation by Calcium*, ed. M. Donowitz, G. W. G. Sharp, pp. 171–91. New York: Liss

34. Donowitz, M., Wicks, J., Madara, J. L., Sharp, G. W. G. 1985. Studies on role of calmodulin in Ca^{2+} regulation of rabbit ileal Na and Cl transport. *Am. J. Physiol.* 248:G726–40

35. Epstein, F. H. 1979. The shark rectal gland model for the active transport of chloride. *Yale J. Biol.* 52:517–23

36. Fan, C. C., Faust, R. G., Powell, D. W. 1983. Ca inhibition of NaCl uptake in rabbit ileal brush border membrane vesicles. *Proc. Natl. Acad. Sci. USA* 80:5248–52

37. Fan, C. C., Powell, D. W. 1983. Coupled sodium-chloride transport by rabbit ileal brush border membrane vesicles. *Am. J. Physiol.* 244:G375–86

38. Field, M. 1981. Secretion of electrolytes and water by mammalian small intestine. In *Physiology of the Gastrointestinal Tract*, ed. L. R. Johnson, pp. 963–82. New York: Raven

39. Fogel, R., Sharp, G. W. G., Donowitz, M. 1982. Chloroquine stimulates absorption, inhibits secretion of ileal water and electrolytes. *Am. J. Physiol.* 243:G117–26

40. Fondacaro, J. D., Madden, T. B. 1984.

Inhibition of Na coupled solute transport by calcium in brush border membrane vesicles. *Life Sci.* 35:1431–38

41. Fondacaro, J. D., Stefankiewicz, J. S., Henderson, L. S. 1985. Phorbol ester induced intestinal hypersecretion. *Fed. Proc.* 44:442 (Abstr.)

42. Foster, E. S., Dudeja, P. K., Brasitus, T. A. 1985. Na/H exchange in brush border membrane vesicles of rabbit colon. *Fed. Proc.* 44:1745 (Abstr.)

43. Foster, E. S., Hayslett, J. P., Binder, H. J. 1984. Mechanism of active potassium absorption and secretion in rat colon. *Am. J. Physiol.* 246:G611–17

44. Frizzell, R. A. 1977. Active chloride secretion by rabbit colon: calcium dependent stimulation by ionophore A23187. *J. Membr. Biol.* 35:175–87

45. Frizzell, R. A., Field, M., Schultz, S. G. 1979. Sodium coupled chloride transport by epithelial tissues. *Am. J. Physiol.* 236:F1–F8

46. Frizzell, R. A., Halm, D. R., Krasny, E. J. Jr. 1984. Relationship between chloride and potassium secretion across large intestine. See Ref. 33, pp. 35–46

47. Fujita, M., Matsui, H., Nagano, K., Nakao, M. 1971. Asymmetrical distribution of ouabain-sensitive ATPase activities in rat intestinal mucosa. *Biochem. Biophys. Acta* 233:404–8

48. Ghijsen, W., Murer, H., Van Os, C. 1984. Regulation of active Ca^{2+} transport in basolateral membranes of small intestinal epithelium. In *Epithelial Calcium and Phosphate Transport: Molecular and Cellular Aspects*, ed. F. Bronner, M. Peterilk, pp. 289–94. New York: Liss

49. Ghijsen, W., Van Os, C. 1982. 1,25-dihydroxy vitamin D-3 regulates ATP-dependent calcium transport in basolateral membranes of rat enterocytes. *Biochim. Biophys. Acta* 689:170–77

50. Gunther, R. D., Wright, E. M. 1983. Na, Li, and Cl transport by brush border membranes from rabbit jejunum. *J. Membr. Biol.* 74:85–94

51. Gunther-Smith, P. J., Grasset, E., Schultz, S. G. 1982. Sodium coupled amino acid and sugar transport by necturus small intestine. *J. Membr. Biol.* 66:25–39

52. Hardcastle, J., Hardcastle, P. T., Noble, J. M. 1984. The involvement of calcium in the intestinal response to secretagogues in the rat. *J. Physiol.* 355:465–78

53. Horvath, P., Ferriola, P., Weiser, M., Duffey, M. 1985. Localization of chloride secretion in rabbit colon by inhibition with anthracene-9-carboxylic acid. *Fed. Proc.* 44:1744 (Abstr.)

54. Hubel, K. A., Callanan, D. 1980. Effects

of Ca^{2+} on ileal transport and electrically induced secretion. *Am. J. Physiol.* 239: G18–G22

55. Ilundain, A., Naftalin, R. J. 1979. Role of Ca^{2+} dependent regulator protein in intestinal secretion. *Nature* 279:446–48

56. Johnson, R. D., Halm, D. R., Kransny, E. J. Jr., Frizzell, R. A., DiBona, D. R. 1984. Cellular specificity for chloride secretion in colonic crypt epithelium from the rabbit. *J. Cell. Biol.* 99:292 (Abstr.)

57. Knickelbein, R., Aronson, P. S., Atherton, W., Dobbins, J. W. 1983. Na and Cl transport across rabbit ileal brush border. I. Evidence for Na/H exchange. *Am. J. Physiol.* 245:G504–10

58. Knickelbein, R. G., Aronson, P. S., Schron, C. M., Seifter, J., Dobbins, J. W. 1985. Na and Cl transport across rabbit ileal brush border. II. Evidence for Cl:HCO$_3$ exchange and mechanism of coupling. *Am. J. Physiol.* 249:G236–45

59. Knickelbein, R. G., Schron, C. M., Aronson, P. S., Dobbins, J. W. 1985. Anion exchange across rabbit ileal brush border membranes. *Gastroenterology* 88:1449 (Abstr.)

60. Korman, L. Y., Lemp, G. F., Jackson, M. J., Gardner, J. D. 1982. Mechanisms of action of ATP on intestinal epithelial cells: cyclic AMP mediated stimulation of active ion transport. *Biochem. Biophys. Res. Commun.* 721:47–54

61. Lazo, P. S., Rivaya, A., Velasco, G. 1984. Regulation by calcium and calmodulin of adenylate cyclase from rabbit intestinal epithelium. *Biochim. Biophys. Acta* 798:361–67

62. Liedtke, C. M., Hopfer, U. 1982. Mechanism of Cl translocation across small intestinal brush-border membrane. I. Absence of NaCl cotransport. *Am. J. Physiol.* 242:G263–71

63. Liedtke, C. M., Hopfer, U. 1982. Mechanism of Cl translocation across small intestinal brush-border membrane. II. Demonstration of Cl/OH exchange and Cl conductance. *Am. J. Physiol.* 242: G272–80

64. Lonnroth, I., Andren, B., Lange, S., Martinsson, K., Holmgren, J. 1979. Chlorpromazine reverses diarrhea in piglets caused by enterotoxigenic *Escherichia coli. Infect. Immun.* 24:900–5

65. Martens, H., Tobey, J. A., Rollin, R. E., Berschneider, H. M., Powell, D. W. 1985. Role of arachidonic acid metabolism in the stimulus-secretion coupling of intestinal secretion. *Gastroenterology* 88:1490 (Abstr.)

66. McCabe, R. D., Cooke, H. J., Sullivan, L. P. 1982. Potassium transport by rabbit

descending colon. *Am. J. Physiol.* 242: C81–C86

67. McCabe, R. D., Smith, P. L. 1985. Colonic potassium and chloride secretion: role of cAMP and calcium. *Am. J. Physiol.* 248:G103–9

68. McCabe, R. D., Smith, P. L., Sullivan, L. P. 1984. Ion transport by rabbit descending colon: mechanisms of transepithelial potassium transport. *Am. J. Physiol.* 246:G594–G607

69. McRoberts, J. A., Erlinger, S., Rindler, M. S., Saier, M. H. Jr. 1982. Furosemide-sensitive salt transport in the Madin-Darby canine kidney cell line. *J. Biol. Chem.* 257:2260–2266

70. Murer, H., Hopfer, U., Kinne, R. 1976. Sodium proton antiport in brush border membrane vesicles isolated from rat small intestine and kidney. *Biochem. J.* 154:597–604

71. Musch, M. W., Orellana, S. A., Kimberg, L. S., Field, M., Halm, D. R., et al. 1982. NaKCl cotransport in the intestine of a marine teleost. *Nature* 300: 351–53

72. Nellans, H. N., Frizzell, R. A., Schultz, S. G. 1973. Coupled sodium chloride influx across the brush border of rabbit ileum. *Am. J. Physiol.* 225:467–75

73. Nellans, H. N., Frizzell, R. A., Schultz, S. G. 1974. Brush border processes and transepithelial Na and Cl transport by rabbit ileum. *Am. J. Physiol.* 226:1131–41

74. Nellans, H. N., Frizzell, R. A., Schultz, S. G. 1975. Effect of acetazolamide on sodium and chloride transport by in vitro rabbit ileum. *Am. J. Physiol.* 228:1808–14

75. Nellans, H. N., Popovitch, J. E. 1981. Calmodulin-regulated ATP-driven calcium transport by basolateral membrane of rat small intestine. *J. Biol. Chem.* 256:9932–36

76. Palfrey, H. C., Rao, M. C. 1983. Na/K/Cl co-transport and its regulation. *J. Exp. Biol.* 106:43–54

77. Powell, D. W. 1985. Ion and water transport in the intestine. In *Physiology of Membrane Disorders,* ed. T. E. Andrioli, D. D. Fanestil, J. F. Hoffman, S. G. Schultz. New York: Plenum. In press

78. Schmidt, W. F., McManus, J. J. 1977. Ouabain-insensitive salt and water movement in duck red cells: III. The role of chloride in the volume response. *J. Gen. Physiol.* 70:99–121

79. Schultz, S. G. 1981. Homocellular regulatory mechanisms in sodium-transporting epithelia: avoidance of extinction by "flush-through". *Am. J. Physiol.* 241:F579–90

80. Sellin, J. H., DeSoignie, R. 1984. Rabbit proximal colon: a distinct transport epithelium. *Am. J. Physiol.* 246:G602–10

81. Smith, P. L., Field, M. 1980. In vitro antisecretory effects of trifluoperazine and other neuroleptics in rabbit and human small intestine. *Gastroenterology* 78:1545–54

82. Smith, P. L., McCabe, R. D. 1984. Mechanism and regulation of transcellular potassium transport by the colon. *Am. J. Physiol.* 247:G445–56

83. Smith, P. L., McCabe, R. D. 1984. A23187-induced changes in colonic K and Cl transport are mediated by separate mechanisms. *Am. J. Physiol.* 247:G695–G702

84. Deleted in proof

85. Sullivan, S. K., Smith, P. L. 1985. Potassium transport by rabbit proximal colon in vitro. *Gastroenterology* 88:1602 (Abstr.)

86. Tanaka, T., Ohmura, T., Hadaka, H. 1982. Hydrophobic interaction of the Ca^{2+}-calmodulin complex with calmodulin antagonists: naphthalenesulfonamide derivatives. *Mol. Pharmacol.* 22:403–7

87. Turnberg, L. A., Bieberdorf, F. A.,

Morawski, S. G., Fordtran, J. S. 1970. Interrelationship of chloride, bicarbonate, sodium and hydrogen transport in human ileum. *J. Clin. Invest.* 49:557–67

88. Weiss, B., Prozialeck, W. C., Wallace, T. L. 1982. Interaction of drugs with calmodulin: biochemical, pharmacologic and clinical implications. *Biochem. Pharmacol.* 31:2217–26

89. Welsh, M. J., Smith, P. L., Frizzell, R. A. 1982. Chloride secretion by canine tracheal epitheliam: II. The cellular electrical potential profile. *J. Membr. Biol.* 70:227–38

90. Welsh, M. J., McCann, J. D., 1985. Intracellular calcium regulates basolateral K channels in a Cl secreting epithelium. *Proc. Natl. Acad. Sci. USA* In press

91. Welsh, M. J., Smith, P. L., Fromm, M., Frizzell, R. A. 1982. Crypts are the site of intestinal fluid and electrolyte secretion. *Science* 218:1219–21

92. Wills, N. K., Biagi, B. 1982. Active potassium transport by rabbit descending colon epithelium. *Am. J. Physiol.* 64:195–203

93. Zimmerman, T. W., Dobbins, J. W., Binder, H. J. 1983. Role of calcium in the regulation of colonic secretion in the rat. *Am. J. Physiol.* 244:G552–60

CELL AND MEMBRANE PHYSIOLOGY

MEMBRANE FUSION

Introduction, Joseph F. Hoffman, *Section Editor*

The focus of the articles contained in this year's section on Cell and Membrane Physiology is on membrane fusion. This is not only because it has become increasingly clear that fusion events are central in membrane and cellular function, but also because there have been substantial advances in our understanding of the processes involved and their functional significance. The articles cover a broad sweep from the detailed examination of the mechanisms of the fusion process itself to the resultant expression of proteins and complexes important in the membrane and the transport of intracellularly synthesized material across the plasma membrane. Many of the processes reviewed are related to, and indeed are natural extensions of, membrane biogenesis and the processing of presumptive plasma membrane and export constituents that occur intracellularly. While only a select range of topics could be covered, because of space limitations, it is hoped that it will be possible in future years to survey other aspects of this burgeoning field.

Ann. Rev. Physiol. 1986. 48:153–61

REGULATION OF TRANSEPITHELIAL H⁺ TRANSPORT BY EXOCYTOSIS AND ENDOCYTOSIS

George J. Schwartz

Departments of Pediatrics and Physiology/Biophysics, Albert Einstein College of Medicine, Bronx, New York 10461

Qais Al-Awqati

Departments of Medicine and Physiology, Columbia University, New York, New York 10032

Introduction

The movement of membrane and secretory proteins from their site of synthesis in the endoplasmic reticulum to their destination occurs by vesicular transport. For plasma membrane proteins in epithelia, these vesicles fuse with either the apical or basolateral membranes, thereby generating and maintaining epithelial polarity. In general, this process is thought to be constitutive, i.e. there is a continuous unregulated turnover of the membrane proteins at either surface. In some epithelia, however, there is another pathway in which vesicle fusion is under hormonal or environmental regulation. The best studied examples include secretion of enzymes by pancreatic acinar cells. Muscarinic agonists increase cell calcium (by activating the phosphoinositide pathway), which in turn causes fusion of the vesicle with the apical membranes, and release of the secreted proteins into the lumen of the ducts. This regulated pathway is similar in many respects to secretion of hormones and neurotransmitters in nonepithelial cells.

Recent studies in epithelia have identified a new regulated process of exocytosis. Similar to the regulated secretion of hormones and enzymes, the response is very rapid. However, in this process it is the vesicle membrane,

153

0066-4278/86/0315-0153$02.00

rather than its contents, that is the target of the response. Although this mechanism is similar to that of membrane turnover, its time course is much more rapid and it occurs in response to a specific stimulus.

Exocytic Insertion of H^+ ATPases into the Apical Plasma Membrane of Urinary Epithelia

H^+ secretion in tight urinary epithelia is mediated by a proton translocating ATPase that is located in the apical plasma membrane (3, 6). We recently discovered that this ATPase is packaged in small endocytic vesicles located underneath the apical plasma membrane of acid-secreting cells (7, 8, 21). These vesicles continuously fuse with the apical membrane and reform; the rate of this membrane turnover is much faster in these cells than in the other cell types, which allows their ready identification. We were able to load these vesicles with macromolecules coupled to the pH sensitive dye, fluorescein, and used a microspectrofluorometer to estimate the pH in them. A patch of cytoplasm that contained a few vesicles was centered in the microscope aperture, and excited at two wavelengths while the emission was measured photometrically. The ratio of the emissions at two different excitation wavelengths is a reasonable function of pH. We found that the mitochondria-rich cells of the turtle bladder, medullary collecting tubule, cortical collecting tubule, and all proximal tubule cells were enriched in vesicles whose pH was acid, varying from 5.0 to 6.5. An acid intravesicular pH could be due to two mechanisms, a proton pump or a Donnan potential created by fixed negative charges. Addition of the electrogenic proton ionophore, CCCP, increased the intravesicular pH, which indicates that the low internal pH is due to a proton pump, since facilitated proton movement down a Donnan potential would lead to a more acidic vesicle pH.

The rate of H^+ secretion in the turtle bladder is sensitive to the ambient pCO_2. Addition of CO_2 rapidly increases the rate of H^+ secretion (7, 25). We developed an assay to test for exocytic insertion of proton pumps, in which we measured the rate of transport simultaneously with secretion of fluorescent dextran from preloaded turtle bladders. We found that increasing the pCO_2 stimulated the H^+ current and simultaneously induced transient secretion of fluorescent macromolecules (1, 7). Since the current increased rapidly to reach a steady high level, but the secretion event was transient, it follows that the cause of the increase in H^+ transport is exocytic insertion of proton pumps which then turn over in the membrane continuously. We have developed a different assay for use in isolated perfused renal tubule (21). Here, we focused the microscope on a single cell that had endocytosed fluorescent macromolecules, and measured the total cellular fluorescence. We found that CO_2 reduced the fluorescence, presumably due to secretion of fluorescent material. Since colchicine prevented this effect of CO_2, microtubules are likely to be involved in mediating exocytosis.

These results provide strong evidence that CO_2 stimulates H^+ secretion in urinary epithelia by exocytic insertion of H^+ ATPases into the apical plasma membrane. Whether this is the sole cause for increased transport or only part of the response is discussed below. Since rapid exocytic insertion of transport proteins is an attractive mechanism for regulation of transport across membranes, which will probably be found in other systems, it is worth discussing the necessary criteria for establishing that such a mechanism operates in epithelia and other cells.

1. The transport protein should be located in vesicles underneath the membrane. The identification is either structural (e.g. immunocytochemical) or functional (e.g. low pH in the case of the H^+ ATPase).
2. Addition of the stimulus should cause fusion of the vesicles that contain the identified transporters with the relevant plasma membrane. This could be tested by the assays described above, as well as by quantitative ultrastructural studies (13, 26).
3. Fusion of vesicles should insert functional transport proteins into the plasma membrane. The time course of the change in transport and fusion should be identical. Substances that preferentially block fusion should also block the change in transport. There should be good correlation between the extent of fusion and the extent of change in transport. Fusion should be measured directly using a method that assays release of pinocytosed fluid phase marker. Measurement of the total surface area of the membrane, e.g. by capacitance or ultrastructural methods, is often used to estimate exocytosis, however, it reflects membrane addition by exocytosis minus that removed by endocytosis. Since we recently found that CO_2 can affect the rate of endocytosis as well (16), measurement of the net change in membrane area will have to be complemented by quantitative determinations of exocytosis or endocytosis. Used in this manner (4) the measurement of the surface capacitance, because of its excellent time resolution, promises to yield important insights into membrane turnover and its role in the regulation of transport.

Any change in transport occurring in the complete absence of exocytosis could then be ascribed to other regulatory events, e.g. increased turnover of individual transporters. However, the methods for measurement of exocytosis suffer from inaccuracies in the assays used and from poor time resolution. More importantly, the density of transporters in exocytic vesicles may be heterogenous, which might confuse the correlation between fusion and transport. A particularly difficult example is the case of vasopressin-mediated water flow in the toad bladder in which the hormone causes fusion of granules (14) and of aggregate-rich tubulovesicles (28). Since fusion of these organelles in response to vasopressin may have different time courses and, at least in principle, different sensitivities to the intracellular signals and to their inhibitors, the relationship between transport and fusion may be further complicated. This relationship has been studied in some systems using the release of pinocytosed fluid phase markers (1, 7, 21). However, these studies have not specifically examined the fusion of vesicles that contain an identified transporter with the plasma membrane.

4. Removal of the stimulus should result in endocytic removal of the transport protein. The time course of the removal should correspond to the time course of the reduction in the transport property measured. Factors which affect endocytosis primarily should also affect the rate of transport. As discussed above, the endocytic vesicles must also be shown to contain the identified transporters.

Endocytic Removal of H^+ Pumps from the Luminal Membrane

When the apical membrane of the turtle bladder or collecting tubule is exposed to macromolecules some of the mitochondria-rich cells rapidly internalize these molecules into vesicles located under the apical plasma membrane. The rate of uptake is much faster in these cells than in the principal or granular cells of the epithelium (1, 7, 21). Since the vesicles that internalize the fluorophore are acidic it follows that the H^+ ATPases are being internalized. In the steady state the H^+ current is constant, hence the number of internalized proton pumps must be balanced by an equal number of exocytically inserted proton pumps. Recent studies showed that certain lectins when added to the luminal fluid inhibit the net rate of H^+ secretion (16). Using an assay that quantitates the initial rate of endocytosis we found that the lectins concanavalin A and wheat germ agglutinin stimulated endocytosis. We also found that removal of CO_2 stimulated endocytosis from the luminal medium. However, the time course of its effect was different from that on exocytosis. The latter effect was almost complete within one minute, while the effect on endocytosis did not start until 15 or more minutes after removal of CO_2. Hence, endocytic removal and exocytic insertion may be regulated by different mechanisms. Because of the disparities in the time courses one would expect the surface area of the apical membrane to change in response to CO_2. That this is the case was demonstrated using ultrastructural morphometry (13, 26), and with much better time resolution by measuring the apical capacitance (4).

One of the problems with all available assays for endocytosis and exocytosis is the fundamental assumption that all of the endocytic and exocytic vesicles contain the same number of proton ATPases. It is likely that this is not the case. We do not know whether the distribution of proton ATPases in the luminal membrane is random. Nor do we know whether the patches of membrane that are endocytosed are randomly chosen, or whether the endocytic process removes a specialized microdomain that is enriched in proton ATPases. Until methods are developed to resolve these questions it will not be possible to quantitate the role of endocytic removal in the regulation of transepithelial transport.

Cellular Signals for Membrane Fusion

To investigate how CO_2 might cause exocytosis we reasoned that cytoplasmic acidification might be the first signal. The best known effect of CO_2 is to acidify the cytoplasm as a result of its cytosolic hydration, which generates carbonic acid (19).(Because we are physiologists rather than chemists we did not consider that CO_2 might cause carbamation of some important protein, e.g. tubulin, which might lead to the fusion event.) In support of the acidification hypothesis we found that the weak acids, butyric and acetic acids, also stimulated exocytic insertion of proton pumps (1). This finding raised another question as to how cell acidification might cause fusion. One possibility is that cell acidification might increase cell calcium. Using the calcium sensitive fluorophore Quin 2, we found that CO_2 and butyric acid increased cell calcium whereas NH_3 and acetazolamide reduced cell calcium (1, 27). These results showed that there is a direct relationship between cytosolic concentrations of Ca and H$^+$ (27). To show that the change in cell calcium was necessary for the exocytic insertion of H$^+$ pumps we attempted to buffer the change in cell calcium with Maptam, a permeable esterified derivative of EGTA. Cytosolic esterases release it in the cytosol where it is trapped. We found that Maptam prevented the effect of CO_2 on exocytosis and on the increased H$^+$ current, but not on the reduction in cell pH (1). That increasing the calcium-buffering power of the cell prevented exocytosis implies that the CO_2-induced change in cell calcium was transient. Indeed, this was found to be the case. We think that the sequence of events is as follows: CO_2 acidifies the cell, which in turn raises cell calcium. Calcium causes exocytic insertion of proton pumps, which then turn over in the plasma membrane and pump protons out of the cell, causing the cell pH to recover towards its original level.

What is the nature of the relationship between cell pH and cell calcium? There are many possible mechanisms that could mediate this relation. One possibility is that Ca and H$^+$ bind to intracellular proteins and simply displace each other from these binding sites. There may also be Ca : H exchangers, either in plasma membranes or in the endoplasmic reticulum, which are driven by the balance of electrochemical gradients for Ca and protons across these membranes. There may be calcium channels that are pH sensitive, opening when the cell is acidified. Another more complex mechanism might be that cell acidification depolarizes the membrane by closing the pH-sensitive K channels. Membrane depolarization could then open voltage-sensitive calcium channels. This latter mechanism was recently invoked as an explanation for glucose-mediated insulin release (2). Other mechanisms, such as the role of phosphoinositides in calcium mobilization and sequestration, will need to be evaluated.

The role of cell pH and cell calcium in endocytosis also remains to be documented. This will probably be more difficult to unravel because at present no mechanism is known to regulate endocytosis.

Role of Exocytosis in Transepithelial H^+ Transport

The increase in H^+ secretion induced by CO_2 is largely or entirely due to exocytic insertion of H^+ pumps. The alternative view is that CO_2 acidifies the cell, which in turn stimulates each proton pump kinetically. Our assertion that there is no major role for a kinetic effect is based on the observation that CO_2 induces exocytic insertion of functional proton pumps, which within several minutes return the cell pH to approximately the initial level (J. van Adelsberg & Q. Al-Awqati, in preparation). The signal for increased turnover of each proton pump is cytoplasmic acidification. Yet after the exocytic event is complete the cell pH is at or near the original level, even though the transepithelial transport rate remains high. Clearly, a kinetic effect cannot be invoked when the cell pH has recovered to the initial level. Our previous studies have shown that the pH optimum of the H^+ ATPase is very broad, with little change in activity in the relevant range of cell pH (8). Also, there is excellent correlation between the increase in H^+ transport and the number of fusing vesicles, as estimated by the release of previously internalized fluid phase marker (1, 7). Finally, removal of CO_2 inhibits H^+ secretion and stimulates endocytosis. However, it will be necessary to measure cell pH, exocytosis, and H^+ transport in the same bladders, and to vary the rate of exocytosis by some agent, before we can conclusively state that all of the increase is due to exocytic insertion of H^+ pumps. At present we conclude that if there is an effect of cell pH on the rate of each pump it must be minor.

Acute addition of CO_2 causes exocytic insertion of H^+ pumps in the renal tubule (21), and increases HCO_3 absorption (11, 12). It is likely that this process is also mediated by intracellular calcium in a manner analogous to the system found in the turtle bladder. Chronic hypercapnea or acid loading was found to increase the surface area of the mitochondria-rich cells of the medullary collecting duct, and to reduce the fractional volume of the cytoplasm occupied by apically located vesicles, which implies the occurrence of exocytosis (13). However, the response to chronic acid loading is much more complex than originally thought: We recently found that there are two types of mitochondria-rich cells in the collecting tubules, an acid-secreting and a bicarbonate-secreting type (23). Acid-secreting cells endocytose luminal macromolecules into vesicles acidified by proton pumps, and respond to CO_2 by exocytosis. Bicarbonate-secreting cells endocytose material from the basolateral but not the luminal side. This raises the question of whether or not CO_2 stimulates basolateral exocytosis in these cells, and hence stimulates bicarbonate secretion. The effect of CO_2 on net bicarbonate transport in cortical and medullary collecting tubules must now be interpreted in the context of these two cell types. Further, chronic acid loading increased the number of acid-secreting cells in the cortical collecting tubule, probably by reversal of the functional polarity of the bicarbonate-secreting cell (22). In this segment, which normally secretes bicarbonate, the majority of the mitochondria-rich cells are of the bicarbonate-secreting variety. This result suggests that chronic alkali loading may reverse the polarity of the acid-secreting cells of the medullary collecting tubule, which normally secretes acid.

Pathways of Endocytosis and Exocytosis

Recent studies on the routes of internalized ligands have uncovered a hitherto unsuspected complexity in these pathways, which shows that intracellular compartmentation is more extensive than previously thought. The pathways of endocytic vesicles that form at the apical membrane include the following (2, 10, 24):

1. The pathway from the apical plasma membrane to lysosomes was the first discovered. Internalized substances that follow this route are delivered to the lysosomes. The membrane of the endocytic vesicle is then recovered and shuttled back to the surface.
2. Another path is from the apical plasma membrane to the endosome. The endosome is a new compartment which has recently attracted much attention (9). There is probably either a stable structure or a constant pool of endocytic vesicles located between the golgi and the apical membrane. The vesicles may fuse with this structure, and then reform to shuttle back to the plasma membrane. This compartment clearly contains a proton ATPase in many (or all) cell types (20).
3. Recent studies have shown that endocytic vesicles from the apical membrane can deliver their contents to the golgi, which suggests that there is traffic between the apical plasma membranes and this organelle (10).
4. Transcytosis from the apical plasma membrane to the basolateral plasma membrane is known to occur in epithelia, although its rate is very low. Transport of IgA in liver and mammary gland, and IgG in neonatal intestine, occurs by this pathway (15, 17). Recently fluid phase transcytosis was also found in cultured MDCK cells.

There is evidence that a large intracellular pool of vesicles is labelled in the mitochondria-rich cell as well as in the proximal tubule cell. Some of these vesicles are "coated," presumably by clathrin (13; G. J. Schwartz, J. Barasch & Q. Al-Awqati, *Nature,* in press). Indeed, Rodman et al have demonstrated the presence of extensive clathrin coats on the apical surface of proximal tubules (18). Clathrin-coated vesicles and endosomes in a variety of cells contain electrogenic proton ATPases (9, 20) that are similar to the ones responsible for urinary acidification. Many of these vesicles also contain a chloride channel in parallel with the proton pump; regulation of this chloride conductance may determine the magnitude of the pH gradients these vesicles can maintain (5).

Since endosomes, clathrin-coated vesicles, golgi, and lysosomes are all acidified by proton pumps, the measurement of the pH in the environment of the endocytosed macromolecules represents an average pH of all these compartments. The vesicles that fuse with the apical plasma membrane in response to CO_2 comprise only a small fraction of the intracellular pool. We found that the average reduction in the total fluorescence of a single cell was ~ 25% of the total (21). Morphometric studies by others showed a similar reduction in the number of apical vesicles (13). Why is the fraction so low? It is possible that the vesicles that fuse with the membrane in response to CO_2 are closely apposed to the membrane, and are in a "ready state" similar to that found in the neuromuscular junction. However, this fusing pool of vesicles clearly exchanges material with the larger (endosomal) pool. This conclusion is based on the observation that when exocytosis of fluorescent dye is induced by one stimulus, e.g. butyric acid, the fusion event is transient. If butyrate is then removed and CO_2 is added it causes another wave of exocytosis, even though no new fluorescent macromolecule has been introduced into the cell (1).

The pathways described for membrane recycling fall into two general classes, a regulated and an unregulated (constitutive) pathway. The constitutive pathway is used for the repair and regeneration of the plasma membrane, and in the steady state the rates of endocytosis and exocytosis are equal. It is likely that the vesicles in the regulated pathway contain proteins that are specific for this pathway. These proteins may comprise the contents of these vesicles, e.g. hormones or enzymes, or they may be receptors, channels, or pumps whose surface number is being regulated by the signal. Vesicles in the regulated pathway must also contain "information" that allows the regulating signal to target them to their destination.

One important question in urinary epithelia is whether the exocytic vesicles that contain the proton ATPase are in the constitutive pathway or only in a separate regulated pathway. CO_2 affects both exocytosis and endocytosis, but the time course of the effect on endocytosis is much slower than that on exocytosis. These observations suggest that membrane recycling in the mitochondria-rich cell is more complex than originally thought, and they highlight the need for probes that can distinguish not only exocytic from endocytic vesicles but also those in the regulated pathway from those in the constitutive one. Using such probes one could then study the time courses of the formation of these vesicles and their fusion with the apical plasma membrane after acute and chronic perturbations in acid-base status. With the development of immunocytochemical markers for the proton ATPase, as well as for the $Cl:HCO_3$ exchanger and the Cl channel, we should be able to map the cellular location of these components of transepithelial H^+ transport and monitor their responses to regulatory stimuli.

Literature Cited

1. Cannon, C., van Adelsberg, J. S., Kelly, S., Al-Awqati, Q. 1985. CO_2 by acidifying the cell increases cell calcium which causes exocytotic insertion of H^+ pumps in turtle bladder luminal membrane. *Nature* 314:443–46

2. Cook, D. L., Ikeuchi, M., Fujimoto, W. Y. 1984. Lowering of pH_i inhibits Ca^{2+}-activated K^+ channels in pancreatic B-cells. *Nature* 311:269–71

3. Dixon, T. E., Al-Awqati, Q. 1979. Urinary acidification in the turtle bladder is due to a reversible proton translocating ATPase. *Proc. Natl. Acad. Sci. USA* 76:3135–39

4. Dixon, T. E., Clausen, C., Coachman, D. 1985. Acetazolamide (AZ) inhibits exocytosis in the turtle urinary bladder (TUB). *Kidney Int.* 27:280 (Abstr.)

5. Glickman, J., Croen, K., Kelly, S., Al-Awqati, Q. 1983. Golgi membranes contain an electrogenic H^+ pump in parallel with a chloride conductance. *J. Cell Biol.* 97:1303–8

6. Gluck, S., Al-Awqati, Q. 1984. An electrogenic investigation of proton-translocating adenosine-triphosphatase from bovine kidney medulla. *J. Clin. Inv.* 73:1704–10

7. Gluck, S., Cannon, C., Al-Awqati, Q. 1982. Exocytosis regulates H^+ transport in the turtle bladder by rapid insertion of H^+ pumps into the luminal membrane. *Proc. Natl. Acad. Sci. USA* 79:4327–31

8. Gluck, S., Kelly, S., Al-Awqati, Q. 1982. The proton translocating ATPase responsible for urinary acidification. *J. Biol. Chem.* 257:9230–33

9. Helenius, A., Mellman, I. S., Wall, D., Hubbard, A. 1983. Endosomes. *Trends Biochem. Sci.* 8:245–50

10. Herzog, V., Farquhar, M. G. 1977. Luminal membrane retrieval after exocytosis reaches most golgi cisternae in secretory cells. *Proc. Natl. Acad. Sci. USA* 74:5073–77

11. Jacobson, H. R. 1981. Effect of CO_2 and acetazolamide on bicarbonate and fluid transport in rabbit proximal tubules. *Am. J. Physiol.* 240:F54–F62

12. Jacobson, H. R. 1984. Medullary collecting duct acidification effect of potassium, HCO_3 concentration, and pCO_2. *J. Clin. Invest.* 74:2107–14

13. Madsen, K. M., Tisher, C. C. 1983. Cellular response to acute respiratory acidosis in rat medullary collecting duct. *Amer. J. Physiol.* 245:F670–79

14. Masur, S. K., Holtzman, E., Walter, R. 1972. Hormone sensitive exocytosois in

the toad urinary bladder. *J. Cell Biol.* 52:211–19

15. Mostov, K., Kraenbuhl, J.-P., Blobel, G. 1980. Receptor-mediated transcellular transport of immunoglobulin: Synthesis of secretory component as multiple and larger transmembrane forms. *Proc. Natl. Acad. Sci. USA* 77:7257–61

16. Reeves, W., Gluck, S., Al-Awqati, Q. 1983. Role of endocytosis in H^+ transport regulation by turtle bladder. *Kidney Int.* 23:232 (Abstr.)

17. Rodewald, R., Kraenbuhl, J.-P. 1984. Receptor-mediated transport of IgG. *J. Cell Biol.* 99:159S–177S

18. Rodman, J. S., Kerjaschki, D., Merisko, E., Farquhar, M. G. 1984. Presence of an extensive clathrin coat on the apical plasmalemma of the rat kidney proximal tubule cell. *J. Cell Biol.* 98:1630–36

19. Roos, A., Boron, W. 1981. Intracellular pH. *Physiol. Rev.* 61:296–434

20. Rudnick, G. 1986. ATP-driven H^+ pumping into intracellular organelles. *Ann. Rev. Physiol.* Vol. 48

21. Schwartz, G. J., Al-Awqati, Q. 1985. CO_2 causes exocytosis of vesicles containing H^+ pumps in isolated perfused proximal and collecting tubules. *J. Clin. Inv.* 75:1638–44

22. Schwartz, G. J., Al-Awqati, Q. 1985. Polarity of H^+ transport in the two types of mitochondria-rich cells (MR) cells of cortical collecting tubules (CCT). *Clin. Res.* 33:497a (Abstr.)

23. Schwartz, G. J., Al-Awqati, Q. 1985. Two functionally distinct types of mitochondria-rich (MR) cells in cortical collecting tubule (CCT) as determined by changes in cell pH (pH_i) in individually identified cells. *Kidney Int.* 27:288 (Abstr.)

24. Steinman, R. M., Mellman, I. S., Muller, W. A., Cohn, Z. A. 1983. Endocytosis and the recycling of plasma membrane. *J. Cell Biol.* 96:1–27

25. Steinmetz, P. R. 1974. Cellular mechanisms of urinary acidification. *Physiol. Rev.* 54:890–956

26. Stetson, D., Steinmetz, P. R. 1983. Role of membrane fusion in CO_2 stimulation of proton secretion by turtle bladder. *Amer. J. Physiol.* 245:C113–20

27. van Adelsberg, J. S., Al-Awqati, Q. 1985. CO_2 causes exocytosis by increasing calcium in turtle bladder epithelial cells. *Kidney Int.* 27:290 (Abstr.)

28. Wade, J. 1980. Hormonal modulation of epithelial structures. *Curr. Top. Memb. Transp.* 15:123–47

Ann. Rev. Physiol. 1986. 48:163–74

OSMOTIC SWELLING OF VESICLES:
Its Role in the Fusion of Vesicles with Planar Phospholipid Bilayer Membranes and its Possible Role in Exocytosis[1]

Alan Finkelstein

Departments of Physiology & Biophysics and Neuroscience, Albert Einstein College of Medicine, 1300 Morris Park Avenue, Bronx, New York 10461

Joshua Zimmerberg

Physical Sciences Laboratory, Division of Computer Research and Technology, Laboratory of Chemical Biology, National Institute of Arthritis, Diabetes, and Digestive and Kidney Diseases, National Institutes of Health, Bethesda, Maryland 20205

Fredric S. Cohen

Department of Physiology, Rush Medical College, Chicago, Illinois 61612

Fusion of intracellular vesicles with the plasma membrane, resulting in the extracellular discharge (exocytosis) of vesicular contents, plays a prominent role in a plethora of biological phenomena. The biochemical and biophysical features of this process have been the subject of extensive and continuing investigation, as witness the other articles in this section. This article focuses on one particular biophysical aspect of the fusion process: the possible role of osmotic forces in exocytosis. It first reviews the part that osmosis plays in the fusion of phospholipid vesicles with planar, phospholipid bilayer membranes, and then considers the evidence that it also acts as a driving force for exocytosis in cells. The review is confined to the possible role of osmosis in exocytosis, and does not consider its role in other biological fusion processes such as intravesicular or intercellular fusion.

[1]The US Government has the right to retain a nonexclusive, royalty-free license in and to any copyright covering this paper.

163

I. FUSION OF PHOSPHOLIPID VESICLES WITH PLANAR BILAYER MEMBRANES

Miller & Racker (29) first drew attention to the participation of osmotic forces in the fusion of vesicles with planar bilayers with their demonstration that the fusion of sucrose-loaded sarcoplasmic reticulum (SR) vesicles with planar bilayers required that the vesicle contents be hyperosmotic with respect to the *cis* solution (the solution, bathing the bilayer, to which vesicles are added). They suggested that for fusion to take place there must be an osmotic gradient ($\approx$ 250 milliosmolal) across the SR membrane. This gradient, however, would have been dissipated long before fusion occurred in their system and, in retrospect, it appears that the fusogenic effect of placing the SR vesicles in a hypo-osmotic solution resulted from their becoming fully swollen (we shall return to this point later). Subsequent experiments with phospholipid vesicles (9) revealed a crucial role of osmotic water flow in vesicle–planar membrane fusion, and more recent studies (2) have clarified to some extent the events underlying the fusion process, although there still remain several important unanswered questions. In this section, we summarize our present understanding of the fusion process in this model system, and draw attention to issues that require further research.

Before discussing the fusion process per se, we wish to note the criterion for fusion that has been employed in virtually all studies of fusion of vesicles (be they of biological origin, as the SR vesicles described above, or formed from phospholipids alone) with planar bilayer membranes. That criterion is the simultaneous group insertion into the planar membrane of integral membrane protein channels originally present in vesicle membranes. [Earlier attempts to study the fusion of phospholipid vesicles with planar membranes using such membrane markers as phospholipids (10), antibiotics (31), and fluorescent probes (37) were bedeviled by nonfusion exchange of marker between vesicles and the planar membrane.] The fact that channels insert as groups, rather than singly, argues for the fusion (or incorporation) of vesicle membranes into the planar membrane, rather than a transfer of channels between membranes (8, 9, 28, 29). In one study, however, direct transfer of intravesicular contents across the planar bilayer membrane was shown to occur under the same conditions that caused channel insertion, and the number of events scored by these two assays was comparable, thus lending credence to group channel insertion as a measure of vesicle–planar membrane fusion (50).

It is now apparent that there are two experimentally distinguishable steps in the fusion of phospholipid vesicles with planar bilayer membranes (2). In the first step, the vesicles form a stable, tightly bound "pre-fusion" state with the planar membrane. If the vesicular and planar membranes are composed of lipids having no net charge, such as phosphatidylcholine (PC) and phosphatidylethanolamine (PE), this state forms in the absence of divalent cation, whereas if the vesicular and/or planar membrane contain negatively charged lipids, millimolar concentrations of divalent cation (Mg^{++} or Ca^{++}) are required for its formation. With negatively charged lipids in the membrane, the pre-fusion state can be achieved with the phospholipid-binding protein fibronectin (48) in place of millimolar concentrations of divalent cation, and if a calcium-binding protein (1) is incorporated into the planar membrane, the pre-fusion state is mediated by micromolar concentrations of Ca^{++}, whereas 1 mM Mg^{++} is ineffective (51). The pre-fusion state has been reported to be manifested by a change in planar membrane capacitance (3), but this interpretation of the reported capacitance changes is not obvious to us.

In the second step, the actual fusion of vesicular and planar membranes occurs via osmotic swelling of vesicles attached (in the pre-fusion state) to the planar membrane. There are two ways in which this swelling has been achieved experimentally. In one (Figure 1), the vesicles are loaded with a solute that is

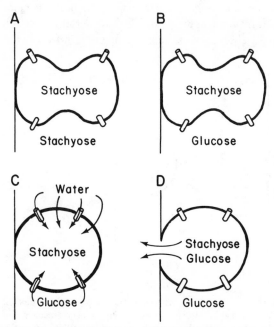

Figure 1   Schematic of the osmotic swelling of a vesicle loaded with an impermeant solute, and its subsequent fusion to a planar lipid bilayer membrane. The vesicle contains stachyose, which is impermeant through the porin channels (drawn as cylinders) in the vesicle membrane. (A) The stachyose-containing vesicle, in an isosmotic stachyose medium, associates tightly with the planar membrane in the pre-fusion state. (B) The external stachyose solution is replaced by an isosmotic glucose solution. The vesicle remains tightly associated with the planar membrane. (C) Glucose diffuses through the porin channels into the vesicle, and water follows (maintaining isosmolality). As a result, the vesicle swells. (D) The vesicle and planar membrane rupture in the region of contact, producing fusion. (From Reference 7.)

impermeant through the channels contained in the vesicular membrane; when this solute is replaced in the *cis* solution by a permeant solute, the vesicles swell as the permeant solute, followed by water, enters them (2, 7). In the other method (Figure 2), an osmotic gradient is created across the planar membrane, either by increasing the osmolality of the *cis* solution or by lowering the osmolality of the *trans* solution; water flowing across the planar membrane in the region of contact with the vesicular membrane crosses the latter and enters the vesicle, causing it to swell (8, 9). It can be argued from the fact that an osmotic gradient across the planar membrane can cause vesicle swelling, that the vesicle and planar membrane are in very intimate contact (2).

The details of the mechanism by which the swelling of vesicles in contact with the planar membrane leads to fusion remain to be elucidated, but the process probably involves stretching of the vesicular and planar membrane in the region of contact, thereby exposing areas of hydrophobic acyl chains, leading to subsequent merger and fusion of the membranes. If the vesicles are fully swollen, the formation of the pre-fusion state itself may induce sufficient stretching of the membranes to produce their merger, thus accounting for fusion that occurs in the absence of osmotic swelling (29, 30). In all these instances,

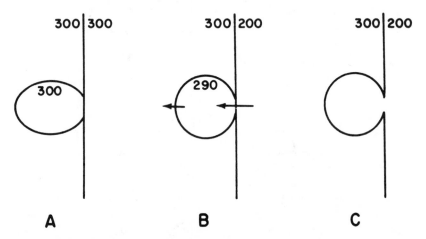

Figure 2   Schematic showing how an osmotic gradient across a planar lipid bilayer membrane causes vesicle swelling and its subsequent fusion with the planar membrane. (A) A shrunken vesicle associates tightly with the planar membrane in the pre-fusion state; the osmolarity on the two sides of the planar membrane and within the vesicle is, for concreteness, taken as 300 mosM. [For simplicity, no space is assumed to exist between the vesicular and planar membrane in the region of contact; a more detailed view of this region is given in (2).] (B) The osmolarity of the *trans* solution has been diluted to 200 milliosmolar. The vesicle has reached a maximally swollen state, but the rate of water entry from the *trans* compartment *(long arrow)* exceeds the rate of osmotic exit of water from the vesicle into the *cis* compartment *(short arrow)*. Consequently, the vesicle bursts and fuses (C). (From Reference 51.)

however, the fusion rates obtained are orders of magnitude higher if an osmotic gradient is applied across the planar membrane (e.g. 4, 11, 20, 24). Two bulged bilayer membranes brought into close contact can meld to form a central single bilayer (18, 32), a process that may be related to the pre-fusion state. In some instances this central bilayer may burst, formally corresponding to the fusion of vesicle and planar membrane.

In addition to the molecular details underlying both the pre-fusion state and the subsequent osmotically induced fusion of vesicular and planar membranes, there are two other unresolved issues that need to be addressed in future studies. One is that stirring in the *cis* compartment (8) is required to induce the fusion of vesicles with decane-containing bilayers; the reason for this is obscure. The other issue is whether or not swelling of vesicles in the pre-fusion state leads to preferential rupture in the region of contact with the planar membrane. The only events that have been scored by the assays so far employed have been *successful* fusions. Attached vesicles, however, may rupture without fusing to the planar membrane, discharging their contents back into the *cis* compartment. What is needed to resolve this point is direct visualization of vesicle-planar membrane fusion, which might be achieved by the study of the fusion of large, dye-filled vesicles with planar membranes.

II.   OSMOTIC FORCES IN EXOCYTOSIS

Both the plasma membrane of cells and the membranes surrounding their internal organelles and vesicles consist of phospholipid bilayers in which are embedded additional components, such as sterols, gangliosides, proteins, and glycoproteins, that are asymmetrically distributed between the two leaflets of the bilayer. It is therefore pertinent to ask, in light of the results described in the previous section for the fusion of phospholipid vesicles with planar bilayer membranes, if cells use osmotic swelling of secretory vesicles as the mechanism to promote their fusion to the comparable planar plasma membrane, or if some other mechanisms are employed to stress these membranes in their region of contact. This section reviews the strength of the evidence that osmotic swelling plays a role in exocytosis and considers what future experiments are required for a definitive conclusion.

Vesicle Swelling During Exocytosis

The association between osmotic swelling and secretion has been considered for some time. In the early part of this century, Jacques Loeb, using light microscopy to study the formation of the fertilization membrane in sea urchin eggs, which we now know to be the result of exocytosis, wrote (26):

"Now it appears to me (so far as the osmotic properties of the [fertilization] membrane are concerned) that this formation of droplets depends upon the fact that a colloidal substance, which lies below the surface layer of the unfertilized egg or is secreted from the egg, suddenly swells by absorption of sea water".

Since then, vesicular swelling during exocytosis has been noted with light microscopy for the cortical granules of the sea urchin egg (52), the mast cell granules of the beige mouse (13), and the nematocysts of the "stinging cells" of *Hydra* (see below); it has also been noted by electron microscopy in such diverse cells as *Limulus* amoebocytes (34), pulmonary mast cells (6), *Tetrahymena* (40), and mammary epithelial cells (14). These observations, however, do not define the temporal relationship between swelling and fusion. This has been, and remains, the sticking point in the interpretation of experiments designed to study the hypothesis that osmotic swelling of vesicles is a driving force for fusion. There is no question that contact of the vesicular contents with the extracellular medium, after fusion has occurred, often results in the swelling of these contents and their subsequent dispersal[1]. It is, after all, well known that the contents of many secretory granules exist as relatively insoluble dense cores, and that they disperse and solubilize (i.e. swell) after discharge.

The key issue that has not yet been conclusively settled, however, is whether there is some swelling of the vesicles that precedes fusion (that is, precedes the exposure of vesicular contents to the extracellular medium), and that can therefore be a possible causal link to the fusion of vesicular membranes with the plasma membrane. Even in those electron microscopic studies that apparently demonstrate vesicle swelling prior to membrane fusion [e.g. (15)] there remains the possibility that "microfusion" of vesicular and plasma membrane, undetected because of the finite thickness of the sections examined, has preceded vesicle swelling. The elegant study by Ornberg & Reese (34) of exocytosis in *Limulus* amoebocytes emphasizes this limitation of microscopy. [In the case of ionophore-activated sea urchin eggs, little of the capacitance increase that normally accompanies secretion is seen when exocytosis is osmotically inhibited (53), which indicates that little or no microfusion has occurred. In contrast, for virus-induced cell-cell fusion, it is argued that microfusion precedes osmotic swelling of the cells (23, 41).]

In a remarkable study of nematocyst discharge from the "stinging cells" of *Hydra,* Holstein & Tardent (21), using high-speed microcinematography (25 μsec/frame), have shown that following stimulation of the cell the nematocyst volume swells by approximately 10% before the (exocytotic) discharge of its

---

[1]This is not to imply that the normal extracellular medium is necessary for swelling of granular contents to occur. In sea urchin cortices, exocytosis occurs even if the external medium is one resembling the cytosolic milieu (39, 45, 52).

contents (stenotele) begins. This swelling is completed in less than 200 μsec, followed by appearance of the stenotele within 25 μsec. The authors propose that the initial volume increase is produced osmotically, but whether this occurs prior to fusion of nematocyst and cell membrane or after, as suggested from earlier studies (27), could not be determined.

Inhibition of Exocytosis by Hyperosmotic Solutions

One experimental approach to testing the osmotic hypothesis of vesicle fusion has been to examine the effect of solution osmolality on exocytosis. In terms of the model depicted in Figure 1, one would expect that in a hyperosmotic milieu, secretory vesicles would shrink, and that therefore the putative stimulus-induced osmotic swelling might not be sufficient to cause them to reach the taut state required for fusion. This predicted inhibition of exocytosis by hyperosmotic media has been demonstrated in a number of intact cell preparations, including parathyroid cells (5), pheochromocytoma cells (16), platelets (38), sea urchin eggs (49), and chromaffin cells (19) (discussed more fully by Holz, this volume). There is, however, an inherent difficulty in attributing the inhibition of exocytosis in these experiments simply to shrinkage of the secretory vesicles; namely, there are numerous other intracellular sequellae to hyperosmotic treatment of cells besides the shrinking of secretory vesicles. Ionic strength, viscosity, concentrations of cyclic nucleotides and calcium, cytoskeletal relationships, and membrane folding are just a few of the intracellular factors that are altered secondary to cell shrinkage in a hyperosmotic medium. Therefore it is difficult to assign the cause of exocytosis inhibition simply to change in vesicle volume. Indeed, at the neuromuscular junction, although hyperosmotic media inhibit stimulus-evoked transmitter release (33), they actually increase spontaneous exocytotic transmitter release; this latter effect has been attributed to changes in the cytosolic concentration of calcium (42).

The experiments of Kachadorian et al (22) on the effect of hyperosmotic luminal solutions, in toad urinary bladder, on the antidiuretic hormone-induced fusion of intracellular tubular vesicles with the luminal membrane attempted to circumvent the problem of cell volume changes that normally accompany changes in the osmolality of the milieu. Because the water permeability of the luminal membrane of the bladder is so much less than that of the basolateral membranes, which are in series with it, changes in the osmolality of the luminal solution are not accompanied by significant changes in cell volume (36). Thus, the situation in their experiments was analogous to that in Figure 2, except that the osmotic gradient was in a direction to withdraw water from the vesicles rather than to cause its entry into them. Their finding that hyperosmotic luminal solutions inhibited vesicle fusion to the luminal membrane is consistent with the idea that vesicle swelling is required for fusion.

A more direct approach to the effect of osmolality on fusion is to modify the osmolality of the cytosol directly, rather than to alter it indirectly via shrinkage of the cell in a hyperosmotic medium. This has been done using the chromaffin cell (see the article by Holz in this volume) and the sea urchin egg. From the latter cell, it is possible to prepare isolated planar cortex consisting of plasma membrane with attached cortical granules (43), thereby giving the investigator direct control of the solution composition bathing the cytoplasmic face of the plasma membrane. In that system it can be shown that exocytosis is reversibly inhibited by hyperosmotic solutions, and that neither increases in viscosity (52) nor increases in ionic strength (53) produced this inhibition. Since the membrane was firmly attached to a solid surface, no membrane folding accompanied the hyperosmotic treatment, and it had previously been shown that it was unlikely that cytoskeletal elements are involved in this fusion system (45). Combined with the demonstrable calcium-induced swelling of vesicles in this system (52), these findings strongly support the view that osmotic swelling of cortical granules to a critical size is essential for their fusion with the plasma membrane.

Even the demonstration that hyperosmolality per se inhibits exocytosis does not establish that an osmotic mechanism drives fusion, as one cannot preclude that solutions of high osmolality are exerting their inhibitory action by direct effects on macromolecular structures, such as altering the hydration states of essential elements in the fusion process. What is needed, in addition, is a clear demonstration that under normal conditions vesicle swelling precedes its fusion with the plasma membrane. Recent experiments on the mast cell of the beige mouse are highly suggestive of this (12, 13; Curran & Brodwick, personal communication). It was first established on permeabilized cells in hypotonic media that vesicles could swell to a critical size, beyond which they lysed, as evidenced by ruthenium red access to, and staining of, vesicular contents. Then, intact cells were observed in the presence of histamine, which is known to cause large shrinkage of the vesicle contents, presumably through cross-linking of gel elements. After addition of secretagogue, the vesicles increased in diameter to the critical size, after which ruthenium red staining was noted and shrinkage occurred. This suggests, within the limits of histamine and ruthenium red diffusion, a swelling of the vesicles to a taut state before exocytosis occurs. What is needed to preclude that microfusion had occurred prior to the increase in vesicle diameter are measurements of membrane capacitance during vesicle swelling. If microfusion has not occurred, no increase in membrane capacitance should be recorded until after the vesicle diameter has increased to a critical size, after which there should be jumps in capacitance corresponding to the increased membrane area inserted by the fusion process; if microfusion occurs prior to vesicle swelling, these capacitance jumps should precede the swelling.

Mechanisms of Osmotic Swelling

If indeed it can be established that vesicle swelling precedes fusion, the question of its mechanism then becomes pertinent. At this stage one can only speculate. One possible explanation is a change in vesicle membrane ion permeability, leading to ion flux and colloid osmotic swelling. The ubiquitous calcium-activated channels found in cell membranes (e.g. 35, 47) are obvious candidates for effectors of these permeability changes, and indeed, the calcium-induced lysis of platelet secretory granules has been ascribed to a calcium-induced increase in the ionic permeability of the granule membrane (44). In the case of rat peritoneal mast cells, however, conductance changes do not accompany exocytosis (17). Alternatively, the stimulation of active ion pumping into the vesicle interior could also lead to swelling. Since a large amount of osmotically inactive material is present in most exocytotic granules, an obvious potential source of osmotic swelling is their activation to osmotically effective particles (for example, by changes in osmotic coefficients or gelation state); solubilization of vesicle contents has been suggested from experiments with pulmonary mast cells (6). Given the hydration and swelling of granular contents that generally follows their exposure to the external medium, one way for this to occur prior to exocytosis would be for a gap-junction like structure to form between the vesicle and the plasma membrane; that is, the stimulus to fusion (e.g. elevated cytosolic calcium concentration) would induce formation of this structure and hence expose granular contents to the external milieu. In this case, capacitance changes would be observed to precede vesicular swelling.

III. SUMMARY

In order for either lipid bilayer membranes or biological membranes to undergo fusion, stresses must somehow be generated in the region of membrane contact. In the fusion of phospholipid vesicles with planar bilayer membranes, the stress can be produced by osmotic swelling of vesicles contacting the planar membrane. On the other hand, fully swollen vesicles may be sufficiently stretched that the additional stress experienced from their adhesion to the planar membrane may in itself suffice to produce fusion (see also Rand & Parsegian, this volume). There is considerable circumstantial evidence that osmotic swelling of vesicles may also be a driving force in exocytosis. This evidence centers both on experiments demonstrating inhibition of excytosis when vesicles are in a hyperosmotic medium, and on observations of vesicle swelling during the secretory process. This article has not reviewed all of the examples in the literature supporting an osmotic mechanism for fusion, but has attempted to suggest the diversity of cell types from which the examples are drawn and to indicate that the evidence is not conclusive. The unambiguous establishment of vesicle swelling prior to fusion would go far in establishing an osmotic mechanism of exocytosis. We must also be prepared to find that osmotic swelling may not be the only biological mechanism of stressing vesicle membranes contacting plasma membranes. The viral membrane fusion proteins (46) provide the precedent for agents that can apparently sufficiently perturb membranes to cause fusion without any additionally imposed stresses, and even direct membrane mechanical stretching may act biologically as a fusogenic stress (25).

ACKNOWLEDGMENTS

AF and FSC were supported by NIH grants GM 29210-08 and GM 31039.

Literature Cited

1. Abood, L. G., Hong, J. S., Takeda, F., Tometsko, A. M. 1976. Preparation and characterization of calcium-binding and other hydrophobic proteins from synaptic membranes. *Biochim. Biophys. Acta* 443:414–27

2. Akabas, M. H., Cohen, F. S., Finkelstein, A. 1984. Separation of the osmotically driven fusion event from vesicle-planar membrane attachment in a model system for exocytosis. *J. Cell Biol.* 98:1063–71

3. Babunashvili, I. N., Silberstein, A. Ya., Nenashev, V. A. 1981. Discrete changes of conductance and capacitance of bimolecular lipid membranes induced by liposomes. *Studia Biophys.* 83:131–37

4. Bell, J. E., Miller, C. 1984. Effects of phospholipid surface charge on ion conduction in the K^+ channel of sarcoplasmic reticulum. *Biophys. J.* 45:279–87

5. Brown, E. M., Pazoles, C. J., Creutz, C. E., Aurbach, G. D., Pollard, H. B. 1978. Role of anions in parathyroid hormone release from dispersed bovine parathyroid cells. *Proc. Natl. Acad. Sci. USA* 75:876–80

6. Caulfield, J. P., Lewis, R. A., Hein, A., Austen, K. F. 1980. Secretion in dissociated human pulmonary mast cells. Evidence for solubilization of granule contents before discharge. *J. Cell. Biol.* 85:299–311

7. Cohen, F. S., Akabas, M. H., Finkelstein, A. 1982. Osmotic swelling of phospholipid vesicles causes them to fuse with a planar phospholipid bilayer membrane. *Science* 217:458–60

8. Cohen, F. S., Akabas, M. H., Zimmerberg, J., Finkelstein, A. 1984. Parameters affecting the fusion of unilamellar phospholipid vesicles with planar bilayer membranes. *J. Cell. Biol.* 98:1054–62

9. Cohen, F. S., Zimmerberg, J., Finkel-stein, A. 1980. Fusion of phospholipid vesicles with planar phospholipid bilayer membranes. II. Incorporation of a vesicular membrane marker into the planar membrane. *J. Gen. Physiol.* 75:251–70

10. Cohen, J. A., Moronne, M. M. 1976. Interaction of charged lipid vesicles with planar bilayer lipid membranes: detection by antibiotic membrane probes. *J. Supramol. Struct.* 5:409–16

11. Coronado, R., Lattore, R. 1982. Detection of K^+ and Cl^- channels from calf cardiac sarcolema in planar lipid bilayer membranes. *Nature* 298:849–52

12. Curran, M., Brodwick, M. S. 1985. Mast cell exocytosis and the gel-swell of granules. *Biophys. J.* 47:172a

13. Curran, M. J., Brodwick, M. S., Edwards, C. 1984. Direct visualization of exocytosis in mast cells. *Biophys. J.* 45:170a

14. Dylewski, D. P., Keenan, T. W. 1983. Compound exocytosis of casein micelles in mammary epithelial cells. *Eur. J. Cell Biol.* 31:114–24

15. Endo, Y. 1961. Changes in the cortical layer of sea urchin eggs at fertilization as studied with the electron microscope. I. *Clypeaster japonicus*. *Exp. Cell Res.* 25:383–97

16. Englert, D. F., Perlman, R. L. 1981. Permeant anions are not required for norepinephrine secretion from pheochromocytoma cells. *Biochim. Biophys. Acta* 674:136–43

17. Fernandez, J. M., Neher, E., Gomperts, B. D. 1984. Capacitance measurements reveal stepwise fusion events in degranulating mast cells. *Nature* 312:453–55

18. Fisher, L. R., Parker, N. S. 1984. Osmotic control of bilayer fusion. *Biophys. J.* 46:253–58

19. Hampton, R. Y., Holz, R. W. 1983. Effects of changes in osmolality on the stability and function of cultured chromaffin cells and the possible role of osmotic forces in exocytosis. *J. Cell Biol.* 96:1082–88

20. Hanke, W., Miller, C. 1983. Single chloride channels from *Torpedo* electroplax. Activation by protons. *J. Gen. Physiol.* 82:25–45

21. Holstein, T., Tardent, P. 1984. An ultrahigh-speed analysis of exocytosis: nematocyst discharge. *Science* 223:830–33

22. Kachadorian, W. A., Muller, J., Finkelstein, A. 1981. Role of osmotic forces in exocytosis: studies of ADH-induced fusion in toad urinary bladder. *J. Cell Biol.* 91:584–88

23. Knutton, S., Pasternak, C. A. 1979. The mechanism of cell-cell fusion. *Trends Biochem. Sci.* 4:220–23

24. Labarca, P., Coronado, R., Miller, C. 1980. Thermodynamic and kinetic studies of the gating behavior of a K^+-selective channel from the sarcoplasmic reticulum membrane. *J. Gen. Physiol.* 76:397–424

25. Lewis, S. A., DeMoura, J. L. C. 1982. Incorporation of cytoplasmic vesicles into apical membrane of mammalian urinary bladder epithelium. *Nature* 297: 685–88

26. Loeb, J. 1919. *Artificial Parthenogenesis and Fertilization*, pp. 209–10. Chicago: Chicago Univ. Press

27. Lubbock, R., Gupta, B. L., Hall, T. A. 1981. Novel role of calcium in exocytosis: Mechanism of nematocyst discharge as shown by x-ray microanalysis. *Proc. Natl. Acad. Sci. USA* 78:3624–28

28. Miller, C. 1982. Open-state substructure of single chloride channels from *Torpedo* electroplax. *Philos. Trans. R. Soc. London B* 299:401–11

29. Miller, C., Racker, E. 1976. Ca^{++}-induced fusion of fragmented sarcoplasmic reticulum with artificial planar bilayers. *J. Membrane Biol.* 30:283–300

30. Miller, C., White, M. W. 1980. A voltage-dependent chloride conductance channel from *Torpedo* electroplax membrane. *Ann. NY Acad. Sci.* 341:534–51

31. Moore, M. R. 1976. Fusion of liposomes containing conductance probes with black lipid films. *Biochim. Biophys. Acta* 426:765–71

32. Neher, E. 1974. Asymmetric membranes resulting from the fusion of two black lipid bilayers. *Biochim. Biophys. Acta* 373:327–36

33. Niles, W. D., Smith, D. O. 1982. Effects

of hyperosmotic solutions on quantal transmitter release at the crayfish neuromuscular junction. *J. Physiol.* 329:185–202

34. Ornberg, R. L., Reese, T. S. 1981. Beginning of exocytosis captured by rapid-freezing of *Limulus* amebocytes. *J. Cell Biol.* 90:40–54

35. Pallota, B. S., Magleby, K. L., Barrett, J. N. 1981. Single channel recordings of Ca^{2+}-activated K^+ currents in rat muscle cell culture. *Nature* 293:471–74

36. Peachey, L. D., Rasmussen, H. 1961. Structure of the toad's urinary bladder as related to its physiology. *J. Biophys. Biochem. Cytol.* 10:529–53

37. Pohl, G. W., Stark, G., Trissl, H. W. 1973. Interaction of liposomes with black lipid membranes. *Biochim. Biophys. Acta* 318:478–81

38. Pollard, H. B., Tack-Goldman, K., Pazoles, C. J., Creutz, C. E., Schulman, N. R. 1977. Evidence for control of serotonin secretion from human platelets by hydroxyl ion transport and osmotic lysis. *Proc. Natl. Acad. Sci. USA* 74:5295–99

39. Sasaki, H., Epel, D. 1983. Cortical vesicle exocytosis in isolated cortices of sea urchin eggs: description of a turbidimetric assay and its utilization in studying effects of different media on discharge. *Dev. Biol.* 98:327–37

40. Satir, B., Schooley, C., Satir, P. 1973. Membrane fusion in a model system. Mucocyst secretion in *Tetrahymena*. *J. Cell Biol.* 56:153–76

41. Sekiguchi, K., Kuroda, K., Ohnishi, S.-I., Asano, A. 1981. Virus induced fusion of human erythrocyte ghosts. I. Effects of macromolecules on the final stages of the fusion reaction. *Biochim. Biophys. Acta* 645:211–25

42. Shimoni, Y., Alnaes, E., Rahamimoff, R. 1977. Is hyperosmotic neurosecretion from motor nerve endings a calcium-dependent process? *Nature* 267:170–72

43. Vacquier, V. D. 1975. The isolation of intact cortical granules from sea urchin eggs. Calcium ions trigger granule discharge. *Dev. Biol.* 40:62–74

44. VanderMeulen, J., Grinstein, S. 1982. Ca^{2+}-induced lysis of platelet secretory granules. *J. Biol. Chem.* 257:5190–95

45. Whitaker, M. J., Baker, P. F. 1983. Calcium-dependent exocytosis in an *in vitro* secretory granule plasma membrane preparation from sea urchin eggs and the effects of some inhibitors of cytoskeletal function. *Proc. R. Soc. London B* 218: 397–413

46. White, J., Kielian, M., Helenius, A. 1983. Membrane fusion proteins of en-

veloped animal viruses. *Q. Rev. Biophys.*
16:151–95

47. Yellen, G. 1982. Single Ca^{2+}-activated nonselective cation channels in neuroblastoma. *Nature* 296:357–59

48. Young, T. M., Young, J., D.-E. 1984. Protein-mediated intermembrane contact facilitates fusion of lipid vesicles with planar bilayers. *Biochim. Biophys. Acta* 775:441–45

49. Zimmerberg, J. 1983. Hyperosmotic treatment inhibits cortical granule exocytosis in the sea urchin *Lytechinus pictus. Biol. Bull.* 165:502

50. Zimmerberg, J., Cohen, F. S., Finkelstein, A. 1980. Fusion of phospholipid vesicles with planar phospholipid bilayer membranes. I. Discharge of vesicular

contents across the planar membrane. *J. Gen. Physiol.* 75:241–50

51. Zimmerberg, J., Cohen, F. S., Finkelstein, A. 1980. Micromolar Ca^{2+} stimulates fusion of lipid vesicles with planar bilayers containing a calcium-binding protein. *Science* 210:906–8

52. Zimmerberg, J., Sardet, C., Epel, D. 1985. Exocytosis of sea urchin egg cortical vesicles *in vitro* is retarded by hyperosmotic sucrose: kinetics of fusion monitored by quantitative light-scattering microscopy. *J. Cell Biol.* In press

53. Zimmerberg, J., Whitaker, M. 1985. Calcium causes irreversible swelling of secretory granules during exocytosis. *Nature* 315:581–84

Ann. Rev. Physiol. 1986. 48:175–89

THE ROLE OF OSMOTIC FORCES IN EXOCYTOSIS FROM ADRENAL CHROMAFFIN CELLS

Ronald W. Holz

Department of Pharmacology, University of Michigan Medical School, Ann Arbor, Michigan 48109

INTRODUCTION

The exocytotic release of catecholamines from bovine adrenal chromaffin cells is normally triggered by nicotinic receptor-activated influx of extracellular Ca^{2+} (15, 28, 33), and a subsequent increase in cytosolic Ca^{2+} concentration (36). Ba^{2+} alone or membrane depolarization in the presence of Ca^{2+} also stimulates exocytosis. Although the mechanism of exocytosis was first described using biochemical techniques in the adrenal medulla (see Reference 64 for review), the underlying mechanisms triggered by Ca^{2+} are not understood. Fusion of artificial vesicles with planar bilayer membranes requires an osmotic gradient across the vesicle membrane, which causes water entry and swelling of the vesicles (10) (see Finkelstein et al, this volume). The chromaffin granule, the secretory granule within chromaffin cells, lyses in hypo-osmotic solutions. The possibility that osmotic stress on the chromaffin granule is a driving force in exocytosis has been raised by a number of investigators and will be critically evaluated in this review.

COMPOSITION AND CHARACTERISTICS OF THE CONTENTS OF CHROMAFFIN GRANULES

The composition of bovine chromaffin granules has been extensively investigated, and has been summarized in a number of reviews (44, 67, 68). Chromaffin granules contain 550 mM catecholamine (72% epinephrine, 27% norepinephrine), 122 mM adenosine triphosphate (ATP), 17–30 mM Ca^{2+}, 5

175

0066-4278/86/0315-0175$02.00

mM Mg^{2+}, and 22 mM ascorbate (44, 52, 67). They also contain enkephalin and enkephalin precursors (58, 65), and a large amount of soluble acidic protein. Dopamine-β-hydroxylase is present in granules as soluble and membrane-bound forms that represent structurally distinct proteins (57).

Although the total concentration of soluble components is approximately 750 mM, the granule interior is iso-osmotic with 300 mOs solutions. Nuclear magnetic resonance (NMR) studies reveal that virtually 100% of the epinephrine and ATP within chromaffin granules is soluble, and such investigations provide evidence for interaction of these molecules (11, 12, 55, 60).

Osmotic pressure measurements of solutions of catecholamine and ATP demonstrate interactions between ATP and catecholamine (epinephrine or norepinephrine) (37, 59), the major osmotic components of the granule interior. For example, at 37°C the osmolality of a solution at pH 6.3 composed of 491 mM epinephrine and 165 mM ATP is 250 mOs (37). The non-ideal behavior of the solution is similar at pH 5.6 and 6.3. The epinephrine-ATP interactions are unaltered by KCl (150 mM), NaCl (150 mM), $MgCl_2$ (150 mM), $CaCl_2$ (90 mM), and EGTA (1 mM) (37). Thus, the low osmolality of the granule interior probably results from the natural interactions of catecholamine and ATP. Na/ATP solutions in the absence of catecholamine also deviate strongly from ideality. Proteins are not necessary for the non-ideal behavior. Consistent with the non-ideality of the solutions is the formation of multimolecular aggregates of catecholamine and ATP, detected by equilibrium centrifugation of solutions at 20°C at pH 6.5 (4). Adding Ca^{2+} to the solution or lowering its temperature increases the size of the aggregates. A phase separation occurs in the presence of Ca^{2+} at 6°C. Chromogranins, the intragranular acidic proteins, although not necessary for aggregate formation, interact with the aggregates at 10–34°C, pH 6.0 (3).

A feature of intact granules not explained by the above data is that intragranular Ca^{2+} is probably tightly bound since Ca^{2+} ionophore does not release Ca^{2+} from the granules (31).

OSMOTIC AND PERMEABILITY PROPERTIES OF CHROMAFFIN GRANULES

Characteristics of Chromaffin Granules In Vitro

Chromaffin granules are relatively impermeant to sucrose. Granules isolated in iso-osmotic sucrose solutions (approximately 300 mOs) at 0–4°C retain their contents for over 24 hr (22), and at 37°C release half of their contents in approximately 2 hr (42). Isolated granules are osmotically sensitive and release 70–90% of their catecholamine when the osmolality is lowered from 300 mOs to 200 mOs at 24–37°C (21, 42, 49) (see Figure 1).

Although chromaffin granules are stable in iso-osmotic sucrose solutions, they lyse rapidly in iso-osmotic solutions of the smaller nonelectrolytes erythri-

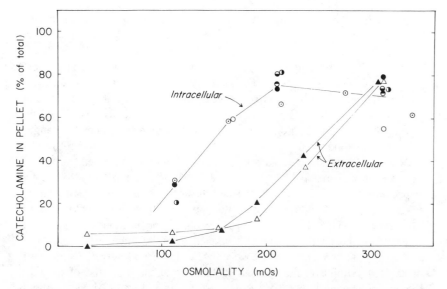

Figure 1 Comparison of the extracellular and intracellular osmotic stability of chromaffin granules. To determine their extracellular osmotic stability chromaffin granules were isolated from cultured chromaffin cells *(dark triangles)*, or from fresh bovine adrenal medulla *(open triangles)* in 260 mM sucrose, 1 mM EGTA, and 10 mM HEPES (pH 7.0) and 0.5 mM ascorbic acid (300 mOs), and were diluted into solutions containing various concentrations of potassium methylsulfate, 0.5 mM ascorbate, 1 mM EGTA, and 10 mM HEPES (pH 7.0) at 25°C. After 10 min the solutions were cooled to 0–4°C, and centrifuged at 35,000 *g* for 20 min. Catecholamine was determined in supernatant and pellet. Intracellular osmotic stability was determined by incubating cells in solutions of differing osmolalities and performing subcellular distributions at 300 mOs. The percentage of catecholamine that sedimented at 35,000 *g* after 20 min is plotted *(circles)*. Data from six experiments are presented and indicated by differently filled circles. The line is drawn through the average value of the percentages at each osmolality. (From Hampton & Holz, Reference 21)

tol ($t_{1/2}$ = 0.6 min), arabitol ($t_{1/2}$ = 4 min), and glucose ($t_{1/2}$ = 9.0 min) (49). Nonelectrolytes smaller than sucrose are, therefore, significantly more permeant than sucrose across the granule membrane.

Chromaffin granules shrink in hyperosmotic sucrose, KCl, or NaCl solutions. They behave as ideal osmometers between 300 and 1000 mOs with an osmotically insensitive space of 0.06 (62) to 0.3 (31, 43, 52) of the total volume. Similarly, chromaffin granule ghosts behave as ideal osmometers from 400 to 670 mOs in medium containing both sucrose and KCl (50).

Chromaffin granules are relatively stable in iso-osmotic KCl, NaCl, and choline chloride in the absence of MgATP (14, 22, 31, 41). When chromaffin granules are incubated in potassium salts, the potassium ionophore valinomycin induces granule lysis with release of granule contents occurring more rapidly in the order SCN⁻, I⁻, Br⁻ > Cl⁻ > acetate, F⁻, isethionate (14). Lysis probably results from the net uptake of potassium salt with transport limited by the intrinsic anion permeability of the granule membrane. Thus, the anion sequence of lysis probably represents the sequence of the anion permeability of the chromaffin granule membrane with SCN^- being more permeable than Cl^-. Valinomycin-induced lysis is not inhibited by SITS (4-acetamido-4'-isothiocyanostilibene-2,2'-disulfonic acid) or pyridoxal phosphate (47), both of which block the anion transport system of red blood cells. A similar anion permeability sequence of the granule membrane ($SCN^- >$ $I^- > Br^- > Cl^- > SO_4^{2-} > CH_3CO_2^- >$ phosphate) is determined by measuring swelling of chromaffin granule ghosts by optical density changes induced by valinomycin in solutions of various potassium salts[1] (50). The SCN^- and Cl^- conductances of the granule membrane calculated from these data are approximately 3×10^{-5} and 3×10^{-7} siemens (S) per cm^2, respectively[2]. The SCN^- conductance of the chromaffin granule membrane is equal to the SCN^- conductance of artificial phosphatidylcholine/chlorodecane bilayers in 0.05 M SCN^- (3×10^{-5} S/cm^2), and is higher than that of solvent-free phosphatidylcholine bilayers (1×10^{-6} S/cm^2) or phosphatidylcholine/decane bilayers (3×10^{-7} S/cm^2), which have lower dielectric constants (13). Similarly, the Cl^- conductance is at the high end of the Cl^- conductance range of 2×10^{-7} to 1×10^{-9} S/cm^2 of artificial phospholipid bilayer membranes of various compositions in the presence of 0.1 to 0.2 M Cl^- (46, 63). Thus, the SCN^- and Cl^- conductances of the chromaffin granule membrane may reflect the intrinsic anion conductances of the bilayer and not a specific anion transport system[3].

[1]Direct measurement of anion uptake also indicates that the chromaffin granule membrane is much less permeable to Cl^- than to SCN^-. The inside positive membrane potential induced by the electrogenic H^+ translocating ATPase of the granule membrane ($+50$ mV) causes a much slower $^{36}Cl^-$ than [^{14}C]SCN^- uptake into chromaffin granules in 320 mM sucrose, 10 mM K_2SO_4, and 10 mM sodium phosphate (pH 7.0) at 31°C (R. W. Holz, unpublished observations). The $^{36}Cl^-$ concentration ratio (inside/outside) increases slowly in the presence of 5 mM MgATP from 0.5 to 1.1 over 1 hr without reaching steady state in the presence of 0.4 or 2.0 mM Cl^-. The [^{14}C]SCN^- concentration ratio increases from 0.8 to a steady state of 8.0 within 15 min. Pazoles & Pollard (48) found that 1 mM MgATP induces an increase in the $^{36}Cl^-$ concentration ratio (inside/out) from 1.83 to 5.92 in 15 min in sucrose medium containing 5.7 mM Cl^- at pH 6.0 at 37°C. The larger uptake of $^{36}Cl^-$ in this experiment may be due to the lower medium pH. SCN^- uptake was not measured at pH 6.0.

[2]Valinomycin-dependent swelling of chromaffin granule ghosts in 0.05 M KSCN was $1/e$ of steady state in 26 sec (50). Conductance was calculated using a ghost diameter of 0.2 μm, assuming the independence of ion movement (23) and ignoring the effects of membrane potential (which probably decays rapidly). Because the initial rate of valinomycin-induced swelling in 0.05 M KCl was approximately 1/100th that in 0.05 M KSCN, the Cl^- conductance was estimated to be 1/100th of the SCN^- conductance.

[3]In contrast, if an anion-selective channel of 1 pS (a very low channel conductance) were in the membrane of a chromaffin granule of 0.2 μm diameter, then the specific conductance would be 1×10^{-3} S/cm^2. Even if this channel were open for only 1% of the time, the time-averaged conductance of the granule membrane would be 1×10^{-5} S/cm^2, which is 100 times the estimated chloride conductance. It is unlikely that a channel with these characteristics exists in the chromaffin granule membrane.

The granule membrane has much lower permeabilities to K^+, Na^+, and choline than to Cl^- (31, 50). The H^+ conductance of the membrane is also very low (31). There is evidence for a Ca^{2+}-Na^+ antiport system in the chromaffin granule membrane (38–40, 51), for Mg^{2+} transport coupled to an inside negative electrical potential (19), and for Mn^{2+} permeability (11; P. S. Yoon, R. R. Sharp, personal communication). The functional significance of divalent ion transport in chromaffin granules is unknown.

The water permeability of the chromaffin granule membrane measured by NMR spin lattice relaxation is 0.37–0.53×10^{-3} cm/sec at 25°C (61), which is within the range for artificial phospholipid bilayers of 0.8–3.0×10^{-3} cm/sec (20). It is likely that water crosses the chromaffin granule membrane by a solubility-diffusion mechanism, as in artificial bilayers, and not through aqueous channels.

Characteristics of Chromaffin Granules Within Cells

Chromaffin granules within cells are more stable than isolated granules (Figure 1). Monolayer chromaffin cells equilibrated at 165 mOs swell but do not lyse (21). Osmolality must be reduced to below 165 mOs to cause significant lysis of intracellular chromaffin granules, whereas isolated granules lyse virtually completely at this osmolality. The osmotic stability of intracellular chromaffin granules in chromaffin cells with plasma membranes permeabilized by intense electric fields (34) or by the detergent digitonin (26) is similar to that in nonpermeabilized cells.

Because it is unlikely that significant pressure differences can be tolerated across membranes of intracellular organelles, a likely explanation for the osmotic stability of intracellular granules is that they are not spherical (5) and can swell without lysis. Isolated granules may contain increased osmotic equivalents as a result of isolation, which would make them almost spherical. They would be subject to lysis with even small increases in volume. Because an approximately 50% reduction of the osmolality is necessary before significant lysis of intracellular chromaffin granules occurs, the intragranular water space probably doubles before the granule membrane is under osmotic stress. If osmotic stress of the granules occurs during exocytosis, then the amount of osmotically active solutes within a granule undergoing exocytosis must at least double.

MgATP, Cl^--DEPENDENT LYSIS OF CHROMAFFIN GRANULES AND THE H^+ ELECTROCHEMICAL GRADIENT ACROSS CHROMAFFIN GRANULE MEMBRANES

Relationship of MgATP, Cl^--Dependent Lysis to Chemiosmotic Processes

Oka and colleagues (45) discovered that chromaffin granules that are stable in sucrose solutions containing MgATP release catecholamine in solutions containing chloride salts and MgATP. Although chromaffin granules contain large amounts of ATP, extragranular ATP is required for the effect. Subsequent studies demonstrated that catecholamine release occurs because of granule lysis (53) and is caused by (at least) Br^- or I^- as well as by Cl^- (47, 54). Acetate (41), phosphate (41, 47), sulfate (47), and isethionate (47) do not cause significant lysis in the presence of MgATP. Thus, Cl^- and anions more permeant than Cl^- across the granule membrane (and not excluded by the low intragranular pH) cause significant lysis in the presence of MgATP.

MgATP, Cl^--dependent lysis is a reflection of chemiosmotic processes in chromaffin granules (see Rudnick, this volume). The intragranular pH of isolated chromaffin granules is 5.6–5.8 when the extragranular pH is approximately 7 (9, 25, 30, 31, 55). In the presence of MgATP and a permeant anion, such as Cl^-, there is a further acidification of the granule interior because of cotransport of H^+ and Cl^- by an electrogenic H^+ translocating ATPase in the granule membrane (8, 9, 48). Cl^- uptake is driven by the inside positive potential induced by the H^+ translocating ATPase. Accompanying water influx causes lysis (8).

Relationship of MgATP, Cl^--Dependent Lysis to Exocytosis

It has been suggested by Pollard and colleagues (48, 54) that during exocytosis extracellular Cl^- is driven into chromaffin granules at the attachment site of the granule to the plasma membrane by the inside positive granule potential that is generated by the H^+ translocating ATPase of the granule membrane. Osmotic stress generated by the accompanying influx of water causes lysis of the granules with extracellular release of their contents. This hypothesis is probably incorrect because: (*a*) Exocytosis from intact chromaffin cells or from closely related pheochromocytoma cells occurs in the absence of anions that are permeant across the granule membrane (16, 18, 32). (*b*) Secretion from chromaffin cells rendered leaky by intense electric fields or by digitonin is maximal in the virtual absence of anions that are permeant across the granule membrane (26, 34). (*c*) Granules *within* digitonin-permeabilized chromaffin cells do not lyse in 140 mM KCl in the presence of 1 mM MgATP, probably because they are more stable osmotically than isolated granules (26). (*d*) The H^+ electrochemical gradient across the chromaffin granule membrane is probably not important in exocytosis (see below). A more extensive critique of these issues by Baker & Knight (2) leads to a similar conclusion.

H^+ Electrochemical Gradient Across the Chromaffin Granule Membrane and Exocytosis

Although MgATP, Cl^--dependent granule lysis probably does not play a role in exocytosis, it is still possible that the chemiosmotic processes of the chromaffin granule are involved in exocytosis. This possibility is attractive since a common feature of many secretory granules is their low internal pH and a membrane-bound, electrogenic H^+ translocating ATPase (see Rudnick, this volume). However, there is compelling evidence from experiments with intact cells (29) and with cells permeabilized by intense electric fields (35) that the H^+ electrochemical gradient across the chromaffin granule membrane does not play an important role in exocytosis. Secretion is not significantly altered when either the pH gradient or the electrical potential across the granule membrane is reduced, or when the H^+ translocating ATPase is inhibited. The recent finding that isolated rat parotid secretory granules have an intragranular pH of 6.8 (1) supports the conclusion that a H^+ concentration gradient across the secretory granule membrane is not necessarily involved in exocytosis.

EFFECTS OF CHANGES IN MEDIUM OSMOLALITY ON SECRETION FROM INTACT CHROMAFFIN CELLS

If osmotic stress on the chromaffin granule membrane is the driving force for fusion of the granule with the plasma membrane during exocytosis, then increasing the osmolality of the extracellular medium should cause water to leave the cells and the intracellular chromaffin granules. Sufficiently shrunken granules should not undergo exocytosis. Indeed, hyperosmotic solutions shrink chromaffin cells in monolayer culture and inhibit nicotinic agonist-induced (Figure 2) and depolarization (elevated K^+)-induced catecholamine secretion (21). The inhibition is reversible, and occurs at a step after Ca^{2+} entry into the cells. Solutions made hyperosmotic with raffinose or NaCl also inhibit secretion. Secretogogue-induced secretion from both monolayer cells (Figure 2) and from suspended cells (54) is half-maximally inhibited when the osmolality is raised from 300 mOs to 400–500 mOs with sucrose or salts. Hyperosmotic solutions inhibit secretagogue-induced hormone release from pheochromocytoma cells (18), parathyroid cells (7), and platelets (56).

If osmotic stress on the chromaffin granule is the driving force for exocytosis, then lowering the osmolality might enhance exocytosis. Although 15% of the total catecholamine is released into the medium when the osmolality is halved (in the absence of secretagogue), the release is not exocytotic (21). Nicotinic agonist-induced secretion is not enhanced by hypo-osmotic solutions (R. W. Holz, unpublished observations).

If a decrease in osmotic stability occurs in a large fraction of chromaffin granules in cells undergoing secretion, then greater intracellular granule lysis should be detectable in hypo-osmotic solution in secreting cells than in nonsecreting cells. However, increased intracellular lysis of chromaffin granules is not observed in cells equilibrated with 165 mOs solution and stimulated to secrete by either carbachol or Ba^{2+} (21). Thus, if there are osmotic changes

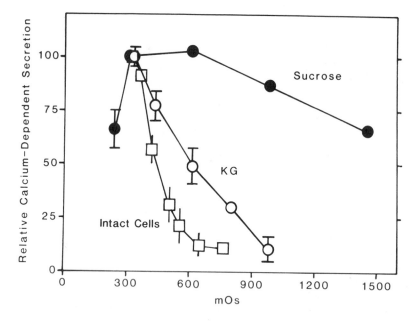

Figure 2   Effects of elevated osmolality on nicotinic agonist-induced secretion from intact cells, and on Ca^{2+}-dependent secretion from digitonin-permeabilized cells. Intact chromaffin cells *(open boxes)* were incubated in physiological salt solution (PSS) containing various amounts of sucrose to increase the osmolality. After 12 min these solutions were replaced by solutions at the same osmolality with or without 10 μM DMPP, a nicotinic agonist. The amount of catecholamine released into the medium was determined after 12 min. Data are expressed as DMPP-induced catecholamine release, which in other experiments was shown to be Ca^{2+}-dependent. Cells were permeabilized with 139 mM potassium glutamate, 20 mM PIPES (pH 6.6), 5 mM EGTA, 1 mM MgATP, and 20 μM digitonin for 5 minutes. In the potassium glutamate experiment (KG, *open circles*) the digitonin-containing solution was replaced with solution containing 20 mM PIPES (pH 6.6), 5 mM EGTA, 1 mM MgATP, and various concentrations of potassium glutamate. After 8 min the solution was replaced with the same composition solution ± 10 μM free Ca^{2+}. Ca^{2+}-dependent secretion was determined after 15 min. In the sucrose experiment *(filled circles)* the digitonin-containing solution was replaced with 20 mM PIPES (pH 6.6), 1 mM MgATP, ± 10 μM Ca^{2+}, and various concentrations of sucrose. Ca^{2+}-dependent secretion was determined after 15 min. The experiments were performed on different preparations of cells. There were four samples per group. (Adapted from References 21 and 27).

in chromaffin granules during secretion, they probably occur in a small proportion of the granules undergoing exocytosis.

The data concerning the effects of hyperosmotic solutions on secretion from intact chromaffin cells are consistent with osmotic stress of the secretory granule playing a role in exocytosis. However, hyperosmotic solutions might inhibit secretion because of effects on the cells other than shrinkage of intracellular chromaffin granules as discussed below.

EFFECTS OF CHANGES IN MEDIUM OSMOLALITY ON SECRETION FROM CHROMAFFIN CELLS WITH LEAKY PLASMA MEMBRANES

Two types of techniques have been developed to permeabilize the plasma membrane of chromaffin cells to constituents of the extracellular medium while still maintaining the ability of the cells to undergo exocytosis: dielectric breakdown induced by intense electric fields (34) and brief treatment of cells with low concentrations of the detergents digitonin (17, 66) or saponin (6). In these preparations, micromolar Ca^{2+} in the presence of ATP stimulates secretion in the absence of nicotinic stimulation. Permeabilized cells allow the investigation of effects of hyperosmotic solutions on secretion while minimizing cell shrinkage, increases in intracellular ionic strength, and changes in spatial relationships between granules and plasma membrane, which confound interpretation of intact cell experiments.

Knight & Baker (34) investigated the effects of solutions made hyperosmotic with sucrose on secretion from cells permeabilized by dielectric breakdown. The plasma membrane of these cells is relatively permeant to low molecular weight species, but is virtually impermeant to lactate dehydrogenase (134,000 daltons). Secretion stimulated by 10 μM Ca^{2+} was inhibited as the osmolality was raised from 300 mOs, with half-maximal inhibition occurring at 700 mOs, and virtually complete inhibition occurring at 1000 mOs. In these experiments the permeabilized cells were incubated for 5 min with solutions containing different concentrations of sucrose before they were challenged with 10 μM Ca^{2+} for 20 min. It is likely that the cells were shrunken since sucrose is probably less permeant than 3-O-methylglucose, which has a $t_{1/2}$ for exit from the cells of 20 min. It is therefore possible that all or part of the inhibition was caused by effects related to cell shrinkage, but not necessarily to shrinkage of the intracellular chromaffin granules.

Monolayer cells treated with low concentrations of digitonin, which interacts with membrane cholesterol, are much leakier than suspended cells subjected to intense electric fields. Lactate dehydrogenase exits from the cells with a $t_{1/2}$ of 10–15 min (17). Membrane permeability assessed by osmotic shrinkage of the cells in hyperosmotic solutions indicates that potassium glutamate and sucrose equilibrate across the plasma membrane of digitonin-treated cells within 2 min, and tetrasaccharides such as stachyose do so within 6–10 min (26). Secretion stimulated by 10 μ M Ca^{2+} from digitonin-treated cells occurs to a similar extent in 300 mOs solutions of potassium glutamate or sucrose. When the osmolality is raised in solutions in which sucrose is the main osmotic constituent there is little inhibition of secretion until osmolalities greater than 1000 mOs are attained (27). Half-maximal inhibition of secretion does not occur until greater than 1500 mOs (Figure 2). Similar results are obtained when sucrose is added to 300 mOs potassium glutamate solution with half-maximal inhibition occurring at 1200 mOs. These data contrast with those from suspended chromaffin cells subjected to intense electric fields, in which secretion is inhibited 50% at 700 mOs in solutions containing potassium glutamate and sucrose (34). The inability of solutions made hyperosmotic with sucrose to inhibit secretion from digitonin-treated cells at less than 1000 mOs may reflect the absence of cell shrinkage in the digitonin-treated cells.

Potassium glutamate solutions made hyperosmotic with the larger carbohydrates stachyose (a tetrasaccharide) or a low molecular weight fraction of maltodextrin (average size a tetrasaccharide) cause one-half maximal inhibition at 900–1000 mOs under conditions in which the cells do not shrink. Prior treatment of permeabilized chromaffin cells with Ca^{2+} in hyperosmotic solutions (containing stachyose) in which secretion was inhibited did not result in enhanced secretion when cells were restored to normal osmolality (27). Significant inhibition of secretion from digitonin-treated cells caused by sucrose, stachyose, and maltodextrin requires large amounts of carbohydrate (approximately 0.3 g/ml for half-maximal inhibition) (27). Although it is possible that the inhibition of secretion results from elevated osmolality, it is also possible that the inhibition results from a pharmacological effect of the carbohydrates on secretion that is independent of their molecular weights or medium osmolality.

Chromaffin granules are relatively impermeant to sucrose (see above) and larger carbohydrates[4]. The inability of solutions made hyperosmotic with carbohydrates to inhibit secretion from digitonin-treated cells until very high osmolalities are attained indicates that *severely shrunken chromaffin granules can undergo secretion.*

If osmotic stress of the granules is a driving force in exocytosis, then lowering the osmolality might enhance secretion. However, Ca^{2+}-dependent secretion from suspended cells subjected to intense electric fields (34) or from digitonin-treated monolayer cells (Figure 2) is inhibited 20–30% rather than enhanced when the osmolality is reduced from 300 mOs to 200–250 mOs.

Secretagogue-induced secretion from intact cells is inhibited 50% when the osmolality of the medium is raised from 300 mOs to 400–500 mOs with

---

[4]The osmotic behavior of intracellular chromaffin granules indicates that they are relatively impermeant to sucrose, stachyose, or a low molecular weight fraction of maltodextrin (average size a tetrasaccharide). Digitonin-treated cells were incubated for 15 min at 25°C in 140 mM potassium glutamate solution containing sucrose, stachyose, or the maltodextrin fraction to increase the osmolality to 1000–1200 mOs. Replacement of the solutions with 140 mM potassium glutamate solution without carbohydrate (300 mOs) released only 7–8% of the total catecholamine from the intracellular chromaffin granules (R. W. Holz, R. A. Senter, unpublished observations). Because the small amount of release was independent of the size of the carbohydrate, it may not have resulted from carbohydrate transport into the granules.

carbohydrate or salt (21, 54). The high sensitivity of secretion from intact cells to increased osmolality contrasts with the virtual absence of effects on secretion from nonshrunken, digitonin-treated cells in hyperosmotic sucrose solutions until much higher osmolalities are attained (Figure 2). Thus, the inhibition of secretion from intact cells by hyperosmotic solutions is probably not caused by shrinkage of the chromaffin granules. One possible cause of the inhibition of secretion from intact cells is the increased ionic strength that is likely to occur when water leaves the cells. Secretion from digitonin-treated cells is sensitive to increased ionic strength, with half-maximal inhibition occurring when the ionic strength is doubled in potassium glutamate (Figure 2, *open circles*) or sodium isethionate (27) solutions. The inhibition also occurs in solutions of increased ionic strength when the osmolality is maintained at 1000 mOs by sucrose. Increased ionic strength does not alter the Ca^{2+} sensitivity of secretion from digitonin-treated cells (27). The experiments suggest that *in intact cells it is probably the increased intracellular ionic strength, rather than granule shrinkage, that contributes to the inhibition of exocytosis by hyperosmotic solutions.* In intact cells if the ionic strength doubles when the water space is halved, then a doubling of the osmolality from 300 to 600 mOs should cause an approximately 50% inhibition of secretion. Secretagogue-induced secretion was inhibited 80–90% by this increase in osmolality (Figure 2) (21, 54). It is, therefore, possible that factors in addition to increased ionic strength (but probably not including osmotic effects on the granules) contribute to the inhibition of secretion from intact cells by hyperosmotic solutions.

If the inhibition of secretion from digitonin-treated cells by large amounts of carbohydrates is caused by osmotic effects, then a mechanism must exist to increase the osmotic equivalents within chromaffin granules sufficiently to cause water influx and granule lysis in solutions of 1000 mOs or greater. Intracellular chromaffin granules are stable at 300 mOs (physiological osmolality). Because inhibition of the lytic effects of a hypothetical increase in intragranular solutes requires solutions of approximately 1000 mOs, there would have to be at least a tripling of osmotic equivalents in granules undergoing exocytosis. In addition, lysis of granules within cells probably requires an approximate doubling of the osmotically active water space, which would necessitate a sixfold increase in osmotic equivalents within intracellular granules undergoing exocytosis.

It is unlikely that decreased solute interactions within chromaffin granules could account for the necessary increase in osmotic equivalents. As discussed above, the granule interior is an extremely non-ideal solution because of interactions between the major osmotic constituents, epinephrine and ATP. The solute interactions are relatively insensitive to changes in pH, divalent ions, NaCl, or KCl. Substitution of Na^+ for catecholamine still results in a very non-ideal solution (37, 59). Physiologically relevent ways of significantly decreasing the non-ideal behavior are unknown. Activation of a pump in the granule membrane that can concentrate solutes within the granule is also an unlikely mechanism to increase the number of osmotically active solutes. H^+, Cl^- cotransport cannot account for the necessary influx (see above). There is no known active transport system in the granule membrane that could cause the necessary large and rapid influx of solutes.

One mechanism which could cause the necessary increase in osmotic equivalents is a permeability increase of the granule membrane to extracellular components at the fusion site with the plasma membrane (or to cytosolic components at non-fusion sites) without a permeability increase to intragranular contents. Because granules would never reach osmotic equilibrium, they would lyse (See Reference 10 for an example of this phenomenon in artificial vesicles.) Inhibition by large amounts of carbohydrate of the rate and maximum degree of secretion from digitonin-permeabilized cells would occur if the extragranular osmoticant equilibrates slowly relative to the lifetime of the permeability change. At present, there is no direct evidence for such a permeability change.

CONCLUSION

In spite of a considerable amount of investigation, it is still uncertain whether osmotic stress on the chromaffin granule is the driving force in the fusion of the granule membrane with the plasma membrane in exocytosis. The relative insensitivity of secretion from digitonin-permeabilized cells to solutions made hyperosmotic with carbohydrate, the inability of hypo-osmotic solutions to enhance secretion from intact or permeabilized cells, and the inability to detect a decrease in osmotic stability of intracellular granules during exocytosis are, in fact, consistent with osmotic stress of the granule not playing a role in exocytosis. Because the data are inconclusive, a role of osmotic forces in exocytosis from adrenal chromaffin cells warrants further consideration.

ACKNOWLEDGMENT

I thank Drs. Joshua Zimmerberg and Alan Finkelstein for many helpful discussions concerning possible osmotic effects in secretion from chromaffin cells. This work was supported by U.S. Public Health Service grant RO-1 AM27959 and NSF grant BNS 8211493. RWH is an Established Investigator of the American Heart Association.

Literature Cited

1. Arvan, P., Rudnick, G., Castle, J. D. 1984. Osmotic properties and internal pH of isolated rat parotid secretory granules. *J. Biol. Chem.* 259:13567–72
2. Baker, P. F., Knight, D. E. 1984. Chemosmotic hypothesis of exocytosis: A critique. *Biosci. Rep.* 4:285–98
3. Berneis, K. H., Goetz, U., DaPrada, M., Pletscher, A. 1973. Interaction of aggregated catecholamine and nucleotides with intragranular proteins. *Naunyn-Schmiedeberg's Arch. Pharmacol.* 277:291–96
4. Berneis, K. H., Pletscher, H., DaPrada, M. 1970. Phase separation in solutions of noradrenaline and adenosine triphosphate: Influence of bivalent cations and drugs. *Br. J. Pharmacol.* 39:382–89
5. Bloom, F. E. 1972. Electron microscopy of catecholamine-containing structures. In *Catecholamines*, ed. H. Blaschko, E. Muscholl, pp. 46–78. New York: Springer-Verlag
6. Brooks, J. C., Treml, S. 1983. Catecholamine secretion by chemically skinned cultured chromaffin cells. *J. Neurochem.* 40:468–73
7. Brown, W. M., Pazoles, C. J., Creutz, C. E., Aurbach, D., Pollard, H. B. 1978. Role of anions on parathyroid hormone release from dispersed bovine parathyroid cells. *Proc. Natl. Acad. Sci. USA* 75:876–80
8. Casey, R. P., Njus, D., Radda, G. K., Sehr, P. A. 1976. Adenosine triphosphate-evoked catecholamine release in chromaffin granules, osmotic lysis as a consequence of proton translocation. *Biochem. J.* 158:583–88
9. Casey, R. P., Njus, D., Radda, G. K., Sehr, P. A. 1977. Active proton uptake by chromaffin granules: Observation by amine distribution and phosphorus-31 nuclear magnetic resonance techniques. *Biochemistry* 16:972–77
10. Cohen, F. S., Akabas, M. H., Finkelstein, A. 1982. Osmotic swelling of phospholipid vesicles causes them to fuse with a planar phospholipid bilayer membrane. *Science* 217:458–60
11. Daniels, A. J., Korda, A., Tanswell, P., Williams, A., Williams, R. J. P. 1974. The internal structure of the chromaffin granule. *Proc. R. Soc. London Ser. B* 187:353–61
12. Daniels, A. J., Williams, R. J. P., Wright, P. E. 1978. The character of the stored molecules in the chromaffin granules of the adrenal medulla: A nuclear magnetic resonance study. *Neuroscience* 3:573–85

13. Digler, J. P., McLaughlin, S. G. A., McIntosh, T. J., Simon, S. A. 1979. The dielectric constant of phospholipid bilayers and the permeability of membranes to ions. *Science* 206:1196–98
14. Dolais-Kitabgi, J., Perlman, R. L. 1975. The stimulation of catecholamine release from chromaffin granules by valinomycin. *Mol. Pharmacol.* 11:745–50
15. Douglas, W. W. 1975. Secretory control of adrenal medullary secretion: membrane and ionic events in stimulus-secretion coupling, in *Handbook of Physiology: Endocrinology*, Sect. 7, ed. H. Blaschko, G. Sayers, A. D. Smith, 6:367–88. Washington DC: Am. Physiol. Soc.
16. Douglas, W. W., Rubin, R. P. 1963. The mechanism of catecholamine release from adrenal medulla and the role of calcium in stimulus-secretion coupling. *J. Physiol.* 167:288–310
17. Dunn, L. A., Holz, R. W. 1983. Catecholamine secretion from digitonin-treated adrenal medullary chromaffin cells. *J. Biol. Chem.* 258:4989–93
18. Englert, D. F., Perlman, R. L. 1981. Permeant anions are not required for norepinephrine secretion from pheochromocytoma cells. *Biochim. Biophys. Acta* 674:136–43
19. Fiedler, J., Daniels, A. J. 1984. Uptake of magnesium by chromaffin granules *in vitro*: Role of the proton electrochemical gradient. *J. Neurochem.* 42:1291–97
20. Finkelstein, A. 1976. Water and nonelectrolyte permeability of lipid bilayer membranes. *J. Gen. Physiol.* 68:127–35
21. Hampton, R. Y., Holz, R. W. 1983. The effects of osmolality on the stability and function of cultured chromaffin cells and the role of osmotic forces in exocytosis. *J. Cell Biol.* 96:1082–88
22. Hillarp, N.-A., Nilson, B. 1954. The structure of the adrenaline and noradrenaline containing granules in the adrenal medullary cells with reference to the storage and release of the sympathomimetic amines. *Acta Physiol. Scand.* 31:113:79–107 (Suppl.)
23. Hodgkin, A. L., Huxley, A. F. 1952. Currents carried by sodium and potassium ions through the membrane of the giant axon of *Loligo. J. Physiol.* 116:449–72
24. Hoffman, P. G., Zinder, O., Bonner, W. M., Pollard, H. B. 1976. Role of ATP and β-γ-aminoadenosinetriphosphate in the stimulation of epinephrine and protein release from isolated adrenal secre-

tory vesicles. *Arch. Biochem. Biophys.* 176:375–88

25. Holz, R. W. 1978. Evidence that catecholamine transport into chromaffin vesicles is coupled to vesicle membrane potential. *Proc. Natl. Acad. Sci. USA* 75:5190–94

26. Holz, R. W., Senter, R. A. 1985. Plasma membrane and chromaffin granule characteristics in digitonin-treated cells. *J. Neurochem.* 45:1548–57

27. Holz, R. W., Senter, R. A. 1986. The effects of osmolality and ionic strength on secretion from adrenal chromaffin cells permeabilized with digitonin. *J. Neurochem.* 46: In press

28. Holz, R. W., Senter, R. A., Frye, R. A. 1982. Relationship between Ca^{2+} uptake and catecholamine secretion in primary dissociated cultures of adrenal medulla. *J. Neurochem.* 39:635–46

29. Holz, R. W., Senter, R. A., Sharp, P. R. 1983. Evidence that the H^+ electrochemical gradient across membranes of chromaffin granules is not involved in exocytosis. *J. Biol. Chem.* 258:7506–13

30. Johnson, R. G., Scarpa, A. 1976. Internal pH of isolated chromaffin granules. *J. Biol. Chem.* 251:2189–91

31. Johnson, R. G., Scarpa, A. 1976. Ion permeability of isolated chromaffin granules. *J. Gen. Physiol.* 68:601–31

32. Kilpatrick, D. L., Slepetis, R., Kirshner, N. 1981. Ion channels and membrane potential in stimulus-secretion coupling in adrenal medulla cells. *J. Neurochem.* 36:1245–55

33. Kilpatrick, D. L., Slepetis, R. J., Corcoran, J. J., Kirshner, N. 1982. Calcium uptake and catecholamine secretion by cultured bovine adrenal cells. *J. Neurochem.* 38:427–35

34. Knight, D. E., Baker, P. F. 1982. Calcium-dependence of catecholamine release from bovine adrenal medullary cells after exposure to intense electric fields. *Membr. Biol.* 68:107–40

35. Knight, D. E., Baker, P. F. 1985. The chromaffin granule proton pump and calcium-dependent exocytosis in bovine adrenal medullary cells. *J. Membr. Biol.* 83:147–56

36. Knight, D. E., Kesteven, N. T. 1983. Evoked transient intracellular free Ca^{2+} changes and secretion in isolated adrenal medullary cells. *Proc. R. Soc. London Ser. B* 218:177–99

37. Kopell, W. N., Westhead, E. W. 1982. Osmotic pressures of ATP and catecholamines relating to storage in chromaffin granules. *J. Biol. Chem.* 257:5707–10

38. Kostron, H., Winkler, H., Geissler, D., Konig, P. 1977. Uptake of calcium by

chromaffin granules *in vitro. J. Neurochem.* 28:487–93

39. Krieger-Brauer, H., Gratzl, M. 1982. Uptake of Ca^{2+} by isolated secretory vesicles from adrenal medulla. *Biochim. Biophys. Acta.* 691:61–70

40. Krieger-Brauer, H. I., Gratzl, M. 1983. Effects of monovalent and divalent cations on Ca^{2+} fluxes across chromaffin secretory membrane vesicles. *J. Neurochem.* 41:1269–76

41. Lishajko, F. 1969. Influence of chloride ions and ATP-Mg^{++} on the release of catecholamine from isolated adrenal medullary granules. *Acta Physiol. Scand.* 75:255–56

42. Lishajko, F. 1970. Osmotic factors determining the release of catecholamines from isolated chromaffin granules. *Acta Physiol. Scand.* 79:64–75

43. Morris, S. J., Schovanka, T. 1977. Some physical properties of adrenal medulla chromaffin granules isolated by a new continuous iso-osmotic density gradient method. *Biochim. Biophys. Acta* 464:53–64

44. Njus, D., Knoth, J., Zallakian, M. 1981. Proton-linked transport in chromaffin granules. *Curr. Top. Bioenerg.* 11:107–47

45. Oka, M., Ohuchi, T., Yoshida, H., Imaizumi, R. 1965. Effect of adenosine triphosphate and magnesium on the release of catecholamine from adrenal medullary granules. *Biochim. Biophys. Acta* 97:170–71

46. Pagano, R., Thompson, T. E. 1968. Spherical lipid bilayer membranes: Electrical and isotopic studies of ion permeability. *J. Mol. Biol.* 38:41–57

47. Pazoles, C. J., Creutz, C. E., Ramu, A., Pollard, H. B. 1980. Permeant anion activation of MgATPase activity in chromaffin granules. *J. Biol. Chem.* 255:7863–69

48. Pazoles, C. J., Pollard, H. B. 1978. Evidence for stimulation of anion transport in ATP-evoked transmitter release from isolated secretory vesicles. *J. Biol. Chem.* 253:3962–69

49. Perlman, R. L. 1976. The permeability of chromaffin granules to nonelectrolytes. *Biochem. Pharmacol.* 25:1035–38

50. Phillips, J. H. 1977. Passive ion permeability of the chromaffin granule membrane. *Biochem. J.* 168:289–97

51. Phillips, J. H. 1981. Transport of Ca^{2+} and Na^{2+} across the chromaffin granule membrane. *Biochem. J.* 200:99–107

52. Phillips, J. H., Allison, Y. P., Morris, S. J. 1977. The distribution of calcium, magnesium, copper and iron in the

bovine adrenal medulla. *Neuroscience* 2:147–52

53. Poisner, A. M., Trifaro, J. M. 1967. The role of ATP and ATPase in the release of catecholamines from adrenal medulla. I. ATP-evoked release of catecholamine, ATP, and protein from isolated chromaffin granules. *Mol. Pharmacol.* 3:561–71

54. Pollard, H. B., Pazoles, C. J., Creutz, C. E., Scott, J. H., Zinder, O., Hotchkiss, A. 1984. An osmotic mechanism for exocytosis from dissociated chromaffin cells. *J. Biol. Chem.* 259:1114–21

55. Pollard, H. B., Shindo, H., Creutz, C. E., Pazoles, C. J., Cohen, J. S. 1979. Internal pH and state of ATP in adrenergic chromaffin granules determined by ^{31}P nuclear magnetic resonance spectroscopy. *J. Biol. Chem.* 254:1170–77

56. Pollard, H. B., Tack-Goldman, K., Pazoles, C. J., Creutz, C. E., Shulman, N. R. 1977. Evidence for control of serotonin secretion from human platelets by hydroxyl ion transport and osmotic lysis. *Proc. Natl. Acad. Sci. USA* 74:5295–99

57. Saxena, A., Fleming, P. J. 1983. Isolation and reconstitution of the membrane-bound form of dopamine-β-hydroxylase. *J. Biol. Chem.* 258:4147–52

58. Schultzberg, M., Lundberg, J. M., Hokfelt, T., Terenius, L., Brandt, J., et al. 1978. Enkephalin-like immunoreactivity in gland cells and nerve terminals of the adrenal medulla. *Neuroscience* 3:1169–86

59. Sen, R., Sharp, R. R. 1982. Molecular mobilities and the lowered osmolality of the chromaffin granule aqueous phase. *Biochim. Biophys. Acta* 74:70–82

60. Sen, R., Sharp, R. R., Domino, L. E., Domino, E. F. 1979. Composition of the aqueous phase of chromaffin granules. *Biochim. Biophys. Acta* 587:75–88

61. Sharp, R. R., Sen, R. 1982. Water permeability of the chromaffin granule membrane. *Biophys. J.* 40:17–25

62. Sudhof, T. C. 1982. Core structure, internal osmotic pressure and irreversible structural changes of chromaffin granules during osmometer behavior. *Biochim. Biophys. Acta* 684:27–39

63. Toyoshima, Y., Thompson, T. E. 1975. Chloride flux in bilayer membranes: The electrically silent chloride flux in semispherical bilayers. *Biochemistry* 14:1518–24

64. Viveros, O. H. 1975. Mechanism of secretion of catecholamines from adrenal medulla. See Reference 15, pp. 389–426

65. Viveros, O. H., Diliberto, E. J., Hazum, E., Chang, K-G. 1979. Opiate-like materials in the adrenal medulla: evidence for storage and secretion with catecholamines. *Mol. Pharmacol.* 16:1101–8

66. Wilson, S. P., Kirshner, N. 1983. Calcium-evoked secretion from digitonin-permeabilized adrenal medullary chromaffin cells. *J. Biol. Chem.* 258:4994–5000

67. Winkler, H. 1976. Composition of adrenal chromaffin granules: An assessment of controversial results. *Neuroscience* 1:65–80

68. Winkler, H., Westhead, E. 1980. The molecular organization of adrenal chromaffin granules. *Neuroscience* 5:1803–23

Ann. Rev. Physiol. 1986. 48:191–200

ELECTRICAL REGULATION OF SPERM-EGG FUSION

Laurinda A. Jaffe

Department of Physiology, University of Connecticut Health Center, Farmington, Connecticut 06032

Nicholas L. Cross

Division of Reproductive Biology and Medicine, Department of Obstetrics and Gynecology, University of California, Davis, California 95616

In this chapter we will describe the control of membrane fusion by membrane potential, a property of the fusion between sperm and egg membranes in a variety of species. Voltage-dependent fusion provides a fast electrical block to polyspermy; the fertilizing sperm causes the egg's membrane potential to change to a level that prevents fusion of additional sperm. We begin with a general description of the membrane fusion between sperm and eggs. We then summarize the evidence that in some, but not all, species this fusion is regulated by membrane potential, and we describe what is known about the mechanism of the voltage dependence.

MEMBRANE FUSION BETWEEN SPERM AND EGGS

In all species of animals and plants, sperm and egg plasma membranes fuse at fertilization, creating a bridge of cytoplasm through which the sperm nucleus enters the egg. Figure 1 illustrates this process in the marine worm *Saccoglossus,* from an early description by Colwin & Colwin (see 7 for a review). In electron micrographs, sperm-egg fusion has been seen in annelid and hemichordate eggs fixed 7–9 sec after insemination (see 7), and in sea urchin eggs fixed 20 sec after insemination (11). It is possible that fusion occurred earlier but was not detected.

191

0066-4278/86/0315-0191$02.00

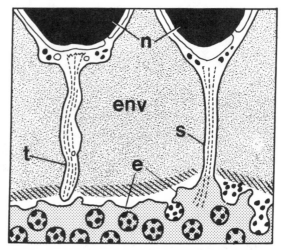

Figure 1   Fusion of sperm and egg plasma membranes in the hemichordate, *Saccoglossus*. *Left:* Anterior region of a sperm penetrating the egg's extracellular envelope *(env)*. The sperm's acrosomal tubule *(t)* approaches the egg plasma membrane *(e)*. *Right:* Fusion of the plasma membranes of the sperm *(s)* and egg *(e)* results in a mosaic membrane and creates a bridge through which the sperm nucleus *(n)* will enter the egg. (Redrawn from Reference 7 with permission of Academic Press).

In what ways are egg and sperm plasma membranes specialized for fusion? In many species, sperm can fuse at any point on the egg surface. In other species, such as frog, mouse, and jellyfish, the fusogenic region may be localized to a particular area (10, 12, 27). However, the differences between fusogenic and nonfusogenic regions are unknown. Although egg factors involved in sperm-egg recognition have been described (e.g. 1, 2, 14), no egg plasma membrane components mediating fusion with the sperm have yet been identified. In most sperm, the fusogenic membrane is localized to a small region of the sperm surface, for example the acrosomal tubule in many invertebrates (see Figure 1) or the equatorial and/or postacrosomal region in mammals (see 43). These regions of the mammalian sperm surface have distinct antigens (36) and lectin receptors (41), but it is not known which if any of these components are important for fusion. The membranes of invertebrate sperm acrosomal tubules have not been characterized biochemically (see 40). There are two recent reports that proteins found on the outside of acrosomal tubule membranes of sea urchin and abalone sperm are fusogenic when added to liposomes (13, 20). These proteins may have hydrophobic regions that insert into both sperm and egg membranes to bring the membranes into contact and allow fusion. An analogy has been made with the fusion proteins of viruses (6, 13).

Normal embryonic development requires that only one sperm nucleus reach the egg nucleus. This regulation can be accomplished at several levels: extra sperm can be stopped at the extracellular envelopes of the egg, at the egg plasma membrane, or in a few species, after entry into the egg cytoplasm (see 25). In this chapter, we discuss only the regulation of plasma membrane fusion by the membrane potential, termed an electrical polyspermy block. (Nonelectrically mediated mechanisms for controlling sperm-egg plasma membrane fusion exist, but are not understood; see 25). The electrical block is always transient, functioning one minute to one hour, depending on the species. A given species often employs a combination of a transient electrical block and a more slowly developing permanent block. For example, in the sea urchin, the electrical block protects the egg from polyspermy during the first minute after fertilization, while a permanent mechanical barrier is being established by the elevation of the fertilization envelope.

FERTILIZATION POTENTIALS AND ELECTRICAL BLOCKS TO POLYSPERMY

In many but not all species, fertilization causes a characteristic sequence of changes in the egg's membrane potential, termed the fertilization potential (Figure 2a). The initial shift is usually in the positive direction, although in some species the deflection is negative (15, 25, 29). Electrical blocks to polyspermy are known in several species that have a positive-going fertilization potential: sea urchin (21), starfish (32), the marine worm *Urechis* (17), and frogs (8). For various other animal groups with positive-going fertilization potentials (annelids, molluscs, tunicates, and nemerteans), there is strong but not yet conclusive evidence for an electrical polyspermy block (see 25 and 29 for references). Voltage-dependent fusion may occur in plants as well (37). Salamanders (5), the teleost fish *Oryzias* (34), and probably most mammals (see 23 for references), do not regulate sperm-egg fusion electrically. Although we will only discuss the role of membrane potential in regulating sperm-egg fusion, membrane potential may also be important in regulating subsequent steps in the fertilization process (30).

What is the evidence that the egg's membrane potential regulates sperm-egg fusion? Two experiments done with sea urchins are shown in Figure 2 (21). Applying current to hold the egg's membrane potential positive blocked fertilization (Figure 2b). Surrounding eggs elevated fertilization envelopes within 1 min of sperm addition, but the experimental egg did not. When the current was turned off, fertilization occurred: a fertilization potential and fertilization envelope were seen. Furthermore, direct observation of the surface of living eggs indicated that sperm fail to enter sea urchin eggs held at positive membrane potentials (30). Studies with *Urechis* showed that sperm nuclei were not found in eggs fixed after insemination at positive potentials (17). The sperm blocked by the positive potential were stopped at the fusion step, since electron

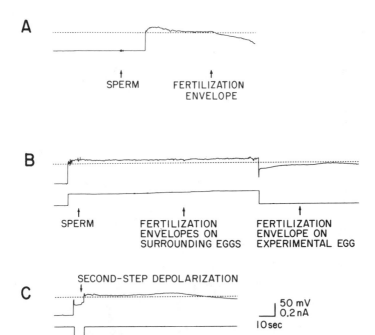

Figure 2   Fertilization potential and demonstration of potential dependence of fertilization in the sea urchin, *Strongylocentrotus purpuratus*. (*a*) Fertilization potential. (*b*) Suppression of fertilization by holding the potential positive. (*c*) Induction of polyspermy by holding the potential negative. Membrane potential is plotted against time and the dotted line indicates 0 mV. The lower trace in *b* and *c* shows applied current. (Reproduced from Reference 21 with permission of Macmillan Journals Ltd).

microscopy of *Urechis* eggs fixed during the positive phase of the fertilization potential showed the acrosomal tubules of many sperm in contact with the egg plasma membrane (35). A positive membrane potential also blocks fertilization of frog eggs (5, 8, 24).

Conversely, holding the egg's membrane potential negative induces polyspermy (Figure 2*c*). After the fertilization potential rise, current was applied to hold the potential at -30 mV. A second step depolarization occurred, then the current was turned off. Multipolar division at first cleavage indicated that this egg was polyspermic, while surrounding eggs were monospermic. Polyspermy can also be induced by changing the ionic composition of the fertilization medium, such that the fertilization potential amplitude is reduced. For example, the fertilization potential in *Urechis* results primarily from Na^+ influx; lowering external Na^+ reduces the potential and induces polyspermy (Figure

3). Similar results were obtained with sea urchin and frog eggs, where the positive potential shift results from Na^+ influx or Cl^- efflux, respectively (4, 8, 18, 22, 33, 38).

Figure 3 also demonstrates that the number of sperm fusing with the egg is not an all-or-none effect, but rather a graded function of the egg's membrane potential, over the range −20 to +30 mV. The probabilistic nature of the voltage-dependence of sperm-egg fusion was also shown by the following two findings: (1) The voltage required to block fertilization depends on the concentration of sperm (21, 26); and (2) the probability that fertilization will occur when a transient shift to a negative potential is superimposed on a longer period of imposed positive potential depends on the value of the negative voltage (39).

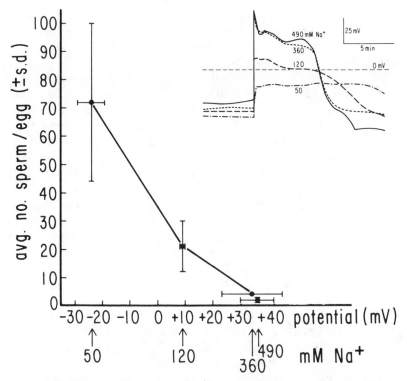

Figure 3   Correlation between the average amplitude of the fertilization potential during the first minute after insemination of *Urechis* eggs and the number of penetrating sperm per egg. The amplitude of the fertilization potential was made more negative by decreasing external Na^+ (replacing with choline$^+$). The inset illustrates typical fertilization potentials in normal and reduced Na^+ seawaters. (Reproduced from Reference 17 with permission of The Rockefeller University Press).

MECHANISM OF THE VOLTAGE-DEPENDENCE OF SPERM-EGG FUSION

An initial question about the mechanism of the voltage-dependence of sperm-egg fusion was whether the fusion block was due to the voltage per se, or to associated ion movements. It might be imagined that depolarization causes Ca^{2+} influx, which in turn causes the fusion block, but a number of observations argue that the voltage-dependence of sperm-egg fusion does not depend on intracellular Ca^{2+} activity. In *Urechis* eggs, there is no correlation between the degree of polyspermy and the magnitude of the Ca^{2+} influx, varied either by altering the composition of the external solution or by treatment with the Ca^{2+} channel blocker, D−600 (17). At 0 mV, Ca^{2+} influx through the voltage-sensitive Ca^{2+} channels of starfish oocytes is less than at −20 mV (19). However, 0 mV blocks sperm-oocyte fusion (in a different species of starfish) while −20 mV does not (32). Finally, the fertilization potential of sea urchin eggs, and hence the electrical polyspermy block, precedes by about 20 sec the increase in Ca^{2+} activity detected by aequorin (9).

Likewise, the Na^+ conductance increase that occurs at fertilization in many marine eggs could increase intracellular Na^+ activity, which might then regulate sperm-egg fusion. However, when the unfertilized starfish egg membrane was clamped at a potential sufficiently positive to prevent fusion, the conductance was only 10% of that measured during the fertilization potential (31), which suggests that it is the potential rather than the Na^+ influx that regulates fusion. Furthermore, when the amount of Na^+ entering *Urechis* eggs during fertilization was experimentally varied, there was no correlation between the magnitude of the Na^+ influx and the establishment of a fusion block (17). A change in intracellular H^+ activity is not important for establishing a fusion block, since the H^+ efflux that normally occurs during fertilization of *Urechis* eggs can be stopped without impairing the electrical polyspermy block (17). In summary, there appears to be no relationship between the fluxes of particular ions and the block to sperm-egg fusion. The block depends on the membrane potential per se.

How might membrane potential regulate fusion? Several models have been proposed (16). One class of models involves a potential-dependent change in some property of the egg membrane, such that it is no longer able to fuse with sperm. This could involve, for example, the potential-dependent exposure of a receptor molecule present in the egg membrane. It could be imagined that an interaction between such a receptor in the egg membrane and a complementary molecule in the sperm membrane could bring sperm and egg membranes into close contact that would allow fusion (Figure 4a). If the receptor molecule had a dipole moment, its conformation or orientation in the egg membrane could change with potential, altering the exposure of a binding site for sperm (Figure

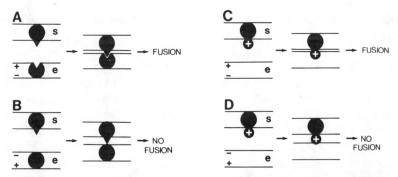

Figure 4   Two models to suggest how the egg's membrane potential might regulate sperm-egg fusion. Parallel lines represent the sperm *(s)* and egg *(e)* plasma membranes; the solid figures represent membrane molecules important in fusion. *(a, b)* Potential-controlled conformational change in an egg membrane component. When the egg's membrane potential is negative *(a)* the successful interaction of egg and sperm components leads to membrane fusion. Positive potential *(b)* prevents fusion. *(c, d)* Potential-controlled insertion of a sperm membrane component into the egg plasma membrane. When the egg's membrane potential is negative *(c)* the positively charged portion of the sperm component inserts fully and fusion follows. Positive potential *(d)* inhibits full insertion and prevents fusion.

4*b*). An example of potential-dependent exposure of a receptor is the potential-dependent binding of saxitoxin to the Na^+ channel (3).

Alternatively, the voltage-dependence of sperm-egg fusion might result from the presence of a charged fusion molecule in the sperm membrane (Figure 4*c*, *d*), analogous to a viral fusion protein (42). Part of the fusion molecule is depicted within the sperm plasma membrane; a second component is shown protruding from the membrane, in a position to insert into the egg membrane. If the protruding portion were positively charged, the extent of its insertion would depend on the egg's membrane potential, because once inserted it would be exposed to the electric field within the egg membrane. If the membrane potential were negative, insertion would proceed and fusion would follow (Figure 4*c*). If the potential were positive, insertion would not proceed (Figure 4*d*). Studies of protein-bilayer interactions have provided precedents for such voltage-dependent protein insertion (28).

In summary, the component responsible for the potential dependence of fusion might reside in either the sperm or the egg membrane. To examine these two possibilities we have been investigating the voltage-dependence of cross-fertilization between species having different voltage-dependent characteristics of sperm-egg fusion. In one series of experiments sea urchin eggs were fertilized with *Urechis* sperm (26). A more positive potential is required to block *Urechis* fertilization compared to sea urchin fertilization. In cross-species fertilization, the blocking voltage was found to be determined by the species of the sperm, not the species of the egg. In a second series of experiments, we tested whether cross-fertilization of frog eggs by salamander sperm is voltage-dependent (24). As described above, frog fertilization is blocked by positive potentials, while salamander fertilization is not. We found that voltage clamping frog eggs at a positive potential did not reduce the frequency of fertilization by salamander sperm. As with the sea urchin X *Urechis* experiments, these results indicate that the voltage-dependence of fertilization depends on the species of sperm. Both findings favor a model for the mechanism of voltage-dependent sperm-egg fusion in which the sperm membrane contains the voltage-sensitive component (Figure 4c, d). However, the model shown in Figure 4a, b is not definitely eliminated.

To test this hypothesis further, it would be informative to examine the voltage-dependence of fertilization between an egg of a species not having voltage-dependent fusion (e.g. salamander or fish) and a sperm of a species in which a more positive potential inhibits fusion. We could then determine whether the sperm contributes this property, in a situation where it is lacking in the egg. An even more direct experiment would be to investigate the voltage-dependence of sperm fusion with an artificial lipid bilayer.

We also think it is important to learn more about the biochemical composition of fusogenic regions of the sperm, e.g. the acrosomal tubule found in many invertebrates. It will be particularly interesting to see if the fusogenic proteins isolated from sperm (13, 20) promote a voltage-dependent fusion. An immunological approach might also be valuable. Antigens localized in the acrosomal tubule membrane, and particularly antigens for which antibodies block sperm-egg fusion, could be identified as possible fusion molecules. Such molecules might be purified and reconstituted into membranes to test whether they could mediate a voltage-dependent fusion.

ACKNOWLEDGMENT

We would like to acknowledge the contributions of Meredith Gould in the development of the ideas described in this paper. We thank Ana Iglesias for helpful comments on the manuscript. Supported by NIH grant HD 14939 to L. A. Jaffe.

Literature Cited

1. Bleil, J. D., Wassarman, P. M. 1980. Mammalian sperm-egg interaction: Identification of a glycoprotein in mouse zonae pellucidae possessing receptor activity for sperm. *Cell* 20:873–82
2. Bolwell, G. P., Callow, J. A., Evans, L. V. 1980. Fertilization in brown algae. III. *J. Cell Sci.* 43:209–24
3. Catterall, W. A. 1979. Binding of scorpion toxin to receptor sites associated with sodium channels in frog muscle. Correla-

tion of voltage-dependent binding with activation. *J. Gen. Physiol.* 74:375–91
4. Chambers, E. L., de Armendi, J. 1979. Membrane potential, action potential and activation potential of eggs of the sea urchin, *Lytechinus variegatus. Exp. Cell Res.* 122:203–18
5. Charbonneau, M., Moreau, M., Picheral, B., Vilain, J. P., Guerrier, P. 1983. Fertilization of amphibian eggs: a comparison of electrical responses between

anurans and urodeles. *Dev. Biol.* 98:304–18

6. Colwin, A. L., Colwin, L. H. 1967. Behavior of the spermatozoon during sperm-blastomere fusion and its significance for fertilization (*Saccoglossus kowalevskii:* Hemichordata). *Z. Zellforsch.* 78:208–20

7. Colwin, L. H., Colwin, A. L. 1967. Membrane fusion in relation to sperm-egg association. In *Fertilization: Comparative Morphology, Biochemistry and Immunology,* ed. C. B. Metz, A. Monroy, pp. 295–367. New York: Academic

8. Cross, N. L., Elinson, R. P. 1980. A fast block to polyspermy in frogs mediated by changes in the membrane potential. *Dev. Biol.* 75:187–98

9. Eisen, A., Kiehart, D. P., Wieland, S. J., Reynolds, G. T. 1984. Temporal sequence and spatial distribution of early events of fertilization in single sea urchin eggs. *J. Cell Biol.* 99:1647–54

10. Elinson, R. P. 1975. Site of sperm entry and a cortical contraction associated with egg activation in the frog *Rana pipiens. Dev. Biol.* 47:257–68

11. Franklin, L. E. 1965. Morphology of gamete membrane fusion and of sperm entry into oocytes of the sea urchin. *J. Cell Biol.* 25:81–100

12. Freeman, G., Miller, R. L. 1982. Hydrozoan eggs can only be fertilized at the site of polar body formation. *Dev. Biol.* 94:142–52

13. Glabe, C. G. 1985. Interaction of the sperm adhesive protein, bindin, with phospholipid vesicles. II. Bindin induces the fusion of mixed-phase vesicles that contain phosphatidylcholine and phosphatidyl serine *in vitro. J. Cell Biol.* 100:800–6

14. Glabe, C. G., Vacquier, V. D. 1978. Egg surface glycoprotein receptor for sea urchin sperm binding. *Proc. Natl. Acad. Sci. USA* 75:881–85

15. Goudeau, H., Goudeau, M. 1985. Fertilization in crabs: IV. The fertilization potential consists of a sustained egg membrane hyperpolarization. *Gamete Res.* 11:1–17

16. Gould-Somero, M., Jaffe, L. A. 1984. Control of cell fusion at fertilization by membrane potential. In *Cell Fusion: Gene Transfer and Transformation,* ed. R. F. Beers Jr., E. G. Bassett, pp. 27–38. New York: Raven

17. Gould-Somero, M., Jaffe, L. A., Holland, L. Z. 1979. Electrically mediated fast polyspermy block in eggs of the marine worm, *Urechis caupo. J. Cell Biol.* 82:426–40

18. Grey, R. D., Bastiani, M. J., Webb, D. J., Schertel, E. R. 1982. An electrical block is required to prevent polyspermy in eggs fertilized by natural mating of *Xenopus laevis. Dev. Biol.* 89:475–84

19. Hagiwara, S., Ozawa, S., Sand, O. 1975. Voltage clamp analysis of two inward current mechanisms in the egg cell membrane of a starfish. *J. Gen. Physiol.* 65:617–44

20. Hong, K., Vacquier, V. D. 1985. Fusion of liposomes induced by a hydrophobic protein from the acrosome granule of abalone spermatozoa. *Biophys. J.* 47:109a

21. Jaffe, L. A. 1976. Fast block to polyspermy in sea urchin eggs is electrically mediated. *Nature* 261:68–71

22. Jaffe, L. A. 1980. Electrical polyspermy block in sea urchins: nicotine and low sodium experiments. *Dev. Growth Differ.* 22:503–7

23. Jaffe, L. A., Cross, N. L. 1983. Electrical properties of vertebrate oocyte membranes. *Biol. Reprod.* 30:50–54

24. Jaffe, L. A., Cross, N. L., Picheral, B. 1983. Studies of the voltage-dependent polyspermy block using cross-species fertilization of amphibians. *Dev. Biol.* 98:319–26

25. Jaffe, L. A., Gould, M. 1985. Polyspermy-preventing mechanisms. In *Biology of Fertilization,* ed. C. B. Metz, A. Monroy, 3:223–50. New York: Academic

26. Jaffe, L. A., Gould-Somero, M., Holland, L. 1982. Studies of the mechanism of the electrical polyspermy block using voltage-clamp during cross-species fertilization. *J. Cell Biol.* 92:616–21

27. Johnson, M. H., Eager, D., Muggleton-Harris, A. 1975. Mosaicism in organization of concanavalin A receptors on surface membrane of mouse egg. *Nature* 257:321–22

28. Kempf, C., Klausner, R. D., Weinstein, J. N., Van Renswoude, J., Pincus, M., Blumenthal, R. 1982. Voltage-dependent trans-bilayer orientation of melittin. *J. Biol. Chem.* 257:2469–76

29. Kline, D., Jaffe, L. A., Tucker, R. P. 1985. Fertilization potential and polyspermy prevention in the egg of the nemertean, *Cerebratulus lacteus. J. Exp. Zool.* In press

30. Lynn, J. W., Chambers, E. L. 1984. Voltage clamp studies of fertilization in sea urchin eggs. I. Effect of clamped membrane potential on sperm entry, activation and development. *Dev. Biol.* 102:98–109

31. Miyazaki, S. 1979. Fast polyspermy block and activation potential. Elec-

200   JAFFE & CROSS

trophysiological bases for their changes during oocyte maturation of a starfish. *Dev. Biol.* 70:341–54
32. Miyazaki, S., Hirai, S. 1979. Fast polyspermy block and activation potential. Correlated changes during oocyte maturation of a starfish. *Dev. Biol.* 70:327–40
33. Nishioka, D., Cross, N. 1978. The role of external sodium in sea urchin fertilization. In *Cell Reproduction,* ed. E. R. Dirksen, D. M. Prescott, C. F. Fox, pp. 403–13. New York: Academic
34. Nuccitelli, R. 1980. The fertilization potential is not necessary for the block to polyspermy or the activation of development in the medaka egg. *Dev. Biol.* 76:499–504
35. Paul, M., Gould-Somero, M. 1976. Evidence for a polyspermy block at the level of sperm-egg plasma membrane fusion in *Urechis caupo. J. Exp. Zool.* 196:105–12
36. Primakoff, P., Myles, D. G. 1983. A map of the guinea pig sperm surface constructed with monoclonal antibodies. *Dev. Biol.* 98:417–28
37. Robinson, K. R., Jaffe, L. A., Brawley,

S. H. 1981. Electrophysiological properties of fucoid algal eggs during fertilization. *J. Cell Biol.* 91:179a
38. Schuel, H., Schuel, R. 1981. A rapid sodium-dependent block to polyspermy in sea urchin eggs. *Dev. Biol.* 87:249–58
39. Shen, S. S., Steinhardt, R. A. 1984. Time and voltage windows for reversing the electrical block to fertilization. *Proc. Natl. Acad. Sci. USA* 81:1436–39
40. Tilney, L. G., Hatano, S., Ishikawa, H., Mooseker, M. S. 1973. The polymerization of actin: Its role in the generation of the acrosomal process of certain echinoderm sperm. *J. Cell Biol.* 59:109–26
41. Virtanen, I., Bradley, R. A., Paasivuo, R., Leyton, V. P. 1984. Distinct cytoskeletal domains revealed in sperm cells. *J. Cell. Biol.* 99:1083–91
42. White, J., Kielian, M., Helenius, A. 1983. Membrane fusion proteins of enveloped animal viruses. *Q. Rev. Biophys.* 16:151–95
43. Yanagimachi, R. 1981. Mechanisms of fertilization in mammals. In *Fertilization and Embryonic Development In Vitro,* ed. L. Mastroianni, Jr., J. B. Biggers, pp. 81–182. New York: Plenum

Ann. Rev. Physiol. 1986. 48:201–12

MIMICRY AND MECHANISM IN PHOSPHOLIPID MODELS OF MEMBRANE FUSION[1]

R. P. Rand

Department of Biological Sciences, Brock University, St. Catharines, Ontario, Canada L2S 3A1

V. A. Parsegian

Physical Sciences Laboratory, National Institutes of Health, Bethesda, Maryland 20205

INTRODUCTION

What have phospholipid model systems taught us about the fusion of bilayer membranes? And how well do these systems mimic the cellular process? One prime objective in using such models is to reduce the chemical complexities of native membraes to identify constituents crucial in the mechanism of fusion. Model studies have taught us much about the properties of phospholipid vesicles that are important for their practical use as delivery systems. However, in order to shed some light on the cellular mechanism, and not on some other behavior peculiar to an artificial preparation, the model system should first match the rather strict topological control shown by cells. A comprehensive review of fusion appeared recently (4). This review considers only those aspects of models that apply to mimicking the cellular process of membrane fusion.

STAGES OF MEMBRANE FUSION

Six possible stages of cell fusion can be defined:

(i) Stable membrane apposition Most membranes do not fuse, maintaining their stability even in close apposition to neighbors. Fusion is an exceptional event under strict control and confined to specific membrane pairs.

(ii) Triggering   Accompanying articles (this volume) indicate that fusion has been associated with: a rise in intracellular calcium that is antagonized by magnesium; osmotic pressure changes; the metabolic turnover of specific lipids, such as phosphatidylinositol; the production of fatty acids; and with specific proteins. The rapidity of events has made it difficult to determine how immediately connected these various triggers are, either with each other or with the events they set in motion.

(iii) Contact   Fusion must involve closer functional approach of membranes than the stable apposition achieved by most membranes. However, enhancing the energy of intermembrane contact can be shown to be independent of fusion. For example, synaptic vesicles subjected to elevated Mg increase their adherence to the extent of bulging the presynaptic membrane, but no fusion results (19).

(iv) Focused destabilization   The structure of the contacting membranes must destabilize, and that destabilization must be restricted to the contact area. Such restriction ensures that the fusion is "leakless," i.e. that the correct aqueous compartments mix.

(v) Membrane coalescence   The destabilized structure leads to the coalescence of two membrane surfaces.

(vi) Restabilization   The fused membrane must restabilize quickly to maintain its and the cell's integrity.
    Stages *iv, v,* and *vi,* and perhaps *iii,* appear to be extremely rapid (microseconds), even if the events leading to them are slow. They are highly localized, which makes them difficult to capture, let alone attribute to specific membrane components. Where extraordinary measures have been taken to visualize them no membrane structural perturbations have been seen during the process and, significantly, the area of contact during coalescence is very small (20, 32).

METHODS OF INVESTIGATING THESE STAGES

Of the wide variety of complementary techniques used to study the interaction and fusion of bilayer membranes we will consider those most directly related to the stages described. Direct measurements of the forces that approaching bilayers experience, within multilayers, have been carried out using an osmotic stress technique combined with X-ray diffraction (34, 39). Micromanipulation measurements on uni- or paucilamellar vesicles and theoretical study of spherical bilayer membranes have taught us much about what to expect when they are deformed by interacting with others (15, 17). Study of the rapid transient events and the topology of mixing of membrane and aqueous compartments is far more difficult. Two ingenious methods of triggering the interaction of phospholipid membranes and assaying the topological response have been developed. In the first (52), unilamellar vesicles made with acidic phospholipids and containing either terbium (Tb) or dipicolinic acid (DPA) are triggered to interact by addition of divalent cations or, more recently (14), by pH-induced structural transitions. Vesicle aggregation is measured by light scattering, the mixing of aqueous contents is assessed by the fluorescence of the Tb-DPA complex, leakage of vesicle contents is measured in parallel experiments by the release of the self-quenching of carboxyfluorescene, and lipid intermixing is measured by energy resonance transfer (53). In the second assay system the fusion of uni- or multilamellar vesicles containing porin or VDAC, high conductance channel-forming proteins, with a planar membrane is assessed by the transfer of the proteins with a planar membrane and of the vesicle contents across it (6, 54). More recently, attempts have been made to see fusion events directly, either by video-enhanced light microscopy (41) or by very rapid-mixing and fast freezing followed by freeze-fracture electron microscopy (2, 30, 41). The lessons learned by this variety of approaches are summarized on the basis of the stages described above.

STABLE MEMBRANE APPOSITION

Understanding why bilayers and membranes for the most part do not achieve contact has led to a better understanding of the prime requirements for fusion. The forces membranes experience on mutual approach have been measured for a wide variety of phospholipid bilayers in multilamellar arrays (39). These physical forces are long-range van der Waals attraction, electrostatic repulsion for bilayers that carry a net surface charge, and hydration repulsion. For separations of 20–30 Å the van der Waals attraction is strong enough to overcome thermal motion and allows the creation of the multilamellar arrays formed by most neutral or zwitterionic lipids. Two to three mole-percent charged lipid adds sufficient electrostatic repulsion for such bilayers to separate indefinitely, sensitive to the usual factors of charge density and ionic conditions (7, 25, 28). However, for separations smaller than 20–30 Å, where contact and fusion must begin, all bilayers experience a strong repulsive force that grows exponentially with a characteristic distance of 2–3 Å (39). McIntosh & Simon (manuscript submitted) have defined bilayer thickness on the basis of electron density profiles of phospholipid bilayers. This has the effect of reducing the bilayer separation as previously defined (26, 29) and suggests that bilayer "contact" occurs with much less work than proposed. Nevertheless it does not change the total energy required to remove water from the bilayers. With either definition of bilayer separation the rapid growth of repulsion ensures that bilayers, even of the smallest area and highest curvature attainable [small unilamellar vesicles (suv)] can approach by thermal collision only a few Å closer than their equilibrium separation (7). This repulsion has been observed for all bilayers regardless of the species or charge of the polar group; the length, heterogeneity, degree of unsaturation, or configuration of the hydrocarbon chains; and the presence or absence of cholesterol; and is neglegibly dependent on the ionic conditions of the medium (26, 39). Hydration forces have subsequently been measured between hydrated mica surfaces (37), between myelin membranes (40), and more recently between DNA double helices (45). It now appears to be ubiquitous, to have a common characteristic length, and to dominate interactions between all hydrophilic groups nearing contact. Its origin is the cost of dehydrating hydrophilic groups. For bilayer surfaces of any significant area this results in mechanical repulsion that extends beyond the "hydration shells" one normally thinks of. This repulsive force is the major barrier to membrane contact.

It is useful to distinguish two different levels of interaction between bilayers because they distinguish two major ways bilayers can react on mutual attraction. Van der Waals attractive energies of the order of $0.01-0.1$ ergs/cm^2 (16, 35, 39) (see Figure 1) hold membranes together, but at the long-range separations of 20–30 Å. Integration of the hydration force measurements shows that attractive energies on the order of 10–100 ergs/cm^2 are required to remove intervening water (35, 39). Such high energies dictate the prime requirements of establishing close bilayer contact and perhaps destabilization during fusion. What mechanisms could establish that contact?

TRIGGER AND CONTACT

A combination that has received the most attention in modeling fusion is that of bilayers containing acidic phospholipids presented with solutions of divalent cations. Charged bilayers in solutions of monovalent ions (7, 28) repel each other: electrostatic repulsion dominates at very long distances, and hydration repulsion prevents closer approach than about 20–30 Å. But millimolar levels of divalent cations trigger a collapse of pure acidic phospholipid systems into multibilayers with little intervening water, for example, none in the case of calcium-phosphatidylserine (PS) and very little in Mg-PS (38). Under such conditions, force measurements cannot be made since once started the collapse proceeds to its final state (27, 42). Apparently divalent ion binding to apposing bilayers can displace the water hydrating the lamellar phase. The affinity for calcium of apposed PS bilayers far exceeds that of the isolated surface (13), although it is still an order of magnitude more than measured affinity of secretory vesicles (12). In the case of pure PS bilayers, from that difference in affinity it can be estimated that 10–100 ergs/cm^2 is available from Ca binding, enough to completely dehydrate the polar groups and to accomplish bilayer contact (35, 42). That energy is reduced by diluting the PS with neutral lipids. The degree of reduction and the subsequent product of bilayer interaction is complicated by the species of divalent cation (11), the degree of dilution, and whether the dilution is with the more hydrated [phosphatidylcholine (PC)] or less hydrated [phosphatidylethanolamine (PE)] phospholipid (10, 11).

However, what has not been widely appreciated are the multiple consequences of triggering such attraction between spherical phospholipid vesicles, or between a spherical vesicle and a planar bilayer. Evans and colleagues have provided a combined experimental and theoretical analysis of what to expect (15, 17). Spherical vesicles will necessarily flatten against each other (Figure 1b); a spherical vesicle will bulge into a large planar membrane (Figure 1a). The attractive energy goes into the stresses that develop as the bilayers deform by bending and changing their curvature (important only for suv's), and by increasing their surface area and bilayer tension (17). However, both the total energy available for contact and the final result depend on many factors involving the intrinsic properties of the bilayers and the constraints that apply before and during their deformation (17, 36). Consider two spherical vesicles, which on interacting necessarily experience increased membrane tension and intravesicular pressure: (i) The relative area of contact, the total energy available for deformation, and the growth of bilayer tension as they deform all will be sensitively dependent on how flaccid or not the vesicles were before contact. (ii) During vesicular deformation a portion of the energy will go into volume loss; the size of the portion depends on the permeabilities of the *stressed* bilayers and the osmotic pressure of the vesicle contents. (iii) These different effects will vary with the individual size of each adhering vesicle. (iv) If the vesicles do not fuse, an equilibrium could be attained only if bilayer tension did not exceed rupture tension [3 dynes/cm, achieved at about 3% increase in area (15)] at any time during their deformation and if the vesicles could maintain their volume, i.e. if they could osmotically support their intracellular pressure. Such an equilibrium is described in Figure 1a, b. However, energies of the order required to remove interbilayer water (see table in Figure 1) would destabilize bilayers by generating tensions that far exceed rupture tension, which is the usual result for many bilayers that contain acidic phosholipids when presented with divalent cations (10, 27, 42, 53).

Two examples of different results obtained by the two different fusion assays illustrate how differing constraints determine the outcome of bilayer interactions. First, interacting spheres of PE-PS (3 : 1) destabilize on the addition of 3 mM calcium (11); similar spheres (PE-PS 4 : 1) do not destabilize on interacting with planar bilayers in 15 mM calcium, unless osmotically stressed (5). Second, bilayer spheres containing high levels of neutral lipids have never

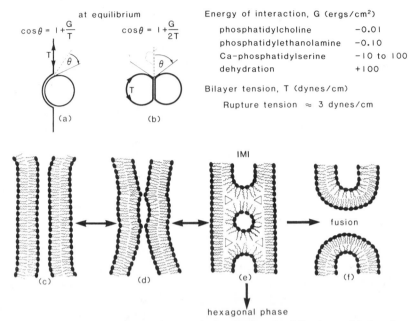

at equilibrium

$$\cos\theta = 1 + \frac{G}{T} \qquad \cos\theta = 1 + \frac{G}{2T}$$

Energy of interaction, G (ergs/cm²)

phosphatidylcholine	−0.01
phosphatidylethanolamine	−0.10
Ca-phosphatidylserine	−10 to 100
dehydration	+100

Bilayer tension, T (dynes/cm)

Rupture tension ≈ 3 dynes/cm

(a)   (b)

IMI

(c)   (d)   (e)   (f)

fusion

hexagonal phase

Figure 1   Macroscopic and microscopic events in the adhesion, destabilization, and fusion of bilayer membranes. See text for discussion of the individual steps.

been observed to destabilize in the sphere-sphere assay (11), but can be made to do so with planar bilayers if stressed osmotically (1). These apparent differences can be reconciled by recognizing that the weaker bilayer tensions developed in sphere-planar interactions require the added tension that results from osmotic swelling to reach destabilizing levels. Taken together these results show that a remarkable lack of specificity of lipid species is required for interaction and destabilization. Bilayer destabilization likely results from the same cause in both assay systems, namely mechanical stretching to rupture tensions.

The vesicle-planar membrane assay clearly identifies two separate steps in the interaction process, vesicle adhesion and destabilization by osmotic stress (1). Significantly, osmotic destabilization occurs even for neutral bilayer spheres that contain PE (1) and that adhere with much weaker attractive energies than the Ca-induced interactions. This suggests that the contact that can be achieved by PE is sufficient for fusion if the destabilizing stress is imposed osmotically.

From the enormous numbers of lipid combinations and aqueous and ionic conditions that have been assessed, it appears that more "fusogenic" conditions are, in general, those that increase the likelihood of bilayer stress and mechanical rupture. However, the integrity of the bilayers and the topology of the aqueous compartments are put at risk under such conditions unless such stresses are relieved by rupture only in the contact area.

FOCUSED DESTABILIZATION AND MEMBRANE COALESCENCE

To what extent is measured fusion only coincidental to random rupture over the whole bilayer surface? Bilayer spheres that differ only in size and flacidity will experience different constraints when they interact. Direct observations of Ca-induced interaction of small or large unilamellar PS vesicles by freeze-fracture electron microscopy and of giant complex vesicles by light microscopy indicate that resultant stresses are rapidly relieved by either fusion or volume loss (30, 41). These two responses appear to occur with about equal probability (41), even though for giant vesicles it is estimated that the probability of rupture of a unit area of contacting bilayers (leading to fusion) is about ten times greater than rupture (and leakage) outside the contact area (41). Volume loss by PS vesicles is by violent vesicle rupture (41). It can occur by more controlled permeation in stressed dioleoylphosphatidyethanolamine (DOPE)-PS vesicles, even if they contain sucrose, and collapse to stable, unfused, adhered vesicles of reduced volume is common (Figure 2; unpublished observations). These observations indicate that the constraints during interaction of specific vesicles under constant conditions are difficult to control and far from uniform.

Such observations raise difficult questions about the meaning of initial fusion and leakage rates measured fluorimetrically (53). Thus far such fluorimetric studies have been interpreted strictly by reaction kinetic schemes without reference to the mechanical and thermodynamic properties of the vesicles. In some conditions and with some lipids, leakage never occurs and fusion reaches near expected values (52). However, most systems show both processes, and it is not clear whether they reflect different populations of vesicles. Constraints may be more uniform, and more like that of vesicular secretion by cells, in the case of sphere-plane interactions. However, in the sphere-planar bilayer assay destabilization outside the contact area (leakage) is not measured (1). The difficult question of what proportion of interacting vesicles fuse remains. If it is not high, observed fusion may be simply coincidental to a random rupturing process.

What in the contact area could lead to its destabilization and preferential rupture? The discovery of lipidic particles in protein-free phospholipid systems has provided the only structural evidence of bilayer perturbation (50). These particles occur only in systems with phospholipids that can form nonbilayer structures, and they have been invoked in models of bilayer fusion (23, 44, 49). Subsequent microscopic (21, 31) and more recent theoretical (46) evidence indicates that such particles form only in interacting, not isolated, bilayers.

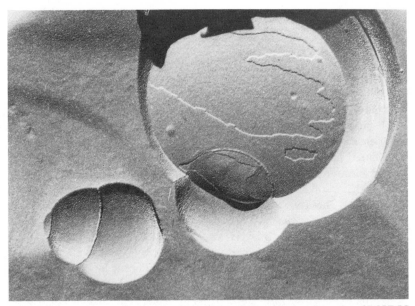

Figure 2   Freeze fracture electron micrograph images of the transient configuration of DOPE-PS (3 : 1) unilamellar vesicles formed within about 100 msec after mixing with 5 mM calcium chloride. Strong adhesion has deformed the vesicles, which were all spherical and isolated before mixing. The large regions of contact are smooth double-bilayer diaphragms with no obvious perturbations. Two of the three adhering vesicles in the lower left have lost considerable volume; this can happen even if they contain 400 mM sucrose. These lipids are en route to forming segregated multilamellar (Ca-PS) and hexagonal (DOPE) phases that exclude most of the aqueous solution.

They are seen in equilibrium conditions, but whether they represent transient structures in the interaction process has yet to be demonstrated (2) (Figure 2). The structure of the particles remains unresolved, but they are probably inverted spherical micelles between adjoining bilayers (Figure 1e); they have been called inverted micellar intermediates, or IMI (46).

This work has rekindled interest in the original lamellar-nonlamellar transitions and in the relevance of these to planar membranes (29). In the lamellar-hexagonal transition particles that resemble the IMI associated with bilayers can be seen associated with the inverted micelles (9, 22). Siegel has provided a very detailed and instructive quantitative analysis of the structural pathways IMI may take in the lamellar-hexagonal transition (47). When applied to the contact region of interacting vesicles, IMI could result in two structural consequences (48) (see Figure 1e). In one, the IMI aggregate, form the hexagonal structure, and vesicles disintegrate. In the other, IMI lead to interlamellar attachment sites, and vesicles fuse (Figure 1f). The relative probabilities of these distinct pathways have a complicated dependence on many structural properties, some that are not easily quantified. The importance of this mechanism is that it is a contact-mediated transition focusing the structural destabilization where it is needed. The importance of the quantitative analysis is that it may provide direction to determining those factors that will make the pathway to fusion much more probable. More quantitative analysis is required, but it is not difficult to imagine that divalent cation concentration, lipid composition, and the effect of bilayer tension (whether produced by adhesion or osmotically) could affect the fusion/leakage ratio. In a cardiolipin (CL)-DOPC system, for example, changes in temperature alone appear to profoundly affect that ratio: at 10°C only fusion occurs (53).

This mechanism hinges on the ability of the lipids of contacting bilayers to form the high curvature structures characteristic of the IMI. That is usually interpreted as a requirement for lipids that can form the hexagonal phase. However, recently it has been demonstrated that many lipids usually found only in the bilayer form can express the high curvatures of the hexagonal phase when chain-packing stresses, illustrated by the open triangles in Figure 1e, are relieved by hydrocarbons (18, 23a, 24) or by phospholipids with very long hydrocarbon chains (S. Gruner, personal communication). This important new consideration means that many more lipids and conditions could result in the formation of the high curvatures of lipidic particles, or IMI.

What might trigger the fluctuations that cause IMI formation? There are many possibilities, both physical, based on measured lipid and bilayer properties, and biochemical, based on phospholipid metabolism. Any change in conditions that results in mutual approach of bilayers into the hydration region will likely result in lipid segregation (43). For example, PE and PC experience such different repulsion that PE would accumulate in the contact region and, because of its propensity to form the hexagonal phase, could form IMI (39). Biochemical alteration of lipids may be translated into such physical mechanisms. The turnover of phosphatidylinositol (PI) is emerging as a ubiquitous transmembrane signalling system (3, 52a). It has been correlated with synaptic transmission, secretion (3), and myoblast fusion (51). One product of the initial reaction is diacylglycerol. Its production removes the PI polar group and associated water, which results in an extremely hydrophobic molecule. Diacylglycerol has now been shown to be a powerful perturber of the bilayer structure (8). Thus, two of the critical steps in triggering fusion, dehydration and destabilization, could be coupled in this one enzymatic reaction.

SUMMARY

In spite of heroic efforts, phospholipid bilayer models of fusion do not mimic the cellular process closely enough to be confident that the cellular mechanism is being probed (36). Probably the experimental factors that are most difficult to control are the uniformity of the vesicles and the constraints that determine their behavior. In most conditions where fusion is triggered, the probability of bilayer mechanical rupture and leakage is increased. Confining that rupture to the contact area remains the most elusive characteristic of cell fusion to mimic. It may depend on fusogenic proteins. Some membrane characteristics, such as lipid asymmetry, may be crucial and may be determined biochemically (33), but they are difficult to duplicate in model systems. The contact-induced formation of nonbilayer lipid structures triggered by phosphatidylinositol turn-over may offer some guidance in how the biochemical and required physical changes may be coupled.

ACKNOWLEDGMENT

We have benefitted from discussions with Sol Gruner and David Seigel and their sharing of recent unpublished observations. RPR acknowledges the expert assistance of Nola Fuller, and the financial support of the Natural Sciences and Engineering Research Council of Canada.

Literature Cited

1. Akabas, M. H., Cohen, F. S., Finkelstein, A. 1984. Separation of the osmotically driven fusion event from vesicleplanar membrane attachment in a model for exocytosis. *J. Cell Biol.* 98:1063–71
2. Bearer, E. L., Duzgunes, N., Friend, D. S., Papahadjopoulos, D. 1983. Fusion of phospholipid vesicles arrested by quick freezing. The question of lipidic particles as intermediates in membrane fusion. *Biochim. Biophys. Acta* 693:93–98
3. Berridge, M. J. 1984. Inositol and diacylglycerol as second messengers. *Biochem. J.* 220:345–60
4. Blumenthal, R. 1985. Membrane fusion. *Curr. Top. Membr. Transp.* 22:
5. Cohen, F. S., Akabas, M. H., Zimmerberg, J., Finkelstein, A. 1984. Parameters affecting the fusion of unilamellar phospholipid vesicles with planar bilayer membranes. *J. Cell Biol.* 98:1054–62
6. Cohen, F. S., Zimmerberg, J., Finkelstein, A. 1980. Fusion of phospholipid vesicles with planar phospholipid bilayer membranes. II. Incorporation of a vesicular membrane marker into the planar membrane. *J. Gen. Physiol.* 75:252–69
7. Cowley, A. C., Fuller, N. L., Rand, R. P., Parsegian, V. A. 1978. Measurement of repulsive forces between charged phospholipid bilayers. *Biochemistry* 17:3163–68
8. Das, S., Rand, R. P. 1984. Diacylglycerol causes major structural transitions in phospholipid bilayer membranes. *Biochem. Biophys. Res. Commun.* 124:491–96

9. De Kruijf, B., Verkleij, A. J., Leunissen-Bijvelt, C. J. A., van Echteld, C. J., Hille, J., Rijnbout, H. 1982. Further aspects of the Ca-dependent polymorphism of bovine heart cardiolipin. *Biochim. Biophys. Acta* 693:1–12
10. Duzgunes, N., Nir, S., Wilschut, J., Bentz, J., Newton, C., et al. 1981. Calcium- and magnesium-induced fusion of mixed phosphatidylserine vesicles: Effect of ion binding. *J. Membr. Biol.* 59:115–25
11. Duzgunes, N., Wilschut, J., Fraley, R., Papahadjopoulos, D. 1981. Studies on the mechanism of membrane fusion: Role of head group composition in calcium- and magnesium-induced fusion of mixed phospholipid vesicles. *Biochim. Biophys. Acta* 642:182–95
12. Ekerdt, R., Dahl, G., Gratzl, M. 1981. Membrane fusion of secretory vesicles and liposomes: Two different types of fusion. *Biochim. Biophys. Acta* 646:10–22
13. Ekerdt, R., Papahadjopoulos, D. 1982. Intermembrane contact affects calcium binding to phospholipid vesicles. *Proc. Natl. Acad. Sci. USA* 79:2273–77
14. Ellens, H., Bentz, J., Szoka, F. C. 1984. pH-Induced destabilization of phosphatidylethanolamine-containing liposome: Role of bilayer contact. *Biochemistry* 23:1532–38
15. Evans, E., Kwok, R. 1982. Mechanical calorimetry of large dimyristoylphosphatidylcholine vesicles in the phase transition region. *Biochemistry* 21:4874–79

16. Evans, E., Metcalfe, M. 1984. Free energy potential for aggregation of giant, neutral lipid bilayer vesicles by van der Waals attraction. *Biophys. J.* 46:423–25
17. Evans, E. A., Parsegian, V. A. 1983. Energetics of membrane deformation and adhesion in cell and vesicle aggregation. *Ann. NY Acad. Sci.* 416:13–33
18. Gruner, S. M., Cullis, P. R., Hope, M. J., Tilcock, C. P. S. 1985. Lipid polymorphism: The molecular basis of nonbilayer phases. *Ann. Rev. Biophys. Biophys. Chem.* 14:211–38
19. Heuser, J. E. 1977. Synaptic vesicle exocytosis revealed in quick-frozen frog neuromuscular junctions treated with 4-amino-pyridine and given a single electric shock. In *Approaches to the Cell Biology of Neurons, Soc. Neurosci. Symp.* ed. W. M. Cowan, J. A. Ferrendelli, 2:215–39
20. Heuser, J. E., Reese, T. S. 1980. Structural changes after transmitter release at the frog neuromuscular junction. *J. Cell Biol.* 88:564–80
21. Hui, S. W., Stewart, T. P. 1981. Lipidic particles are intermembrane attachment sites. *Nature* 290:427–28
22. Hui, S. W., Stewart, T. P., Boni, L. T. 1983. The nature of lipidic particles and their roles in polymorphic transitions. *Chem. Phys. Lipids* 33:113–26
23. Hui, S. W., Stewart, T. P., Boni, L. T., Yeagle, P. L. 1981. Membrane fusion through point defects in bilayers. *Science* 212:921–23
23a. Kirk, G. L., Gruner, S. M. 1985. Hypotropic effects of alkanes and head group composition of the L-H lipid liquid crystal phase transition: hydrocarbon packing versus intrinsic curvature. *J. Physique* 46: In press
24. Kirk, G. L., Gruner, S. M., Stein, D. L. 1984. A thermodynamic model of the lamellar to inverse hexagonal phase transition of the lipid membrane water systems. *Biochemistry* 23:1093–1102
25. Lis, L. J., Lis, W. T., Parsegian, V. A., Rand, R. P. 1981. Adsorption of divalent cations to a variety of phosphatidylcholine bilayers. *Biochemistry* 20:1771–77
26. Lis, L. J., McAlister, M., Fuller, N. L., Rand, R. P., Parsegian, V. A. 1982. Interactions between neutral phospholipid bilayer membranes. *Biophys. J.* 37:657–66
27. Loosley-Millman, M. E. 1980. PhD thesis. Guelph Univ., Guelph, Canada
28. Loosley-Millman, M. E., Rand, R. P., Parsegian, V. A. 1982. Effects of monovalent ion binding and screening on measured electrostatic forces between charged phospholipid bilayers. *Biophys. J.* 40:221–32

29. Luzzati, V., Husson, F. 1962. The structure of the liquid-crystalline phases of lipid water systems. *J. Cell. Biol.* 12:207–19
30. Miller, D. C., Dahl, G. P. 1982. Early events in calcium-induced liposome fusion. *Biochim Biophys. Acta* 689:165–69
31. Miller, R. G. 1980. Do lipidic particles represent intermembrane attachment sites? *Nature* 287:166–67
32. Ornberg, R. L., Reese, T. S. 1981. Beginning of exocytosis captured by rapid-freezing of limulus amebocytes. *J. Cell Biol.* 90:40–54
33. Parsegian, V. A. 1977. Considerations in determining the mode of influence of calcium on vesicle-membrane interaction. See Ref. 19, pp. 161–71
34. Parsegian, V. A., Fuller, N. L., Rand, R. P. 1979. Measured work of deformation and repulsion of lecithin bilayers. *Proc. Natl. Acad. Sci. USA* 76:2750–54
35. Parsegian, V. A., Rand, R. P. 1983. Membrane interaction and deformation. *Ann. NY Acad. Sci.* 416:1–12
36. Parsegian, V. A., Rand, R. P., Gingell, D. 1984. Lessons for the study of membrane fusion from membrane interactions in phospholipid systems. In *Cell Fusion. CIBA Found. Symp.* 103:9–27 London: Pitman Books
37. Pashley, R. M., Israelachivili, J. N. 1981. Hydration forces between mica surfaces in aqueous electrolyte solutions. *J. Colloid. Interface Sci.* 80:153–62
38. Portis, A., Newton, C., Pangborn, W., Papahadjopolous, D. 1979. Studies on the mechanism of membrane fusion: Evidence for an intermembrane Ca-phospholipid complex, synergism with Mg, and inhibition by spectrin. *Biochemistry* 18:780–90
39. Rand, R. P. 1981. Interacting phospholipid bilayers: Measured forces and induced structural changes. *Ann. Rev. Biophys. Bioeng.* 10:277–314
40. Rand, R. P., Fuller, N. L., Lis, L. J. 1979. Myelin swelling and measurement of forces between myelin membranes. *Nature* 279:258–60
41. Rand, R. P., Kachar, B., Reese, T. S. 1985. Dynamic morphology of interacting phosphatidylserine vesicles. *Biophys. J.* 47:483–89
42. Rand, R. P., Parsegian, V. A. 1984. Physical force considerations in model and biological membranes. *Can. J. Biochem. Cell. Biol.* 62:752–59
43. Rand, R. P., Parsegian, V. A., Henry, J. A. C., Lis, L. J., McAlister, M. 1980. The effect of cholesterol on measured interaction and compressibility of dipalmitoylphosphatidylcholine bilayers. *Can. J. Biochem.* 58:959–68

44. Rand, R. P., Reese, T. S., Miller, R. G. 1981. Phospholipid bilayer deformations associated with interbilayer contact and fusion. *Nature* 293:237–38

45. Rau, D. C., Lee, B. K., Parsegian, V. A. 1984. Measurement of the repulsive forces between parallel DNA double helices. *Proc. Natl. Acad. Sci. USA* 81:2621–25

46. Siegel, D. 1984. Inverted micellar structures in bilayer membranes. Formation rates and half-lives. *Biophys. J.* 45:399–420

47. Siegel, D. 1985. Mechanism of the transitions between lamellar and inverted hexagonal phases. *Biophys. J.* 47:250a

48. Siegel, D. 1985. Membrane-membrane interactions via intermediates in the La-HII transition. *Biophys. J.* 47:250a

49. Verkleij, A. J., Mombers, C., Gerritsen, W. J., Leunissen-Bijvelt, L., Cullis, P. R. 1979. Fusion of phospholipid vesicles in association with the appearance of lipidic particles a visualized by freeze fracturing. *Biochim. Biophys. Acta* 555:358–61

50. Verkleij, A. J., Mombers, C., Leunissen-Bijvelt, J., Ververgaert, P. H. 1979. Lipidic intermembraneous particles. *Nature* 279:162–63

51. Wakelam, M. J. O. 1983. Inositol phospholipid metabolism and myoblast fusion. *Biochem. J.* 214:77–82

52. Wilschut, J., Duzgunes, N., Fraley, R., Papahadjopoulos, D. 1980. Studies on the mechanism of membrane fusion: Kinetics of calcium ion-induced fusion of phosphatidylserine vesicles followed by a new assay for mixing of aqueous vesicle contents. *Biochemistry* 19:6011–21

52a. Whitaker, M., Aitchison, M. 1985. Calcium-dependent polyphosphoinositide hydrolysis is associated with exocytosis in vitro. *FEBS Lett.* 182:119–24

53. Wilschut, J., Duzgunes, N., Hong, K., Hoekstra, D., Papahadjopoulos, D. 1983. Retention of aqueous contents during divalent cation-induced fusion of phospholipid vesicles. *Biochim. Biophys. Acta* 734:309–18

54. Zimmerberg, J., Cohen, F. S., Finkelstein, A. 1980. Fusion of phospholipid vesicles with planar phospholipid bilayer membranes. I. Discharge of vesicular contents across the planar membrane. *J. Gen. Physiol.* 75:241–50

Ann. Rev. Physiol. 1986. 48:213–223

ROLE OF MEMBRANE FUSION IN HORMONAL REGULATION OF EPITHELIAL TRANSPORT

James B. Wade

Department of Physiology, University of Maryland School of Medicine, Baltimore, Maryland 21201

INTRODUCTION

For some time it has been apparent that cellular mechanisms of membrane biogenesis must play an important role in the synthesis and insertion of the transport systems responsible for the characteristic permeability and active transport capacities of cell membranes. In recent years there has been growing evidence that many cells maintain a population of membrane transport proteins in specific intracellular membrane vesicles. In such cells an important mechanism of transport regulation involves fusion of these vesicles with the plasma membrane and the resulting insertion of additional transport proteins into the plasma membrane. Although this review focuses on the role of this mechanism in epithelial hormonal responses, there are a growing number of transport responses that appear to utilize this type of mechanism. The importance of membrane fusion as a transport regulatory mechanism was first recognized in the oxyntic cells of the stomach (16). Parallel regulatory responses have also been described in the urinary bladders of the toad (60, 88), turtle (23, 83), and rabbit (50). There also appears to be an analogous system responsible for the action of insulin on glucose transport by the adipocyte (9, 85). These systems vary in many respects, but in each case cellular transport activity is regulated by fusion of cytoplasmic vesicles with the plasma membrane.

213

0066-4278/86/0315-0213$02.00

REGULATION OF THE APICAL MEMBRANE

Water Permeability Response

Structure-function analysis of the amphibian urinary bladder's response to vasopressin has provided compelling evidence that a membrane fusion mechanism plays an important role in regulating apical membrane permeability. A distinctive feature of this system is a specialized organization of intramembrane particles, identified in freeze-fracture studies of the bladder's response to vasopressin (7, 41). These intramembrane particle aggregates appear to represent sites of specialized transmembrane water channels that are responsible for the bladder's hydroosmotic response to vasopressin (37, 41). In the absence of vasopressin the aggregates occur in the membrane of long tubular vesicles in the cytoplasm (35, 87) that have been named aggrephores by Muller & Kachadorian (59). When the bladder epithelial cells are stimulated by vasopressin, the aggrephores shift from a horizontal position in the cytoplasm to fuse with the apical membrane (76). Many aggregates leave the site of membrane fusion and are found on the flat surface of the apical membrane (30, 60). Fused aggrephores are not just associated with induction of the response but are observed in equal numbers long after initiation of the hormone response (60). It has been suggested that a given aggrephore remains fused with the apical surface continuously during hormone exposure (60). Alternatively, the association of aggrephores with the apical surface may be a dynamic process since vasopressin-stimulated bladders internalize large molecular weight tracers into cytoplasmic membrane vesicles that are the same size and shape as the aggrephores (55, 88). Following removal of vasopressin from the bathing medium there is a rapid reduction in water permeability that is sensitive to certain inhibitors (54), and both aggregates and aggrephore fusion sites disappear from the apical membrane (59).

The ultrastructural evidence for a membrane fusion mechanism in the action of vasopressin has been augmented by electrical capacitance measurements, which indicate an increase in apical membrane area following vasopressin exposure (65, 66, 82, 91). The close correspondence between changes in capacitance and fusion of aggrephores with the apical membrane suggests that the capacitance measurements can be used to monitor addition of aggregate-containing membrane to the apical membrane. Remarkably, the vasopressin-induced capacitance change is much larger (18% or more) than expected based on early measurements of the area occupied by those aggregates that occur in the flat portion of the apical membrane (41). Although it is possible that membrane other than that involved in the aggrephore system is added to the apical surface (24, 84), the most likely explanation is that the major portion of the area change results from the fusion of aggrephores with the apical membrane (65). Aggrephores have been estimated to be 0.1 μm in diameter and as long as 2 μm (38), and the incidence of fusion sites is thought to be as great as 15 fused aggrephores per 100 μm^2 (60). These data yield a substantially greater area of aggregate-containing membrane that is added to the apical surface than was previously estimated.

The possibility that aggregates in the walls of the fused aggrephores may be important sites of water movement has been evaluated by Levine et al (46). The diameter of these tubules is sufficiently large that only a small fall in driving force along the tubule would be expected (46). It appears that the osmotic gradient across the wall of the tubule can be largely maintained if the mucosal fluid is sufficiently dilute. In addition, the identification of an amiloride-insensitive current that appears to be related to aggrephore fusion (82) may mean that sufficient solute permeability is associated with aggregates to prevent solute concentration from rising in the tubule to a level high enough to retard osmotic flow.

The analysis of Levine et al (46) indicates that diffusional water permeability, $P_d(w)$, may be much more impaired by water movement through these structures than is osmotic permeability, (P_f). This realization is important for interpreting the significance of P_d and P_f measurements. Although high values for $P_f/P_d(w)$ had been observed in early studies of vasopressin-treated tissues (31, 44), their accuracy appeared to be severely limited by the presence of unstirred layers and tissue-related series barriers that could significantly affect the values obtained (12, 29). The recognition that these values could be used to estimate channel length if water molecules moved through the channels in single file (48) reawakened interest in these parameters. A number of laboratories have now estimated these values with corrections for unstirred layers, and all have obtained high values for P_f/P_d after administration of vasopressin (32, 46, 67). While this may arise from a long narrow channel, the result can also be explained by other configurations, including the fused-aggrephore model (46). Although the fused-aggrephore model is attractive in several respects, it has not yet been possible to rigorously evaluate the contribution of these structures to water flow across the apical membrane. This is particularly important because under certain circumstances the number of fused aggrephores has not been found to be closely correlated with changes in the magnitude of water flow (39, 60).

Solute Permeability Response

Although vasopressin increases the apical membrane's permeability to sodium and a number of nonelectrolytes such as urea, the possible involvement of membrane fusion in these responses is less certain than for the water permeability response. The finding that it is possible to dissociate these responses by a variety of maneuvers, including use of inhibitors, indicates that water and solutes move via very different channels (3, 26, 45). Since the responses are mediated by cAMP (25) and occur in the same cell type (13, 73), the nature of the post-cAMP responses involved is especially puzzling. It is clear from studies using fluctuation analysis that vasopressin increases the number of amiloride-inhibitable sodium channels in the apical membrane (33, 52). Aldosterone has also been found to increase the number of active channels (64). An increase in the number of active channels could occur by activation of electrically silent channels that are continuously present in the membrane, or additional active channels might be inserted into the apical membrane by fusion of channel-rich vesicles with the apical surface.

The analysis by Lewis and colleagues of the rabbit urinary bladder has provided compelling evidence that vesicles in the cytoplasm of this epithelium contain amiloride-sensitive sodium channels that fuse with the apical surface when the epithelium is stretched or the epithelial cells are swollen (50, 51). Previous observations indicate that stretching induces a striking increase in sodium transport in frog skin (62) and toad urinary bladder (90). While this indicates that a cytoplasmic pool of vesicles with sodium channels may also be available in these tissues, it is not certain to what extent the transfer of these channels to the apical membrane plays an important role in the response to hormones.

In the case of aldosterone a variety of evidence indicates that channels preexisting in the apical membrane are activated (20, 43, 63), but Garty & Edelman raise the possibility that vasopressin's action may involve insertion of additional sodium channels into the membrane (20). Although trypsin exposure from the mucosal side irreversibly inactivated a substantial fraction of sodium transport, the vasopressin response was unaffected by a prior trypsin treatment (20). This observation is in contrast to work with other reagents where pretreatments did reduce the subsequent response to vasopressin (63, 69). One explanation for the latter result would be that these reagents may impair the vesicle fusion mechanism as well as act on apical membrane sodium channels. Alternatively, a conformational change produced by vasopressin could alter the sensitivity of channels to trypsin such that the result of Garty & Edelman might be observed without requiring the addition of channels to the surface from vesicles. Thus the role of membrane fusion in the sodium transport response to vasopressin is uncertain at this time.

REGULATION OF THE BASOLATERAL MEMBRANE

The possibility that fusion of cytoplasmic vesicles mediates transport responses at the basolateral surface has not been extensively evaluated. Basolateral membrane transport systems are undoubtedly synthesized and transferred to the plasma membrane by intracellular membrane biogenesis. However, it is not certain that a significant pool of these vesicles is maintained in the cytoplasm nor that vesicle fusion with the basolateral surface is an important means of regulating transport.

Many studies have evaluated the possibility that effects of aldosterone on renal sodium and potassium excretion may, at least in part, involve modulation of the number of Na,K-ATPase pumps. Striking effects of corticosteriod exposure on NaK-ATPase activity have been demonstrated with long-term exposures to hormone (5, 14, 18, 58). Ultrastructural studies have demonstrated remarkably parallel changes in basolateral membrane area associated with such long-term treatments (42, 81, 89). Although the detailed mechanism for this stimulation remains uncertain, apparently the relatively rapid effects of aldosterone on pump activity that occur with 3 hr exposures are secondary to increased sodium entry across the luminal membrane (71). There is also evidence for an additional long-term effect of aldosterone on transport that involves biosynthesis of Na,K-ATPase (21, 22). The multiphase model for aldosterone action proposed by Rossier (75) may also explain the finding that the renal transport response to brief aldosterone exposures is not associated with a detectable change in membrane area, while long-term exposure greatly enhances both transport and basolateral membrane area (80). The increase in membrane area associated with the long-term response indicates that fusion of membrane vesicles with the basolateral surface may be the mechanism for the increase in sodium pump activity. There is no definitive evidence at this time to indicate whether this occurs by new membrane biogenesis subsequent to aldosterone stimulation or via fusion of cytoplasmic vesicles rich in Na-K-ATPase from a preexisting pool.

Recent work suggests that insertion and removal of basolateral K channels may be an important regulatory mechanism (17, 49). K exit from the cell changes when rates of active transport are altered in order to minimize effects on cell volume. The finding by Foskett & Spring (17) that the regulatory volume decrease is sensitive to cytochalasin B raises the possibility that microfilament-mediated translocation of vesicles may be involved in regulating basolateral permeability. Recent observations suggest that vasopressin may have actions at the basolateral surface in addition to its well-established apical membrane action (40, 79), but there is no evidence to indicate whether or not these effects are mediated by a membrane fusion mechanism.

REGULATION BY INTRACELLULAR COMPONENTS

Cytoskeleton

The possible role of the cytoskeleton in epithelial transport responses has been of major interest because translocation of vesicles into apposition with the plasma membrane is a necessary precondition for membrane fusion. In the case of the water permeability response to vasopressin, the observation by Taylor and colleagues that the inhibitors of microtubules and microfilaments (colchicine and cytochalasin B, respectively) were potent inhibitors of the response (86) gave an early indication that the cytoskeleton was involved. The proposal that these cytoskeletal elements mediate vesicle translocation leading to insertion of transport elements has provided a useful rationale for a variety of observations (36, 65, 70). However, some observations are not easily explained by this model. For example, colchicine has been reported to have effects on prostaglandin E biosynthesis and action (1). Although inhibition by cytochalasin B of the water permeability response has been consistently observed in the presence of an osmotic gradient (27, 86), the failure to detect inhibition when no osmotic gradient is present has led Hardy & DiBona to question the prevailing model (27). However, use of cytochalasin B to evaluate the role of microfilaments may be complicated by possible effects of the drug at multiple sites (70). Since sites other than the apical membrane appear to influence measured rates of water movement under some circumstances (28, 40), measurements of overall transepithelial water permeability may not necessarily be an accurate quantitative assessment of changes in apical membrane permeability.

Calcium

Calcium promotes membrane fusion responses in many systems. Vasopressin treatment of toad bladder cells is known to enhance $^{45}Ca^{2+}$ efflux (11), and it has recently been reported that this effect is transient and precedes measureable changes in water permeability (2). Burch & Halushka suggest that release of calcium from the plasma membrane may be related to the fusion of intracellular vesicles with the apical membrane. Their measurements of quin-2 fluorescence indicate that intracellular calcium decreases with vasopressin exposure (2). This decrease may be important in the permeability response since a variety of maneuvers expected to increase intracellular calcium inhibit the water permeability response to vasopressin (reviewed in 47).

It is also possible that changes in intracellular calcium have a role in the stimulation of sodium transport by vasopressin. Extensive work indicates that regulation of apical membrane sodium permeability is mediated by variations in cytoplasmic calcium (reviewed in 6, 92). While some observations suggest that such responses may involve changes in the density of sodium channels (10), the recent finding that calcium can directly inhibit sodium permeability of isolated luminal membrane vesicles argues against the possibility that endocytosis and exocytosis of Na^+ channel-containing membranes are necessary for calcium-related regulation of Na permeability (6).

Protein Kinase C

In recent years intensive investigations have demonstrated a role for polyphosphoinositol turnover in receptor responses of a wide range of tissues (reviewed in 61). For example, this pathway may be involved in the response of hepato-cytes to vasopressin and angiotensin (19). A primary product of receptor-linked phosphatidylinositol breakdown is diacylglycerol, which can supply arachi-donate for prostaglandin synthesis and, perhaps most importantly, is a potent activator of protein kinase C (61). Phorbol esters can effectively substitute for diacylglycerol as stimulators of protein kinase C at physiologically low con-centrations of Ca^{2+} (4). A number of systems have been described in which phorbol esters dramatically stimulate exocytotic responses (34, 56, 74). Cal-cium-mediated exocytotic responses are greatly enhanced by phorbol esters and in some cases appear to be activated in the absence of changes in cytosolic calcium activity (74). Recent investigations of epithelia indicate that the protein kinase C system interfaces with cAMP-regulated transport responses (57, 77, 78). It appears likely that these systems interact to elicite and modulate a variety of important receptor-mediated responses (72).

Intracellular pH

Intracellular pH also appears to play a role in modulating membrane fusion responses. The water permeability response to vasopressin is inhibited by acidification of the bathing medium (53). Analysis of this effect in the toad bladder suggests that there may be effects of pH at multiple steps in the response. There is an important effect of pH on formation of cAMP that may result from enhanced PGE_2 synthesis (15). The pH inhibition of the water permeability response to vasopressin is reflected by a decrease in the in-tramembrane particle aggregates under ordinary circumstances (8); however, medium acidification at low temperature (8) or in cAMP-stimulated bladders (68) appears to reduce transepithelial water flow even when a high incidence of the aggregates is maintained in the membrane. This finding has raised the possibility that the water permeability of the aggregates may be directly in-fluenced by intracellular pH (8, 68). However, in view of the recent evidence that post-apical membrane regulation of water permeability may occur (40), the possibility of pH effects at another site cannot be ruled out.

SUMMARY

Fusion of cytoplasmic vesicles with the plasma membrane represents an impor-tant mechanism whereby additional transport proteins can be introduced into the cell membrane. Although it is apparent that some epithelial hormone responses, such as the vasopressin-induced change in water permeability, utilize this mechanism, the mechanism of some other responses remains un-certain. In addition, many details concerning the intracellular systems responsi-ble for controlling vesicle translocation and membrane fusion in epithelial hormone responses remain to be elucidated.

Literature Cited

1. Burch, R. M., Halushka, P. V. 1982. Inhibition of prostaglandin synthesis antagonizes the colchicine-induced reduction of vasopressin-stimulated water flow in the toad urinary bladder. *Mol. Pharmacol.* 21:142–49

2. Burch, R. M., Halushka, P. V. 1984. ADH or theophylline-induced changes in intracellular free and membrane-bound calcium. *Am. J. Physiol.* 247:F939–45

3. Carvounis, C. P., Franki, N., Levine, S. D., Hays, R. M. 1979. Membrane pathways for water and solutes in the toad bladder: I. Independent activation of water and urea transport. *J. Membr. Biol.* 49:253–68

4. Castagna, M., Takai, Y., Kaibuchi, K., Sano, K., Kikkawa, U., Nishizuka, Y. 1982. Direct activation of calcium-activated, phospholipid-dependent protein kinase by tumor-promoting phorbol esters. *J. Biol. Chem.* 257:7847–51

5. Charney, A. N., Silva, P., Besarab, A., Epstein, F. H. 1974. Separate effects of aldosterone, DOCA, and methylprednisolone on renal Na-K-ATPase. *Am. J. Physiol.* 227:345–50

6. Chase, H. S. 1984. Does calcium couple the apical and basolateral membrane permeabilities in epithelia? *Am. J. Physiol.* 247:F869–76

7. Chevalier, J., Bourguet, J., Hugon, J. S. 1974. Membrane associated particles: distribution in frog urinary bladder epithelium at rest and after oxytocin treatment. *Cell Tissue Res.* 152:129–40

8. Chevalier, J., Parisi, M., Bourguet, J. 1983. The rate-limiting step in hydrosmotic response of frog urinary bladder. A freeze-fracture study at different temperatures and medium pH. *Cell Tissue Res.* 228:345–55

9. Cushman, S. W., Wardzala, L. J. 1980. Potential mechanism of insulin action on glucose transport in the isolated rat adipose cell. *J. Biol. Chem.* 255:4758–62

10. Cuthbert, A. W., Shum, W. K. 1977. Does intracellular sodium modify membrane permeability to sodium ions? *Nature* 266:468–69

11. Cuthbert, A. W., Wong, P. Y. D. 1974. Calcium release in relation to permeability changes in toad bladder epithelium following antidiuretic hormone. *J. Physiol.* 241:407–22

12. Dainty, J., House, C. R. 1966. An examination of the evidence for membrane pores in frog skin. *J. Physiol.* 185:172–84

13. DiBona, D. R., Civan, M. M., Leaf, A. 1969. The cellular specificity of the effect of vasopressin on toad urinary bladder. *J. Membr. Biol.* 1:79–91

14. El Mernissi, G., Chabardés, D., Doucet, A., Hus-Citharel, A., Imbert-Teboul, M., et al. 1983. Changes in tubular basolateral membrane markers after chronic DOCA treatment. *Am. J. Physiol.* 245:F100–9

15. Forrest, J. N., Schneider, C. J., Goodman, D. B. P. 1982. Role of prostaglandin E$_2$ in mediating the effects of pH on the hydroosmotic response to vasopressin in the toad urinary bladder. *J. Clin. Invest.* 69:499–506

16. Forte, T. M., Machen, T. E., Forte, J. G. 1977. Ultrastructural changes in oxyntic cells associated with secretory funtion: A membrane recycling hypothesis. *Gastroenterology* 73:941–55

17. Foskett, J. K., Spring, K. R. 1985. Involvement of calcium and cytoskeleton in gallbladder epithelial cell volume regulation. *Am. J. Physiol.* 248:C27–C36

18. Garg, L. C., Knepper, M. A., Burg, M. B. 1981. Mineralocorticoid effects on Na-K-ATPase in individual nephron segments. *Am. J. Physiol.* 240:F536–44

19. Garrison, J. C., Johnsen, D. E., Campanile, C. P. 1984. Evidence for the role of phosphorylase kinase, protein kinase C, and other Ca^{2+}-sensitive protein kinases in the response of hepatocytes to angiotensin II and vasopressin. *J. Biol. Chem.* 259:3283–92

20. Garty, H., Edelman, I. S. 1983. Amiloride-sensitive trypsinization of apical sodium channels. Analysis of hormonal regulation of sodium transport in toad bladder. *J. Gen. Physiol.* 81:785–803

21. Geering, K., Claire, M., Gaeggeler, H. P., Rossier, B. C. 1985. Receptor occupancy vs. induction of Na$^+$-K$^+$-ATPase and Na$^+$ transport by aldosterone. *Am. J. Physiol.* 248:C102–8

22. Geering, K., Girardet, M., Bron, C., Kraehenbühl, J. P., Rossier, B. C. 1982. Hormonal regulation of (Na$^+$, K$^+$) ATPase biosynthesis in the toad bladder. *J. Biol. Chem.* 257:10338–43

23. Gluck, S., Cannon, C., Al-Awqati, Q. 1982. Exocytosis regulates urinary acidification in turtle bladder by rapid insertion of H$^+$ pumps into the luminal membrane. *Proc. Natl. Acad. Sci. USA* 79:4327–31

24. Gronowicz, G., Masur, S. K., Holtzman, E. 1980. Quantitative analysis of exocytosis and endocytosis in the

hydroosmotic response of toad bladder. *J. Membr. Biol.* 52:221–35
25. Handler, J. S., Butcher, R. W., Sutherland, E. W., Orloff, J. 1965. The effect of vasopressin and of theophylline on the concentration of adenosine 3',5'-phosphate in the urinary bladder of the toad. *J. Biol. Chem.* 240:4524–26
26. Hardy, M. A. 1985. Urea and Na$^+$ permeabilities in toad urinary bladder: one or two solute pathways? *Am. J. Physiol.* 248:F56–F63
27. Hardy, M. A., DiBona, D. R. 1982. Microfilaments and the hydrosmotic action of vasopressin in toad urinary bladder. *Am. J. Physiol.* 243:C200–4
28. Hardy, M. A., DiBona, D. R. 1982. Extracellular Ca^{++} and the effect of antidiuretic hormone on the water permeability of the toad urinary bladder: an example of flow-induced alteration of flow. *J. Membrane Biol.* 67:27–44
29. Hays, R. M. 1968. A new proposal for the action of vasopressin, based on studies of a complex synthetic membrane. *J. Gen. Physiol.* 51:385–98
30. Hays, R. M., Chevalier, J., Gobin, R., Bourguet, J. 1985. Fusion images and intramembrane particle aggregates during the action of antidiuretic hormone. A rapid-freeze study. *Cell Tissue Res.* 240:433–39
31. Hays, R. M., Leaf, A. 1962. Studies on the movement of water through the isolated toad bladder and its modification by vasopressin. *J. Gen. Physiol.* 45:905–19
32. Hebert, S. C., Andreoli, T. E. 1980. Interactions of temperature and ADH on transport processes in cortical collecting tubules. *Am. J. Physiol.* 238:F470–80
33. Helman, S. I., Cox, T. C., Van Driessche, W. 1983. Hormonal control of apical membrane Na transport in epithelia. Studies with fluctuation analysis. *J. Gen. Physiol.* 82:201–20
34. Hubinont, C. J., Best, L., Sener, A., Malaisse, W. J. 1984. Activation of protein kinase C by a tumor-promoting phorbol ester in pancreatic islets. *FEBS Lett.* 170:247–53
35. Humbert, F., Montesano, R., Grosso, A., deSousa, R. C., Orci, L. 1977. Particle aggregates in plasma and intracellular membranes of toad bladder (granular cell). *Experientia* 33:1364–67
36. Kachadorian, W. A., Ellis, S. A., Muller, J. 1979. Possible roles for microtubules and microfilaments in ADH action on toad urinary bladder. *Am. J. Physiol.* 236:F14–F20
37. Kachadorian, W. A., Levine, S. D., Wade, J. B., DiScala, V. A., Hays, R. M. 1977. Relationship of aggregated intramembranous particles to water permeability in vasopressin-treated toad urinary bladder. *J. Clin. Invest.* 59:576–81
38. Kachadorian, W. A., Muller, J., Finkelstein, A. 1981. Role of osmotic forces in exocytosis: studies of ADH induced fusion in toad urinary bladder. *J. Cell Biol.* 91:584–88
39. Kachadorian, W. A., Muller, J., Rudich, S., DiScala, V. A. 1981. Relation of ADH effects to altered membrane fluidity in toad urinary bladder. *Am. J. Physiol.* 240:F63–F69
40. Kachadorian, W. A., Sariban-Sohraby, S., Spring, K. R. 1985. Regulation of water permeability in toad urinary bladder at two barriers. *Am. J. Physiol.* 248:F260–65
41. Kachadorian, W. A., Wade, J. B., Uiterwyk, C. C., DiScala, V. A. 1977. Membrane structural and functional responses to vasopressin in toad bladder. *J. Membr. Biol.* 30:381–401
42. Kaissling, B., LeHir, M. 1982. Distal tubular segments of the rabbit kidney after adaptation to altered Na- and K-intake. I. Structural changes. *Cell Tissue Res.* 224:469–92
43. Kipnowski, J., Park, C. S., Fanestil, D. D. 1983. Modification of carboxyl of Na$^+$ channel inhibits aldosterone action on Na$^+$ transport. *Am. J. Physiol.* 245:F726–34
44. Koefoed-Johnsen, V., Ussing, H. H. 1953. The contributions of diffusion and flow to the passage of D$_2$O through living membranes. *Acta Physiol. Scand.* 28:60–76
45. Levine, S., Franki, N., Hays, R. M. 1973. The effect of phloretin on water and solute movement in the toad bladder. *J. Clin. Invest.* 52:1435–42
46. Levine, S. D., Jacoby, M., Finkelstein, A. 1984. The water permeability of toad urinary bladder II. The value of P_f/P_d(w) for the antidiuretic hormone-induced water permeation pathway. *J. Gen. Physiol.* 83:543–61
47. Levine, S. D., Schlondorff, D. 1984. The role of calcium in the action of vasopressin. *Semin. Nephrol.* 4:144–58
48. Levitt, D. G. 1974. A new theory of transport for cell membrane pores. I. General theory and application to red cell. *Biochim. Biophys. Acta* 373:115–31
49. Lewis, S. A., Butt, A. G., Bowler, M. J., Leader, J. P., MacKnight, A. D. C. 1985. Effects of anions on cellular volume and transepithelial Na$^+$ transport across toad urinary bladder. *J. Membr. Biol.* 83:119–37
50. Lewis, S. A., de Moura, J. L. C. 1984.

Apical membrane area of rabbit urinary bladder increases by fusion of intracellular vesicles: An electrophysiological study. *J. Membr. Biol.* 82:123–36

51. Lewis, S. A., Ifshin, M. S., Loo, D. D. F., Diamond, J. M. 1984. Studies of sodium channels in rabbit urinary bladder by noise analysis. *J. Membr. Biol.* 80:135–51

52. Li, J. H. Y., Palmer, L. G., Edelman, I. S., Lindemann, B. 1982. The role of sodium-channel density in the natriferic response of the toad urinary bladder to an antidiuretic hormone. *J. Membr. Biol.* 64:77–89

53. Lorenzen, M., Taylor, A., Windhager, E. E. 1983. pH effect on osmotic response of collecting tubules to vasopressin and 8-cpt-cAMP. *Am. J. Physiol.* 245:F188–97

54. Masters, B. R., Fanestil, D. D. 1979. Metabolic dependence of the offset of antidiuretic hormone-induced osmotic flow of water across the toad urinary bladder. *J. Membr. Biol.* 48:237–47

55. Masur, S. K., Cooper, S., Rubin, M. S. 1984. Effect of an osmotic gradient on antidiuretic hormone-induced endocytosis and hydroosmosis in the toad urinary bladder. *Am. J. Physiol.* 247:F370–79

56. Masur, S. K., Rivero, D., Sapirstein, V. 1985. Phorbol myristate acetate induces exocytosis, endocytosis and hydroosmosis in the toad urinary bladder. *Kidney Int.* 27:330 (Abstr.)

57. Mauro, T., Rubenstein, D., O'Brien, T., Civan, M. M. 1985. Effects of tumor promoters in Na^+ transport across frog skin. *Fed. Proc.* 44:1567 (Abstr.)

58. Mujais, S. K., Chekal, M. A., Jones, W. J., Hayslett, J. P., Katz, A. I. 1984. Regulation of renal Na-K-ATPase in the rat. Role of the natural mineralo- and glucocorticoid hormones. *J. Clin. Invest.* 73:13–19

59. Muller, J., Kachadorian, W. A. 1984. Aggregate-carrying membranes during ADH stimulation and washout in toad bladder. *Am. J. Physiol.* 247:C90–C98

60. Muller, J., Kachadorian, W. A., Di-Scala, V. A. 1980. Evidence that ADH-stimulated intramembrane particle aggregates are transferred from cytoplasmic to luminal membranes in toad bladder epithelial cells. *J. Cell Biol.* 85:83–95

61. Nishizuka, Y. 1984. The role of protein kinase C in cell surface signal transduction and tumour promotion. *Nature* 308:693–98

62. Nutbourne, D. M. 1968. The effect of small hydrostatic pressure gradients on the rate of active sodium transport across isolated frog-skin membranes. *J. Physiol.* 195:1–18

63. Palmer, L. G., Edelman, I. S. 1981. Control of apical sodium permeability in the toad urinary bladder by aldosterone. *Ann. NY Acad. Sci.* 372:1–14

64. Palmer, L. G., Li, J. H. Y., Lindemann, B., Edelman, I. S. 1982. Aldosterone control of the density of sodium channels in the toad urinary bladder. *J. Membrane Biol.* 64:91–102

65. Palmer, L. G., Lorenzen, M. 1983. Antidiuretic hormone-dependent membrane capacitance and water permeability in the toad urinary bladder. *Am. J. Physiol.* 244:F195–F204

66. Palmer, L. G., Speez, N. 1984. Modulation of antidiuretic hormone-dependent capacitance and water flow in toad urinary bladder. *Am. J. Physiol.* 246:F501–8

67. Parisi, M., Bourguet, J. 1983. The single file hypothesis and the water channels induced by antidiuretic hormmone. *J. Membrane Biol.* 71:189–93

68. Parisi, M., Bourguet, J. 1984. Effects of cellular acidification on ADH-induced intramembrane particle aggregates. *Am. J. Physiol.* 246:C157–59

69. Park, C. S., Kipnowski, J., Fanestil, D. D. 1983. Role of carboxyl group in Na^+—entry step at apical membrane of toad urinary bladder. *Am. J. Physiol.* 245:F707–15

70. Pearl, M., Taylor, A. 1983. Actin filaments and vasopressin-stimulated water flow in toad urinary bladder. *Am. J. Physiol.* 245:C28–C39

71. Petty, K. J., Kokko, J. P., Marver, D. 1981. Secondary effect of aldosterone on Na-K ATPase activity in the rabbit cortical collecting tubule. *J. Clin. Invest.* 68:1514–21

72. Rasmussen, H., Barrett, P. Q. 1984. Calcium messenger system: an integrated view. *Physiol. Rev.* 64:938–84

73. Rick, R., Roloff, C., Dorge, A., Beck, F. X., Thurau, K. 1984. Intracellular electrolyte concentrations in the frog skin epithelium: Effect of vasopressin and dependence on the Na concentration in the bathing media. *J. Membr. Biol.* 78:129–45

74. Rink, T. J., Sanchez, A., Hallam, T. J. 1983. Diacylglycerol and phorbol ester stimulate secretion without raising cytoplasmic free calcium in human platelets. *Nature* 305:317–19

75. Rossier, B. C. 1983. Biosynthesis of (Na^+, K^+)-ATPase in amphibian epithelial cells. *Curr. Topics Membr. Transport* 20:125–45

76. Sasaki, J., Tilles, S., Condeelis, J., Car-

boni, J., Meiteles, L., et al. 1984. Electron-microscopic study of the apical region of the toad bladder epithelial cell. *Am. J. Physiol.* 247:C268–81

77. Schlondorff, D., Levine, S. D. 1985. Protein kinase C inhibits vasopressin (VP)-stimulated water flow in toad urinary bladder. *Kidney Int.* 27:334 (Abstr.)

78. Schlondorff, D., Satriano, J. A. 1985. Interactions of vasopressin, cAMP, and prostaglandins in toad urinary bladder. *Am. J. Physiol.* 248:F454–58

79. Schoen, H. F., Erlij, D. 1985. Neurohypophyseal peptides influence both apical and basolateral membranes of frog skin. *Fed. Proc.* 44:1567 (Abstr.)

80. Stanton, B., Biemesderfer, D., Kashgarian, M., Wade, J., Giebisch, G. 1985. Mechanism and time course of aldosterone (aldo) induced stimulation of Na$^+$ and K$^+$ transport by renal collecting tubule. *Fed. Proc.* 44:1566 (Abstr.)

81. Stanton, B., Janzen, A., Klein-Robbenhaar, G., DeFronzo, R., Giebisch, G., Wade, J. 1985. Ultrastructure of rat initial collecting tubule: Effect of adrenal corticosteroid treatment. *J. Clin. Invest.* 75:1327–34

82. Stetson, D. L., Lewis, S. A., Alles, W., Wade, J. B. 1982. Evaluation by capacitance measurements of antidiuretic hormone induced membrane area changes in toad bladder. *Biochim. Biophys. Acta* 689:267–74

83. Stetson, D. L., Steinmetz, P. R. 1983. Role of membrane fusion in CO$_2$ stimulation of proton secretion by turtle bladder. *Am. J. Physiol.* 245:C113–20

84. Stetson, D. L., Wade, J. B. 1983. Ultrastructural characterization of cholesterol distribution in toad bladder

using filipin. *J. Membrane Biol.* 74:131–38

85. Suzuki, K., Kono, T. 1980. Evidence that insulin causes translocation of glucose transport activity to the plasma membrane from an intracellular storage site. *Proc. Natl. Acad. Sci. USA* 77:2542–45

86. Taylor, A., Mamelak, M., Reaven, E., Maffly, R. 1973. Vasopressin: Possible role of microtubules and microfilaments in its action. *Science* 181:347–50

87. Wade, J. B. 1978. Membrane structural specialization of the toad urinary bladder revealed by the freeze-fracture technique. III. Location, structure and vasopressin dependence of intramembrane particle arrays. *J. Membr. Biol.* 40 (Spec. issue):281–96

88. Wade, J. B., Stetson, D. L., Lewis, S. A. 1981. ADH action: Evidence for a membrane shuttle mechanism. *Ann. NY Acad. Sci.* 372:106–17

89. Wade, J. B., O'Neil, R. G., Pryor, J. L., Boulpaep, E. L. 1979. Modulation of cell membrane area in renal collecting tubules by corticosteroid hormones. *J. Cell Biol.* 81:439–45

90. Walser, M. 1969. Reversible stimulation of sodium transport in the toad bladder by stretch. *J. Clin. Invest.* 48:1714–23

91. Warncke, J., Lindemann, B. 1981. Effect of ADH on the capacitance of apical epithelial membranes. In *Int. Congr. Physiol. Sci. 28th, Budapest, 1980. Proc., Adv. Physiol. Sci.*, 3:129–33. New York: Pergamon

92. Windhager, E. E., Taylor, A. 1983. Regulatory role of intracellular calcium ions in epithelial Na transport. *Ann. Rev. Physiol.* 45:519–32

Ann. Rev. Physiol. 1986. 48:225–38

REGULATION OF MEMBRANE FUSION IN SECRETORY EXOCYTOSIS

Robert C. De Lisle and John A. Williams

Department of Physiology, University of California, San Francisco, California 94143;
Cell Biology Laboratory, Mount Zion Hospital and Medical Center, San Francisco,
California 94117

INTRODUCTION

Exocytosis is a ubiquitous cell function that involves the intracellular transport and fusion of membrane-bound cytoplasmic vesicles or granules with the plasma membrane. Once the cytoplasmic granule and the plasma membrane have fused, their membranes are continuous and the granule interior now faces outside the cell. Hence, exocytosis serves both to incorporate membrane proteins into the plasma membrane and to secrete the contents of the granule. Since this review will focus on secretion, the membrane undergoing fusion with the plasma membrane will be referred to as the secretory organelle (or granule), and the end result of exocytosis will be referred to as secretion.

There appear to be two pathways for exocytosis, constitutive and regulated (24). Constitutive exocytosis, which occurs independently of extracellular stimuli and proceeds at a steady rate, is thought to be responsible for the insertion of plasma membrane proteins and secretion of extracellular matrix components. In contrast, regulated exocytosis, which is triggered by extracellular stimuli, is responsible for episodic secretion of hormones, neurotransmitters, digestive enzymes, etc. In addition, regulated exocytosis provides a mechanism for the rapid insertion of membrane transport proteins into the plasma membrane (38).

The basic scheme outlined by Palade (50) is still adequate to describe the overall morphological sequence of events in exocytosis. This sequence includes: (*a*) translocation of the secretory organelle from its point of formation,

225

0066-4278/86/0315-0225$02.00

usually near the center of the cell, to a position near the plasma membrane; (*b*) close apposition of secretory organelle and the plasma membrane; (*c*) fusion of secretory organelle and the plasma membrane; and (*d*) retrieval of the secretory organelle membrane. Since exocytosis is present in all cell types, yet serves somewhat different functions in each, one might expect some variation in the morphology and biochemistry of exocytosis. Nevertheless, the underlying process is expected to be the same, and the variations that do exist should help in the discovery of the common factors and basic mechanisms of exocytosis.

THE MORPHOLOGY OF EXOCYTOSIS

Translocation of Secretory Organelles

Before a secretory organelle can fuse with the plasma membrane the two must be closely apposed. The positioning of secretory organelles in resting cells varies among cell types. Most secretory cells have some organelles close to the plasma membrane and others deeper in the cytoplasm. These cells can rapidly release only 10–20% of their secretory content upon stimulation (70), which may be a function of the proportion of organelles near the plasma membrane that are ready for secretion. For prolonged secretion or recovery for future secretion, more organelles must be recruited from deeper in the cytoplasm to replace those exocytosed. Other cells, such as mast cells, goblet cells, and parotid acinar cells, release more than 50% of their secretory product in a short time via compound exocytosis. In compound exocytosis an organelle can fuse to another organelle when the latter is already fused with the plasma membrane or another organelle. Somehow organelles "recognize" an organelle that has fused as "plasma membrane."

Plattner et al (52) described the intracellular transport and positioning of secretory organelles (trichocysts) in growing *Paramecium tetraurelia*. Three levels of control of the movement of trichocysts were proposed. First, trichocysts were seen associated with microtubules as the trichocysts were moved from the cytoplasm to nearer the plasma membrane. Second, near the plasma membrane the trichocysts seemed to be guided to a specific area of the plasma membrane by a microfilament network. Finally, the trichocysts were attached to the plasma membrane at a "plug" of material.

These observations suggest involvement of microtubules and microfilaments in organelle transport. Isolated secretory organelles bind to microtubules in a manner dependent on the presence of microtubule-associated proteins (MAPs) and may be regulated by MgATP and cAMP (64). A system of in vitro reconstituted microtubules was recently developed (67) that can translocate axoplasmic organelles in a manner dependent on ATP and soluble cytoplasmic protein(s) that are not MAPs. With the development of such in vitro reconstituted systems it will be possible to define the molecular mechanisms of intracellular organelle transport, including those of secretory granules.

Morphologically it appears that microfilaments are important for short-range translocation of secretory organelles to the site of secretion (52). If microfilaments do act in this fashion, they probably utilize the contractile interactions of actin and myosin. Immunofluorescence studies of a variety of exocrine glands have demonstrated the presence of actin, myosin, and actin-associated proteins around the luminal border of cells (17).

Positioning of Secretory Organelles at the Plasma Membrane

In some cells, once the secretory organelle is closely apposed to the plasma membrane it becomes associated with a morphologically defined release site. In *Tetrahymena* the mucocyst is in apposition to a rosette of prominent intramembrane particles (60); in *Paramecium* the trichocyst becomes attached to the plasma membrane at a "plug" of material (52), which may serve as a receptor for the secretory organelle membrane. Other cells that exhibit "prepositioning" of secretory organelles at release sites are neurons (28) and oocytes (59).

The common characteristic of cells that exhibit prepositioning of secretory organelles is that they respond rapidly to a secretory stimulus. Exocytosis at a synapse takes a few milliseconds. Prepositioning secretory organelles at the site of membrane fusion reduces the response time that would otherwise be needed to translocate and position organelles following cell stimulation. Most other cells do not respond so rapidly, and exocytosis begins seconds after stimulation. It is not known whether these slower-responding cells form structural membrane specializations, like those seen in prepositioning cells, that are present so transiently that their observation is unlikely.

Membrane Fusion

In various cell types the plasma membrane has been observed to invaginate and become apposed to the secretory organelle membrane as a prelude to secretion (37, 48, 51). This kind of observation suggests that the force-generating machinery is attached to the plasma membrane and the secretory organelle and that it pulls on the plasma membrane, causing it to invaginate. At one time it was thought that intramembraneous particles (IMP) were cleared from the membranes about to fuse (2, 51). It has since been demonstrated that this was an artifact of fixation; IMP clearing is not seen in rapidly frozen, unfixed tissues (28, 48).

Once the secretory organelle and plasma membranes are closely apposed their contact becomes so intimate that it appears as if the outer lipid leaflets of the two membranes have fused (48, 50). Fusion of membranes appears to begin at small localized areas where "pores" in the fusing membranes are seen (2, 48).

Based on the rarity of these observations and the fact that only small pores or large areas of fusion are seen, it seems likely that once fusion begins it proceeds quite rapidly.

Certain cell types, especially those of exocrine tissues such as pancreas and salivary gland, are highly polarized. In such cells exocytosis normally is strictly localized to the apical pole of the cell (39). In endocrine cells, such as adrenal medulla chromaffin cells, exocytosis can occur along most of the cell surface (27). The localization of exocytosis in exocrine cells probably involves structural specializations of the secretory surface. Differences between the apical and basolateral plasma membrane domains have been observed for the distribution of IMPs (14) and the localization of specific enzymes and hormone receptors (22). Filipin, an antibiotic that binds to cholesterol and creates a pattern visible in electron microscopy, has been used to demonstrate a paucity of cholesterol in luminal membranes of pancreatic acinar cells, which were proposed as sites of altered membrane fluidity (47).

STIMULUS-SECRETION COUPLING

Although the term stimulus-secretion coupling was originally coined to describe the role of Ca^{2+} in mediating secretion by chromaffin and other cells (15), it is now generally used in a broader sense to describe the regulatory events following reception of a signal that culminate in the secretion of proteins or ions. The focus in stimulus-secretion coupling has generally been on characterizing "second" or "intracellular" messengers, which will be discussed here; the next section will discuss the mechanisms activated by intracellular messengers.

The traditionally recognized intracellular messengers that control secretion are cAMP and calcium (58). Recent evidence suggests that diacylglycerol (DAG) and inositol-1,4,5-trisphosphate (IP_3) released during secretatogogue-evoked phosphoinositide (PI) breakdown also serve as important intracellular messengers (4, 44). Cyclic GMP is another possible secretory intracellular messenger, but its levels generally follow those of Ca^{2+}.

Different intracellular messengers may act differently in different tissues (58). cAMP mediates secretion by certain endocrine and exocrine cells, whereas it inhibits secretion by mast cells and platelets. A rise in intracellular Ca^{2+} initiates secretion in most cells, but in the parathyroid gland and renin-secreting cells of the juxtaglomerular apparatus it inhibits secretion (58). Thus, intracellular messengers are informational signals that can be utilized differently in different cell types.

Although there is little that is unique about the generation of cAMP in secretory cells, there have been a number of recent advances in our understanding of the role of Ca^{2+} and lipids as intracellular messengers (4, 44, 56). Direct evidence for the importance of Ca^{2+} as an intracellular messenger controlling secretion has been obtained using permeabilized cells. Following the work of Baker & Knight (3), who used high electrical fields to induce dielectric breakdown of the plasma membrane of chromaffin cells, a number of other means of selectively permeabilizing the plasma membrane now have been described. These include permeabilizing cells by using digitonin (7), Sendai virus (26), and ATP (23). These methods allow manipulation of the concentrations of specific ions, and in some cases small proteins, within the intracellular environment. Permeabilized cells in a medium containing MgATP secrete in a manner consistent with exocytosis in response to Ca^{2+} in the range of 1–100 μM (3, 26, 70). While these levels of Ca^{2+} are higher than observed physiologically, other factors may be necessary for secretion; recently GTP analogs have been shown to greatly enhance the Ca^{2+} sensitivity of permeabilized blood platelets (26). The authors of this study suggested that a GTP binding protein is involved in production of DAG, which would act synergistically with $Ca^{2+}{}_i$.

The methods used until recently to directly measure intracellular free Ca^{2+} were difficult to apply to small secretory cells. The development by Tsien et al of fluorescent chelate probes such as Quin-2 (66) have made it possible to monitor $Ca^{2+}{}_i$ continuously in secretory cells. Studies on both secretory and other cells have generally revealed a resting $Ca^{2+}{}_i$ of about 100 nM (45, 57, 66). Studies on platelets, pancreatic acinar cells, chromaffin cells, and pituitary tumor cells have shown a secretagogue-induced rise of $Ca^{2+}{}_i$ to 300–1000 nM within seconds. Usually $Ca^{2+}{}_i$ then declines within minutes to a smaller sustained increase. The extent to which the probe slows down or attenuates the rise in $Ca^{2+}{}_i$ is still uncertain. The use of Quin-2 has made it possible to demonstrate in cells such as pancreatic acinar cells that Ca^{2+} is mobilized from intracellular stores, since the initial secretagogue-induced rise in $Ca^{2+}{}_i$ is unaffected by Ca^{2+} removal from the medium (45). However, in some cases, such as thrombin-stimulated platelets, Quin-2 studies have indicated that presumed Ca^{2+}-mediated secretion can occur without a rise in $Ca^{2+}{}_i$ (57).

The elucidation of the influence of phosphatidylinositol (PI) turnover has been important in our understanding of Ca^{2+} as an intracellular messenger. In 1975 Michell noted that PI turnover (breakdown and resynthesis) accompanied the action of Ca^{2+}-mediated agonists in a number of systems (42). Recently it has been observed that cellular levels of polyphosphorylated inositol phospholipids, particularly phosphatidylinositol-4,5-bisphosphate (PIP$_2$), fall more rapidly than that of phosphatidylinositol when cells are activated. This finding suggests that the breakdown of these phospholipids may be the initial event that follows receptor activation (4). This breakdown occurs via a phospholipase C–like mechanism that leads to the production of DAG and the water-soluble inositol phosphates, inositol bis- and trisphosphate (IP$_2$ and IP$_3$). The suggestion by Berridge (4) that these water-soluble metabolites could be intracellular messengers was confirmed in permeabilized pancreatic acinar cells, in which IP_3 was shown to release sequestered Ca^{2+} (62). IP_3 has subsequently been shown in other cells and isolated vesicular fractions to release intracellular Ca^{2+}, primarily from the endoplasmic reticulum (49, 55). This demonstration of the role of IP_3 provides the missing link between the stimulation at the plasma membrane and the release of intracellular Ca^{2+} stores in cells that utilize intracellular Ca^{2+} as a messenger. The DAG produced during PI turnover can also be considered an intracellular messenger in light of its ability to activate protein kinase C.

In some neurally related secretory cells $Ca^{2+}{}_i$ is believed to increase following activation of membrane Ca^{2+} channels. In chromaffin cells Ca^{2+} channels have been demonstrated by patch clamp recording (19). In other cells, however, the existence of plasma membrane Ca^{2+} channels has only been deduced from the rapid inactivation of secretion upon removal of extracellular Ca^{2+}. Evidence has been presented recently for a guanine nucleotide binding protein in mast cells that is involved in coupling the IgE receptor to the Ca^{2+} channel (23). Whether or not IP_3 has any influence on membrane Ca^{2+} channels is also under investigation.

EFFECTOR MECHANISMS

Neutralization of Negatively Charged Membranes

Both secretory organelles and plasma membranes are known to possess a net negative surface charge, which generates a repulsive force that must be overcome to allow fusion. An early theory of the role of Ca^{2+} in secretion invoked neutralization of fixed negative surface charges. In simple artificial systems consisting of pure phospholipid vesicles, Ca^{2+} can induce membrane fusion, but only at concentrations in the millimolar range (18). In the presence of synexin, a cytosolic Ca^{2+}-binding protein (see below), and 1 mM Mg^{2+} the threshold for Ca^{2+}-induced fusion of negative phospholipid vesicles is reduced to about 10 μM (30). Thus, charge neutralization by Ca^{2+}, potentiated by cytosolic protein(s), may be involved in membrane fusion in exocytosis. This view, however, does not explain membrane fusion in cAMP- or DAG-mediated (Ca^{2+}-independent) secretion.

Cytoskeleton and Contractile Proteins

Although the cytoskeleton and associated contractile proteins are clearly involved in the transposition of newly synthesized secretory organelles (see above), it is not clear whether they are involved in the regulation of exocytosis. Agents that perturb cytoskeletal proteins, such as colchicine, inhibit intracellular translocation of newly synthesized proteins but do not block secretion of proteins from secretory granules already at the plasma membrane (1, 68). Thus it seems unlikely that microtubules are directly involved in regulation of exocytosis.

Studies on the possible roles of contractile proteins have generally taken two forms. First, many studies have evaluated the effects of cytochalasins on secretion. These agents disrupt the actin-containing microfilament network located just under the plasma membrane. Cytochalasin B enhances glucose-stimulated insulin secretion (46) but has no effect on or inhibits secretion by a variety of other secretory cells (1, 58). However, this agent is also known to interact with cellular components other than microfilaments.

The second type of study is based on the premise that force must be applied to bring about fusion and that the actinomyosin system exists in all cells. It is now clear that actin is frequently associated with secretory organelles (7). The actin-binding protein α-actinin also has been shown to be associated with chromaffin granules (32). Since the interaction of actin and α-actinin is Ca^{2+} sensitive, this could be a regulated process. Recently, the binding of F-actin by isolated chromaffin granules was shown to be inhibited by Ca^{2+} with a K_i of 0.3 μM (53). In a separate approach, physiological secretagogues have been shown to increase polymerization of actin (65), but the implications for secretion are unclear. Myosin, tropomyosin, and other muscle proteins also have been localized in secretory cells (17). Moreover, myosin light chains are phosphory-lated in both platelets and the pancreatic beta cell by a Ca^{2+}-regulated kinase (see below). How these observations are related to secretion remains to be established.

Protein Kinases and Phosphatases

Although not proven in detail for any secretory systems, it seems likely that reversible changes in protein phosphorylation are involved in the regulation of secretion. Reversible phosphorylation is the most common type of covalent protein modification and is clearly involved in metabolic regulation (10). All cells studied have cAMP-, Ca^{2+}-, and diacylglycerol-activated protein kinases, which would be affected by these intracellular messengers which are active in secretory cells. Moreover, the necessity of ATP in phosphorylation reactions could account in part for the energy dependence of secretion. Evidence for the importance of reversible phosphorylation also has been provided by the demon-stration that thiophosphorylation, which is not readily reversible, blocks chro-maffin cell secretion (6). However, in contrast to metabolic regulation, in which the enzymes regulated by phosphorylation are known, in the secretory process, the specific proteins involved are largely unknown. Therefore, most work to date has attempted to demonstrate changes in protein phosphorylation induced by secretagogues, or the presence of specific kinases and phosphatases in secretory cells.

While a single form of cAMP-activated protein kinase exists, there are a number of distinct Ca^{2+}-activated kinases that have different substrate specificities (10), most of which contain a calmodulin or closely related protein subunit or are activated by the Ca^{2+}-calmodulin complex. In contrast to these, protein kinase C is a Ca^{2+}- and phospholipid-dependent enzyme that is activated by DAG (44). A small amount of DAG can increase the apparent affinity for Ca^{2+} and may fully activate the enzyme without a change in Ca^{2+}_i. The tumor-promoting phorbol esters, such as 12-O-tetradecanoyl-phorbol-13-acetate (TPA), can substitute for DAG as activators of C kinase and are frequently used to determine a functional role for this kinase (44), just as Ca^{2+} ionophores such as A23187 are used to artificially activate Ca^{2+}-activated kinases.

In platelets, neither a small increase in Ca^{2+}_i induced by A23187 or TPA alone can initiate secretion, but combined they lead to exocytosis (72). Moreover, A23187 leads to enhanced phosphorylation of a 20-kilodalton (kDa) protein identified as myosin light chain, while TPA or synthetic DAG leads to phosphorylation of a 40-kDa protein whose function is unknown. Physiological secretagogues such as thrombin and platelet activating factor increase Ca^{2+}_i, DAG production, and the phosphorylation of both aforementioned proteins. A number of attempts have been made to generalize this model (56). However, in some cells, such as the guinea pig pancreatic acinar cell, TPA alone is a potent secretagogue (25), while in the intact chromaffin cell TPA has little or no effect (33). Moreover, in most secretory cells there are a number of changes in protein phosphorylation but changes in the 20 and 40-kDa proteins are not prominent.

In several cells specific protein dephosphorylation correlates best with secretion. In pancreatic acinar cells two low molecular weight (20 kDa) cytosolic proteins are rapidly and reversibly dephosphorylated by Ca^{2+}-mediated secretagogues (71). In *Paramecium tetraurelia* a 65-kDa membrane protein is dephosphorylated by secretory stimulus; this effect is absent in a mutant cell line incapable of secretory organelle (trichocyst) fusion (21).

Although the aforementioned work involved proteins identified only by molecular weight and isoelectric point, a number of studies have focused directly on the secretory organelle. In the chromaffin cell, calmodulin was shown to bind with high affinity to the secretory granule membrane in a Ca^{2+}-dependent manner and to activate a protein kinase that phosphorylates the granule membrane (8). Two of the phosphorylated proteins in the chromaffin granule were subsequently identified as tyrosine hydroxylase and the cAMP protein kinase regulatory subunit. It is doubtful that these are involved in regulation of exocytosis, and the role of the other phosphorylated proteins remains to be established. Recently, protein kinase C has also been shown to phosphorylate membrane proteins in isolated insulin granules (5) and zymogen granules of pancreatic acinar cells (71). To date, however, no specific phosphorylation of a secretory granule protein has been shown to occur within an intact cell as a response to stimulation.

Cytosolic Proteins

It is not surprising that most postulated effector mechanisms in exocytosis involve proteins, given the wide range of protein structures and their specificity. One of the clearest examples of a cytosolic protein involved in exocytosis is calmodulin. The antipsychotic drugs, which include trifluoperazine, inhibit exocytosis (16), probably by interacting with calmodulin or similar calcium-binding proteins. In the chromaffin cell, trifluoperazine inhibits membrane fusion but does not affect the intracellular transport of chromaffin granules (9). In addition, calmodulin associates with isolated synaptic vesicles in a calcium-independent manner (31). The most dramatic demonstration of calmodulin's involvement in exocytosis is the observation that an anti-calmodulin antibody inhibits cortical granule exocytosis in cortices from sea urchin eggs (61). From these data it is apparent that calmodulin action is fairly late in the series of events involved in exocytosis. The way in which calcium and calmodulin act to promote exocytosis is unclear, but protein kinases or phosphatases are probably involved.

Another well-studied cytosolic protein, synexin, was first isolated from chromaffin cells based on its ability to cause the aggregation of isolated granules (53). Initially, it was reported that synexin caused chromaffin granule aggregation in a Ca^{2+}-dependent manner, with the half-maximal effect at about 200 μM Ca^{2+}. More recent work (12) shows that synexin binding to chromaffin granules is half-maximal at about 4 μM Ca^{2+}, which is much closer to physiological $Ca^{2+}{}_i$ levels. Synexin-aggregated chromaffin granules will fuse with each other in the presence of small amounts of a fusogenic lipid such as arachidonic acid (53), which may also be produced during stimulus-response coupling by a phospholipase A_2–like enzyme. Fusion of isolated secretory organelles is used as a model of compound exocytosis. Interestingly, synexin also dramatically lowers the Ca^{2+} needed to fuse negatively charged phospholipid vesicles (30) to about 10 μM.

A promising approach taken by a number of groups is to use immobilized purified membranes in columns for affinity adsorption of cytosolic proteins. Creutz et al (11) have isolated a number of cytosolic proteins based on their ability to bind to Sepharose-linked chromaffin granule membranes in a Ca^{2+}-dependent manner. These proteins, termed chromobindins, include synexin, protein kinase C, and an endogenous C kinase substrate of 37 kDa (63). Using a similar approach, a protein from solubilized plasma membranes was isolated by virtue of its ability to bind to immobilized chromaffin granule membranes (41). This protein had a M_r of 51,000 and was postulated to be a receptor for granule-plasma membrane recognition during secretion. Another possible receptor was suggested by the demonstration that lectins bind to isolated chromaffin granules, which indicates the presence of a glycoprotein whose sugar residues are on the granule's cytoplasmic face (40). The presence of a glycoprotein with its carbohydrate portion in the cytoplasm is unusual, but most classical peptide hormone receptors are glycoproteins, albeit with oppositely-oriented glycosyl residues.

Other Possible Effectors

Other effector mechanisms have been studied with less conclusive results. Inhibitors of metalloendoprotease, such as 1-10 phenanthroline, blocked fusion of myoblasts and secretion from isolated chromaffin and mast cells (43). Since Ca^{2+} ionophore-induced secretion was also inhibited, Mundy & Strittmatter concluded that metalloendoprotease activity may be necessary for the terminal steps in secretion.

Another proposed effector mechanism is the methylation of carboxyl groups on granules and other organelles by the enzyme protein carboxyl methylase (PCM), which has been observed to increase methylation in pancreas, parotid, and chromaffin cells in response to appropriate secretagogues (54). Such methylation would neutralize negative charges on the substrate and is known to be a readily reversible process. However, inhibitors of PCM, although they largely blocked protein carboxylation, failed to inhibit pancreatic secretion (54). Thus, at best only a small part of cellular PCM activity is related to secretion.

MODEL SYSTEMS AND MECHANISMS OF MEMBRANE FUSION

A number of artificial systems have been designed to allow examination of fusion by intermixing the contents of two phospholipid vesicle populations. Such studies have yielded a good deal of information on the physical and chemical parameters important in membrane fusion. These physicochemical constraints on membrane fusion include the phospholipid composition of the membranes, the ionic strength and pH of the cell and medium, and the concentrations of divalent cations, notably Ca^{2+} (30). Such a system provides a well-defined model with which to test the effects of incorporated biological compounds on membrane interactions and fusion (30).

Another artificial system allows study of the interactions of phospholipid vesicles with a planar lipid bilayer (20). A distinct advantage of this system over one involving vesicle-vesicle interactions is that the planar lipid bilayer can simulate the plasma membrane. This allows the experimenter to test the effects of differences, such as ionic composition and osmotic strength, that may occur across the plasma membrane. As in the other system, putative biological mediators can be added to either of the membranes.

Systems based on compound exocytosis have been used; they involve the in vitro interaction of secretory organelles. Such a system provided the setting for the discovery of synexin (see above, and 53) and for the observations that served as the basis of the chemiosmotic hypothesis of exocytosis (29). With a similar approach, secretory organelle fusion was observed by freeze fracture electron microscopy (13). In some of these freeze fracture images, fusion of secretory organelles with plasma membrane contaminants was observed. Since secretory organelles do not normally fuse with one another, except in compound exocytosis in which at least one organelle must be fused with the plasma membrane, the interaction of secretory organelles with the plasma membrane is a more general model of exocytosis.

A system based on the interactions of chromaffin granules and plasma membranes has been developed by Konings and De Potter (36). They found that release of granule contents requires added plasma membranes in a dose-dependent manner and has a half-maximal Ca^{2+} dependency of about 1 μM (35). It is not yet known, however, whether the plasma membrane fraction in these experiments is in the form of membrane sheets or vesicles, nor has fusion of granules with plasma membranes been demonstrated by freeze fracture. In further studies they demonstrated that sialic acid residues on the plasma membrane were required for release of granule content (34). They suggested that this plasma membrane component is a receptor for secretory granule–plasma membrane recognition. They also demonstrated that ATP is required and that several proteins in the secretory granule and plasma membrane are phosphorylated in vitro (35). Phosphorylation of one of the plasma membrane proteins ($M_r =$ 60,000) was Ca^{2+}-dependent. Such an in vitro reconstitution of exocytosis offers the possibility of identifying the molecular components of exocytosis and how they are regulated by the cell.

ACKNOWLEDGMENT

This work was supported by grant AM 34992 from the National Institutes of Health.

Literature Cited

1. Allison, A. C., Davies, P. 1974. Interaction of membranes, microfilaments, and microtubules in endocytosis and exocytosis. In *Advances in Cytopharmacology,* ed. B. Ceccarelli, F. Clementi, J. Meldolesi, 2:237–48. New York: Raven

2. Anuis, D., Hesketh, J. E., Devilliers, G. 1979. Freeze-fracture study of the chromaffin cell during exocytosis: Evidence for connections between the plasma membrane and secretory granules and for movements of plasma membrane-associated particles. *Cell Tissue Res.* 197:433–41

3. Baker, P. F., Knight, D. E. 1981. Calcium control of exocytosis and endocytosis in bovine adrenal medullary cells. *Philos. Trans. R. Soc. London Ser. B* 296:83–103

4. Berridge, M. J. 1984. Inositol triphosphate and diacylglycerol as second messengers. *Biochem. J.* 220:345–60

5. Brockelhurst, K. W., Hutton, J. C. 1984. Involvement of protein kinase C in the phosphorylation of an insulin-granule membrane protein. *Biochem. J.* 220:283–90

6. Brooks, J. C., Treml, S., Brooks, M.

1984. Thiophosphorylation prevents catecholamine secretion by chemically skinned chromaffin cells. *Life Sci.* 35:569–74

7. Burgoyne, R. D. 1984. Mechanisms of secretion from adrenal chromaffin cells. *Biochim. Biophys. Acta* 779:201–16

8. Burgoyne, R. D., Geisow, M. J. 1981. Specific binding of ^{125}I-calmodulin to and protein phosphorylation in adrenal chromaffin granule membranes. *FEBS Lett.* 131:127–31

9. Burgoyne, R. D., Geisow, M. J., Barron, J. 1982. Dissection of stages in exocytosis in the adrenal chromaffin cell with use of trifluoperazine. *Proc. R. Soc. London Ser. B* 216:111–15

10. Cohen, P. 1982. The role of protein phosphorylation in neural and hormonal control of cellular activity. *Nature* 296: 613–20

11. Creutz, C. E., Dowling, L. G., Sandro, J. J., Villar-Sando, C., Whipple, J. H., Zaks, W. J. 1983. Characterization of the chromobindins. *J. Biol. Chem.* 258: 14664–74

12. Creutz, C. E., Sterner, D. C. 1983. Calcium dependence of the binding of synexin to isolated chromaffin granules. *Biochem. Biophys. Res. Commun.* 114: 355–64

13. Dahl, G., Ekerdt, R., Gratzl, M. 1979. Models for exocytotic membrane fusion. *Symp. Soc. Exp. Biol.* 33:349–68

14. DeCamilli, P., Peluchetti, D., Meldolesi, J. 1974. Structural difference between luminal and lateral plasmalemma in pancreatic acinar cells. *Nature* 248: 245–47

15. Douglas, W. W. 1968. Stimulus-secretion coupling: The concept and clues from chromaffin and other cells. *Br. J. Pharmacol.* 34:451–74

16. Douglas, W. W., Nemeth, E. F. 1982. On the calcium receptor activating exocytosis: Inhibitory effects of calmodulin-interacting drugs on rat mast cells. *J. Physiol.* 323:229–44

17. Drenckhahn, D., Mannherz, H. G. 1983. Distribution of actin and the actin-associated proteins myosin, tropomyosin, alpha-actinin, vinculin, and villin in rat and bovine exocrine glands. *Eur. J. Cell Biol.* 30:167–76

18. Duzgunes, N., Papahadjopolous, D. 1983. Ionotropic effects on phospholipid membranes: Calcium/magnesium specificity in binding, fluidity, and fusion. In *Membrane Fluidity in Biology*, ed. R. C. Aloia, 2:186–216. Academic: New York

19. Fenwick, E. M., Marty, A., Neher, E. 1982. Sodium and calcium channels in bovine chromaffin cells. *J. Physiol.* 331:599–635

20. Finkelstein, A., Cohen, F. S., Zimmerberg, J. 1986. Osmatic swelling of vesicles: Its role in the fusion of vesicles with planar phospholipid bilayer membranes and its possible role in exocytosis. *Ann. Rev. Physiol.* 48:163–74

21. Gilligan, D. M., Satir, B. H. 1982. Protein phosphorylation/dephosphorylation and stimulus-secretion coupling in wild type and mutant *Paramecium*. *J. Biol. Chem.* 257:13903–6

22. Goldfine, I. D., Williams, J. A. 1983. Receptors for insulin and CCK in the acinar pancreas: Relationship to hormone action. *Int. Rev. Cytol.* 85:1–38

23. Gomperts, B. D. 1983. Involvement of guanine nucleotide-binding protein in the gating of Ca^{2+} by receptors. *Nature* 306:64–66

24. Gumbiner, B., Kelly, R. B. 1982. Two distinct intracellular pathways transport secretory and membrane glycoproteins to the surface of pituitary tumor cells. *Cell* 28:51–59

25. Gunther, G. R. 1981. Effect of 12-O-tetradecanoyl-phorbol-13-acetate on Ca^{2+} efflux and protein discharge in pancreatic acini. *J. Biol. Chem.* 256:12040–45

26. Haslam, R. J., Davidson, M. M. L. 1984. Guanine nucleotides decrease the free $[Ca^{2+}]$ required for secretion of serotonin from permeabilized blood platelets. Evidence of a role for a GTP-binding protein in platelet activation. *FEBS Lett.* 174:90–95

27. Helle, K. B., Serck-Hanssen, G. 1975. The adrenal medulla: A model for studies of hormonal and neuronal storage and release mechanisms. *Mol. Cell. Biochem.* 6:127–46

28. Heuser, J. E., Reese, T. S., Dennis, M. J., Jan, Y., Jan, L., Evans, L. 1979. Synaptic vesicle exocytosis captured by quick freezing and correlated with quantal transmitter release. *J. Cell Biol.* 81:275–300

29. Holz, R. W. 1986. The role of osmotic forces in exocytosis from adrenal chromaffin cells. *Ann. Rev. Physiol.* 48:175–89

30. Hong, K., Duzgunes, N., Papahadjopoulos, D. 1982. Modulation of membrane fusion by calcium-binding proteins. *Biophys. J.* 37:297–305

31. Hooper, J. E., Kelly, R. B. 1984. Calmodulin is tightly associated with synaptic vesicles independent of calcium. *J. Biol. Chem.* 259:148–53

32. Jockusch, B. M., Burger, M. M., DePrada, M., Richards, J. G., Chaponnier,

C., Gabbiani, G. 1977. Alpha-actinin attached to membranes of secretory vesicles. *Nature* 270:628–29

33. Knight, D. E., Baker, P. F. 1983. The phorbol ester TPA increases the affinity of exocytosis for calcium in 'leaky' adrenal medullary cells. *FEBS Lett.* 160:98–100

34. Konings, F., De Potter, W. 1982. A role for sialic acid containing substrates in the exocytosis-like in vitro interaction between isolated adrenal medullary plasma membranes and chromaffin granules. *Biochem. Biophys. Res. Commun.* 106:1191–95

35. Konings, F., De Potter, W. 1983. Protein phosphorylation and the exocytosis-like interaction between isolated adrenal medullary plasma membranes and chromaffin granules. *Biochem. Biophys. Res. Commun.* 110:55–60

36. Konings, F., Majchrowicz, B., De Potter, W. 1983. Release of chromaffin granule content on interaction with plasma membranes. *Am. J. Physiol.* 244:C309–12

37. Lawson, D. 1980. Rat peritoneal mast cells: A model system for studying membrane fusion. In *Membrane-Membrane Interactions*, ed. N. B. Gilula, 34:27–44. New York: Raven

38. Lienhard, G. E. 1983. Regulation of cellular membrane transport by the exocytotic insertion and endocytic retrieval of transporters. *Trends Biochem. Sci.* 8:125–27

39. Meldolesi, J. 1974. Secretory mechanisms in pancreatic acinar cells. Role of cytoplasmic membranes. See Ref. 1, pp. 71–85

40. Meyer, D. I., Burger, M. M. 1976. The chromaffin granule surface. Localization of carbohydrate on the cytoplasmic surface of an intracellular organelle. *Biochim. Biophys. Acta* 433:428–36

41. Meyer, D. I., Burger, M. M. 1979. Isolation of a protein from the plasma membrane of adrenal medulla which binds to secretory vesicles. *J. Biol. Chem.* 254:9854–59

42. Michell, R. H. 1975. Inositol phospholipids and cell surface receptor function. *Biochim. Biophys. Acta* 415:81–147

43. Mundy, D. I., Strittmatter, W. J. 1985. Requirement for metalloendoprotease in exocytosis: Evidence in mast cells and adrenal chromaffin cells. *Cell* 40:645–56

44. Nishizuka, Y. 1984. The role of proteins kinase C in cell surface signal transduction and tumor promotion. *Nature* 308:693–98

45. Ochs, D. L., Korenbrot, J. I., Williams, J. A. 1983. Intracellular free calcium

concentrations in isolated pancreatic acini; effects of secretagogues. *Biochem. Biophys. Res. Commun.* 117:122–28

46. Orci, L., Gabbay, K. H., Malaisse, W. J. 1972. Pancreatic beta-cell web: Its possible role in insulin secretion. *Science* 175:1128–30

47. Orci, L., Perrelet, A., Montesano, R. 1983. Differential filipin labeling of the luminal membranes lining the pancreatic acinus. *J. Histochem. Cytochem.* 31: 952–55

48. Ornberg, R. L., Reese, T. S. 1981. Beginning of exocytosis captured by rapid-freezing of *Limulus* amebocytes. *J. Cell Biol.* 90:40–54

49. O'Rourke, F. A., Halenda, S. P., Zavoico, G. B., Feinstein, M. B. 1985. Inositol 1,4,5-triphosphate releases Ca^{2+} from a Ca^{2+}-transporting membrane vesicle fraction derived from human platelets. *J. Biol. Chem.* 260:956–62

50. Palade, G. E. 1975. Intracellular aspects of protein synthesis. *Science* 189:347–58

51. Plattner, H. 1981. Membrane behavior during exocytosis. *Cell Biol. Int. Rep.* 5:435–59

52. Plattner, H., Westphal, C., Tiggemann, R. 1982. Cytoskeleton-secretory vesicle interactions during the docking of secretory vesicles at the cell membrane in *Paramecium tetraurelia* cells. *J. Cell Biol.* 92:368–77

53. Pollard, H. B., Creutz, C. E., Fowler, V., Scott, J., Pazoles, C. J. 1981. Calcium-dependent regulation of chromaffin granule movement, membrane contact, and fusion during exocytosis. *Cold Spring Harbor Symp. Quant. Biol.* 46: 819–34

54. Povilaitis, V., Gagnon, C., Heisler, S. 1981. Stimulus-secretion coupling in exocrine pancreas: Role of protein carboxyl methylation. *Am. J. Physiol.* 240:G199–G205

55. Prentki, M., Biden, T. J., Janjic, D., Irvine, R. F., Berridge, M. J., Wollheim, C. B. 1984. Rapid mobilization of Ca^{2+} from rat insulinoma microsomes by inositol-1,4,5-trisphosphate. *Nature* 309:562–64

56. Rasmussen, H., Barrett, P. Q. 1984. Calcium messenger system: An integrated view. *Physiol. Rev.* 64:938–84

57. Rink, T. J., Smith, S. W., Tsien, R. Y. 1982. Cytoplasmic free Ca^{2+} in human platelets: Ca^{2+} thresholds and Ca-independent activation for shape-change and secretion. *FEBS Lett.* 148:21–26

58. Rubin, R. P. 1982. *Calcium and Cellular Secretion*. New York: Plenum

59. Sasaki, H., Epel, D. 1983. Cortical vesi-

cle exocytosis in isolated cortices of sea urchin eggs: Description of a turbidometric assay and its utilization in studying effects of different media on discharge. *Dev. Biol.* 98:327–37

60. Satir, B., Schooley, C., Satir, P. 1973. Membrane fusion in a model system. Mucocyst secretion in *Tetrahymena. J. Cell Biol.* 56:153–76

61. Steinhardt, R. A., Alderton, J. M. 1982. Calmodulin confers calcium sensitivity on secretory exocytosis. *Nature* 295:154–55

62. Streb, H., Irvine, R. F., Berridge, M. J., Schulz, I. 1983. Release of Ca^{2+} from a nonmitochondrial store in pancreatic acinar cells by inositol-1,4,5-trisphosphate. *Nature* 306:67–69

63. Summers, T. A., Creutz, C. E. 1985. Phosphorylation of a chromaffin granule-binding protein by protein kinase C. *J. Biol. Chem.* 260:2437–43

64. Suprenant, K. A., Dentler, W. L. 1982. Association between endocrine pancreatic secretory granules and in-vitro-assembled microtubules is dependent upon microtubule-associated proteins. *J. Cell Biol.* 93:164–74

65. Swanston, S. K., Carlsson, L., Gylfe, E. 1980. Actin filament formation in pancreatic β-cells during glucose stimulation of insulin secretion. *FEBS Lett.* 117:299–302

66. Tsien, R. Y., Pozzan, T., Rink, T. J. 1982. Calcium homeostasis in intact lymphocytes: Cytoplasmic free calcium monitored with a new, intracellularly trapped fluorescent indicator. *J. Cell Biol.* 94:325–34

67. Vale, R. D., Schnapp, B. J., Reese, T. S., Scheetz, M. P. 1985. Organelle, bead, and microtubule translocations promoted by soluble factors from the squid giant axon. *Cell* 40:559–69

68. Williams, J. A. 1981. Effects of antimitotic agents on ultrastructure and intracellular transport of protein in pancreatic acini. In *Methods in Cell Biology*, ed. A. R. Hand, C. Oliver, 23:247–58. New York: Academic

69. Williams, J. A., Burnham, D. B. 1985. Calcium and stimulus-secretion coupling in pancreatic acinar cells. In *Calcium in Biological Systems*, ed. R. P. Rubin, G. B. Weiss, J. W. Putney, p. 83–91. New York: Plenum

70. Wilson, S. P., Kirshner, N. 1983. Calcium-evoked secretion from digitonin-permeabilized adrenal medullary chromaffin cells. *J. Biol. Chem.* 258: 4994–5000

71. Wrenn, R. W. 1984. Phosphorylation of a pancreatic zymogen membrane protein by endogenous calcium/phospholipid-dependent protein kinase. *Biochim. Biophys. Acta* 775:1–6

72. Yamanishi, J., Takai, Y., Kaibuchi, K., Sano, K., Castagna, M., Nishizuka, Y. 1983. Synergistic functions of phorbol ester and calcium in serotonin release from human platelets. *Biochem. Biophys. Res. Commun.* 112:778–86

CARDIOVASCULAR PHYSIOLOGY

ENDOTHELIAL CELL FUNCTION

Introduction, Harvey V. Sparks, Section Editor

The importance of endothelial cells in the regulation of the cardiovascular system has become widely recognized during the past decade. The reviews collected in this section are intended to reflect recent developments in this fascinating field. Betz and Goldstein review the ability of brain capillary endothelium to regulate the exchange of solute between plasma and interstitium. They emphasize the asymmetry of endothelial cells of the brain and their distinctly epithelial function. Smith addresses the compartmentation of prostaglandin biosynthesis in the vascular wall. It is now clear that smooth muscle and endothelial cells make prostanoids in response to different stimuli. Furthermore, PGI_2 is formed at several subcellular sites within these cells. It appears that synthesis of PGI_2 directed at the luminal surface can modulate the function of circulating blood cells, whereas synthesis on the abluminal surface may relate to communication with smooth muscle. Ryan discusses new findings concerning the all-important metabolic role of endothelial cells in the lung. These cells are crucial for the regulation of the plasma concentration of a number of hormones and autacoids. She emphasizes the cellular and subcellular localization of the enzymes responsible for this function. The Simionescus describe the heterogeneity of locations of specific functions on the endothelial cell surface. They review the studies that demonstrate the location of a number of surface proteins that determine transport, enzymatic transformation, and receptor binding of vasoactive substances and a variety of plasma proteins. They also discuss the new information concerning the role of endothelial cell surface in the regulation of thrombosis. The Campbells present new information regarding the role of endothelial cells in regulating cell division and cell phenotype in the arterial wall. In particular, they emphasize the role of a heparin-like glycosaminoglycan. Vanhoutte and his colleagues report on recent developments in the rapid growth in our understanding of the role of endothelial cells as modulators of vascular smooth muscle tone. In addition, they discuss the physiological and pathological significance of the inhibitory and excitatory effects of endothelial cells. Shepro and Dunham review the transport of biogenic amines by endothelial cells and point to new evidence that biogenic amines are capable of modulating the shape of endothelial cells by their action on stress fibers. Finally, Bassingthwaighte and Sparks review the use of mathematical modeling and indicator dilution techniques for the quantative analysis of in situ endothelial cell transport functions. The interested reader should also be aware of the article by Pearson and Gordon on adenine nucleotide metabolism by endothelial cells, which appeared in Volume 47 of the Annual Review of Physiology.

Ann. Rev. Physiol. 1986. 48:241–50

SPECIALIZED PROPERTIES AND SOLUTE TRANSPORT IN BRAIN CAPILLARIES

A. Lorris Betz and Gary W. Goldstein

Departments of Pediatrics and Neurology, University of Michigan, Ann Arbor, Michigan 48109

INTRODUCTION

The capillaries in brain are formed by a specialized endothelium whose function is to regulate the movement of solutes between blood and brain. In contrast to other vascular beds, the endothelial cells in brain capillaries are sealed together by continuous tight junctions, do not contain fenestrations or transendothelial channels, and have little transcellular vesicular transport. In addition to these barrier properties, the brain capillary endothelial cells exhibit other special features that play an important role in the function of the blood-brain barrier (BBB). For example, brain capillaries facilitate the entry of glucose into brain. Transport of this important energy substrate has been the subject of numerous investigations and several reviews (10, 52, 63). Also present at the BBB are transport systems for amino acids (11, 58, 62), organic acids (56), amines (20), purines (7, 21), and nucleosides (21). Comprehensive reviews of BBB structure and function are available elsewhere (13, 14, 66).

During the past decade we and others developed methods to isolate and study microvessels from brain, and to grow the endothelial cells in tissue culture. These new techniques permit a more detailed characterization of the specialized cell physiology of the brain endothelium. In this review we present selected advances in the field and relate them, when possible, to the function of the BBB.

0066-4278/86/0315-0241$02.00

EPITHELIAL PROPERTIES OF BRAIN CAPILLARY ENDOTHELIUM

It is well established that energy-dependent secretory activity by the choroid plexus epithelium is important in producing and regulating the composition of the cerebrospinal fluid. Brain interstitial fluid is also closely regulated, and active transport pumps in the endothelial cells of brain capillaries appear to maintain the volume and composition of this extracellular fluid (14). The high density of mitochondria in the endothelial cells of brain capillaries supports the role of these cells in energy-dependent processes (57). In addition, the brain capillary endothelium appears to have other epithelial properties that provide further support for a fluid secretory activity. For example, both brain capillary endothelium and typical epithelial cells are joined together by continuous tight junctions (24, 68). In part because of the tight junctions these cell types have a low transcellular permeability and a high transcellular resistance to many polar solutes. Recently, Crone & Olesen (22) measured the electrical resistance across the brain capillary and found that it averaged nearly 2000 ohms·cm². This very high resistance is similar to that found across tight epithelia, and is a strong testament to the low permeability of the tight junctions in brain capillaries. Consequently, this special endothelial cell layer can support transcellular concentration gradients for proteins, ions, and amino acids, and an electrical potential difference of 3–5 mV (22).

As in epithelial cells, certain transport systems in the brain capillary appear to work in a one-way or vectorial direction as a result of the asymmetric distribution of active pumps between the two surfaces of the cell layer. While the movement of potassium from blood to brain is extremely limited (32), its flux in the opposite direction is more rapid. Bradbury & Stulcova (17) determined that this efflux in vivo occurs by means of a saturable transport system with a K_m of about 3 mM. This asymmetry in permeability may be responsible for maintaining the concentration of potassium in the extracellular fluid of brain at 2.8 mM, which is significantly lower than its 3–5 mM concentration in blood. Furthermore, changes in the blood concentration of potassium do not result in changes in its interstitial fluid concentration (16). A possible role for the brain capillary in this regulation of interstitial fluid potassium was suggested by the observation that isolated brain capillaries exhibit saturable, energy-dependent uptake of potassium (31). The K_m of this potassium transport system is approximately 3 mM. The uptake of potassium by isolated brain capillaries is nearly completely inhibited by ouabain and, therefore, probably mediated by Na,K-ATPase. Since the luminal membrane of the brain capillary has a low potassium permeability (32), these results suggest that Na,K-ATPase might be located on only the antiluminal membrane. This polar distribution of Na,K-ATPase was confirmed by cytochemical localization and by fractionation of membranes prepared from isolated brain capillaries (9). More recent cytochemical investigations indicate that Na,K-ATPase may not be entirely absent from the luminal membrane, but rather it may be present occasionally (74) or at lower activity than on the antiluminal membrane (70). Nevertheless, the demonstration of endothelial cell polarity strongly supports the proposition that brain capillaries have epithelial properties.

The antiluminal location of Na,K-ATPase in brain capillary endothelial cells is similar to the location of this enzyme in many fluid-transporting epithelia, and it could provide the basis for the active production of interstitial fluid by brain capillaries. The transendothelial secretion of fluid is likely to be coupled to sodium transport. Recent experiments have focused on identifying the transport systems that allow sodium to enter the endothelial cell as it moves across the capillary wall. Studies using the single pass, intracarotid injection technique suggest the presence of two separate saturable sodium entry mechanisms (5). One is inhibited by low concentrations of amiloride, and has some of the features of an epithelial sodium pore. The other is inhibited by furosemide, and may represent Na-Cl cotransport. Experiments with isolated brain capillaries also indicate the presence of a Na/H exchanger, which we believe is located primarily on the antiluminal membrane (6).

Figure 1 shows a schematic diagram depicting the apparent distribution of sodium transport systems between the two sides of the brain capillary endothelial cell. Transcellular secretion of fluid would involve entry of sodium down its concentration gradient across the luminal membrane through either Na-Cl cotransport or the amiloride-sensitive uptake system. Then intracellular sodium would be pumped out of the endothelial cell against a gradient into the brain extracellular space. Simultaneous movement of an anion such as chloride (69) is required to maintain neutrality. Finally, a transcellular flux of water would follow the net movement of salt from blood to brain and maintain isotonicity.

RELATIONSHIP BETWEEN ASTROCYTES AND ENDOTHELIAL CELLS

A special relationship exists between capillaries and astrocytes of the brain (15, 77). With few exceptions, cerebral capillaries are nearly completely ensheathed by astrocytic processes. In fact, early investigators thought that glial cells were the anatomic site of the BBB. However, studies with horseradish peroxidase demonstrated that proteins can freely permeate the space between astrocytic foot processes and enter the basement membrane up to, but not past, the tight junctions joining endothelial cells together (18).

The close contact between astrocytes and endothelial cells suggests a functional interaction. This possibility is supported by the fact that processes of the same astrocyte contact neurons or ependymal cells (15, 77). Potential in-

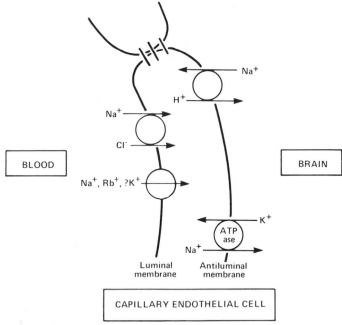

Figure 1   Schematic diagram for the proposed distribution of ion transport systems in brain capillary endothelial cells. (Reproduced with permission from Reference 5.)

teractions include transfer of substances (31), regulation of capillary activity, and induction of specialized endothelial properties (15).

Recent studies with cultured brain capillary endothelial cells provide support for an inductive interaction. Under normal circumstances, brain capillary endothelial cells contain a polar distribution of certain neutral amino acid transport systems that is similar to the distribution of Na,K-ATPase shown in Figure 1. The L-system for amino acid transport is present on both the luminal and antiluminal membranes, while the A-system appears to be present only on the antiluminal membrane (11). When brain capillary endothelial cells are grown in tissue culture, they demonstrate both A and L transport systems; however, amino acid uptake by the A-system is stimulated after contact of the endothelial cells with a cell line derived from astrocytes (C_6 glioma), or after exposure to glial-conditioned medium (19). If endothelial cells are cultured on polycarbonate filters, they can be used to measure the rate of transcellular transport in either direction across the cell monolayer. Under these conditions A-system amino acid transport occurs at equal rates in both directions. However, if C_6 glioma cells are grown on the underside of the filter, then A-system transport occurs more rapidly from the glial surface across the endothelium than in the opposite direction (3). Coculture with vascular smooth muscle cells does not produce this effect. Thus, in tissue culture, glial cells appear to be able to induce in cultured endothelial cells a polar distribution of amino acid carriers that is similar to the distribution of these carriers observed in vivo.

RELATIONSHIP BETWEEN TRANSPORT AND METABOLISM

Glucose

Glucose is the primary energy substrate of the brain, and its metabolism accounts for nearly all of the brain's oxygen consumption. Since entry of glucose into the brain is critical, mechanisms for glucose transport across the BBB are particularly well studied (10, 52, 63). Brain uptake of glucose occurs by a saturable, stereospecific transport system that is inhibited by phloretin and cytochalasin B. A similar glucose transport system has been demonstrated in isolated brain capillaries in vitro, and these studies also indicate that capillary glucose transport is not energy- or sodium-dependent (8). Furthermore, brain capillaries transport glucose much faster than they metabolize it. In fact, they appear to metabolize other substrates in preference to glucose (12, 31). Thus, as expected, glucose transport and metabolism by brain capillary endothelial cells is well suited to facilitate the transcellular passage of this important metabolic fuel. It is not surprising, therefore, that the recent quantitative analysis of Dick et al (25) indicated that brain capillaries contain a larger number of glucose carriers than does the cerebral cortex.

Neurotransmitters

In contrast to glucose, monoamine neurotransmitters are more rapidly metabolized than they are transported by brain capillaries. In part, this is due to the low permeability of the luminal membrane to monoamines (55). The neurotransmitter precursor L-DOPA readily enters brain capillaries because it is transported by the L-system for amino acids (58, 62). Nevertheless, L-DOPA penetration from blood to brain is limited by the presence of the enzyme L-DOPA decarboxylase (4, 30, 34, 35), which converts L-DOPA to dopamine within the capillary endothelial cell. Since capillaries also contain monoamine oxidase (12, 33–35, 51), the dopamine generated after L-DOPA uptake is eventually degraded to inactive products.

Intracapillary monoamine oxidase may also inactivate neurotransmitters released by neuronal activity, since monoamines are actively accumulated and metabolized by isolated brain capillaries (36, 71). Thus, monoamine oxidase would degrade monoamines that are released into brain interstitial fluid and taken up by capillaries, those formed by L-DOPA decarboxylase within the capillary, as well as the small amount that might enter the endothelial cell from the blood (35). The result is the production by the brain capillary endothelial cell of a "metabolic" BBB that limits the transcapillary exchange of neurotransmitters and their precursors.

RECEPTORS ON BRAIN CAPILLARIES

The presence on brain capillaries of receptors for various agents has been an area of active investigation during the past six years. Early investigators studied increases in the cyclic AMP content of isolated brain microvessels after their exposure to potential agonists to show the presence of a receptor. More recent studies have used binding of radioactive ligands. Table 1 lists the receptors that have been described as being associated with brain capillaries, although some receptors have not been demonstrated by all investigators.

Since isolated capillaries contain more than one cell type, the question arises as to where these receptors and enzymes are located. Cytochemical studies demonstrate adenylate cyclase activity along the luminal and antiluminal surfaces of the endothelial cell (46, 72, 75), as well as on smooth muscle cells (75) and astrocytic foot processes (46). Smooth muscle cells and membranes of astrocytic foot processes are sometimes found in isolated brain capillaries (76), and these may contribute to receptor binding. Axon terminals with presynaptic

Table 1   Receptors present in brain capillaries[1]

Receptor	Assay	References
Beta-adrenergic	Cyclic AMP	2, 39, 40, 53, 54, 59, 61
	Binding	23, 37, 49, 50, 64
Beta$_2$	Cyclic AMP	53
	Binding	37, 49
Alpha-adrenergic	Binding	64
Alpha$_2$	Binding	37
Dopamine	Cyclic AMP	2, 54, 59, 61
Histamine	Cyclic AMP	2, 40
H$_1$	Binding	64
H$_2$	Cyclic AMP	47
Adenosine	Cyclic AMP	39, 40, 60, 67
	Binding	60
Muscarinic cholinergic	Binding	26, 27
Prostaglandins	Cyclic AMP	40
Insulin	Binding	28, 73
Transferrin	Binding	43
Vasoactive intestinal peptide	Cyclic AMP	41
Parathyroid hormone	Cyclic AMP	41

[1]The presence of neurotransmitter or hormonal receptors was assayed either by measuring a stimulation in cyclic AMP production or by quantitating the binding of radioligands.

receptors might also contribute to measurable microvascular binding sites. Finally, histamine, presumed to be within mast cells of the capillary wall, is found in isolated brain capillaries (38, 42), and the presence of mast cells may also influence results. Because of the multiple possible binding sites present in isolated microvessels, caution is advised in assuming that the receptors described above are located exclusively in endothelial cells.

Despite these limitations, the possibility that endothelial cells in brain capillaries are under hormonal regulation is appealing. For example, a functional significance for receptors in endothelial cells may be found in the observation of Raichle et al (65) that changes in cerebral blood flow and water permeability at the BBB follow adrenergic stimulation, or in the enhanced pinocytosis within endothelial cells described by Joo after administration of dibutyryl cyclic AMP (44) or dibutyryl cyclic GMP (45).

Some of the hormone receptors present in brain capillaries are not directly involved in regulating endothelial cell function. Rather, they may be part of a transcapillary transport system that allows hormones to enter the brain from the blood. Receptor-mediated transendothelial transport of insulin was recently demonstrated in cultured aortic endothelial cells (48), and the brain capillary receptors for insulin (1, 29) and transferrin (43) were proposed to play a similar role. This could explain why the brain concentration of some hormones is high compared to other plasma proteins.

CONCLUSIONS

The past decade has seen a great interest in information concerning brain capillary structure and function. Traditional histological and physiological approaches to the study of the BBB are now being expanded by the use of the latest techniques in cell isolation and biochemistry. The goal is to understand the unique properties of the brain capillary and the cellular and molecular processes that underlie their regulation. It now appears likely that the brain capillary contains a specialized type of endothelial cell that is structurally and functionally much like an epithelial cell. These properties are undoubtedly important in regulating the amount and composition of the brain's interstitial fluid.

ACKNOWLEDGMENT

This work was supported in part by grants ES02380, EY03772, and HL26840 from the National Institutes of Health. Dr. Betz is an Established Investigator of the American Heart Association.

Literature Cited

1. Albrecht, J., Wroblewska, B., Mossa-kowski, M. J. 1982. The binding of insulin to cerebral capillaries and astrocytes of the rat. *Neurochem. Res.* 7:489–94
2. Baca, G. M., Palmer, G. C. 1978. Presence of hormonally-sensitive adenylate cyclase receptors in capillary-enriched fractions from rat cerebral cortex. *Blood Vessels* 15:286–98
3. Beck, D. W., Vinters, H. V., Hart, M. N., Cancilla, P. A. 1984. Glial cells influence polarity of the blood-brain barrier. *J. Neuropathol. Exp. Neurol.* 43: 219–24
4. Bertler, A., Falck, B., Owman, C., Rosengren, E. 1966. The localization of monoaminergic blood-brain mechanisms. *Pharmacol. Rev.* 18:369–85
5. Betz, A. L. 1983. Sodium transport from blood to brain: Inhibition by furosemide and amiloride. *J. Neurochem.* 41:1158–64
6. Betz, A. L. 1983. Sodium transport in capillaries isolated from rat brain. *J. Neurochem.* 41:1150–57
7. Betz, A. L. 1985. Identification of hypoxanthine transport and xanthine oxidase activity in brain capillaries. *J. Neurochem.* 44:574–79
8. Betz, A. L., Csejtey, J., Goldstein, G. W. 1979. Hexose transport and phosphorylation by capillaries isolated from rat brain. *Am. J. Physiol.* 236:C96–C102
9. Betz, A. L., Firth, J. A., Goldstein, G. W. 1980. Polarity of the blood-brain barrier: Distribution of enzymes between the luminal and antiluminal membranes of the brain capillary endothelial cell. *Brain Res.* 192:17–28
10. Betz, A. L., Gilboe, D. D., Drewes, L. R. 1978. The characteristics of glucose transport across the blood brain barrier and its relation to cerebral glucose metabolism. In *Transport Phenomena in the Nervous System,* ed. G. Levi, L. Battistin, A. Lajtha, pp. 133–49. New York: Plenum
11. Betz, A. L., Goldstein, G. W. 1978. Polarity of the blood-brain barrier: Neutral amino acid transport into isolated brain capillaries. *Science* 202:225–27
12. Betz, A. L., Goldstein, G. W. 1981. Developmental changes in metabolism and transport properties of capillaries isolated from rat brain. *J. Physiol.* 312:365–76
13. Betz, A. L., Goldstein, G. W. 1984. Brain capillaries. Structure and function. In *Handbook of Neurochemistry,* ed. A. Lajtha, 7:465–84. New York: Plenum
14. Bradbury, M. 1979. *The Concept of a Blood-Brain Barrier.* Chichester, England: Wiley. 465 pp.
15. Bradbury, M. 1979. Why a blood-brain barrier? *Trends in Neurosci.* 2:36–38
16. Bradbury, M. W. B., Kleeman, C. R. 1967. Stability of potassium content of cerebrospinal fluid and brain. *J. Physiol.* 213:519–28
17. Bradbury, M. W. B., Stulcova, B. 1970. Efflux mechanism contributing to the stability of the potassium concentration in cerebrospinal fluid. *J. Physiol.* 208: 415–30
18. Brightman, M. W., Reese, T. S. 1969. Junctions between intimately apposed cell membranes in the vetebrate brain. *J. Cell. Biol.* 40:648–77
19. Cancilla, P. A., DeBault, L. E. 1983. Neutral amino acid transport properties of cerebral endothelial cells in vitro. *J. Neuropath. Exp. Neurol.* 42:191–99
20. Cornford, E. M., Braun, L. D., Oldendorf, W. H. 1978. Carrier mediated blood-brain barrier transport of choline and certain choline analogs. *J. Neurochem.* 30:299–308
21. Cornford, E. M., Oldendorf, W. H. 1975. Independent blood-brain barrier transport systems for nucleic acid precursors. *Biochim. Biophys. Acta* 394: 211–19
22. Crone, C., Olesen, S. P. 1982. Electrical resistance of brain microvascular endothelium. *Brain Res.* 241:49–55
23. Culvenor, A. J., Jarrott, B. 1981. Comparison of beta-adrenoceptors in bovine intracerebral microvessels and cerebral grey matter by [^{3}H]dihydroalprenolol binding. *Neuroscience* 6:1643–48
24. Dermietzel, R. 1978. Junctions in the central nervous system of the cat: IV. Interendothelial junctions of cerebral blood vessels from selected areas of the brain. *Cell Tissue Res.* 164:46–62
25. Dick, A. P. K., Harik, S. I., Klip, A., Walker, D. M. 1984. Identification and characterization of the glucose transporter of the blood-brain barrier by cytochalasin B binding and immunological reactivity. *Proc. Natl. Acad. Sci. USA* 81:7233–37
26. Estrada, C., Hamel, E., Krause, D. N. 1983. Biochemical evidence for cholinergic innervation of intracerebral blood vessels. *Brain Res.* 266:261–70
27. Estrada, C., Krause, D. N. 1982. Muscarinic cholinergic receptor sites in cerebral blood vessels. *J. Pharmacol. Exp. Ther.* 221:85–90
28. Frank, H. J. L., Pardridge, W. M. 1981.

A direct in vitro demonstration of insulin binding to isolated brain microvessels. *Diabetes* 30:757–61

29. Frank, H. J. L., Pardridge, W. M. 1983. Insulin binding to brain microvessels. *Adv. Metab. Disorders* 10:291–302

30. Garnett, E. S., Firnau, G., Nahmias, C., Sood, S., Belbeck, L. 1980. Blood-brain barrier transport and cerebral utilization of dopa in living monkeys. *Am. J. Physiol.* 238:R318–27

31. Goldstein, G. W. 1979. Relation of potassium transport to oxidative metabolism in isolated brain capillaries. *J. Physiol.* 286:185–95

32. Hansen, A. J., Lund-Anderson, H., Crone, C. 1977. K⁺-permeability of the blood-brain barrier, investigated by aid of a K⁺-sensitive microelectrode. *Acta Physiol. Scand.* 101:438–45

33. Hardebo, J. E., Emson, P. C., Falck, B., Owman, C., Rosengren, E. 1980. Enzymes related to monoamine transmitter metabolism in brain microvessels. *J. Neurochem.* 35:1388–93

34. Hardebo, J. E., Falck, B., Owman, C. 1979. A comparative study on the uptake and subsequent decarboxylation of monoamine precursors in cerebral microvessels. *Acta Physiol. Scand.* 107:161–67

35. Hardebo, J. E., Owman, C. 1980. Barrier mechanisms for neurotransmitter monoamines and their precursors at the blood-brain barrier. *Ann. Neurol.* 8:1–11

36. Hardebo, J. E., Owman, C. 1980. Characterization of the in vitro uptake of monoamines into brain microvessels. *Acta Physiol. Scand.* 108:223–29

37. Harik, S. I., Sharma, V. K., Wetherbee, J. R., Warren, R. H., Banerjee, S. P. 1981. Adrenergic and cholinergic receptors of cerebral microvessels. *J. Cereb. Blood Flow Metab.* 1:329–38

38. Head, R. J., Hjelle, J. T., Jarrot, B., Berkowitz, B., Cardinale, G., Spector, S. 1980. Isolated brain microvessels: Preparation, morphology, histamine and catecholamine contents. *Blood Vessels* 17:173–86

39. Herbst, T. J., Raichle, M. E., Ferrendelli, J. A. 1979. Beta-adrenergic regulation of adenosine 3',5'-monophosphate concentration in brain microvessels. *Science* 204:330–32

40. Huang, M., Drummond, G. I. 1979. Adenylate cyclase in cerebral microvessels: Action of guanine nucleotides, adenosine, and other agonists. *Mol. Pharmacol.* 16:462–72

41. Huang, M., Rorstad, O. P. 1984. Cerebral vascular adenylate cyclase: Evidence for coupling to receptors for vasoactive intestinal peptide and parathyroid hormone. *J. Neurochem.* 43:849–56

42. Jarrot, B., Hjelle, J. T., Spector, S. 1979. Association of histamine with cerebral microvessels in regions of bovine brain. *Brain Res.* 168:323–30

43. Jefferies, W. A., Brandon, M. R., Hunt, S. V., Williams, A. F., Gatter, K. C., Mason, D. Y. 1984. Transferrin receptor on endothelium of brain capillaries. *Nature* 312:162–63

44. Joo, F. 1972. Effect of N⁶O²-dibutyryl cyclic 3',5'-adenosine monophosphate on the pinocytosis of brain capillaries of mice. *Experientia* 28:1470–71

45. Joo, F., Temesvari, P., Dux, E. 1983. Regulation of the macromolecular transport in the brain microvessels: The role of cyclic GMP. *Brain Res.* 278:165–74

46. Joo, F., Toth, I. 1975. Brain adenylate cyclase: its common occurrence in the capillaries and astrocytes. *Naturwissenschaften* 62:397–98

47. Karnushina, I. L., Palacios, J. M., Barbin, G., Dux, E., Joo, F., Schwartz, J. C. 1980. Studies on a capillary-rich fraction isolated from brain: Histaminic components and characterization of the histamine receptors linked to adenylate cyclase. *J. Neurochem.* 34:1201–8

48. King, G. L., Johnson, S. M. 1985. Receptor-mediated transport of insulin across endothelial cells. *Science* 227:1583–86

49. Kobayashi, H., Maoret, T., Ferrante, M., Spano, P., Trabucchi, M. 1981. Subtypes of beta-adrenergic receptors in rat cerebral microvessels. *Brain Res.* 220:194–98

50. Kobayashi, H., Memo, M., Spano, P. F., Trabucchi, M. 1981. Identification of beta-adrenergic receptor binding sites in rat brain microvessels, using [¹²⁵I]iodohydroxybenzylpindolol. *J. Neurochem.* 36:1383–88

51. Lai, F. M., Udenfriend, S., Spector, S. 1975. Presence of norepinephrine and related enzymes in isolated brain microvessels. *Proc. Natl. Acad. Sci. USA* 72:4622–25

52. Lund-Anderson, H. 1979. Transport of glucose from blood to brain. *Physiol. Rev.* 59:305–52

53. Nathanson, J. A. 1980. Cerebral microvessels contain a beta₂-adrenergic receptor. *Life Sci.* 26:1793–99

54. Nathanson, J. A., Glaser, G. H. 1979. Identification of beta-adrenergic-sensitive adenylate cyclase in intracranial blood vessels. *Nature* 278:567–69

55. Oldendorf, W. H. 1971. Brain uptake of radiolabeled amino acids, amines, and hexoses after arterial injection. *Am. J. Physiol.* 221:1629–39

56. Oldendorf, W. H. 1973. Carrier-mediated blood-brain barrier transport of short-chain monocarboxylic organic acids. *Am. J. Physiol.* 224:1450–53

57. Oldendorf, W. H., Cornford, M. E., Brown, W. J. 1977. The large apparent work capacity of the blood-brain barrier: A study of the mitochondrial content of capillary endothelial cells in brain and other tissues of the rat. *Ann. Neurol.* 1:409–17

58. Oldendorf, W. H., Szabo, J. 1976. Amino acid assignment to one of three blood-brain barrier amino acid carriers. *Am. J. Physiol.* 230:94–98

59. Palmer, G. C. 1979. Diminished adenylate cyclase responses in frontal cortex and cerebral capillaries of spontaneously hypertensive rats. *Biochem. Pharmacol.* 28:2847–49

60. Palmer, G. C., Ghai, G. 1982. Adenosine receptors in capillaries and pia-arachnoid of rat cerebral cortex. *Eur. J. Pharmacol.* 81:129–32

61. Palmer, G. C., Palmer, S. J. 1978. 5'guanylyl-imidodiphosphate actions on adenylate cyclase in homogenates of rat cerebral cortex plus neuronal and capillary fractions. *Life Sci.* 23:207–16

62. Pardridge, W. M. 1977. Kinetics of competitive inhibition of neutral amino acid transport across the blood-brain barrier. *J. Neurochem.* 28:103–8

63. Pardridge, W. M. 1983. Brain metabolism: A perspective from the blood-brain barrier. *Physiol. Rev.* 63:1481–1535

64. Peroutka, S. J., Moskowitz, M. A., Reinhard, J. F. Jr., Snyder, S. H. 1980. Neurotransmitter receptor binding in bovine cerebral microvessels. *Science* 208:610–12

65. Raichle, M. E., Hartman, B. K., Eichling, J. O., Sharpe, L. G. 1975. Central noradrenergic regulation of cerebral blood flow and vascular permeability. *Proc. Natl. Acad. Sci. USA* 72:3726–30

66. Rapoport, S. I. 1976. *Blood-Brain Barrier in Physiology and Medicine.* New York: Raven. 316 pp.

67. Schutz, W., Steurer, G., Tuisl, E. 1982. Functional identification of adenylate

cyclase-coupled adenosine receptors in rat brain microvessels. *Eur. J. Pharmacol.* 85:177–84

68. Shivers, R. R., Betz, A. L., Goldstein, G. W. 1984. Isolated rat brain capillaries possess intact, structurally complex, interendothelial tight junctions; Freeze-fracture verification of tight junction integrity. *Brain Res.* 324:313–22

69. Smith, Q. R., Rapoport, S. I. 1984. Carrier-mediated transport of chloride across the blood-brain barrier. *J. Neurochem.* 42:754–63

70. Spatz, M. 1984. Attenuated blood-brain barrier. In *Handbook of Neurochemistry*, ed. A. Lajtha, 7:501–43. New York: Plenum

71. Spatz, M., Maruki, C., Abe, T., Rausch, W. D., Abe, K., Merkel, N. 1981. The uptake and fate of the radiolabeled 5-hydroxytryptamine in isolated cerebral microvessels. *Brain Res.* 220:214–19

72. Szumanska, G., Palkama, A., Lehtosalo, J. I., Uusitalo, H. 1984. Adenylate cyclase in the microvessels of the rat brain. A histochemical study with light and electron microscopy. *Acta Neuropathol.* 62:219–24

73. van Houten, M., Posner, B. I. 1979. Insulin binds to brain blood vessels in vivo. *Nature* 282:623–25

74. Vorbrodt, A. W., Lossinsky, A. S., Wisniewski, H. M. 1982. Cytochemical localization of ouabain-sensitive, K⁺-dependent p-nitro-phenylphosphatase (transport ATPase) in the mouse central and peripheral nervous systems. *Brain Res.* 243:225–34

75. Vorbrodt, A. W., Szumanska, G., Dobrogowska, D. H. 1984. Cytochemical studies of adenylate cyclase in the choroid plexus and brain vessels of rat and mouse. *J. Histochem. Cytochem.* 32:275–84

76. White, F. P., Dutton, G. R., Norenberg, M. D. 1981. Microvessels isolated from rat brain: Localization of astrocyte processes by immunohistochemical techniques. *J. Neurochem.* 36:328–32

77. Wolff, J. R. 1970. The astrocyte as link between capillary and nerve cell. *Triangle* 9:153–64

Ann. Rev. Physiol. 1986. 48:251–62

PROSTAGLANDIN BIOSYNTHESIS AND ITS COMPARTMENTATION IN VASCULAR SMOOTH MUSCLE AND ENDOTHELIAL CELLS

William L. Smith

Department of Biochemistry, Michigan State University, East Lansing, Michigan 48824

Introduction

This review is intended to serve two functions: first, to provide a synopsis of and a bibliographic guide to eicosanoid biochemistry in vascular smooth muscle and endothelium, and second, to outline what is known about where prostaglandin biosynthesis occurs in vascular cells and to discuss the potential functional consequences of this compartmentation.

Prostaglandin Metabolism and Function: An Overview

The term "eicosanoid" is a colloquialism for oxygenated twenty-carbon fatty acids, including the prostaglandins, thromboxanes, leukotrienes, and epoxy, mono-, and dihydroxy eicosenoic acids. The vasculature responds both to leukotrienes (15, 19, 35) and prostaglandins (8, 51); however, the major eicosanoids synthesized by vascular smooth muscle and endothelia are the prostaglandins (51, 58). These compounds are formed via the "cyclooxygenase" pathway, most commonly from arachidonic acid (Figure 1). Biosynthesis occurs in three stages (51, 65, 70): (*a*) a rate-limiting, stimulus-induced mobilization of arachidonic acid from membrane phosphoglycerides; (*b*) conversion of arachidonate to the prostaglandin endoperoxide PGH_2 by PGH synthase; and (*c*) isomerization of PGH_2 to a biologically active end-product (PGD_2, PGE_2, PGI_2 or TxA_2). Factors that can elicit arachidonate release from phospholipids of endothelial cells from one or more sources include α-thrombin (18, 44, 87), histamine (2, 4), bradykinin (2, 44, 89), leukotriene C_4 (15),

0066-4278/86/0315-0251$02.00

certain neutrophil-derived products (43, 50, 58), and shear forces (28). Serotonin and platelet-derived growth factor cause arachidonate release from smooth
muscle cells (51). Few of the steps in stimulus-induced arachidonate release are
defined; however, arachidonate mobilization itself is catalyzed by a combination of phospholipase A_2 acting on phosphatidylcholine (56, 62) and phospholipase C plus diglyceride lipase acting on phosphatidylinositol (52, 66, 90). The
properties of PGH synthase and PGH_2 isomerases have recently been reviewed
(65).

Much less is known about the mechanism(s) of prostanoid action than about
biosynthesis. The only effects of prostaglandins that have been defined biochemically are those on cAMP metabolism (although prostaglandins cause
some effects that appear to be independent of cAMP; cf 26). Prostanoids can
both stimulate and inhibit cAMP synthesis. One type of physiological function
of prostaglandins is to attenuate responses to circulating hormones (e.g. vasopressin, epinephrine) that stimulate adenylate cyclase (30, 40, 60, 86). In these

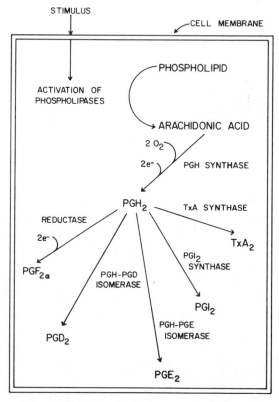

Figure 1   Enzymic pathways for prostaglandin formation.

cases prostaglandins apparently bind receptors that act through the inhibitory guanine nucleotide binding protein, N_i, to inhibit hormone-induced cAMP synthesis (3, 57, 60); TxA_2 may act via N_i to block the activation of platelet adenylate cyclase. The other major effect of prostanoids is to increase cellular cAMP levels. Presumably, this involves another class of prostaglandin receptors functioning through the stimulatory guanine nucleotide binding protein, N_s (34, 80). A widely recognized example is the stimulation of platelet adenylate cyclase by PGI_2 (38); the biological effect in this case is to desensitize platelets to the actions of thrombogenic agents. PGI_2 can also stimulate endothelial cell adenylate cyclase (45), but the physiological importance of this effect is unclear (37, 88). The PGI_2-induced relaxation of smooth muscle appears to be mediated by cAMP (61).

Prostaglandins are "local hormones" that act near their sites of synthesis. This concept has arisen from four types of observations. First, with a few notable exceptions (31, 67), the plasma concentrations of vasoactive prostaglandins such as PGE_2, PGD_2, and PGI_2 are too low ($\leq 10^{-11}$ M) to elicit responses (6, 14, 23, 27, 39, 64, 77, 83). Second, different catabolic systems in the lung, kidney, and liver effectively bar passage of prostanoids through the circulation (25, 48, 65, 91, 92). Third, prostaglandins are synthesized in most organs, not by any central exocrine gland (13, 78). And finally, prostaglandins cause effects upon cells in which they are formed and often affect anatomically adjacent cells (cf. 78, 86).

Which Prostaglandins Are Produced by the Vasculature?

Each of the major prostanoids can be found in media bathing endothelial cells cultured from several different sources (Table 1). Prostacyclin (PGI_2) is the major prostanoid present in incubates of freshly isolated endothelial cells from large arteries and veins (1, 12, 32, 35, 46, 53). The rate of PGI_2 production ranges from 0.5–5.0 pmoles/hr/10^6 arterial endothelial cells (2, 36, 44). The capacity of arteries to form PGI_2 is three to ten times that of veins (76). Microvessels also synthesize prostanoids, but at less than one tenth the rate of arterial endothelial cells (32). Furthermore, Gerritsen & Cheli (32) have established that PGE_2 is produced in greater amounts than PGI_2 by coronary microvessels. In general, prostanoids other than PGI_2 appear to be the major products of microvessels (12, 32, 33). Freshly prepared smooth muscle cells from aorta synthesize primarily PGI_2 (Table 1), but following passage of the cells, PGE_2 becomes the major product (1).

With the exception of microvessels (12, 32, 33), it is still questionable whether PGE_2, $PGF_{2\alpha}$, PGD_2, or TxB_2 are formed by endothelial cells or smooth muscle in significant amounts in vivo. One can reasonably argue that these products only arise in vitro via nonenzymic synthesis. Accordingly, bovine vascular rings produce mainly PGI_2 and only minor amounts of PGE_2

Table 1 Prostanoids synthesized by cells of the vasculature[a]

Source of Cells and Assay Conditions	Relative Proportion of Prostanoids					
	$6KF_{1\alpha}$	$PGF_{2\alpha}$	PGE_2	PGD_2	TxB_2	Ref.
BAE plus 20:4	1	0.11	0.51	0.04	0.22	46
BAE plus 20:4	1	0.38	0.53	—	—	53
BAE plus 20:4	1	—	0.11	—	0.082	36
Bovine vascular rings plus 20:4	1	—	0.04	—	0.005	36
HUA plus BK	1	0.52	0.20	—	—	2
HUV	1	1.0	0.20	—	—	12
PAE 1°(< 24 hr)	1	—	0.59	—	—	1
PAE (24–48 hr)	1	—	5.6	—	—	1
Rabbit heart microvessels	1	—	3	—	—	32
Human foreskin microvessels	1[b]	4	3	—	—	12
PASM						
1° (0–24 hr)	1	—	0.47	—	—	1
1° (24–48 hr)	1	—	1.0	—	—	1
2° (0–24 hr)	1	—	13	—	—	1
2° (24–48 hr)	1	—	13	—	—	1

[a]Abbreviations are $6KF_{1\alpha}$ = 6-keto-$PGF_{1\alpha}$ (the stable acid hydrolysis product of PGI_2); BAE = bovine aortic endothelial cells; PAE, porcine aortic endothelial cells; HUA = human umbilical arterial endothelial cells; HUV, human umbilical vein endothelial cells; PASM = porcine aortic smooth muscle cells; 20:4 = arachidonic acid; 1° = primary cultures; 2° = subcultures; BK = bradykinin.

[b]$6KF_{1\alpha}$ was detected but no changes in the level of this product were observed upon addition of exogenous arachidonic acid.

and TxB_2, although these latter products represent more than 20% of the prostaglandins formed in cultures of bovine aortic endothelial cells (35). Similarly, Ager et al (1) have shown that the ratio of PGI_2 to PGE_2 production by freshly isolated porcine endothelial cells decreases from a value of 5 after 5 hr of culture to 0.9 by 48 hr; analogous results were reported for smooth muscle. Cellular levels of PGI_2 synthase can fall rapidly following cell isolation (1). When PGH_2 accumulates as a result of decreased PGI_2 synthase activity, PGE_2, $PGF_{2\alpha}$, PGD_2, and even TxB_2 can be formed nonenzymically from PGH_2 (63). For example, the PGE_2 formed by freshly isolated smooth muscle or aorta must be produced nonenzymically since homogenates of aorta lack PGH-PGE isomerase activity (1, 32, 69).

There is good evidence that coronary microvessels form PGE_2 as well as PGI_2 enzymically (32). Microvessel endothelia are derived from mixtures of arterioles, capillaries, and venules, and hence it is unclear if PGE_2 and PGI_2 can be formed within the same cells. In fact, it is not known whether any differentiated cell can form more than one prostanoid enzymically. It would be of interest to determine whether or not cultured rabbit coronary microvessel endothelia, which possess both PGI_2 synthase and PGH-PGE isomerase activities (32), stain uniformly with anti-PGI_2 synthase antibodies (79). If so, at least some of the cells must synthesize both PGI_2 and PGE_2 enzymically.

Comparison of PGI_2 Synthesis by Smooth Muscle and Endothelium

The results of Weksler and coworkers (24) illustrate that with arachidonic acid as a substrate, endothelial cells synthesize ten to twenty times more PGI_2 than smooth muscle cells. Biochemically, this difference is attributable to the fact that the concentration of PGH synthase, and thus the capacity to form PGH_2, is twenty times greater in endothelial cells than in smooth muscle. [Although the concentrations of PGI_2 synthase in endothelial cells and smooth muscle cells are virtually identical (20).] The physiological relevance of endothelial cells having a much higher capacity for PGI_2 synthesis is a matter of speculation. It is thought that the major role of PGI_2 formed by the endothelium is to modulate the activities of circulating blood cells, most notably platelets (8, 10, 16, 24, 38, 51). Since PGI_2 released by the endothelium into the blood would be diluted quickly, endothelial cells may need a high capacity for PGI_2 synthesis to accommodate the dilution problem (20). Dilution would not be an important problem in the case of smooth muscle were PGI_2 formed by smooth muscle to act only within the medial layer. One can infer that this is the case since PGI_2 is synthesized by all smooth muscle and not just vascular smooth muscle (79).

Subcellular Location of Prostacyclin Synthesis

Information regarding the subcellular location of the enzymes involved in prostacyclin formation is incomplete. As discussed in subsequent paragraphs, prostaglandin biosynthesis can be associated with several different organelles within the same cell, but the reasons for this complex distribution are not understood.

Phosphatidylinositol-specific phospholipase C is the only enzyme likely to be involved in prostacyclin synthesis that is a soluble protein (52). Phospholipase A_2, diglyceride lipase, PGH synthase, and PGI_2 synthase are integral membrane proteins (78). The subcellular locations of phospholipase A_2 and diglyceride lipase involved in supplying arachidonic acid for prostaglandin synthesis have not been identified. However, it is likely that arachidonate is released near its site of oxygenation, and hence that the relevant lipases will be found in close proximity to PGH synthase. It should be noted in this regard that the subcellular locations of PGH_2 isomerases, such as PGI_2 synthase, TxA synthase, and PGH-PGE isomerase, correspond to those of PGH synthase (79, 81), which indicates that arachidonate oxygenation and PGH_2 isomerization occur on the same membrane.

LOCATION OF PGH SYNTHASE AND PGI_2 SYNTHASE IN SMOOTH MUSCLE CELLS   When used for immunocytochemistry, antibodies to PGH synthase and PGI_2 synthase stain both the nuclear and plasma membranes of smooth muscle cells (79). Moreover, PGI_2 synthase activity of bovine aorta is also present in a subcellular fraction enriched in endoplasmic reticulum (82). The immunocytochemical work (79) needs to be extended to verify that nuclear and plasma membrane PGH synthase and PGI_2 synthase immunoreactivities are equivalent to catalytic activities. Nevertheless, the present data suggest that conversion of arachidonic acid to prostacyclin can occur on the plasma membranes, the endoplasmic reticulum, and the nuclear membranes of smooth muscle cells.

Staining of smooth muscle cells with anti-PGH synthase or anti-PGI_2 synthase antibodies is only possible after the cells have been permeabilized (82). This implies that the antigenic determinants of those synthase molecules associated with the plasma membrane are on the cytosolic surface; presumably, the same is true of the catalytic sites of the enzymes. It is known that the active site of the PGH synthase that is present on the endoplasmic reticulum is on the cytoplasmic surface of this membrane system (21). It has not been determined whether the PGH synthase and the PGI_2 synthase associated with the nuclear membrane of smooth muscle cells are on the inner or outer membrane of the nuclear envelope. However, based on the distribution of other enzymes present on both the endoplasmic reticulum and nuclear membrane (55), it is likely that the prostaglandin biosynthetic enzymes are on the outer membrane of the envelope, which is continuous with the endoplasmic reticulum.

LOCATION OF PGH SYNTHASE AND PGI_2 SYNTHASE IN ENDOTHELIAL CELLS   Cultured vascular endothelial cells stained for PGH synthase immunoreactivity and then viewed by light microscopy exhibit diffuse cytoplasmic and intense perinuclear staining (81). This pattern is identical to that seen with Swiss mouse 3T3 fibroblasts where PGH synthase was shown by immunoelectron microscopy to be present on the endoplasmic reticulum and nuclear membrane but not the plasma membrane (68). However, as discussed earlier, changes in the levels of prostaglandin biosynthetic enzymes occur as cells adapt to culture conditions (1), and it is quite conceivable that a plasma membrane component of synthesis is selectively lost in cultured endothelial and 3T3 cells. Several studies based on separation of subcellular organelles have been performed to determine the location of prostaglandin biosynthesis (7, 21, 29, 41). In each case most of the activity was found in association with the endoplasmic reticulum and a plasma membrane activity could have easily been overlooked.

IMPLICATIONS OF MULTIPLE SUBCELLULAR SITES OF PROSTACYCLIN SYNTHESIS   Data on the subcellular location of PGH synthase and PGI_2 synthase suggest that these enzymes are associated with several different membrane systems in smooth muscle cells and perhaps endothelial cells. The consequences of this unusual distribution are unknown, but there exist a number of intriguing possibilities. Biosynthesis at different sites within a cell would likely be regulated independently. As noted earlier, a variety of stimuli can elicit PGI_2 synthesis by vascular endothelial or smooth muscle cells, and these stimuli may each act to cause PGI_2 synthesis only on one membrane. PGI_2 formed at different subcellular locations could be channeled to interact with different receptors, perhaps subserving different biochemical functions. There is evidence that prostaglandin binding proteins are associated with plasma membrane, endoplasmic reticulum, and nuclear membrane fractions (42, 59, 75).

In general, arachidonate is released from phospholipids and transformed to end-products without leaving cells. Exceptions occur when the rate of PGH_2 production exceeds the rate of PGH_2 isomerization. Clearly a portion of the PGH_2 molecules originating in platelet cells are converted to PGI_2 by endothelial cells (8, 54, 71). As discussed below, prostaglandins do not readily enter cells. Thus, transformation of exogenous PGH_2 may occur through the action of PGI_2 synthase present on the plasma membrane.

Both phosphatidylinositol and phosphatidylcholine can act as precursors of the arachidonate that is converted to prostaglandins (52, 56, 62, 66, 90). It is not clear why or the extent to which arachidonate is derived from these two phosphoglycerides. One simple possibility is that these lipids are derived from different subcellular membranes and serve as precursors for synthesis at different subcellular sites.

It is obviously important at this stage to determine if PGH synthase and PGI_2 synthase are present on the plasma membranes of endothelial as well as smooth muscle cells. If so, one can envision using plasma membrane cell fusion techniques (11, 22, 49) to determine (a) if different stimuli elicit prostaglandin formation by plasma membranes and endoplasmic reticula, and (b) whether different phospholipids are used as precursors for prostaglandin synthesis on different membranes.

Is There an Asymmetric Release of Prostacyclin from Endothelia?

Endothelial cells are asymmetric (74). The fact that lower concentrations of PGI_2 are required to cause vasodilation in denuded than in intact arteries (9) indicates that the arterial endothelium, like most other cells (5, 30, 47, 73), provides a transcellular permeability barrier to the movement of PGI_2. As noted earlier, a major role of PGI_2 formed by the endothelium is to modulate platelet function, and there is no question that PGI_2 can be released on the luminal surface of the endothelium (24). In vitro, PGI_2 formed by the endothelium can cause relaxation of underlying smooth muscle (9). These data would suggest that, at least in large arteries, newly synthesized PGI_2 can also exit endothelial cells on the abluminal surface. It is not clear whether this is the case for all endothelial cells. It should be recognized that some cells do release prostaglandins in an asymmetric manner (17, 72), and that some cells exhibit a sidedness in their responses to prostaglandins (72, 84, 85).

Summary

PGI$_2$ is the major, if not the only, eicosanoid formed by smooth muscle and endothelial cells of large arteries and veins. PGI$_2$ is not the major prostanoid synthesized by microvessels. Different stimuli elicit prostanoid production by smooth muscle and endothelial cells. PGI$_2$ is formed at several subcellular sites within smooth muscle and perhaps endothelial cells, but the consequences of this highly unusual distribution are unknown. PGI$_2$ formed by the endothelium can exit on the luminal surface to modulate the functions of circulating blood cells, and probably on the abluminal surface to relax underlying smooth muscle. PGI$_2$ formed by smooth muscle probably acts only upon smooth muscle cells.

ACKNOWLEDGMENT

Portions of the work performed in the author's laboratory were supported in part by US Public Health Service grants HL29685 and AM22042, a grant-in-aid from the American Heart Association of Michigan, and an Established Investigatorship from the American Heart Association.

Literature Cited

1. Ager, A., Gordon, J. L., Moncada, S., Pearson, J. D., Salmon, J. A., Trevethick, M. A. 1982. Effects of isolation and culture on prostaglandin synthesis by porcine aortic endothelial and smooth muscle cells. *J. Cell. Physiol.* 110:9–16

2. Alhenc-Gelas, F., Tsai, S. J., Callahan, K. S., Campbell, W. B., Johnson, A. R. 1982. Stimulation of prostaglandin formation by vasoactive mediators in cultured human endothelial cells. *Prostaglandins* 24:723–42

3. Anderson, R. J., Wilson, P. D., Dillingham, M. A., Breckon, R., Schwertschlaf, U., Garcia-Sainz, J. A. 1984. Pertussis toxin reverses prostaglandin E$_2$ inhibition of arginine vasopressin (AVP) and forskolin in rabbit collecting tubular epithelium. *Am. Soc. Nephrol. Meet. Abstr.* 154A

4. Baenziger, N. L., Force, L. E., Becher-er, P. R. 1980. Histamine stimulates prostacyclin synthesis in cultured human umbilical vein cells. *Biochem. Biophys. Res. Commun.* 92:1435–44

5. Bito, L. A., Baroody, R. A. 1975. Impermeability of rabbit erythrocytes to prostaglandins. *Am. J. Physiol.* 229:1580–84

6. Blair, I. A., Barrow, S. E., Waddell, K. A., Lewis, P. J., Dollery, C. T. 1982. Prostacyclin is not a circulating hormone in man. *Prostaglandins* 23:579–89

7. Bohman, S-O., Larsson, C. 1975. Prostaglandin synthesis in membrane fractions from the rabbit renal medulla. *Acta Physiol. Scand.* 94:244–58

8. Bunting, S., Gryglewski, R., Moncada, S., Vane, J. R. 1976. Arterial walls generate from prostaglandin endoperoxides a substance (prostaglandin X) which relaxes strips of mesenteric and coeliac arteries and inhibits platelet aggregation. *Prostaglandins* 12:897–913

9. Busse, R., Forstermann, U., Matsuda, H., Pohl, U. 1984. The role of prostaglandins in the endothelium-mediated vasodilatory response to hypoxia. *Pflügers Arch.* 401:77–83

10. Cazenave, J.-P., Dejana, E., Kinlough-Rathbone, R., Packham, M. A., Mustard, J. F. 1979. Platelet interactions with the endothelium and the subendothelium: the role of thrombin and prostacyclin. *Haemostasis* 8:183–92

11. Cerione, R. A., Strulovich, B., Benovic, J. L., Strader, C. D., Caron, M. G., Lefkowitz, R. J. 1983. Reconstitution of β-adrenergic receptors in lipid vesicles: affinity chromatography-purified receptors confer catecholamine responsiveness on a heterologous adenylate cyclase system. *Proc. Natl. Acad. Sci. USA* 80:4899–4903

12. Charo, I. F., Shak, S., Karasek, M. A., Davison, P. M., Goldstein, I. M. 1984. Prostaglandin I$_2$ is not a major metabolite

of arachidonic acid in cultured endothelial cells from human foreskin microvessels. *J. Clin. Invest.* 74:914–19

13. Christ, E. J., Nugteren, D. H. 1972. Comparative aspects of prostaglandin biosynthesis in animal tissues. *Biochim. Biophys. Acta* 270:537–45

14. Christ-Hazelhof, E., Nugteren, D. H. 1981. Prostacyclin is not a circulating hormone. *Prostaglandins* 22:739–46

15. Cramer, E. B., Pologe, L., Pawlowski, Z., Cohn, A., Scott, W. A. 1983. Leukotriene C promotes prostacyclin synthesis by human endothelial cells. *Proc. Natl. Acad. Sci. USA* 80:4109–13

16. Curwen, K. D., Gimbrone, M. A. Jr., Handin, R. I. 1980. In vitro studies of thromboresistance. The role of prostacyclin (PGI$_2$) in platelet adhesion to cultured normal and virally transformed human vascular endothelial cells. *Lab. Invest.* 42:366–74

17. Cuthbert, A. W., Halushka, P. V., Margolius, H. S., Spayne, J. A. 1984. Mediators of the secretory response to kinins. *Br. J. Pharmacol.* 82:597–607

18. Czervionke, R. L., Smith, J. B., Hoak, J. C., Fey, G. L., Haycraft, D. L. 1979. Use of a radioimmunoassay to study thrombin-induced release of PGI$_2$ from cultured endothelium. *Thromb. Res.* 14:781–86

19. Dahlen, S.-E., Bjork, J., Hedqvist, P., Arfors, K.-E., Hammarstrom, S., et al. 1981. Leukotrienes promote plasma leakage and leukocyte adhesion in postcapillary venules: in vitro effects with relevance to the acute inflammatory response. *Proc. Natl. Acad. Sci. USA* 78:3887–91

20. DeWitt, D. L., Day, J. S., Sonnenburg, W. K., Smith, W. L. 1983. Concentrations of prostaglandin endoperoxide synthase and prostaglandin I$_2$ synthase in the endothelium and smooth muscle of bovine aorta. *J. Clin. Invest.* 72:1882–88

21. DeWitt, D. L., Rollins, T. E., Day, J. S., Gauger, J. A., Smith, W. L. 1981. Orientation of the active site and antigenic determinants of prostaglandin endoperoxide synthase in the endoplasmic reticulum. *J. Biol. Chem.* 256:10375–82

22. Dufau, M. L., Hayashi, K., Sala, G., Baukal, A., Catt, K. J. 1978. Gonadal luteinizing hormone receptors and adenylate cyclase: transfer of functional ovarian luteinizing hormone receptors to adrenal fasciculata cells. *Proc. Natl. Acad. Sci. USA* 75:4769–78

23. Dunn, M. J., Liard, J., Dray, F. 1978. Basal and stimulated rates of renal secretion and excretion of prostaglandins E$_2$,

F$_\alpha$, and 13,14-dihydro-15-keto-F$_\alpha$ in the dog. *Kidney Int.* 13:136–43

24. Eldor, A., Falcone, D. J., Hajjar, D. P., Minick, C. R., Weksler, B. B. 1981. Recovery of prostacyclin production by deendothelized rabbit aorta: critical role of the neointimal smooth muscle cells. *J. Clin. Invest.* 67:735–41

25. Ferreira, S. H., Vane, J. R. 1967. Prostaglandins: their disappearance from and release into the circulation. *Nature* 216:868–73

26. Fitz, T. A., Hoyer, P. B., Niswender, G. D. 1984. Interaction of prostaglandins with subpopulations of ovine luteal cells. I. Stimulatory effects of prostaglandins E$_1$, E$_2$ and I$_2$. *Prostaglandins* 28:116–26

27. Fitzgerald, G. W., Brash, A. R., Falardeau, P., Oates, A. 1981. Estimated rate of prostacyclin secretion into the circulation of normal man. *J. Clin. Invest.* 68:1272–76

28. Francos, J. A., Eskin, S. G., McIntire, L. V., Ives, C. L. 1985. Flow effects on prostacyclin production by cultured human endothelial cells. *Science* 227:1477–79

29. Friedman, Y., Lang, M., Burke, G. 1975. Further characterization of bovine thyroid prostaglandin synthase. *Biochim. Biophys. Acta* 397:331–41

30. Garcia-Perez, A., Smith, W. L. 1984. Apical-basolateral membrane asymmetry in canine cortical collecting tubule cells. Bradykinin, arginine vasopressin, prostaglandin E$_2$ interrelationships. *J. Clin. Invest.* 74:63–74

31. Gerber, J. B., Payne, N. A., Murphy, R. C., Nies, A. S. 1981. Prostacyclin produced by the pregnant uterus in the dog may act as a circulating vasodepressor substance. *J. Clin. Invest.* 67:632–36

32. Gerritsen, M. E., Cheli, C. D. 1983. Arachidonic acid metabolism and prostaglandin endoperoxide metabolism in isolated rabbit coronary microvessel and isolated and cultivated coronary microvessel endothelial cells. *J. Clin. Invest.* 72:1658–71

33. Gesce, A., Ottlecz, A., Mezei, Z., Telegday, G., Joo, F., et al. 1982. Prostacyclin and prostaglandin synthesis in isolated brain capillaries. *Prostaglandins* 74:1552–55.

34. Gilman, A. G. 1984. Guanine nucleotide-binding regulatory proteins and dual control of adenylate cyclase. *J. Clin. Invest.* 73:1–4

35. Goldsmith, J. C., Needleman, S. W. 1982. A comparative study of thromboxane and prostacyclin release from ex vivo and cultured bovine vascular endothelium. *Prostaglandins* 24:173–78

36. Deleted in proof

37. Gorman, R. R., personal communication.
38. Gorman, R. R., Fitzpatrick, F. A., Miller, O. V. 1978. Reciprocal regulation of human platelet cAMP levels by thromboxane A_2 and prostacyclin. *Adv. Cyclic Nucleotide Res.* 9:597–609
39. Granstrom, E., Kindahl, H. 1978. Radioimmunoassay for prostaglandins. *Adv. Prost. Thrombox. Res.* 5:119–210
40. Grantham, J. J., Orloff, J. 1968. Effect of prostaglandin E_2 on the permeability response of the isolated collecting tubule to vasopressin, adenosine 3',5'-monophosphate, and theophylline. *J. Clin. Invest.* 47:1154–61
41. Hack, N., Carey, F., Crawford, N. 1984. The inhibition of platelet cyclooxygenase by aspirin is associated with the acetylation of a 72 kDa polypeptide in the intracellular membranes. *Biochem. J.* 223:105–11
42. Hammarstrom, S. 1982. A receptor for prostaglandin $F_{2\alpha}$ from corpora lutea. *Methods Enzymol.* 86:202–9
43. Harlan, J. M., Callahan, K. S. 1984. Role of hydrogen peroxide in the neutrophil-mediated release of prostacyclin from cultured endothelial cells. *J. Clin. Invest.* 74:442–48
44. Hong, S. L. 1980. Effect of bradykinin and thrombin on prostacyclin synthesis in endothelial cells from calf and pig aorta and human umbilical cord vein. *Thromb. Res.* 18:787–95
45. Hopkins, N. K., Gorman, R. R. 1981. Regulation of endothelial cell cyclic nucleotide metabolism of prostacyclin. *J. Clin. Invest.* 67:540–46
46. Ingerman-Wojenski, C., Silver, M. J., Smith, J. B., Macarak, E. 1981. Bovine endothelial cells in culture produce thromboxane as well as prostacyclin. *J. Clin. Invest.* 67:1292–96
47. Irish, J. J. 1979. Secretion of prostaglandin E_2 by rabbit proximal tubules. *Am. J. Physiol.* 237:F268–73
48. Jarabek, J. 1982. Isolation and properties of a NAD^+-dependent 15-hydroxyprostaglandin dehydrogenase from human placenta. *Methods Enzymol.* 86:126–30
49. Kassis, S., Fishman, P. H. 1984. Functional alteration of the β-adrenergic receptor during desensitization of mammalian adenylate cyclase by β-agonists. *Proc. Natl. Acad. Sci. USA* 81:6686–90
50. LeRoy, E. C., Ager, A., Gordon, J. L. 1984. Effects of neutrophil elastase and other proteases on porcine endothelial cell prostaglandin I_2 production, adenosine nucleotide release and responses to vasoactive agents. *J. Clin. Invest.* 74:1003–10
51. Majerus, P. W. 1983. Arachidonate metabolism in vascular disorders. *J. Clin. Invest.* 72:1521–25
52. Majerus, P. W., Neufeld, E. J., Wilson, D. B. 1984. Production of phosphoinositide-derived messengers. *Cell* 37:701–3
53. Marcus, A. J., Weksler, B. B., Jaffe, E. A. 1978. Enzymatic conversion of prostaglandin endoperoxide H_2 and arachidonic acid to prostacyclin by cultured human endothelial cells. *J. Biol. Chem.* 253:7138–41
54. Marcus, A. J., Weksler, B. B., Jaffe, E. A., Broekman, M. J. 1980. Synthesis of prostacyclin from platelet-derived endoperoxides by cultured human endothelial cells. *J. Clin. Invest.* 66:979–86
55. Matsuura, S., Masuda, R., Omori, K., Negishi, M., Tashiro, Y. 1981. Distribution and induction of cytochrome P-450 in rat liver nuclear envelope. *J. Cell Biol.* 91:212–20
56. McKean, M. W., Smith, J. B., Silver, M. J. 1981. Formation of lysophosphatidylcholine by human platelets in response to thrombin: support for the phospholipase A_2 pathway for the liberation of arachidonic acid. *J. Biol. Chem.* 256:1522–24
57. Michelangeli, V. P., Livesey, S. A., Martin, T. J. 1984. Effects of pertussis toxin on adenylate cyclase responses to prostaglandin E_2 and calcitonin in human breast cancer cells. *Biochem. J.* 224:371–77
58. Miller, D. K., Sadowski, S., Soderman, D. D., Kuehl, F. A. Jr. 1985. Endothelial cell prostacyclin production induced by activated neutrophils. *J. Biol. Chem.* 260:1006–14
59. Mitra, S., Rao, Ch. V. 1978. Gonadotropin and prostaglandins binding sites in rough endoplasmic reticulum and Golgi fractions of bovine corpora lutea. *Arch. Biochem. Biophys.* 191:331–40
60. Murayama, T., Ui, M. 1983. Loss of the inhibitory function of the guanine nucleotide regulatory component of adenylate cyclase due to its ADP-ribosylation by islet-activating protein, pertussis toxin, in adipocyte membranes. *J. Biol. Chem.* 258:3319–26
61. Nakahata, N., Suzuki, T. 1981. Effects of prostaglandin E_1, I_2 and isoproterenol on the tissue cyclic AMP content in longitudinal muscle of rabbit intestine. *Prostaglandins* 22:159–65
62. Neufeld, E. J., Majerus, P. W. 1983. Arachidonate release and phosphatidic acid turnover in stimulated human platelets. *J. Biol. Chem.* 258:2461–67
63. Nugteren, D. H., Christ-Hazelhof, E. 1980. Chemical and enzymic conver-

sions of the prostaglandin endoperoxide PGH$_2$. *Adv. Prost. Thrombox. Res.* 6:129–37

64. Oates, J. A., Roberts, L. J., Sweetman, B. J., Maas, R. L., Gerkens, J. F., Taber, D. F. 1980. Metabolism of the prostaglandins and thromboxanes. See Ref. 63, pp. 35–41

65. Pace-Asciak, C. R., Smith, W. L. 1983. Enzymes in the biosynthesis and catabolism of the eicosanoids: prostaglandins, thromboxanes, leukotrienes and hydroxy fatty acids. *Enzymes* 16:544–604

66. Rittenhouse-Simmons, S. 1979. Production of diglyceride from phosphatidylinositol in activated human platelets. *J. Clin. Invest.* 63:580–87

67. Roberts, L. J., Sweetman, B. J., Lewis, R. A., Austen, K. F., Oates, J. A. 1980. Increased production of prostaglandin D$_2$ in patients with systemic mastocytosis. *N. Eng. J. Med.* 303:1400–4

68. Rollins, T. E., Smith, W. L. 1980. Subcellular localization of the prostaglandin-forming cyclooxygenase in Swiss mouse 3T3 fibroblasts by electron microscopic immunocytochemistry. *J. Biol. Chem.* 255:4872–75

69. Salmon, J. A., Smith, D. R., Flower, R. J., Moncada, S., Vane, J. R. 1978. Further studies on the enzymatic conversion of prostaglandin endoperoxide into prostacyclin by porcine aorta microsomes. *Biochim. Biophys. Acta* 523:250–62

70. Samuelsson, B., Goldyne, M., Granstrom, E., Hamberg, M., Hammarstrom, S., Malmsten, C. 1978. Prostaglandins and thromboxanes. *Ann. Rev. Biochem.* 47:994–1030

71. Schafer, A. I., Crawford, D. D., Gimbrone, M. A. Jr. 1984. Unidirectional transfer of prostaglandin endoperoxides between platelets and endothelial cells. *J. Clin. Invest.* 73:1105–12

72. Schuster, V. L., Kokko, J. P., Jacobson, H. R. 1984. Interactions of lysylbradykinin and anti-diuretic hormone in the rabbit cortical collecting tubule. *J. Clin. Invest.* 73:1659–69

73. Siegl, A. M., Smith, J. B., Silver, M. J., Nicolaou, K. C., Ahern, D. 1979. Selective binding site for ^{3}H-prostacyclin on platelets. *J. Clin. Invest.* 63:215–20

74. Simionescu, M., Simionescu, N., Palade, G. E. 1982. Biochemically differentiated microdomains of the cell surface of capillary endothelium. *Ann. NY Acad. Sci.* 401:9–24

75. Sinha, A. K., Colman, R. W. 1980. Persistence of increased platelet cAMP induced by prostaglandin E$_1$ after removal

of the hormone. *Proc. Natl. Acad. Sci. USA* 77:2946–50

76. Skidgel, R. A., Printz, M. P. 1978. PGI$_2$ production by rat blood vessels: diminished prostacyclin formation in veins compared to arteries. *Prostaglandins* 16:1–16

77. Smith, J. B., Ogletree, M. L., Lefer, A. M., Nicolaou, K. C. 1978. Antibodies which antagonize the effects of prostacyclin. *Nature* 274:64–65

78. Smith, W. L. 1985. Cellular and subcellular compartmentation of prostaglandin and thromboxane synthesis. In *Biochemistry of Arachidonic Acid Metabolism*, ed. W. E. M. Lands, 1:77–93. Boston: Kluwer-Nijhoff.

79. Smith, W. L., DeWitt, D. L., Allen, M. L. 1983. Bimodal distribution of the prostaglandin I$_2$ synthase antigen in smooth muscle cells. *J. Biol. Chem.* 258:5922–26

80. Smith, W. L., Garcia-Perez, A. 1985. A two receptor model for the mechanism of action of prostaglandins in the renal collecting tubule. In *Prostaglandins, Leukotrienes and Lipoxins*, ed. J. M. Bailey. New York: Plenum. In press

81. Smith, W. L., Rollins, T. E., DeWitt, D. L. 1981. Subcellular localization of prostaglandin forming enzymes using conventional and monoclonal antibodies. In *Progress in Lipid Research*, ed. R. T. Holman, 20:103–10. Oxford: Pergammon. 911 pp.

82. Sonnenburg, W. K., Smith, W. L., unpublished results.

83. Steer, M. L., Macintyre, D. E., Levine, L., Salzman, E. W. 1980. Is prostacyclin a physiologically important circulating anti-platelet agent? *Nature* 283:194–95

84. Stokes, J. B. 1985. Modulation of vasopressin-induced water permeability of the cortical collecting tubule by endogenous and exogenous prostaglandins. *Mineral Electrolyte Metab.* In press

85. Stokes, J. B., Kokko, J. P. 1977. Inhibition of sodium transport by prostaglandin E$_2$ across the isolated perfused rabbit collecting tubule. *J. Clin. Invest.* 59:1099–1104

86. Torikai, S., Kurokawa, K. 1983. Effect of PGE$_2$ on vasopressin-dependent cell cAMP in isolated single nephron segments. *Am. J. Physiol.* 245:F58–66

87. Weksler, B., Ley, C. W., Jaffe, B. A. 1978. Stimulation of endothelial cell prostaglandin production by thrombin, trypsin, and the ionophore A23187. *J. Clin. Invest.* 62:923–30

88. Whorton, A. R., Collawn, J. B., Montgomery, M. E., Young, S. L., Kent, R. S. 1985. Arachidonic acid

metabolism in cultured aortic endothelial cells. Effect of cAMP and 3-isobutyl-1-methylxanthine. *Biochem. Pharmacol.* 34:119–23

89. Whorton, A. R., Young, S. L., Data, J. L., Barchowsky, A., Kent, R. S. 1982. Mechanism of bradykinin stimulated prostacyclin synthesis in porcine aortic endothelial cells. *Biochim. Biophys. Acta* 712:79–87

90. Wilson, D. B., Neufeld, E. J., Majerus,

P. W. 1985. Phosphoinositide interconversion in thrombin-stimulated human platelets. *J. Biol. Chem.* 260:1046–51

91. Wong, P. Y-K. 1982. Purification of PGD$_2$ 11-keto-reductase from rabbit liver. *Methods Enzymol.* 86:117–25

92. Wong, P. Y.-K., McGiff, J. C., Cagen, L., Malik, K. U., Sun, F. F. 1978. Metabolism of prostacyclin in the rabbit kidney. *J. Biol. Chem.* 254:12–14

Ann. Rev. Physiol. 1986. 48:263–77

METABOLIC ACTIVITY OF PULMONARY ENDOTHELIUM: Modulations of Structure and Function

Una S. Ryan

Department of Medicine, University of Miami School of Medicine, Miami, Florida 33101

INTRODUCTION

Endothelium can be considered an ubiquitous cell type permeating all parts of the body or a very extensive but continuous organ. The main functions of endothelial cells are shared throughout the vascular tree, but certain properties are most significant in particular organs or in vessels of particular dimensions. All endothelial cells are probably capable of metabolic activities that alter the composition of substances flowing in the bloodstream but, as originally pointed out by Vane and colleagues (4, 82), it is at the level of the lungs that the metabolic processing of vasoactive substances is most important, since it is in the lungs that the entire cardiac output is processed and its composition of bioactive materials adjusted before delivery to the systemic circulation. Since many of the metabolic activities of the lungs result from the actions of enzymes, receptors, and transport molecules situated on the luminal surface of pulmonary endothelial cells, the pulmonary endothelium plays a role in maintaining and regulating the entry of hormones and other active substances destined for circulation to target organs throughout the body (45, 46, 48, 51). Similarly, the pulmonary endothelium can be said to influence blood pressure, salt and water balance, hemostasis, blood pH, and a number of functions important in maintaining general homeostasis (48, 51).

This chapter will restrict discussion chiefly to pulmonary endothelial cells, especially those of the microvasculature, where metabolic activities are likely to have the greatest effect. Although, like all cells, pulmonary endothelial cells conduct a number of metabolic activities important for cell maintenance

263

0066-4278/86/0315-0263$02.00

and turnover, most of the reactions relevant to blood-borne substances occur on the luminal surface. Thus our discussion will be further restricted to surface reactions and ultrastructural characteristics of the cell surface.

Finally, the metabolic activities of endothelium have been treated extensively in previous reviews (4, 20, 21, 22a, 48, 51, 82), so this chapter will focus on modulations of endothelial cell functions and surface structures that alter the endothelium from its normally actively nonthrombogenic disposition and relative lack of immunologic reactivity into a surface fully equipped for initiation and progression of events leading to vascular obstruction.

FUNCTIONAL PROPERTIES OF PULMONARY ENDOTHELIUM

As pointed out above, pulmonary endothelial cells are capable of acting on a wide range of circulating vasoactive substances, including polypeptide hormones, biogenic amines, nucleotides, lipoproteins, and products of arachidonic acid (3, 4, 20, 21, 22a, 24, 29, 45, 48, 51, 56, 73, 82). Despite the wide range of substances processed, the reactions are selective and show a fine discrimination among molecules of the various categories, and the reactions are fast and efficient. Much of the selectivity and efficiency can be accounted for by the architecture and ultrastructure of the pulmonary capillary bed (48). For example, the degradation of bradykinin and the conversion of angiotensin I to angiotensin II are completed almost quantitatively during one transit through the pulmonary vasculature (see references in 51). In fact, metabolic activities of endothelial cells, such as amine uptake, are now considered indices of pulmonary vascular injury (7, 17, 19), and hydrolysis of synthetic substrates of angiotensin-converting enzyme is viewed as an indicator of pulmonary vascular perfusion (8). These well-established endothelial properties may be altered in disease states. For example, plasma levels of angiotensin-converting enzyme are elevated in a number of pulmonary diseases such as sarcoidosis, silicosis, tuberculosis, and lung cancer, but their modulation under physiologic conditions, such as changes in blood pO_2, has not been demonstrated (8, 37, 80). Therefore we will discuss processing of vasoactive peptides, amines, and nucleotides only where they influence properties described below.

Alterations in Expression of Hemostatic Properties

From earliest descriptions (see 2) endothelium was known to provide an effective barrier separating the blood from the tissues and a nonthrombogenic surface over which blood can flow unimpeded. Some of the "passive" thromboresistance of the vessel wall can be attributed to heparin-like membrane proteoglycans (81). However, it is now known that endothelium is actively antithrombogenic by virtue of its ability to synthesize and release prostacyclin (PGI_2) (12, 33, 85) and its ADPase activity (13, 38). This activity is located on the surface, probably in endothelial caveolae, as are ATPase and 5'-nucleotidase (75, 76). In addition, there are a number of cellular mechanisms that tend to promote the antithrombogenicity of the endothelial surface, such as secretion of a plasminogen activator (31), uptake and clearance of circulating thrombin (30) and synthesis of antithrombin III (9b). Basal levels of prostacyclin release appear to be quite low, but in response to a variety of substances, such as bradykinin (12), thrombin, ionophore A23187, and trypsin (84), the levels of PGI_2 released are increased dramatically. PGI_2 is markedly antiaggregatory (35) and is also a vasodilator. Since bradykinin is a vasodilator, the bradykinin-induced release of PGI_2 has clear implications both for hemostasis and for vascular tone. Angiotensin converting enzyme (kininase II), the enzyme largely responsible for degradation of bradykinin in the pulmonary circulation, is important in limiting the actions of bradykinin on PGI_2 release (63). The bradykinin-stimulated release of PGI_2 is inhibited by a number of substances, including EDTA, indomethacin, verapamil, nifedipine, trifluoperazine, and hydrocortisone (12, 14, 63).

Despite the impressive number of mechanisms capable of rendering the endothelial surface resistant to thrombus formation, it is now becoming apparent that a number of stimuli can change the normally antithrombogenic nature of the endothelium. Substances such as endotoxin cause endothelial cells to express procoagulant (tissue factor) activity (10, 72). Endotoxin exposure also alters the fibrinolytic potential of endothelial cells, causing them to release an inhibitor of plasminogen activator (11). At the same time endotoxin appears to unmask Fc receptors on endothelial cells (see below). It now appears that procoagulant activity of endothelial cells can also be induced by the action of interleukin 1, an inflammatory mediator (5, 71). The procoagulant potential of endothelial cells by themselves has now been shown by a number of studies; for example, prothrombin can be activated on endothelial cells by factor Xa and calcium (44). The cofactor necessary for this reaction, factor V, has been shown to be synthesized by endothelial cells in culture (9), factors IX and X have also been shown to be bound to endothelium (26).

Clearly, the normally actively antithrombogenic surface of endothelium can be transformed into one that is fully capable of supporting procoagulant activities. Furthermore, these modulations of activity occur in response to stimuli that though they may be regarded as injurious, fall far short of damaging the endothelium and are not the result simply of exposure of subendothelial connective tissue. Since the experiments leading to the data presented above were carried out using endothelial cells in culture, the effects of platelets, macrophages, and smooth muscle cells, or their growth factors, were not operative.

Alterations in Expression of Immunologic Properties

Endothelium is relatively unreactive in immunologic terms under normal conditions. Ia antigen can be detected on endothelium under a number of conditions (1, 42), but it appears that constitutively it is not expressed. Ia antigen can be induced, however, by exposure of endothelial cells to γ-interferon (39).

Normal pulmonary endothelial cells do not express receptors for the Fc portion of IgG nor for the C3b component of complement (65). However, when the endothelial cells are damaged by virus infection (influenza or cytomegalovirus) or exposure to white cell lysates, Fc and C3b receptors become expressed (66). Other injurious stimuli that result in a similar unmasking of endothelial Fc receptors include incubation of endothelial cells with antibodies to endothelial surface enzymes, such as angiotensin-converting enzyme or carboxypeptidase N, in the presence of complement (58, 59), and exposure to trypsin or endotoxin (63). Another condition that results in the expression of Fc receptors on endothelial cells is incubation with C1q; endothelial cells bind C1q but not C1 itself (58, 59). Recently, we have been able to demonstrate that the binding of C1q to pulmonary endothelial cells is receptor-mediated and occurs via the collagenous tail region of the C1q molecule (87). Each bound molecule of C1q exposes the six globular head regions (Fc binding portion) on the endothelial cell (63) (Figure 1b). Both unmasking of latent Fc receptors on endothelium and expression of Fc receptors resulting from C1q binding may involve the endothelial glycocalyx (see below). Receptors for the collagenous tail region of C1q on the endothelial surface may provide a mechanism whereby C1q-bearing soluble immune complexes can bind to endothelium. Such bound immune complexes would result in complement activation with release of the anaphylatoxins. C5a would be expected to attract neutrophils directly to the endothelial surface; once there they would be likely to engulf bound immune complexes, which would result in release of neutrophil products such as the toxic oxygen radicals and proteases. Release of proteases would be expected to unmask further Fc receptors on the endothelium (66). This hypothetical sequence of events, in combination with activation of the coagulation cascade and contributions by other unflammatory mediators, could create conditions that would lead to the severe microvascular occlusion seen in aggregate anaphylaxis in guinea pigs (46) and in a variety of inflammatory reactions (59).

The developing picture indicates that endothelial cells can participate actively in the events associated with inflammatory or other vascular damage. Although normally actively antithrombogenic and immunologically privileged, the endothelial surface can respond to injurious, but subtle, stimuli and become fully capable of vigorous procoagulant activities and of initiating and sustaining complement-linked and immune reactions.

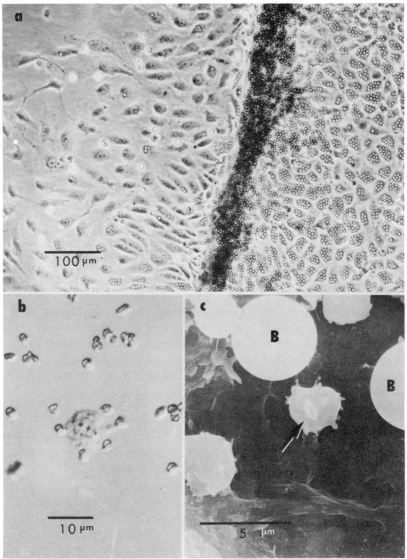

Figure 1 (*a*) Monolayer of bovine pulmonary endothelial cells after phagocytosis of 5–10 μm beads. In the intact monolayer *(right)* each cell may contain many beads. After wounding the monolayer by removal of cells on the left with a rubber policeman the "activated" endothelial cells rapidly migrate out from the wound edge. (*b*) Expression of Fc receptors on an endothelial cell after reaction with C1q. Positive rosette assay (binding of IgG-coated red cells) indicates expression of Fc receptors. (*c*) Expression of Fc receptors after phagocytosis. (Scanning electron micrograph of cells treated as in Figure 3*a*). EA7s (sheep erythrocytes coated with IgG) are bound to the surface, which indicates that Fc receptors have been unmasked. The red cell marked with an arrow is apparently attached to the endothelial cell by a stalk. Uningested beads (*B*) are also seen on the surface.

Structural Correlates: The Role of the Glycocalyx

The luminal surfaces of endothelial cells possess a number of ultrastructural specializations that are important in the interactions of blood cells and blood-borne substances with the endothelium. Endothelial cells viewed by scanning electron microscopy are seen to be covered with projections of varying distribution, size, and density (78). These projections can also be seen in thin sections and on surface replicas (58, 78). The projections greatly increase the surface area of the endothelium and promote the formation of a layer of plasma that is free of blood cells over the endothelial surface. Both effects facilitate the processing of circulating vasoactive substances by endothelial surface enzymes (48).

In addition to projections, the endothelial surface characteristically possesses large numbers of caveolae, many of which directly face the vascular lumen (48, 56, 77). Like endothelial projections, endothelial caveolae have the effect of increasing the vascular surface area for the interaction of blood solutes with endothelial cells. In addition, the luminal stoma is spanned by a delicate diaphragm (77, 79), which provides a specialized microenvironment for selective processing of circulating substrates by endothelial enzymes and for the rapid return of metabolized products to the circulation. Endothelial caveolae possess many of the enzymes important in the processing of vasoactive substances. For example, the adenine nucleotides are metabolized during a single passage through the pulmonary vascular bed (47) by enzymes specifically located in caveolae (75, 76). Bradykinin is inactivated and angiotensin I is converted to angiotensin II by a single enzyme, angiotensin-converting enzyme (kininase II) (see references in 51). Angiotensin-converting enzyme is localized by immunocytochemical techniques on the endothelial plasma membrane, including caveolae (48, 60, 62, 67). Carboxypeptidase N, which may play a role in the pulmonary metabolism of the anaphylatoxins (64), is similarly localized by immunocytochemical methods on the plasma membrane and caveolae of endothelial cells (59). Carbonic anhydrase is localized on endothelial cells but is not preferentially localized to caveolae (69). Caveolae thus appear to be important not only for their large numbers and their position in direct communication with the circulation (54), but also for their enzymic activities (48, 60).

Endothelial projections and caveolae taken together may account for the discrepancy in vascular volumes measured by using tagged red cells versus those using tagged albumin. This difference indicates that the space not accessible to red cells is sizeable. However, there is another layer on the endothelial surface that may by itself, or in combination with endothelial projections, account for discrepancies in hematocrit measurements (18) and for the solute-excluded volumes found near the cell surface (41). This layer is the endothelial glycocalyx; it is not visible by conventional electron microscopic techniques. It can be visualized using special stains (32, 43), which give it an amorphous fuzzy appearance of a coating on the endothelial surface. It has been detected by a number of other techniques, such as exclusion of ferritin label (60) and by con A-hemocyanin reaction (83). In vivo the glycocalyx contains adsorbed plasma proteins such as albumin that help to maintain the permeability characteristics of the endothelial layer (70). The glycocalyx is probably responsible for the distribution of anionic sites on the endothelial surface and the differentiated microdomains on the luminal surface of capillary endothelium (74).

The glycocalyx can be observed directly by surface replica techniques (Figure 2) (25, 58). The surface replicas can be tilted to yield three-dimensional images that show that the glycocalyx is not an amorphous fuzz but is similar to a deep-pile carpet (100 to several hundred angstroms thick) that covers and enmeshes the endothelial enzymes and receptors embedded in the plasma membrane (58). The glycocalyx may serve as a filter that can facilitate or restrict the access of certain substrates to these enzymes and receptors. It can admit molecules of the size of IgG since peroxidase-labeled antibodies can be used for localization of endothelial enzymes (61). It can also act as a size, shape, and charge barrier for small molecules (74), and within junctions it may act as a fiber matrix (15) capable of determining permeability properties.

When endothelial cells are reacted with antibodies to endothelial antigens (such as angiotensin-converting enzyme or carboxypeptidase N) in the presence of a source of complement, such as serum, the endothelial glycocalyx becomes disarrayed (Figure 2b) (58, 60, 63). Note that the same conditions that cause disarray of the endothelial glycocalyx also cause unmasking of Fc receptors on endothelial cells, as described above. Thus the glycocalyx may act as a physical mask or barrier shielding latent receptors on the endothelial surface (63). The glycocalyx may also play a role in the binding of C1q since the collagenous portion of the molecule that binds to endothelium (87) has a high affinity for fibronectin. Since fibronectin is an endothelial cell product (6) and is likely to be a component of the glycocalyx, it may well be that C1q binds to endothelium via the glycocalyx. The glycocalyx may play a significant role in maintaining the normal recognition processes between endothelium and blood cells and between endothelium and blood-borne substances. Its disarray may accompany changes in immunologic properties, and it may play a role in the initiation of immune complex deposition.

Evidence of a role for the glycocalyx in the modulations of hemostatic activities described above is more circumstantial. However, it was recently shown that conditioned media from stimulated leukocytes (containing interleukins) cause the appearance of a glycosaminoglycan-rich pericellular matrix, which is stainable with alcian blue, on the surface of endothelial cells (36). This effect was partially replicated by incubating endothelial cells with interleukin 1 and γ-interferon in combination (36). Interleukin 1 markedly alters

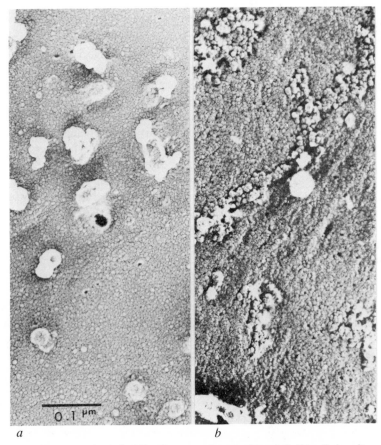

Figure 2 Surface replicas of rabbit pulmonary microvascular endothelial cells in culture: (*a*) shows a control endothelial cell with glycocalyx appearing as a regular carpetwork over the surface; (*b*) shows an endothelial cell after reaction with antibodies to angiotensin-converting enzyme in the presence of complement. The glycocalyx is disarrayed and shows pits, furrows, and clumps.

endothelial cell shape; it may mediate both the expression of tissue factor activity (5, 71) and alterations in the endothelial glycocalyx.

Endotoxin directly affects the structure and permeability of the endothelial layer (34). The effects of endotoxin on the endothelial glycocalyx are not yet known; however, endotoxin affects the expression of procoagulant (10, 72) and the fibrinolytic potential of endothelium (11) and also causes unmasking of Fc receptors (63). In other instances unmasking of the Fc receptors is accompanied by disarray of the glycocalyx.

Recently it was reported (27) that specific injury to the endothelium causes the appearance of a dense amorphous layer covering the endothelial surface and that this layer is the focus for platelet adhesion. We found (unpublished data) that trypsin alters the glycocalyx to yield widely separated blobs of alcian blue staining material and a complete absence of the normal layer. (Trypsin has a number of injurious effects on the endothelial surface, see below.)

Studies of the ultrastructural specializations of the endothelial surface have contributed to our understanding of the cellular mechanisms involved in the normal functions of endothelium, such as processing of vasoactive substances, maintenance of an antithrombogenic surface, and control of permeability barriers. Various researchers have shown that both endothelial projections and caveolae may be altered in response to injury (16, 54, 59). It may now be important to correlate changes in the glycocalyx with changes in the expression of hemostatic and immunologic potential in the response of endothelium to injury.

Quality of Endothelial Cell Cultures

Unlike studies of the metabolic processing of vasoactive substances by endothelium, which were first conducted in intact lungs and then confirmed in vitro, the large majority of the studies described in the previous three sections were conducted using endothelial cells in culture. This attests to the convenience and great utility of endothelial cultures; however, it also serves as a warning that many endothelial properties await verification in vivo. Nonetheless, isolated endothelial cells in culture should continue to provide a useful system for studying changes in structure or function produced by subtle injuries or stimuli, as long as the endothelial cells are not unduly injured or stimulated by the practice of culture itself. Some substances that are commonly used for cell culture impart alterations to endothelial cells. For example, trypsin concentrations lower or the same as those used for routine processing cause removal of endothelial surface enzymes (59), loss of high-affinity binding sites and junctional proteins (57), exposure of Fc receptors (63), and strand breaks in DNA (9a). In our laboratory, endothelial cells are not exposed to proteolytic enzymes for isolation or for subculture. Rather, the cells are isolated mechanically, using a scalpel to scrape endothelium from large vessels (55), or using microcarrier beads (35–40 μm) (28) to remove cells from the microvasculature (61, 68). Endothelium can be collected from either the pre- (68) or postcapillary vessels (61). The cells can be passaged with a rubber policeman or microcarriers (100–150 μm) can be used in roller bottle cultures. The cells will migrate off confluent microcarriers onto flasks or coverslips and, conversely, the cells from confluent monolayers will colonize naked beads seeded onto them (49). The microcarrier suspensions containing cell-covered beads can be passaged by dividing them among new roller bottles and then adding fresh medium and additional microcarriers. We have been able to sustain culture lines for over five years and more than 125 passages by methods that avoid enzymes, and we have maintained cultures that retain differentiated properties, such as cobblestone monolayer morphology, normal levels of angiotensin-converting enzyme, and the ability to synthesize and release PGI_2. The ability to culture endothelial cells over the long term without loss of phenotypic characteristics may be important in applications such as seeding of prostheses (50), but is essential for studies of endothelial surface properties in response to injury.

Phagocytosis and Endothelial Cell Activation

The success experienced using 35–40-μm microcarrier beads to obtain microvascular endothelial cells suggests that perfusion of blood-free lungs with 5–10-μm beads might be a suitable method for collecting capillary endothelium. However, when blood-free rat lungs were embolized with 5–10-μm beads we did not obtain the usual harvest of endothelial cell-covered beads. Instead, capillary endothelial cells engulfed the beads. The experiment was repeated using endothelial cells in monolayer culture, and again endothelial cells ingested the beads by phagocytosis in a time-dependent fashion. Within 1 hr of exposure most cells had ingested one bead, after 48 hr some cells contained as many as nine beads (52). In later experiments we found that endothelial cells in culture can engulf heat-killed Staphylococcus aureus, hardened, swelled red cells, and microcarrier beads 1–15 μm in diameter. The beads become totally embedded in the cytoplasm, and a limiting membrane is hard to discern. There is considerable rearrangement of internal organelles to accomodate the beads, as seen by staining of, for example, vimentin, stress fibers, Golgi apparatus, and mitochondria using monoclonal antibodies (gift of Dr. Marina Glukhova, Cardiology Research Center, Moscow, USSR).

When endothelial monolayers, replete with phagocytosed beads, were wounded by removal of a portion of the monolayer with a rubber policeman, the endothelial cells appeared to be markedly stimulated in their ability to migrate out from the wound edge (Figure 1a). In previous studies we had shown that wounding of this type accelerated division and migration rates in a small population of cells dedicated to repairing the wound (53); however, after phagocytosis all the cells appeared markedly "activated." It is not yet known whether endothelial enzyme systems are activated, like those of macrophages, to digest the beads, nor is it known what role phagocytosis by endothelial cells may play in intact vessels. It is clear, however, that endothelial cells that have phagocytosed several beads express Fc receptors (Figure 1c), while control cells that have not engaged in phagocytosis do not. Under normal conditions of flow it is unlikely that small particles passing the vessel wall would have sufficient time for attachment and phagocytosis. However, when flow is slowed or stopped it is conceivable that endothelial cell phagocytosis could play a role in removing intravascular debris from occluded vessels.

CONCLUDING COMMENTS AND FUTURE DIRECTIONS

Endothelial cells play a number of active roles: They act as a barrier with limited permeability; they process circulating hormones and other bioactive materials with great efficiency and selectivity; they share the responsibility for hemostatic reactions with cells and components of blood, but under normal conditions interact very little with blood cells or blood-borne clotting factors. The enzymes, enzyme inhibitors, receptors, and transport proteins responsible for the outcome of interactions of endothelial cells with circulating substances are in many cases known. Some of the active substances released by endothelial cells have also been documented, but undoubtedly many remain to be discovered. The active antithrombogeneity of endothelium is probably due in part to release of prostacyclin, but even when prostacyclin is inhibited endothelium does not become thrombogenic. In fact, only when endothelial cells in vitro are transformed do they become thrombogenic (22, 23, 86). Under these circumstances the polarity of the endothelium may be lost and the distinction between the glycocalyx on the luminal surface and the basement membrane materials on the abluminal surface may become confused.

The full range of properties and functions of the normal glycocalyx (Figure 2a) are not known, but it is clear that endothelium can play an active role in the events leading to microvascular occlusion and damage. The endothelial surface over which blood normally flows unimpeded can become a focus for procoagulant and complement-linked reactions, and such changes may be accompanied by a disarray of the glycocalyx (Figure 2b). It is tempting to speculate that the glycocalyx is important in the recognition processes between endothelial cells and blood elements and that alterations in hemostatic and immunologic potential are accompanied by alterations in the endothelial glycocalyx.

ACKNOWLEDGMENT

This work was supported by NHLBI grants HL21568 and HL33064, and by a grant from the Council for Tobacco Research, USA, Inc.

Literature Cited

1. Alejandro, R., Schienvold, F. L., Hajek, S. V., Ryan, U. S., Miller, J., et al. 1982. Immunocytochemical localization of HLA-DR in human islets of langerhans. *Diabetes* 31:17–22
2. Altschul, R. 1954. *Endothelium. Its Development, Morphology, Function and Pathology.* New York: MacMillan. 157 pp.
3. Bakhle, Y. S., Ferreira, S. H. 1985. Lung metabolism of eicosanoids: pros-

taglandins, prostacyclin, thromboxane, and leukotrienes. In *Handbook of Physiology—The Respiratory System*, ed. A. P. Fishman, A. B. Fisher, Vol. 1, pp. 365–86. Bethesda, MD: Am. Physiol. Soc.
4. Bakhle, Y. S., Vane J. R. 1974. Pharmacokinetic function of the pulmonary circulation. *Physiol. Rev.* 54:1007–45
5. Bevilaqua, M. P., Pober, S. J., Majeau,

G. R., Cotran, R. S., Gimbrone, M. A. 1984. Interleukin 1 (IL-1) induces biosynthesis and cell surface expression of procoagulant activity in human vascular endothelial cells. *J. Exp. Med.* 160:618–23

6. Birdwell, G. R., Gospodarowicz, D., Nicolson, G. L. 1978. Identification, localization and role of fibronectin in cultured bovine endothelial cells. *Proc. Natl. Acad. Sci. USA* 75:3273–77

7. Block, E. R., Fisher, A. B. 1977. Depression of serotonin clearance by rat lungs during oxygen exposure. *J. Appl. Physiol. Respirat. Environ. Exercise Physiol.* 42:33–38

8. Catravas, J. D., Gillis, C. N. 1981. Metabolism of [³H]-benzoyl-phenylalanyl-alanyl-prolin by pulmonary angiotensin converting enzyme in vivo: effects of bradykinin, SQ 14225 or acute hypoxia. *J. Pharmacol. Exp. Ther.* 217:263–70

9. Cerveny, T. J., Fass, D. N., Mann, K. G. 1984. Synthesis of coagulation factor V by cultured aortic endothelium. *Blood* 63:1467–74

9a. Cesarone, C. F., Fugassa, E., Gallo, G., Voci, A., Orunesu, M. 1984. Collagenase perfusion of rat liver induces DNA damage and DNA repair in hepatocytes. *Muta. Res.* 141:113–16

9b. Chan, T. K., Chan, V. 1981. Antithrombin III, the major modulator of intravascular coagulation, is synthesized by human endothelial cells. *Thromb. Haemostas.* 46:504–6

10. Colucci, M., Balconi, G., Lorenzet, R., Pietra, A., Locati, I., et al. 1983. Cultured human endothelial cells generate tissue factor in response to endotoxin. *J. Clin. Invest.* 71:1893–96

11. Crutchley, D. J., Conanan, L. B., Ryan, U. S. 1985. Endotoxin induction of a plasminogen activator inhibitor in bovine pulmonary artery endothelial cells. *Fed. Proc.* 44:1844 (Abstr. 8369)

12. Crutchley, D. J., Ryan, J. W., Ryan, U. S., Fisher, G. M. 1983. Bradykinin-induced release of prostacyclin and thromboxanes from bovine pulmonary artery endothelial cells. Studies with lower homologs and calcium antagonists. *Biochem. Biophys. Acta* 751:99–107

13. Crutchley, D. J., Ryan, U. S., Ryan, J. W. 1980. Effects of aspirin and dipyridamole on the degradation of adenosine diphosphate by cultured cells derived from bovine pulmonary artery. *J. Clin. Invest.* 66:29–35

14. Crutchley, D. J., Ryan, U. S., Ryan, J. W. 1985. Glucocorticoid modulation of prostacyclin production in cultured

bovine pulmonary endothelial cells derived from bovine pulmonary arteries. *J. Pharmacol. Exp. Ther.* 233:650–55

15. Curry, F. E., Michel, C. C. 1980. A fiber matrix model of capillary permeability. *Microvasc. Res.* 20:96–99

16. Davies, P., Ross, R. 1978. Mediation of pinocytosis in cultured arterial smooth muscle and endothelial cells by platelet-derived growth factor. *J. Cell Biol.* 79:663–71

17. Dobuler, K. J., Catravas, J. D., Gillis, C. N. 1982. Early detection of oxygen-induced lung injury in conscious rabbits. *Am. Rev. Respir. Dis.* 126:534–39

18. Duling, B. R., Sarelius, I. M., Jackson, W. F. 1982. A comparison of microvascular estimates of capillary blood flow with direct measurements of total muscle flow. *Int. J. Microcirc. Clin. Exp.* 1:409–24

19. Fisher, A. B., Block, E. R., Pietra, G. G. 1980. Environmental influences on uptake of serotonin and other amines. *Environ. Health Perspect.* 35:191–98

20. Fishman, A. P., Pietra, G. G. 1974. Handling of bioactive materials by the lung. Pt. 1. *N. Engl. J. Med.* 291:884–90

21. Fishman, A. P., Pietra, G. G. 1974. Handling of bioactive materials by the lung. Pt. 2. *N. Engl. J. Med.* 291:953–59

22. Fry, G. L., Czervionke, R. L., Hoak, J. C., Smith, J. B., Haycraft, D. L. 1980. Platelet adherence to cultured vascular cells: influence of prostacyclin (PGI₂). *Blood* 55:271–75

22a. Gillis, C. N., Pitt, B. R. 1982. The fate of circulating amines within the pulmonary circulation. *Ann. Rev. Physiol.* 44:269–81

23. Gimbrone, M. A., Fareed, G. C. 1976. Transformation of cultured human vascular endothelium by SV40 DNA. *Cell* 9:685–93

24. Hamosh, M., Hamosh, P. 1985. Lipoproteins and lipoprotein lipase. In *Handbook of Physiology—The Respiratory System*, ed. A. P. Fishman, A. B. Fisher, Vol. 1, pp. 387–418

25. Hart, M. A., Ryan, U. S. 1978. Surface replicas of pulmonary endothelial cells in culture. *Tissue Cell* 10:441–49

26. Heimark, R., Schwartz, S. M. 1983. Binding of coagulation factors X and XI to the endothelial surface. *Biochem. Biophys. Res. Commun.* 111:723–31

27. Herrmann, K. S., Voigt, W. H. 1984. Ultrastructural observations of an electron dense amorphous layer on selectively damaged endothelial cells, a possible trigger of thrombogenesis in vivo, and its inhibition by nafazatrom. *Thromb. Res.* 36:205–15

28. Jacobson, B. S., Ryan, U. S. 1982. Growth of endothelial and Hela cells on a new multipurpose microcarrier that is positive, negative or collagen coated. *Tissue Cell* 14:69–83

29. Junod, A. F. 1985. 5-Hydroxytryptamine and other amines in the lungs. In *Handbook of Physiology—The Respiratory System*, ed. A. P. Fishman, A. B. Fisher, Vol. 1, pp. 337–50

30. Lollar, P., Owen, W. G. 1980. Clearance of thrombin from the circulation by high affinity binding sites on endothelium: Possible role in the inactivation of thrombin by antithrombin III. *Circulation* 62:1222–30

31. Loskutoff, D. J., Edgington, T. S. 1977. Synthesis of a fibrinolytic activator and inhibitor by endothelial cells. *Proc. Natl. Acad. Sci. USA* 74:3903–7

32. Luft, J. H. 1966. Fine structure of capillary and endocapillary layer as revealed by ruthenium red. *Fed. Proc.* 25:1773–83

33. MacIntyre, D. E., Pearson, J. D., Gordon, J. L. 1978. Localisation and stimulation of prostacyclin production in vascular cells. *Nature* 271:549–51

34. Meyrick, B. O., Ryan, U. S., Brigham, K. L. 1986. Direct effects of *E. coli* endotoxin on structure and permeability of pulmonary endothelial monolayers and the endothelial layer of intimal explants. *Am. J. Path.* In press

35. Moncada, S., Gryglewski, R., Bunting, S., Vane, J. R. 1976. An enzyme isolated from arteries transforms prostaglandin endoperoxides to an unstable substance that inhibits platelet aggregation. *Nature* 263:663–65

36. Montesano, R., Mossaz, A., Ryser, J. E., Orci, L., Vassalli, P. J. 1984. Leukocyte interleukins induce cultured endothelial cells to produce a highly organized glycosaminoglycan-rich pericellular matrix. *J. Cell Biol.* 99:1706–15

37. Oparil, S., Winternitz, S., Gould, V., Baerwald, M., Szidon, P. 1982. Effect of hypoxia on the conversion of angiotensin I to II in the isolated perfused rat lung. *Biochem. Pharmacol.* 31:1375–79

38. Pearson, J. D., Carleton, J. S., Gordon, J. L. 1980. Metabolism of adenine nucleotides by ectoenzymes of vascular endothelial and smooth-muscle cells in culture. *Biochemistry* 190:421–29

39. Pober, J. S., Gimbrone, M. A., Cotran, R. S., Reiss, C. S., Burakoff, S. J., et al. 1983. Ia expression by vascular endothelium is inducible by activated T cells and by human gamma interferon. *J. Exp. Med.* 157:1339–53

40. Deleted in proof

41. Polefka, T. G., Garrick, R. A., Redwood, W. R., Swislocki, N. I., Chinard, F. P. 1984. Solute excluded volumes near the Novikoff cell surface. *Am. J. Physiol.* 247:C350–56

42. Rabinovitch, A., Alejandro, R., Noel, J., Brunschwig, J. P., Ryan, U. S. 1982. Tissue culture reduces Ia antigen-bearing cells in rat islets and prolongs islet allograft survival. *Diabetes* 31:48–54

43. Rambourg, A., Leblond, C. P. 1967. Electron microscope observations on the carbohydrate-rich cell coat present at the surface of cells in the rat. *J. Cell Biol.* 32:27–53

44. Rodgers, G. M., Schuman, M. A. 1983. Prothrombin is activated on vascular endothelial cells by factor Xa and calcium. *Proc. Natl. Acad. Sci. USA* 80:7001–5

45. Ryan, J. W., Ryan, U. S. 1977. Pulmonary endothelial cells. *Fed. Proc.* 36:2683–91

46. Ryan, J. W., Ryan, U. S. 1984. Endothelial surface enzymes and the dynamic processing of plasma substrates. *Int. Rev. Exp. Pathol.* 26:1–43

47. Ryan, J. W., Smith, U. 1971. Metabolism of adenosine-5'-monophosphate during circulation through the lungs. *Trans. Assoc. Am. Physcns.* 84:297–306

48. Ryan, U. S. 1982. Structural bases for metabolic activity. *Am. Rev. Physiol.* 44:223–39

49. Ryan, U. S. 1984. Culture of pulmonary endothelial cells on microcarriers. In *Biology of the Endothelial Cell*, ed. E. A. Jaffe, pp. 35–50. The Netherlands: Nijhoff

50. Ryan, U. S. 1984. New uses for endothelial cell culture. *BioEssays* 1:114–16

51. Ryan, U. S. 1985. Processing of angiotensin and other peptides by the lungs. In *Handbook of Physiology—The Respiratory System*, ed. A. P. Fishman, A. B. Fisher, Vol. 1, pp. 351–64

52. Ryan, U. S. 1986. The endothelial surface and responses to injury. *Fed. Proc.* In press

53. Ryan, U. S., Absher, M., Olazabal, B. M., Brown, L. M., Ryan, J. W. 1982. Proliferation of pulmonary endothelial cells: time-lapse cinematography of growth to confluence and restitution of monolayer after wounding. *Tissue Cell* 14:637–49

54. Ryan, U. S., Frokjaer-Jensen, J. 1985. Pulmonary endothelium and processing of plasma solutes: structure and function. In *The Pulmonary Circulation and Pulmonary Vascular Injury*, ed. S. I. Said. Mount Kisko, NY: Futura

55. Ryan, U. S., Mortara, M., Whitaker, C. 1980. Methods for microcarrier culture

of bovine pulmonary artery endothelial cells avoiding the use of enzymes. *Tissue Cell* 12:619–35

56. Ryan, U. S., Ryan, J. W. 1977. Correlations between the fine structure of the alveolar-capillary unit and its metabolic activities. In *Lung Biology in Health and Disease*, ed. C. Lenfant, Vol. 4, pp. 197–232. New York/Basel: Dekker

57. Ryan, U. S., Ryan, J. W. 1982. Vital and functional activities of endothelial cells. In *Pathobiology of the Endothelial Cell*, ed. H. L. Nossel, H. J. Vogel, pp. 455–69. New York: Academic

58. Ryan, U. S., Ryan, J. W. 1983. Surface properties of pulmonary endothelial cells. *Ann. NY Acad. Sci.* 416:441–56

59. Ryan, U. S., Ryan, J. W. 1983. Endothelial cells and inflammation. *Clin. Lab. Med.* 3:577–99

60. Ryan, U. S., Ryan, J. W. 1984. Cell biology of pulmonary endothelium. *Circulation* 70:III-46–III-62

61. Ryan, U. S., Ryan, J. W. 1984. Inflammatory mediators, contraction and endothelial cells. In *Progress in Microcirculation Research II*, ed. F. C. Courtice, D. G. Garlick, M. A. Perry, pp. 424–38. Sydney: Comm. Postgrad. Med. Educ. Univ. New South Wales

62. Ryan, U. S., Ryan, J. W., Chin, A. T. 1976. Kininase II (angiotensin converting enzyme) and endothelial cells in culture. *Adv. Exp. Med. Biol.* 70:217–27

63. Ryan, U. S., Ryan, J. W., Crutchley, D. J. 1985. The pulmonary endothelial surface. *Fed. Proc.* 44:2603–9

64. Ryan, U. S., Ryan, J. W., Plummer, T. H. 1982. Carboxypeptidase N is a surface enzyme of pulmonary endothelial cells. *Circulation* 66:II-167 (Abstr. 667)

65. Ryan, U. S., Schultz, D. R., Del Vecchio, P., Ryan, J. W. 1980. Endothelial cells of bovine pulmonary artery lack receptors for C3b and for the Fc portion of immunoglobulin G. *Science* 208:748–49

66. Ryan, U. S., Schultz, D. R., Ryan, J. W. 1981. Fc and C3b receptors on pulmonary endothelial cells: induction by injury. *Science* 214:557–59

67. Ryan, U. S., Ryan, J. W., Whitaker, C., Chiu, A. 1976. Localization of angiotensin converting enzyme (kininase II). Immunocytochemistry and immunofluorescence. *Tissue Cell* 8:125–146

68. Ryan, U. S., White, L., Lopez, M., Ryan, J. W. 1982. Use of microcarriers to isolate and culture pulmonary microvascular endothelium. *Tissue Cell* 14:597–606

69. Ryan, U. S., Whitney, P. L., Ryan, J. W. 1982. Localization of carbonic anhydrase on pulmonary endothelial cells in culture. *J. Appl. Physiol.* 53:914–19

70. Schneeberger, E. E., Hamelin, M. 1984. Interaction of serum proteins with lung endothelial glycocalyx: its effect on endothelial permeability. *J. Physiol.* 247:H206–H217

71. Schorer, A. E., Moldow, C. F., Rao, G. H. R., Oken, M., Kaplan, M. 1985. Interleukin 1 (IL1) promotes tissue factor expression in human endothelial cells. *Clin. Res.* In press

72. Schorer, A. E., Rick, P. D., Swain, W. R., Moldow, C. F. 1985. Structural features of endotoxin required for stimulation of endothelial cell tissue factor production: Exposure of preformed tissue factor after oxidant-mediated endothelial injury. *J. Lab. Clin. Med.* 106:38–42

73. Shepro, D. 1986. The metabolism of biogenic amines by endothelial cells. *Am. Rev. Physiol.* 48:335–45

74. Simionescu, M., Simionescu, N. 1986. Functions of the endothelial cell surface. *Ann. Rev. Physiol.* 48:279–93

75. Smith, U., Ryan, J. W. 1971. Pinocytotic vesicles of the pulmonary endothelial cell. *Chest* 59:125–55

76. Smith, U., Ryan, J. W. 1972. Pulmonary endothelial cells and metabolism of adenine nucleotides, kinins and angiotensin I. *Adv. Exp. Med. Biol.* 21:267–76

77. Smith, U., Ryan, J. W. 1973. Electron microscopy of endothelial and epithelial components of the lungs: correlations of structure and function. *Fed. Proc.* 32:1957–66

78. Smith, U., Ryan, J. W., Michie, D. D., Smith, D. S. 1971. Endothelial projections: As revealed by scanning electron microscopy. *Science* 173:925–27

79. Smith, U., Ryan, J. W., Smith, D. S. 1973. Freeze-etch studies of the plasma membrane of pulmonary endothelial cells. *J. Cell Biol.* 56:492–99

80. Szidon, P., Bairey, N., Oparil, S. 1980. Effect of acute hypoxia on the pulmonary conversion of angiotensin I to angiotensin II in dogs. *Circ. Res.* 46:221–26

81. Thorgiersson, G., Robertson, A. L. 1978. The vascular endothelium–pathobiologic significance. *Am. J. Path.* 93:803–48

82. Vane, J. R. 1969. The release and fate of vaso-active hormones in the circulation. *Br. J. Pharmacol.* 35:209–42

83. Weber, G., Fabrini, P., Resi, L., Toti, P. 1977. Aortic surface coat scanning

electron-microscopic modifications after short-term hypercholesterolic diet, visualized in rabbits by con A-haemocyanin reaction. *Atherosclerosis* 27:141–45

84. Weksler, B. B., Ley, C. W., Jaffe, E. A. 1978. Stimulation of endothelial prostacyclin production by thrombin, trypsin and ionophore A23187. *J. Clin. Invest.* 62:923–30

85. Weksler, B. B., Marcus, A. J., Jaffe, E. A. 1977. Synthesis of prostaglandin I_2 (prostacyclin) by cultured human and bovine endothelial cells. *Proc. Natl. Acad. Sci. USA* 74:3922–26

86. Zetter, B. R., Johnson, L. K., Shuman, M. A., Gospodarowicz, D. 1978. The isolation of vascular endothelial cell lines with altered cell surface and platelet-binding properties. *Cell* 14:501–9

87. Zhang, S. C., Schultz, D. R., Ryan, U. S. 1986. Receptor-mediated binding of C1q on pulmonary endothelial cells. *Tissue Cell* 18: In press

Ann. Rev. Physiol. 1986. 48:279–93

FUNCTIONS OF THE ENDOTHELIAL CELL SURFACE

Maya Simionescu and Nicolae Simionescu

Institute of Cellular Biology and Pathology, Bucharest-79691, Romania

INTRODUCTION

The primary interactions between the blood components and the vessel wall take place at the luminal surface of vascular endothelium. The blood-endothelial interface is a composite of the endothelial cell coat proper and some plasma proteins temporarily associated with the former. The endothelial cell coat actually represents the ectodomains of membrane proteins and glycoproteins, and proteoglycans. It is still uncertain whether proteoglycans are true membrane constituents or are only attached to the glycocalyx.

Endothelial cell surface (ECS) occupies a special strategic position. It is continuously exposed to the dynamic internal milieu, and it senses, transmits, and participates in adjustments to deviations in homeostasis. To fulfill these very complex and vital activities ECS has been endowed with an intricate chemical and functional machinery that is responsible for the blood-tissue exchanges, active monitoring of plasma molecules, and maintenance of a nonthrombogenic surface.

The inability, so far, to obtain a pure fraction of endothelial plasma membrane explains the lack of detailed information on its chemistry, including the molecular organization of the glycocalyx. Data currently available emerged mostly from indirect investigations using membrane markers, and from physiologic inquiries on some activities significantly associated with endothelial membrane and implicitly with its cell coat. Our present information comes from studies on both microvascular and large vessel endothelia, and is often affected by the unavoidable limitations of the in-culture conditions.

The main purpose of this review is to consider some of the significant advances in (*a*) the chemical mapping of ECS, (*b*) the cell surface-associated plasma proteins, and (*c*) some cell surface- and membrane-associated activi-

279

0066-4278/86/0315-0279$02.00

ties. It is not an exhaustive account, and we leave the technical details to the original literature. Endothelial cell (EC) metabolic activities leading to releasable substances will not be discussed.

CHEMICAL MAPPING OF CELL SURFACE

In chemically fixed specimens the luminal front of vascular endothelium displays a "fuzzy" but actually highly organized coat ~15–40 nm thick. Its visualization in the electron microscope can be enhanced by staining with ruthenium red, ionic lanthanum, uranyl acetate, or tannic acid. Depending on the location, this plasma membrane coat continues into open plasmalemmal vesicles and transendothelial channels, is often thicker on coated pits and fenestral diaphragms, and is excluded at the level of intercellular junctions. As detected by various procedures, the EC coat contains the external moieties of a variety of membrane components, e.g. proteins, glycoproteins, sialoconjugates, and proteoglycans. These may function either as (a) a sieving meshwork; (b) a locally differentiated charge barrier; or (c) as specific binding sites and receptors for plasma molecules to be either adsorbed to the cell coat, internalized into the cell itself (endocytosis), or selectively transported across the cell (transcytosis). Cell coat molecules may represent either the ectodomains of transmembrane proteins synthesized by the endothelial cells and incorporated into the plasmalemma (e.g. sialoconjugates), or molecules produced in other tissues and secondarily attached to the ECS where they perform their activity (e.g. lipoprotein lipase, thrombin). Some ECS components are continuously active (e.g. angiotensin converting enzyme), while others are dormant in the absence of a stimulus (e.g. Fc and C_3b receptors) (43).

Proteoglycans

From a relatively early demonstration (8) we learned that heparan sulfate and probably chondroitin sulfate A are present at the ECS. Heparan sulfate may exert an anticoagulant effect by enhancing the inactivation of both thrombin and activated coagulant factor X (activated by antithrombin III). Recently it was shown that EC's can produce heparin; this may be related to the presence on the ECS of β-thromboglobulin (a platelet-specific protein) known to bind heparin. Since platelet factor 4 also binds with high affinity to some glycosaminoglycans, it seems likely that ECS proteoglycans may be of considerable importance in regulating the balance between coagulating and anticoagulating systems in vivo (20). It is also generally accepted that the lipoprotein lipase is attached to the ECS via glycosaminoglycan chains. Heparin and related compounds may serve a modulating function in vivo and in situ on the receptor-mediated uptake of low density lipoproteins (64). Sulfated proteoglycans are among the contributors to the net negative charge of vascular endothelium in situ (50).

A minute differentiated distribution of some glycosaminoglycans (GAG) was indirectly demonstrated on capillary endothelium by decorating the anionic sites with cationic ferritin after ECS digestion with GAG-degrading enzymes. It appeared that heparan sulfates and chondroitin sulfates are present in small amounts and are patchily distributed on plasma membrane, and are absent on vesicle membrane. The luminal aspect of fenestral diaphragm is particularly rich in heparan sulfate. Conversely, the abluminal surface of the same diaphragm is devoid of cationic ferritin-detectable anionic sites (47). There is a suggestion that keratan sulfate is present at the level of intercellular junctions, which open after keratanase perfusion in situ (M. Simionescu, unpublished observations).

Sialoglycoconjugates

In the vascular endothelium of bone marrow at pH 1.8, colloidal iron and cationic ferritin (CF) bind to the plasma membrane, but not on coated pits. CF binding is markedly reduced by neuraminidase, which indicates that the ECS of these cells has exposed sialic acid residues which are almost absent at endocytic sites. In addition, anionic moieties with a pK_a higher than that of sialic acid (pK_a = 2.6) are presumed to exist on the entire ECS in these vessels (15). After preferential oxidation of sialyl residues with sodium periodate, the sialic acid–bearing glyco- and lipoconjugates of the ECS of mouse pancreatic capillaries were detected with ferritin hydrazide. The tracer concentration was prominent on plasmalemma proper, decreased on coated pits, and was practically absent on the membranes of vesicles and transendothelial channels (35). It appears that sialyl groups are largely but not exclusively responsible for the negative charge of plasmalemma. Like sulfated GAGs, sialic acids are virtually absent from vesicles and channels, but unlike GAGs they do not contribute to the dense negative charge of fenestral diaphragms. It has been shown that enzymatic removal of sialic acids from the ECS of rabbit carotid arteries increases the uptake of low density lipoprotein and fibrinogen (21), and the adhesion of blood platelets to EC's (22).

Glycoproteins

A variety of labeled lectins have been used to detect specific monosaccharide residues on the ECS of arteries (68), heart (45), pancreas, and intestine (48). In the latter organs, evidence was produced that while the mannosyl, glucosyl, and to a certain extent, fucosyl residues have a relatively patchy distribution on the ECS, other monosacchrides are more homogeneously displayed on plasmalemma. However, membranes of plasmalemmal vesicles and transendothelial channels, and their associated diaphragms, are particularly rich in β-D-galactosyl and β-N-acetylglucosaminyl residues. These defined microdomains appear to be to a certain extent complementary to those generated by the preferential distribution of anionic sites (see section on cell surface charge). A similar distribution of monosaccharides was detected on the ECS of bone marrow sinusoids, except for the absence of binding of Ulex europeus agglutinin (specific for fucosyl residues), and their relation to features involved in the endothelial transport was emphasized (56).

Endogenous Lectins

Sugar-binding proteins, such as those specific for N-acetylglucosamine-terminated glycoproteins or galactoorosomucoid, were identified in the rat hepatic sinusoidal endothelial cells. These receptors can be modulated by glucose and during diabetes mellitus (60). In the marrow sinusoid endothelium, experiments with glycosylated ferritin failed to detect lectin-like molecules (56). The possible occurrence of endogenous lectins within ECS is of great interest, but its investigation to date has been technically difficult. The absence of an expressed sugar-binding protein does not rule out its existence as a dormant species that can only be identified using isolated endothelial plasma membrane.

Enzymes

Several enzymes or enzymatic activities have been ascribed to the ECS: ATPase, ADPase, 5'-nucleotidase, and nonspecific esterase. Carbonic anhydrase (present on pulmonary endothelial cells) is assumed to facilitate egress of CO_2; carboxypeptidase N is believed to contribute to the degradation of bradykinin and the conversion of C_5a to C_5a des Arg (41). The best-explored ECS enzymes are the angiotensin converting enzyme and the lipoprotein lipases.

ANGIOTENSIN I CONVERTING ENZYME (ACE)   ACE (EC 3.4.15.1) is a carboxyl-terminal dipeptidyl peptidase that releases the His-Leu from angiotensin I (a decapeptide) to form the more potent angiotensin II (an octapeptide); this enzyme also inactivates kinins (67). ACE has been found in a variety of species and tissues, and has been immunocytochemically localized to the endothelial cell surface (42). Membrane-associated ACE has also been detected in nonvascular sites (67).

LIPOLYTIC ENZYMES   Two lipid ester hydrolases acting selectively on triglycerides and phospholipids of the plasma lipoproteins have been associated with ECS: lipoprotein lipase (LPL) and hepatic endothelial lipase (HEL). LPL hydrolyzes triglycerides of chylomicrons and very low density lipoproteins (VLDL) in extrahepatic tissues, and is partly responsible for the plasma concentration of high density lipoproteins (HDL and HDL_2), the lipolytic products of VLDL and chylomicrons (Scow, in Reference 11). LPL was immunocytochemically localized to the luminal ECS (38) and appeared to be particularly concentrated in the aorta (11). LPL is synthesized by the paren-chymal cells of several tissues and secondarily becomes associated with the ECS via an interaction with GAG chains. It was estimated that 3.75×10^6 LPL molecules bind to each EC (11). HEL is present on liver sinusoids and acts mostly as a phospholipase: it splits phospholipid moieties of VLDL remnants and removes HDL. The activities of LPL and HEL are genetically controlled, and are influenced by a variety of physiological factors and pathological conditions. Disturbances in these enzymes are partly responsible for abnormal concentrations of plasma VLDL and HDL (37).

Molecules Related to the Coagulation System

Endothelial cells have the capability to produce both coagulant and anti-coagulant factors; only some of these are directly associated with the ECS. Tissue factor (thromboplastin) is essential for rapid extrinsic coagulation, which may influence generation of traces of thrombin. This was demonstrated at the ECS by immunocytochemistry (45). Factor VIII–related antigen (VIIIR : Ag) is synthesized by EC's and megakaryocytes as a large polymeric glycoprotein, which circulates in plasma as a major component of the factor VIII/von Willebrand factor complex. VIIIR : Ag has an important role in intravascular coagulation and platelet aggregation. It was localized im-munocytochemically to the ECS of activated platelets and to endothelial base-ment membrane (associated with fibronectin) (24). It is presumed that VIIIR : Ag is either adsorbed nonspecifically to the ECS, or is an integral part of the endothelial cell membrane (28). Although suggestive, the localization of plasminogen activator at the ECS (20) remains to be convincingly demon-strated.

Receptors and Binding Sites

HISTAMINE   Using ferritin conjugates with either histamine, 2-pyridyl-ethylamine (H_1 agonist), or 4-methylhistamine (H_2 agonist) perfused in situ in various vascular beds, it was demonstrated that histamine receptors are largely represented on the cell membrane of vascular endothelium, particularly in venules that express mainly H_2 receptors. The latter are preferentially located on regions rich in filaments, such as parajunctional area of the luminal ECS. This may explain the special involvement of venules in inflammation (23, 53; Majno in Reference 52). The binding of histamine-ferritin conjugate to micro-vascular endothelium is specific, as assessed by competition with histamine, mepyramine (H_1 antagonist), cimetidine (H_2 antagonist), and telemethylhista-mine (a compound chemically similar to histamine). Telemethylhistamine-ferritin conjugate binds nonspecifically to microvascular endothelium (Antohe et al, manuscript in preparation).

LIPOPROTEINS   Both in situ and in vitro studies have demonstrated that arterial endothelium is able to take up low density lipoproteins (LDL) by saturable high affinity receptors located in coated pits, and by low affinity receptors confined to plasmalemmal vesicles. LDL receptors were visualized immunocytochemically (64) and by LDL-gold conjugates (34). EC's also possess receptors for chemically modified LDL (acetyl-LDL, malondialde-hyde-altered LDL), identified as "scavenger receptors", as well as high affinity receptors for β-VLDL. The latter is genetically distinct from the LDL receptor. Except for EC's, only monocyte macrophages express all three of these receptors (4). The marked uptake of acetylated LDL has been used for identification of isolated EC's (66). The removal of modified LDL from the circulation in vivo seems to be mediated preferentially by the sinusoidal EC's of liver, spleen, bone marrow, adrenal cortex, and ovary (40). Attempts were made to isolate the EC scavenger receptor, which reportedly has a M_r of 200,000–285,000 and can bind various charge-modified lipoprotein and nonlipoprotein ligands; the receptor is common to both EC's and monocytes (65).

HORMONES   Thus far, EC specific binding sites have been detected for only a few hormones; the best characterized of these is the insulin receptor present on most endothelial cells (2). The receptor was identified using ^{125}I-insulin, which revealed low affinity binding sites on liver sinusoids (7), human umbilical vein, brain vessels (45), bovine aorta (2, 3), and the capillaries of fat tissue (58). Insulin receptors are distinct from receptors for insulin-like growth factors (2). It is now considered that insulin transcytosis across EC is a specific receptor-mediated process (29, 58).

TRANSPORT PROTEINS   Specific binding sites on EC's for plasma transport proteins have been reported for transferrin and albumin.

Transferrin   Receptors for the iron-carrier protein have been detected on the EC's of two organs, liver and brain. Using latex minibeads covalently linked to transferrin or ^{125}I-transferrin, it was found that in rat liver cell suspensions, transferrin receptors are restricted to the coated pits of EC's. Neither hepatocytes nor Kupffer cells bind the ligand. These findings suggest that iron is first taken up by sinusoid endothelium and then transported to parenchymal cells (57). Monoclonal antibodies against rat and human transferrin receptors when applied on cryostat sections or injected intravenously in rats were found to label the ECS of brain blood capillaries but not of other tissues (26). It is assumed that transcytosis of transferrin across the blood-brain barrier is receptor-mediated.

Albumin   Bovine or mouse serum albumin-gold complex perfused in situ was found to bind specifically to high affinity binding sites restricted to EC uncoated pits and plasmalemmal vesicles. The latter transport the albumin-gold complex across capillary endothelium of mouse heart, lung, and diaphragm. Their receptor-mediated transcytosis may deliver to some tissues not only albumin but also other molecules such as fatty acids and testosterone, known to be carried by albumin (Ghitescu et al, manuscript submitted for publication).

LYMPHOCYTE RECOGNITION   One of the most remarkable ECS recognition functions is the highly specific binding of some populations of circulating lymphocytes to the high endothelium of postcapillary venules of the lymphoid organs. The peripheral lymph nodes and the gut-associated Peyer's patches present different, distinct determinants for lymphocyte recognition. These receptors direct the lymphocyte migration through particular regions of the body, especially their programmed passage from the bloodstream into the surrounding lymphoid parenchyma (9).

Antigenic Determinants

Blood group antigens (AB0) as well as the H antigen have been localized with immunofluorescent antibodies to the ECS in most large vessels and capillaries examined. In cultured human umbilical vein EC's express ABH antigens appropriate to the donor's blood type. The ECS also contains the histocompatibility or transplantation antigens. These have been detected on fresh and cultured EC's, and are thought to be a key for immunologic compatibility in organ transplants (45).

CELL SURFACE CHARGE-DIFFERENTIATED MICRODOMAINS

The luminal ECS appears to be made up of microdomains of different charge and/or charge density generated by the preferential distribution of sialoconjugates, proteoglycans, and glycoproteins. These domains correspond to structures involved in endocytosis and transcytosis of capillary endothelium (46–55). Under local variations from one vascular bed to another (15, 44, 49, 52, 62) anionic sites are provided by proteoglycans and sialoglycoconjugates on plasma membrane and coated pits, and by heparan sulfate proteoglycans on fenestral diaphragms. In liver sinusoids, EC coated pits contain both anionic and cationic sites (19). On the membranes and diaphragms of plasmalemmal vesicles and transendothelial channels some components are largely excluded (e.g. high affinity anionic sites, sialoconjugates, proteoglycans), whereas others are accumulated (low affinity anionic and cationic sites, Gal- and NAcGlc-rich glycoproteins) (52, 54). Especially in old animals, neuraminidase decreases the extent and density of anionic sites (14, 49), particularly on the plasma membrane of venular enodthelium (49). Angiotensin-induced hypertension in rats generates a marked reduction of anionic sites on the arteriolar endothelium accompanied by increased permeability (36). From the differentiated distribution of the electric charge on ECS it appears that plasmalemmal vesicles and channels are features designed to facilitate the uptake and transport of anionic molecules, which is the case with most plasma proteins. Recently it was discovered that in some capillaries vesicle membrane contains specific binding sites for albumin (Ghitescu et al, manuscript submitted for publication), and probably for other macromolecules (70).

CELL SURFACE-ASSOCIATED PLASMA PROTEINS

Plasma molecules approach the endothelial features within the thin immobile layer of plasma adjacent to the EC luminal glycocalyx. Some plasma molecules are taken up (permeant molecules) whereas others remain associated with the cell surface for a relatively extended period (adsorbed molecules). The chemical organization of this association is unknown.

α_2-*Macroglobulin*   This potent antiproteolytic protects EC's by modulating the activities of various proteases, including those involved in fibrinolysis, coagulation, and the Kallikrein system. By immunofluorescence microscopy α_2-macroglobulin was localized on the luminal ECS in arteries, veins, and lymphatics (6).

Fibrinogen-Fibrin   An endo-endothelial lining of fibrin was postulated as a physiologic constituent with a complex role that included anticoagulant and antithrombotic actions (10). It was demonstrated that fluorescein-FITC-conjugated fibrinogen injected intravenously in vivo accumulates inhomogenously at the ECS, mostly in venules. Rhodamin B-isothiocyanate-conjugated fibronectin injected concomitantly with FITC-fibrinogen accumulates in the same places as the latter. Albumin and gammaglobulin did not show any affinity for the vessel wall (71).

Albumin   The above mentioned negative experiments (71) and the lack of evidence that albumin (an anionic protein) binds to the negatively-charged ECS make unlikely the hypothetical model of an ECS "fiber matrix" (13) organized mostly by albumin that would play a sieving and electrostatic role in endothelial permeability. Moreover, recent findings indicate that albumin-gold conjugates do not bind to EC plasma membrane but to restricted microdomains such as uncoated pits and plasmalemmal vesicles (Ghitescu et al, manuscript submitted for publication).

CELL SURFACE- AND MEMBRANE-ASSOCIATED ACTIVITIES

The hemorrheological conditions at the blood–vessel wall interface and the complex biochemical composition of the endothelial cell coat render ECS a particular multifunctional entity operating in a special chemical and physical microenvironment. Some ECS functions are common to the entire vascular endothelium, others have been particularly developed and diversified in certain vascular beds. Of this broad spectrum of activities only some are satisfactorily understood.

Sorting and Gating of Permeant Molecules

In recent years we learned that plasma molecules are selectively transported across the endothelium not only according to their size, but also according to their charge and chemistry.

ELECTROSTATIC SORTING   The existence on capillary ECS of microdomains of different electrical charge associated with structures potentially involved in transport enables the EC's to discriminate among permeant molecules according to their charge. Tracer experiments show that molecules of pI in the range of 4.5 to 7.2 do not bind significantly to plasma membrane. Coated pits represent a special case: While in most capillary endothelia they bind almost exclusively cationic ligands, in liver sinusoids they are labeled both by polycations and anionic markers (19). In aortic endothelium, it was shown that binding sites for oppositely charged particles coexist in the same microdomains (1). Polycations of pI between 7.2 and 9.0 fail to label plasmalemmal vesicles and channels and their diaphragms, but bind strongly to fenestral diaphragms, plasma membrane, and coated pits. By internalization of coated pits polycations can be delivered to the lysosomal compartment (adsorptive endocytosis). Molecules of pI higher than 9.0 [e.g. cationized hemeundecapeptide, pI $= 10.6$ (18); cationic ferritin, pI > 9.2; cytochrome C, pI $= 10.6$] decorate the entire ECS, including open plasmalemmal vesicles (18). It appears, therefore, that these vesicles and their derived transendothelial channels are transcytotic carriers designed to facilitate the uptake and transport of anionic molecules, which include most plasma proteins (52). Vesicle membrane has an upper limit for charge discrimination at pI ~ 9.0 (18). As revealed by recent experiments with albumin-gold complex, a small fraction of plasmalemmal vesicles perform fluid-phase pinocytosis (54). The extent of this process may vary from one type of EC to another (49, 54). Physiological experiments have already stressed the charge effect on permeability (1, 12, 13, 39, 63), but their accurate interpretation has to wait until additional studies characterize the exact type of interaction between the probe and the ECS (electrostatic, chemical). An interesting finding was that fenestrated capillaries have a greater permeability to water and small lipid-insoluble solutes than do continuous capillaries, but they have a similar protein permeability (32; see also in Reference 52). This suggests that anionic plasma proteins are largely repelled from the negatively charged fenestral diaphragms. All these findings substantiate the idea that EC is not only a size barrier, but also a refined charge barrier (52).

CHEMICAL SORTING   Evidence is now available that some plasma constituents can be selectively taken up by EC's via specific binding sites or receptors, and delivered either to the cell itself (receptor-mediated endocytosis) or to the surrounding tissue (receptor-mediated transcytosis). Some molecular species can be transported by both processes (e.g. LDL) (64). EC receptor-mediated endocytosis of LDL uses the same pathway as in other cells: coated pits to coated vesicles to endosomes to lysosomes. This high affinity pathway is saturable and temperature-dependent, and provides EC's with the cholesterol needed for membrane biogenesis (34, 64). EC can also take up altered LDL and β-VLDL via separate, distinct receptors, but the physiopathologic significance of this process is still unclear.

Receptor-mediated transcytosis of LDL by a low affinity pathway involving plasmalemmal vesicles of arterial endothelium was first demonstrated in situ (64), then in vitro (61). Comparative studies with native LDL and methylated LDL demonstrated that in normal rabbit aorta LDL transcytosis is largely receptor-independent: less than 30% of LDL entering the arterial wall undergoes degradation (69).

Other plasma molecules that have been shown to be transported by EC's via a receptor-mediated mechanism are insulin (27, 29, 58), transferrin (26, 57), and albumin (54). This type of transport occurs preferentially or exclusively in some capillary beds (26, 57). In microvessels isolated from rat epididimal fat, vesicle ingestion of glycosylated albumin was more pronounced than that of albumin (70). It is very likely that in vivo transcytosis of most molecules occurs by combined fluid phase and adsorptive mechanisms (54). Factors governing the intracellular sorting and membrane recycling during endocytosis and transcytosis in EC remain to be elucidated.

Monitoring of Plasma Lipids

There are several ways ECS participates in the regulation of lipid metabolism. One activity is the adsorption of circulating lipoprotein lipase (LPL) and hepatic lipase (see section entitle Lipolytic Enzymes), another is the binding, via various mechanisms, of lipoprotein particles that carry triglycerides, cholesteryl esters, and free fatty acids. Triglycerides are contained in the circulating chylomicrons, which once attached to the ECS are hydrolyzed by LPL; most of the released fatty acid is taken up directly by the tissue. Very low density lipoprotein (VLDL) also attaches nonspecifically or to a receptor of the extrahepatic ECS, where some of its triglycerides are hydrolyzed by LPL. The remaining low density lipoprotein (LDL) carries most of the circulating cholesterol, in humans and some other species. LDL is taken up by EC high or low affinity receptors to be endocytosed or transcytosed, respectively. The endocytosed LDL is catabolized within EC's, while by transcytosis most LDL is delivered to the other tissues for their own metabolic needs, or is recirculated through interstitial fluid and lymph back into blood. According to some investigators, the removal of chemically modified LDL (acetylated, acetoacetylated) from the circulation in vivo is mediated preferentially by the sinusoid EC's of liver, spleen, bone marrow, adrenal cortex, and ovary (40). In normal conditions endothelial cells are able to control efficiently the excess plasma cholesterol. In abnormal conditions, still poorly understood, the further cholesterol egress from the arterial wall is hampered, leading to local lipid accumulation, and eventually to formation of atherosclerotic plaque. Since free fatty acid derived primarily from adipocyte triglycerides is transported as a physical complex with plasma albumin, it would be of high interest to elucidate whether the specific albumin binding sites detected on some capillary endothelia represent a selective mechanism for transport of these lipids to some tissues. (For a more detailed account of lipoprotein binding to ECS see Reference 16.)

Maintenance of a Nonthrombogenic Surface

The antithrombogenic ECS is the cumulative result of several local factors, such as the net negative charge, the presence of sulfated GAG (especially heparin), occurrence of some of the fibrinolytic system components, etc. Concomitantly, the ECS participates in and controls the intravascular blood coagulation and haemostasis by producing both coagulant (e.g. tissue factor, plasminogen inhibitor, factor VIII) and anticoagulant substances (e.g. plasminogen activator, prostacyclin). The coagulation and fibrinolytic systems must maintain a dynamic equilibrium at the blood-endothelium interface. Only some of the factors involved in these processes are associated with the ECS (see pertinent chapters in this volume). The endothelium appears to be fibrinolytically active, but the molecular basis of this function is largely hypothetical. One reason for this is the difficulty of distinguishing between synthesis of fibrinolytic enzymes by EC's and the adsorption of such molecules to the ECS.

An interesting behavior at the ECS is ascribed to thrombin and some of the related components of the fibrinolytic system. Thrombin binds directly to EC and plays a dual role in hemostasis. It has procoagulant functions, such as conversion of fibrinogen to fibrin, activation of coagulation factors, and platelet activation. However, thrombin also stimulates anticoagulant activities, such as prostacyclin release from EC's, and (in conjunction with ECS-associated thrombomodulin) activates protein C (31). In cultured human umbilical vein or aortic bovine EC's, thrombin adsorption to specific binding sites on the ECS also results in the inactivation of EC plasminogen activator, release of ADP, and synthesis and release of fibronectin (25, 30). Covalent thrombin binding is markedly enhanced after endothelial injury (25). Thrombin inactivation by antithrombin III occurs both in plasma and at the ECS (31). α_2-Macroglobulin, which is an important antithrombin agent, is synthesized by EC's and associated with the ECS. Studies on cultured porcine aortic EC suggest that plasmin also binds to the ECS in a time- and concentration-dependent fashion. The binding sites for thrombin and plasmin are different, and they do not compete for this binding. The interaction of plasmin with the ECS seems to be specific in the fibrinolytic system, since under similar conditions plasminogen does not bind to these cells (5). Another component of the fibrinolytic system produced by EC's, and assumed to be associated with ECS, is plasminogen activator which contributes to the catalysis of plasminogen to plasmin, the major enzyme responsible for fibrin degradation.

The data reviewed above clearly show that much remains to be done to elucidate the functions of the ECS and its molecular basis. Certain lines of available information are at least starting points that suggest working hypotheses for further research.

ACKNOWLEDGMENT

The work performed in the authors' laboratories and herein reported was supported by the Ministry of Education, Romania, by NIH Grant HL-26343, by funds from Wellcome Trust, England, and the A. and L. Lucian Award, Canada. Those studies carried out in collaboration with G. E. Palade were supported by NIH Grant HL-17080, and NSF Grant INT-80–16156.

Literature Cited

1. Baldwin, A. L., Chien, S. 1984. Endothelial transport of anionized and cationized ferritin in the rabbit aorta and vasa vasorum. *Arteriosclerosis* 4:372–82
2. Bar, R. S., Boes, M. 1984. Distinct receptors for IGF-I, IGF-II, and insulin are present on bovine capillary endothelial cells. *Biochim. Biophys. Res. Commun.* 124:203–9
3. Bar, R. S., Hoak, J. C., Peacock, M. L. 1978. Insulin receptors in human endothelial cells: identification and characterization. *J. Clin. Endocrinol. Metab.* 47:699–702
4. Baker, D. P., Van Lenten, B. J., Fogelman, A. M., Edwards, P. A., Kean, C., Berliner, J. A. 1984. LDL, scavenger, and β-VLDL receptors on aortic endothelial cells. *Arteriosclerosis* 4:248–55
5. Bauer, P. I., Machovich, R., Buki, K.

G., Csonka, E., Koch, S. A., Horvath, J. 1984. Interaction of plasmin with endothelial cell. *Biochem. J.* 218:119–24
6. Becker, C. G., Harpel, P. C. 1976. α_2-Macroglobulin on human vascular endothelium. *J. Exp. Med.* 144:1–9
7. Bergeron, J. J., Sikstrom, R., Hand, A. R., Posner, B. I. 1979. Binding and uptake of ^{125}I-insulin into rat liver hepatocytes and endothelium. An in vivo radioautographic study. *J. Cell Biol.* 80:427–43
8. Buonassisi, V., Colburn, P. 1982. Biological significance of heparan sulfate. *Ann. NY Acad. Sci.* 401:76–84
9. Butcher, E. C., Kraal, G., Stevens, S. K., Weissman, I. L. 1980. A recognition function of endothelial cells: directing lymphocyte traffic. In *Pathology of the Endothelial Cell*, ed. H. L. Nosel, H. J.

FUNCTIONS OF ENDOTHELIAL SURFACE   291

Vogel, pp. 409–24. New York: Academic. 486 pp.
10. Copley, A. L. 1983. The endo-endothelial fibrin lining. A historical account. *Thromb. Res. Suppl.* 5:1–26
11. Cryer, A. 1983. Lipoprotein lipase-endothelial interactions. In *Biochemical Interactions at the Endothelium*, ed. A. Cryer, pp. 245–74. Amsterdam: Elsevier. 438 pp.
12. Curry, F. E. 1983. The effect of charge on the transport of intermediate sized protein probes across the capillary wall. In *Pathogenicity of Cationic Probes*, ed. P. P. Lambert, P. Bergmann, R. Beauwens, pp. 120–24. New York: Raven. 385 pp.
13. Curry, F. E., Michel, C. C. 1980. A fibre matrix model of capillary permeability. *Microvasc. Res.* 20:96–99
14. Danon, D., Laver-Rudich, R., Skutelsky, E. 1980. Surface charge and flow properties of endothelial membranes in aging rats. *Mech. Aging Dev.* 14:145–53
15. De Bruyn, P. P. H., Michelson, S. 1979. Changes in the random distribution of sialic acid at the surface of the myeloid sinusoidal endothelium resulting from the presence of diaphragmed fenestrae. *J. Cell Biol.* 82:708–14
16. Fielding, C. J., Fielding, P. E. 1983. Lipoprotein binding to the endothelial surface. See Ref. 11, pp. 275–99
17. Furchgott, R. F. 1984. The role of endothelium in the response of vascular smooth muscle to drugs. *Ann. Rev. Pharmacol. Toxicol.* 24:175–97
18. Ghinea, N., Simionescu, N. 1985. Anionized and cationized hemeundecapeptides as probes for cell surface charge and permeability studies: differentiated labeling of endothelial plasmalemmal vesicles. *J. Cell Biol.* 100:606–12
19. Ghitescu, L., Fixman, A. 1984. Surface charge distribution on the endothelial cell of liver sinusoids. *J. Cell Biol.* 99:639–47
20. Giddings, J. C. 1983. The control of intravascular blood coagulation and haemostasis at endothelial surfaces. See Ref. 11, pp. 167–206
21. Görög, P., Born, G. V. R. 1982. Increased uptake of circulating low-density lipoproteins and fibrinogen by arterial walls after removal of sialic acid from the endothelial surface. *Br. J. Exp. Pathol.* 63:447–51
22. Görög, P., Schraufstätter, I., Born, G. V. R. 1982. Effect of removing sialic acids from endothelium on the adherence of circulating platelets in arteries in vivo. *Proc. R. Soc. London Ser. B* 214:471–80

23. Heltianu, C., Simionescu, M., Simionescu, N. 1982. Histamine receptors of the microvascular endothelium revealed in situ with a histamine-ferritin conjugate: Characteristic high-affinity binding sites in venules. *J. Cell Biol.* 93:357–64
24. Hormia, M., Lehto, V. P., Virtanen, I. 1983. Factor VIII-related antigen. A pericellular matrix component of cultured human endothelial cells. *Exp. Cell Res.* 149:483–97
25. Isaacs, J., Savion, N., Gospodarowicz, D., Shuman, M. A. 1981. Effect of cell density on thrombin binding to a specific site on bovine vascular endothelial cells. *J. Cell Biol.* 90:670–74
26. Jefferies, W. A., Brandon, M. R., Hunt, S. V., Williams, A. F., Gater, K. C., Mason, D. Y. 1984. Transferrin receptors on endothelium brain capillaries. *Nature* 312:162–63
27. Jialal, J., King, G. L., Buchwald, S., Kahu, C. R., Crettaz, M. 1984. Processing of insulin by bovine endothelial cells in culture. Internalization without degradation. *Diabetes* 33:794–800
28. Jones, T. R., Kao, K. J., Pizzo, S. V., Bigner, D. D. 1981. Endothelial cell surface expression and binding of factor VIII/von Willebrand factor. *Am. J. Pathol.* 103:304–8
29. King, G. L., Jialal, I., Johnson, S. 1984. Transport of insulin across endothelial cells by a specific receptor-mediated process. *J. Cell Biol.* 99(2):208a (Abstr.)
30. Lollar, P., Hoak, J. C., Owen, W. G. 1980. Binding of thrombin to cultured human endothelial cells. Nonequilibrium aspects. *J. Biol. Chem.* 255:10279–83
31. Lollar, P., MacIntosh, S. C., Owen, W. G. 1984. Reaction to antithrombin III with thrombin bound to the vascular endothelium. Analysis in a recirculating perfused rabbit heart preparation. *J. Biol. Chem.* 259:4335–38
32. Mann, G. E., Smaje, L. H., Yudilevich, D. L. 1979. Permeability of the fenestrated capillaries in the cat submandibular gland to lipid-insoluble molecules. *J. Physiol.* 297:335–54
33. Maruki, C., Spatz, M., Ueki, Y., Negatsu, I., Bembry, J. 1984. Cerebrovascular endothelial cell culture: metabolism and synthesis of 5-hydroxytryptamine. *J. Neurochem.* 43:316–19
34. Mommoas-Kienhuis, A. M., Krijbolder, L. H., Van Hinsberg, W. M., Daems, W. T., Vermeer, B. J. 1985. Visualization of binding and receptor-mediated uptake of low density lipoproteins by human endothelial cells. *Eur. J. Cell Biol.* 36:201–8

35. Muresan, V., Constantinescu, M. C. 1985. Distribution of sialoglyco-conjugates on the luminal surface of the endothelial cell in fenestrated capillaries of the pancreas. *J. Histochem. Cytochem.* 33:5474–76

36. Nag, S. 1984. Cerebral endothelial surface in hypertension. *Acta Neuropathol.* 63:276–81

37. Nikkilä, E. A., Kuusi, T., Taskinen, M.-R., Tikkanen, M. J. 1984. Relation of lipoprotein metabolism by endothelial lipolytic enzymes. In *Treatment of Hyperlipoproteinemia*, ed. L. A. Carlson, A. G. Olsson, pp. 77–84. New York: Raven

38. Pedersen, M. E., Cohen, M., Schotz, M. C. 1983. Immunocytochemical fraction of lipoprotein lipase in the perfused heart. *J. Lipid Res.* 24:512–21

39. Perry, M. A., Benoit, J. N., Kvietys, P. R., Granger, D. N. 1983. Restricted transport of cationic macromolecules across intestinal capillaries. *Am. J. Physiol.* 245:G568–72

40. Pitas, R. E., Boyles, J., Mahley, R. W., Bissell, D. M. 1985. Uptake of chemically modified low density lipoproteins in vivo is mediated by specific endothelial cells. *J. Cell Biol.* 100:103–17

41. Ryan, U. S., Ryan, J. W., Plummer, T. H. 1982. Carboxypeptidase N is a surface enzyme of pulmonary endothelial cells. *Circulation* 66:II–242 (Abstr.)

42. Ryan, U. S., Ryan, J. W., Whitaker, C., Chin, A. 1976. Localization of angiotensin converting enzyme (kininase II). II. Immunocytochemistry and immunofluorescence. *Tissue Cell* 8:125–46

43. Ryan, U. S., Schultz, D. R., Ryan, J. W. 1981. Fc and C3b receptors on pulmonary endothelial cells: induction by injury. *Science* 214:557–58

44. Seno, S., Ono, T., Tsujii, T. 1983. Macromolecular charge and cellular surface charge in adhesion, ingestion, and blood vessel leakage. *Ann. NH Acad. Sci.* 416:410–25

45. Shepro, D., D'Amore, P. A. 1984. Physiology and biochemistry of vascular wall endothelium. In *Handbook of Physiology*, Sect. 2: *The Cardiovascular System*, Vol. IV: *Microcirculation*, Part I, ed. E. M. Renkin, C. C. Michel, pp. 103–64. Bethesda, MD: Am. Physiol. Soc., 626 pp.

46. Simionescu, D., Simionescu, M. 1983. Differentiated distribution of the cell surface charge on the alveolar-capillary unit. Characteristic paucity of anionic sites on the air-blood barrier. *Microvasc. Res.* 25:85–100

47. Simionescu, M., Simionescu, N.,

Palade, G. E. 1982. Preferential distribution of anionic sites on the basement membrane and the abluminal aspect of the endothelium in fenestrated capillaries. *J. Cell Biol.* 95:425–34

48. Simionescu, M., Simionescu, N., Palade, G. E. 1982. Differentiated microdomains on the luminal surface of capillary endothelium: Distribution of lectin receptors. *J. Cell Biol.* 94:406–13

49. Simionescu, M., Simionescu, N., Santoro, F., Palade, G. E. 1985. Differentiated microdomains on the luminal plasmalemma of murine muscle capillaries. Segmental variations in young and old animals. *J. Cell Biol.* 100:1396–1407

50. Simionescu, M., Simionescu, N., Silbert, J. E., Palade, G. E. 1981. Differentiated microdomains on the luminal surface of the capillary endothelium. II. Partial characterization of their anionic sites. *J. Cell Biol.* 90:614–21

51. Simionescu, N. 1981. Transcytosis and traffic of membranes in the endothelial cell. In *International Cell Biology 1980–1981*, ed. H. G. Schweiger, pp. 657–72. Berlin: Springer-Verlag. 1033 pp.

52. Simionescu, N. 1983. Cellular aspects of transcapillary exchange. *Physiol. Rev.* 63:1536–68

53. Simionescu, N., Heltianu, C., Antohe, F., Simionescu, M. 1982. Endothelial cell receptors for histamine. *Ann. NY Acad. Sci.* 401:132–49

54. Simionescu, N., Simionescu, M. 1984. Fluid-phase and adsorptive transcytosis in the endothelial cell. In *International Symposium on "Membrane Biogenesis and Recycling"*, Abstr. Vol. V-1, Kanami, Japan. 96 pp.

55. Simionescu, N., Simionescu, M., Palade, G. E. 1981. Differentiated microdomains on the luminal surface of the capillary endothelium. I. Preferential distribution of anionic sites. *J. Cell Biol.* 90:605–13

56. Soda, R., Tavassoli, M. 1983. Mapping of the bone marrow sinus endothelium with lectins and glycosylated ferritins: identification of differentiated microdomains and their functional significance. *J. Ultrastr. Res.* 84:299–310

57. Soda, R., Tavassoli, M. 1984. Liver endothelium and not hepatocytes or Kupffer cells have transferrin receptors. *Blood* 63:270–76

58. Solenski, N. J., Williams, S. K. 1984. Insulin binding and endocytosis on cultured and freshly isolated endothelium. *J. Cell Biol.* 99(2):209a (Abstr.)

59. Steinberg, S. F., Jaffe, E. A., Bilezikian, J. P. 1984. Endothelial cells contain be-

ta adrenoreceptors. *Naunyn-Schmiedeberg's-Arch. Pharmacol.* 325:310–13

60. Summerfield, J. A., Vergalla, J., Jones, E. A. 1982. Modulation of a glycoprotein recognition system on rat hepatic endothelial cells by glucose and diabetes mellitus. *J. Clin. Invest.* 69:1337–47

61. Takano, T., Hashida, R., Kimura, J., Anamizu, C., Ohkuma, S. 1984. Transendothelial transport of lipoprotein in monolayer culture, See Ref. 54, pp. VI-3

62. Tsujii, T., Ono, T., Akita, M., Seno, S. 1984. Role of ionized anionic groups on endothelial cell surface. In *International Cell Biology 1984*, ed. S. Seno, Y. Okada, p. 84. Tokyo: Academic. 594 pp.

63. Turner, M. R., Clough, G., Michel, C. C. 1983. The effects of cationized ferritin and native ferritin upon the filtration coefficient of single frog capillaries. Evidence that proteins in the endothelial cell coat influence permeability. *Microvasc. Res.* 25:205–22

64. Vasile, E., Simionescu, M., Simionescu, N. 1983. Visualization of the binding, endocytosis, and transcytosis of low-density lipoprotein in the arterial endothelium in situ. *J. Cell Biol.* 96:1677–89

65. Via, D. P., Dressel, H. A., Gotto, A. Jr. 1984. Purification to homogeneity of a receptor for modified lipoproteins from macrophage tumors, endothelial cells, and monocytes. *Arteriosclerosis* 4:567a (Abstr.)

66. Voyta, J. C., Via, D. P., Butterfield, C. E., Zetter, B. R. 1984. Identification and isolation of endothelial cells based on their uptake of acetylated-low density lipoprotein. *J. Cell Biol.* 99:2034–40

67. Ward, P. E., Sheridan, M. A. 1982. Angiotensin I converting enzyme of rat intestinal and vascular surface membrane. *Biochim. Biophys. Acta* 716:208–16

68. Weber, G., Fabbrini, P., Resi, L. 1973. On the presence of a concanavalin A reactive coat over the endothelial aortic surface and its modifications during early experimental cholesterol atherogenesis in rabbits. *Virchows Arch. A* 359:299–307

69. Wiklund, O., Carew, T. E., Steinberg, D. 1984. Transendothelial transport of low-density lipoprotein is largely receptor-independent in normal rabbit aortas. *Arteriosclerosis* 4:532a (Abstr.)

70. Williams, S. K. 1983. Vesicular transport of proteins by capillary endothelium. *Ann. NY Acad. Sci.* 416:457–67

71. Witte, S. 1983. The endothelial lining as studied by a fluorescent labeling technique in situ. *Thromb. Res. Suppl.* 5:93–104

Ann. Rev. Physiol. 1986. 48:295–306
Copyright © 1985 by Annual Reviews, Inc. All rights reserved

ENDOTHELIAL CELL INFLUENCES ON VASCULAR SMOOTH MUSCLE PHENOTYPE

Julie H. Campbell

Cell Biology Laboratory, Baker Medical Research Institute, Commercial Road, Prahran, Victoria 3181, Australia

Gordon R. Campbell

Cardiovascular Research Unit, Department of Anatomy, University of Melbourne, Parkville, Victoria 3052, Australia

INTRODUCTION

In the normal arterial wall the smooth muscle cells and abluminal surface of the endothelium are surrounded by a basal lamina consisting of (among other substances) laminin, heparan sulfate proteoglycan, and type IV collagen (59, 75). In turn the basal laminae are closely associated with the continuum of collagen, elastin, and proteoglycans of the extracellular matrix. This association maintains spatial arrangements of components within the vessel wall (93), but may also regulate the proper homeostatic balance of the cellular constituents.

In this article, the relationship between the endothelium, smooth muscle, and an extracellular matrix molecule they produce is explored. In particular, we will discuss the proposal that a heparin-like glycosaminoglycan present in the basal lamina of both smooth muscle and endothelium plays an important role in controlling the phenotype the smooth muscle expresses, and its response to serum mitogens. Change in smooth muscle phenotype leads to many changes in the biology of the cell, and these will also be reviewed.

295

0066-4278/86/0315-0295$02.00

ENDOTHELIAL DENUDATION

Injury to the endothelium has been caused experimentally by a variety of methods (3, 7, 42, 60, 82, 84, 89, 90). If the injury is of sufficent size, smooth muscle cells from the media migrate to the intima, where they subsequently proliferate and form a neo-intima of longitudinally orientated smooth muscle cells. These cells contain large amounts of rough endoplasmic reticulum, free ribosomes, and mitochondria for up to three weeks following the injury (15, 30, 54, 60, 62). Studies using antibodies to the heavy meromyosin end of smooth muscle myosin (49) demonstrate a loss of myosin by 14 days after endothelial denudation (12). The cells have decreased amounts of actin and desmin, and increased amounts of vimentin (45, 61). Moreover, beta-actin is the predominant actin isotype in these cells, and significant amounts of gamma-actin appear, whereas alpha-actin decreases. Seventy-five days after injury, when the endothelium has completely regenerated, the cytoskeletal elements of the neo-intimal smooth muscle cells are similar to those of the media. The smooth muscle cells of the neo-intima also regain an apparently normal complement of myosin and myofilaments, with a concomitant decrease in the amount of synthetic organelles (12, 30, 62).

Extensive Endothelial Injury

The response of the vessel wall varies according to the extent of endothelial denudation. Where large areas of endothelium have been removed, smooth muscle cells are capable of forming a pseudoendothelium lining the luminal surface. Luminal smooth muscle cells contain large amounts of rough endoplasmic reticulum and free ribosomes within the central body of the cell, which is embedded within the neo-intima. The filament bundles are small and localized towards the luminal surface of the vessel (28, 31, 82, 88). These luminal cells, like true endothelium, are nonthrombogenic (6, 7, 85), and with time produce increasing amounts of prostaglandin I_2 (PGI_2). By 35–70 days after de-endothelialization these cells produce an amount of PGI_2 similar to that produced by the endothelium of the normal vessel (38). Larrue et al (62) suggest that this activation of PGI_2 production by smooth muscle is associated with their phenotypic expression. The luminal smooth muscle cells lack Weibel-Palade bodies, have loose cell-to-cell contacts, do not stain with antibodies to factor VIII, and do not exclude horseradish peroxidase, Evans blue, or ferritin (28).

The absence of endothelial cells suggests that these sites might be subject to increased lipoprotein transport, predisposing them to atherosclerosis. However, in rabbits, lipid accumulates preferentially in areas covered by regenerated endothelium (70, 71). This accumulation is not a result of passive filtration, but is due to metabolic differences in the re-endothelialized neo-intima (39, 40, 52), which persist for up to one year after a single balloon catheter deendothelialization and re-endothelialization (79). There are also significant increases in the glycosaminoglycans heparan sulfate and chondroitin sulfate in re-endothelialized aortas compared to de-endothelialized or uninjured aortas (94). Since glycosaminoglycans and proteoglycans can form insoluble and soluble complexes with plasma lipoproteins (10, 11, 93), this may be another mechanism whereby changes in smooth muscle metabolism contribute to the increased deposition of lipid in re-endothelialized regions of injured aorta. Further studies in vivo (34, 77) and in vitro (69) demonstrate that aortic glycosaminoglycan content is markedly influenced by the presence or absence of endothelium.

Critical Lesion Size

If the segment of endothelium removed from an artery is less than 1 cm long, an intimal thickening does not occur (32, 80, 81); in such cases endothelial replacement is complete within 5–7 days of injury. If small tracks (2–20 cells wide) of endothelium are removed, no proliferation of smooth muscle occurs (57, 76). Thus there is a critical lesion size, or time for endothelial regeneration to occur, before smooth muscle cells proliferate in the intima. It does not appear to be related to the release of platelet-derived growth factor from the alpha-granules of platelets since most platelet adhesion occurs within the first 24 hr of denudation with granule release in the first 4 hr (48, 50).

Factors Suppressing Myointimal Proliferation After Endothelial Denudation

Several factors have been shown to modify smooth muscle responses to endothelial denudation. These include interference with platelet number and/or function (44, 72), and hypophysectomy (5, 87). Smooth muscle proliferation at 14 days can also be markedly reduced by the continuous post-injury infusion of heparin (29). Anticoagulant and non-anticoagulant heparin are equally effective (51).

PHENOTYPIC MODULATION OF SMOOTH MUSCLE IN CULTURE

When the media of adult arteries is enzyme-dispersed into single smooth muscle cells and seeded into primary culture, the cells are morphologically and functionally similar to those of the intact vessel. However, if they are seeded below a critical cell density, the cells undergo a spontaneous change in phenotype after 6–8 days (24). They lose the capacity to contract, and gain the capacity to divide, which they do logarithmically in response to serum mitogens (27). They also synthesize greatly increased amounts of collagen and noncollagen protein (14). Morphologically the cells lose their thick, myosin-containing filaments, and greatly increase the amount of organelles involved with synthesis, such as rough endoplasmic reticulum and free ribosomes (26), to resemble immature smooth muscle cells. The two distinct phenotypes have been termed "contractile" and "synthetic" (25). These are only two points at the ends of a continuous spectrum of smooth muscle phenotypic expression, and cells having features of both contractile and synthetic cells occur. Cells that have modulated from a contractile to synthetic state on days 6–8 in primary culture, then proliferated to a confluent monolayer within another 7 days, undergoing fewer than 5 cell doublings, spontaneously revert to a contractile state 1 or 2 days after achieving confluence ("reversible synthetic" cells). But cells that have been seeded so sparsely that the synthetic state cells require more than 2–3 weeks to achieve confluence do not return to a contractile state, and appear "irreversibly synthetic." Subcultured cells, beyond passage one or two, are in the irreversible synthetic state.

As well as becoming responsive to serum mitogens and capable of enhanced collagen synthesis, there are several other important metabolic changes that occur in smooth muscle cells when they alter from a contractile to synthetic phenotype in culture. Cytochrome c oxidase and NADPH-dependent cytochrome c reductase increase 2.3-fold and 12.8-fold, respectively, concomitant with the change to the synthetic state. Increases of three- to fourfold in activity of the lysosomal enzymes, acid phosphatase and N-acetyl-β-glucosaminidase, are also found, which is in agreement with the larger number of lysosomes present in synthetic state cells. However, acid cholesteryl esterase, which is also found in lysosomes and is responsible for the hydrolysis of cholesterol esters, decreases slightly upon alteration to the synthetic state (15). Synthetic state (particularly "irreversible synthetic") cells, also have an altered ability to metabolize β-very low density lipoprotein (β-VLDL) from hyperlipemic serum, resulting in substantial lipid accumulation in these cells compared with "contractile state" cells (16).

ENDOTHELIAL-SMOOTH MUSCLE INTERACTIONS IN CULTURE

Effect on Smooth Muscle Phenotype

Spontaneous phenotypic modulation of isolated smooth muscle from a contractile to synthetic phenotype in primary cell culture is prevented if the cells are grown in co-culture with a confluent monolayer of endothelial cells (13, 23, 25). The two cell layers do not have to be in contact, just bathed by the same nutrient medium, as occurs in modified Rose chambers, in which the test and feeder cell layers are grown on opposite coverslips (25). A feeder layer of confluent, contractile smooth muscle cells that is above the critical cell density and does not undergo the spontaneous phenotypic change also prevents the test, sparsely seeded contractile smooth muscle cells from spontaneously modulating their phenotype. In contrast, co-culture with confluent adventitial fibroblasts, confluent subcultured synthetic state smooth muscle cells, or subconfluent proliferating endothelial cells does not prevent the spontanous phenotypic change of contractile smooth muscle (25).

The approximate molecular weight of the inhibitory substance or substances produced by confluent endothelial cells and contractile smooth muscle cells is 10,000–15,000, as determined by the insertion of Spectrapor wet cellulose dialysis membranes of different molecular weight cut-off between the feeder and test layers (13). This is in agreement with an earlier study showing that a glycosaminoglycan extract of about 12,000 daltons from the artery wall inhibits smooth muscle phenotypic change (25). Treatment of the aortic glycosaminoglycan extract with 4 units/ml heparinase from $Flavobacterium\ heparinum$ for 6 hr at 37°C destroys the active factor, suggesting that it is heparin or a related glycosaminoglycan. Addition of sodium heparin to culture medium inhibits smooth muscle phenotypic change (25, 68).

Cultured endothelial cells secrete about 50% of their glycosaminoglycan as a highly sulfated (heparin-like) heparan sulfate (9, 47, 74, 92). They also produce a factor or factors able to stimulate glycosaminoglycan synthesis by smooth muscle cells (69). Heparan sulfate is the predominant glycosaminoglycan in the pericellular coat immediately adjacent to the plasma membrane of cultured smooth muscle cells (56, 73, 96). However, by the seventh subculture heparan sulfate is replaced by dermatan sulfate as the predominant species (96).

Effect on Smooth Muscle Proliferation

Endothelial cells produce both growth inhibitors and stimulators of smooth muscle. Several laboratories have reported the existence of a potent mitogen produced by endothelial cells in culture (17, 41, 46, 91, 95). This polypeptide, the endothelial-derived growth factor (EDGF) (46), is mitogenic for many mesenchymally derived cells, but not for endothelial cells themselves. EDGF is not homogeneous, and it contains one factor that is similar to the platelet-derived growth factor (PDGF). The PDGF-like factor accounts for about 25% of the mitogenic effect, at least with 3T3 cells as the target (8, 35, 36).

Our studies suggest that the proliferative state of the endothelial cell determines whether a stimulator or inhibitor is released or which one predominates. When synthetic state smooth muscle is the test tissue and proliferating endothelium the feeder layer in a co-culture situation, the rate of proliferation of the test smooth muscle is stimulated. But when the feeder layer consists of confluent, quiescent endothelium, the normal growth of the test synthetic state smooth muscle is totally inhibited (13, 25).

In 1936, Simms & Stillman (83) first discovered that the aorta contains growth inhibitory substances. Florentin et al (43) showed that alcoholprecipitable components of an aqueous extract of pig aorta injected intraperitoneally into 8-week-old living swine, in quantities as low as 500 μg of protein, drastically reduced the rate of entry of arterial smooth muscle cells into mitosis, with no demonstrable effect on epidermal mitosis. Eisenstein et al (37) reported two classes of molecules in fractions of bovine aortic extracts that inhibit cell growth. One was of low molecular weight and inhibited only endothelial cells, and the other was composed of structural polyanions, including heparin and a proteoglycan, and inhibited the growth of both smooth muscle and endothelial cells. However, more recent reports show that heparin stimulates the proliferation of endothelial cells (58, 86).

Alcohol precipitates from aqueous extracts of pig aorta can be fractionated to produce both stimulators and inhibitors of synthetic state smooth muscle in culture (25). Conditioned medium containing 20% whole blood serum from confluent endothelial cells inhibits the proliferation of subcultured smooth muscle cells, while conditioned medium from proliferating endothelial cells and from proliferating or confluent subcultured smooth muscle cells and fibroblasts does not inhibit smooth muscle cell growth (17). The inhibitory activity is heat stable and not affected by proteases. It is sensitive to *Flavobacterium* heparinase, but not to hyaluronidase or chondroitin sulfate ABC lyase. A crude isolate of glycosaminoglycans from endothelial cell–conditioned medium reconstituted in 20% serum inhibits smooth muscle cell growth, but no inhibition is seen if the glycosaminoglycan preparation is treated with heparinase. Exogenous heparin at 1–10 μg/ml inhibits growth, while most other glycosaminoglycans have no effect (17, 20, 25, 53, 58, 73). While there are reports of an antiproliferative effect of heparin on various cell types, the dose required for 50% inhibition is very high, usually about 1 mg/ml (19, 21, 64). Anticoagulant and non-anticoagulant heparin are equally effective in inhibiting smooth muscle cell growth, as they are in vivo in preventing the formation of myointimal thickening following endothelial denudation (29, 51). The smallest heparin fragment with antiproliferative activity is the pentasaccharide, while maximum activity requires a 12-saccharide heparin molecule (21). Both N- and O-sulfates are required for antiproliferative activity (18). Heparin binds to smooth muscle cells via specific, saturable binding sites on the cell surface with a $K_d = 10^{-9}$ M (22). Quiescent cells bind eight times more heparin than exponentially growing cells (22). It is internalized by receptor-mediated endocytosis (21), and can both induce and suppress the synthesis of specific proteins (33, 65–67).

In summary, confluent quiescent monolayers of endothelial cells produce heparin-like substances that appear to have two effects: first, they maintain smooth muscle cells in a contractile phenotype, in which state they are unresponsive to serum mitogens; and second, they inhibit the proliferation of serum-stimulated synthetic state smooth muscle cells.

PROPOSED MECHANISMS OF ARTERIAL REPAIR FOLLOWING ENDOTHELIAL DENUDATION

In primary culture, isolated smooth muscle cells in a contractile phenotype (as they exist in the aortic media of adult animals) do not normally divide when challenged with serum mitogens, but will do so after 6–8 days when the cells have undergone a spontaneous change in phenotype to the synthetic state (27). Therefore we suggest that before smooth muscle proliferation can occur as a result of damage to the vessel wall, the injury must fulfill at least two requirements: the smooth muscle cells must phenotypically modulate to a synthetic state, and mitogens must contact these cells after they have modulated. This is in line with the studies of Reidy & Schwartz (76) who have shown that there is a critical lesion size of endothelial denudation below which smooth muscle proliferation will not occur. That is, myointimal thickening occurs only in those areas requiring more than 7 days for endothelial regeneration.

Following endothelial denudation, platelets are deposited on the sub-endothelium, releasing PDGF from their alpha-granules, and platelet heparitinase (endoglycosidase) from their lysosomes. The endoglycosidase cleaves the heparin-like substance from the basal laminal proteoglycans of the smooth muscle cells closest to the damaged lumen and from remaining endothelial cells, and is removed (20, 78). If a heparin-like glycosaminoglycan is the low molecular weight substance in the artery wall that maintains smooth muscle in a contractile phenotype, then the loss of this substance would result in smooth muscle cells close to the lumen modulating to the synthetic phenotype if the area of denudation is larger than a critical lesion size (in primary cell culture it would be due to dilution of the factor with decreasing cell seeding concentration). The synthetic state muscle cells become responsive to substances from the blood and/or regenerating endothelium, and the cells migrate into the intima and proliferate. Upon restitution of the endothelial lining, the confluent, quiescent endothelium releases a growth inhibitor for synthetic state cells, and development of the myointimal thickening is halted. The smooth muscle cells then return to a contractile state, except for those which have undergone more than five cell doublings. These remain permanently in a synthetic phenotype ("irreversible synthetic"). If the area of denudation is less than the critical lesion size then the rapid restitution of the endothelium and its underlying extracellular matrix prevents smooth muscle phenotypic change and subsequent proliferation.

The notion that extracellular matrix components can control the phenotype a cell expresses is not new. For example, collagen type II and certain proteoglycans are influential in chondrogenic differentiation and regulation of phenotype (1, 55, 63). Altered endothelial morphology is accompanied by changes in secretion of heparan sulfate proteoglycans, which suggests that they play a role in regulating the phenotype of endothelial cells (74). In embryonic mouse salivary tissue, hyaluronic acid is the predominant glycosaminoglycan in proliferating regions, whereas the heparan sulfates predominate in terminally differentiated regions (4). Similarly, hyaluronic acid occurs in the actively developing microvascular beds in the rabbit eye, while the heparan sulfates predominate in quiescent beds surrounding the smooth muscle cells, as well as on the abluminal side of the endothelial cells (2).

Literature Cited

1. Archer, C. W., Rooney, P., Wolpert, L. 1982. Cell shape and cartilage differentiation of early chick limb bud cells in culture. *Cell Differ.* 11:245–51
2. Ausprunk, D. H., Boudreau, C. L., Nelson, D. A. 1981. Proteoglycans in the microvasculature. II. Histochemical localization in proliferating capillaries of the rabbit cornea. *Am. J. Pathol.* 103:367–75
3. Baumgartner, H. R., Studer, A. 1966. Consequences of vessel catheterization in normo- and hypercholesterolaemic rabbits. *Pathol. Microbiol.* 29:393–405 (In German)
4. Bernfield, M. R., Banerjee, S. D., Cohn, R. H. 1972. Dependence of salivary epithelial morphology and branching morphogenesis upon acid mucopolysaccharide-protein (proteoglycan) at the epithelial surface. *J. Cell Biol.* 52:674–89
5. Bettmann, M. A., Stemerman, M. B., Ransil, B. J. 1981. The effect of hypophysectomy on experimental endothelial cell regrowth and intimal thickening in the rat. *Circ. Res.* 48:907–12
6. Björkerud, S., Bondjers, G. 1971. Arterial repair and atherosclerosis after mechanical injury. I. Permeability and light microscopic characteristics of endothelium in non-atherosclerotic and atheroscerotic lesions. *Atherosclerosis* 13:355–63
7. Björkerud, S., Bondjers, G. 1973. Arterial repair and atherosclerosis after mechanical injury. Part 5. Tissue response after induction of a large superficial transverse injury. *Atherosclerosis* 18:235–55
8. Bowen-Pope, D. F., Vogel, A., Ross, R. 1984. Production of platelet-derived growth factor-like molecules and reduced expression of platelet-derived growth factor receptors accompany transformation by a wide spectrum of agents. *Proc. Natl. Acad. Sci. USA* 81:2396–2400
9. Busch, C., Ljungman, C., Heldin, C.-M., Waskson, E., Öbrink, B. 1979. Surface properties of cultured endothelial cells. *Haemostasis* 8:142–48
10. Camejo, G. 1982. The interaction of lipids and lipoproteins with the intercellular matrix of arterial tissue: Its possible role in atherogenesis. *Adv. Lipid Res.* 19:1–53
11. Camejo, G., Ponce, E., López, F., Starosta, R., Hurt, E., et al. 1983. Partial structure of the active moiety of a lipoprotein complexing proteoglycan from human aorta. *Atherosclerosis* 49:241–54
12. Campbell, G. R., Campbell, J. H. 1985. Smooth muscle cells. In *The Biology and Clinical Science of Atherosclerosis*. European Atherosclerosis Group. Edinburgh: Churchill Livingstone. In press
13. Campbell, J. H., Campbell, G. R. 1984. Cellular interactions in the artery wall. In *The Peripheral Circulation*, ed. S. Hunyor, J. Ludbrook, J. Shaw, M. McGrath, pp. 33–39. New York: Elsevier. 288 pp.
14. Campbell, J. H., Campbell, G. R. 1985. Chemical stimuli of the hypertrophic response in smooth muscle. In *Hypertrophic Response of Smooth Muscle*, ed. C. L. Seidel, N. Weisbrodt. Boca Raton, Fla.: CRC Press. In press
15. Campbell, J. H., Popadynec, L., Nestel, P. J., Campbell, G. R. 1983. Lipid accumulation in arterial smooth muscle cells. Influence of phenotype. *Atherosclerosis* 47:279–95
16. Campbell, J. H., Reardon, M. F., Campbell, G. R., Nestel, P. J. 1985. Metabolism of atherogenic lipoproteins by smooth muscle cells of different phenotype in culture. *Arteriosclerosis* 5:318–28
17. Castellot, J. J. Jr., Addonizio, M. L., Rosenberg, R., Karnovsky, M. J. 1981. Cultured endothelial cells produce a

heparinlike inhibitor of smooth muscle cell growth. *J. Cell Biol.* 90:372–79
18. Castellot, J. J. Jr., Beeler, D. L., Rosenberg, R. D., Karnovsky, M. J. 1984. Structural determinants of the capacity of heparin to inhibit the proliferation of vascular smooth muscle cells. *J. Cell. Physiol.* 120:315–20
19. Castellot, J. J. Jr., Cochran, D. L., Karnovsky, M. J. 1985. Effect of heparin on vascular smooth muscle cells. I Cell metabolism. *J. Cell. Physiol.* 124:21–28
20. Castellot, J. J. Jr., Favreau, L. V., Karnovsky, M. J., Rosenberg, R. D. 1982. Inhibition of vascular smooth muscle cell growth by endothelial cell-derived heparin. Possible role of a platelet endoglycosidase. *J. Biol. Chem.* 257:11256–60
21. Castellot, J. J. Jr., Karnovsky, M. J. 1985. Heparin and the regulation of growth in the vascular wall. In *Vascular Smooth Muscle in Culture,* ed. J. H. Campbell, G. R. Campbell. Boca Raton, Fla.: CRC Press. In press
22. Castellot, J. J. Jr., Wong, K., Herman, B., Hoover, R. L., Albertini, D. F., et al. 1985. Binding and internalization of heparin by vascular smooth muscle cells. *J. Cell. Physiol.* 124:13–20
23. Chamley, J. H., Campbell, G. R., Burnstock, G. 1974. Dedifferentiation, redifferentiation and bundle formation of smooth muscle cells in tissue culture: the influence of cell number and nerve fibres. *J. Embryol. Exp. Morphol.* 32:297–323
24. Chamley, J. H., Campbell, G. R., McConnell, J. D., Gröschel-Stewart, U. 1977. Comparison of vascular smooth muscle cells from adult human, monkey and rabbit in primary culture and in subculture. *Cell Tissue Res.* 177:503–22
25. Chamley-Campbell, J. H., Campbell, G. R. 1981. What controls smooth muscle phenotype? *Atherosclerosis* 40:347–57
26. Chamley-Campbell, J., Campbell, G. R., Ross, R. 1979. The smooth muscle cell in culture. *Physiol. Rev.* 59:1–61
27. Chamley-Campbell, J. H., Campbell, G. R., Ross, R. 1981. Phenotype-dependent response of cultured aortic smooth muscle to serum mitogens. *J. Cell Biol.* 89:379–83
28. Clowes, A. W., Collazzo, R. E., Karnovsky, M. J. 1978. A morphologic and permability study of luminal smooth muscle cells after arterial injury in the rat. *Lab. Invest.* 39:141–50
29. Clowes, A. W., Karnovsky, M. J. 1977. Suppression by heparin of smooth muscle cell proliferation in injured arteries. *Nature* 265:625–26

30. Clowes, A. W., Reidy, M. A., Clowes, M. M. 1983. Kinetics of cellular proliferation after arterial injury. I. Smooth muscle growth in the absence of endothelium. *Lab. Invest.* 49:327–33
31. Clowes, A. W., Reidy, M. A., Clowes, M. M. 1983. Mechanisms of stenosis after arterial injury. *Lab. Invest.* 49:208–15
32. Clowes, A. W., Ryan, G. B., Breslow, J. L., Karnovsky, M. J. 1976. Absence of enhanced intimal thickening in the response of the carotid arterial wall to endothelial injury in hypercholesterolemic rats. *Lab. Invest.* 35:6–17
33. Cochran, D. L., Castellot, J. J., Karnovsky, M. J. 1985. Effect of heparin on vascular smooth muscle cells. II. Specific protein synthesis. *J. Cell. Physiol.* 124:29–36
34. Collatz-Christensen, B., Chemnitz, J., Tkocz, I., Kim, C. M. 1979. Repair in arterial tissue: 2. Connective tissue changes following embolectomy catheter lesion: The importance of endothelial cells to repair and regeneration. *Acta Pathol. Microbiol. Scand. Sect. A* 87:275–83
35. Di Corleto, P. E. 1984. Cultured endothelial cells produce multiple growth factors for connective tissue cells. *Exp. Cell Res.* 153:167–72
36. Di Corleto, P. E., Bowen-Pope, D. F. 1983. Cultured endothelial cells produce a platelet-derived growth factor-like protein. *Proc. Natl. Acad. Sci. USA* 80:1919–23
37. Eisenstein, R., Harper, E., Kuettner, K. E., Schumacher, B., Matijevitch, B. 1979. Growth regulators in connective tissues. II. Evidence for the presence of several growth inhibitors in aortic extracts. *Paroi Arter.* 5:163–69
38. Eldor, A., Falcone, D. J., Hajjar, D. P., Minick, C. R., Weksler, B. B. 1981. Recovery of prostacyclin production by de-endothelialized rabbit aorta. Critical role of neointimal smooth muscle cells. *J. Clin. Invest.* 67:735–41
39. Falcone, D. J., Hajjar, D. P., Minick, C. R. 1980. Enhancement of cholesterol and cholesteryl ester accumulation in re-endothelialized aorta. *Am. J. Pathol.* 99:81–104
40. Falcone, D. J., Hajjar, D. P., Minick, C. R. 1984. Lipoprotein and albumin accumulation in reendothelialized and de-endothelialized aorta. *Am. J. Pathol.* 114:112–20
41. Fass, D. N., Downing, M. R., Meyers, P., Bowie, E. J. W., Witte, L. D. 1978. Cell growth stimulation by normal and von Willebrand porcine platelets and en-

dothelial cells. *Blood* 52(Suppl. 1): 181 (Abstr.)

42. Fishman, J. A., Ryan, G. B., Karnovsky, M. J. 1975. Endothelial regeneration in the rat carotid artery and the significance of endothelial denudation in the pathogenesis of myointimal thickening. *Lab. Invest.* 32:339–51

43. Florentin, R. A., Nam, S. C., Janakidevi, K., Lee, K. T., Reiner, J. M., et al. 1973. Population dynamics of arterial smooth-muscle cells. II. In vivo inhibition of entry into mitosis of swine arterial smooth-muscle cells by aortic tissue extracts. *Arch. Pathol.* 95:317–20

44. Friedman, R. J., Stemerman, M. B., Wenz, B., Moore, S., Gauldie, J., et al. 1977. The effect of thrombocytopenia on experimental arteriosclerotic lesion formation in rabbits. Smooth muscle cell proliferation and re-endothelialization. *J. Clin. Invest.* 60:1191–1201

45. Gabbiani, G., Rungger-Brändle, E., De Chastonay, C., Franke, W. W. 1982. Vimentin-containing smooth muscle cells in aortic intimal thickening after endothelial injury. *Lab. Invest.* 47:265–69

46. Gajdusek, C., Di Corleto, P., Ross, R., Schwartz, S. M. 1980. An endothelial cell-derived growth factor. *J. Cell Biol.* 85:467–72

47. Gamse, G., Fromme, H. G., Kresse, H. 1978. Metabolism of sulfated glycosaminoglycans in cultured endothelial cells and smooth muscle cells from bovine aorta. *Biochim. Biophys. Acta* 544:514–28

48. Goldberg, I. D., Stemerman, M. B., Handin, R. I. 1980. Vascular permeability of platelet factor IV after endothelial injury. *Science* 209:610–12

49. Gröschel-Stewart, U., Schreiber, C., Mahlmeister, C., Weber, K. 1976. Production of specific antibodies to contractile proteins, and their use in immunofluorescence microscopy. I. Antibodies to smooth and striated chicken muscle myosins. *Histochemie* 46:229–36

50. Groves, H. M., Kinlough-Rathbone, R. L., Richardson, M., Moore, S., Mustard, F. 1979. Platelet interaction with damaged rabbit aorta. *Lab. Invest.* 40: 194–200

51. Guyton, J. R., Rosenberg, R. D., Clowes, A. W., Karnovsky, M. J. 1980. Inhibition of rat arterial smooth muscle cell proliferation by heparin. In vivo studies with anticoagulant and nonanticoagulant heparin. *Circ. Res.* 46:625–34

52. Hajjar, D. P., Falcone, D. J., Fowler, S., Minick, C. R. 1981. Endothelium modifies the altered metabolism of the injured aortic wall. *Am. J. Pathol.* 102:28–39

53. Hatcher, V. B., Tsien, G., Oberman, M. S., Burk, P. G. 1980. Inhibition of cell proliferation and protease activity by cartilage factors and heparin. *J. Supramol. Struct.* 14:33–46

54. Haudenschild, C. C., Schwartz, S. M. 1979. Endothelial regeneration. II. Restitution of endothelial continuity. *Lab. Invest.* 41:407–18

55. Hay, E. D. 1981. Collagen and embryonic development. In *Cell Biology of Extracellular Matrix*, ed. E. D. Hay, pp. 379–409. New York: Plenum. 417 pp.

56. Heickendorff, L., Ledet, T. 1984. Glycosaminoglycans of arterial basement membrane-like material from cultured rabbit aortic myomedial cells. *Biochim. Biophys. Acta* 798:276–82

57. Hirsch, E. Z., Robertson, A. L. 1977. Selective acute arterial endothelial injury and repair, Part 1. Methodology and surface characteristics. *Atherosclerosis* 28: 271–87

58. Hoover, R. L., Rosenberg, R., Haering, W., Karnovsky, M. J. 1980. Inhibition of rat arterial smooth muscle cell proliferation by heparin. II. In vitro studies. *Circ. Res.* 47:578–83

59. Kjellén, L., Pettersson, I., Höök, M. 1981. Cell-surface heparan sulfate: an intercalated membrane proteoglycan. *Proc. Natl. Acad. Sci. USA* 78:5371–75

60. Knieriem, H-J., Bondjers, G., Björkerud, S. 1973. Electron microscopy of intimal plaques following induction of large superficial mechanical injury (transverse injury) in the rabbit aorta. *Virchows Arch. A* 359:267–82

61. Kocher, O., Skalli, O., Bloom, W. S., Gabbiani, G. 1984. Cytoskeleton of rat aortic smooth muscle cells. Normal conditions and experimental intimal thickening. *Lab. Invest.* 50:645–52

62. Larrue, J., Daret, D., Demond-Henri, J., Allières, C., Bricaud, H. 1984. Prostacyclin synthesis by proliferative aortic smooth muscle cells. A kinetic in vivo and in vitro study. *Atherosclerosis* 50: 63–72

63. Lash, J. W., Vasan, N. S. 1978. Somite chondrogenesis in vitro. Simulation by exogenous matrix components. *Dev. Biol.* 66:151–71

64. Lippman, M., Mathews, M. B. 1977. Heparins: varying effects on cell proliferation in vitro and lack of correlation with anticoagulant activity. *Fed. Proc.* 36:55–59

65. Majack, R. A., Bornstein, P. 1983. Heparin-like glycosaminoglycans regulate the collagen phenotype of cultured vascular smooth muscle cells: Induced

synthesis of a novel short-chain collagen. *J. Cell Biol.* 97:2a (Abstr.)

66. Majack, R. A., Bornstein, P. 1984. Heparin and related glycosaminoglycans modulate the secretory phenotype of vascular smooth muscle cells. *J. Cell Biol.* 99:1688–95

67. Majack, R. A., Bornstein, P. 1985. Biosynthesis and modulation of extracellular matrix components by cultured vascular smooth muscle cells. In *Vascular Smooth Muscle in Culture*, ed. J. H. Campbell, G. R. Campbell. Boca Raton, Fla.: CRC. In press

68. Melzig, M., Teuscher, E. 1983. The influence of blood factors on the myosin content of vascular smooth muscle cells in culture. *Acta Histochem.* 73:289–91 (In German)

69. Merrilees, M. J., Scott, J. 1981. Interaction of aortic endothelial and smooth muscle cells in culture. Effect on glycosaminoglycan levels. *Atherosclerosis* 39:147–61

70. Minick, C. R., Stemerman, M. B., Insull, W. Jr. 1977. Effect of regenerated endothelium on lipid accumulation in the arterial wall. *Proc. Natl. Acad. Sci. USA* 74:1724–28

71. Minick, C. R., Stemerman, M. B., Insull, W. Jr. 1979. Role of endothelium and hypercholesterolaemia in intimal thickening and lipid accumulation. *Am. J. Pathol.* 95:131–58

72. Moore, S., Friedman, R. J., Singal, D. P., Gauldie, J., Blajchman, M. A., et al. 1976. Inhibition of injury induced thromboatherosclerotic lesions by antiplatelet serum in rabbits. *Thromb. Haemostasis* 35:70–81

73. Nilsson, J., Ksiazek, T., Thyberg, J., Wasteson, Å. 1983. Cell surface components and growth regulation in cultivated arterial smooth muscle cells. *J. Cell Sci.* 64:107–21

74. Oohira, A., Wight, T. N., Bornstein, P. 1983. Sulfated proteoglycans synthesized by vascular endothelial cells in culture. *J. Biol. Chem.* 258:2014–21

75. Palotie, A., Tryggvason, K., Peltonen, L., Seppä, H. 1983. Components of subendothelial aorta basement membrane. Immunohistochemical localization and role in cell attachment. *Lab. Invest.* 49:362–70

76. Reidy, M. A., Schwartz, S. M. 1981. Endothelial regeneration. III. Time course of intimal changes after small defined injury to rat aortic endothelium. *Lab. Invest.* 44:301–8

77. Richardson, M., Ihnatowycz, I., Moore, S. 1980. Glycosaminoglycan distribution in rabbit aortic wall following balloon catheter deendothelialization. An ultrastructural study. *Lab. Invest.* 43:509–16

78. Rosenberg, R. D., Castellot, J. J. Jr., Karnovsky, M. J. 1983. Role of heparin-like molecules in atherogenesis. In *Heparin. New Biochemical and Medical Aspects*, ed. I. Witt, pp. 261–73. Berlin: de Gruyter. 372 pp.

79. Rosenfeld, R. S., Paul, I., Spaet, T. H. 1983. Long-term effects of deendothelialization of rabbit aorta: In vitro synthesis of DNA, protein and lipid. *Proc. Soc. Exp. Biol. Med.* 173:427–35

80. Schwartz, S. M. 1982. Vascular Integrity. In *Biologic and Synthetic Vascular Prosthesis*, ed. J. C. Stanley, pp. 27–36. New York: Grune & Stratton. 720 pp.

81. Schwartz, S. M., Gajdusek, C. M., Owens, G. K. 1982. Vessel wall growth control. In *Pathobiology of the Endothelial Cell*, ed. H. L. Nossel, H. J. Vogel, pp. 63–78. New York: Academic. 496 pp.

82. Schwartz, S. M., Stemerman, M. B., Benditt, E. P. 1975. The aortic intima. II. Repair of the aortic lining after mechanical denudation. *Am. J. Pathol.* 81:15–42

83. Simms, H. S., Stillman, N. P. 1936. Substances affecting adult tissue in vitro. II. A growth inhibitor in adult tissue. *J. Gen. Physiol.* 20:621–29

84. Stemerman, M. B., Ross, R. 1972. Experimental arteriosclerosis. I. Fibrous plaque formation in primates, an electron microscope study. *J. Exp. Med.* 136:769–89

85. Stemerman, M. B., Spaet, T. H., Pitlick, F., Cintron, J., Lejnieks, I., Tiell, M. L. 1977. Intimal healing. The pattern of reendothelialization and intimal thickening. *Am. J. Pathol.* 87:125–42

86. Thornton, S. C., Mueller, S. N., Levine, E. M. 1983. Human endothelial cells: use of heparin in cloning and long-term serial cultivation. *Science* 222:623–25

87. Tiell, M. L., Stemerman, M. B., Spaet, T. H. 1978. The influence of the pituitary on arterial intimal proliferation in the rat. *Circ. Res.* 42:644–49

88. Ts'ao, C.-H. 1968. Myointimal cells as a possible source of replacement for endothelial cells in the rabbit. *Circ. Res.* 23:671–82

89. van Pelt-Verkuil, E., van Pelt, W., Jense, D. 1983. Morphometry of air-drying-induced arteriosclerosis in rat carotid artery. Effect of air-flow rate. *Arteriosclerosis* 3:441–51

90. Veress, B., Kádár, A., Jellinek, H. 1969. Ultrastructural elements in ex-

306   CAMPBELL & CAMPBELL

perimental intimal thickening. I. Electron microscopic study of the development and cellular elements of intimal proliferation. *Exp. Mol. Pathol.* 11:200–11

91. Wang, C-H., Largis, E. E., Schaffer, S. A. 1981. The effects of endothelial cell-conditioned media on the proliferation of aortic smooth muscle cells and 3T3 cells in culture. *Artery* 9:358–71

92. Wasteson, Å., Glimelius, B., Busch, C., Westermark, B., Heldin, C.-H., et al. 1977. Effect of a platelet endoglycosidase on cell surface associated heparan sulphate of human cultured endothelial and glial cells. *Thrombosis Res.* 11:309–21

93. Wight, T. N. 1980. Vessel proteoglycans and thrombogenesis. *Progress in Hemostasis and Thrombosis,* ed. T. Spaet, pp.

1–39. New York: Grune & Stratton. 298 pp.

94. Wight, T. N., Curwen, K. D., Litrenta, M. M., Alonso, D. R., Minick, C. R. 1983. Effect of endothelium on glycosaminoglycan accumulation in injured rabbit aorta. *Am. J. Pathol.* 113:156–64

95. Witte, L. D., Cornicelli, J. A., Miller, R. W., Goodman, D. S. 1982. Effects of platelet-derived and endothelial cell-derived growth factors on the low density lipoprotein receptor pathway in cultured human fibroblasts. *J. Biol. Chem.* 257:5392–5401

96. Yamamoto, H., Kanaide, H., Nakamura, M. 1983. Metabolism of glycosaminoglycans of cultured rat aortic smooth muscle cells altered during subculture. *Br. J. Exp. Pathol.* 64:156–65

Ann. Rev. Physiol. 1986. 48:307–20

MODULATION OF VASCULAR SMOOTH MUSCLE CONTRACTION BY THE ENDOTHELIUM

Paul M. Vanhoutte, Gabor M. Rubanyi, Virginia M. Miller, and Donald S. Houston

Department of Physiology and Biophysics, Mayo Clinic and Mayo Foundation, Rochester, Minnesota 55905

INTRODUCTION

The vascular endothelium is the layer of squamous epithelial cells that is in direct contact with the blood. In addition to its other important functions, which include capillary transport, regulation of plasma lipids, and participation in the control of hemostasis, it modulates the reactivity of vascular smooth muscle. This regulatory role is accomplished through several mechanisms: The layer (*a*) interposes a physical barrier between the vascular smooth muscle and hormones and other vasoactive substances circulating in blood; (*b*) it extracts or metabolically degrades vasoactive substances such as norepinephrine, serotonin, and kinins and thereby prevents or diminishes their activity in vascular smooth muscle; (*c*) it converts precursors (e.g. angiotensin I) into vasoactive products; (*d*) it secretes known vasoactive substances, primarily prostacyclin; and (*e*) it releases other still unidentified inhibitory and excitatory mediators in response to vasoactive stimuli. This review will summarize the evidence that the latter mechanism exists in mammalian blood vessels.

ENDOTHELIUM-DEPENDENT INHIBITORY RESPONSES

Acetylcholine

Furchgott and colleagues studied the paradoxical finding that acetylcholine generally was noted to cause vasodilatation in vivo but not in isolated blood vessels in vitro, and they discovered that the presence of endothelial cells is

307

0066-4278/86/0315-0307$02.00

obligatory for acetylcholine to relax isolated rings of the rabbit thoracic aorta mounted for isometric tension measurements (36, 41, 42). Subsequently, acetylcholine has been shown to produce endothelium-dependent relaxations in most isolated mammalian pulmonary and systemic arteries (7, 8, 11, 14, 22, 41, 66). The relaxations result from activation of muscarinic receptors on the endothelial cells (27, 41, 66, 83). In isolated rings of rabbit thoracic aorta (27, 38) and canine femoral artery (27, 83) endothelium-dependent relaxations are mediated by a low-affinity muscarinic receptor subtype only. In contrast, during intraluminal perfusion of intact canine femoral arteries, acetylcholine stimulates the release of relaxing substances by acting on both high- and low-affinity muscarinic receptor subtypes (83).

The endothelium-dependent inhibitory effect of acetylcholine is much less pronounced in isolated venous preparations (22). Although most of the preparations studied have been large conduit arteries, experiments carried out in smaller arteries or in vascular beds indicate that acetylcholine may induce endothelium-mediated relaxations in resistance vessels as well (71).

CHEMICAL NATURE OF THE ENDOTHELIUM-DERIVED RELAXING FACTOR RELEASED BY ACETYLCHOLINE   That endothelial cells exposed to acetylcholine release a diffusable substance (or substances) is demonstrated by transfer experiments ("sandwich" or "layered" preparations; 41, 42, 80, 92). In these experiments vascular strips without endothelium were layered with strips containing it, and the strips without endothelium regained the ability to relax in response to acetylcholine. Further evidence that endothelial cells exposed to acetylcholine release a diffusable vasodilator substance comes from bioassay experiments in which the perfusate flowing through blood vessels with endothelium was passed over or through a blood vessel without endothelium (32, 47, 78). The half-life of the relaxing material released by acetylcholine varies from 6 to 80 sec, depending upon the experimental conditions and the species (32, 47, 78, 82). Early studies ruled out adenosine and adenosine monophosphate as possible mediators of endothelium-dependent relaxations (41). The chemical nature of the diffusable mediator is still unknown. Thus, to differentiate it from known vasoactive substances (like prostacyclin), the term "endothelium-derived relaxing factor" or "EDRF" was introduced for the description of the still unidentified vasodilator mediator(s).

Involvement of arachidonic acid   Of all putative mediators, arachidonic acid and its metabolites have received the most attention. Quinacrine, an inhibitor of phospholipase A_2 (the calcium-sensitive enzyme that liberates arachidonate from membrane phospholipids), prevents the endothelium-dependent relaxations in a variety of blood vessels from different species (9, 19, 41, 42, 74, 80, 88, 92). It prevents the release of endothelium-derived relaxing factor in bioassay experiments without affecting the substance in transit or altering its action on smooth muscle (47). However, the effect of quinacrine can be attributed to actions other than phospholipase A_2 inhibition (42, 88). Another inhibitor of phospholipase A_2, bromophenacyl bromide, also inhibits the relaxations caused by acetylcholine and other substances that cause endothelium-dependent relaxations in the aorta of rabbit and rat (37, 75), but this compound usually caused desquamation of endothelial cells (37). Despite the problems with interpreting the effects of inhibitors of phospholipase A_2, it is believed that this enzyme is probably involved in the generation of the endothelium-derived relaxing factor. Indeed, melittin (a polypeptide present in bee venom, which activates phospholipase A_2) causes endothelium-dependent relaxation of the aorta of the rabbit, an effect that is prevented by quinacrine (31).

Consistent with the hypothesis that phospholipase activation followed by release and metabolism of arachidonic acid produces endothelium-derived relaxing factor is the observation that endothelium-mediated relaxation is calcium dependent. In various blood vessels the Ca^{2+}-ionophore A 23187 causes endothelium-dependent relaxations (37, 42, 86). Incubation in Ca^{2+}-free medium or the addition of calcium entry blockers, such as nifedipine and verapamil, inhibit endothelium-dependent responses to muscarinic receptor activation in the aorta of the rabbit (86). Bioassay studies with the perfused aorta of the rabbit demonstrated that removal of Ca^{2+} from the perfusate inhibits the release of endothelium-derived relaxing factor (26). Thus, the entry of extracellular Ca^{2+} may be a key step in the production and/or release of endothelium-derived relaxing factor.

If endothelium-derived relaxing factor is a product of the metabolism of arachidonic acid, its formation is not likely to be catalyzed by cyclo-oxygenase. Indeed several inhibitors of the enzyme, as well as inhibitors of prostacyclin synthetase, fail to affect the endothelium-dependent relaxations induced by acetylcholine in various blood vessels (for reviews see 37, 72).

Exogenous arachidonic acid, however, evokes endothelium-dependent relaxations in a number of isolated arteries. This finding has been taken as evidence that arachidonate is the precursor of endothelium-derived relaxing factor. In most blood vessels these endothelium-dependent relaxations can be reduced only in part by inhibitors of cyclo-oxygenase (19, 22, 40, 81, 87). Experiments with layered preparations demonstrated that, in a manner similar to that of acetylcholine, arachidonic acid releases a diffusable nonprostaglandin relaxing factor from canine coronary artery endothelium (81).

Endothelial cells can metabolize exogenous arachidonic acid through the lipoxygenase pathway (19, 55, 65). The labile 15-hydroperoxy intermediate (15 HPETE) has inhibitory properties on isolated blood vessels (19); the more stable 12- and 15-HETEs and the dihydroxy metabolites do not (29). C-6-sulfidopeptide leukotrienes, although they can be produced by the blood vessel wall, do not cause relaxation of vascular smooth muscle; the leukotriene antagonist FPL 55712 and inhibitors of leukotriene production (diethyl maleate or 2-cyclohexen-1-one) do not alter the relaxations caused by acetylcholine in the aorta of the rabbit (30). The concept of involvement of products of lipoxygenase in the endothelium-dependent relaxations emerged early on: It was noted that certain inhibitors of the enzyme [5,8,11,14-eicosatetraynoic acid (ETYA), nordihydroguaiaretic acid (NDGA), and phenidone] could prevent the relaxations induced by acetylcholine in a variety of blood vessels (for review see 37, 75). Another inhibitor of lipoxygenase, BW 755C, had this effect in renal arteries of the dog (8), but not in the aorta of the rabbit (37).

Bioassay experiments with blood vessels of the rabbit demonstrated that the inhibitory effects of phenidone and NDGA can reasonably be attributed to their chemical interaction with the endothelium-derived relaxing factor(s) rather than to their inhibition of its production (47). Actually, these studies demonstrated that inhibitors of lipoxygenase do not prevent the response to acetylcholine unless they also possess antioxidant properties (47). This casts serious doubt on the potential role of a product of lipoxygenase in endothelium-dependent relaxations evoked by acetylcholine.

Endothelial cells contain cytochrome P-450 mono-oxygenases, which can oxidize arachidonic acid to various epoxygenase metabolites (3, 55, 56). In the aorta of the rabbit, the inhibitors of this enzyme (SKF 525A and metyrapone) antagonize endothelium-dependent responses to cholinergic activation (89). This observation suggests that an epoxygenase metabolite of arachidonic acid may be involved in the phenomenon. However, inhibitors of cytochrome P 450 mono-oxygenases do not affect endothelium-dependent responses to acetylcholine in the aorta of the rat (75). Part of the effect of SKF 525A noted in the blood vessels of the rabbit could be related to an inhibitory effect on Ca^{2+} entry (58).

Like arachidonate, several other nonmetabolizing unsaturated and saturated fatty acids evoke endothelium-dependent relaxations (40, 81); it has been suggested that these lipids (including arachidonate) are not precursors of the endothelium-derived relaxing factor(s), but rather promote its synthesis or release by changing the fluidity of the endothelial cell membrane (40).

It is possible that multiple pathways for the formation of endothelium-derived relaxing factor exist, or that there is more than one relaxing factor, which could explain the contradictory evidence of the involvement of arachidonic acid metabolic pathways in endothelium-mediated inhibitory responses. Indeed, in bioassay experiments with canine blood vessels, acetylcholine can cause biphasic inhibitory responses in the bioassay tissue. Some antioxidants prevent only the second phase of relaxation (78), which may indicate the release of two (or more) relaxing factors by acetylcholine.

Oxidative mechanisms and free radicals   Antioxidants and nonspecific radical scavengers inhibit endothelium-dependent relaxations evoked by acetylcholine in the aorta of the rabbit (29, 42, 47). These experiments suggest that oxidative mechanisms play an important role in the production of endothelium-derived relaxing factor; this hypothesis would also explain why anoxia can prevent the relaxations induced by acetylcholine (20, 23, 42).

Under conditions of bioassay, some antioxidants do not affect the *release* of endothelium-derived relaxing factor, but inactivate it in transit (47, 78). Catecholamines, which have antioxidant properties, also can inactivate the relaxing factor (78). Chemical interaction with endothelium-derived relaxing factor also explains the inhibitory effect that hemoglobin (but not methemoglobin) has on endothelium-dependent relaxations in response to acetylcholine (40). Since hemoglobin is a large protein that cannot pass across cell membranes it must inactivate the factor during its diffusion through the extracellular space (40). These observations suggest that the relaxing factor is an oxidized substance whose oxidized state is essential for its biological activity.

Experiments using isolated vascular rings of the rabbit (85) and dog (95) and perfused canine femoral artery segments (82) have ruled out the possibility that oxygen-derived free radicals are the endothelium-derived relaxing factor(s), since scavengers of these free radicals do not eliminate the response. However, oxygen-derived free radicals can affect endothelium-dependent responses in opposite ways. Generation of oxidizing free radicals (hydrogen peroxide, hydroxyl radical) by xanthine oxidase, or exogenously administered hydrogen peroxide facilitate the release of endothelium-derived relaxing factor and its action on smooth muscle. In contrast, superoxide anions depress acetylcholine-induced relaxations in rings of canine coronary artery (95).

In bioassay experiments, when the relaxing factor is in prolonged contact with physiological salt solution, superoxide anions accelerate its destruction (82). As a consequence, superoxide dismutase considerably prolongs the half-life of endothelium-derived relaxing factor, in particular if the P_{O_2} is lowered (82). Under certain experimental conditions, lowering the P_{O_2} per se may prolong the half-life of the factor (32). These techniques may be useful in further analysis of the chemical identity of endothelium-derived relaxing factor. The endothelium-dependent actions of these free radicals may contribute to the vasodilation and permeability changes during inflammatory processes when the radicals are released from activated polymorphonuclear neutrophils (18).

ACTION ON VASCULAR SMOOTH MUSCLE   The relaxations caused by acetylcholine are associated with increased production of cyclic GMP in the aorta of the rabbit and the rat, and in bovine coronary arteries (25, 40, 52, 74). Removal of the endothelium abolishes the relaxation and the accumulation of cyclic GMP caused by acetylcholine, but not those evoked by sodium nitroprusside (75). Methylene blue, a known inhibitor of guanylate cyclase, has effects similar (52, 75) to those caused by removal of the endothelium (52, 75). The inhibitor of cyclic GMP phosphodiesterase (M-B 22,948) augments the response to acetylcholine (52). Thus, it appears likely that the inhibitory effect of endothelium-derived relaxing factor released by acetylcholine is mediated by guanylate cyclase via the production of cyclic GMP and the activation of cyclic GMP-dependent protein kinase in vascular smooth muscle. This results in altered protein phosphorylation and in dephosphorylation of the myosin light chain, which may lead to relaxation (75).

In bioassay experiments, the release of endothelium-derived relaxing factor by acetylcholine from canine femoral arteries hyperpolarizes the smooth muscle of canine coronary arteries. However, when the hyperpolarization is prevented by ouabain the relaxation in response to acetylcholine persists (28). This finding suggests that smooth muscle hyperpolarization may not be the conditio sine qua non of endothelium-mediated relaxation.

Basal and Flow-Dependent Release of Endothelium-Derived Relaxing Factor

POSSIBLE ROLE OF HEMODYNAMIC FACTORS   Effluent from perfused rabbit aortic (47) or canine femoral artery preparations with endothelium (78) relaxes bioassay coronary arteries without endothelium. As in the case of relaxations induced by acetylcholine, cyclo-oxygenase inhibitors have no effect on these responses, but antioxidants (e.g. phenidone and catecholamines) prevent them (78). These studies demonstrate that a nonprostaglandin endothelium-derived relaxing factor is released from perfused artery segments. Thus, a basal release of a relaxing factor(s), in the absence of vasoactive agents, can be stimulated by shear stress imposed by flow on the luminal surface of the endothelial cells. Hemodynamic shear stress plays an important role in both the physiology and pathobiology of the vascular endothelium. Morphologic (24, 35, 77) and functional changes, such as increased histamine-forming capacity (17), increased fluid endocytosis (15), and increased production of prostacyclin (34, 93), occur in endothelial cells subjected to steadily increasing or pulsatile shear stresses. Increments in flow through arteries in situ (43, 49, 50, 57) or in vitro (51) induce vasodilatation, which cannot be prevented by cyclo-oxygenase inhibitors (50), but can be abolished by removal of the endothelium (51) or depressed by methylene blue (57). The flow-induced endothelium-dependent regulation of the tone of large arteries may be of physiological importance in the complex interaction between regional hemodynamics and the elements of the vessel wall.

Substances Involved in Hemostasis

Increasing evidence indicates that substances generated during the process of hemostasis can cause endothelium-dependent relaxations. Thrombin, which is generated abundantly during activation of the coagulation cascade, causes endothelium-dependent relaxation in basilar, coronary, femoral, saphenous, splenic, and pulmonary arteries of the dog and in aorta of the rat (19, 22, 62, 64, 73). This relaxation can be prevented by heparin. Although thrombin can stimulate the production of prostacyclin by endothelial cells (97), inhibitors of cyclo-oxygenase do not block the thrombin-induced relaxation. The endothelium-mediated relaxing effect of thrombin is counteracted in many tissues by a direct contractile action on the smooth muscle (19, 64).

A number of canine vascular preparations, including coronary arteries, as well as human digital arteries and rat caudal arteries will contract in response to products released during platelet aggregation (11, 12, 16, 70, 94). In coronary artery rings such contractions are greater in the absence of endothelium (11). If contraction is first induced with prostaglandin $F_{2\alpha}$, canine or human platelets can induce an endothelium-dependent relaxation, in contrast to further contraction in rings without endothelium (11, 12, 53, 54). In isolated physiological saline-perfused segments of canine coronary artery, relaxation in response to platelets is observed if the platelets are added to the perfusion fluid, but not if they are exposed only to the abluminal surface of the vessel. The relaxation does not occur if the endothelium has been removed (13). Thus, substances released from platelets can trigger the endothelium to send a potent inhibitory signal to the smooth muscle of the vessel wall.

A potential mediator of the platelet-induced relaxation is serotonin. Platelets are the carriers of almost all of the serotonin in blood, which they release during aggregation. Most blood vessels contract in response to serotonin; in the canine coronary artery in vitro and in vivo, however, this contraction is diminished in the presence of endothelium (5, 11, 12). As with aggregating platelets, if the ring is first contracted with prostaglandin $F_{2\alpha}$, serotonin can induce a modest endothelium-dependent relaxation (10–12). This relaxation is not affected by the selective S_2-serotonergic antagonist, ketanserin, but is abolished by the S_1- and S_2-serotonergic antagonist, methiothepin (53). Whereas the contractile response to platelets is reduced in most situations by serotonergic antagonists, which suggests that released serotonin contributes to the contraction, inhibition of the serotonergic relaxation with methiothepin does not affect the relaxation in response to platelets in the coronary artery (53).

In addition to serotonin, platelets release large quantities of adenosine di- and triphosphate (ADP and ATP) during aggregation. These substances induce endothelium-dependent relaxations in arterial tissues, such as the canine femoral and coronary arteries, and pig and rabbit aorta (19, 21, 22, 36, 45, 53). Apyrase, an adenosine di- and triphosphatase, inhibits the relaxations to exogenous ADP and ATP; furthermore, it almost abolishes relaxations in response to platelets. These observations indicate that the principal mediators of the endothelium-dependent relaxation in response to aggregating platelets are ADP and ATP (53). In canine coronary artery the endothelium facilitates relaxations in response to adenosine (79).

Finally, platelet-activating factor, a potent mediator of platelet aggregation and a vasodilator in a number of animal models, is released during aggregation (96). Platelet-activating factor induces endothelium-dependent relaxations in isolated canine coronary and femoral arteries and rat aortae, but only at very high concentrations (59, 60, 94). This probably represents a nonspecific action of platelet-activating factor (94), perhaps akin to that produced at high concentrations by other lipids (40). Therefore, it seems unlikely that platelet-activating factor contributes importantly to platelet-induced relaxations.

Thus several substances—thrombin, adenine nucleotides, and serotonin—could contribute to endothelium-dependent relaxation in the face of thrombogenesis. This may serve, particularly in a vital and precarious vascular bed such as the coronary, to dilate the vessel and "flush away" the evolving clot. Endothelial dysfunction or damage, perhaps in the form of atherosclerosis, could promote the development of arterial spasm. In the periphery, disruption of the endothelium during trauma would promote hemostasis by facilitating vasoconstriction.

Hormones and Other Autocoids

Norepinephrine and selective alpha$_2$-adrenergic agonists can cause relaxation of canine and porcine coronary and systemic arteries and canine pulmonary arteries and veins if the endothelium is present (10, 67). In the canine pulmonary artery and femoral vein, which are chronically exposed to low oxygen tension, the inhibitory effects of endothelial alpha$_2$-adrenergic stimulation are masked in part by the contractions induced by stimulation of alpha$_2$-adrenoceptors on the vascular smooth muscle (67). The expression of the alpha$_2$-adrenergic relaxations of the femoral vein can be exaggerated when that vessel is chronically exposed to high flow and high arterial levels of oxygen tension by the creation of an arteriovenous fistula between the femoral artery and vein (69).

In the canine coronary artery the relaxing effects of beta-adrenergic agonists, in particular norepinephrine and isoproterenol, are reduced following removal of the endothelium (79). It is uncertain whether the greater responsiveness to beta-adrenergic agonists in the presence of endothelial cells is due to the continuous (basal) release of an endothelium-derived relaxing factor or to activation of beta-adrenoceptors on the endothelial cells.

The presence of inhibitory alpha$_2$-adrenoceptors on the endothelial cells, and the augmented beta-adrenergic relaxations that these cells provide, may help to explain the vasodilatory effects of catecholamines in certain vascular beds. Conversely, absence of the endothelium would favor vasoconstriction due to activation by catecholamines of alpha-adrenergic receptors on vascular smooth muscle cells. Therefore, contractions evoked by nonselective alpha-adrenergic agonists, in particular epinephrine and norepinephrine, are augmented following removal of the endothelium (6, 10, 33, 44).

In canine cerebral arteries (and to a lesser extent in coronary arteries, but not in peripheral vessels) vasopressin, along with the related peptide oxytocin, causes endothelium-dependent relaxations via activation of V_1-vasopressinergic receptors (61, 62). Vasopressin has a better-known direct contractile effect on most peripheral vessels. This, coupled with the endothelium-dependent vasodilatory effect of vasopressin in cerebral arteries, may favor the redistribution of blood flow from the periphery to the brain during shock and hemorrhage.

Another hormone generally regarded as a vasoconstrictor, angiotensin II, can induce endothelium-dependent relaxation of canine renal arteries; this effect is apparently mediated by the production of prostacyclin (91).

Several other substances present normally or pathologically in blood have been demonstrated to induce endothelium-dependent relaxations in certain vessels. Bradykinin can induce endothelium-dependent relaxations in human, porcine, and canine arteries (1, 7–9, 46, 76). These relaxations may involve the metabolism of arachidonic acid through the lipoxygenase pathway (8). In the aorta of the rat and pulmonary artery of the guinea pig, histamine induces an endothelium-dependent relaxation that is blocked by H_1-histaminergic antagonists (14, 74, 84, 92). These effects of bradykinin and histamine could conceivably contribute to the vasodilatation and edema associated with inflammation.

The peptidergic transmitter, substance P, can induce endothelium-dependent relaxations in certain isolated rat, dog, and rabbit arteries, and in the canine femoral artery in vivo (2, 39). In certain circumstances, relaxations induced by vasoactive intestinal polypeptide may also be endothelium-dependent (14). Another putative neuropeptide, calcitonin gene-related peptide, is a potent stimulator of endothelium-dependent relaxation (4).

ENDOTHELIUM-DEPENDENT EXCITATORY RESPONSES

Several lines of evidence suggest that endothelial cells also can facilitate contractile responses of the vascular smooth muscle. Studies on cultured bovine aortic endothelial cells demonstrate that these cells release a potent vasoconstrictor polypeptide (48), which may be at least in part responsible for endothelium-mediated excitatory responses.

Exogenous arachidonic acid causes endothelium-dependent increases in the tension of canine veins; this effect can be prevented by inhibitors of cyclo-oxygenase. Inhibition of prostacyclin synthetase or thromboxane synthetase does not antagonize the endothelium-dependent increases in tension caused by the fatty acid. Thus a prostanoid, other than prostacyclin or thromboxane A_2, or an endoperoxide intermediate of cyclo-oxygenase metabolism may be responsible for the endothelium-dependent effect of arachidonic acid in canine veins

(68). Stimulation of the cyclo-oxygenase pathway by exogenous arachidonic acid induces opposite responses in arteries and veins: an endothelium-dependent relaxation in arteries, an endothelium-dependent contraction in veins. This heterogeneity in endothelium-dependent responses observed between these blood vessels may reflect a difference in behavior of the arterial and venous smooth muscle in response to a common prostanoid produced by the endothelial cells or, alternatively, arterial and venous endothelium may produce different prostanoids (90).

Sudden hypoxia/anoxia augments contractile responses in a number of canine blood vessels. In femoral, splenic, coronary, cerebral, and pulmonary arteries, and in splenic and pulmonary veins, removal of the endothelium reduces this augmentation (22, 23, 63, 80). Transfer experiments with layered canine coronary and femoral arteries provide evidence that the hypoxic/anoxic facilitation is mediated by a still unidentified diffusable vasoconstrictor substance(s) released from the endothelium (80). Although contractions of rings of canine femoral veins are not facilitated by hypoxia, studies with mixed-layer preparations show that the venous endothelium releases facilitatory mediators that can cause contraction of arterial vascular smooth muscle (80).

CONCLUDING REMARKS

The discovery of the ability of the endothelium to modulate vascular smooth muscle contractility under experimental conditions suggests another physiologic role for these cells. The phenomenon was originally observed with acetylcholine, and it has become clear that the endothelium releases a diffusible factor in response to muscarinic stimulation. Despite several efforts to characterize the endothelium-derived relaxing factor, its chemical nature remains to be determined. A consensus has emerged, nonetheless, that the relaxation of smooth muscle in response to this endothelium-derived factor occurs through the activation of guanylate cyclase.

The physiological significance of acetylcholine-induced endothelium-dependent responses remains obscure. However, the endothelial inhibitory responses initiated by hemodynamic shear stresses, circulating vasoactive hormones (vasopressin, angiotensin, and catecholamines), mediators of local blood flow regulation (adenosine, histamine, and bradykinin), and substances involved in hemostasis (thrombin, serotonin, and adenine nucleotides) could contribute to the physiological regulation of circulation. In contrast, the absence or dysfunction of endothelial cells may play a role in pathological vascular events associated with atherosclerosis, thrombogenesis, and vasospasm.

In view of the considerable heterogeneity in the endothelial responses among species, tissues, and stimulating agents, the possibility remains that more than one mechanism of production, or more than one factor exists. A shift from inhibitory to excitatory function of endothelial cells by conditions of hypoxia or thrombogenesis may be of importance in the pathogenesis of various vascular diseases.

Literature Cited

1. Altura, B. M., Chand, N. 1981. Bradykinin-induced relaxation of renal and pulmonary arteries is dependent upon intact endothelial cells. *Br. J. Pharmacol.* 74:10–11
2. Angus, J. A., Campbell, G. R., Cocks, T. M., Manderson, J. A. 1983. Vasodilatation by acetylcholine is endothelium-dependent: A study by sonomicrometry in canine femoral artery in vivo. *J. Physiol.* 344:209–22
3. Baird, W. M., Chemerys, R., Grinspan, J. B., Mueller, S. N., Levine, E. M. 1980. Benzo(a)pyrene metabolism in bovine aortic endothelial and bovine lung fibroblast-like cell culture. *Cancer Res.* 40:1781–86
4. Brain, S., Williams, T., Tippins, J., Morris, H., MacIntyre, I. 1985. Calcitonin gene-related peptide is a potent vasodilator. *Nature* 313:54–56
5. Brum, J. M., Sufan, Q., Lane, G., Bove, A. A. 1984. Increased vasoconstrictor activity of proximal coronary arteries with endothelial damage in intact dogs. *Circulation* 70:1066–73
6. Carrier, G. O., White, R. E. 1985. Enhancement of alpha-1 and alpha-2 adrenergic agonists induced vasoconstriction by removal of endothelium in rat aorta. *J. Pharmacol. Exp. Ther.* 232:682–87
7. Chand, N., Altura, B. M. 1981. Acetylcholine and bradykinin relax intrapulmonary arteries by acting on endothelial cells: Role in lung vascular diseases. *Science* 213:1376–79
8. Chand, N., Altura, B. M. 1981. Inhibition of endothelial cell-dependent relaxations to acetylcholine and bradykinin by lipoxygenase inhibitors in canine isolated renal arteries. *Microcirculation* 1:211–23
9. Cherry, P. D., Furchgott, R. F., Zawadzki, J. V., Jothianandan, D. 1982. Role of endothelial cells in relaxation of isolated arteries by bradykinin. *Proc. Natl. Acad. Sci. USA* 79:2106–10
10. Cocks, T. M., Angus, J. A. 1983. Endothelium-dependent relaxation of coronary arteries by noradrenaline and serotonin. *Nature* 305:627–30
11. Cohen, R. A., Shepherd, J. T., Vanhoutte, P. M. 1983. Inhibitory role of the endothelium in the response of isolated coronary arteries to platelets. *Science* 221:273–74
12. Cohen, R. A., Shepherd, J. T., Vanhoutte, P. M. 1983. 5-Hydroxytryptamine can mediate endothelium-dependent relaxation of coronary arteries. *Am. J. Physiol.* 245:H1077–80
13. Cohen, R. A., Shepherd, J. T., Vanhoutte, P. M. 1984. Endothelium and asymmetrical responses of the coronary arterial wall. *Am. J. Physiol.* 247:H403–8
14. Davies, J. M., Williams, K. I. 1984. Endothelial-dependent relaxant effects of vasoactive intestinal polypeptide and arachidonic acid in rat aortic strips. *Prostaglandins* 27:195–202
15. Davies, P. F., Dewey, C. F. Jr., Brussolari, S. R., Gordon, E. J., Gimbrone, M. A. Jr. 1984. Influence of hemodynamic forces on vascular endothelial function. *J. Clin. Invest.* 73:1121–29
16. De Clerck, F., Van Nueten, J. M. 1982. Platelet-mediated vascular contractions: Inhibition of the serotonergic component by ketanserin. *Thromb. Res.* 27:713–27
17. De Forrest, J. M., Hollis, T. M. 1978. Shear stress and aorbic histamine synthesis. *Am. J. Physiol.* 234:H701–5
18. Del Maestro, R. F. 1982. Role of superoxide anion radicals in microvascular permeability and leukocyte behavior. *Can. J. Physiol. Pharmacol.* 60:1406–14
19. De Mey, J. G., Claeys, M., Vanhoutte, P. M. 1982. Endothelium-dependent inhibitory effects of acetylcholine, adenosine triphosphate, thrombin and arachidonic acid in the canine femoral artery. *J. Pharmacol. Exp. Ther.* 222:166–73
20. De Mey, J. G., Vanhoutte, P. M. 1980. Interaction between Na^+,K^+ exchanges and the direct inhibitory effect of acetylcholine on canine femoral arteries. *Circ. Res.* 46:826–36
21. De Mey, J. G., Vanhoutte, P. M. 1981. Role of the intima in cholinergic and purinergic relaxation of isolated canine femoral arteries. *J. Physiol.* 316:347–55
22. De Mey, J. G., Vanhoutte, P. M. 1982. Heterogeneous behavior of the canine arterial and venous wall: Importance

318   VANHOUTTE ET AL

of the endothelium. *Circ. Res.* 51:439–47
23. De Mey, J. G., Vanhoutte, P. M. 1983. Anoxia and endothelium dependent reactivity of the canine femoral artery. *J. Physiol.* 335:65–74
24. Dewey, C. F. Jr., Bussolari, S. R., Gimbrone, M. A. Jr., Davies, P. F. 1981. The dynamic response of vascular endothelial cells to fluid shear stress. *J. Biomech. Eng.* 103:177–85
25. Diamond, J., Chu, E. B. 1983. Possible role for cyclic GMP in endothelium-dependent relaxation of rabbit aorta by acetylcholine. Comparison with nitroglycerin. *Res. Commun. Chem. Pathol. Pharmacol.* 41:369–81
26. Edwards, D. H., Griffith, T. M., Henderson, A. H., Lewis, M. J., Newby, A. C. 1985. Production of endothelium-derived relaxant factor is both ATP and calcium dependent. *Br. J. Pharmacol.* 84:P64 (Abstr.)
27. Eglen, R. M., Whiting, R. L. 1985. Determination of the muscarinic receptor subtype mediating vasodilatation. *Br. J. Pharmacol.* 84:1–4
28. Feletou, M., Vanhoutte, P. M. 1985. Endothelium-derived relaxing factor(s) hyperpolarizes coronary vascular smooth muscle. *Physiologist* 28:325 (Abstr.)
29. Förstermann, U., Neufang, B. 1984. The endothelium-dependent relaxation of rabbit aorta: Effects of antioxidants and hydroxylated eicosatetraenoic acids. *Br. J. Pharmacol.* 82:765–67
30. Förstermann, U., Neufang, B. 1984. C-6-sulfidopeptide leukotrienes are unlikely to be involved in the endothelium dependent relaxation of rabbit aorta by acetylcholine. *Prostaglandins* 27:181–93
31. Förstermann, U., Neufang, B. 1985. Endothelium-dependent vasodilation by melittin: Are lipoxygenase products involved? *Am. J. Physiol.* In press
32. Förstermann, U., Trogisch, G., Busse, R. 1985. Species-dependent differences in the nature of endothelium-derived vascular relaxing factor. *Eur. J. Pharmacol.* 106:639–43
33. Fortes, Z. B., Leme, J. G., Scivoletto, R. 1983. Vascular reactivity in diabetes mellitus: Role of the endothelial cell. *Br. J. Pharmacol.* 79:771–81
34. Frangos, J. A., Eskin, S. G., McIntire, L. V., Ives, C. L. 1985. Flow effects on prostacyclin production by cultured human endothelial cells. *Science* 227:1477–79
35. Franke, R.-P., Gräfe, M., Schnittler, H., Seiffge, D., Mittermayer, C., Drenckhahn, D. 1984. Induction of human

vascular endothelial stress fibers by fluid shear stress. *Nature* 307:648–49
36. Furchgott, R. F. 1981. The requirement for endothelial cells in the relaxation of arteries by acetylcholine and some other vasodilators. *Trends Pharmacol. Sci.* 2:173–76
37. Furchgott, R. F. 1983. Role of the endothelium in responses of vascular smooth muscle. *Circ. Res.* 53:557–73
38. Furchgott, R. F., Cherry, P. D. 1984. The muscarinic receptor of vascular endothelium that subserves vasodilatation. *Trends Pharmacol. Sci.* 5:45–48
39. Furchgott, R. F., Cherry, P. D., Zawadzki, J. V. 1983. Endothelium-dependent relaxation of arteries by acetylcholine, bradykinin, and other agents. In *Vascular Neuroeffector Mechanisms,* ed. J. Bevan, M. Fujiwara, R. A. Maxwell, K. Mohri, S. Shibata, et al, pp. 37–43. New York: Raven
40. Furchgott, R. F., Jothianandan, D., Cherry, P. D. 1984. Endothelium-dependent responses: The last three years. In *Vasodilator Mechanisms,* ed. P. M. Vanhoutte, S. F. Vatner, pp. 1–15. Karger: Basel
41. Furchgott, R. F., Zawadzki, J. V. 1980. The obligatory role of endothelial cells in the relaxation of arterial smooth muscle by acetylcholine. *Nature* 288:373–76
42. Furchgott, R. F., Zawadzki, J. V., Cherry, P. D. 1981. Role of endothelium in the vasodilator response to acetylcholine. In *Vasodilatation,* ed. P. M. Vanhoutte, I. Leusen, pp. 49–66. New York: Raven
43. Gerova, M., Smiesko, V., Gero, J., Barta, E. 1983. Dilatation of conduit coronary artery induced by high blood flow. *Physiol. Bohemoslov.* 32:55–63
44. Godfraind, T., Egleme, C., Alosachie, I. H. 1985. Role of endothelium in the contractile response of rat aorta to α-adrenoceptor agonists. *Clin. Sci.* 68 (Suppl. 10):65s–71s
45. Gordon, J. L., Martin, W. 1983. Endothelium-dependent relaxation of the pig aorta: Relationship to stimulation of ⁸⁶Rb efflux from isolated endothelial cells. *Br. J. Pharmacol.* 79:531–41
46. Gordon, J. L., Martin, W. 1983. Stimulation of endothelial prostacyclin production plays no role in endothelium-dependent relaxation of pig aorta. *Br. J. Pharmacol.* 80:179–86
47. Griffith, T. M., Edwards, D. H., Lewis, M. J., Newby, A. C., Henderson, A. H. 1984. The nature of endothelium-derived vascular relaxant factor. *Nature* 308:645–47
48. Hickey, K. A., Rubanyi, G. M., Paul, R. J., Highsmith, R. F. 1985. Characteriza-

tion of a coronary vasoconstrictor produced by cultured endothelial cells. *Am. J. Physiol.* 248:C550–56

49. Hintze, T. H., Vatner, S. F. 1983. Mechanism of large coronary artery dilatation in response to brief periods of coronary occlusion and myocardial ischemia. *Circulation* 68 (Suppl. III):32 (Abstr.)

50. Holtz, J., Förstermann, U., Pohl, U., Giesler, M., Bassenge, E. 1984. Flow-dependent, endothelium-mediated dilation of epicardial coronary arteries in conscious dogs: effects of cyclooxygenase inhibition. *J. Cardiovasc. Pharmacol.* 6:1161–69

51. Holtz, J., Pohl, U., Kellner, C., Busse, R. 1984. Effect of endothelial removal or damage on the flow-dependent dilation of canine femoral arteries in vivo and in vitro (abstract). *Pflügers Arch.* 400:R9

52. Holzmann, S. 1982. Endothelium-induced relaxation by acetylcholine associated with large rises in cyclic GMP in coronary arterial strips. *J. Cyclic Nucl. Res.* 8:409–19

53. Houston, D. S., Shepherd, J. T., Vanhoutte, P. M. 1985. Adenine nucleotides, serotonin and endothelium-dependent relaxations to platelets. *Am. J. Physiol.* 248:H389–95

54. Houston, D. S., Vanhoutte, P. M. 1985. Direct contraction and endothelium-mediated relaxation of isolated canine coronary arteries by aggregating human platelets. *Fed. Proc.* 44:1562 (Abstr.)

55. Johnson, A., Revtyak, G., Campbell, W. 1985. Arachidonic acid metabolites and endothelial injury: studies with cultures of human endothelial cells. *Fed. Proc.* 44:19–24

56. Juchau, M. R., Bond, J. A., Benditt, E. P. 1976. Aryl-4-monooxygenase and cytochrome P-450 in the aorta: Possible role in atherosclerosis. *Proc. Natl. Acad. Sci. USA* 73:3723–25

57. Kaiser, L., Hull, S. S., Sparks, H. V. 1985. Methylene blue inhibits flow-dependent dilation in the canine femoral artery. *Fed. Proc.* 44:808 (Abstr.)

58. Kalsner, S., Nickerson, M., Boyd, G. N. 1978. Selective blockade of potassium-induced contractions of aortic strips by β-diethylaminodiphenyl propylacetate (SKF-525A). *J. Pharmacol. Exp. Ther.* 174:500–8

59. Kamitani, T., Katamoto, M., Tatsumi, M., Katsuta, K., Ono, T., et al. 1984. Mechanism(s) of the hypotensive effect of synthetic 1-0-octadecyl-2-0-acetyl-glycero-3-phosphorylcholine. *Eur. J. Pharmacol.* 98:357–66

60. Kasuya, Y., Masuda, Y., Shigenobu, K. 1984. Possible role of endothelium in the vasodilator response of rat thoracic aorta to platelet-activating factor (PAF). *J. Pharmacobio–Dyn.* 7:138–42

61. Katusic, Z., Shepherd, J. T., Vanhoutte, P. M. 1984. Oxytocin induces endothelium-dependent relaxation of canine basilar arteries. *Physiologist* 27:282 (Abstr.)

62. Katusic, Z. S., Shepherd, J. T., Vanhoutte, P. M. 1984. Vasopressin causes endothelium-dependent relaxations of the canine basilar artery. *Circ. Res.* 55:575–79

63. Katusic, Z., Vanhoutte, P. M. 1985. Anoxic contractions in isolated cerebral arteries. Contribution of endothelium-derived factors, metabolites of arachidonic acid and calcium entry. *J. Cardiovasc. Pharmacol.* In press

64. Ku, D. D. 1982. Coronary vascular reactivity after acute myocardial ischemia. *Science* 218:576–78

65. Kühn, H., Pönicke, K., Halle, W., Schewe, T., Förster, W. 1983. Evidence for the presence of lipoxygenase pathway in cultured endothelial cells. *Biomed. Biochim. Acta* 42:K1–K4

66. Lee, T. J. F. 1982. Cholinergic mechanism in large cat cerebral artery. *Circ. Res.* 50:870–79

67. Miller, V. M., Vanhoutte, P. M. 1984. Muscular and endothelial responsiveness to alpha$_2$-adrenergic activation in canine blood vessels *Physiologist* 27:282 (Abstr.)

68. Miller, V. M., Vanhoutte, P. M. 1985. Endothelium-dependent contractions to arachidonic acid are mediated by products of cyclo-oxygenase in canine veins. *Am. J. Physiol.* 248:H432–37

69. Miller, V. M., Vanhoutte, P. M. 1985. Endothelium-dependent responses can be modulated chronically in canine arteries and veins. *Fed. Proc.* 44:455 (Abstr.)

70. Moulds, R. F. W., Iwanov, V., Medcalf, R. L. 1984. The effects of platelet-derived contractile agents on human digital arteries. *Clin. Sci.* 66:443–51

71. Owen, M., Bevan, J. 1985. Acetylcholine induced endothelial-dependent vasodilatation increases as artery diameter decreases in the rabbit ear. *Experientia.* In press

72. Peach, M. J., Loeb, A. L., Singer, H. A., Saye, J. A. 1985. Endothelium-derived vascular relaxing factor. *Hypertension* 7 (Suppl. I):I94–I100

73. Rapoport, R. M., Draznin, M. B., Murad, F. 1984. Mechanisms of the adenosine triphosphate-, thrombin-, and trypsin-induced relaxation of rat thoracic aorta. *Circ. Res.* 55:468–79

74. Rapoport, R. M., Murad, F. 1983. Agonist-induced endothelium-dependent

relaxation in rat thoracic aorta may be mediated through cGMP. *Circ. Res.* 52:352–57

75. Rapoport, R. M., Murad, F. 1983. Endothelium-dependent and nitrovasodilator-induced relaxation of vascular smooth muscle: Role of cyclic GMP. *J. Cyclic Nucl. Protein Phosph. Res.* 9: 281–96

76. Regoli, D., Mizrahi, J., D'Orleans-Juste, P., Caranikas, S. 1982. Effects of kinins on isolated blood vessels. Role of endothelium. *Can. J. Physiol. Pharmacol.* 60:1580–83

77. Reidy, M. A., Langille, B. L. 1980. The effects of local blood flow patterns on endothelial cell morphology. *Exp. Mol. Pathol.* 32:276–89

78. Rubanyi, G. M., Lorenz, R. R., Vanhoutte, P. M. 1985. Bioassay of endothelium-derived relaxing factor(s). Inactivation by catecholamines. *Am. J. Physiol.* 249:H95–H101

79. Rubanyi, G. M., Vanhoutte, P. M. 1985. Endothelium-removal decreases relaxations of canine coronary arteries caused by beta-adrenergic agonists and adenosine. *J. Cardiovasc. Pharmacol.* 7:139–44

80. Rubanyi, G. M., Vanhoutte, P. M. 1985. Hypoxia releases a vasoconstrictor substance from the canine vascular endothelium. *J. Physiol.* 364:45–56

81. Rubanyi, G. M., Vanhoutte, P. M. 1985. Ouabain inhibits endothelium-dependent relaxations to arachidonic acid in canine coronary arteries. *Fed. Proc.* 44:1234 (Abstr.)

82. Rubanyi, G. M., Vanhoutte, P. M. 1985. Superoxide dismutase prolongs the half-life of endothelium-derived relaxing factor(s) *Clin. Res.* 33:522A (Abstr.)

83. Rubanyi, G. M., Vanhoutte, P. M. 1985. Muscarinic receptor subtypes mediating the release of endothelium-derived relaxing factor(s) from canine femoral arteries. *Physiologist.* (Abstr.) 28:325

84. Satoh, H., Inui, J. 1984. Endothelial cell-dependent relaxation and contraction induced by histamine in the isolated guinea-pig pulmonary artery. *Eur. J. Pharmacol.* 97:321–24

85. Silin, P. J., Strulowitz, J. A., Wolin, M. S., Belloni, F. L. 1985. Absence of a role of superoxide anion, hydrogen peroxide and hydroxyl radical in endothelium-mediated relaxation of rabbit aorta. *Blood Vessels* 22:65–73

86. Singer, H. A., Peach, M. J. 1982. Calcium- and endothelial-mediated vascular smooth muscle relaxation in rabbit aorta. *Hypertension* 4 (Suppl. II):II19–II25

87. Singer, H. A., Peach, M. J. 1983. Endothelium-dependent relaxation of rabbit aorta. 1. Relaxation stimulated by arachidonic acid. *J. Pharmacol. Exp. Ther.* 226:790–95

88. Singer, H. A., Peach, M. J. 1983. Endothelium-dependent relaxation of rabbit aorta. II. Inhibition of relaxation stimulated by methacholine and A23187 with antagonists of arachidonic acid metabolism. *J. Pharmacol. Exp. Ther.* 226:796–801

89. Singer, H. A., Saye, J. A., Peach, M. J. 1984. Effects of cytochrome P-450 inhibitors on endothelium-dependent relaxation in rabbit aorta. *Blood Vessels* 21:223–30

90. Skidgel, R. A., Printz, M. P. 1978. PGI_2 production by rat blood vessels: Diminished prostacyclin formation in veins compared to arteries. *Prostaglandins* 16:1–16

91. Toda, N. 1984. Endothelium-dependent relaxation induced by angiotensin II and histamine in isolated arteries of dog. *Br. J. Pharmacol.* 81:301–7

92. Van de Voorde, J., Leusen, I. 1983. Role of the endothelium in the vasodilator response of rat thoracic aorta to histamine. *Eur. J. Pharmacol.* 87:113–20

93. van Grondelle, A., Worthen, G. S., Ellis, D., Mathias, M. M., Murphy, R. C., et al. 1984. Altering hydrodynamic variables influences PGI_2 production by isolated lungs and endothelial cells. *J. Appl. Physiol.* 57:388–95

94. Vanhoutte, P. M., Houston, D. S. 1985. Platelets, endothelium and vasospasm. *Circulation.* In press

95. Vanhoutte, P. M., Rubanyi, G. M. 1985. Oxygen-derived free radicals and endothelium-mediated relaxation in canine coronary arteries *Clin. Res.* 33:523A (Abstr.)

96. Vargaftig, B. B., Benveniste, J. 1983. Platelet-activating factor today. *Trends Pharmacol. Sci.* 4:341–43

97. Weksler, B. B., Ley, C. W., Jaffe, E. A. 1978. Stimulation of endothelial cell prostacyclin production by thrombin, trypsin, and the ionophore A23187. *J. Clin. Invest.* 62:923–30

Ann. Rev. Physiol. 1986. 48:321–34
Copyright © 1986 by Annual Reviews, Inc. All rights reserved

INDICATOR DILUTION ESTIMATION OF CAPILLARY ENDOTHELIAL TRANSPORT

James B. Bassingthwaighte

Center for Bioengineering, University of Washington, Seattle, Washington 98195

Harvey V. Sparks

Michigan State University, East Lansing, Michigan 48824

INTRODUCTION

A multitude of recent findings have raised the incentive to develop quantitative approaches to studying endothelial cellular metabolism in vivo. Among these are the demonstration of the role of endothelial cells in regulating vascular smooth muscle tone (see review by Vanhoutte, this volume) and the large number of enzymatic and transport phenomena now known to occur on their surfaces in culture and in vivo (see reviews by Ryan, Betz & Goldstein, and Simionescu & Simionescu, this volume; and 31).

Our approach to quantitating endothelial transport has been to develop two techniques in parallel: (*a*) the formulation of a mathematically expressible, quantitative hypothesis describing the events, and (*b*) the definition of an experimental approach based on the multiple indicator dilution method. These go hand in hand because the hypothesis is expressed as a computer-programmed mathematical model whose behavior can be explored to aid in the design of the experiments, and the hypothesis is tested by determining whether or not the model parameters can be adjusted within realistic ranges to provide a good fit of the model solution to the data. The models should account for rapid transformation of substrate, for example, as for angiotensin-converting enzyme in the lung (30), as well as for slower events.

321

0066-4278/86/0315-0321$02.00

THE TOOLS OF THE TRADE

The Multiple Indicator Dilution Technique

The multiple indicator technique, introduced by Chinard et al (8) and developed further for studies of capillary permeability by Crone (9), is based on the principle of multiple inbuilt controls. It makes use of the principles of conservation of mass and of steady-state physiological conditions. The injection of "indicator" should not change the physiological state, so only inert substances or substances introduced in tracer, nonpharmacological amounts are considered appropriate. For studies of endothelial cells several indicators can be used simultaneously, including (a) an intravascular tracer that does not penetrate the vessel wall nor bind to its luminal surface, usually albumin or other large hydrophilic molecule; (b) an extracellular marker with characteristics similar to the test solute, such as the same molecular weight (e.g. L-glucose as the extracellular reference for D-glucose); and (c) the test solute.

The three or more tracers are injected simultaneously as a bolus into the arterial inflow to the organ, and the effluent blood is collected as a series of samples at short intervals (1 or 2 sec) for the first half minute, and then at longer intervals (4 to 10 sec) for the next few minutes, as illustrated in Figure 1. The duration of the sampling depends on the substances and the flow; it should be longer for low flows or for substances with larger volumes of distribution. The basis of outflow detection experiments is that tracer must be returned to the outflow from any region whose characterization is needed. This outflow can be difficult or impossible to detect in the presence of recirculation in the intact animal or in an isolated organ that consumes the test solute so completely that there is no detectable return.

The same mathematical approach can be used with other techniques, for example constant tracer infusion into the inflow with outflow sampling, or brief inflow injections with recording of intraorgan concentration by external detection of positron- or gamma-emitting radioisotopes. In practice these alternative techniques are not as good as the bolus injection-outflow detection method, because the latter gives the high temporal resolution needed for accurate determination of the endothelial cell parameters. Since transport rates around or through the endothelial cells are rapid, the dilution curves must contain high frequency information with a sharply peaked outflow dilution curve to provide good resolving power for the differences between the test solute and the reference substances.

Models for Blood-Tissue Exchange

DESIGN OF TRANSENDOTHELIAL EXCHANGE MODELS   A general approach to describing intravascular transport and exchange between capillary plasma, the interstitium, and the parenchymal cells of an organ has been outlined by Bassingthwaighte & Goresky (3). They showed that it is essential to account for

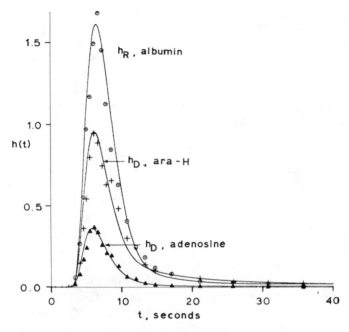

Figure 1   Outflow dilution curves from dog hindlimb skeletal muscle following injection into the femoral arterial inflow. The ordinate is the fraction of the injected dose emerging per second. The indicators were ^{125}I-albumin (intravascular reference), ^{3}H-araH (arabinofuranosylhypoxanthine, extracellular reference) and ^{14}C-adenosine (the "test solute"). The symbols are the data; ^{14}C-labelled metabolites of adenosine have been separated in each sample, but are not shown. The smooth curves are model solutions, using a model composed of an aggregate of 4-region units (capillary, endothelial cell, ISF, parenchymal cell) in parallel to account for the measured distribution of regional flows.

flow heterogeneity as well as for exchange and chemical reaction. The new feature to be emphasized here is the role of the endothelial cell.

The basic conceptual unit is a single capillary-tissue exchange region. Because intraorgan regional flows are heterogeneous (16), each is one of a set of units arrayed in parallel. For multiple solutes or for a substrate and a set of metabolites there would be a set of units for each.

Each capillary-tissue unit is axially distributed, i.e. it has the potential to vary in properties or status along its length to allow for the normal concentration gradients between inflow and outflow. Radially, there are five regions: erythrocytes, plasma, endothelial cells separated by aqueous clefts, interstitial fluid (ISF), and parenchymal cells. Metabolic reactions take place along the length of the unit in both the myocardial and endothelial cells, and in certain cases, also in the erythrocytes. The heterogeneity of the regional flows used in the modeling analysis was defined experimentally by the distributions of markers deposited in each region following arterial injection (16, 24).

To account for the production of metabolites of an injected substrate or agonist and the time course of the appearance of such products in the outflow, a separate set of capillary-tissue units is required for each of the metabolites and, where necessary, for the products of their reactions as well. The input to the model for each reaction product (metabolite) is the rate of transformation of substrate; for example, the rate of adenosine removal is the sum of the rates of production of inosine and of its incorporation into adenosine monophosphate and S-adenosylhomocysteine.

FORMULATION OF MODELS FOR SOLUTION   Equations have previously been developed for plasma-ISF (two-region models) and plasma-ISF-cell (three-region) models that take into account axial concentration gradients. Analytic solutions have been obtained for models with parameter values constant along the length. Solutions for the two-region model are accurate and fast in the absence of axial diffusion using either analytic (32) or numerical solutions (1). The three-region analytic solution of Rose et al (29) loses accuracy at long solution times. Numerical solutions for a two-region model with axial diffusion are within 1% of accurate values (1, 19) and are also very fast. Numerical solutions for three-region models with axial diffusion (18) appear accurate since they have the correct areas and mean transit times, but they await further checking when or if analytic solutions become available.

Convection-diffusion equations for four- and five-region axially distributed capillary-tissue models (erythrocytes, plasma, endothelial cells, interstitium, parenchymal cells) are very similar to those for compartmental models and can be readily defined following the fashion of Bassingthwaighte & Goresky (3). Bassingthwaighte et al (7) provide analytic and numeric solutions for a four-region model (without erythrocytes). A practical way to develop insight into the behavior of the system is to solve the equations and observe the forms of the solutions while changing parameter values. Fast execution times are of great practical importance since repetitive solutions are needed, and they have been obtained by using new numerical techniques, which can be more than a million times faster than using analytic solutions.

Flow heterogeneity is large; in the heart, a seemingly compact unifunctional organ, the regional flow per unit mass of tissue varies five- to sixfold from minimum to maximum, with a standard deviation of 30% around the mean flow (16). It is essential to take this variation into account in the analysis of the dilution curves to avoid systemic biases in the estimates of the parameters describing the exchange. A heterogeneity model is required to account properly for it, but there are many different possible forms of heterogeneous vascular networks. We are currently using a simple arrangement of parallel noninteracting units that differ only in their flows; each receives as input the same arterial concentration-time curve. Very heterogeneous networks such as skeletal muscle may need other representations, some of which have been outlined by Bassingthwaighte & Goresky (3). One model based on dispersionless transport in both large and small vessels has been used extensively (28). We prefer our approach because there is intravascular dispersion in vessels of all sizes, but their dispersionless model has the virtue of linking slow-flow large vessels with slow-flow capillaries, and fast with fast. A configuration intermediate between theirs and ours may be the most realistic.

USING MODELS TO ANALYZE DATA   Models can be used to interpret data in a variety of fashions and with varying degrees of precision. The simplest approach is to analyze by analogy. The more complex and accurate techniques involve careful fitting of the model to the observed data or the observed sets of data. In general, the more data that are obtained simultaneously and analyzed with a single composite model, the stronger the inference concerning the physiology because the degrees of freedom are lower.

Analyzing by analogy is usually done by using the data in a calculation based on a model, but the model often can be fitted only to a part of the data. An example is the use of the Crone-Renkin equation $PS_c = -F_s \log_e (1-E)$, where PS_c is the capillary permeability surface area product, F_s is the flow of solute-containing fluid, and E is a chosen apparent extraction that represents the normalized difference between an intravascular reference tracer and the permeating tracer at a time point following a bolus injection. This model assumes that tracer that has escaped from the capillary never returns. The analogy is acceptable when the extraction is low, i.e. PS_c is only mildly underestimated when E is calculated from the upslope of the outflow indicator dilution curves. But the value for E changes as a function of time, and diminishes to zero during the downslope phase of the curve as tracer returns from the ISF to the capillary. The inconstancy of E illustrates that the Crone-Renkin expression is an incomplete capillary-tissue exchange model.

Fitting of all of the data is the best test of a model; it tests how precisely the model accounts for the experimentally observed data. In indicator-dilution experiments the data that must be fitted include: the direct measurement of flow; the observed set of indicator dilution curves; the regional heterogeneity of flows [estimated using deposited tracer such as microspheres, or highly retained markers, such as desmethylimipramine (23)]; and observations of the steady-state volumes of distribution for the vascular, interstitial, and total water space in the organ. Ideally it is not merely the indicator dilution curves that are fitted by the model, but all of these other observations as well.

Optimization of the model solutions to fit the data is achieved using automated routines that adjust the parameters until good fits are obtained. The procedures can take into account all of the data listed above. Sensitivity functions, which measure the degree to which each of the parameters influence the fit of the experimental data, can be obtained from the model solutions in order to determine whether a parameter can be reliably determined from the data (2). These functions can also be used in the optimization technique outlined by Levin et al (20). The method of optimization is not as important as the precision of the fit with the model solutions over the full extent of the data sets. If there are systematic deviations of the model solutions from the data, assuming the data are accurate, the model is either incorrect or incomplete. Such systematic biases are the incentive to continue to refine one's hypothesis concerning the physiological system.

The development of a model as a statement of a hypothesis concerning the function of the microcirculation involves acquiring data, fitting the data with the models, developing the models further, and improving the experiment designs. Any model of the microcirculation is necessarily a simplification of the actual situation. Despite this it is important that the model not only predict the available data but also have a structure that is physiologically valid, i.e. that agrees with observations made using a variety of techniques. For example, although no practical model can represent the biological variability of a vascular bed, it should represent a reasonable statistical abstraction of that heterogeneity. Model development should continue as long as new information that can serve as a test of the model becomes available. The ultimate goal is a model that represents all of the functionally significant elements of the microcirculation in such a way as to accurately predict, i.e. fit, all of the available data.

MECHANISMS OF TRANSPORT ACROSS THE CAPILLARY ENDOTHELIAL BARRIER

There are two routes for solute escape from the capillary blood into the interstitium. Tracers injected into the arterial inflow can escape through the clefts between endothelial cells or enter endothelial cells by traversing the cell membrane. Those tracers that bind to the cell membrane can also be removed from the blood without any transport. For many substrates there are facilitating transporters on the endothelial cell membranes (see Reference 7 for a discussion of the relationship between PS and parameters of facilitated transport.) For adenosine in the heart there is a special transporter that can be blocked by dipyridamole. Passive diffusional transport through the clefts is unaffected by competitors or blockers (6, 14). In experiments such as that shown in Figure 1, ^{14}C-adenosine, ^{3}H-AraH (an inert, nontransported adenosine analog), and ^{125}I-albumin were injected simultaneously into the inflow to isolated perfused hearts and skeletal muscle. Despite the fact that adenosine and AraH have the same molecular weight, the extraction of adenosine was more than twice that of AraH. Since AraH traverses only the water-filled clefts between endothelial cells, this indicates that adenosine is transported across the plasmalemma of the endothelial cell as well as through the aqueous channels between cells. The blocking effect of dipyridamole showed that the cellular entry was carrier-mediated. When dipyridamole was administered the adenosine curve had the same shape as that of AraH; both behaved as inert hydrophilic solutes traversing only the clefts.

Analyses of adenosine indicator dilution curves from heart and skeletal muscle indicate that under normal circumstances the flux via the endothelial luminal transporter is about twice that through the clefts between the cells. This high flux is still not high enough to explain completely the magnitude of the accumulation of tracer adenosine in endothelial cells observed by Nees et al (26). However, it is sufficiently high to explain the very rapid appearance of adenosine metabolites in the outflow under conditions in which no deamination occurs in the vascular space (14).

In skeletal muscle studies Gorman et al (14) observed that after tracer-labeled adenosine was injected into the inflow the peaks of the outflow dilution curves for tracer-labeled metabolites, inosine and hypoxanthine, were almost coincident with the peak of that for tracer adenosine. In the case of inosine, an ectodeaminase may be present on the luminal plasmalemma of the endothelial cell; the formation of hypoxanthine cannot be so readily explained since there has been no suggestion that an extracellular form of the enzyme could be involved. The appearance of these metabolites therefore suggests that the metabolism is intracellular. The time it takes for metabolites to emerge from an extravascular volume should have caused some delay, but very little was observed, which is in accord with the small volume of the endothelial cells. (The volume is estimated by multiplying the capillary surface area and the endothelial cell thickness. In skeletal muscle this value is about $50 \, \text{cm}^2/\text{g} \times 0.2 \times 10^{-4}$ cm, or about 0.1% of the muscle volume. In heart the value is ten times larger, i.e. about 1%.) The rapid appearance of metabolites also suggests that there is no significant binding of either inosine or hypoxanthine within the cells, which would have resulted in a larger delay. The magnitude of the outflow curves for inosine and hypoxanthine provides a measure of what fraction of the adenosine was deaminated rather than being incorporated into adenine nucleotide. In the first few seconds about 10–15% of the tracer emerges on inosine and another 2–4% as hypoxanthine.

The modeling analysis can account for the chemical reactions occurring within endothelial and parenchymal cells. Model solutions with permeabilities that fit adenosine curves show very early emergence of inosine and hypoxanthine, with the peaks of their curves lagging only a small fraction of a second behind the peak of the adenosine curve. This result shows that the rapid appearance of products does not require an ectodeaminase on the luminal surface, but that endothelial cell uptake, intracellular deamination to inosine and hydrolysis to hypoxanthine, followed by outward transport of these two metabolites into the effluent plasmas are fast enough to explain quantitatively the appearance of both metabolites.

The form of the effluent curves for inosine and hypoxanthine show early peaks like adenosine. This observation implies that their concentrations inside the cell have transient peaks, and that the production slacks off quickly. This differs from the lung data of Hellewell & Pearson (15), which showed a prolonged increase in the release of both metabolites. Our modeling did account for adenosine phosphorylation to AMP. The rapid incorporation of adenosine into nucleotide, which reduces intraendothelial free adenosine levels, explains the brief peaking of the inosine and hypoxanthine curves. [Incorporation of adenosine into adenine-nucleotide was observed by Nees et al (26) and by Pearson et al (27) in monolayer endothelial cell cultures.] Single pass adenosine extraction was about 75%, while the extraction of AraH was only about 25% (Figure 1); given that 25% of adenosine traverses the clefts along with the AraH, the 50% difference is accounted for by adenosine entering the endothelial cells via the luminal surface.

Figure 1 shows that the four-region axially distributed model can fit the dilution curves for adenosine, even with the constraints imposed by the need to fit the albumin and AraH dilution curves. The combination of the microsphere data, defining flow heterogeneity, and the albumin curve delimits the vascular dispersion of the adenosine and AraH. The form of the AraH curve further constrains the interpretation of the adenosine curve by fixing the estimates of the permeability of the aqueous clefts between endothelial cells and of the interstitial volume of distribution for adenosine. However, not all the curves fit so well: A recurring problem is that the tails of model curves are often above the observed adenosine curves, which indicates that the model did not adequately account for the adenosine uptake and retention in the slower transit time pathways. The tail is almost insensitive to the luminal endothelial PS (2), and the close fit of the upslope and peak provides assurance that the relative importance of diffusion via the paracellular pathway and transport into endothelial cells is reasonably well evaluated. Even so, such misfitting demonstrates incompleteness or incorrectness of the model, and demands that the model be developed further. Better heterogeneity models (for regional volumes and PS's as well as for flows) are needed, as well as better geometric descriptions of the microvasculature and, in this particular case where a constant PS_c was used, a concentration-dependent PS_c in accord with a facilitated transport mechanism.

ESTIMATION OF TRANSPORTER KINETICS WITH INDICATOR DILUTION

The multiple indicator dilution technique was designed for use in steady-state situations. The formal requirements are for stationary (steady flow and distribution) and linear (transport rates unaffected by changes in concentration) conditions. High frequency fluctuations in flow are not a significant problem for estimating membrane transport rates of tracers; Bassingthwaighte et al (4) found that so long as flow oscillations were so frequent that at least several occurred during the time of passage of the main part of the bolus (usually 8–20 sec), the estimates of flows and mean transit times had little error. Explorations with a blood-tissue exchange model that allowed fluctuating flows suggested that for substances with permeabilities similar to that of sucrose in the heart the rate of equilibration between blood and tissue was unaffected by fluctuations in flow or even intermittent emptying of the capillaries (5).

The other condition, linearity, raises more difficult issues. There is no likelihood of an artifactual change in PS when one uses radioactive tracer techniques in which the specific activity of the tracer is very high and the chemical concentration is constant. However, there are two situations in which problems occur: (a) when the chemical levels are changed by the injection of tracer, and (b) when one wishes to characterize saturable transport kinetics using the indicator dilution approach. In the first instance, an observed rate constant for exchange will be less than in the steady state because of self-competition (between additional nontracer and tracer). In the second instance, when the relationship between transport rate and concentration over the whole range is needed, a set of experiments can be designed to elicit the desired information.

The Steady-State Tracer Bolus Technique

The determination of the endothelial luminal surface conductance (PS_{ecl}) over a range of substrate concentrations can be accomplished by a series of experiments each of which fulfills the requirement of stationary, linear conditions. The technique involves the use of tracer-labeled substrates with high specific activity in the multiple indicator dilution experiment in the presence of a set of different fixed concentration levels of the nontracer substrate. At low concentrations of the nontracer mother substance, tracer access to the transporter is unimpeded and PS_{ecl} is maximal. At higher concentrations of mother substance the competition reduces the observed PS_{ecl} for tracer. In order to determine the form of the relationship the investigator must perform indicator dilution studies at concentrations well below and well above the K_m. Transport via other mechanisms must be either identified or eliminated from consideration. Such experiments provide the "raw data" for another level of analysis, namely, that at which we determine whether an observed PS-concentration relationship can be well fitted by a model for transporter kinetics. Higher-order binding will result in steeper slopes in the mid-portion of the curve. Information about the effects of competitors and inhibitors is also necessary for more detailed evaluation, and may reveal further complexities such as sidedness or asymmetry of the transporter (e.g. 17). Many transporters exhibit countertransport, in which a rise in concentration on one side of the membrane increases flux from the opposite side toward the first side. While first order Michaelis-Menten kinetics have been considered (12, 21), no blood-tissue exchange model that accounts for bidirectional, saturable transport with countertransport has been published.

If a substance is consumed in the tissue, then at steady-state the nontracer substrate level will diminish along the capillary. In this circumstance one must account for the rise in effective PS between inflow and outflow. Goresky et al (12) developed expressions suitable for galactose uptake in the liver (11), where there is no capillary barrier. Their expressions are suitable for a first-order Michaelis-Menten transporter in the special case in which the complexed and uncomplexed transporter have equal permeabilities, there is passive transport in parallel, and there is no return flux. Goresky et al (13) applied this model to a kinetically similar situation, namely ethanol consumption within the liver. There is no effective barrier at the hepatocyte plasmalemma for ethanol, and the first rate-limiting reaction within the cell is a first-order process, which means that it is analogous to a saturable transporter at the membrane. At present, in order to account for the transporter characteristics in the analysis of each dilution curve we must search for two parameters, the K_m and V_{max}, instead of one, the PS. Although this appears to be a disadvantage, it can be offset by acquiring additional data (the concentrations of the substrate in the inflow and outflow) which are often needed anyway for the interpretation.

Transients in Tracer and Mother Substance

Another approach has been taken by Linehan & Dawson (21). They worked from the same basic premises as Goresky (i.e. a Michaelis-Menten transporter acting across a single barrier with no back diffusion of tracer from the extravascular region), which is equivalent to modeling an infinitely large extravascular space that dilutes away the tracer entering the space. Tracer-labeled and nontracer prostaglandin were simultaneously injected into the pulmonary artery, along with a reference (tracer-labeled albumin), to collect a sequence of outflow samples in the usual fashion. This is known colloquially as the "bolus sweep" technique; the concentration of mother substance is low at the initial portion of the curve, high at the peak, then low again at the tail, so the effective PS of the transporter changes from moment to moment as the bolus sweeps through a wide range of concentrations while passing through the capillary.

In the early applications of this technique (10, 21, 22) the concentrations of the nontracer mother substrate were not measured, so the accuracy of the estimates of K_m and V_{max} were questioned because the actual degree of dilution between inflow and outflow was unknown. Malcorps et al (24) measured the chemical and tracer concentrations, and found almost a twofold difference in K_m between the bolus sweep and the steady state technique described above. The bolus sweep technique has the virtues of providing estimates of K_m and

V_{max} with each intraarterial injection of a set of tracers, and of avoiding the unphysiologic effects of prolonged infusion at concentrations above the K_m. In their studies of PGE_1 and serotonin their model solutions fit only the first 4–10 sec of the dilution curves, namely the upslope portions, since back diffusion of tracer from tissue into the blood was not accounted for. In their most recent study, Linehan et al (21a) showed that the model solution did fit the whole of pulmonary outflow dilution curves for tracer-labeled BPAP, an angiotensin analog that is hydrolyzed at the endothelial surface by angiotensin-converting enzyme and whose products are immediately released into the blood. Linehan et al model flow heterogeneity assuming a dispersed input function and random coupling between large vessels and capillaries, as we do, and estimate the capillary transit time distribution from the dilution curves, as did Rose & Goresky (28). Since hydrolysis is a nonlinear, concentration-dependent process, this result is persuasive that the approach is a good one. To document the method completely we would recommend measuring the flow heterogeneity as well as the chemical concentrations in each sample.

Use of Small Reference Solutes

Yudilevich & de Rose (33) explored the rates of transport of glucose and amino acids across the blood-brain barrier. In that situation the intravascular reference tracer can be any inert hydrophilic solute for which there is not a special transporter. The blood-brain barrier is composed of endothelial cells joined together circumferentially by tight junctions that allow no passage of hydrophilic molecules by passive diffusion between cells. Thus the size of the reference molecule is of little consequence, and sucrose and albumin serve equally well. The instantaneous extraction of a transported solute gives a measure of the endothelial transport alone. These investigators did not fit the model to the data, but used the historically interesting technique of Martin & Yudilevich (25) in which correction for back-diffusion is attempted by a "back-extrapolation" to estimate extraction.

This experimental technique was employed by Hellewell & Pearson (15) in their study on adenosine uptake by pulmonary endothelium. They used bolus injections of tracer sucrose and adenosine because sucrose remains extracellular and the endothelial uptake of adenosine can thus be measured by comparison with it. The problem is that both sucrose and adenosine escape through the clefts between the cells; the endothelial permeability-surface area (PS_{ecl}) for adenosine cannot be calculated directly from its extraction relative to sucrose unless the two tracers have the same cleft permeability. Sucrose ($M_r = 342$) would be expected to permeate the clefts between endothelial cells less readily than does adenosine ($M_r = 287$), so the difference between the two extractions would represent endothelial uptake plus some excess escape of adenosine into the interstitium via the clefts. However, Hellewell & Pearson

(15) found that high concentrations of dipyridamole resulted in the adenosine curves that were superimposed on the sucrose curves. This suggests that diffusion coefficients for sucrose and adenosine are nearly identical, in which case they could indeed estimate PS_{ecl}. In their particular studies error due to failure to use a precisely analogous reference solute does not appear to be great, but such errors are potentially large whenever the reference and test solute do not have identical conductances through the aqueous channels between cells.

This "uptake" technique was extended by Yudilevich & colleagues (34, 35), who used only a small inert extracellular solute (usually sucrose) as a reference marker and no intravascular reference in an attempt to measure uptake by parenchymal cells. The advantages of reducing the number of radioactive tracers used simultaneously are offset by the restriction this places on the conditions under which one can accurately estimate parameter values. In the brain sucrose is restricted to the intravascular space, but it is not in tissues with open clefts between endothelial cells. When applied to the estimation of permeability-surface area products of parenchymal cells (PS_{pc}) the method gives correct answers if the permeability of the capillary wall is extremely high. If it is not, PS_{pc} is underestimated, usually to a considerable extent. Our calculations with a two-barrier model show that the capillary permeability-surface area product should be higher than 100 ml g^{-1} min^{-1} to have less than a few percent error in PS_{pc}. Even when passive capillary PS is as high as 10 ml g^{-1} min^{-1} their technique gives a severalfold error in PS_{pc}. Therefore, the values of PS_{pc} obtained by Yudilevich & Mann (34) are probably underestimated significantly, but by exactly how much is not known since estimates of PS_g were not obtained.

SUMMARY

Mechanisms of transport of substrates and small solutes across the endothelial lining of the capillaries include passive diffusion (through clefts between cells or across the plasmalemma) and transporter-mediated flux across the plasmalemma. Because the transport rates are typically high, the multiple indicator dilution technique is usually the method of choice, as it provides the high temporal resolution required. In the simplest version of this technique, a test solute is injected into the inflow simultaneously with reference solutes that are restricted to intravascular and extracellular space. Interpretation of the resulting data requires models; the most precise approach is to fit the model solutions to the data. When appropriate combinations of indicators and sufficiently complex models (those that account for flow heterogeneity, arteriovenous gradients, passive and saturable transport, reaction, and diffusion in multicomponent systems) are used the transporters can be characterized. Features such as the rapidity of intracellular reaction can also be revealed by this technique.

ACKNOWLEDGMENT

The authors appreciate the assistance of Malcolm McKay in the preparation of this manuscript.

Literature Cited

1. Bassingthwaighte, J. B. 1974. A concurrent flow model for extraction during transcapillary passage. *Circ. Res.* 35: 483–503
2. Bassingthwaighte, J. B., Chaloupka, M. 1984. Sensitivity functions in the estimation of parameters of cellular exchange. *Fed. Proc.* 43:180–84
3. Bassingthwaighte, J. B., Goresky, C. A. 1984. Modeling in the analysis of solute and water exchange in the microvasculature. *Handbook of Physiology, Sec. 2*, ed. E. M. Renkin, C. C. Michel, 4:549–626. Bethesda, MD: Am. Physiol. Soc.
4. Bassingthwaighte, J. B., Knopp, T. J., and Anderson, D. U. 1970. Flow estimation by indicator dilution (bolus injection): Reduction of errors due to time-averaged sampling during unsteady flow. *Circ. Res.* 27:277–91
5. Bassingthwaighte, J. B., Knopp, T. J., Hazelrig, J. B. 1970. A concurrent flow model for capillary-tissue exchanges. *Capillary Permeability (Alfred Benzon Symp. II)*, ed. C. Crone, N. A. Lassen, pp. 60–80. New York: Academic
6. Bassingthwaighte, J. B., Sparks, H. V. Jr., Chan, I. S., DeWitt, D. F., Gorman, M. W. 1985. Modeling of transendothelial transport. *Fed. Proc.* 44:2623–26
7. Bassingthwaighte, J. B., Wang, C. Y., Gorman, M., DeWitt, D., Chan, I. S., Sparks, H. V. 1985. Endothelial regulation of agonist and metabolite concentrations in the interstitium. *Carrier-Mediated Transport of Solutes from Blood to Tissue*, ed. D. L. Yudilevich, G. E. Mann, pp. 185–97. London: Pitman
8. Chinard, F. P., Vosburgh, G. J., Enns, T. 1955. Transcapillary exchange of water and of other substances in certain organs of the dog. *Am. J. Physiol.* 183: 221–34
9. Crone, C. 1963. The permeability of capillaries in various organs as determined by the use of the "indicator diffusion" method. *Acta Physiol. Scand.* 58:292–305
10. Gillis, C. N., Cronau, L. H., Mandel, S., Hammond, G. L. 1979. Indicator dilution measurement of 5-hydroxytryptamine clearance by human lung. *J. Appl. Physiol.* 46:1178–83
11. Goresky, C. S., Bach, G. G., Nadeau, B. E. 1973. On the uptake of materials by the intact liver—the transport and net re-

moval of galactose. *J. Clin. Invest.* 53:991–1009
12. Goresky, C. A., Bach, G. G., Rose, C. P. 1983. The effects of saturating metabolic uptake on space profiles and tracer kinetics. *Am. J. Physiol.* 244: G215–32
13. Goresky, C. A., Gordon, E. R., Bach, G. G. 1983. Uptake of monohydric alcohols by liver: Demonstration of a shared enzymatic shape. *Am. J. Physiol.* 244: G198–G214
14. Gorman, M. W., Bassingthwaighte, J. B., Olsson, R. A., Sparks, H. V. 1985. Endothelial cell uptake of adenosine in canine skeletal muscle. *Am. J. Physiol.* Submitted for publication
15. Hellewell, P. G., Pearson, J. D. 1983. Metabolism of circulating adenosine by the porcine isolated perfused lung. *Circ. Res.* 53:1–7
16. King, R. B., Bassingthwaighte, J. B., Hales, J. R. S., Rowell, L. B. 1985. Stability of heterogeneity of myocardial blood flow in normal awake baboons. *Circ. Res.* 57:285–95
17. Krupka, R. M., Deves, R. 1979. The membrane valve: A consequence of asymmetrical inhibition of membrane carriers.: I. Equilibrating transport systems. *Biochim. Biophys. Acta* 550:77–91
18. Kuikka, J., Levin, M., Bassingthwaighte, J. B. 1985. Multiple tracer dilution estimates of D- and 2-deoxy-D-glucose uptake by the heart. *Am. J. Physiol.* In press
19. Lenhoff, A. M., Lightfoot, E. N. 1982. The effects of axial diffusion and permeability barriers on the transient response of tissue cylinders. I. Solution in transform space. *J. Theor. Biol.* 97:663–77
20. Levin, M., Kuikka, J., Bassingthwaighte, J. B. 1980. Sensitivity analysis in optimization of time-distributed parameters for a coronary circulation model. *Med. Prog. Technol.* 7:119–24
21. Linehan, J. H., Dawson, C. A. 1979. A kinetic model of prostaglandin metabolism in the lung. *J. Appl. Physiol.* 47:404–11
21a. Linehan, J. H., Dawson, C. A., Rickaby, D. A., Bronikowski, T. A., Gillis, C. N., Pitt, B. R. 1985. Pulmonary endothelial angiotensin-converting enzyme kinetics. See Ref. 7

22. Linehan, J. H., Dawson, C. A., Wagner-Weber, V. M. 1981. Prostaglandin E₁ uptake by isolated cat lungs perfused with physiological salt solution. *J. Appl. Physiol.* 50:428–34

23. Little, S. E., Bassingthwaighte, J. B. 1983. Plasma-soluble marker for intraorgan regional flows. *Am. J. Physiol.* 245:H707–12

24. Malcorps, C. M., Dawson, C. A., Linehan, J. H., Bronikowski, T. A., Rickaby, D. A., et al. 1984. Lung serotonin uptake kinetics from indicator dilution and constant infusion methods. *J. Appl. Physiol.* 57:720–30

25. Martin, P., Yudilevich, D. L. 1964. A theory for the quantification of transcapillary exchange by tracer-dilution curves. *Am. J. Physiol.* 207:162–68

26. Nees, S., Herzog, V., Bock, M., Gerlach, E. 1984. Vasoactive adenosine-perfused through isolated hearts is selectively trapped within the coronary endothelium. *Fed. Proc.* 43:900

27. Pearson, J. D., Carleton, J. S., Hutchings, A., Gordon, J. L. 1978. Uptake and metabolism of adenosine by pig aortic endothelial and smooth muscle cells in culture. *Biochem. J.* 170:265–71

28. Rose, C. P., Goresky, C. A. 1976. Vasomotor control of capillary transit time heterogeneity in the canine coronary circulation. *Circ. Res.* 39:541–54

29. Rose, C. P., Goresky, C. A., Bach, G. G. 1977. The capillary and sarcolemmal barriers in the heart: An exploration of labeled water permeability. *Circ. Res.* 41:515–33

30. Ryan, J. W. 1983. Assay of peptidase and protease enzymes *in vivo. Biochem. Pharmacol.* 32:2127–37

31. Ryan, U. S. 1982. Structural basis for metabolic activity. *Ann. Rev. Physiol.* 44:223–39

32. Sangren, W. C., Sheppard, C. W. 1953. A mathematical derivation of the exchange of a labeled substance between a liquid flowing in a vessel and an external compartment. *Bull. Math. Biophys.* 15:387–94

33. Yudilevich, D. L., de Rose, N. 1971. Blood-brain transfer of glucose and other molecules measured by rapid indicator dilution. *Am. J. Physiol.* 220:841–46

34. Yudilevich, D. L., Mann, G. E. 1982. Unidirectional uptake of substrates at the blood side of secretory epithelia: stomach, salivary gland, pancreas. *Fed. Proc.* 41:3045–53

35. Yudilevich, D. E., Sepúlveda, F. V., Bustamante, J. C., Mann, G. E. 1979. A comparison of amino acid transport and ouabain binding in brain endothelium and salivary epithelium studied *in vivo* by rapid paired-tracer dilution. *J. Neural Transm.* 15:15–27

Ann. Rev. Physiol. 1986 48:335–45

ENDOTHELIAL CELL METABOLISM OF BIOGENIC AMINES

David Shepro and Bernadette Dunham

Departments of Biology and Surgery, Boston University, 2 Cummington Street, Boston, Massachusetts 02215

PROLOGUE

Endothelial cell "housekeeping" functions are regulated by specific amines, and with only the rarest of exceptions these amines are cleared, sequestered, and released or catabolized by intimal and microvascular endothelial cells. From 1980 to 1984, approximately 1300 articles were published with titles including the expression *biogenic amine*. If you add to this prudent total another conservative statistic, that the word *endothelial* or *endothelium* in the same span of time appeared in some form or other in over 5500 article titles, it is not unreasonable to anticipate an impressive literature on biogenic amine metabolism by endothelial cells. The truth of the matter is that there are only about 270 articles with both descriptors in the title.

The emphasis of this review is on catecholamines, serotonin (5-hydroxytryptamine, 5-HT), and histamine, which are cleared and metabolized to varying degrees by endothelium. Some data is also provided on acetylcholine (ACh) metabolism because of its involvement in the obligatory role ascribed to certain intimal endothelial cells and those cells regulating endogenous polyamines.

BACKGROUND

Endothelium

It is an axiom in endothelial cell research that metabolism may vary not only between intimal and microvessel cells, but from organ to organ, and even within a given microvascular bed. For example, the pulmonary microvascula-

335

0066-4278/86/0315-0335$02.00

ture does not significantly metabolize prostacyclin (18) via 15-hydroxyprosta-glandin dehydrogenase. However, when nonpulmonary vessels such as the aorta are perfused or incubated in vitro with prostacyclin, the fatty acid is degraded to 6,15-ketometabolites via 15-hydroxyprostaglandin dehydrogenase (61). Also, rat cardiac microvessel endothelial cells do not appear to synthesize an inhibitor of plasminogen activators (56) that has been identified in aortic intimal endothelium (36). Hence, in this review the specific type of endothelial cell studied will be identified whenever possible. For additional endothelial cell metabolic characteristics, please see the recent review entitled "The Physiology and Biochemistry of the Vascular Wall Endothelium" in *The Handbook of Physiology* (54).

Acetylcholine

The history of receptors and ACh is closely tied to the studies of Langley (34) and Dixon (17), which date back to the first decade of the twentieth century. The amine is formed by acetylation of the hydroxyl group of choline with acetyl coenzyme A in the presence of the enzyme choline acetyltransferase. The degradation of ACh with acetylcholinesterase quickly hydrolyzes ACh to choline and acetic acid.

Catecholamines

It was almost 100 years ago that Oliver & Schafer observed pressor effects with adrenal gland extracts (42). Today we know these compounds as catechol-amines, a group of agonists derived from 3,4-dihydroxyphenylamine. Three catecholamines, norepinephrine, epinephrine, and dopamine, present in mam-mals are so called because of the hydroxy substitution at the 3 and 4 positions of the benzene ring. Broadly speaking, catechols stimulate muscle tissue, liberate fatty acids, increase gluconeogenesis, act upon the nervous system, and mod-ulate pituitary and other endocrine secretions. There is recent evidence to suggest that specific catecholamines also affect cytoskeletal contractile ele-ments of nonmuscle tissue, such as endothelium. Norepinephrine and epinephrine promote the assembly of *stress fibers,* bundles of actin and other contractile proteins, which have been identified in the cytoskeleton of cultured bovine aortic and retinal microvessel endothelial cells (55, 64). Interestingly, dopamine's effect is opposite that of norepinephrine: it decreases stress fiber numbers (64). Catecholamines for the most part are metabolized by catechol-O-methyl transferase, which is located in the cytoplasm, and/or monoamine oxidase (MAO), located on the mitochondria (50).

Histamine

The principal sites of synthesis of histamine or β-aminoethylimidazole are the tissue mast cell and the basophil. The predominant histamine action is mediated by two distinct classes of receptors, an H_1 receptor, classically antagonized by a wide variety of antihistamines, and a structurally different H_2 receptor, which is blocked by specific drugs such as cimetidine. The mechanism of histamine action on endothelium is generally described as that of isotonic contraction. Recent reports suggest that postcapillary venule endothelial functional apposition may be a function of stress fiber numbers (57, 64, 65) and their isometric contraction (26). Histamine has been shown to disassemble endothelial stress fibers, and the stimulus-coupled response appears to be receptor mediated (64). Hence, histamine-induced loss of the endothelial barrier function may be a consequence of decreasing stress fiber isometric contraction.

The degradation of histamine is catalyzed by the enzyme imidazole-N-methyltransferase (INMT), which converts histamine to N-methylhistamine by ring methylation. This product is then further catabolized to N-methylimidazole acetic acid under the catalytic action of MAO. Diamine oxidase (DAO) a group of enzymes otherwise known as *histaminase*) may also degrade histamine to the imidazole acetic acid by oxidative deamination.

Serotonin

This monoamine, found in vertebrates, invertebrates, and plants, is truly one of nature's ubiquitous molecules, but in spite of its widespread occurrence its function in mammalian circulation is still obscure. Serotonin is an agonist in search of a vascular target. First identified by Ludwig & Schmidt (37), who over a century ago observed 5-HT's vasoconstrictive action, this amine is currently believed to be involved in the motility of and within animal cells. For example, we have shown that 5-HT inhibits cultured aortic endothelial cell motility as measured by the gold chloride tracking assay (6). We also reported that exogenous 5-HT reverses the loss of microvessel structural integrity associated with severe thrombocytopenia (57). We postulate that the cytoprotective action of 5-HT is related to its action in promoting stress fiber assembly (64).

Serotonin is synthesized by the hydroxylation of L-tryptophan in a two-step reaction, which occurs principally in the enterochromaffin cells of the gastrointestinal tract and in the central nervous system. The prime 5-HT metabolite, 5-hydroxyindoleacetic acid (5-HIAA), results from the oxidative deamination of 5-HT to an aldehyde in the presence of MAO. At least two types of MAO activity have been identified: type A, which acts principally upon 5-HT and norepinephrine, and type B, which deaminates phenylethylamine and benzylamine (63).

Polyamines

Several thousand works exist that are related to the biology of putrescine, spermidine, spermine, and other polyamines. Nonetheless, the physiological importance of these amines remains a conundrum. Because of their polycationic character, polyamines have an exceedingly high affinity for acidic constituents, which may provide a clue to their physiological function. In mammalian tissue polyamines are derived principally from L-ornithine through the rate-limiting action of ornithine decarboxylase. Metabolism of polyamines may include a putrescine cycle in which spermidine and spermine are converted to putrescine by acetyltransferase and polyamine oxidase. Putrescine is converted to gamma-aminobutyric by acetylation. Enzyme mechanisms such as the oxidation of terminal amino groups by amine oxidases have also been shown.

METABOLISM

The uptake and metabolism of vasoactive biogenic amines from the circulation is essential for the maintenance of homeostasis in the vascular system. The pulmonary endothelial cell is the cell type that is most likely to be responsible for sequestering and/or inactivating many biogenic amines. With the advent of tissue culture techniques, the metabolic role played by endothelium can be directly demonstrated.

Much of the inactivation of biogenic amines has been shown to occur in the lung (1, 2, 20, 24, 28, 47, 60, 66). Isolated, perfused lungs remove 5-HT, norepinephrine, and phenylethylamine from the perfusate in a single passage, whereas levels of epinephrine and histamine remain largely unchanged (23). Strum & Junod (60) demonstrated via autoradiography that [^{3}H]-5-HT is localized in the capillaries and in large vessel endothelium of the lung, provided the perfusate contains a monoamine oxidase inhibitor to prevent intracellular degradation of the amine. Within the lung, 5-HT is transported by a saturable, high affinity receptor system (1). The process is inhibited by imipramine or by removal of Na^+ from the perfusate (1, 28).

One of the first attempts at demonstrating directly that endothelial cells can transport and metabolize vasoactive amines was made by our laboratory in 1975. Using primary cultures of bovine aortic endothelium, we found that [^{14}C]-5-HT uptake was partially inhibited by imipramine (10^{-4} M) (53). Similar results were reported by Junod & Ody (29) using freshly isolated porcine aortic or pulmonary artery endothelium. Pearson et al (44, 45) studied 5-HT uptake in cultures of porcine endothelium and reported a saturable component with an apparent $K_m = 1$ μM. However, the observation that 5-HT is highly unstable in culture medium (43) was crucial to these studies. Stringent precautions must be taken to minimize nonenzymic oxidation. Olverman et al (43) did not find any evidence for a specific, high affinity uptake process for 5-HT in either cultured porcine aortic endothelium or smooth muscle cells. Their data suggest that cells from large vessels may not share the same capacity for transporting and/or metabolizing amines as that possessed by the lung microvasculature. Upon reinvestigation, our laboratory reported again that cultured bovine aortic endothelium do not exhibit a saturable 5-HT uptake system (8).

A recent cytochemical study utilizing rat pulmonary artery endothelium in culture has shown that uptake of 5-HT is antagonized by either imipramine or ouabain (31). Monolayers of cultured cells were treated according to the Hillarp-Falck fluorescence technique (10) and studied cytofluorimetrically to estimate intracellular 5-HT. Uptake of 5-HT was observed after inhibition of MAO and was antagonized with either imipramine or ouabain, which suggests that this amine was taken up via an active pump mechanism. Autoradiographic studies have indicated that the endothelial cells of pulmonary arterioles and capillaries are predominantly responsible for 5-HT uptake (11, 60). A recent study using cultured cerebrovascular endothelial cells found that these cells can clear and metabolize 5-HT and can synthesize 5-HT from its precursor L-tryptophan (39). Robinson-White et al (49) further reported 5-HT uptake by capillary endothelium from rat adipose, and their data reveal that 5-HT uptake in these cells has a saturable component with an apparent $K_m = 0.3$ μM.

The literature does not provide a unified mechanism for endothelial cell clearance of 5-HT. This can be explained by variations in experimental design and procedure: First, the most critical difference is whether microvessel endothelial cells or large vessel endothelia were used in the in vitro assays; second, some experiments utilized endothelial cells in suspension, others worked with primary cultures, and still others used subcultures; and third, tissue culture techniques varied from laboratory to laboratory. In addition, comparisons between in vivo and in vitro systems or among species leave room for variation. And finally, the paucity of experimentation makes fully characterizing 5-HT clearance a difficult and perhaps questionable task.

Other amines are removed from the circulation by the pulmonary endothelium. Phenylethylamine is rapidly cleared and deaminated by the action of MAO (63), and norepinephrine (NE) is removed during a single circuit through the lung by a carrier-mediated process (27, 41). The uptake of NE has been examined in endothelial cells of pig pulmonary artery, aorta, and lung slices (29). The data obtained in the studies using lung slices only provide evidence for a saturable uptake mechanism that is sensitive to cold, imipramine, and Na^+-free medium. Histamine deamination occurs via DAO, and methylation occurs via histamine methyltransferase (HMT); both enzymes are present in the cytosolic fraction of cell homogenates (3, 52). Karnushina et al (30), using microvessels isolated from guinea pig cerebral cortex, reported that H_2 receptors were involved in the activation of adenylate cyclase within the capillary fraction. Robinson-White et al (48) demonstrated high HMT activity in microvascular endothelial cell preparations from guinea pig perirenal fat pad, heart ventricles, and brain cortex, but the same preparations from rat had no detectable HMT activity. Diamine oxidase, in contrast, was found in all preparations from both guinea pig and rat. Rabbit intimal endothelial cell homogenates deaminate biogenic amines most rapidly in the following decreasing order of activity: phenylamine > tyramine > 5-HT > dopamine > NE (50).

The synthesis of polyamines by endothelial cells and the fates of those products have not been studied to any extent. D'Amore & Shepro (12) were the first to demonstrate the presence of ornithine decarboxylase (ODC), the rate limiting enzyme in polyamine synthesis, in cultured bovine aortic endothelium. They also observed that serum, serotonin, and thrombin stimulated ODC synthesis. Since these investigators had shown previously that these agonists also produced a rapid calcium influx of as much as 24 times the control levels (13), the effect of calcium channel blockers on ODC induction was investigated. The experimental results indicate that calcium is required to initiate ODC synthesis and to maintain ODC levels when cultured endothelial cells are at equilibration with the medium (14). We have unpublished data that show that blocking ODC synthesis with retinol significantly decreases stress fiber numbers in cultured bovine aortic endothelial cells. However, a cell regulatory function for polyamines, such as a role as second messengers, has not been documented for endothelial cells in culture or in vivo.

RECEPTOR MEDIATION

The presence of β-adrenergic-responsive adenylate cyclase activity in cultured endothelial cells provides indirect evidence that a β-adrenoceptor exists in endothelial cells (7, 25, 38, 40, 51). Through the development of a new iodinated radioligand, (^{125}I)-iodocyanopindolol, Steinberg et al (59) directly identified β-adrenoceptors in cultured bovine aortic endothelial cells. They reported that specific binding at 37°C was saturable, stable, and reversible. Moreover, there was a single class of binding site (21,500 ± 2,900 sites/cell) with an equilibrium dissociation constant (K_d) of 109 ± 26 pM. The presence of β-adrenoceptors and an adenylate cyclase system in endothelial cells strengthens the hypothesis that endothelial cells actively mediate the physiologic response of the vasculature to adrenergic stimulation.

The physiological activities of histamine are mediated by at least two different types of receptors (4, 5, 9). Simionescu et al (58) have directly detected histamine receptors in situ and have mapped their topographical distribution using conjugates of ferritin covalently coupled to histamine (for both types of histamine receptors), 2-pyridylethylamine (for H_1 receptors), or 4-methylhistamine (for H_2 receptors). Their data revealed that the density of histamine binding sites was characteristically high in venules, but much lower in arterioles and veins. Moreover, the conjugates were localized to restricted areas of the endothelial cell, including regions rich in filaments and near endothelial junctions. These findings indicate that venular endothelium contains mainly H_2 receptors.

Receptor binding studies for 5-HT in neurological tissues and nonendothelial cells have led to two subclasses of putative serotonin receptor sites: 5-HT$_1$

binding sites (saturable binding sites on brain membrane preparations that label [^{3}H]-5-HT with high affinity at nanomolar concentrations, and which are antagonized by compounds having an indole-nucleus) and 5-HT$_2$ binding sites ([^{3}H]-spiperone-labelled binding sites that are distinct from dopamine receptor sites, and to which all known 5-HT antagonists belonging to different chemical classes bind with nanomolar affinity) (46). A physiological or pharmacological role, however, has not been demonstrated for the 5-HT$_1$ binding site (35). Although large vessel vasomotor responses to the presence of 5-HT are well documented, 5-HT binding sites have not been identified conclusively on intimal endothelial cells, either in vivo or in vitro.

FACTORS INFLUENCING METABOLISM

Oxygen therapy is required in many clinical situations, but it carries the risk of tissue damage, particularly to the lungs (33). Hyperoxia has been shown to decrease several pulmonary endothelial cell functions including: (a) conversion of angiotensin I to angiotensin II [a reduction in this conversion has been shown to be an early biochemical marker of cell injury (62)] and (b) the active removal of both 5-HT and NE (19). Lahr et al (33), however, reported that the lung was capable of recovering from moderate oxygen-induced injury (exposure of mice to 100% oxygen for 72 hr), as indicated by pulmonary deposition of [^{3}H]-5-HT. This activity was significantly elevated during the period of oxygen exposure, but returned to control levels following 72 hr of air recovery.

Anoxia, on the other hand, has been shown to abolish the relaxant effect of ACh (16) and to increase the contractile response to NE in the canine femoral artery (15); both of these effects are endothelial cell–dependent. The observation that increased contractions caused by anoxia during exposure to NE depended upon the presence of functional endothelium has led to the suggestion that anoxia interrupts the production (by endothelial cells) of a vasodilator signal.

Using a diabetic rat model, Fortes et al (21) demonstrated that responses to permeability factors such as histamine and bradykinin were impaired in rat mesenteric microvessels. Twentyfold higher concentrations of both substances were required to antagonize the vasoconstrictor effect of NE on mesenteric microvessels. Furthermore, Fortes and his coworkers, using isolated diabetic rat aortae (with an intact endothelium), noted that the median effective concentrations of NE were greatly increased. These observations led these researchers to hypothesize that the observed changes resulted from an alteration of endothelial cell function due to a relative lack of insulin. Garcia Leme et al (22) reported that exposure to permeability factors readily induced interendothelial openings in the venules of control rats, whereas this effect was rarely observed in diabetic animals. These findings suggest a role for insulin as a modulator of endothelial cell functions.

EPILOGUE

Autoregulation may be the *modus operandi* for altering microvascular permeability by way of local production of biogenic substances that are then delivered to the restricted milieu of the microcirculation. In essence this supposition is an extension of August Krogh's keen perception some sixty years ago that microvessel perfusion is independent, at least in part, of neurogenic control and events occurring upstream (32). There are a number of naturally occurring metabolites that could affect homeostatic regulation of permeability. The use of the portmanteau term *autocoids* to identify these local regulators is growing. Autocoids include the agonists discussed in this chapter and others such as the prostanoids prostacyclin and thromboxanes, and the polypeptides angiotensin and bradykinin.

There are a number of naturally occurring substances that could collectively be responsible for homeostatic regulation of permeability. Hence the consequence of abnormal autocoid titers, which could result in part from endothelial cell dysfunction, could be responsible for permeability changes that occur in many clinical settings. For example, the autocoids 5-HT, NE, and prostacyclin strengthen the microvascular barrier, especially at the level of postcapillary venules. In contrast, thromboxanes and histamine decrease endothelial structural integrity. Whether or not these different autocoids have disparate mechanisms for regulating permeability and whether or not they mediate one anothers' actions are still to be determined.

ACKNOWLEDGMENT

The authors would like to thank our colleagues Drs. Patricia D'Amore (Harvard Medical School) and Raymond Petryshyn (Massachusetts Institute of Technology) for their critiques of the manuscript, and Gerald Norris for its preparation.

Literature Cited

1. Alabaster, V. A., Bakhle, Y. S. 1970. Removal of 5-hydroxytryptamine by rat isolated lung. *Br. J. Pharmacol.* 40:468–82
2. Alabaster, V. A., Bakhle, Y. S. 1973. The removal of noradrenaline in the pulmonary circulation of rat isolated lungs. *Br. J. Pharmacol.* 47:325–31
3. Beaven, M. A., Horakora, Z. 1978. The enzymatic isotopic assay of histamine. In *Handbook of Experimental Pharmacology,* ed. M. Rocha e Silva, 18(Pt. 2):151–73 New York: Springer-Verlag
4. Black, J. W. 1979. Histamine receptors. In *Proc. A. N. Richards Symp.,* ed. T. O. Yellin, 5:3–16. New York: Spectrum
5. Black, J. W., Duncan, W. A. M.,

Durant, C. J., Ganellin, C. R., Parson, E. M. 1972. Definition and antagonism of histamine H_2 receptors. *Nature* 236:385–90
6. Bottaro, D., Shepro, D., Peterson, S., Hechtman, H. B. 1985. Serotonin, histamine and norepinephrine mediation of endothelial and vascular smooth muscle cell movement. *Am. J. Physiol.* 248:C252–57
7. Buonassisi, V., Venter, J. C. 1976. Hormone and neurotransmitter receptors in an established vascular endothelial cell line. *Proc. Natl. Acad. Sci. USA* 73:1612–16
8. Carson, M. P., Peterson, S. W., Hechtman, H. B., Shepro, D. 1981. Serotonin

uptake in [³H]thymidine-selected cultures of bovine aortic endothelium. *Fed. Proc.* 40:610 (Abstr.)

9. Chand, N., Eyre, P. 1975. Classification and biological distribution of histamine receptor subtypes. *Agents Actions* 5(4): 277–96

10. Corrodi, H., Jonsson, G. 1967. The formaldehyde fluorescence method for the histochemical demonstration of biogenic monoamines. *J. Histochem. Cytochem.* 15:65–78

11. Cross, S. A. M., Albaster, V. A., Bakhle, Y. S., Vane, J. R. 1974. Sites of uptake of [³H]-5-hydroxytryptamine in rat isolated lung. *Histochemistry* 39:83–91

12. D'Amore, P. A., Shepro, D. 1978. Calcium flux and ornithine decarboxylase activity in cultured endothelial cells. *Life Sci.* 22:571–76

13. D'Amore, P. A., Shepro, D. 1977. Stimulation of growth and calcium influx in cultured bovine aortic endothelial cells by platelets and vasoactive substances. *J. Cell. Physiol.* 92:177–84

14. D'Amore, P. A., Hechtman, H. B., Shepro, D. 1978. Ornithine decarboxylase activity in cultured endothelial cells stimulated by serum, thrombin and serotonin. *Thromb. Haemostasis* 29:496–503

15. De Mey, J. G., Vanhoutte, P. M. 1981. Contribution of the endothelium to the response to anoxia in the canine femoral artery. *Arch. Int. Pharmacodyn. Ther.* 253:325–26

16. De Mey, J. G., Vanhoutte, P. M. 1980. Interaction between Na⁺, K⁺ exchanges and the direct inhibitory effect of acetylcholine on canine femoral arteries. *Circ. Res.* 46:826–36

17. Dixon, W. E. 1907. On the mode of action of drugs. *Med. Mag.* 16:454–57

18. Dusting, G. J., Moncada, S., Vane, J. R. 1978. Recirculation of prostacyclin (PGI₂) in the dog. *Br. J. Pharmacol.* 64:315–20

19. Fisher, A. B., Block, E. R., Pietra, G. 1980. Environmental influences on uptake of serotonin and other amines. *Environ. Health Perspect.* 35:191–98

20. Fishman, A. P., Pietra, G. G. 1974. Handling of bioactive materials by the lung. *N. Engl. J. Med.* 291:953–59

21. Fortes, Z. B., Garcia Leme, J., Sciroletto, R. 1983. Vascular reactivity in diabetes mellitus: Role of the endothelial cell. *Br. J. Pharmacol.* 79:771–81

22. Garcia Leme, J., Bohm, G. M., Migliorini, R. H., Souza, M. Z. A. 1974. Possible participation of insulin in the

control of vascular permeability. *Eur. J. Pharmacol.* 29:298–306

23. Gillis, C. N., Roth, J. A. 1976. Pulmonary disposition of circulating vasoactive hormones. *Biochem. Pharmacol.* 25: 2547–53

24. Gillis, C. N., Roth, J. A. 1977. The fate of biogenic monoamines in perfused rabbit lung. *Br. J. Pharmacol.* 59:585–90

25. Herbst, T. J., Raichle, M. E., Ferrendelli, J. A. 1979. Beta-adrenergic regulation of adenosine 3'-5'-monophosphate concentration in brain microvessels. *Science* 204:330–32

26. Herman, I. M., Pollard, T. D., Wong, A. J. 1982. Contractile proteins in endothelial cells. *Ann. NY Acad. Sci.* 401:50–60

27. Iwasawa, Y., Gillis, C. N. 1974. Pharmacological analysis of norepinephrine and 5-hydroxytryptamine removal from the pulmonary circulation: Differentiation of uptake sites for each amine. *J. Pharmacol. Exp. Ther.* 188(3):386–93

28. Junod, A. F. 1972. Uptake, metabolism and efflux of [¹⁴C]-5-hydroxytryptamine in isolated perfused rat lungs. *J. Pharmacol. Exp. Ther.* 183:341–55

29. Junod, A. F., Ody, C. 1977. Amine uptake and metabolism by endothelium of pig pulmonary artery and aorta. *Am. J. Physiol.* 232:C88–C94

30. Karnushina, I. L., Palacies, J. M., Barbin, G., Dux, E., Joo, F., Schwartz, J. C. 1980. Studies on the capillary rich fraction isolated from brain: Histamine component and characterization of the histamine receptors linked to adenylate cyclase. *J. Neurochem.* 34(5):1201–8

31. Kjellstrom, T., Ahlman, H., Dahlstrom, A., Hansson, G. K., Risberg, B. 1984. The uptake of 5-hydroxytryptamine in endothelial cells cultured from the pulmonary artery in rats. *Acta Physiol. Scand.* 120:243–50

32. Krogh, A. 1959. *The Anatomy and Physiology of Capillaries.* New York: Hafner. Reprinted from the original version published by Yale Univ. Press, New Haven, 1922, pp. 47–69

33. Lahr, P., Mais, D. E., Bosin, T. R. 1983. Reparative changes following oxygen-induced lung injury: Effect on serotonin disposition and metabolism. *Toxicol. Appl. Pharmacol.* 70:188–94

34. Langley, J. N. 1901. Observations on the physiological action of extracts of the supra-renal bodies. *J. Physiol.* 27:237–56

35. Leysen, J. 1983. Serotonin receptor binding sites: Is there pharmacological and clinical significance? *Med. Biol.* 61:138–43

36. Loskutoff, D. S., Edgington, T. S. 1977.

Synthesis of a fibrinolytic activator and inhibitor by endothelial cells. *Proc. Natl. Acad. Sci. USA* 74:3903–7

37. Ludwig, C., Schmidt, A. 1868. Das Verhalten der Gase, welch mit dem Blut durch den reizbaren Saugethiermuskel strömen. *Arb. Physiol. Anstalt Leipzig* pp. 1–61

38. Makarski, J. S. 1981. Stimulation of cyclic AMP production by vasoactive agents in cultured bovine aortic and pulmonary artery endothelial cells. *In Vitro* 17:450–58

39. Maruki, C., Spatz, M., Ueki, Y., Nagatsu, I., Bembry, J. 1984. Cerebrovascular endothelial cell culture: Metabolism and synthesis of 5-hydroxytryptamine. *J. Neurochem.* 43:316–19

40. Nathanson, J. A. 1980. Cerebral microvessels contain a beta$_2$-adrenergic receptor. *Life Sci.* 26:1793–99

41. Nicholas, T. E., Strum, J. M., Angelo, L. S., Junod, A. F. 1974. Site and mechanism of uptake of [^{3}H]-1-norepinephrine by isolated perfused rat lungs. *Circ. Res.* 35:670–80

42. Oliver, G., Schafer, E. A. 1895. The physiological effects of extracts from the suprarenal capsules. *J. Physiol.* 18:230–76

43. Olverman, H. J., Pearson, J. D., Gordon, J. L. 1979. Transport of biogenic amines by blood platelets and cultured vascular cells. *Blood Vessels* 16:219

44. Pearson, J. D., Gordon, J. L. 1984. Metabolism of serotonin and adenosine. In *Biology of Endothelial Cells*, ed. E. A. Jaffe, pp. 330–42. Boston/The Haague/Dordrecht/Lancaster/Nijhoff

45. Pearson, J. D., Olverman, H. J., Gordon, J. L. 1977. Transport of 5-hydroxytryptamine by endothelial cells. *Biochem. Soc. Trans.* 5:1181–83

46. Peroutka, R. B., Snyder, S. H. 1979. Multiple serotonin receptors: Differential binding of [^{3}H]-5-hydroxytryptamine, [^{3}H]-lysergic acid diethylamide and [^{3}H]-spiroperidol. *Mol. Pharmacol.* 16:687–99

47. Pickett, R. D., Anderson, N. W., Orton, T. C., Eling, T. E. 1975. The pharmacodynamics of 5-hydroxytryptamine uptake and metabolism by the isolated perfused rabbit lung. *J. Pharmacol. Exp. Ther.* 194:545–53

48. Robinson-White, A., Beaven, M. A. 1982. Presence of histamine and histamine-metabolizing enzyme in rat and guinea-pig microvascular endothelial cells. *J. Pharmacol. Exp. Ther.* 223 (2):440–45

49. Robinson-White, A., Peterson, S., Hechtman, H. B., Shepro, D. 1981.

50. Roth, J. A., Venter, J. C. 1978. Predominance of the B form of monamine oxidase in cultured vascular intimal endothelial cells. *Biochem. Pharmacol.* 27:2371–73

51. Schafer, A. I., Gimbrone, M. A., Handin, R. I. 1980. Endothelial cell adenylate cyclase: Activation by catecholamines and prostaglandin I$_2$. *Biochem. Biophys. Res. Commun.* 96:1640–47

52. Schayer, R. W. 1966. Catabolism of histamine *in vivo*. See Ref. 3, pp. 672–83

53. Shepro, D., Batbouta, J. C., Robblee, L. S., Carson, M. P., Belamarich, F. A. 1975. Serotonin transport by cultured bovine aortic endothelium. *Circ. Res.* 36:799–806

54. Shepro, D., D'Amore, P. A. 1984. The physiology and biochemistry of the vascular wall endothelium. In *The Handbook of Physiology. The Cardiovascular System, Microcirculation*, ed. E. M. Renkin, C. Michel, 4:103–63. Baltimore, MD: Am. Physiol. Soc.

55. Shepro, D., Hechtman, H. B. 1985. Endothelial serotonin uptake and mediation of prostanoid secretion and stress fiber production. *Fed. Proc.* 44:2616–19

56. Shepro, D., Li, S., Hechtman, H. B. 1980. Plasminogen activator activity of isolated cardiac muscle microvessel endothelial cells. *Thromb. Res.* 18:609–16

57. Shepro, D., Welles, S. L., Hechtman, H. B. 1984. Vasoactive agonists prevent erythrocyte extravasation in thrombocytopenic hamsters. *Thromb. Res.* 35:421–30

58. Simionescu, N., Heltianu, C., Antone, F., Simionescu, M. 1982. Endothelial cell receptors for histamine. *Ann. NY Acad. Sci.* 401:132–49

59. Steinberg, S. R., Jaffe, E. A., Bilezikian, J. P. 1984. Endothelial cells contain beta adrenoceptors. *Naunyn-Schmiedeberg's Arch. Pharmacol.* 325:310–13

60. Strum, J. M., Junod, A. F. 1972. Radioautographic demonstration of 5-hydroxytryptamine-[^{3}H] uptake by pulmonary endothelial cells. *J. Cell Biol.* 54:456–67

61. Sun, F. F., Taylor, B. M. 1978. Metabolism of prostacyclin in rat. *Biochemistry* 17(19):4096–4101

62. Toivonen, H., Hartiala, J., Bakhle, Y. 1981. Effects of high oxygen tension on the metabolism of vasoactive hormones in isolated perfused rat lungs. *Acta Physiol. Scand.* 111:185–92

63. Trevethick, M. A., Pearson, J. D.,

Olverman, H. J., Gordon, J. L. 1979. Metabolism of phenylethylamine and 5-hydroxytryptamine by cultured vascular cells. *Biochem. Soc. Trans.* 7:1063–65

64. Welles, S. L., Shepro, D., Hechtman, H. B. 1985. Vasoactive amines modulate actin cables (stress fibers) and surface area in cultured bovine endothelium. *J. Cell Physiol.* 123:337–42

65. Welles, S. L., Shepro, D., Hechtman, H. B. 1985. Eicosanoid modulation of stress fibers in cultured bovine aortic endothelial cells. *Inflammation* 9:439–50

66. Wiersma, D. A., Roth, R. A. 1980. Clearance of 5-hydroxytryptamine by rat lung and liver: The importance of relative perfusion and intrinsic clearance. *J. Pharmacol. Exp. Ther.* 212(1):97–102

SPECIAL TOPIC: ACID/BASE PHYSIOLOGY

Introduction, Walter F. Boron, *Section Editor*

In the past decade, the field of acid/base physiology has experienced a flurry of research activity, and a series of important advances having been made at the level of single cells and subcellular organelles. Progress has been made possible largely by the availability of new electrophysiological (e.g. see Reference 2) and optical techniques (e.g. see Reference 1) for measuring the pH inside these cells and organelles. Attention has focused primarily on the mechanisms by which acid/base equivalents are transported across membranes, how these transport processes are regulated, and how the pH values determined by these transport processes affect cell function.

It is widely appreciated that almost all cellular processes are sensitive to changes in pH, some exquisitely so. For that reason, it is not surprising that cells have gone to great lengths to appropriately regulate their intracellular pH (pH_i). In the first article in this section, Claire Aickin reviews ion-transport mechanisms such as Na-H and $Cl-HCO_3$ exchange that participate in pH_i homeostasis in muscle. Rather than being peculiar to muscle, these and similar transporters appear to play a role in pH_i regulation in a wide variety of cells.

Although one might think it best for homeostatic mechanisms to maintain pH_i at a fixed value, it seems that the "normal" pH_i of certain cells can be modified under special conditions. In the second article in this series, Wouter Moolenaar surveys the effects of growth factors on intracellular pH. Work in this area has helped clarify how certain cells (e.g. fibroblasts) respond to specific stimuli (e.g. platelet-derived growth factor) and thereby participate in an important biological process (e.g. wound healing). Furthermore, such research may shed light on the more general issue of cell growth control.

347

348

Another example of how pH_i regulation can be important for the whole organism is the role of pH_i-regulating mechanisms in transporting acid/base equivalents across certain epithelia. In the third article in this special section, I examine pH_i regulation in epithelial cells, which generally have different transport systems at their apical and basolateral plasma membranes. Because one or more of the acid/base transport mechanisms of some epithelial cells are restricted to a single side of the cell, the transporters not only regulate pH_i, but in the process also secrete acid/base equivalents across the epithelium.

As noted above, the reason for expecting pH_i regulation to be of such importance to the cell, both in the normal steady state and during cell activation, is the large number of cellular processes that are pH sensitive. In the fourth article in this section, William Busa analyzes the mechanisms and consequences of regulating cellular processes by changes in pH_i.

Although the acid/base status of the cytoplasm is of crucial importance for cell function, pH is also vitally important for various cellular organelles. The pH inside of certain organelles (e.g. lysosomes and chromaffin granules) must be maintained at a relatively low value in order for them to function properly. In the final article in this series, Gary Rudnick discusses the ATP-driven proton pumps responsible for maintaining the low internal pH of these organelles.

Thus, the review articles in this special topic section cover a broad range of interrelated subjects, and should provide the reader with some insight into this rapidly evolving area of physiology.

Literature Cited

1. Thomas, J. A., Buchsbaum, R. N., Zimniak, A., Racker, E. 1979. Intracellular pH measurements in Ehrlich ascites tumor cells utilizing spectroscopic probes generated in situ. *Biochemistry* 81:2210–18

2. Thomas, R. C. 1974. Intracellular pH of snail neurones measured with a new pH-sensitive glass microelectrode. *J. Physiol.* 238:159–80

Ann. Rev. Physiol. 1986. 48:349–61

INTRACELLULAR pH REGULATION BY VERTEBRATE MUSCLE

C. Claire Aickin

Department of Pharmacology, Oxford University, South Parks Road, Oxford OX1 3QT, United Kingdom

INTRODUCTION

Several reviews on intracellular pH (pH_i) and the mechanism of its regulation have been recently published, ranging from the exhaustive work of Roos & Boron (37) to the concise review lecture of Thomas (43). This reflects the rapid advance in our understanding of the subject, largely conferred by the development of pH-sensitive electrodes small enough to be inserted into living cells. The microelectrode not only allows direct, but also, perhaps more importantly, continuous measurement of pH_i. It has confirmed that pH_i is more alkaline than predicted for a passive H^+ distribution and has revealed that pH_i recovers relatively rapidly from imposed changes. Investigation of the recovery from intracellular acidosis clearly provides an ideal method for studying the mechanisms responsible for the maintenance of pH_i. These mechanisms are generally assumed to involve active transport of H^+, HCO_3^-, or OH^- ions, although contribution from intracellular sequestration cannot be excluded.

The majority of work covered in previous reviews, and indeed the source of most of our knowledge, comes from invertebrate preparations. Yet even the pioneering experiments in the technically more difficult vertebrate preparations (7, 24) illustrated that the invertebrate was not a valid model. Recent research in the three classes of vertebrate muscle has considerably advanced our understanding, and it is to this work that the critique is unashamedly restricted. Details of the techniques used for the measurement and alteration of pH_i, and their theoretical basis, have been adequately described elsewhere (e.g. 31, 37, 43), and are not within the scope of this short article.

349

0066-4278/86/0315-0349$02.00

SKELETAL MUSCLE

Mammalian

The mouse soleus muscle was the first vertebrate preparation in which the ionic mechanism responsible for pH_i regulation was studied directly with microelectrodes (7). Fibers were acid loaded by removal of NH_4^+ from the superfusing solution, and the subsequent recovery was observed. Typical examples of the resultant transients are shown in Figures 1–3, and a formal description of the underlying events has been published (11). In brief, this approach depends on the intracellular accumulation of NH_4^+ ions and their subsequent dissociation in NH_4^+-free solution to NH_3, which is rapidly lost, and H^+ ions, which are not. The resultant acidification is followed by recovery of pH_i as the cell actively extrudes H^+ or accumulates HCO_3^- or OH^- ions.

Several of the transport mechanisms previously suggested to account for the nonpassive distribution of H^+ ions were tested by observing the effect of altering the concentration of their putative substrates on this recovery. The lack of effect of more than an hour's removal of external K^+ (K_o^+) or of application of ouabain excluded the involvement of both K^+-H^+ exchange and H^+ ion transport by the outward limb of the Na pump. Tests for participation of Ca^{2+}-H^+ exchange were less conclusive. Recovery was unaffected by changes of Ca_o^{2+} between 10 and 1 mM, but much lower levels would be required to exclude contribution by this mechanism, particularly at the mitochondrial membrane. Complete removal of Na_o^+ (substituted by Li^+), however, greatly slowed recovery (see Figure 1). It may be argued that the Na^+-dependence of the recovery was in fact greater than indicated by this experiment since Li^+ has subsequently been shown to be capable of activating the Na^+-H^+ exchanger in other preparations (see Figure 2) (12, 22, 30, 33). Nevertheless, substitution with K^+ caused the same degree of inhibition, and amiloride, a putative Na^+-H^+ exchange inhibitor (14), did not add to the inhibition seen in Li^+-substituted, Na^+-free solution. Further evidence for involvement of Na^+ ions was seen in an amiloride-sensitive increase in intracellular Na^+ activity (a_{Na}^i) during the period of pH_i recovery. It is notable that a reduction of only 11% in Na_o^+ caused a 57% decrease in the rate constant of pH_i recovery. This implies that the apparent affinity for Na^+ is low: a condition that is, so far, unique to the regulating mechanism of mouse soleus. Studies in marine animals have revealed K_m values of the same order of magnitude, but these represent only 14% of the normal Na_o^+ in barnacle muscle (12) and 18% in squid giant axon (13).

Although the results clearly showed considerable Na^+-dependence, its inhibition did not cause the failure of recovery envisaged for a totally blocked regulating mechanism. The suspected involvement of another mechanism was confirmed by experiments in which nominally CO_2-free solutions or the anion

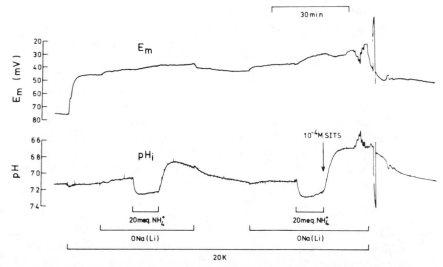

Figure 1. Pen recording of an experiment showing the combined inhibitory effect of removal of Na_o^+ (substituted by Li^+) and application of SITS on pH_i recovery in mouse soleus muscle. Intracellular acidification was induced by removal of $(NH_4)_2SO_4$, and the muscle was superfused with CO_2-buffered solutions throughout. K_o^+ was increased to 20 mM to minimize contraction caused by removal of Na_o^+. The equal and opposite changes in potential in the E_m and pH_i traces during the last 30 min were caused by disturbance of the voltage electrode.

exchange inhibitor SITS (4-acetamide-4'-isothiocyanostilbene-2,2'-disulphonic acid) were applied. Both decreased the rate of recovery by about 30%, and added to the inhibition caused by removal of Na_o^+ or application of amiloride (see Figure 1). Thus it was concluded that both Na^+-H^+ exchange and Cl^--HCO_3^- exchange are involved in pH_i regulation, and that they are entirely separate mechanisms. Cl^--HCO_3^- exchange was calculated to comprise about 20% of the pH_i regulating system and to have a Q_{10} of 6.9, while the more dominant Na^+-H^+ exchange had a Q_{10} of 1.4. This independence of the two exchange mechanisms is in complete contrast to their obligatory coupling found in snail neurones (42), the squid giant axon (13), and barnacle muscle (12).

Roos & Boron (36) subsequently confirmed these findings in rat diaphragm using the distribution of the weak acid DMO (5,5-dimethyloxazolidine-2,4-dione) to estimate pH_i. They too calculated a 20% contribution from Cl^--HCO_3^- exchange, and observed a further 50% reduction of acid extrusion on removal of Na_o^+ (Mg^{2+} substituted). Yet, intriguingly, they observed a 50% reduction in acid extrusion on removal of Cl_o^- when Cl^--HCO_3^- exchange should already have been largely blocked by nominally CO_2-free conditions.

Amphibian

At much the same time as the mouse soleus work was done, Bolton & Vaughan-Jones (9) made the first direct measurements of transient pH_i changes in frog skeletal muscle. They found that, despite a clearly nonpassive distribution, pH_i showed no tendency to recover from acidosis induced by application of CO_2. More recently, this apparently anomalous behavior was studied in detail by Roos and his colleagues (1, 2, 35). They confirmed the earlier finding, but showed that depolarized fibers recover quite rapidly (1, 2). This was explained by a significant HCO_3^- permeability (P_{HCO_3}), which would permit a passive outward leak of HCO_3^- ions in normally polarized fibers, obscuring the operation of the regulating mechanism, but would allow only negligible leakage on depolarization, when membrane potential (E_m) is close to the HCO_3^- equilibrium potential. Recent demonstration of considerable recovery from NH_4Cl-induced acidosis in normally polarized fibers in the nominal absence of CO_2 convincingly supports this conclusion (35).

Various methods of depolarization were tested, and it was found that elevation of neither K_o^+ nor Cl_i^- were prerequisites for pH_i recovery to be observed following application of CO_2. However, recovery was fastest when Cl_i^- was elevated, and in this condition alone, recovery was SITS sensitive (1, 2, 35). Complete removal of Na_o^+ (substituted by N-methyl-D-glucamine) and, to a lesser extent, application of amiloride inhibited recovery. The Na^+ dependence could be fitted to a Michaelis-Menten curve with an apparent K_m of 12 mM (35), and the mechanism appeared to be electroneutral (2, 35). Investigation in hypertonic solutions again showed marginal recovery from CO_2-induced acidosis in normally polarized fibers, and appearance of recovery following depolarization (2). However, under these conditions amiloride caused a degree of inhibition similar to that elicited by complete removal of Na_o^+. There was no sensitivity to SITS, regardless of the method of depolarization. Yet, paradoxically, the fastest recovery was observed when Cl_i^- was elevated.

Superficially, the presence of both a SITS- and an amiloride-sensitive mechanism at normal tonicity appears the same as in the mammal. But the important difference is that although amiloride and SITS were additive, the absence of Na_o^+ produced a greater degree of inhibition than the presence of amiloride. Thus it was concluded that an amiloride-sensitive mechanism (probably Na^+-H^+ exchange) and a SITS-sensitive, Na^+-dependent mechanism (probably like the much-studied Na^+-dependent $Cl^--HCO_3^-$ exchange; 12, 13, 42) can be involved in pH_i regulation in frog skeletal muscle. The latter only appears to be active at normal tonicity when Cl_i^- is elevated and CO_2 is present (see also 38, 42). It is interesting that this combination of mechanisms has also been observed in crayfish neurones in which Cl_i^- is relatively high (30).

Although the pH$_i$ regulating mechanism appeared to operate in normally polarized fibers (1), its activation could have been caused by depolarization-induced release of Ca^{2+}. Application of caffeine in normal (34) or hypertonic (2) solutions, however, did not stimulate recovery. Nevertheless, both depolarization and caffeine induced an acidification, possibly caused by Ca^{2+}-H^+ exchange at shared intracellular buffers, and Ca^{2+} activation of glycogenolysis. Unexpectedly, elevation of Ca_o^{2+} to 10 mM completely inhibited the amiloride-sensitive fraction of pH$_i$ regulation without affecting the SITS-sensitive fraction (34). Ni^{2+} and Cd^{2+} at 1 mM produced the same effect.

CARDIAC MUSCLE

Mammalian

Direct observation of the rapid recovery of pH$_i$ from acidosis in mammalian cardiac muscle was first made by Ellis & Thomas (23, 24). Following the finding that the active outward transport of H^+ and Na^+ ions in the snail neurone are independent and selectively inhibitable by SITS and ouabain, respectively (41), they looked for the same pharmacological distinction in the sheep heart Purkinje fiber (24). Recovery from a CO_2-induced acidosis was again unaffected by ouabain. But it was also unaffected by SITS. At the time, the unimpressive effect of SITS on an otherwise uninhibited recovery in mouse soleus was also, mistakenly, taken to be insignificant. The error was realized in mouse soleus (7), but despite repeated attempts to find an effect, pH$_i$ recovery from acidosis in the Purkinje fiber has remained resolutely resistant to SITS or DIDS (4-4'-diisothiocyanostilbene-2,2'-disulfonic acid; 19, 22, 46, 49, 50). In addition, it is unaffected by the presence or nominal absence of CO_2 (44–46), and unaffected by Cl^--depletion (26, 45, 46). Thus it seems fair to conclude that Cl^--HCO_3^- exchange, Na^+-dependent or otherwise, is not involved in pH$_i$ recovery from an acidosis.

The search for a Na^+-dependence of pH$_i$ regulation was initiated by Deitmer & Ellis (19). Their careful work with both Na^+- and pH-sensitive microelectrodes, however, failed to produce an unequivocal answer. Their most convincing results were: (a) that recovery from acidosis was slowed by 90% removal of Na_o^+ (substituted by Li^+ or $Tris^+$) and by application of amiloride; (b) that the attendant rise in a_{Na}^i was abolished by amiloride; and (c) that pH$_i$ fell on application of amiloride. But, disturbingly, they observed that when the Na pump was inhibited, reduction of Na_o^+ caused a rapid fall not only in a_{Na}^i (18) but also in pH$_i$. Although this is in the right direction to be consistent with Na^+-H^+ exchange, the fall in pH$_i$ was too large to be accounted for by a $1:1$ stoichiometry. Since these authors had previously shown that Na^+-Ca^{2+} exchange is at least partially responsible for control of a_{Na}^i when the Na pump is inhibited (18), this raised the possibility of indirect effects of the Na^+ gradient on pH_i through Na^+-Ca^{2+} exchange and subsequent Ca^{2+}-H^+ exchange at shared intracellular buffers and/or the sarcolemma.

Evidence for a close relationship between the intracellular Na^+, Ca^{2+}, and H^+ ion activities then grew. The rapid fall in pH_i on reduction of Na_o^+ when the Na pump was inhibited was shown to be accompanied by a large rise in a_{Ca}^i and a contracture, which are consistent with the operation of Na_i^+-Ca_o^{2+} exchange (21). Alteration of pH_i caused opposite changes in a_{Ca}^i (8) and similarly, when the Na pump was inhibited, alteration of Ca_o^{2+} caused opposite changes in pH_i (51). Changes in pH_i which could not be attributed to Na^+-H^+ exchange but were consistent with Na^+-Ca^{2+} exchange and common intracellular buffering of Ca^{2+} and H^+ ions were elegantly demonstrated (51). Although all these results cannot exclude the existence of Na^+-H^+ exchange, they demonstrate that under certain conditions, dependence of pH_i on Na^+ is indirect. How then is pH_i regulated? Is it dependent on Ca^{2+}-H^+ exchange, or does Na^+-H^+ exchange exist?

Ellis & MacLeod (22) recently addressed these questions. They found that complete removal of Na_o^+ [bis(2-hydroxyethyl)dimethylammonium$^+$, BDA^+, substituted] not only prevented recovery from acidosis but caused a continued slow fall in pH_i (as shown in Figure 2), which suggests a complete block of the regulating mechanism. When the Na^+ substitute was altered to Li^+, pH_i began to recover, indicating that Li^+ can substitute for Na^+ on this mechanism. Na_o^+ had to be lowered to about 8 mM before a 50% reduction in the rate of pH_i recovery was observed. Amiloride slowed, but did not completely inhibit, recovery (see also 19, 49), and it now seems likely that the incomplete inhibition may be explained by the relatively high apparent affinity for Na^+ and competition between Na^+ and amiloride (28). Despite the fact that these results strongly suggest the presence of Na^+-H^+ exchange, the authors were keenly aware that they could equally be explained by a rise in a_{Ca}^i under conditions of low Na_o^+ and by an action of amiloride on Na^+-Ca^{2+} exchange (16). Differentiation between these alternatives was achieved, with what must have been great technical difficulty, by repeating the Na^+-free experiments at $< 10^{-8}$ M Ca_o^{2+}, a concentration unable to support the expression of Na^+-Ca^{2+} exchange in Na^+-withdrawal contractures (29). Complete removal of Na_o^+ still fully inhibited recovery, but no longer caused an acidification when the Na pump was inhibited. Finally, they showed that this Ca^{2+}-dependent acidification was unaffected by amiloride. Thus the prolonged uncertainty in sheep heart Purkinje fibers was laid to rest. Na^+-H^+ exchange, perhaps exclusively, is involved in pH_i recovery from an acid load. But changes in a_{Ca}^i, readily induced by alteration of the transmembrane Na^+ gradient, have profound effects on pH_i.

Although no attempt has yet been made to determine the stoichiometry, the lack of significant effect on E_m during recovery from acidosis (see Figure 2) suggests that the exchange is electroneutral. The fact that alteration of E_m has no

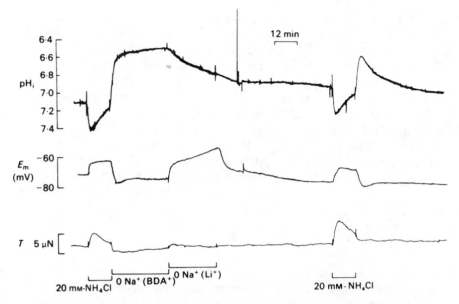

Figure 2. Pen recording of an experiment showing inhibition of pH_i recovery by removal of Na_o^+, substituted by BDA^+, and its partial reactivation by Li^+ in the sheep heart Purkinje fiber. Intracellular acidification was induced by removal of NH_4Cl and all solutions were nominally CO_2-free. Reproduced with permission (22).

effect on the recovery is consistent with this conclusion (17, 22). Nevertheless, de Hemptinne (17) has suggested that E_m does influence pH_i regulation because depolarization removes the difference between the steady state pH_i values recorded in the presence and in the nominal absence of CO_2. He explained this observation by assuming a significant P_{HCO_3}, calculated to be close to the apparent P_{Cl} (46, 47). It is, however, not easy to explain why a significant HCO_3^- leak should affect the steady state pH_i but not the recovery in normally polarized fibers (see 1). It is worth noting that simultaneous measurements of pH_i, a_{Na}^i, and tension in voltage-clamped Purkinje fibers (15) have shown that in the nominal absence of CO_2, E_m has virtually no effect on pH_i. However, when a_{Na}^i is elevated, E_m significantly affects pH_i via its effects on a_{Ca}^i.

Despite the repeated inability to find a contribution of anion exchange to pH_i recovery from acidosis, Cl^--HCO_3^- exchange is present in the cardiac Purkinje fiber, and is capable of affecting pH_i (48). In a novel approach to the concept of pH_i regulation, Vaughan-Jones has demonstrated that recovery from alkalinization is slowed by the presence of DIDS or the nominal absence of CO_2 (49, 50; see also 46). The recovery is accompanied by a DIDS-sensitive rise in a_{Cl}^i. These findings indicate that Cl^--HCO_3^- exchange is involved in recovery from an *alkaline* load, and similar observations have recently been made in human neutrophils (40). Formerly, mechanisms of pH_i regulation were believed to be switched off at high pH_i or at least only operative in a self exchange mode, with recovery from alkalinization occurring simply through the acidifying effects of passive ion fluxes and metabolism (see 37). Carrier-mediated recovery from alkalinization in the cardiac Purkinje fiber may, however, be a consequence of the specialization of Cl^--HCO_3^- exchange for maintenance of a high a_{Cl}^i, and its relative affinities for Cl^- and HCO_3^-. It seems significant that intracellular alkalinization without a concomitant increase in HCO_{3i}^- does not activate Cl^--HCO_3^- exchange (49). From purely theoretical considerations of the apparent affinities of the system, low HCO_{3i}^- (low pH_i) should reverse the exchange mechanism so that it extrudes acid equivalents (R. D. Vaughan-Jones, personal communication). Some evidence for this has been seen by Vanheel et al (46) in a greater rate of acid extrusion at low pH_i in the presence of CO_2 than in its nominal absence. However, as the authors point out, other explanations are not excluded.

Avian

Investigation of pH_i regulation in cardiac muscle has recently been extended to cultured chick cells using a microfluorometric technique (32, 33). Basically the same conclusions have been drawn. Recovery from an acidosis showed half maximal activation at 15 mM Na_o^+, could be supported by Li^+, was accompanied by a rise in total Na^+ content, and was inhibited by amiloride. Measurements were consistent with a 1:1 stoichiometry. DIDS, Cl^--free, and nominally CO_2-free solutions had no effect on the acid-induced Na^+ uptake, indicating that Na^+-H^+ exchange rather than Na^+-dependent Cl^--HCO_3^- exchange was responsible. Interestingly, an inhibitory action of Ca_o^{2+} on Na^+-H^+ exchange was concluded.

SMOOTH MUSCLE

Mammalian

Smooth muscle, the least amenable to impalement by microelectrodes, has the least predictable pH_i transients to what can now be regarded as classical manipulations (3). The underlying cause of its unique behavior is not yet fully understood, but recent research has revealed some of the characteristics of its pH_i regulation (4).

The first direct recording was reported by Yamaguchi & Stephens (52, 53) but the irreproducibility of their electrode design cast doubt on the validity of the results (see 37). Subsequently a trustworthy electrode was developed, and pH_i of the smooth muscle from guinea pig vas deferens (3) and ureter (4) was found to be very similar to that of the other two types of mammalian muscle (7, 23, 24). However, application of increasing CO_2 levels revealed a rapid, complete recovery of pH$_i$, unlike the partial recovery observed in both skeletal and cardiac muscle. This greater stability may reflect a very low P_{HCO_3} (see 1, 17, 35). As in many other preparations (see 37), pH$_i$ recovery was inhibited by low pH$_o$. The striking finding was that the nominal absence of CO_2 caused a steady state *acidification*. Readdition of CO_2 caused such a pronounced recovery that the acidification predicted from the rapid passage of CO_2 into the cell could be almost obscured. This suggests that a CO_2/HCO_3^--dependent mechanism confers a powerful part of the pH$_i$ regulating mechanism. Indeed, recovery from acidification induced by NH_4^+ removal was considerably slowed by the nominal absence of CO_2 (4). However, the obvious candidate, Cl^--HCO_3^- exchange, although present (6), does not appear to be involved in recovery from acidosis. Removal of CO_2 had no effect on a_{Cl}^i, while its readdition caused an as yet unexplained transient rise; a contribution of Cl^--HCO_3^- exchange to the effective H^+ ion extrusion would cause a fall in a_{Cl}^i. Furthermore, pH$_i$ rapidly recovered on reapplication of CO_2 in the complete absence of Cl^- (6). A similar situation has been reported in the renal proximal tubule, in which an electrogenic Na^+-$2HCO_3^-$ transporter has been implicated (10). However, this mechanism seems equally unlikely to form the CO_2/HCO_3^--dependent recovery in smooth muscle because the recovery occurs without significant change in E_m (see Figure 3). Recovery from acidosis is, nevertheless, dependent upon Na_o^+, (as shown in Figure 3), and preliminary measurements of a_{Na}^i have shown changes consistent with the presence of a Na^+ gradient–driven mechanism (C. C. Aickin, unpublished observations). Na_o^+ had to be lowered to about 1 mM in the presence of CO_2 before recovery from acidosis was prevented, which suggests a relatively high apparent affinity. Significantly, readdition of Na_o^+ caused a dramatic intracellular alkalinization. The Na^+-dependence remained apparent in the nominal absence of CO_2, although recovery was then prevented at about 12 mM Na_o^+. Clearly part of the CO_2/HCO_3^--dependent mechanism is Na^+ independent since the progressive fall in pH$_i$ in the absence of Na_o^+ was slowed or even halted by application of CO_2 (4). More experiments are required before the ionic mechanisms involved in recovery from acidosis can be fully characterized, but the results to date suggest a system that is unlike any so far described.

The concept of pH$_i$ regulation does not, however, only involve recovery from acidosis (49, 50). The intracellular acidification in the nominal absence of CO_2 seems much too fast to be accounted for by passive ion fluxes or metabolic production of acid (3). Not surprisingly, Cl^--HCO_3^- exchange is not involved (a_{Cl}^i is unaffected; 6), but it is possible that the mechanisms responsible for recovery from acidosis may reverse under these conditions (see 25, 39). Nevertheless, alkalinization involving elevation of HCO_{3i}^- may activate Cl_o^--HCO_{3i}^- exchange since the internal site of this exchanger has a higher affinity for HCO_3^- than for Cl^- (5). It is interesting that recent observations of

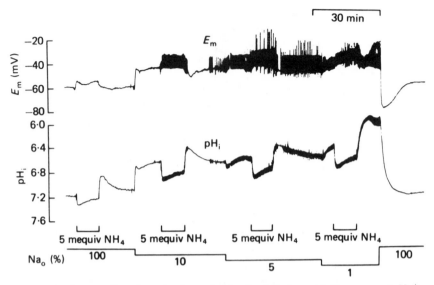

Figure 3. Pen recording of an experiment showing the dependence of pH_i recovery on Na_o^+ (substituted by $Tris^+$) in the smooth muscle of guinea-pig ureter. Intracellular acidification was induced by removal of $(NH_4)_2SO_4$, and the preparation was maintained in CO_2-buffered solutions throughout. Reproduced with permission (4).

changes in vascular smooth muscle tone, interpreted to be caused by changes in pH_i, are consistent with Cl^--HCO_3^- exchange involvement in recovery from alkalosis, but not acidosis (27a). Furthermore, they are consistent with an amiloride-sensitive, Na^+-dependent mechanism underlying recovery from acidosis (25a, 27a). However, other interpretations of the changes in tension cannot be excluded.

SUMMARY

Regulation of pH_i in the face of acidosis resulting from contracture would appear to be of such fundamental importance to the physiology of the muscle cell that a process common to all muscle types seems a reasonable prediction. However, this has not been found to be the case. The transmembrane Na^+ gradient clearly plays a major role and the process appears to be electroneutral in all three classes of muscle, but the transport mechanisms, even within the mammal, are different. It is an interesting observation that the ability of the muscle cell to regulate pH_i in the presence of CO_2, presumably governed by P_{HCO_3}, is related to P_{Cl} although there is little evidence for HCO_3^- permeation through Cl^- channels (20). Virtually no recovery from CO_2-induced acidosis is observed in normally polarized frog skeletal muscle, where P_{Cl} forms a large part of the resting conductance (27), whereas the same steady state pH$_i$ is recorded in the presence of various CO_2 levels in mammalian smooth muscle, where P$_{Cl}$ is very low (5).

The study of pH$_i$ regulation in vertebrate muscle has provided important lessons for the subject as a whole. Experience in cardiac muscle has shown that if Na^+-Ca^{2+} exchange is present, great care is required in interpretation of results where the transmembrane Na^+ gradient is altered or where Ca^{2+} levels are changed. Interpretation may be even more complex, bearing in mind the recent reports that Ca^{2+} inhibits Na^+-H^+ exchange. "Indeed," it seems appropriate to conclude, "if a little knowledge is dangerous, where is the man who has so much as to be out of danger?" (Thomas Huxley).

ACKNOWLEDGMENT

I am extremely grateful to Drs. D. Ellis and A. Roos for sending me copies of manuscripts in press, to Dr. A. F. Brading for critical comments on an early version of this article, to Professor E. Bülbring for the quotation, and to my husband for unfailing tolerance of the frustrations of authorship. This review was written during the tenure of an MRC Senior Research Fellowship.

Literature Cited

1. Abercrombie, R. F., Putnam, R. W., Roos, A. 1983. The intracellular pH of frog skeletal muscle: its regulation in isotonic solutions. *J. Physiol.* 345:175–87

2. Abercrombie, R. F., Roos, A. 1983. The intracellular pH of frog skeletal muscle: its regulation in hypertonic solutions. *J. Physiol.* 345:189–204

3. Aickin, C. C. 1984. Direct measurement of intracellular pH and buffering power in smooth muscle cells of guinea-pig vas deferens. *J. Physiol.* 349:571–85.

4. Aickin, C. C. 1985. The effect of Na^+ and HCO_3^- ions on recovery from an acid load in the smooth muscle of guinea-pig ureter. *J. Physiol.* In press

5. Aickin, C. C., Brading, A. F. 1983. Towards an estimate of chloride permeability in the smooth muscle of guinea-pig vas deferens. *J. Physiol.* 336:179–97

6. Aickin, C. C., Brading, A. F. 1984. The role of chloride-bicarbonate exchange in the regulation of intracellular chloride in guinea-pig vas deferens. *J. Physiol.* 349:587–606

7. Aickin, C. C., Thomas, R. C. 1977. An investigation of the ionic mechanism of intracellular pH regulation in mouse soleus muscle fibres. *J. Physiol.* 273: 295–316

8. Bers, D. M., Ellis, D. 1982. Intracellular calcium and sodium activity in sheep heart Purkinje fibres: effect of changes of external sodium and intracellular pH. *Pflügers Arch.* 393:171–78

9. Bolton, T. B., Vaughan-Jones, R. D. 1977. Continuous direct measurement of intracellular chloride and pH in frog skeletal muscle. *J. Physiol.* 270:801–33

10. Boron, W. F., Boulpaep, E. L. 1983. Intracellular pH regulation in the renal proximal tubule of the salamander. Basolateral HCO_3^- transport. *J. Gen. Physiol.* 81:53–94

11. Boron, W. F., De Weer, P. 1976. Intracellular pH transients in squid giant axons caused by CO_2, NH_3 and metabolic inhibitors. *J. Gen. Physiol.* 67:91–112

12. Boron, W. F., McCormick, W. C., Roos, A. 1981. pH regulation in barnacle muscle fibers: dependence on extracellular sodium and bicarbonate. *Am. J. Physiol.* 240:C80–89

13. Boron, W. F., Russell, J. M. 1983. Stoichiometry and ion dependencies of the intracellular-pH-regulating mechanism in squid giant axons. *J. Gen. Physiol.* 81:373–99

14. Bull, M. B., Laragh, J. H. 1968. Amiloride, a potassium-sparing natriuretic. Clinical trial-amiloride appears to act in

distal nephron by blocking both Na/H and Na/K exchange. *Circulation* 37:45–53

15. Cannell, M. B., Lederer, W. J., Vaughan-Jones, R. D. 1984. The effect of membrane potential on intracellular pH in sheep cardiac Purkinje fibres. *J. Physiol.* 349:45P

16. Cragoe, E., Kaczorowski, G. L., Reeves, J. P., Slaughter, R. S. 1984. Amiloride analogs interact with the monovalent cation binding site of the bovine heart sodium-calcium exchange carrier. *J. Physiol.* 353:74P.

17. de Hemptinne, A. 1981. Has the membrane potential an influence on the regulation of intracellular pH in cardiac Purkinje fibres? *Arch. Int. Physiol. Biochim.* 89:P23–24

18. Deitmer, J. W., Ellis, D. 1978. Changes in the intracellular sodium activity of sheep heart Purkinje fibres produced by calcium and other divalent cations. *J. Physiol.* 227:437–53

19. Deitmer, J. W., Ellis, D. 1980. Interactions between the regulation of the intracellular pH and sodium activity of sheep cardiac Purkinje fibres. *J. Physiol.* 304:471–88

20. Edwards, C. 1982. The selectivity of ion channels in nerve and muscle. *Neurosci.* 7:1335–66

21. Ellis, D., Deitmer, J. W., Bers, D. M. 1981. Intracellular pH, Na^+ and Ca^{2+} activity measurements in mammalian heart muscle. In *Progress in Enzyme and Ion-selective Electrodes,* ed. D. W. Lübbers, H. Acker, R. P. Buck, G. Eisenman, M. Kessler, W. Simon, pp. 148–55. Berlin: Springer-Verlag.

22. Ellis, D., MacLeod, K. T. 1985. Sodium-dependent control of intracellular pH in Purkinje fibres of sheep heart. *J. Physiol.* 359:81–105

23. Ellis, D., Thomas, R. C. 1976. Microelectrode measurement of the intracellular pH of mammalian heart cells. *Nature* 262:224–25

24. Ellis, D., Thomas, R. C. 1976. Direct measurement of the intracellular pH of mammalian cardiac muscle. *J. Physiol.* 262:755–71

25. Evans, M. G., Thomas, R. C. 1984. Acid influx into snail neurones caused by reversal of the normal pH_i-regulating system. *J. Physiol.* 346:143–54

25a. Garnier, D., Roulet, M. J. 1985. Is pH_i involved in the temperature-sensitivity of the oxygen-mediated response in the smooth muscle of guinea-pig ductus arteriosus? *J. Physiol.* In press

26. Gonzalez, N. C., Clancy, R. L. 1981. Myocardial intracellular pH regulation during chloride depletion. *J. Appl. Physiol.* 51:1630–34

27. Hodgkin, A. L., Horowicz, P. 1959. The influence of potassium and chloride ions on the membrane potential of single muscle fibres. *J. Physiol.* 148:127–60

27a. Ighoroje, A. D., Spurway, N. C. 1985. How does vascular muscle in the isolated rabbit ear artery adapt its tone after alkaline or acid loads? *J. Physiol.* In press

28. Kinsella, J. L., Aronson, P. S. 1980. Properties of the $Na^+ - H^+$ exchanger in renal microvillus membrane vesicles. *Am. J. Physiol.* 238:F461–69

29. Miller, D. J., Moisescu, D. G. 1976. The effects of very low external calcium and sodium concentrations on cardiac contractile strength and calcium-sodium antagonism. *J. Physiol.* 259:283–308

30. Moody, W. J. 1981. The ionic mechanism of intracellular pH regulation in crayfish neurones. *J. Physiol.* 316:293–308

31. Nuccitelli, R., Deamer, D. W., eds. 1982. *Intracellular pH: Its Measurement, Regulation, and Utilization in Cellular Functions.* New York: Liss. 594 pp.

32. Piwnica-Worms, D., Lieberman, M. 1983. Microfluorometric monitoring of pH_i in cultured heart cells: $Na^+ - H^+$ exchange. *Am. J. Physiol.* 244:C422–28

33. Piwnica-Worms, D., Jacob, R., Horres, C. R., Lieberman, M. 1985. Na/H exchange in cultured chick heart cells. pH_i regulation. *J. Gen. Physiol.* 85:43–64

34. Putnam, R. W., Roos, A. 1985. External divalent cations inhibit Na/H exchange in frog skeletal muscle. *Biophys. J.* 47:489a

35. Putnam, R. W., Roos, A. 1985. Aspects of pH_i regulation in frog skeletal muscle. In *Current Topics in Membranes and Transport. Na-H Exchange, Intracellular pH and Cell Function,* ed. W. F. Boron, P. Aronson, In press. New York: Academic.

36. Roos, A., Boron, W. F. 1978. Intracellular pH transients in rat diaphragm muscle measured with DMO. *Am. J. Physiol.* 235:C49–54

37. Roos, A., Boron, W. F. 1981. Intracellular pH. *Physiol. Rev.* 61:296–434

38. Russell, J. M., Boron, W. F. 1976. Role of chloride transport in regulation of intracellular pH. *Nature* 264:73–74

39. Russell, J. M., Boron, W. F., Brodwick, M. S. 1983. Intracellular pH and Na fluxes in barnacle muscle with evidence for reversal of the ionic mechanism of intracellular pH regulation. *J. Gen. Physiol.* 82:47–78

40. Simchowitz, L., Roos, A. 1985. Regula-

tion of intracellular pH in human neutrophils. *J. Gen. Physiol.* 85:443–70

41. Thomas, R. C. 1976. Ionic mechanism of the H$^+$ pump in a snail neurone. *Nature* 262:54–55

42. Thomas, R. C. 1977. The role of bicarbonate, chloride and sodium ions in the regulation of intracellular pH in snail neurones. *J. Physiol.* 273:317–38

43. Thomas, R. C. 1985. Experimental displacement of intracellular pH and the mechanism of its subsequent recovery. *J. Physiol.* 354:3–22P

44. Vanheel, B. 1982. Recovery from intracellular acidosis in cardiac Purkinje cells superfused with bicarbonate-containing and bicarbonate-free solutions. *Arch. Int. Physiol. Biochim.* 90: P44–45

45. Vanheel, B., de Hemptinne, A. 1982. Recovery from intracellular acidosis of sheep cardiac Purkyne strands in chloride-free solution. *Arch. Int. Physiol. Biochim.* 90:P109–10

46. Vanheel, B., de Hemptinne, A., Leusen, I. 1985. Analysis of Cl-HCO$_3$ exchange during recovery from intracellular acidosis in cardiac Purkinje strands. *Am. J. Physiol.* 246:C391–400

47. Vaughan-Jones, R. D. 1979. Non-passive chloride distribution in mammalian heart muscle: micro-electrode measurement of the intracellular chloride activity. *J. Physiol.* 295:83–109

48. Vaughan-Jones, R. D. 1979. Regulation of chloride in quiescent sheep heart Purkinje fibres studied using intracellular chloride and pH-sensitive microelectrodes. *J. Physiol.* 295:111–37

49. Vaughan-Jones, R. D. 1982. Chloride-bicarbonate exchange in the sheep cardiac Purkinje fibre. See Ref. 31, pp. 239–52

50. Vaughan-Jones, R. D. 1982. Chloride activity and its control in skeletal and cardiac muscle. *Philos. Trans. R. Soc. London Ser.* B 299:537–48

51. Vaughan-Jones, R. D., Lederer, W. J., Eisner, D. A. 1983. Ca^{2+} ions can affect intracellular pH in mammalian cardiac muscle. *Nature* 301:522–24

52. Yamaguchi, H., Stephens, N. L. 1977. A new method of fabricating recessed tip, pH microelectrode. *Fed. Proc.* 36: 499

53. Yamaguchi, H., Stephens, N. L. 1977. Determination of intracellular pH of airway smooth muscle using recessed tip pH microelectrode. *Proc. Int. Congr. Physiol. Sci. Paris* 13:824

Ann. Rev. Physiol. 1986. 48:363–76

EFFECTS OF GROWTH FACTORS ON INTRACELLULAR pH REGULATION

Wouter H. Moolenaar

Hubrecht Laboratory, International Embryological Institute, Uppsalalaan 8, 3584 CT Utrecht, The Netherlands

INTRODUCTION

One decade ago it was reported that within the first minutes after fertilization, sea urchin eggs show a striking increase in intracellular pH (pH_i), apparently due to an amiloride-sensitive exchange of extracellular Na^+ for intracellular H^+ across the plasma membrane (26). There is now good evidence that this rise in pH_i is a necessary signal for the initiation of growth and development of the egg (10, 74). The studies of the pH_i response to fertilization in sea urchin eggs were the first to suggest that a rise in pH_i, mediated by Na^+/H^+ exchange, might be a common event in the metabolic activation of quiescent animal cells. In recent years, a convincing role for Na^+/H^+ exchange and changes in pH_i in the action of extracellular growth stimuli has been documented with a variety of cell types in culture.

The purpose of this review is to describe the effects of growth factors on Na^+/H^+ exchange and pH_i, with emphasis on those studies that have examined the mechanisms by which the Na^+/H^+ exchanger is activated. Because of space limitations, only the most pertinent results can be discussed. A review of the role of pH_i in the regulation of cell metabolism and growth can be found elsewhere (10; W. B. Busa, this volume) and is beyond the scope of this chapter.

363

0066-4278/86/0315-0363$02.00

GROWTH FACTORS ACTIVATE Na^+/H^+ EXCHANGE

Transmembrane Signalling by Growth Factors: A Role for Na^+/H^+ Exchange

Growth factors are polypeptide hormones that induce replicative DNA synthesis and cell division in their target cells. The molecular mechanisms of action and the in vivo functions of growth factors are not well understood. By far the most extensively studied growth factors are epidermal growth factor (EGF) and platelet-derived growth factor (PDGF). EGF is a single polypeptide chain (molecular weight 6045), routinely isolated from the mouse submaxillary gland, that stimulates the proliferation of epithelial cells in vivo and of various other cell types in culture (12). PDGF is a highly basic glycoprotein (30–33 kDa) that is released from platelets during blood clotting and at sites of blood vessel injury, where it may serve to promote wound healing by stimulating the proliferation of fibroblasts, glial cells, and smooth muscle cells (18, 73).

Growth factors initiate their action by binding to specific cell surface receptors. The activated receptor mediates a cascade of rapid biochemical and physiological changes in the cell, which ultimately lead to DNA synthesis and cell proliferation. One of the immediate consequences of growth factor receptor interaction is protein phosphorylation (11, 12, 18, 73). The receptors for growth factors like EGF and PDGF are transmembrane glycoproteins that possess intrinsic and ligand-stimulated protein tyrosine kinase activity (11, 18, 73). This intrinsic tyrosine-specific kinase activity is shared with several viral oncogene products, such as the transforming protein of Rous sarcoma virus (6). This suggests that tyrosine-specific protein phosphorylations may initiate a set of common mitogenic pathways in virus-transformed and growth factor–stimulated cells. Yet it is currently not possible to relate an increase in tyrosine-specific protein kinase activity to specific metabolic alterations in intact cells.

Other immediate consequences of receptor activation include the rapid breakdown of inositol phospholipids (23, 59), a transient rise in cytoplasmic free Ca^{2+} (24, 40), and the stimulation of monovalent ion transport across the plasma membrane (36, 37, 58). Of the known ionic transport changes in growth factor–stimulated cells, the activation of amiloride-sensitive Na^+/H^+ exchange is best characterized. Smith & Rozengurt (64) first reported that serum increases the rate of an amiloride-sensitive Li^+ uptake system in mouse embryo fibroblasts, and Koch & Leffert (27) observed a rapid increase in amiloride-sensitive $^{22}Na^+$ uptake after addition of mitogenic peptides to rat hepatocytes. However, these initial results were not interpreted in terms of Na^+/H^+ exchange. The first direct evidence for the notion that growth factors stimulate Na^+/H^+ exchange came from studies on serum-stimulated neuroblastoma cells (35, 38). In these cells it was shown that serum activates an electrically silent Na^+ entry pathway, which is sensitive to amiloride and can be stimulated by acidifying the cytoplasm. Furthermore, it was demonstrated that amiloride-sensitive Na^+ uptake in acid-loaded cells is coupled in a 1 : 1 ratio to the efflux of H^+. Similarly, EGF-induced Na^+ influx in human fibroblasts was shown to be amiloride-sensitive, electroneutral, and enhanced by cytoplasmic acid loads (43). Although these results provided suggestive evidence for the involvement of Na^+/H^+ exchange in growth factor action, measurement of dynamic changes in the key variable, pH_i, was technically difficult.

With the advent of novel fluorescent pH indicators that can be trapped in the cytoplasm of small cells (42, 55, 57), it has become possible to demonstrate that (a) the Na^+/H^+ exchanger is normally involved in the close regulation of pH_i; and (b) activation of the Na^+/H^+ exchanger by growth factors results in a rapid and persistent increase in pH_i.

Regulation of pH_i by Na^+/H^+ Exchange

An electroneutral Na^+/H^+ exchange system appears to be present in the plasma membrane of virtually all vertebrate cells, where it efficiently regulates pH_i by virtue of its sensitivity to intracellular H^+ (1, 8, 33, 56). The functioning of pH_i regulating mechanisms in intact cells is usually assessed by rapidly acidifying the cytoplasm, for example by an NH_4^+ prepulse, and monitoring the ensuing recovery of pH_i to its baseline level (8, 56). In HCO_3^--free media, pH_i recovery after an acute acid load follows an exponential time course, and is entirely due to H^+ extrusion through the Na^+/H^+ exchanger, which utilizes the energy stored in the transmembrane Na^+ gradient. In HCO_3^--containing media, a Na^+-dependent HCO_3^-/Cl^- exchange mechanism becomes operative, and contributes to acid extrusion in many different cell types (8, 56), including mammalian fibroblasts, neuroblastoma, and carcinoma cells (30, 57; W. H. Moolenaar, unpublished data).

Some of the basic properties of the mammalian Na^+/H^+ exchanger have been inferred from the kinetics of pH_i recovery and/or concomitant Na^+ and H^+ fluxes in such diverse cell types as neuroblastoma cells, muscle cells, fibroblasts, and lymphocytes (18a, 22, 35, 39, 42, 50, 69). The major determinant of the Na^+/H^+ exchange rate is pH_i. At normal pH_i (about 7.0–7.3) the Na^+/H^+ exchanger is relatively inactive, although the steep transmembrane Na^+ gradient could theoretically raise pH_i ~1.0 unit more alkaline. As pH_i falls below a certain "threshold," the rate of Na^+/H^+ exchange is increasingly stimulated. Aronson et al (1, 1a) were the first to report that intracellular H^+ can allosterically activate the exchanger by binding to an inward-facing modifier site that is distinct from the internal H^+ transport site. In principle, by changing the affinity of the modifier site for cytoplasmic H^+, physiologic stimuli could control the activity of the Na^+/H^+ exchanger and thereby affect the value of pH_i.

The diuretic amiloride has generally been found to inhibit Na^+/H^+ exchange activity by competing with Na^+ for binding to the same external site ($K_i \simeq$ 2–5 μM). Because the reported K_M' for external Na^+ is about 15–50 mM, rather high ($\gtrsim$ 1 mM) concentrations of amiloride are required to effectively inhibit Na^+/H^+ exchange at physiologic Na^+ levels. Several amiloride analogues have been found to be 10–100 times more potent than amiloride in blocking Na^+/H^+ exchange (28, 68, 76). It should be emphasized, however, that amiloride and many of its potent analogues may interfere with protein synthesis and protein kinase activity both in intact cells and in cell-free preparations (4, 16, 32, 76). Thus, extreme caution is needed in attributing amiloride-sensitive changes in cellular functions to inhibition of Na^+/H^+ exchange.

Growth Factors Raise pH_i

The first evidence that stimulation of Na^+/H^+ exchange by growth factors causes an increase in pH_i, rather than being secondary to a fall in pH_i, was obtained from studies on mouse 3T3 cells and human diploid fibroblasts. These studies showed by weak-acid distribution measurements that addition of mitogenic peptides or serum produces an amiloride-sensitive rise in pH_i of about 0.15 unit (37, 60). Subsequently, the use of intracellularly-trapped fluorescent pH indicators has revealed that the increase in pH_i induced by mitogens like EGF and PDGF is detectable within $\sim$ 30 seconds, and is virtually complete after 10 minutes (13, 42, 57). The elevated pH_i persists for at least several hours as long as the ligand is present. Table 1 summarizes the various kinds of mitogens and other external stimuli that rapidly raise pH_i by activating Na^+/H^+ exchange in their target cells. In general, the observed alkalinizations range from 0.1–0.3 pH unit; they are inhibited by amiloride and by Na^+ removal and/or accompanied by amiloride-sensitive $^{22}Na^+$ uptake. Importantly, when mutant fibroblasts that lack functional Na^+/H^+ exchange activity are stimulated by mitogens, there is no increase in pH_i detectable (29). Although most of the experiments listed in Table 1 have been conducted in HCO_3^--free media, the pH_i response to mitogenic stimulation in mouse 3T3 cells has been observed in the presence of HCO_3^- (9, 24, 31, 60; but see 14 for opposite results in A431 cells). Among those hormones not listed that do cause a significant increase in amiloride-sensitive Na^+ influx, but for which concomitant pH_i shifts have not yet been documented, are nerve growth factor (7), bradykinin (49), and angiotensin (63).

Of interest is the case of insulin, for which most cells have functional cell surface receptors. By itself, insulin fails to activate Na^+/H^+ exchange and to raise pH_i in quiescent fibroblasts, but it markedly potentiates the cytoplasmic alkalinization induced by other mitogens (29, 36, 42). Likewise, insulin has no effect on Na^+/H^+ exchange in chick skeletal muscle (70) or human A431 carcinoma cells (57). In contrast, insulin does increase pH_i by activating Na^+/H^+ exchange in frog skeletal muscle (44, 54) and rat adipocytes (45). This suggests that there is not a direct functional link between the hormone receptor

Table 1 Summary of stimuli that raise pH_i by activating Na^+/H^+ exchange in their target cells[a]

Stimulus	Cell Type	Reference
Sperm	Sea urchin eggs	26, 74
Serum	Human fibroblasts	42
	Human A431 cells	57
	Mouse 3T3 cells	9
	Mouse NR6 cells	13
EGF	Human fibroblasts	42
	Human A431 cells	57
	Mouse 3T3 cells	24
PDGF	Mouse NR6 cells	13
	Human fibroblasts	41, 42
	Mouse 3T3 cells	31
Insulin[b]	Frog skeletal muscle	44, 54
	Rat adipocytes[c]	45
Thrombin	Hamster fibroblasts	29
	Human blood platelets	25, 62
Vanadate	Human A431 cells	15
Vasopressin	Mouse 3T3 cells	9, 24
Con A	Mouse thymocytes	24
	Mouse 3T3 cells	24
Chemotactic peptide (f-Met-Leu-Phe)	Rabbit neutrophils	34, 61, 72
Tumor-promoting phorbol esters	Human fibroblasts	41
	Human HeLa cells	41
	Human A431 cells[d]	75
	Mouse 3T3 cells	9, 24
	Mouse neuroblastoma cells	41
	Murine thymocytes	19a, 20, 21, 24
	Rabbit neutrophils	72
	Sea urchin eggs	67
1-Oleoyl-2-acetyl-glycerol	Human HeLa cells	41
	Mouse neuroblastoma cells	41
	Rat thymocytes	19a, 21
	Mouse 3T3 cells	67a
Hypertonic medium	Human A431 cells	14
	Human lymphocytes	21
	Rat thymocytes	19a

[a]Reported alkalinizations range from ~0.1–0.3 pH unit.
[b]Insulin alone fails to raise pH_i in fibroblasts (29, 42), A431 cells (57), and chick skeletal muscle cells (70), but it potentiates the pH_i response to EGF, PDGF, and thrombin in fibroblasts (29, 36, 42).
[c]Insulin effect is mimicked by H_2O_2.
[d]Pre-incubation with phorbol ester inhibits the pH_i response to EGF and serum, but not the response to hypertonicity.

and the Na^+/H^+ exchanger, but that post-receptor signalling pathways determine the degree of coupling specific for each cell type. As is obvious from Table 1, mitogens are not the only stimuli that activate Na^+/H^+ exchange and raise pH_i. For example, the chemotactic N-formyl peptide raises pH_i in mammalian neutrophils, apparently by activating Na^+/H^+ exchange. Activation of Na^+/H^+ exchange and subsequent cytoplasmic alkalinization can also be induced by exposure of cells to hyperosmotic stress, as reported for A431 cells (14) and lymphocytes (19a, 21). It seems that hypertonic cell shrinking incidentally triggers a sequence of events normally involved in hormone action (21, 66). Hence, the use of hypertonic stimuli may help to elucidate the molecular mechanisms by which physiologic agents normally activate the Na^+/H^+ exchanger.

MECHANISM OF ACTIVATION OF Na^+/H^+ EXCHANGE

Change in pH_i-Dependence

Recent studies have revealed the mechanism for physiologic activation of the otherwise quiescent Na^+/H^+ exchanger. By analyzing the kinetics of pH_i recovery from an acid load in growth factor-stimulated versus quiescent human fibroblasts, Moolenaar et al (42) concluded that activation of the Na^+/H^+ exchanger results from an alkaline shift in the pH_i sensitivity of the exchanger, as illustrated in Figure 1. A similar conclusion was reached by Paris & Pouysségur (51) from $^{22}Na^+$ uptake studies in acid-loaded hamster fibroblasts, and by Grinstein et al (20), who analyzed the effects of tumor-promoting phorbol esters on pH_i in rat lymphocytes.

As mentioned above, the pH_i sensitivity of the Na^+/H^+ exchanger is largely determined by an allosteric H^+-binding modifier site on the cytoplasmic face of the exchanger. It thus seems likely that the altered pH_i-sensitivity of the exchanger is due to a conformational change that results in an increased apparent affinity of the modifier site for cytoplasmic H^+. In other words, the physiologic effect of external stimuli on the Na^+/H^+ exchanger is to increase its pH_i threshold, that is, the level to which pH_i must rise before the exchanger virtually shuts off. This implies that the activation process persists only until pH_i has reached its new, more alkaline value. Indeed, the available evidence indicates that the Na^+/H^+ exchanger is only transiently stimulated by EGF in human fibroblasts (36) and by phorbol esters in rat lymphocytes (20), and that Na^+/H^+ exchange activity returns to the control level once pH_i has attained a new stable value. Similarly, activation of Na^+/H^+ exchange by hypertonicity has a transient character (66), and also appears to reflect an 0.2–0.3 unit alkaline shift of the pH_i-dependence of the exchanger, as reported for lymphocytes (21).

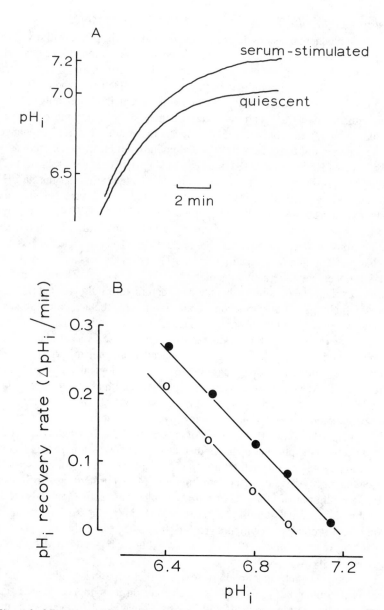

Figure 1 Mitogens modify the pH$_i$ sensitivity of the Na$^+$/H$^+$ exchanger. (*a*) Superimposed recordings of exponential pH$_i$ recovery from an NH$_4$$^+$-induced acidification in quiescent and serum-stimulated human fibroblasts. (*b*) Relationship between rate of pH$_i$ recovery, i.e. Na$^+$/H$^+$ exchange activity, and pH$_i$ in quiescent *(open circles)* and serum-stimulated cells *(dark circles)*. Redrawn from 42 with permission.

Role of Cytosolic Free Ca^{2+} and Protein Kinase C

By which biochemical steps do growth factors modify the pH_i sensitivity of the Na^+/H^+ exchanger? It has been speculated that activation of the Na^+/H^+ exchanger is brought about via a rise in cytosolic free Ca^{2+} ($[Ca^{2+}]_i$) and formation of Ca^{2+}-calmodulin complexes (47, 48, 71). This hypothesis relies heavily on rather indirect results obtained with the calcium ionophore A23187 and with putative Ca^{2+} and calmodulin "antagonists". In some cell types, including human fibroblasts, A23187 appears to stimulate Na^+/H^+ exchange, while treatment of the cells with Ca^{2+}-calmodulin inhibitors blocks activation by mitogens. However, A23187 induces a fall in pH_i in human fibroblasts (42), perhaps by poisoning the mitochondria, and thereby may stimulate the Na^+/H^+ exchange rate. Furthermore, Ca^{2+} ionophore fails to activate Na^+/H^+ exchange in neuroblastoma cells (38), lymphocytes (22), and 3T3 cells (18a; but see 24 for an opposite result). Perhaps more important is the finding that the tumor promoter tetradecanoyl-phorbol-acetate (TPA) can activate the Na^+/H^+ exchanger without any change in $[Ca^{2+}]_i$ (41). It thus appears that a rise in free Ca^{2+} is not essential for activation of the Na^+/H^+ exchanger. This does not, of course, exclude the possibility that there is a certain threshold value of $[Ca^{2+}]_i$, below which this parameter becomes rate-limiting for the activation process.

Several lines of evidence strongly suggest that activation of Na^+/H^+ exchange by external stimuli is mediated by protein kinase C, a cellular enzyme normally activated by diacylglycerol produced from inositol phospholipids through the action of phospholipase C (46). First, biologically active phorbol esters like TPA, which bind to and directly activate kinase C (46), stimulate Na^+/H^+ exchange, and thereby raise pH_i in a wide variety of cell types (Table 1). Second, addition of a synthetic diacylglycerol can mimic phorbol esters in raising pH_i (19a, 41, 67a). In physiologic conditions, 1,2-diacylglycerols are produced from the phospholipase C–mediated breakdown of inositol phospholipids, in particular phosphatidylinositol-4,5-bisphosphate (2, 3), and serve as the endogenous activator of protein kinase C (46). Furthermore, trifluoperazine, an inhibitor of kinase C in vitro, can block the activation of Na^+/H^+ exchange by external stimuli (21, 41; cf 48). Finally, TPA does not further alkalinize fibroblasts or lymphocytes that have been already stimulated by PDGF (41) or hypertonicity (21), respectively (but see 24 for additive effects of TPA and EGF in 3T3 cells).

The simplest molecular model to explain these findings is that kinase C directly phosphorylates the Na^+/H^+ exchanger on its cytoplasmic face, and thereby increases its apparent affinity for intracellular H^+. However, we cannot yet exclude the possibility that kinase C acts in a more indirect way to activate the Na^+/H^+ exchanger. The apparent involvement of protein kinase C strongly suggests that a rise in pH_i, mediated by Na^+/H^+ exchange, may be a common cellular response to those stimuli that activate phospholipase C to trigger the breakdown of inositol phospholipids and thereby activate kinase C. Indeed, of the physiologic stimuli listed in Table 1, many are known stimulators of inositol lipid hydrolysis in their specific target cells (see 2, 3 for references).

When analyzing the long-term effects of phorbol esters on EGF-induced Na$^+$/H$^+$ exchange in A431 cells, Whiteley et al (75) observed that TPA attenuates the stimulation of Na$^+$/H$^+$ exchange by EGF. This result, together with the fact that TPA may inhibit diacylglycerol formation (65) and Ca^{2+} mobilization by EGF (24; W. H. Moolenaar, unpublished data), suggests that kinase C, in addition to activating Na$^+$/H$^+$ exchange, may somehow antagonize the breakdown of inositol phospholipids following EGF addition to responsive cells.

Further support for the notion that the stimulus-induced Na$^+$/H$^+$ exchange activity and resultant rise in pH$_i$ is a consequence of the activation of phospholipase C comes from experiments on rabbit neutrophils (72). Pretreatment of these cells with pertussis toxin inhibits both the N-formyl peptide-induced breakdown of inositol phospholipids and the rise in pH$_i$ mediated by Na$^+$/H$^+$ exchange. Inhibition by this bacterial toxin is specific, in that the pH$_i$ response to TPA is not affected. The membrane substrate for pertussis toxin is a GTP-binding regulatory protein that in addition to mediating inhibition of adenylate cyclase (19) may be responsible for activation of phospholipase C.

Future experiments should reveal whether growth factors utilize additional pathways to activate the Na$^+$/H$^+$ exchanger, or that protein kinase C is the final common regulator of Na$^+$/H$^+$ exchange activity. We note that the intrinsic tyrosine protein kinase activity of certain mitogen receptors seems to have no direct role in regulating Na$^+$/H$^+$ exchange. Evidence for this notion comes from experiments using anti-EGF receptor monoclonal antibodies on A431 cells (17). Some of these antibodies can act as agonists in that they activate the EGF receptor tyrosine kinase activity both in vitro and in vivo, but none of these antibodies is capable of inducing a pH$_i$ response, which suggests that activation of the EGF receptor tyrosine kinase is not sufficient, by itself, to activate Na$^+$/H$^+$ exchange (17, 36).

Figure 2 is a schematic representation of the receptor-linked signal pathways. In this simplified scheme, activation of Na$^+$/H$^+$ exchange and Ca^{2+} mobilization occur in parallel but independently of each other through the action of phospholipase C, whereas the tyrosine-specific protein kinase initiates a distinct pathway.

CONCLUDING REMARKS

The physiological significance of cytoplasmic alkalinization is a crucial question, both in the action of external stimuli in general and that of growth factors

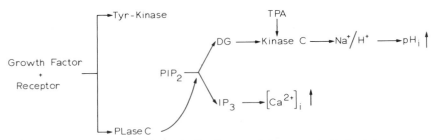

Figure 2   Proposed sequence of events leading from growth factor-receptor binding to increase in pH_i. Abbreviations used: Tyr-kinase = tyrosine-specific protein kinase; PLase C = phospholipase C; PIP_2 = phosphatidylinositol 4,5-bisphosphate; DG = 1,2-diacylglycerol; IP_3 = inositol 1,4,5-trisphosphate; TPA = 12-O-tetradecanoyl phorbol-13-acetate. For details of the PIP_2 hydrolosis pathway see References 2, 3, and 46.

in particular. Perhaps the clearest demonstration of a role for pH_i in the initiation of a mitogenic response has been made with fertilized sea urchin eggs, where pH_i must rise from 6.8 to above 7.0 to permit DNA synthesis to begin (74). One of the critical pH_i-dependent steps in fertilized eggs appears to be the stimulation of protein synthesis (10, 67, 74). Using mutant fibroblasts that lacked functional Na^+/H^+ exchange activity, Pouysségur et al (52, 53) showed that the initiation of DNA synthesis in mitogen-stimulated cells is extremely sensitive to pH_i. It appears that below a critical threshold value (around 7.2) pH_i becomes limiting for cell proliferation. The mutant cells resume growth as soon as their pH_i is artificially elevated, either by raising external pH or by incubating them in HCO_3^-/CO_2 buffered media (52, 53; see also 5 for a HCO_3^- effect that is probably similar). Addition of bicarbonate apparently raises pH_i into the "permissive range" due to the operation of the Na^+-dependent HCO_3^-/Cl^- exchanger (30).

In summary, evidence is accumulating that Na^+/H^+ exchange, in addition to its role in pH_i regulation, may take part in transmembrane signalling by growth factors and other hormones. Receptor occupancy alters the pH_i sensitivity of the exchanger, and this causes pH_i to rise to a more alkaline value. This intrinsic modification of the exchanger is probably mediated by protein kinase C as a consequence of the receptor-linked activation of phospholipase C. Information concerning the molecular structure of the Na^+/H^+ exchanger may become available in the near future, and this should facilitate further exploration of the biochemical steps underlying the activation of the exchanger by physiologic stimuli.

ACKNOWLEDGEMENT

The author is supported by a grant from the Netherlands Cancer Foundation (Koningin Wilhelmina Fonds).

Literature Cited

1. Aronson, P. S. 1985. Kinetic properties of the plasma membrane Na$^+$-H$^+$ exchanger. *Ann. Rev. Physiol.* 47:545–60

1a. Aronson, P. S., Nee, J., Suhm, M. A. 1982. Modifier role of internal H$^+$ in activating the Na-H exchanger in renal microvillus membrane vesicles. *Nature* 299:161–63

2. Berridge, M. J. 1984. Inositol trisphosphate and diacylglycerol as second messengers. *Biochem. J.* 220:345–60

3. Berridge, M. J., Irvine, R. F. 1984. Inositol trisphosphate, a novel second messenger in cellular signal transduction. *Nature* 312:315–21

4. Besterman, J. M., May, W. S., LeVine, H., Cragoe, E. J., Cuatrecasas, P. 1985. Amiloride inhibits phorbol ester–stimulated Na$^+$/H$^+$ exchange and protein kinase C. *J. Biol. Chem.* 260:1155–59

5. Besterman, J. M., Tyrey, S. J., Cragoe, E. J., Cuatrecasas, P. 1984. Inhibition of epidermal growth factor-induced mitogenesis by amiloride and an analog: Evidence against a requirement for Na$^+$/H$^+$ exchange. *Proc. Natl. Acad. Sci. USA* 81:6762–66

6. Bishop, J. M. 1983. Cellular oncogenes and retroviruses. *Ann. Rev. Biochem.* 53:301–54

7. Boonstra, J., Moolenaar, W. H., Harrison, P. H., Moed, P., van der Saag, P. T., de Laat, S. W. 1983. Ionic responses and growth stimulation induced by nerve growth factor and epidermal growth factor in rat pheochromocytoma (PC12) cells. *J. Cell Biol.* 97:92–98

8. Boron, W. F. 1983. Transport of H$^+$ and of ionic weak acids and bases. *J. Membr. Biol.* 72:1–16

9. Burns, C. P., Rozengurt, E. 1983. Serum, platelet-derived growth factor, vasopressin and phorbol ester increase intracellular pH in Swiss 3T3 cells. *Biochem. Biophys. Res. Commun.* 116:931–38

10. Busa, W. B., Nuccitelli, R. 1984. Metabolic regulation via intracellular pH. *Am. J. Physiol.* 246:R409–38

11. Carpenter, G. 1984. Properties of the receptor for epidermal growth factor. *Cell* 37:357–58

12. Carpenter, G., Cohen, S. 1979. Epidermal growth factor. *Ann. Rev. Biochem.* 48:193–216

13. Cassel, D., Rothenberg, P., Zhuang, Y. X., Deuel, T. F., Glaser, L. 1983. Platelet-derived growth factor stimulates Na$^+$/H$^+$ exchange and induces cytoplasmic alkalinization in NR6 cells. *Proc. Natl. Acad. Sci. USA* 80:6224–28

14. Cassel, D., Whiteley, B., Zhuang, Y. X., Glaser, L. 1985. Mitogen-independent activation of Na$^+$/H$^+$ exchange in human epidermoid carcinoma A431 cells: regulation by medium osmolarity. *J. Cell. Physiol.* 122:178–86

15. Cassel, D., Zhuang, Y. X., Glaser, L. 1984. Vanadate stimulates Na$^+$/H$^+$ exchange activity in A431 cells. *Biochem. Biophys. Res. Commun.* 118:675–81

16. Davis, R. J., Czech, M. P. 1985. Amiloride directly inhibits growth factor receptor tyrosine kinase activity. *J. Biol. Chem.* 260:2543–51

17. Defize, L. H. K., Moolenaar, W. H., van der Saag, P. T., de Laat, S. W. 1986. Dissociation of cellular responses to epidermal growth factor by anti-receptor monoclonal antibodies. *EMBO J.* In press

18. Deuel, T. F., Huang, J. S. 1984. Platelet-derived growth factor. *J. Clin. Invest.* 74:669–76

18a. Frelin, C., Vigne, P., Lazdunski, M. 1983. The amiloride-sensitive Na$^+$/H$^+$ antiport in 3T3 fibroblasts. *J. Biol. Chem.* 258:6272–76

19. Gilman, A. G. 1984. G proteins and dual control of adenylate cyclase. *Cell* 36:577–79

19a. Grinstein, S., Cohen, S., Goetz, J. D., Rothstein, A. 1985. Osmotic and phorbol ester-induced activation of Na$^+$/H$^+$ exchange: possible role of protein phosphorylation in lymphocyte volume regulation. *J. Cell Biol.* 101:269–76

20. Grinstein, S., Cohen, S., Goetz, J. D., Rothstein, A., Gelfand, E. W. 1985. Characterization of the activation of Na$^+$/H$^+$ exchange in lymphocytes by phorbol esters: Change in cytoplasmic pH dependence of the antiport. *Proc. Natl. Acad. Sci. USA* 82:1429–33

21. Grinstein, S., Cohen, S., Goetz, J. D., Rothstein, A., Mellors, A., Gelfand, E. W. 1985. Activation of the Na$^+$/H$^+$ antiport by changes in cell volume and by phorbol esters. Possible role of protein kinase. *Current Top. Membr. Transp.* In press

22. Grinstein, S., Cohen, S., Rothstein, A. 1984. Cytoplasmic pH regulation in thymic lymphocytes by an amiloride-sensitive Na$^+$/H$^+$ antiport. *J. Gen. Physiol.* 83:341–69

23. Habenicht, A. J. R., Glomset, J. A., King, N. C., Nist, C., Mitchell, C. D., Ross, R. 1981. Early changes in phosphatidylinositol and arachidonic acid metabolism in quiescent Swiss 3T3 cells stimulated to divide by platelet-derived

growth factor. *J. Biol. Chem.* 256: 12329–35

24. Hesketh, T. R., Moore, J. P., Morris, J. D. H., Taylor, M. V., Rogers, J., et al. 1985. A common sequence of calcium and pH signals in the mitogenic stimulation of eukaryotic cells. *Nature* 313:481–84

25. Horne, W. C., Norman, N. E., Schwartz, D. B., Simons, E. R. 1981. Changes in cytoplasmic pH and in membrane potential in thrombin-stimulated human platelets. *Eur. J. Biochem.* 120:295–302

26. Johnson, J. J., Epel, D., Paul, M. 1976. Intracellular pH and activation of sea urchin eggs after fertilization. *Nature* 262:661–64

27. Koch, K. S., Leffert, H. L. 1979. Increased sodium ion flux is necessary to initiate rat hepatocyte proliferation. *Cell* 18:153–63

28. l'Allemain, G., Franchi, A., Cragoe, E. J., Pouysségur, J. 1984. Blockade of the Na^+/H^+ antiport abolishes growth factor-induced DNA synthesis in fibroblasts. *J. Biol. Chem.* 259:4313–19

29. l'Allemain, G., Paris, S., Pouysségur, J. 1984. Growth factor action and intracellular pH regulation in fibroblasts. *J. Biol. Chem.* 259:5809–15

30. l'Allemain, G., Paris, S., Pouysségur, J. 1985. Role of Na^+-dependent Cl^-/HCO_3^- exchange in regulation of intracellular pH in fibroblasts. *J. Biol. Chem.* 260:4877–83

31. Lopez-Rivas, A., Stroobant, P., Waterfield, M. D., Rozengurt, E. 1984. Ionic responses rapidly elicited by porcine platelet-derived growth factor in Swiss 3T3 cells. *EMBO J.* 3:939–44

32. Lubin, M., Cahn, F., Coutermarsh, B. A. 1982. Amiloride, protein synthesis, and activation of quiescent cells. *J. Cell. Physiol.* 113:247–51

33. Mahnensmith, R. L., Aronson, P. S. 1985. The plasma membrane Na^+-H^+ exchanger and its role in physiologic and pathophysiologic processes. *Circ. Res.* 56:773–88

34. Molski, T. F. P., Naccache, P. H., Volpi, M., Wolpert, L. M., Sha'afi, R. I. 1980. Specific modulation of the intracellular pH of rabbit neutrophils by chemotactic factors. *Biochem. Biophys. Res. Commun.* 94:508–14

35. Moolenaar, W. H., Boonstra, J., van der Saag, P. T., de Laat, S. W. 1981. Sodium/proton exchange in mouse neuroblastoma cells. *J. Biol. Chem.* 256:12883–87

36. Moolenaar, W. H., Defize, L. H. K., van der Saag, P. T., de Laat, S. W. 1986. The

generation of ionic signals by growth factors. *Current Top. Membr. Transp.* In press

37. Moolenaar, W. H., de Laat, S. W., Mummery, C. L., van der Saag, P. T. 1982. Na^+/H^+ exchange in the action of growth factors. In *Ions, Cell Proliferation, and Cancer*, ed. A. L. Boynton, W. L. McKeehan, J. F. Whitfield, pp. 151–62. New York/London: Academic. 551 pp.

38. Moolenaar, W. H., Mummery, C. L., van der Saag, P. T., de Laat, S. W. 1981. Rapid ionic events and the initiation of growth in serum-stimulated neuroblastoma cells. *Cell* 23:789–98

39. Moolenaar, W. H., Tertoolen, L. G. J., de Laat, S. W. 1984. The regulation of cytoplasmic pH in human fibroblasts. *J. Biol. Chem.* 259:7563–70

40. Moolenaar, W. H., Tertoolen, L. G. J., de Laat, S. W. 1984. Growth factors immediately raise cytoplasmic free Ca^{2+} in human fibroblasts. *J. Biol. Chem.* 259:8066–69

41. Moolenaar, W. H., Tertoolen, L. G. J., de Laat, S. W. 1984. Phorbol ester and diacylglycerol mimic growth factors in raising cytoplasmic pH. *Nature* 312:371–74

42. Moolenaar, W. H., Tsien, R. Y., van der Saag, P. T., de Laat, S. W. 1983. Na^+/H^+ exchange and cytoplasmic pH in the action of growth factors in human fibroblasts. *Nature* 304:645–48

43. Moolenaar, W. H., Yarden, Y., de Laat, S. W., Schlessinger, J. 1982. Epidermal growth factor induces electrically silent Na^+ influx in human fibroblasts. *J. Biol. Chem.* 257:8502–6

44. Moore, R. D. 1981. Stimulation of Na : H exchange by insulin. *Biophys. J.* 33:203–10

45. Mukherjee, S. P., Mukherjee, C. 1981. Metabolic activation of adipocytes by insulin accompanied by an early increase in intracellular pH. *Ann. NY Acad. Sci.* 372:347–51

46. Nishizuka, Y. 1984. The role of protein kinase C in cell surface signal transduction and tumour promotion. *Nature* 308:693–98

47. Owen, N. E. 1984. Platelet-derived growth factor stimulates Na^+ influx in vascular smooth muscle cells. *Am. J. Physiol.* 247:C501–5

48. Owen, N. E., Villereal, M. L. 1982. Evidence for a role of calmodulin in serum stimulation of Na^+ influx in human fibroblasts. *Proc. Natl. Acad. Sci. USA* 79:3537–41

49. Owen, N. E., Villereal, M. L. 1983. Lys-bradykinin stimulates Na^+ influx

and DNA synthesis in cultured human fibroblasts. *Cell* 32:979–85

50. Paris, S., Pouysségur, J. 1983. Biochemical characterization of the amiloride sensitive Na⁺/H⁺ antiport in Chinese hamster lung fibroblasts. *J. Biol. Chem.* 258:3503–8

51. Paris, S., Pouysségur, J. 1984. Growth factors activate the Na⁺/H⁺ antiporter in quiescent fibroblasts by increasing its affinity for intracellular H⁺. *J. Biol. Chem.* 259:10989–94

52. Pouysségur, J., Chambard, J.-C., Franchi, A., l'Allemain, G., Paris, S., van Obberghen-Shilling, E. 1985. Growth factor activation of the Na⁺/H⁺ antiporter controls growth of fibroblasts by regulating intracellular pH. In *Cancer Cells*, Vol. 3, ed. J. Feramisco, B. Ozanne, C. Stiles, pp. 409–16. Cold Spring Harbor, NY: Cold Spring Harbor Lab.

53. Pouysségur, J., Sardet, C., Franchi, A., l'Allemain, G., Paris, S. 1984. A specific mutation abolishing Na⁺/H⁺ antiport activity in hamster fibroblasts precludes growth at neutral and acidic pH. *Proc. Natl. Acad. Sci. USA* 81:4833–37

54. Putnam, R. W. 1985. Effect of insulin on intracellular pH in frog skeletal muscle fibers. *Am. J. Physiol.* 248:C330–36

55. Rink, T. J., Tsien, R. Y., Pozzan, T. 1982. Cytoplasmic pH and free Mg²⁺ in lymphocytes. *J. Cell Biol.* 95:189–96

56. Roos, A., Boron, W. 1981. Intracellular pH. *Physiol. Rev.* 61:296–434

57. Rothenberg, P., Glaser, L., Schlessinger, P., Cassel, D. 1983. Activation of Na⁺/H⁺ exchange by epidermal growth factor elevates intracellular pH in A431 cells. *J. Biol. Chem.* 258:12644–53

58. Rozengurt, E. 1981. Stimulation of Na⁺ influx, Na⁺,K⁺ pump activity and DNA synthesis in quiescent cultured cells. *Adv. Enzyme Regul.* 19:61–85

59. Sawyer, S. T., Cohen, S. 1981. Enhancement of calcium uptake and phosphatidylinositol turnover by epidermal growth factor in A431 cells. *Biochemistry* 20:6280–86

60. Schuldiner, S., Rozengurt, E. 1982. Na⁺/H⁺ antiport in Swiss 3T3 cells: Mitogenic stimulation leads to cytoplasmic alkalinization. *Proc. Natl. Acad. Sci. USA* 79:7778–82

61. Sha'afi, R. I., Naccache, P. H., Molski, T. F. P., Volpi, M. 1982. Chemotactic stimuli-induced changes in the pH_i of rabbit neutrophils. In *Intracellular pH: Its Measurement, Regulation, and Utilization in Cellular Functions*, ed. R. Nuccitelli, D. W. Deamer, pp. 513–25. New York: Liss. 594 pp.

62. Siffert, W., Fox, G., Mückenhoff, K., Scheid, P. 1984. Thrombin stimulates Na⁺-H⁺ exchange across the human platelet membrane. *FEBS Lett.* 172:272–74

63. Smith, J. B., Brock, T. A. 1983. Analysis of angiotensin-stimulated sodium transport in cultured smooth muscle cells from rat aorta. *J. Cell. Physiol.* 114:284–90

64. Smith, J. B., Rozengurt, E. 1978. Lithium transport by fibroblastic mouse cells: characterization and stimulation by serum and growth factors in quiescent cultures. *J. Cell. Physiol.* 97:441–50

65. Smith, K. B., Losonczy, I., Sahai, A., Pannerselvam, M., Fehnel, P., Salomon, D. S. 1983. Effect of TPA on the growth inhibitory and increased phosphatidylinositol responses induced by EGF in A431 cells. *J. Cell. Physiol.* 117:91–100

66. Spring, K. R., Ericson, A. C. 1982. Epithelial cell volume modulation and regulation. *J. Membr. Biol.* 69:167–76

67. Swann, K., Whitaker, M. 1985. Stimulation of the Na/H exchanger of sea urchin eggs by phorbol ester. *Nature* 314:274–77

67a. Vara, F., Schneider, J. A., Rozengurt, E. 1985. Ionic responses rapidly elicited by activation of protein kinase C in Swiss 3T3 cells. *Proc. Natl. Acad. Sci. USA* 82:2384–88

68. Vigne, P., Frelin, C., Cragoe, E. J., Lazdunski, M. 1984. Structure-activity relationships of amiloride and certain of its analogues in relation to the blockade of the Na⁺/H⁺ exchange system. *Mol. Pharmacol.* 25:131–36

69. Vigne, P., Frelin, C., Lazdunski, M. 1982. The amiloride-sensitive Na⁺/H⁺ exchange system in skeletal muscle cells in culture. *J. Biol. Chem.* 257:9394–9400

70. Vigne, P., Frelin, C., Lazdunski, M. 1984. The Na⁺-dependent regulation of the internal pH in chick skeletal muscle cells. *EMBO J.* 3:1865–70

71. Villereal, M. L. 1981. Sodium fluxes in human fibroblasts: Effect of serum, Ca²⁺ and amiloride. *J. Cell. Physiol.* 107:359–69

72. Volpi, M., Naccache, P. H., Molski, T. F. P., Shefcyk, J., Huang, C.-K., et al. 1985. Pertussis toxin inhibits the FMLP but not the phorbol ester stimulated changes in rabbit neutrophils: role of the "G-proteins" in excitation response coupling. *Proc. Natl. Acad. Sci. USA* 82:2708–12

73. Westermark, B., Heldin, C.-H., Ek, B., Johnsson, A., Mellström, K., et al.

1983. Biochemistry and biology of platelet-derived growth factor. In *Growth and Maturation Factors,* ed. G. Guroff, 1:75–115. New York: Wiley
74. Whitaker, M. J., Steinhardt, R. A. 1982. Ionic regulation of egg activation. *Q. Rev. Biophys.* 15:593–666
75. Whiteley, B., Cassel, D., Zhuang, Y. X., Glaser, L. 1984. The tumor promoter

phorbol 12-myristate 13-acetate inhibits mitogen-stimulated Na^+/H^+ exchange in human epidermoid carcinoma A431 cells. *J. Cell Biol.* 99:1162–66
76. Zhuang, Y. X., Cragoe, E. J., Shaikewitz, T., Glaser, L., Cassel, D. 1984. Characterization of potent Na^+/H^+ exchange inhibitors of the amiloride series in A431 cells. *Biochemistry* 23:4481–88

Ann. Rev. Physiol. 1986. 48:377–88

INTRACELLULAR pH REGULATION IN EPITHELIAL CELLS

Walter F. Boron

Department of Physiology, Yale University School of Medicine, New Haven, Connecticut 06510

INTRODUCTION

The regulation of intracellular pH (pH_i) in epithelial cells is expected to be extremely important because virtually every biological process is pH sensitive. In addition, changes in pH_i may be important in modulating transepithelial solute transport, in modifying biochemical or endocrinological function, and in controlling cell growth and differentiation. Certain epithelial cells are specialized for transporting acid/base equivalents through the cell, from one side of the epithelium to the other. In these cells pH_i regulation may be intimately interwoven with transepithelial acid/base traffic. This brief review will be confined to ion-transport processes, studied in intact epithelial cells, that affect pH_i regulation. Other reviews have considered epithelial acid/base transport studies at the level of whole epithelia (26) or isolated membrane vesicles (5).

APPROACHES TO STUDYING pH_i REGULATION IN EPITHELIAL CELLS

The methods available for examining epithelial pH_i regulation, as for nonepithelial cells, fall into two broad categories: First, ion flux measurements (e.g. of Na^+ or Cl^-) provide vital data on the coupling of acid/base transport processes (e.g. Na-H or Cl-HCO_3 exchange). Second, rates of pH_i change reflect acid/base transport rates across one or both of the epithelial cell membranes. The technologies available for measuring pH_i have recently been reviewed (37, 45). The most useful approach to studying a pH_i-regulating transporter involves rapidly perturbing the cell by loading it with acid (see 37) and then monitoring its recovery toward its initial pH_i value. For example,

377

Na-H exchange produces such a pH_i recovery by exchanging extracellular Na^+ for intracellular H^+. Alternately, pH_i can be monitored after rapidly changing the extracellular (o) concentration of a relevant solute. In response to a reduction of $[Cl^-]_o$, for example, Cl-HCO$_3$ exchange raises pH_i by increasing the rate at which it exchanges internal Cl^- for external HCO_3^-. Additional information on the mechanism of ion transport can be obtained by performing the aforementioned maneuvers in the presence of potential inhibitors of transport, or in the absence of various solutes.

REGULATION OF pH_i BY EPITHELIAL ACID/BASE TRANSPORT SYSTEMS

As in other cells, the steady-state pH_i of epithelial cells is determined by the balance between the chronic rates of intracellular acid loading and extrusion[1]. Chronic *intracellular acid loading* can result from (*a*) cellular metabolism (see 15, 37), (*b*) the passive flux of acid/base equivalents across the cell membrane (37), or (*c*) carrier-mediated transport of acid/base equivalents. This last category includes Cl-HCO$_3$ exchange and electrogenic Na/HCO_3^- cotransport, discussed below.

Acid extrusion, defined as the sum of acid efflux and base influx, normally occurs by three major classes of transporter: (*a*) specialized transporters (e.g. Na/HCO_3-Cl/H and Na-H exchangers) regulated by pH_i, (*b*) H^+-translocating ATPases (e.g. H-K exchangers and electrogenic H^+ pumps) located at the cell membrane, or (*c*) other acid/base transporters (e.g. Na/lactate and Na/acetate cotransport).

Cl-HCO$_3$ Exchange

This transporter, or family of transporters, exchanges anions on opposite sides of the cell membrane in a stoichiometry of 1 : 1, and is inhibited or blocked by disulfonic stilbene derivatives (16). This exchanger has been examined in considerable detail in erythrocytes and Ehrlich cells (see 49), and has also been studied using ion-sensitive microelectrodes in sheep cardiac Purkinje fibers (46). Although Cl-HCO$_3$ exchange has been widely hypothesized to account for HCO_3^- transport in various epithelia, it has been directly demonstrated in only two preparations, *Necturus* gallbladder (35) and the pig-kidney cell line LLC-PK$_1$ (17).

Because the inward gradient for Cl^- generally exceeds that for HCO_3^-, the direction of net transport predicted by a 1 : 1 stoichiometry is net Cl^- influx/ HCO_3^- efflux. This represents a chronic intracellular acid load. Lowering pH_i

---

[1]Acute processes, such as passive fluxes of neutral weak acids (e.g. CO_2) and bases (e.g. NH_3), only transiently influence pH_i, and will not be considered in this review.

or $[Cl^-]_o$ enough to reverse the sum of the Cl^- and HCO_3^- gradients should cause HCO_3^- to enter in exchange for Cl^-, thereby alkalinizing the cell. Such a reversal of Cl-HCO_3 exchange apparently occurs in acid-loaded mouse skeletal muscle (2), though the actual transition between forward and reverse Cl-HCO_3 exchange has yet to be well documented in any cell. In epithelial cells, the exchanger has been studied by monitoring pH_i while modifying the transmembrane Cl^- or HCO_3^- gradients. For example, in single, isolated PK_1 cells (17), reducing $[Cl^-]_o$ also leads to a reversible increase in pH_i that is inhibited by stilbenes and depends on HCO_3^-. Conversely, reducing pH_o causes a reversible fall of pH_i that is blocked by stilbenes and depends on Cl^- and HCO_3^-.

Electrogenic Na/HCO₃⁻ Cotransport

In the proximal tubule (PT) of the salamander *Ambystoma tigrinum,* a novel transport mechanism normally mediates the net efflux of Na^+, HCO_3^- (or a related species), and negative charge (10). This cotransporter, which is inhibited by stilbenes but is independent of Cl^-, has also been found in cultured bovine corneal endothelial cells (24, 25), the proximal convoluted tubule (PCT) of the rat (4, 52), and the *Necturus* PT (27). Transport can be detected by monitoring pH_i, intracellular Na^+ activity (a$_i^{Na}$), and/or cell voltage. In the *Ambystoma* PT (10), for example, reducing basolateral (b) $[HCO_3^-]$ causes a rapid fall of both pH_i and a$_i^{Na}$, as well as a spiking basolateral depolarization (i.e. the cell interior transiently becomes more positive). Similarly, reducing $[Na^+]_b$ leads to a rapid and reversible fall of pH_i and a spiking basolateral depolarization. These changes are all severely depressed by adding stilbenes or by performing the maneuvers in nominally HCO_3^--free solutions.

The voltage changes indicate that more than one HCO_3^- equivalent accompanies each Na^+, though the precise ratio is unknown. The simplest stoichiometry that would account for the *Ambystoma* PT data (10) is two HCO_3^- equivalents for each Na^+. When applied to the rat PCT, however, this predicts that the cotransporter should mediate a steady-state net influx of HCO_3^-, rather than the net efflux needed to account for transepithelial HCO_3^- reabsorption[2]. Assuming that Na/HCO_3^- cotransport is indeed responsible for basolateral HCO_3^- efflux in the rat PCT, and not merely an epiphenomenon, Yoshitomi et al (52) have suggested a HCO_3^- : Na^+ stoichiometry of 3 : 1. This ratio predicts a net HCO_3^- efflux under normal conditions for the rat PCT, and also appears to be consistent with the *Ambystoma* data.

[2]Given $[Na^+]_i = 17.2$ mM, $[HCO_3^-]_i = 18.5$ mM, $[Na^+]_b = 144$ mM, and $[HCO_3^-]_b = 30$ mM (51), the 2 : 1 stoichiometry predicts a reversal potential of ~ -82 mV. This is slightly more negative than the observed basolateral membrane potential of ~ -75 mV, and therefore predicts a net Na/HCO_3^- influx. The 3 : 1 stoichiometry predicts a reversal potential of -47 mV, and thus a net Na/HCO_3^- efflux.

Na/HCO₃-Cl/H Exchange

A transporter, or family of transporters, that normally exchanges extracellular Na^+ and HCO_3^- (or a similar species) for intracellular Cl^- and H^+ (see 8, 37) regulates pH_i in several invertebrate cells (12, 13, 44). It is also present in the basolateral membrane of the *Necturus* PT (23), and perhaps in certain cultured mammalian cells (see 38). The transporter is inhibited by stilbenes, but is unaffected by amiloride. The stoichiometry is 1 Na^+ : 1 Cl^- : 2 acid/base equivalents (13). Although the mechanism of ion transport is not known, kinetic data from the squid axon (7, 13) suggest that the extracellular ion pair $NaCO_3^-$ may be exchanged for intracellular Cl^-. However, the ion-pair model has been ruled out for a superficially similar transporter in barnacle muscle (12). In both barnacle muscle (39) and snail neurons (20) net transport is reversed when the gradients for one or more of the transported ions are sufficiently altered. This finding suggests that the transporter is driven solely by ion gradients. The comparable system in the squid axon, however, has yet to be reversed and requires ATP. The hallmark of this transporter is that it is nearly inactive at alkaline pH_i values, and is gradually activated as pH_i falls below a certain threshold (14). This same pH_i dependence has also been identified for the Na-H exchanger. This pH_i dependence identifies Na/HCO₃-Cl/H and Na-H exchangers as "smart" transporters, conceptually distinguishing them from processes, such as Cl-HCO₃ exchange and Na/HCO₃⁻ cotransport, that appear to be rather pH_i insensitive.

Na-H Exchange

A transporter that normally exchanges external Na^+ for intracellular H^+ in a 1 : 1 stoichiometry is responsible for pH_i regulation in a variety of vertebrate cells (see 1, 5). The transporter requires Na^+, and is inhibited by large doses of amiloride (e.g. 1 mM) or smaller doses of more potent amiloride analogs (see 28). It differs from the Na/HCO₃-Cl/H exchanger in that it does not require HCO_3^- or Cl^- and it is insensitive to stilbene derivatives (9). The Na-H exchanger is readily reversed by manipulating the Na^+ gradient and has a pH_i dependence virtually the same as that of the Na/HCO₃-Cl/H exchanger. Activation of the Na-H exchanger is thought to play a crucial role in activation of cells by growth factors and mitogens (see 28).

Proton Pumps

ATP-driven H^+ pumps play a central role in acid secretion by certain epithelia. An electrogenic H^+ pump is responsible for HCO_3^- reabsorption in the mammalian distal nephron and in the turtle urinary bladder (3). An electroneutral K-H exchange pump is responsible for gastric acid secretion (21). Because ATP hydrolysis generally releases far more energy than the flux of an ion (e.g. Na^+) down its electrochemical gradient, these pumps are able to transport H^+

against very large transmembrane pH gradients. The vast majority of the work on these pumps has been carried out at the level of the whole epithelium or that of isolated membrane vesicles. The role these transporters normally play in pH_i regulation is not entirely clear. A Na^+-independent component of pH_i recovery from an intracellular acid load has been identified in several preparations (see Table 1). In separated rabbit proximal tubules (6) and rabbit medullary collecting duct cells (53), the Na-independent pH_i recovery has been inhibited by depleting the cells of ATP. In the rabbit proximal straight tubule (PST) the Na-independent pH_i recovery drives pH_i to a value 0.1–0.2 higher than the value that normally prevails in the presence of Na^+.

Cotransport of Na^+ with Anionic Weak Bases

A number of Na^+/organic-anion transport systems have been identified in membrane vesicles derived from epithelial cells (see 50). The addition of 3.6 mM D- or L-lactate to the lumen of an isolated *Ambystoma* PT incubated in nominally HCO_3^--free solutions causes pH_i, as measured with microelectrodes, to reversibly rise by ~ 0.20 (42). This effect requires luminal Na^+ and occurs with no change in basolateral membrane potential, which is consistent with an electroneutral luminal Na/lactate cotransport system. For the isolated rabbit PST in nominally HCO_3^--free solutions, bilateral removal of 10 mM acetate causes pH_i, as measured with a dye (31), to transiently increase and then slowly fall to a value ~ 0.4 below the normal level. Readdition of acetate elicits a rapid, transient acidification, followed by a slower recovery of pH_i to its normal level. In the absence of Na^+, however, the slower pH_i changes are completely absent; this is consistent with the existence of a Na/acetate cotransporter at the luminal and/or basolateral membrane of the rabbit PST. Thus, in both the amphibian and mammalian PT, Na^+-coupled organic-anion transport systems are capable of producing large pH_i changes.

pH_i REGULATION IN SELECTED EPITHELIAL CELLS

Amphibian Proximal Tubules

The amphibian PT is perhaps the epithelial cell whose pH_i physiology has been studied most extensively. Although the amphibian PT does not develop a significant transepithelial pH gradient, it reabsorbs substantial amounts of HCO_3^- isosmotically (22, 32). Furthermore, in stop-flow perfusion experiments in which the initial luminal $[HCO_3^-]$ is elevated from the normal 10 mM to 25 or 50 mM, the rate constant of HCO_3^- reabsorption is more than 40 times greater than that of volume reabsorption (32). At least some of the HCO_3^- reabsorbed under free-flow conditions is therefore likely to be actively transported through the PT cell.

In cells for which there is reason to suspect separate H^+ and HCO_3^- transport-

Table 1 Ion transport systems that have been shown to affect pH_i in intact epithelial cells[1]

System and tissue	Method	Comments	Reference
$C1$-HCO_3^- Exchange			
Necturus gallbladder	ISE	isolated glands	35
LLC-PK_1	dye (a)	single cultured cells	17
Rabbit CCT	dye (f)	isolated perfused tubules	41
Electrogenic Na/HCO_3 Cotransport			
Ambystoma PT	ISE	isolated perfused tubules	10
Bovine corneal endothelium	VE, ^{22}Na	cultured cells	24, 25
Necturus PT	ISE	isolated perfused tubules	27
Rat PT	ISE, dye (f)	microperfused tubules	4, 52
Na/HCO_3-$C1$/H Exchange			
Necturus PT	ISE	microperfused tubules	23
Na-H Exchange			
Ambystoma PT	ISE	isolated perfused tubules	9
Necturus gallbladder	ISE, ^{22}Na	isolated glands	47, 48
Necturus gallbladder	ISE	isolated glands treated with cyclic AMP	36
Rabbit stomach	dye (f)	isolated glands, mixed cell types	33
Bovine corneal endothelium	^{22}Na	cultured cells	25
Hepatocytes	dye (f)	cells in primary culture	34
Rabbit CCT	dye (a)	isolated tubules, mixed cell types	18
Na-Independent pH_i Recovery (possible H^+ pump)			
Rabbit collecting duct	dye (f)	cell suspensions isolated from inner stripe of outer medulla	53
Rabbit PT	DMO	tubule suspensions	6
Rabbit PST	dye (a)	isolated tubules	30
Rat PCT	ISE	microperfused tubules	52
Rabbit CCT	dye (a)	isolated tubules	18
Na/Organic Weak Base Cotransport			
Ambystoma PT	ISE	isolated perfused tubule	42
Rabbit PST	dye (a)	isolated perfused tubule	31

[1]Abbreviations: PT = proximal tubule (S = straight, C = convoluted), CCT = cortical collecting tubule, ISE = ion-selective microelectrodes, a = absorbance, f = fluorescence

ers, the simplest approach is to first study pH_i regulation in the nominal absence of HCO_3^-, and then begin the more complicated task of analyzing HCO_3^- transport. In experiments in which ion-sensitive microelectrodes were employed in isolated perfused tubules in the nominal absence of HCO_3^-, pH_i in the *Ambystoma* PT was found to recover rapidly from an acute acid load. Further experiments demonstrated that this pH_i recovery is mediated by luminal and basolateral Na-H exchangers (9). More recent work has also implicated a Na-dependent, luminal lactate transporter that, like the Na-H exchanger, normally alkalinizes the PT cell (42). In the presence of HCO_3^-, basolateral electrogenic Na/HCO_3^- cotransport normally mediates a net efflux of HCO_3^-, which acid loads the cell and causes the steady-state pH_i to fall to a value ~ 0.15 below that found in the absence of HCO_3^- (10). Inhibition of Na/HCO_3^- cotransport by acetazolamide reduces this acid load and allows pH_i to rise (W. F. Boron & P. Fong, unpublished). The acetazolamide probably reduces HCO_3^- transport by inhibiting intracellular carbonic anhydrase (thereby reducing the intracellular conversion of CO_2 to HCO_3^-), although an additional direct inhibition of the transporter cannot yet be ruled out.

Evidence suggests that the main route for basolateral Cl^- exit in the *Necturus* PT is Na/HCO_3-Cl/H exchange (23). The major basolateral pathway for HCO_3^-, however, is a Cl-independent electrogenic Na/HCO_3^- cotransporter (27), similar to that of *Ambystoma*. Thus, although Na/HCO_3-Cl/H exchange plays an important role in Cl^- transport, it is eclipsed by Na/HCO_3^- cotransport as far as HCO_3^- transport is concerned. Indeed, data obtained on *Ambystoma* suggest that the maximal rate of basolateral transport for Cl^- is substantially less than for HCO_3^- (10).

Mammalian Proximal Tubules

The existence of an Na-H exchanger in mammalian brush-border membrane vesicles (see 5) is supported by studies of pH_i regulation. Microelectrode measurements of pH_i on the isolated rabbit PST have shown that luminal Na^+ removal produces a reversible fall in pH_i (40). Dye studies (30, 31), conducted in nominally HCO_3^--free solutions, have confirmed this observation and have shown that pH_i recovery from an acute acid load can occur by at least three routes. These are: (*a*) luminal Na-H exchange, (*b*) Na-dependent acetate uptake, and (*c*) a Na-independent mechanism. Na-dependent acid extrusion is far greater at the luminal than basolateral membrane. The Na-independent pH_i recovery from an acid load, which could represent the activity of a H^+ pump, has also been detected with DMO in a suspension of rabbit PT's (6) and with microelectrodes in cells of the rat PCT (51). Microelectrode data support the existence of a basolateral electrogenic Na/HCO_3^- transporter in the rat PCT (51). In the rabbit PST, dye studies indicate that $\sim 30\%$ of the pH_i change caused by altering $[HCO_3^-]_b$ requires Cl^-, which suggests a component of Cl-HCO_3 exchange (29).

Amphibian Gallbladder

Necturus gallbladder epithelial cells possess both Na-H and Cl-HCO_3 exchangers at the luminal (i.e. mucosal) membrane. As measured with a miniature pH-sensitive electrode under stop-flow conditions, the luminal Na-H exchanger acidifies the luminal solution in a process that is Na^+ dependent and amiloride sensitive (47). Studies in which Na^+ transport was assessed either by measuring ^{22}Na fluxes or by monitoring rates of change of a a_i^{Na} suggest that this Na-H exchange activity accounts for about half of the luminal Na^+ influx under the conditions of these experiments (48). Application of 8-Br-cyclic AMP, the phosphodiesterase inhibitor theophylline, or the adenylate cyclase activator forskolin reduced both pH_i and a a_i^{Na} (36). Elevation of [cyclic AMP]$_i$ reduced the rates of luminal acidification and pH_i recovery from an acute acid load, which is also consistent with inhibition of luminal Na-H exchange by cyclic AMP. Although a net luminal acidification occurs under normal circumstances, inhibition of the luminal Na-H exchanger with amiloride causes a brief luminal alkalinization. This, as well as the observation that removal of luminal Cl^- produces a short-lived stimulation of luminal acidification, is suggestive of a luminal Cl-HCO_3 exchanger. Indeed, removal of luminal Cl^- also causes a rapid, reversible rise in pH_i that is dependent on the presence of HCO_3^- and is inhibited by SITS (35). Observed changes in a_i^{Cl} are also in the direction expected in the presence of a Cl-HCO_3 exchanger.

Measurements of cell volume (19) indicate that luminal Na-H and Cl-HCO_3 exchangers are stimulated during cell shrinkage and are responsible for the subsequent increase in cell volume (19). If the Na-H and Cl-HCO_3 exchange rates were equal, then the net effect would be NaCl uptake, without any effect on pH_i or pH_o. The luminal acidification observed under what were presumably euvolemic conditions (47) suggests that Na-H exchange outstrips Cl-HCO_3 exchange. Thus the net effect is acid extrusion plus NaCl uptake, at least under these conditions.

RELATION BETWEEN TRANSEPITHELIAL ACID TRANSPORT AND pH_i REGULATION

The current model of HCO_3^- reabsorption by the PT, developed and refined from the late 1940s through the 1950s (see 26, 43), proposes that luminal HCO_3^- is not directly removed from the lumen, but titrated with H^+ secreted by the PT cell. This acid extrusion step would be achieved by Na-H exchange. The reaction sequence $H_2O + CO_2 \rightarrow H_2CO_3 \rightarrow H^+ + HCO_3^-$, the first step of which is catalyzed by carbonic anhydrase, would be the source of the intracellular H^+ as well as the by-product HCO_3^-, which would exit at the basolateral membrane. The model's essential features have since been verified experimentally. The only fundamental modifications that may be required are the inclusion of two possible acid-extruding mechanisms, a H^+ pump and Na-coupled uptake of anionic weak bases (see above). The philosophical foundation for interpreting how ion-transport systems interact to produce HCO_3^- reabsorption was formulated well before modern studies on pH_i regulation began (see 37). As a result, the PT cell has been thought of as a black box. The prevailing view is that (a) the primary event in acid secretion is Na-H exchange, (b) its purpose is to acidify the tubule lumen, (c) basolateral HCO_3^- efflux is a secondary event, and (d) it serves to provide sufficient substrate (i.e. H^+) for the luminal Na-H exchanger. More recent data on pH_i regulation suggest a slight shift in the emphasis of our philosophy of proximal tubule HCO_3^- reabsorption, toward the idea that acid secretion occurs as a by-product of pH_i regulation (9, 10).

The data reviewed in the previous sections suggest that pH_i regulation is a general property of epithelial cells, regardless of whether they engage in transepithelial acid/base transport. One might argue that transporters such as Na-H exchangers evolved in nonepithelial cells in order to regulate pH_i, and quite separately evolved in certain epithelial cells to secrete acid/base equivalents, regulating pH_i in these cells only by chance. However, a simpler alternative is to suppose that such transporters evolved to regulate pH_i, and that later modifications in the distribution of such transporters conferred upon the cells the ability to transport acid/base equivalents across the epithelium. Stages in this hypothetical evolutionary process might be represented by barnacle muscle, mammalian skeletal muscle, amphibian PT cells, and mammalian PT cells, all of which are discussed below.

Barnacle muscle has no discernible acid-loading transporters and a very low rate of chronic acid loading (see 37). Its $Na/HCO_3-Cl/H$ exchanger is nearly inactive at its threshold pH_i of ~ 7.4, and gradually increases its acid extrusion rate as pH_i falls below this point. Because the acid-loading rate is low, the steady-state pH_i need be only slightly below the threshold to dictate an acid extrusion rate sufficient to balance acid loading. A sudden fall in pH_i would stimulate acid extrusion in an attempt to return pH_i to the threshold level. Although this arrangement is ideal for defending against acid loads, restoring pH_i following an alkali load could be accomplished only by halting acid extrusion and waiting for metabolism and passive ion fluxes to slowly lower pH_i.

In mammalian skeletal muscle (see 1), acid is extruded by a Na-H exchanger that is kinetically similar to the $Na/HCO_3-Cl/H$ exchanger. In addition, there appears to be a $Cl-HCO_3$ exchanger (2), which presumably acid loads the cell under normal circumstances. pH_i probably stabilizes relatively far below the threshold, which dictates an acid extrusion rate high enough to counter Cl-HCO_3 exchange. The relatively high steady-state energetic cost of Na-H exchange may be the price paid for $Cl-HCO_3$ exchange. During severe pH_i decreases the latter may act as an adjunct acid extruder. During alkali loads, when Na-H exchange should slow or halt, $Cl-HCO_3$ exchange should produce a relatively rapid pH_i decline. Although the $Cl-HCO_3$ exchanger may help defend against alkali loads, the crucial element for pH_i regulation in this cell is the "smart" Na-H exchanger, which is highly sensitive to pH_i.

Any epithelial cell with symmetrically distributed acid-extruding and acid-loading activity is expected, like mammalian skeletal muscle, to efficiently regulate pH_i, but to be incapable of significant transcellular acid/base transport. The same is true of cells that lack a significant acid-loading mechanism or that have both acid-extruding and -loading mechanisms asymmetrically confined to the same side. The amphibian PT cell apparently has acid-extruding mechanisms on both its luminal (e.g. Na-H exchange, Na/lactate cotransport) and basolateral membranes (e.g. Na-H exchange), but its acid-loading mechanisms (e.g. Na/HCO_3^- cotransport) are confined to the basolateral membrane. This partial asymmetry enables the cell to efficiently regulate pH_i and to transfer a small amount of acid from its basolateral to its luminal surface.

The mammalian PT may represent the evolutionary culmination of acid/base regulating mechanisms in the epithelial cell. It has retained an excellent pH_i regulatory system and has developed an efficient, high-capacity acid-secreting scheme. This is achieved by confining acid-loading processes to the basolateral membrane (as in the amphibian PT) and acid-extruding processes to the luminal membrane, creating a cell with doubly asymmetric acid/base transporters. A modified view of HCO_3^- reabsorption by the PT would be that (a) the primary event is basolateral HCO_3^- efflux, (b) the latter serves to lower pH_i below the threshold of the Na-H exchanger, (c) the secondary event is Na-H exchange, and (d) the latter responds to the intracellular acid load by extruding acid across the luminal membrane. pH_i regulation in acid-secreting epithelial cells is thus philosophically identical to pH_i regulation in other cells. Appropriate modifications in the distribution of preexisting acid/base transport systems, however, cause transepithelial acid/base transport to occur as a by-product of pH_i regulation.

ACKNOWLEDGMENT

I thank Drs. A. W. Siebens and N. L. Nakhoul for their helpful comments on an earlier draft of this review. My work has been supported by NIH grants AM-01022 (Research Career Development Award) and AM-17433.

Literature Cited

1. Aickin, C. C. 1986. Intracellular pH regulation by vertebrate muscle. *Ann. Rev. Physiol.* 48:349–61
2. Aickin, C. C., Thomas, R. C. 1977. An investigation of the ionic mechanism of intracellular pH regulation in mouse soles muscle fibres. *J. Physiol.* 273:295–316
3. Al-Awqati, Q. 1978. H^+ transport in urinary epithelia. *Am. J. Physiol.* 235: F77–88
4. Alpern, R. J. 1985. Mechanism of basolateral membrane $H^+/OH^-/HCO_3^-$ trans-

port in the rat proximal convoluted tubule: A sodium-coupled electrogenic process. *J. Gen. Physiol.* 86:613–36
5. Aronson, P. S. 1985. Kinetic properties of the plasma membrane Na^+-H^+ exchanger. *Ann. Rev. Physiol.* 47:545–60
6. Bichara, M., Paillard, M., Leviel, F., Prigent, A., Gardin, J. -P. 1983. Na:H exchange and the primary H pump in the proximal tubule. *Am. J. Physiol.* 244: F165–71
7. Boron, W. F. 1985. Intracellular-pH-

regulating mechanism of the squid axon: Relation between the external Na^+ and HCO_3^- dependencies. *J. Gen. Physiol.* 85:325–45

8. Boron, W. F. 1985. Control of intracellular pH. In *The Kidney: Physiology and Pathophysiology*, ed. D. W. Seldin, G. Giebisch, pp. 1417–39. New York: Raven

9. Boron, W. F., Boulpaep, E. L. 1983. Intracellular pH regulation in the renal proximal tubule of the salamander: Na-H exchange. *J. Gen. Physiol.* 81:29–52

10. Boron, W. F., Boulpaep, E. L. 1983. Intracellular pH regulation in the renal proximal tubule of the salamander: Basolateral HCO_3^- transport. *J. Gen. Physiol.* 81:53–94

11. Boron, W. F., Fong, P. 1983. Effects of carbonic anhydrase inhibitors on basolateral HCO_3^- transport in salamander proximal tubules. *Kidney Int.* 23:230

12. Boron, W. F., McCormick, W. C., Roos, A. 1981. pH regulation in barnacle muscle fibers: Dependence on extracellular sodium and bicarbonate. *Am. J. Physiol.* 240:C80–89

13. Boron, W. F., Russell, J. M. 1983. Stoichiometry and ion dependencies of the intracellular-pH-regulating mechanism in squid giant axons. *J. Gen. Physiol.* 81:373–99

14. Boron, W. F., Russell, J. M., Brodwick, M. S., Keifer, D. W., Roos, A. 1978. Influence of cyclic AMP on intracellular regulation and chloride fluxes in barnacle muscle fibres. *Nature* 276:511–13

15. Busa, W. B., Nuccitelli, R. 1984. Metabolic regulation via intracellular pH. *Am. J. Physiol.* 246:R409–38

16. Cabantchik, Z. I., Knauf, P. A., Rothstein, A. 1978. The anion transport system of the red blood cell. The role of membrane protein evaluated by the use of "probes". *Biochem. Biophys. Acta* 515: 239–302

17. Chaillet, J. R., Amsler, K., Boron, W. F. Optical measurement of intracellular pH in single $LLC-PK_1$ cells: Demonstration of $Cl-HCO_3$ exchange. *Proc. Natl. Acad. Sci. USA.* In press

18. Chaillet, J. R., Lopes, A. G., Boron, W. F. 1985. Basolateral Na-H exchange in the rabbit cortical collecting tubule. *J. Gen. Physiol.* In press

19. Ericson, A.-C., Spring, K. R. 1982. Volume regulation by *Necturus* gallbladder: Apical Na^+-H^+ and $Cl^--HCO_3^-$ exchange. *Am. J. Physiol.* 243:C146–50

20. Evans, M. G., Thomas, R. C. 1984. Acid influx into snail neurones caused by reversal of the normal pH_i-regulating system. *J. Physiol.* 346:143–54

21. Forte, J. G., Machen, T. E., Obrink, K. J. 1980. Mechanisms of gastric H^+ and Cl^- transport. *Ann. Rev. Physiol.* 42: 111–26

22. Giebisch, G. 1956. Measurement of pH, chloride and insulin concentrations in proximal tubule fluid of *Necturus*. *Am. J. Physiol.* 185:171–75

23. Guggino, W. B., London, R., Boulpaep, E. L., Giebisch, G. 1983. Chloride transport across the basolateral cell membrane of the *Necturus* proximal tubule: Dependence on bicarbonate and sodium. *J. Membr. Biol.* 71:227–40

24. Jentsch, T. J., Matthes, H., Keller, S. K., Wiederholt, M. 1985. Anion dependence of electrical effects of bicarbonate and sodium on cultured bovine corneal endothelial cells. *Pflügers Arch.* 403: 175–85

25. Jentsch, T. J., Stahlknecht, T. L., Hollwede, H., Fischer, D. F., Keller, S. K., Wiederholt, M. 1985. A bicarbonate-dependent process inhibitable by disulfonic stilbenes and a Na^+/H^+ exchange mediate $^{22}Na^+$ uptake into cultured bovine corneal endothelium. *J. Biol. Chem.* 260:795–801

26. Koeppen, B., Giebisch, G., Malnic, G. 1985. Mechanism and regulation of renal tubular acidification. See Ref. 8, pp. 1491–1525

27. Lopes, A. G., Siebens, A. W., Giebisch, G., Boron, W. F. Electrogenic Na/HCO_3 cotransport in isolated perfused *Necturus* proximal tubules. *Kidney Int.* In press

28. Moolenaar, W. H. 1986. Effects of growth factors on intracellular pH regulation. *Ann. Rev. Physiol.* 48:363–76

29. Nakhoul, N., Boron, W. F. 1985. Intracellular pH regulation in rabbit proximal straight tubules: Basolateral HCO_3^- transport. *Kidney Int.* 27:286

30. Nakhoul, N., Boron, W. F. 1985. Intracellular-pH regulation in rabbit proximal straight tubules: Dependence on external sodium. *Fed. Proc.* 44:1898

31. Nakhoul, N., Boron, W. F. 1986. Effect of Na-dependent acetate transport on the intracellular pH of isolated rabbit proximal straight tubules. *Kidney Int.* In press

32. O'Regan, M. G., Malnic, G., Giebisch, G. 1982. Cell pH and luminal acidification in *Necturus* proximal tubule. *J. Membr. Biol.* 69:99–106

33. Paradiso, A. M., Tsien, R. Y., Machen, T. E. 1984. Na^+-H^+ exchange in gastric glands as measured with a cytoplasmic-trapped, fluorescent pH indicator. *Proc. Natl. Acad. Sci. USA* 81:7436–40

34. Pollock, A. S. 1984. Intracellular pH of

hepatocytes in primary monolayer culture. *Am. J. Physiol.* 246:F738–44

35. Reuss, L., Costantin, J. L. 1984. Cl⁻/ HCO₃⁻ exchange at the apical membrane of *Necturus* gallbladder. *J. Gen. Physiol.* 83:801–18

36. Reuss, L., Petersen, K.-U. 1985. Cyclic AMP inhibits Na⁺/H⁺ exchange at the apical membrane of *Necturus* gallbladder epithelium. *J. Gen. Physiol.* 85:409–29

37. Roos, A., Boron, W. F. 1981. Intracellular pH. *Physiol. Rev.* 61:296–434

38. Rothenberg, P., Glaser, L., Schlesinger, P., Cassel, D. 1983. Activation of Na⁺/ H⁺ exchange by epidermal growth factor elevates intracellular pH in A431 cells. *J. Biol. Chem.* 258:12644–53

39. Russell, J. M., Boron, W. F., Brodwick, M. S. 1983. Intracellular pH and Na fluxes in barnacle muscle with evidence for reversal of the ionic mechanism of intracellular pH regulation. *J. Gen. Physiol.* 82:47–78

40. Sasaki, S., Iino, Y., Shiigai, T., Takeuchi, J. 1984. Intracellular pH of isolated perfused rabbit proximal tubule: Effects of luminal Na and Cl. *Kidney Int.* 25:282

41. Schwartz, G. J., Al-Awqati, Q. 1985. Two functionally distinct types of mitochondria-rich (MR) cells in cortical collecting tubule (CCT) as determined by changes in cell pH (pHᵢ) in individually identified cells. *Kidney Int.* 27:288

42. Siebens, A. W., Boron, W. F. 1985. A luminal, electroneutral Na/lactate cotransporter and its effect on intracellular pH of salamander proximal tubules. *Kidney Int.* In press

43. Smith, H. W. 1951. *The Kidney. Structure and Function in Health and Disease.* New York: Oxford Univ. Press. 1049 pp.

44. Thomas, R. C. 1977. The role of bicarbonate, chloride and sodium ions in the regulation of intracellular pH in small neurones. *J. Physiol.* 273:317–38

45. Thomas, R. C. 1984. Experimental displacement of intracellular pH and the mechanism of its subsequent recovery. *J. Physiol.* 354:3P–22P

46. Vaughan-Jones, R. D. 1979. Regulation of chloride in quiescent sheep heart Purkinje fibres studied using intracellular chloride and pH-sensitive microelectrodes. *J. Physiol.* 295:111–37

47. Weinman, S. A., Reuss, L. 1982. Na⁺- H⁺ exchange at the apical membrane of *Necturus* gallbladder. *J. Gen. Physiol.* 80:299–321

48. Weinman, S. A., Reuss, L. 1984. Na⁺- H⁺ exchange and Na⁺ entry across the apical membrane of *Necturus* gallbladder. *J. Gen. Physiol.* 83:57–74

49. Wieth, J. O., Brahm, J. 1985. Cellular anion transport. See Ref. 8, pp. 49–89.

50. Wright, E. M. 1985. Transport of carboxylic acids by renal membrane vesicles. *Ann. Rev. Physiol.* 47:127–41

51. Yoshitomi, K., Fromter, E. 1985. How big is the electrochemical potential difference of Na⁺ across rat renal proximal tubular cell membranes in vivo? *Pflügers Arch.* In press

52. Yoshitomi, K., Burckhardt, B.-Ch., Fromter, E. 1985. Rheogenic sodium-bicarbonate cotransport in the peritubular cell membrane of rat renal proximal tubule. *Pflügers Arch.* Submitted for publication

53. Zeidel, M. L., Silva, P., Seifter, J. L. 1985. ATP-dependent intracellular pH (pHᵢ) regulation in rabbit medullary collecting duct (MCD) cells. *Kidney Int.* 27:291

Ann. Rev. Physiol. 1986. 48:389–402

MECHANISMS AND CONSEQUENCES OF pH-MEDIATED CELL REGULATION

William B. Busa

Department of Zoology, University of California, Davis, California 95616

INTRODUCTION

The activity of hydrogen ions (commonly expressed in terms of pH) has long been recognized as a parameter of fundamental importance in aqueous chemistry. Although the same would logically be expected to be true for that rather specialized branch of aqueous chemistry known as cell biology, the technical difficulties of measuring this parameter within the confines of the intact cell have greatly retarded experimental assessment of the roles intracellular pH (pH_i) might play in regulating the behavior of cells. Fortunately, recent technical advances have provided cell biologists with a growing armory of techniques with which to measure pH_i (see References 46 and 57 for reviews), and their application has uncovered a large (and still growing) number of instances in which pH_i changes accompany defined events in the lives of cells. In a total of nineteen genera these events include gamete activation and fertilization, cyst and spore germination, various examples of stimulus-response coupling, progression through the cell cycle, and changes in cellular energy balance (see References 13 and 47 for review). Most recently, pH_i changes have been detected or inferred in the sequence of events involved in differentiation of the slime mold *Dictyostelium* (24, 32), in the maturation of nematode spermatids to active spermatozoa (78), in the chemotactic response of the myxomycete *Physarum* (28), in motility initiation of mammalian spermatozoa (5), in germination of zoospores of the phycomycete *Blastocladiella* (74), and in mitogenic stimulation of numerous mammalian cell lines (see W. H. Moolenaar, this volume). Conclusive evidence that these pH_i changes play a regulatory role in the processes they accompany has proven difficult to achieve, in

389

0066-4278/86/0315-0389$02.00

part because of the lack of highly specific inhibitors and stimulators of pH_i changes. Nonetheless, it is now widely accepted that pH_i plays a central role in regulating sea urchin egg and sperm activation, the stimulation of glycolysis in frog muscle by insulin, and the *Artemia* embryo dormancy/development transition (see Reference 13 for review). Recent results suggest an important permissive role for pH_i in the mitogenic activity of serum growth factors in mammalian fibroblasts (W. H. Moolenaar, this volume).

Given this recent explosion of examples of cell systems in which pH_i changes may play a regulatory role, it is important to consider the potential targets at which pH_i changes might act. As discussed in the conclusion of this review, these targets are necessarily manifold. I shall discuss and review recent evidence concerning some of the better-defined targets, including pH-dependent enzyme activities, cytoskeletal protein polymerization and cross-linking, gap junctional conductance; and the dependence of intracellular free Ca^{2+} and cyclic AMP levels on intracellular pH. This treatment will necessarily be somewhat speculative, principally due to the relative youth of this field of inquiry. Nonetheless, I will emphasize systems and mechanisms for which some evidence exists that the proposed responses are in fact observed under physiologically relevant conditions.

pH DEPENDENCES OF INTRACELLULAR PROCESSES

Enzyme pH Activity Profiles

An obvious starting point in any search for the targets of pH_i-mediated metabolic regulation is to consider the pH activity profiles of enzymatic activities. In cells that undergo significant pH_i changes, the behavior of enzymes (and pathways) with sharp pH dependences within the physiological range of pH_i should conform to their pH activity profiles. Indeed, this seems to be the case for such important pathways as glycolysis and protein synthesis in several of the cell systems listed above (11), as well as for cAMP synthesis and hydrolysis in yeast cells and mammalian liver (13, 15a). Rather than repeat this evidence here, I shall discuss briefly some of the less obvious pitfalls that await those who would draw conclusions concerning the physiological significance of enzyme pH activity profiles determined in vitro.

Considerable caution must be exercised in judging the regulatory significance of pH activity profiles, since apparently modest changes in assay conditions can sometimes dramatically alter the researcher's conclusions. For example, the activity of rat liver pyruvate carboxylase is not markedly pH dependent when assayed in the presence of saturating concentrations of its allosteric effector, acetyl-CoA (63). In contrast, at physiological acetyl-CoA levels the activity of pyruvate carboxylase displays pronounced pH dependence, due largely to the pH dependence of the activator constant (K_A) of acetyl-CoA for pyruvate carboxylase (60). This effect may explain the recent observation that the rate of glucose synthesis from lactate in isolated rat hepatocytes is depressed by about 80% as pH_i is decreased from 7.1 to 6.9, a response also observed in earlier studies with intact, perfused livers (Reference 33 and works cited therein). A similar effect of allosteric effector levels on the pH dependence of enzymes is also seen in the classic example of phosphofructokinase, which is fully active at a pH value just 0.1 unit higher than the pH at which it is completely inactive (70). This marked pH dependence is observed only in the ATP-inhibited enzyme, and the absolute value of pH at which this transition occurs is markedly dependent on both the fructose-6-phosphate and AMP levels present. Thus, intracellular levels of three different effectors determine whether the enzyme will display pH dependence in vivo. While this might seem to hopelessly complicate assessment of the regulatory significance of phosphofructokinase's pH activity profile, it is encouraging to note that compelling evidence now exists implicating pH_i changes in the activation of phosphofructokinase in vivo, in the insulin-stimulated frog skeletal muscle (21). Similarly, the dramatic inhibition of carbohydrate catabolism seen during anaerobic dormancy in *Artemia* embryos (which appears to be regulated by the >1 unit pH_i decrease during dormancy initiation; see Reference 13 for review) can be explained in terms of the pH activity profile of trehalase, a central regulatory point in this pathway (14a).

Interaction With Other Effectors

INTRACELLULAR FREE Ca^{2+} Using various means to manipulate either pH_i or intracellular free Ca^{2+} levels ($[Ca^{2+}]_i$), numerous investigators have observed either inverse or direct relationships (depending on the cell type under investigation) between these two parameters in such diverse cell types as vertebrate and invertebrate muscle fibers, snail and squid neurons, insect salivary gland, frog blastomeres, and mammalian myocardium (see works cited in Reference 13). Unfortunately, the physiological significance of these observations remains unclear. First, none of these cell types are known to undergo physiological pH_i changes under biologically meaningful conditions; thus, the observed dependence of $[Ca^{2+}]_i$ on pH_i in these systems might simply represent a pathological response. Second, direct measurements of pH_i and $[Ca^{2+}]_i$ in "typical" cells are technically demanding and fraught with potential artifacts. For example, $[Ca^{2+}]_i$ has been reported to be either *inversely* (8) or *directly* (80) related to pH_i in the mammalian cardiac Purkinje fiber under nearly identical conditions (perhaps due to difficulties in accurately determining $[Ca^{2+}]_i$ in the latter study). Similarly, studies of the pH_i dependence of $[Ca^{2+}]_i$ that use the photoprotein aequorin to measure $[Ca^{2+}]_i$ are complicated by uncertainties regarding the pH dependence of aequorin's light output in vivo

(42, 62). Despite all these objections, the most reliable data available (3, 36, 37, 41, 56) strongly suggest that, in some cell types at least, pH_i and $[Ca^{2+}]_i$ may be interdependent variables. This finding suggests one potentially significant means by which pH_i changes could influence metabolism, and further research is clearly called for.

A more subtle interrelationship between pH_i and $[Ca^{2+}]_i$ under *physiological* conditions has also been observed in a number of cell types, although in this case the related changes in these parameters are sequential rather than simultaneous. In the fertilized sea urchin egg, for example, $[Ca^{2+}]_i$ increases dramatically but transiently within about 1 min following fertilization, followed shortly thereafter by a permanent increase of pH_i (see Reference 82 for review). A similar sequence of $[Ca^{2+}]_i$ and pH_i changes follows frog egg fertilization as well (14, 79). Similarly, the activation of mammalian neutrophils (by formyl-Met-Leu-Phe) and platelets (by thrombin) is marked by sequential increases in $[Ca^{2+}]_i$ (55, 77) and pH_i (31, 43, 61). Finally, a variety of mitogens trigger sequential $[Ca^{2+}]_i$ and pH_i increases in such cultured mammalian cells as thymocytes (26) and fibroblasts (10, 26, 44). Thus, such diverse processes as fertilization, mitotic initiation, and activation of secretion and chemotaxis in certain cells share this pattern of a transient $[Ca^{2+}]_i$ increase followed by a long-term pH_i increase, although the mechanism and possible significance of this common pattern remain obscure. Interestingly, these events apparently share another common factor: the extracellular agents that elicit these intracellular responses appear to do so by activating the polyphosphoinositide cycle (see Reference 7 for review). Briefly, this involves the transient hydrolysis of the plasma membrane lipid phosphatidylinositol-4,5-bisphosphate (PIP$_2$) to yield the water soluble compound inositol-1,4,5-trisphosphate (IP$_3$) and the lipid-soluble compound diacylglycerol (DAG). Considerable evidence indicates that IP$_3$ potently and specifically activates intracellular Ca^{2+} release, while DAG specifically activates protein kinase C. Evidence for triggering of the polyphosphoinositide cycle is most complete in cases of mitogenic stimulation of fibroblasts by growth factors (30, 45, 75, 76) and neutrophil and platelet activation (2, 77), but growing evidence implicates this cycle in egg activation at fertilization as well (12, 73, 81). Perhaps the two-pronged nature of this cycle (production of both IP$_3$ and DAG) may explain the two-pronged response: IP$_3$ triggers a transient release of intracellular Ca^{2+}, while DAG (by stimulating protein kinase C?) activates intracellular alkalinization. Although the physiological significance of this dual $[Ca^{2+}]_i$/pH_i response is still unknown, one role of the intracellular alkalinization may be to *prolong* the effect of the $[Ca^{2+}]_i$ increase on calmodulin-regulated processes (see below).

CALMODULIN   A previous review (13) considered the implications for metabolic regulation of the extreme pH dependence of calmodulin's (CaM) K_d

for Ca^{2+} reported by Tkachuk & Men'shikov (69), who observed an order of magnitude decrease in K_d as pH increased from 6.5 to 7.5 in media of fairly low ionic strength ($I \approx 0.03-0.06$). More recent studies, using media of higher ionic strength (containing 100–150 mM KCl) have failed to detect significant changes in K_d between pH 6.8 and 7.2 (49) or between 6.8 and 7.8 (34). A seemingly plausible (but as yet untested) explanation for these conflicting results is that the pK_a of the ionizable group giving rise to the pH dependence of CaM's Ca^{2+} dissociation constant (at low ionic strength) is shifted out of the physiological pH range at higher ionic strengths; however, the similarly extreme pH dependence of Ca^{2+}-binding by the closely related protein troponin C is observed at physiological pH values even in 150 mM KCl (27). An explicit study of CaM's pH dependence under physiologically relevant conditions of ionic strength, $[Mg^{2+}]$, etc, is called for.

Should the pH dependence of Ca^{2+}-binding by CaM previously reported by Tkachuk & Men'shikov prove to hold true under intracellular conditions, a potential role for the sequential $[Ca^{2+}]_i$ and pH_i changes seen in various cells (see above) would be that a long-term increase in pH_i could serve to "lock in" the activation of CaM by the prior, transient $[Ca^{2+}]_i$ increase. The alkalinization would increase the degree of activation of CaM at resting Ca^{2+} levels by decreasing CaM's K_d for Ca^{2+}.

Despite these uncertainties regarding the effect of pH on CaM's affinity for Ca^{2+}, several recent studies demonstrate that both its Ca^{2+}-dependent conformation changes and its association with other proteins display pronounced pH dependences. Pundak & Roche (53) observed a strong pH dependence of the intrinsic tyrosine fluorescence (apparent $pK_a = 7$) of the bovine testis Ca^{2+}-CaM complex, and proposed that pH_i plays a role in regulating the Ca^{2+}-dependent conformation change of calmodulin in vivo. In support of this hypothesis they also cited unpublished evidence that CaM's activation of cyclic nucleotide phosphodiesterase increases by fivefold as pH is increased from 6 to 7, even in the presence of excess Ca^{2+}-CaM. In contrast, Ca^{2+}-CaM's activation of the sea urchin sperm flagellar dynein ATPase *decreases* by fourfold as pH increases from 6.8 to 8 (29). These findings suggest that the nature of CaM's pH dependence may depend in part on the range of the pH change and/or the enzyme under consideration. By far the most pronounced pH dependence yet reported for Ca^{2+}-CaM interaction with a protein is that of its association with the 110 kDa protein of the intestinal epithelial microvillus; a pH increase from about 6.1 to 7.4 increases the $[Ca^{2+}]$ at which this association is half-maximal from 0.1 to 100 μM (22). Thus, the pH dependences of Ca^{2+}-CaM's association with other proteins (here, at reasonably physiological ionic strengths) might provide a mechanism for "tuning" the responses of CaM-mediated processes to $[Ca^{2+}]_i$ changes. Depending on the absolute value of pH_i at the time of the $[Ca^{2+}]_i$ transient, certain CaM-mediated responses might be activated while others would remain unaffected. Such a mechanism could provide considerable flexibility to metabolic regulation via CaM, since $[Ca^{2+}]_i$ transients at different pH_i values would activate different sets of processes.

CYCLIC AMP   Evidence from various laboratories has previously been suggested to show that, like $[Ca^{2+}]_i$, intracellular cAMP levels ($[cAMP]_i$) might be a function of pH_i, or vice versa, in such diverse cell types as barnacle muscle fibers, mammalian liver and myocardium, and yeast cells (see Reference 13 for review). This conclusion was based both on the pronounced pH dependences of adenylyl cyclase and/or cyclic nucleotide phosphodiesterase from various systems, as well as on observations that exogenous cAMP can trigger pH_i changes under certain experimental conditions in these cells. In keeping with predictions based on the opposed pH activity profiles of adenylyl cyclase and phosphodiesterase in the yeast *Saccharomyces* (Reference 13 and works cited therein), it has recently been shown that a variety of treatments that depress pH_i in this cell (low external pH, treatment with protonophore, or refeeding of starved cells) all elevate $[cAMP]_i$ (14a). This may prove to be the first example of $[cAMP]_i$ dependence on pH_i under physiologically relevant conditions (starvation/refeeding). Conversely, further evidence of the dependence of pH_i on cyclic nucleotide levels has recently been provided by Conner & Hockberger (18), who demonstrated that pressure injection of cAMP or cGMP into gastropod neurons elicits pH_i changes that cannot be attributed simply to hydrolysis of the exogenous nucleotide.

Further evidence that pH_i changes can modulate $[cAMP]_i$, as well as a potential physiological role for such coupling between pH_i and $[cAMP]_i$, have recently emerged from studies of differentiation in cells of the cellular slime mold, *Dictyostelium discoideum*. In the presence of adequate food supplies these eukaryotic cells exist as free-living amoebae, but when starved they aggregate (under the influence of extracellular cAMP as a chemotactic signal) to form large, multicellular "slugs". These slugs can migrate for considerable distances before forming fruiting bodies consisting of two cell types, stalk cells and spore cells. Differentiation of these two cell types apparently occurs in the early slug, and displays remarkable precision. Cells in the anterior 25% of the slug differentiate into "prestalk" cells, while those of the posterior 75% become "prespore" cells. This remarkable system has thus long been considered an exceptional experimental model of differentiation and pattern formation (see Reference 40 for review).

High levels of ammonia (usually several millimolar) normally accumulate in and around aggregating *D. discoideum* amoebae and slugs (due to amino acid catabolism), and much evidence indicates that external ammonia concentrations can dictate whether the aggregates form slugs or proceed directly to fruiting bodies (see Reference 83 for early work). Further, as recently demonstrated by Gross and coworkers (24), ammonia influences the choice of differentiation pathway of individual cells, promoting the differentiation of prespore cells and inhibiting prestalk cell formation. Because this effect is observed at external pH 7.5, but not at pH 6.2, the active species was presumed to be the membrane-permeant weak base NH_3, which led these workers to propose that high pH_i promotes prespore cell differentiation. This conclusion is also supported by the ability of other weak bases to promote prespore cell formation. In contrast, membrane permeant weak *acids* promote *prestalk* cell differentiation, as do inhibitors of the plasma membrane proton pump (52) of these cells.

How might variations in local $[NH_3]$ influence the developmental choices of *D. discoideum* cells in the slug? Because the migrating slug is surrounded by a slime sheath that is minimal at its apical tip and progressively thickened posteriorly, this diffusion barrier can create a gradient of $[NH_3]$ along the slug (58, 68, 84), and thus a gradient of pH_i, as is strongly suggested by the graded staining of slugs by the pH indicator neutral red (85). Such a pH_i gradient, in turn, would be expected to give rise to a gradient of total (intracellular plus extracellular) cAMP, since NH_3 (15 mM, pH 7.2) inhibits both the intracellular and extracellular accumulation of cAMP in these cells (83). Indeed, such a cAMP gradient (highest at the apical tip) has been observed via immunoflourescence (50) and biochemical assay of slug sections (9), and differential [cAMP] values have been suggested to regulate both the migration and differentiation of the two cell types in the slug (68, 83).

The data presently available do not permit speculation concerning the means by which ammonia modulates $[cAMP]_i$ in these cells. Indeed, the in vitro pH activity profile of *D. discoideum's* adenylyl cyclase (twentyfold greater activity at pH 8 than at pH 6) (35) suggests that intracellular alkalinization via NH_3 should *stimulate* rather than inhibit cAMP production. However, a recent preliminary report has noted that "low" ammonia concentrations increase pH_i in *D. discoideum* cells, whereas ". . . high concentrations have the opposite effect" (1). This response can be explained by a finite permeability of the cell's plasma membrane to the conjugate acid NH_4^+ (due either to passive diffusion or active transport, e.g. via the Na,K-ATPase), which would liberate its proton intracellularly and thus tend to *acidify* pH_i—a phenomenon previously observed in numerous cell types (see Reference 57 for review). Thus, direct measurements of pH_i along the length of the differentiating slug, as well as in single cells differentiating in suspension culture in response to NH_3, are clearly called for in order to clarify the role(s) of ammonia and pH_i in modulating $[cAMP]_i$ and differentiation in these cells. The interrelated actions of cAMP and NH_3 in regulating the migration and differentiation of *D. discoideum* suggest that pH_i and $[cAMP]_i$ powerfully influence each other's effects, not only in this system, but in other cells as well.

Cytoskeletal Protein Interactions

A large number of the physiological processes known to involve pH_i changes are also accompanied by either cell shape changes or changes in motility, i.e. by modifications of the cytoskeleton. While many of these cytoskeletal modifications are understood to be regulated by changes in free Ca^{2+} levels and/or by protein phosphorylation, increasing evidence suggests that the pH_i changes accompanying these processes may also play a significant modulatory role.

As previously discussed (13), evidence exists that implicates the 0.4 unit pH_i increase upon fertilization of the sea urchin egg in regulation of actin filament cross-linking to form the microvillar core bundles of the zygote (6, 15). Although to my knowledge no information is available regarding the pH dependence of fascin, the major microfilament cross-linker of the sea urchin egg microvillus, such data is available for microfilament cross-linking proteins from other systems. Filamin, a major actin-binding protein found in many cell types, forms gels under appropriate conditions by cross-linking actin filaments. The low-shear viscosity of such gels at pH 7.5–7.7 is three- to tenfold higher than at pH 7.2, apparently due to modulation of filamin's cross-linking ability rather than to some effect of pH on the microfilaments themselves (48). The 95 kDa actin-binding protein from *Dictyostelium* cytoplasm likewise gels F-actin in a pH-dependent fashion; the viscosity of such gels decreases by about four- to twentyfold as pH is increased from 6.8 to 7.5 (17, 20). Such observations suggest that physiological pH_i changes of the magnitudes observed in many cell types (13) may have profound effects on the structure and motility of the actin-based cytoskeleton. This is also indicated by observations of pH-dependent gelation and contraction of crude cytosolic extracts from *Dictyostelium* amoebae (16, 25), cells that, as discussed above, appear to undergo rather large pH_i changes during differentiation. Similarly, activated platelets, which undergo both pH_i and $[Ca^{2+}]_i$ increases (see above) in conjunction with shape changes, form extended meshworks of microfilament bundles. This microfilament bundling can be elicited in cytosolic extracts of quiescent platelets by raising pH from 6.8 to 7.6 in the presence of elevated free Ca^{2+} levels (23). In this instance, however, the pH dependences of the actin-binding protein(s) involved have not been characterized. Thus, while alkalinization appears to promote microfilament bundling and cross-linking in sea urchin eggs, mammalian platelets, and filamin-containing systems, it can *decrease* such interactions in *Dictyostelium* cytosol, apparently depending only upon the identity of the cross-linking agents involved.

Microfilament-based systems are not the only cytoskeletal structures that show pronounced pH dependence. While no information is available regarding microtubule-binding proteins, polymerization of tubulin itself has been shown to be markedly pH sensitive. As demonstrated by Regula and coworkers (54), the critical concentration for tubulin polymerization increases about sixfold as pH is raised from 6.4 to 7.8, giving rise to a rapid and reversible depolymerization (to a new steady state) when microtubule suspensions are alkalinized from, for example, 6.7 to 7.6. In keeping with these in vitro results, it has been observed that incubation of PtK2 cells at pH 5 or 6 (which should depress pH_i) triggers an abundant polymerization of free microtubules and (in mitotic cells) microtubules radiating from the centrosomes (19). A similar relationship between pH_i and microtubule polymerization may exist under physiologically relevant conditions in the germinating zoospores of the water mold *Blastocladiella*, in which both 0.3 unit pH_i increase (74) and the rapid disassembly of both flagellar and cytoplasmic microtubules occurs (see Reference 39 for review).

Gap Junctional Conductance

In 1977, Turin & Warner (71) first demonstrated that treatment of frog early embryos with 100% CO_2 completely and reversibly abolished the normally high degree of electrical coupling between these cells. They proposed that this was due to the depression of pH_i under these conditions. These observations were confirmed and expanded to include a variety of coupled cell systems (Reference 72 and works cited therein). Decreases in pH_i of as little as 0.3 unit can profoundly inhibit junctional communication in amphibian embryos (decreasing it by about fourfold); this effect displays an apparent pK_a of 7.3 (64, 66). In contrast, the $[Ca^{2+}]_i$ required to disrupt cell coupling in fish embryos was at least 0.1 mM, about 2–3 orders of magnitude above the physiological value of $[Ca^{2+}]_i$ in most cell systems (67). Hence, the uncoupling induced by intracellular acidification is not mediated by the comparatively minor increases in $[Ca^{2+}]_i$ that such treatments evoke in some cell systems (see Reference 13). Interestingly, the ability of CO_2 to uncouple embryonic chick lens cells (as judged by inhibition of fluorescent dye transfer) is lost as the embryos progress from Stage 14 to Stage 15 (59). However, since pH_i was not measured in this study, the result may reflect either an increase in cell buffering capacity or a loss of gap junctional pH sensitivity.

Several recent studies raise the possibility that calmodulin may mediate the closure of gap junctions in response to elevation of $[Ca^{2+}]_i$ or depression of pH_i (Reference 51 and works cited therein). This evidence includes the observation that such calmodulin inhibitors as trifluoperazine and calmidazolium block the Ca^{2+}- and pH_i-mediated inhibition of junctional communication. Unfortunately, it is difficult to explain the very high $[Ca^{2+}]_i$ required to inhibit junctional communication (apparent $pK_{Ca} = 3.3$; see above) if calmodulin is involved in this response, since CaM is usually activated at physiological $[Ca^{2+}]_i$ ($pK_{Ca} \approx 6$). However, the involvement of CaM in pH_i-mediated modulation of junctional communication is entirely in keeping with the pH sensitivity of both its Ca^{2+}-binding and Ca^{2+}-dependent conformation changes discussed above.

At present, it is difficult to assess the potential physiological significance of these pH_i effects on gap junctional communication, not least because the role(s) of cell coupling in nonexcitable cells remains largely obscure, though theories abound (see Reference 38 for review). In some systems, such as rat liver, in which the pH dependence of junctional communication lies ≥ 0.7 units below the typical value of pH_i (57, 65), pH_i is unlikely to play a role in physiological regulation of ionic cell-cell coupling. Nevertheless, as has previously been pointed out, under conditions where ionic cell coupling (as measured by the electrical coupling coefficient) remains high, cell–cell communication of higher molecular weight substances (as observed, for example, in dye transfer experiments) may be radically inhibited by agents that alter junctional permeability (4). Thus, pH_i changes too small to dramatically affect ionic cell coupling may still modulate this latter form of communication. In the embryonic systems investigated to date (see above), the potential for pH_i-mediated regulation of junctional permeability for both ions and larger molecules seems more promising, since in these systems the pH dependence of cell coupling falls at or near typical values of pH_i.

CONCLUSION

Substantial intracellular pH changes under physiologically relevant conditions are now recognized to occur in a very broad range of cell types and systems during a variety of metabolic and developmental transitions (13; see also W. H. Moolenaar, this volume). That such changes are not merely fortuitous is strongly suggested by a variety of evidence, not least of which is the observation that mechanisms such as Na^+/H^+ exchange, thought to function in many cell systems to maintain constant pH_i during steady state metabolism (see Reference 57 for review), actually work to *actively alter* pH_i during many of these metabolic transitions. Based solely on fundamental biochemical principles, such pH_i changes would be expected to have considerable effects on the behavior of these cells. Nevertheless, with only a few exceptions, it has proven quite difficult to unambiguously assign regulatory roles to these pH_i changes, and a growing consensus among workers in the field holds that such pH_i changes generally play *permissive* rather than strictly obligatory regulatory roles. In this sense pH_i differs greatly from the more classical regulatory agents such as $[Ca^{2+}]_i$ and $[cAMP]_i$. Perhaps this is to be expected, however, in light of the fact that these latter agents are essentially *arbitrary* regulators, in the sense that their roles probably could have been filled by any of a variety of compounds, subject only to the "whim" of evolution. In contrast, the regulatory potential of pH_i is *inherent* to life based on the aqueous chemistry of ionizable compounds. As such, its effects on intracellular processes are manifold, as I have attempted to suggest in this and previous reviews (see References 11, 13), and need not be mediated by specialized receptors such as those required by $[Ca^{2+}]_i$ and $[cAMP]_i$. Thus, as previously suggested (13), the principle regulatory role of pH_i may be to establish a *metabolic context*, i.e. to coordinate the activities of diverse pathways, structures, and regulatory agents in a manner appropriate to the task at hand. Unfortunately, such a role, however significant, would be expected to be exceedingly difficult to demonstrate via a single "crucial experiment," as has indeed proven to be the case. Hopefully, future reviews based on more extensive experimental data will be able to address this issue decisively.

ACKNOWLEDGMENT

I thank Dr. R. Nuccitelli for his patience, encouragement, and support. This work was supported by NSF grant PCM 81 18174 to R. Nuccitelli.

Literature Cited

1. Aerts, R., Durston, T., Moolenaar, W. 1984. The dependence of DNA and protein biosynthesis on cytoplasmic pH during the cell cycle in *Dictyostelium discoideum*. *J. Embryol. Exp. Morphol. (Suppl.)* 82:164

2. Agranoff, B. W., Murthy, P., Seguin, E. B. 1983. Thrombin-induced phosphodiesteratic cleavage of phosphatidylinositol bisphosphate in human platelets. *J. Biol. Chem.* 258:2076–78

3. Alvarez-Leefmans, F. J., Rink, T. J., Tsien, R. Y. 1981. Free calcium ions in neurones of *Helix aspersa* measured with ion-selective microelectrodes. *J. Physiol.* 315:531–48

4. Azarnia, R., Loewenstein, W. R. 1984. Intercellular communication and the control of growth: X. Alteration of junctional permeability by the *src* gene. A study with temperature-sensitive mutant Rous sarcoma virus. *Membr. Biol.* 82:191–205

5. Babcock, D. F., Rufo, G. A., Lardy, H. A. 1983. Potassium-dependent increases in cytosolic pH stimulate metabolism and motility of mammalian sperm. *Proc. Natl. Acad. Sci. USA* 80:1327–31

6. Begg, D. A., Rebhun, L. I., Hyatt, H. 1982. Structural organization of actin in the sea urchin egg cortex: microvillar elongation in the absence of actin filament bundle formation. *J. Cell Biol.* 93:24–32

7. Berridge, M. J. 1984. Inositol trisphosphate and diacylglycerol as second messengers. *Biochem. J.* 220:345–60

8. Bers, D. M., Ellis, D. 1982. Intracellular calcium and sodium activity in sheep heart Purkinje fibres. Effect of changes of external sodium and intracellular pH. *Pflugers Arch.* 393:171–78

9. Brenner, M. 1977. Cyclic AMP gradient in migrating pseudoplasmodia of the cellular slime mold *Dictyostelium discoideum*. *J. Biol. Chem.* 252:4073–77

10. Burns, C. P., Rozengurt, E. 1983. Serum, platelet-derived growth factor, vasopressin and phorbol esters increase intracellular pH in Swiss 3T3 cells. *Biochem. Biophys. Res. Commun.* 116: 931–38

11. Busa, W. B. 1985. The proton as an integrating effector in metabolic activation. In *Na+-H+ Exchange, Intracellular pH, and Cell Function*, ed. W. F. Boron, P. S. Aronson. New York: Academic. In press

12. Busa, W. B., Ferguson, J. E., Joseph, S. K., Williamson, J. R., Nuccitelli, R. 1985. Activation of frog *(Xenopus laevis)* eggs by inositol trisphosphate. I. Characterization of Ca^{2+} release from intracellular stores. *J. Cell Biol.* 101:677–82

13. Busa, W. B., Nuccitelli, R. 1984. Metabolic regulation via intracellular pH. *Am. J. Physiol.* 246:R409–38

14. Busa, W. B., Nuccitelli, R. 1985. An elevated free cytosolic Ca^{2+} wave follows fertilization in eggs of the frog, *Xenopus laevis*. *J. Cell Biol.* 100:1325–29

14a. Carpenter, J. F., Hand, S. C. 1986. Arrestment of carbohydrate metabolism during anaerobic dormancy and aerobic acidosis in *Artemia* embryos: Determination of pH-sensitive control points. *J. Comp. Physiol. B.* In press

15. Carron, C. P., Longo, F. J. 1982. Relation of cytoplasmic alkalinization to microvillar elongation and microfilament formation in the sea urchin egg. *Dev. Biol.* 89:128–37

15a. Caspani, G., Tortora, P., Hanozet, G. M., Guerritore, A. 1985. Glucose-stimulated cAMP increase may be mediated by intracellular acidification in Saccharomyces cerevisiae. *FEBS Lett.* 186: 75–79

16. Condeelis, J. S., Taylor, D. L. 1977. The contractile basis of amoeboid movement. V. The control of gelation, solation, and contraction in extracts from *Dictyostelium discoideum*. *J. Cell Biol.* 74:901–27

17. Condeelis, J., Vahey, M. 1982. A calcium- and pH-regulated protein from *Dictyostelium discoideum* that cross-links actin filaments. *J. Cell Biol.* 94:466–71

18. Connor, J. A., Hockberger, P. 1984. Intracellular pH changes induced by injection of cyclic nucleotides into gastropod neurones. *J. Physiol.* 354:163–72

19. De Brabander, M., Geuens, G., Nuydens, R., Willebrords, R., De Mey, J. 1982. Microtubule stability and assembly in living cells: the influence of metabolic inhibitors, taxol and pH. *Cold Spring Harbor Symp. Quant. Biol.* 46:227–40

20. Fechheimer, M., Brier, J., Rockwell, M., Luna, E. J., Taylor, D. L. 1982. A calcium- and pH-regulated actin binding protein from *D. discoideum*. *Cell Motility* 2:287–308

21. Fidelman, M. L., Seeholzer, S. H., Walsh, K. B., Moore, R. D. 1982. Intracellular pH mediates action of insulin on glycolysis in frog skeletal muscle. *Am. J. Physiol.* 242:C87–93

22. Glenney, J. R., Glenney, P. 1985. Comparison of Ca^{++}-regulated events in the intestinal brush border. *J. Cell Biol.* 100:754–63

23. Gonnella, P. A., Nachmias, V. T. 1981. Platelet activation and microfilament bundling. *J. Cell Biol.* 89:146–51

24. Gross, J. D., Bradbury, J., Kay, R. R., Peacey, M. J. 1983. Intracellular pH and the control of cell differentiation in *Dictyostelium discoideum*. *Nature* 244–45

25. Hellewell, S. B., Taylor, D. L. 1979. The contractile basis of ameboid movement: VI. The solation-contraction coupling hypothesis. *J. Cell Biol.* 83:633–48

26. Hesketh, T. R., Moore, J. P., Morris, J. D. H., Taylor, M. V., Rogers, J., et al. 1985. A common sequence of calcium and pH signals in the mitogenic stimulation of eukaryotic cells. *Nature* 313:481–84

27. Hincke, M. T., McCubbin, W. D., Kay, C. M. 1978. Calcium-binding properties of cardiac and skeletal troponin C as determined by circular dichroism and ultraviolet difference spectroscopy. *Can. J. Biochem.* 56:384–95

28. Hirose, T., Ueda, T., Kobatake, Y. 1982. Changes in intracellular pH accompanying chemoreception in the plasmodia of *Physarum polycephalum*. *J. Gen. Microbiol.* 128:2647–51

29. Hisanaga, S., Pratt, M. M. 1984. Calmodulin interaction with cytoplasmic and flagellar dynein: calcium-dependent binding and stimulation of adenosinetriphosphatase activity. *Biochemistry* 23: 3032–37

30. Hoffmann, R., Erzberger, P., Frank, W., Ristow, H. 1980. Increased phosphatidylinositol synthesis in rat embryo fibroblasts after growth stimulation and its inhibition by d-hexachlorocyclohexane. *Biochim. Biophys. Acta* 618:282–92

31. Horne, W. C., Norman, N. E., Schwartz, D. B., Simons, E. R. 1981. Changes in cytoplasmic pH and in membrane potential in thrombin-stimulated human platelets. *Eur. J. Biochem.* 120: 295–302

32. Jamieson, G. A., Frazier, W. A., Schlesinger, P. H. 1984. Transient increase in intracellular pH during *Dictyostelium* differentiation. *J. Cell Biol.* 99:1883–87

33. Kashiwagura, T., Deutsch, C. J., Taylor, J., Erecinska, M., Wilson, D. F. 1984. Dependence of gluconeogenesis, urea synthesis, and energy metabolism of hepatocytes on intracellular pH. *J. Biol. Chem.* 259:237–43

34. Keller, C. H., Olwin, B. B., LaPorte, D. C., Storm, D. R. 1982. Determination of the free-energy coupling for binding of calcium ions and troponin I to calmodulin. *Biochemistry* 21:156–62

35. Klein, C. 1976. Adenylate cyclase activity in *Dictyostelium discoideum* amoebae and its changes during differentiation. *FEBS Lett.* 68:125–28

36. Lea, T. J., Ashley, C. C. 1978. Increase in free Ca^{2+} in muscle after exposure to CO$_2$. *Nature* 275:236–38

37. Lea, T. J., Ashley, C. C. 1981. Carbon dioxide or bicarbonate ions release Ca^{2+}

from internal stores in crustacean myofibrillar bundles. *J. Membr. Biol.* 61:115–25

38. Loewenstein, W. R. 1981. Junctional intercellular communication: the cell-to-cell membrane channel. *Physiol. Rev.* 61:829–913

39. Lovett, J. S. 1975. Growth and differentiation of the water mold *Blastocladiella emersonii:* cytodifferentiation and the role of ribonucleic acid and protein synthesis. *Bacteriol. Rev.* 39:345–404

40. MacWilliams, H. K., David, C. N. 1984. Pattern formation in *Dictyostelium.*

41. Meech, R. W., Thomas, R. C. 1980. Effect of measured calcium chloride injections on the membrane potential and internal pH of snail neurones. *J. Physiol.* 298:111–29

42. Moisescu, D. G., Ashley, C. C., Campbell, A. K. 1975. Comparative aspects of the calcium-sensitive photoproteins aequorin and obelin. *Biochim. Biophys. Acta.* 396:133–40

43. Molski, T. F. P., Naccache, P. H., Volpi, M., Wolpert, L. M., Sha'afi, R. I. 1980. Specific modulation of the intracellular pH of rabbit neutrophils by chemotactic factors. *Biochem. Biophys. Res. Commun.* 94:508–14

44. Moolenaar, W. H., Tertoolen, L. G. J., de Laat, S. W. 1984. Growth factors immediately raise cytoplasmic free Ca^{2+} in human fibroblasts. *J. Biol. Chem.* 259:8066–69

45. Moolenaar, W. H., Tertoolen, L. G. J., de Laat, S. W. 1984. Phorbol ester and diacylglycerol mimic growth factors in raising cytoplasmic pH. *Nature* 312:371–74

46. Nuccitelli, R., 1982. Intracellular pH measurement techniques: their advantages and limitations. See Ref. 47, pp. 161–69

47. Nuccitelli, R., Deamer, D. W., eds. 1982. *Intracellular pH: Its Measurement, Regulation, and Utilization in Cellular Functions.* New York: Liss. 594 pp.

48. Nunnally, M. H., Craig, S. W. 1980. Small changes in pH within the physiological range cause large changes in the consistency of actin-filamin mixtures. *J. Cell Biol.* 87:218a

49. Ogawa, Y., Tanokura, M. 1984. Calcium binding to calmodulin: effects of ionic strength, Mg^{2+}, pH and temperature. *J. Biochem.* 95:19–28

50. Pan, P., Bonner, J. T., Wedner, H. J., Parker, C. W. 1974. Immunofluorescence evidence for the distribution of cyclic AMP in cells and cell masses of the cellular slime molds. *Proc. Natl. Acad. Sci. USA* 71:1623–25

51. Perracchia, C., Bernardini, G. 1984. Gap junction structure and cell-to-cell coupling regulation: is there a calmodulin involvement? *Fed. Proc.* 43:2681–91

52. Pogge-von Strandmann, R., Kay, R. R., Dufour, J-P. 1984. An electrogenic proton pump in plasma membranes from the cellular slime mould *Dictyostelium discoideum. FEBS Lett.* 175:422–28

53. Pundak, S., Roche, R. S. 1984. Tyrosine and tyrosinate fluorescence of bovine testes calmodulin: calcium and pH dependence. *Biochemistry* 23:1549–55

54. Regula, C. S., Pfeiffer, J. R., Berlin, R. D. 1981. Microtubule assembly and disassembly at alkaline pH. *J. Cell Biol.* 89:45–53

55. Rink, T. J., Smith, S. W., Tsien, R. Y. 1982. Cytoplasmic free Ca^{2+} in human platelets: Ca^{2+} thresholds and Ca-independent activation for shape-change and secretion. *FEBS Lett.* 148:21–26

56. Rink, T. J., Tsien, R. Y., Warner, A. E. 1980. Free calcium in *Xenopus* embryos measured with ion-selective microelectrodes. *Nature* 283:658–60

57. Roos, A., Boron, W. F. 1981. Intracellular pH. *Physiol. Rev.* 61:296–434

58. Schindler, J., Sussman, M. 1977. Ammonia determines the choice of morphogenetic pathways in *Dictyostelium discoideum. J. Mol. Biol.* 116:161–69

59. Schuetze, S. M., Goodenough, D. A. 1982. Dye transfer between cells of the embryonic chick lens becomes less sensitive to CO_2 treatment with development. *J. Cell Biol.* 694–705

60. Scrutton, M. C., Utter, M. F. 1967. Pyruvate carboxylase. IX. Some properties of the activation by certain acyl derivatives of coenzyme A. *J. Biol. Chem.* 242:1723–35

61. Sha'afi, R. I., Naccache, P. H., Molski, T. F. P., Volpi, M. 1982. Chemotactic stimuli-induced changes in the pH_i of rabbit neutrophils. See Ref. 47, pp. 513–25

62. Shimomura, O., Johnson, F. H. 1973. Further data on the specificity of aequorin luminescence to calcium. *Biochem. Biophys. Res. Commun.* 53:490–94

63. Soling, H.-D., Willms, B., Kleineke, J., Gehlhoff, M. 1970. Regulation of gluconeogenesis in the guinea pig liver. *Eur. J. Biochem.* 16:289–302

64. Spray, D. C., Harris, A. L., Bennett, M. V. L. 1981. Gap junctional conductance is a simple and sensitive function of intracellular pH. *Science* 211:712–15

65. Spray, D. C., Hertzberg, E. L. 1985.

Biophysical properties of rat liver gap junction channels. *Biophys. J.* 47:505a

66. Spray, D. C., Nerbonne, J., Campos de Carvalho, A., Harris, A. L., Bennett, M. V. L. 1984. Substituted benzyl acetates: a new class of compounds that reduce gap junctional conductance by cytoplasmic acidification. *J. Cell Biol.* 99:174–79

67. Spray, D. C., Stern, J. H., Harris, A. L., Bennett, M. V. L. 1982. Gap junctional conductance: comparison of sensitivities to H and Ca ions. *Proc. Natl. Acad. Sci. USA* 79:441–45

68. Sussman, M., Schindler, J., Kim, H. 1977. Toward a biochemical definition of the morphogenetic fields in *D. discoideum. Developments and Differentiation in the Cellular Slime Moulds*, pp. 31–50. Amsterdam: Elsevier. 241 pp.

69. Tkachuk, V. A., Men'shikov, M. Y. 1981. Effect of pH on Ca-binding properties of calmodulin and its interaction with the Ca-dependent form of cyclic nucleotide phosphodiesterase. *Biokhimia* 46:779–88 (English translation)

70. Trivedi, B., Danforth, W. H. 1966. Effect of pH on the kinetics of frog muscle phosphofructokinase. *J. Biol. Chem.* 241:4110–14

71. Turin, L., Warner, A. 1977. Carbon dioxide reversibly abolishes ionic communication between cells of early amphibian embryo. *Nature* 270:56–59

72. Turin, L., Warner, A. E. 1980. Intracellular pH in early *Xenopus* embryos: its effect on current flow between blastomeres. *J. Physiol.* 300:489–504

73. Turner, P. R., Sheetz, M. P., Jaffe, L. A. 1984. Fertilization increases the polyphosphoinositide content of sea urchin eggs. *Nature* 310:414–15

74. Van Brunt, J., Harold, F. M. 1980. Ionic control of germination of *Blastocladiella emersonii* zoospores. *J. Bacteriol.* 141: 735–44

75. Vicentini, L. M., Miller, R. J., Villereal, M. L. 1984. Evidence for a role of phospholipase activity in the serum stimulation of Na^+ influx in human fibroblasts. *J. Biol. Chem.* 259:6912–19

76. Vicentini, L. M., Villereal, M. L. 1984.

Serum, bradykinin and vasopressin stimulate release of inositol phosphates from human fibroblasts. *Biochem. Biophys. Res. Commun.* 123:663–70

77. Volpi, M., Yassin, R., Tao, W., Molski, T. F. P., Naccache, P. H., Sha'afi, R. I. 1984. Leukotriene B_4 mobilizes calcium without the breakdown of polyphosphoinositides and the production of phosphatidic acid in rabbit neutrophils. *Proc. Natl. Acad. Sci. USA* 81:5966–69

78. Ward, S., Hogan, E., Nelson, G. A. 1983. The initiation of spermiogenesis in the nematode *Caenorhabditis elegans. Dev. Biol.* 98:70–79

79. Webb, D. J., Nuccitelli, R. 1981. Direct measurement of intracellular pH changes in *Xenopus* eggs at fertilization and cleavage. *J. Cell Biol.* 91:562–67

80. Weingart, R., Hess, P., Reber, W. R. 1982. Influence of intracellular pH on cell-to-cell coupling in sheep Purkinje fibers. In *Normal and Abnormal Conduction in the Heart. Biophysics, Physiology, Pharmacology, and Ultrastructure*. ed. A. P. de Carvalho, B. F. Hoffman, M. Lieberman. pp. 73–84. Mount Kisco, NY: Futura. 279 pp.

81. Whitaker, M., Irvine, R. F. 1984. Inositol 1,4,5-trisphosphate microinjection activates sea urchin eggs. *Nature* 312: 636–39

82. Whitaker, M. J., Steinhardt, R. A. 1982. Ionic regulation of egg activation. *Q. Rev. Biophys.* 15:593–644

83. Williams, G. B., Elder, E. M., Sussman, M. 1984. Modulation of the cAMP relay in *Dictyostelium discoideum* by ammonia and other metabolites: possible morphogenetic consequences. *Dev. Biol.* 105:377–88

84. Wilson, J. B., Rutherford, C. L. 1978. ATP, trehalose, glucose and ammonium ion localization in the two cell types of *Dictyostelium discoideum. J. Cell Physiol.* 94:37–46

85. Yamamoto, A., Takeuchi, I. 1983. Vital staining of autophagic vacuoles in differentiating cells of *Dictyostelium discoideum. Differentiation* 24:83–87

Ann. Rev. Physiol. 1986. 48:403–13

ATP-DRIVEN H⁺ PUMPING INTO INTRACELLULAR ORGANELLES

Gary Rudnick

Department of Pharmacology, Yale University School of Medicine, New Haven, Connecticut 06510

Introduction

The existence of acidic intracellular organelles has been known since the 1890's, when Metchnikoff (30) observed that protozoans change the color of ingested litmus particles from blue to red. Subsequently, many individual acidic organelles have been found in both plant and animal cells. These organelles, which include components of both the endocytic and the secretory pathways, use their acidic interior for a variety of physiological functions, including solute storage, protein degradation and processing, recycling of surface receptors, and entry of viruses and other pathological agents. Despite this functional heterogeneity, all of the organelles studied use the same mechanism, an ATP-driven H⁺ pump (40), to maintain their interior at a pH lower than that of the cytoplasm. Recent evidence suggests that this ATPase is distinct from previously characterized ion pumps. This review will focus on the evidence that intracellular organelles are acidic, the mechanism by which the organelle ATPase pumps H⁺ ions, and the way that various organelles utilize the ATP-generated H⁺ potential.

Techniques of Measuring Organelle Acidity

The interior of many isolated organelles has been found to be acidic by a variety of techniques. The most widely useful of these involves measuring the distribution of a weakly basic amine that is permeant only in its unprotonated form, and which therefore accumulates inside acidic compartments. From the equilibrium distribution ratio, the external pH, and the amine's pK_a, the internal pH is readily calculated (39). To accurately determine the distribution ratio, many workers have measured the distribution of radioactive weak bases such as

403

methylamine, but a qualitative estimate of the transmembrane pH difference (ΔpH) can be obtained using weak bases, such as 9-amino acridine, acridine orange, and quinacrine, whose optical properties change with concentration. With these probes, fluorescence or absorbance or both decrease when the probe is concentrated within an acidic organelle. Hence, absorbance or fluorescence quenching is associated with acidification.

Another class of optical probes takes advantage of the pH dependence of a fluorophore. Ohkuma & Poole (33) measured the internal pH of lysosomes in intact cells by incubating with fluorescein-dextran, a fluorescent polymer that accumulates in lysosomes by a process of constitutive endocytosis. From the characteristic changes in fluorescein's excitation spectrum the investigators concluded that lysosomes in vivo maintain an internal pH of 4.7–4.8. In the case of acidic vacuoles in plants, endogenous chromophores have been used as indicators of internal pH in tulip and amaryllis petals. By comparing the absorbance of endogenous anthocyanin in intact petals with free anthocyanin at various pH values, Lin et al (25) estimated that vacuoles in situ have an internal pH close to 4.

The fact that some secretory granules contain a high concentration of ATP provides an endogenous probe for measuring internal pH by nuclear magnetic resonance (NMR). The ATP γ-phosphate gives a ^{31}P NMR peak that shifts in frequency as the degree of protonation changes. Using this γ-phosphate resonance Njus et al (32) measured an internal pH of 5.5–5.7 in chromaffin granules, which compares well with estimates of 5.3–5.7 using methylamine distribution.

A less quantitative but morphologically more informative technique has recently been developed by Anderson and coworkers (3). 3-(2,4-dinitro-anilino)-3'-amino-N-methyldipropylamine (DAMP) is a weakly basic amine that accumulates, like methylamine, in the acidic organelles of cells with which it is incubated. When cells incubated with DAMP are fixed and stained with antibodies against dinitrophenol, the antibodies label acidic compartments. From these experiments, lysosomes, endosomes, some coated vesicles, and parts of the Golgi apparatus appear acidic.

Which Organelles are Acidic?

Acidic intracellular organelles belong, in general, to either the pinocytic or the secretory pathway. In the pinocytic pathway, lysosomes and endosomes (pre-lysosomal endocytic vesicles) are acidic (33, 45). The coated vesicles that give rise to endosomes may also be acidic, and isolated brain coated vesicles (whose origin is not necessarily endocytic) acidify in vitro (15, 43). Among secretory organelles, biogenic amine storage granules in platelets, chromaffin cells, and mast cells are acidic, as are peptide storage granules in the pituitary and the endocrine pancreas (see 40 for review), although amylase-containing granules in parotid acinar cells are not acidic (5). Moreover, there are indications that earlier secretory compartments are also acidified. Glickman et al (17) measured acidification of isolated Golgi and endoplasmic reticulum preparations in vivo, and mutants deficient in the ability to acidify endosomes also show defects in the glycosylation of secreted and surface proteins, which is a Golgi function (38). Additional evidence that the Golgi apparatus is normally acidified comes from labeling experiments with DAMP (3).

Generation of ΔpH

How can the interior of a lysosome, vacuole, or secretory granule maintain its acidic pH? The initial observations of isolated lysosomes correctly suggested that the ΔpH was maintained, in the absence of added energy sources, by a diffusion potential for H^+. In the presence of ATP, however, H^+ is pumped into lysosomes, chromaffin granules, and other acidic organelles. H^+ is not at electrochemical equilibrium across the membrane, and the H^+ potential generates a significant driving force for H^+ efflux. When the potential is high enough, net H^+ influx ceases, either because H^+ leaks out faster, or because the increased work of pumping H^+ against a larger potential slows down the ATPase, or for both reasons.

ELECTROGENICITY OF THE ATPASE   Hydrogen ion pumps can be either electroneutral or electrogenic, depending on participation of counterions in the catalytic cycle. The electroneutral K^+,H^+-ATPase of gastric mucosa, for example, is believed to pump out one H^+ for each K^+ it pumps into the cell (42). The H^+-pumping ATPases of plant and fungal plasma membranes, in contrast, pump H^+ with no counterion and are therefore electrogenic (18). If H^+ pumping into intracellular organelles is electrogenic, we expect two consequences: the organelle interior should become both acidic and electrically positive with respect to the suspending medium. In the case of an electroneutral pump, the pH change would be accompanied by a change in the counterion concentration, without a change in ΔΨ (the transmembrane electrical potential).

All available evidence indicates that an electrogenic ATPase acidifies the interior of endocytic and secretory organelles. In chromaffin granules, for example, ATP addition has little effect on ΔpH in the absence of external permeant anions. Instead, ΔΨ swings from $-80\,mV$ to $+50\,mV$ (21). The high internal buffering capacity prevents a significant change in ΔpH. When a permeant anion such as Cl^- is present it can flow into the vesicle, down the electrical potential, and result in net pumping of HCl. In chromaffin granule membrane vesicles, ATP generates either ΔpH or ΔΨ, or both, depending on the presence of permeant external anions (23). In their absence only ΔΨ is generated. As Cl^- is added ΔΨ decreases to zero and ΔpH increases to a maximum. The total transmembrane electrochemical potential for H^+ ($\Delta\bar{\mu}_{H^+}$) varies little during this manipulation. Similar results have been obtained for other secretory organelles (40), lysosomes (19), and coated vesicles (49).

The external anion requirement for acidification and ATP hydrolysis has led to the suggestion that the ATPase transports Cl^- in addition to H^+ (35). In coated vesicles, both ATPase activity and Cl^- permeability are inhibited by DIDS (4,4'-diisothiocyanostilbene-2,2'-disulfonic acid), but separate sites of action are involved since only the ATPase can be protected by pretreatment with DTNB [5,5'-dithiobis-(2-nitrobenzoic acid)]. In the absence of Cl^-, other permeant ions such as K^+ in the presence of valinomycin fulfill the role of a counterion (49). Different organelles show markedly different Cl^- requirements for acidification. Lysosomes acidified almost as well in the absence of Cl^- as in its presence, synaptosomes (presumably containing synaptic vesicles) absolutely required Cl^-, and chromaffin granules were intermediate in their Cl^- requirement (9). Rather than implying different ion requirements for ATP hydrolysis in different organelles, these differences presumably reflect differences in ion content and membrane permeability in the various preparations.

EVIDENCE THAT THE ATPASE IS UNIQUE   Two approaches have been used to distinguish the acidic organelle ATPase from other ion pumping ATPases. The first approach has been to use antibodies against the mitochondrial F_1F_0 ATPase to test for similarities between the chromaffin granule H^+ pump and the mitochondrial enzyme. Apps & Schatz (4) first detected mitochondrial-like ATPase in preparations of chromaffin granules, and they concluded that this represented the H^+ pump that acidifies the granule. Cidon & Nelson (10) demonstrated, however, that chromaffin granule membrane vesicles from which all immunoreactive F_1 β-subunit had been removed by NaBr extraction still retained 70% of their ATPase activity, and that this remaining ATPase would reconstitute ATP-dependent H^+ influx (9). Since the β-subunit is highly conserved in F_1F_0 ATPase from all known sources, it is extremely unlikely that the chromaffin granule ATPase represents a typical F_1F_0 enzyme.

The second approach has been to compare the inhibitor sensitivity of H^+ pumping in secretory granules, endosomes, coated vesicles, and kidney vesicles with that of known ion pumping ATPases. Dean et al (12, 13) demonstrated that in platelet and chromaffin granules the H^+-pumping ATPase is insensitive to concentrations of inhibitors (oligomycin, efrapeptin, and azide) that maximally inhibit F_1F_0 ATPase. At least one of these inhibitors, azide, inhibits F_1F_0 from all known sources. Na^+,K^+-ATPase inhibitors (vanadate and ouabain) also fail to block H^+ pumping in secretory granules. Lack of inhibition by vanadate is significant since all transport ATPases known to proceed through a phosphoenzyme intermediate are strongly inhibited by vanadate (27).

Acidification of endosomes, lysosomes, coated vesicles, yeast, and *Neurospora* vesicles and kidney vesicles is also insensitive to azide and vanadate (8, 16, 34, 43, 44, 46). Despite its resistance to the above reagents, the acidic organelle H^+ pump is rapidly inactivated by sulfhydryl reagents such as NEM (N-ethylmaleimide), Nbd-Cl (7-chloro-4-nitrobenz-2-oxa-1,3-diazole), and DTNB at concentrations that fail to inhibit F_1F_o or Na^+,K^+-ATPases (8, 12, 13, 16, 34, 43, 44, 46). This distinctly different pattern of inhibition between the organelle ATPase and other classes of transport ATPase suggests that it represents a new class of ATP-dependent ion pump.

NUCLEOTIDE SPECIFICITY   If the same enzyme is responsible for acidifying all acidic organelles, we would expect it to show the same substrate specificity in all cases. Relative to ATP, however, other nucleotide triphosphates are utilized to a greater or lesser extent depending on their origin. The largest discrepancy is for GTP. In lysosomes and some preparations of endosomes, coated vesicles, and secretory granules, GTP serves as a substrate for the pump (12, 15, 34). Xie et al (49) have noted that contamination by ADP and nucleotide-5'-diphosphokinase can, by synthesizing ATP, mimic the ability of GTP to serve as a true substrate. In some preparations of coated vesicles, endosomes, and chromaffin granule membrane vesicles GTP fails to drive H^+ pumping (13, 29, 49), which suggests that GTP hydrolysis is not an innate property of the H^+ pump. In lysosomes, however, GTP consistently drives H^+ influx (29, 34). Whether this observation indicates that the lysosomal H^+ pump is different from other acidic organelle H^+ pumps or rather that lysosomes are more difficult to free of contamination by ADP and nucleotide-5'-diphosphokinase remains to be seen.

STOICHIOMETRY AND REVERSIBILITY   The H^+ pump of acidic organelles differs fundamentally in function from the F_1F_o ATPase of energy transducing membranes such as chloroplasts, mitochondria, and bacteria. F_1F_o functions predominantly as an ATP synthetase in vivo, using the $\Delta\bar{\mu}_{H^+}$ generated by metabolic or light energy. The acidic organelle ATPase, in contrast, consumes ATP to acidify the organelle interior. As might be predicted from their function, the stoichiometries of the two enzymes are different. Berry & Hinkle (6) measured the stoichiometry of F_1F_o ATPase in submitochondrial particles and concluded that three H^+ ions are transported for each molecule of ATP synthesized or hydrolyzed. Two estimates have been made of the chromaffin granule ATPase stoichiometry, using either the γ-phosphate resonance of intragranular ATP (32) or accumulation of methylamine (24) as an internal pH indicator. Both groups estimated the rate of H^+ pumping taking into account the estimated buffering capacity, related the pumping rate to the ATP hydrolytic rate, and concluded that two H^+ ions were transported per ATP hydrolyzed.

A difference in stoichiometry between the two enzymes is reasonable considering their opposite functions. To synthesize ATP, it is an advantage to have many H^+ ions participating in each catalytic cycle. This insures that ATP will be synthesized at a minimum $\Delta\bar{\mu}_{H^+}$. For an enzyme whose function is to generate $\Delta\bar{\mu}_{H^+}$, if fewer H^+ ions participate in the reaction the ATPase can generate a larger $\Delta\bar{\mu}_{H^+}$ with a given phosphorylation potential (ΔG_p) for ATP hydrolysis. For a given stoichiometry, n, the $\Delta\bar{\mu}_{H^+}$ in equilibrium with a given ΔG_p is given by $\Delta G_p = n \cdot \Delta\bar{\mu}_{H^+}$. It is clear that as n increases, the $\Delta\bar{\mu}_{H^+}$ which is in equilibrium with ΔG_p decreases. The apparent difference in stoichiometry is reflected in the reversibility of the two ATPases. F_1F_o ATPase is easier to drive in the direction of ATP synthesis either by respiratory H^+ pumping or by artificially imposed $\Delta\bar{\mu}_{H^+}$. The acidic organelle H^+ pump is rather difficult to reverse. The only evidence of reversal is the uncoupler sensitive incorporation of ^{32}Pi into ATP by coated vesicles (49). This probably represents the rapid breakdown and resynthesis of ATP after H^+ pumping has generated a $\Delta\bar{\mu}_{H^+}$ in equilibrium with ΔG_p.

MECHANISM OF ATP HYDROLYSIS   Previously studied transport ATPases catalyze ATP hydrolysis by one of two distinct pathways. The phospho-enzyme type ATPases, such as Na^+,K^+-ATPase, catalyze transfer of the γ-phosphate of ATP to form an enzyme-phosphate intermediate, which is then hydrolyzed in a separate step (7). The F_1F_o ATPase probably catalyzes direct transfer of the γ-phosphate to water (48). Since vanadate inhibits all of the transport ATPases known to utilize the phospho-enzyme mechanism, the lack of vanadate inhibition in the acidic organelle ATPase suggests that it does not proceed through a phospho-enzyme intermediate. Attempts to isolate a phospho-enzyme intermediate in the coated vesicle ATPase reaction have also failed (14). It is difficult, however, to definitively rule out the participation of such an intermediate.

PURIFICATION AND STRUCTURE   The acidic organelle H^+ pump has been purified from yeast vacuoles and chromaffin granules (31, 46). In each tissue more than one polypeptide is associated with the purified pump. In the case of the yeast vacuole the sizes of these peptides are 89, 64, and 19.5 kilodaltons (kDa), while the chromaffin granule polypeptides associated with pump activity are 115, 72, 57, and 39 kDa. In chromaffin granules the 115 and 57 kDa peptides are labeled with NEM, and the 115 kDa polypeptide has tentatively been identified as the active site subunit. In coated vesicles the pump has been resolved into a detergent-soluble ATPase fraction and a membrane residue, both of which are required for H^+ pumping (50). In addition, both the coated vesicle and chromaffin granule ATPases are stabilized and activated by the presence of phosphatidyl serine, which may represent an additional component of the complete H^+ pump.

How the $\Delta\bar{\mu}_{H^+}$ is Used

LYSOSOMAL PROTEIN DEGRADATION   The observation that many lysosomal hydrolytic enzymes have acidic pH optima prompted early suggestions that the lysosome actively maintained an acidic interior (11). The rate of intralysosomal protein hydrolysis varies with internal pH and has been used as a measure of acidification (37). ATP increases the rate of protein hydrolysis, and the increase is blocked by dinitrophenol and nigericin, both of which are expected to prevent ATP-driven acidification (28). The intralysosomal hydrolysis of amino acid methyl esters and their accumulation as free amino acids represents a potential model system for lysosomal proteolysis (36). This process is stimulated by ATP and inhibited by agents which dissipate the ΔpH.

RECEPTOR-MEDIATED ENDOCYTOSIS   Many nutrients, hormones, enzymes, and other macromolecules enter animal cells by binding to receptors on the plasma membrane, which are subsequently internalized by the process of endocytosis (20). Although the ligands are delivered with high efficiency to an intracellular location (usually the lysosome), the receptors often return to the cell surface free of ligand, and participate in many cycles of endocytosis and return during their lifetime. The recycling process requires release of internalized ligand prior to reutilization of the receptor, and recent studies suggest that acidification of an intracellular compartment triggers receptor-ligand dissociation.

The two compartments likely to serve as the sites of receptor-ligand sorting are the endocytic coated vesicle and the endosome. Although coated vesicles isolated from brain (43) and liver (47) acidify in the presence of ATP in vitro, there is no direct evidence that endocytic coated vesicles are acidic in vivo. Endosomes, however, are known to be acidic in vivo (45) and to acidify their interiors in vitro using an H^+-pumping ATPase similar to the one in secretory granules, lysosomes, and coated vesicles (16).

In addition to physiological ligands whose intracellular accumulation depends on endosomal acidification, a variety of pathogens also require an acid internal compartment for their activity. These include a variety of envelope viruses, such as Semliki Forest Virus, and polypeptide endotoxins like diphtheria toxin. In both cases infection or intoxication is blocked by either lysosomotropic weak bases or by ionophores, such as monensin and nigericin, which are known to increase lysosomal pH. Moreover, virus or toxin bound to the cell surface can act if the medium is briefly acidified, even in the presence of monensin or a weak base (20).

INTRAORGANELLE SOLUTE STORAGE   Cells secreting biogenic amines store them in secretory granules using the ΔpH and $\Delta\Psi$ generated by the H^+-pumping ATPase. The evidence for coupling amine transport to ATP hydrolysis through an H^+ potential consists of three major observations: (a) ATP hydrolysis generates both $\Delta\Psi$ and ΔpH; (b) artificial imposition of $\Delta\Psi$, ΔpH, or both drives biogenic amine accumulation; and (c) agents that dissipate $\Delta\Psi$ or ΔpH uncouple the ATPase from amine transport (see 40 for review). The membranes of these granules contain, in addition to the ATPase, a reserpine-sensitive amine transporter that exchanges internal H^+ ions for cytoplasmic amines. The transporter is rather nonspecific; it uses norepinephrine, epinephrine, serotonin, dopamine, and histamine as substrates. Since net positive charge moves out of the granule as amines enter, the transporter is believed to exchange one H^+ for a neutral amine, or two H^+ ions for a protonated amine.

In synaptic vesicles isolated from *Torpedo californica*, ATP also drives influx of acetylcholine. ATP-dependent accumulation is blocked by H^+ ionophores, such as FCCP [carbonyl cyanide p-(trifluoromethoxy)phenyl-hydrazone], at the same concentration that they increase ATP hydrolysis (2). This observation is consistent with an ATPase that generates a $\Delta\Psi$ or ΔpH or both across the membrane. The $\Delta\Psi$ or ΔpH act both to limit the rate of ATP hydrolysis and to drive acetylcholine transport. Furthermore, both nigericin and ammonia inhibit ATP-dependent acetylcholine accumulation. Although neither agent dissipates $\Delta\Psi$, both dissipate ΔpH.

Cytoplasmic vacuoles from many yeast, fungal, and plant cells store a variety of metabolites. Although the mechanism is not known in detail, the process is apparently similar to biogenic amine accumulation by mammalian secretory granules (40). The vacuoles contain a membrane-bound H^+-pumping ATPase. ATP addition acidifies the vacuole and stimulates solute transport, which is a saturable process. Addition of substrate in the absence of ATP causes medium acidification, and an artificially imposed ΔpH stimulates solute influx in the absence of ATP.

URINARY ACIDIFICATION   Urinary acidification in the turtle bladder is thought to represent the same process by which mammalian urine is acidified in the renal collecting tubule. In the turtle bladder, specialized cells containing acidic organelles pump H^+ from the cell to the bladder lumen in response to stimulation by CO_2 (see Schwartz & Al-Awqati, this volume). The data suggest that a specific organelle reversibly inserts H^+ pumps into the plasma membrane when the cell is stimulated.

EXOCYTOSIS   The $\Delta\bar{\mu}_{H^+}$ generated by H^+ influx has been invoked as a driving force for exocytosis. According to this hypothesis the $\Delta\Psi$ generated by H^+ pumping leads to anion influx, which in turn causes osmotic swelling of the secretory organelle and facilitates its fusion with the plasma membrane. Many lines of evidence now argue against this mechanism. The osmotic properties of secretory granules and their relation to exocytosis are reviewed by Holz elsewhere in this volume.

PROCESSING OF SECRETION GRANULE CONTENTS   Some secreted substances are formed or modified within the secretory granule. In adrenergic neurons and chromaffin cells dopamine is converted to epinephrine by intragranular dopamine-β-hydroxylase. In peptide secreting cells the limited proteolytic digestion required to convert precursors into active peptides is believed to occur within the secretory organelle. This peptide processing consists of at least three reactions: cleavage, C-terminal digestion, and amidation (26).

Each of these reactions is at least partially dependent on H^+-pumping ATPase activity. In proteolytic reactions the endopeptidases and carboxypeptidases thought to be responsible for peptide processing are most active at low pH (26). Amidation and dopamine hydroxylation both depend on the availability of intragranular ascorbate, which is oxidized to semidehydroascorbate. To replenish intragranular ascorbate the semiquinone is reduced through the action of a membrane-bound electron carrier (probably cytochrome b-561), which presumably uses cytoplasmic ascorbate as a reductant (41). The H^+-pumping ATPase drives this reaction toward internal ascorbate reduction for two reasons. The $\Delta\Psi$ (interior positive) generated by electrogenic H^+ pumping will facilitate the influx of electrons through the cytochrome. Moreover, the midpoint potential for ascorbate reduction is higher at lower pH. This leads to more facile reduction of intragranular semidehydroascorbate with cytoplasmic ascorbate when a ΔpH is generated by the ATPase.

OTHER FUNCTIONS   Does H^+ pumping into intracellular organelles serve other physiological functions in addition to those described above? The answer is probably yes. For example, protein glycosylation is inhibited both by monensin (which increases the pH of acidic organelles) and by mutations that block endosome acidification (38). These findings suggest a role for the H^+-pumping ATPase in the Golgi apparatus. Other uses in intracellular signalling and energy transduction will doubtless be discovered for this versatile H^+ pump.

Literature Cited

1. Deleted in proof
2. Anderson, D. C., King, S. C., Parsons, S. M. 1982. Proton gradient linkage to active uptake of [³H]acetylcholine by *Torpedo* electric organ synaptic vesicles. *Biochemistry* 21:3037–43
3. Anderson, R. G. W., Pathak, R. K. 1985. Vesicles and cisternae in the *trans* golgi apparatus of human fibroblasts are acidic compartments. *Cell* 40:635–43

4. Apps, D. K., Schatz, G. 1979. An adenosine triphosphatase isolated from chromaffin granule membranes is closely similar to F_1-adenosine triphosphatase of mitochondria. *Eur. J. Biochem.* 100:411–19
5. Arvan, P., Rudnick, G., Castle, J. D. 1984. Osmotic properties and internal pH of isolated rat parotid secretory granules. *J. Biol. Chem.* 259:13567–72

412   RUDNICK

6. Berry, E. A., Hinkle, P. C. 1983. Measurement of the electrochemical proton gradient in submitochondrial particles. *J. Biol. Chem.* 258:1474–86

7. Bastide, F., Meissner, G., Fleisher, S., Post, R. L. 1973. Similarity of the active site of phosphorylation of the adenosine triphosphatase for transport of sodium and potassium ions in kidney to that for transport of calcium ions in the sarcoplasmic reticulum of muscle. *J. Biol. Chem.* 248:8385–91

8. Bowman, E. J. 1983. Comparison of the vacuolar membrane ATPase of *Neurospora crassa* with the mitochondrial and plasma membrane ATPases. *J. Biol. Chem.* 258:15238–44

9. Cidon, S., Ben-David, H., Nelson, N. 1983. ATP-driven proton fluxes across membranes of secretory organelles. *J. Biol. Chem.* 258:11684–88

10. Cidon, S., Nelson, N. 1983. A novel ATPase in the chromaffin-granule membrane. *J. Biol. Chem.* 258:2892–98

11. Coffey, J. W., de Duve, C. 1968. Digestive activity of lysosomes. I. The digestion of proteins by extracts of rat liver lysosomes. *J. Biol. Chem.* 243:3255–63

12. Dean, G. E. Fishkes, H., Nelson, P. J., Rudnick, G. 1984. The hydrogen ion-pumping adenosine triphosphatase of platelet dense granule membrane. Differences from F_1F_0- and phosphoenzyme-type ATPases. *J. Biol. Chem.* 259:9569–74

13. Dean, G. E., Nelson, P. J., Rudnick, G. 1986. Characterization of the native and reconstituted hydrogen ion-pumping adenosine triphosphatase of chromaffin granules. Submitted for publication

14. Forgac, M., Cantley, L. 1984. Characterization of the ATP-dependent proton pump of clathrin-coated vesicles. *J. Biol. Chem.* 259:8101–5

15. Forgac, M., Cantley, L., Wiedenmann, B., Altstiel, L., Branton, D. 1983. Clathrin-coated vesicles contain an ATP-dependent proton pump. *Proc. Natl. Acad. Sci. USA* 80:1300–3

16. Galloway, C. J., Dean, G. E., Marsh, M., Rudnick, G., Mellman, I. 1983. Acidification of macrophage and fibroblast endocytic vesicles in vitro. *Proc. Natl. Acad. Sci. USA* 80:3334–38

17. Glickman, J., Croen, K., Kelly, S., Al-Awqati, Q. 1983. Golgi membranes contain an electrogenic H^+ pump in parallel to a chloride conductance. *J. Cell Biol.* 97:1303–8

18. Goffeau, A., Slayman, C. W. 1981. The proton translocating ATPase of the fungal plasma membrane. *Biochim. Biophys. Acta* 639:197–223

19. Harikumar, P., Reeves, J. P. 1983. The lysosomal proton pump is electrogenic. *J. Biol. Chem.* 258:10403–10

20. Helenius, A., Mellman, I., Wall, D., Hubbard, A. 1983. Endosomes. *Trends Biochem. Sci.* 8:245–50

21. Holz, R. W. 1979. Measurement of membrane potential of chromaffin granules by the accumulation of triphenylmethylphosphonium cations. *J. Biol. Chem.* 254:6703–9

22. Deleted in proof

23. Johnson, R. G., Pfister, D., Carty, S. E., Scarpa, A. 1979. Biological amine transport in chromaffin ghosts. Coupling to the transmembrane proton and potential gradients. *J. Biol. Chem.* 254:10963–72

24. Johnson, R. G., Beers, M. F., Scarpa, A. 1982. H^+ ATPase of chromaffin granules. kinetics, regulation, and stoichiometry. *J. Biol. Chem.,* 257:10701–7

25. Lin, W., Wagner, G. J., Siegelman, H. W., Hind, G. 1977 Membrane-bound ATPase of intact vacuoles and tonoplasts isolated from mature plant tissue. *Biochim. Biophys. Acta* 465:110–17

26. Loh, Y. P., Brownstein, M. J., Gainer, H. 1984. Proteolysis in neuropeptide processing and other neural functions. *Ann. Rev. Neurosci.* 7:189–222

27. Macara, I. 1980. Vanadium—an element in search of a role. *Trends Biochem. Sci.,* 5:92–94

28. Mego, J. L., Farb, R. M., Barnes, J. 1972. An ATP-dependent stabilization of proteolytic activity in heterolysosomes. *Biochem. J.* 128:763–69

29. Merion, M., Schlesinger, P., Brooks, R. M., Moehring, J. M., Moehring, T. J., Sly, W. S. 1983. Defective acidification of endosomes in Chinese hamster ovary cell mutants cross-resistant to toxins and viruses. *Proc. Natl. Acad. Sci. USA* 80:5315–19

30. Metchnikoff, E. 1893. *Lectures on the Comparative Pathology of Inflammation.* London: Kegan. 218 pp.

31. Nelson, N., Cidon, S. 1986. Chromaffin granule proton pump. *Methods Enzymol.* In press

32. Njus, D., Sehr, P. A., Radda, G. K., Ritchie, G. A., Seeley, P. J. 1978. Phosphorus-31 nuclear magnetic resonance studies of active proton translocation in chromaffin granules. *Biochemistry* 17: 4337–43

33. Ohkuma, S., Poole, B. 1978. Fluorescence probe measurement of the intralysosomal pH in living cells and the perturbation of pH by various agents. *Proc. Nat. Acad. Sci. USA* 75:3327–31

34. Ohkuma, S., Moriyama, Y., Takano, T.

1982. Identification and characterization of a proton pump on lysosomes by fluorescein-isothiocyanate-dextran fluorescence. *Proc. Natl. Acad. Sci. USA* 79:2758–62

35. Pazoles, C. J., Creutz, C. E., Ramu, A., Pollard, H. B. 1980. Permeant anion activation of MgATPase activity in chromaffin granules. Evidence for direct coupling of proton and anion transport. *J. Biol. Chem.* 255:7863–69

36. Reeves, J. P., Reames, T. 1981. ATP stimulates amino acid accumulation by lysosomes incubated with amino acid methyl esters. *J. Biol. Chem.* 256:6047–53

37. Reijngoud, D.-J., Oud, P. S., Kas, J., Tager, J. M. 1976. Relationship between medium pH and that of the lysosomal matrix. *Biochim. Biophys. Acta* 448:290–302

38. Robbins, A. R., Oliver, C., Bateman, J. L., Krag, S. S., Galloway, C. J., Mellman, I. 1984. A single mutation in Chinese hamster ovary cells impairs both Golgi and endosomal functions. *J. Cell. Biol.* 99:1296–1308

39. Rottenberg, H. 1979. The measurement of membrane potential and ΔpH in cells, organelles, and vesicles. *Methods Enzymol.* 55:547–69

40. Rudnick, G. 1985. Acidification of intracellular organelles. Mechanism and function. In *Physiology of Membrane Disorders*, ed. T. E. Andreoli, D. D. Fanestil, J. F. Hoffman, S. G. Schultz, Vol. 25. New York: Plenum. In press. 2 ed.

41. Russell, J. T., Levine, M., Njus, D. 1985. Electron transfer across posterior pituitary neurosecretory vesicle membranes. *J. Biol. Chem.* 260:226–31

42. Sachs, G., Chang, H. H., Rabon, E., Schackman, R., Lewin, M., Saccomani, G. 1976. A nonelectrogenic H⁺ pump in plasma membranes of hog stomach. *J. Biol. Chem.* 251:7690–98

43. Stone, D. K., Xie, X.-S., Racker, E. 1982. An ATP-driven proton pump in clathrin-coated vesicles *J. Biol. Chem.* 258:4059–62

44. Stone, D. K., Xie, X.-S., Wu, L.-T., Racker, E. 1984. Proton translocating ATPases of clathrin-coated vesicles, renal medulla, and Ehrlich ascites tumor cells. In *Hydrogen Ion Transport in Epithelia*, ed. J. G. Forte, D. G. Warnock, F. C. Rechter Jr., pp. 219–30. New York: Wiley

45. Tycko, B., Maxfield, F. R. 1982. Rapid acidification of endocytic vesicles containing α-2-macroglobulin. *Cell* 28:643–51

46. Uchida, E., Ohsumi, Y., Anraku, Y. 1985. Purification and properties of H⁺-translocating, Mg²⁺-adenosine triphosphatase from vacuolar membranes of *Saccharomyces cerevisiae.*, *J. Biol. Chem.* 260:1090–95

47. Van Dyke, R. W., Steer, C. J., Scharschmidt, B. F. 1984. Clathrin-coated vesicles from rat liver: Enzymatic profile and characterization of ATP-dependent proton transport. *Proc. Natl. Acad. Sci. USA* 81:3108–12

48. Webb, M. R., Grubmeyer, C., Penefsky, H. S., Trentham, D. R. 1980. The stereochemical course of phosphoric residue transfer catalyzed by beef heart mitochondrial ATPase. *J. Biol. Chem.* 255:11637–39

49. Xie, X.-S., Stone, D. K., Racker, E. 1983. Determinants of clathrin-coated vesicle acidification. *J. Biol. Chem.* 258:14834–38

50. Xie, X.-S., Stone, D. K., Racker, E. 1984. Activation and partial purification of the ATPase of clathrin-coated vesicles and reconstitution of the proton pump. *J. Biol. Chem.* 259:11676–78

SPECIAL TOPIC: CELL BIOLOGICAL APPROACHES TO BRAIN FUNCTION

Introduction, Paul Greengard, *Section Editor*

Progress in our understanding of the molecular and cellular bases of neuronal function has been fairly remarkable during the past decade. As one example, we now know of three distinct classes of neurotransmitters, namely, amino acids, biogenic amines, and peptides; moreover, the list of peptides that appear to be involved in neurotransmission now numbers more than sixty. The multiple neurotransmitters/neuromodulators, the multiple receptors for these ligands, the multiple ion channels, and the multiple intracellular regulatory molecules that have been discovered provide some biochemical equipment for investigating the molecular basis of neuronal function, e.g. the mechanisms by which different types of nerve cells respond to various extracellular signals with appropriate physiological responses. This investigation is being facilitated by the powerful new methodologies developed in recent years: patch clamping, monoclonal antibodies, immunocytochemistry, radioactive ligands, tissue culture techniques (e.g. *in vitro* reaggregation of dispersed brain cells into histiotypic patterns), intracranial transplantation techniques, techniques for the isolation of intraneuronal organelles (e.g. small synaptic vesicles and postsynaptic densities), procedures for purification of receptors, ion channels, and other integral membrane proteins, techniques for functional reconstitution of receptors and ion channels into artificial membranes, cloning of receptors and ion channels, site-directed mutagenesis of receptors and ion channels, etc.

   This section contains reviews of four of the many exciting areas of neurobiological research. Gerald Edelman reviews important advances in our knowledge of cell adhesion molecules and their role in the development of the nervous system. Solomon Snyder has chosen a few receptors to illustrate a number of

416

principles in the receptor field. Mayo et al review the basic structural characteristics common to those neuroendocrine genes thus far analyzed and explore new
methodologies that promise to be useful for the identification and analysis of
genes encoding neuroendocrine peptides. Finally, Gage & Björklund discuss
recent advances in the rapidly growing field of neural grafting. Regretfully,
space limitations prohibit the inclusion of numerous other exciting areas of
research on the molecular and cellular basis of function in the nervous system.

Ann. Rev. Physiol. 1986. 48:417–30

CELL ADHESION MOLECULES IN NEURAL HISTOGENESIS

Gerald M. Edelman

Laboratory of Developmental and Molecular Biology, The Rockefeller University, New York, New York 10021

Introduction

Aside from evolutionary change itself, there are three main sources of variability in neural networks: the somatic developmental sequence, which is responsible for network formation and neuroanatomy; the chemical and structural variation at synapses (particularly that related to neurotransmitters and channels); and the electrical variation that depends both upon intrinsic cellular metabolism and external signals. These processes emerge in a clear-cut order of development. It is just as clear, however, that none of these processes is fully independent of the others, although their relative contributions vary in time. While much has been done to study neurotransmitters and electrical activity in the last three decades, only recently has it become possible to study the molecular bases of constancy and variation in network formation, fiber tract mapping, and the establishment of the earliest contacts of nerve and muscle.

One of the key elements in this molecular analysis has been the development of a concerted series of assays (4, 12, 13, 32) that unequivocally establish criteria for the isolation and structural and functional characterization of cell adhesion molecules (CAMs). Prior to this approach, the evidence for the existence of such molecules was sparse and unconvincing, but since its application at least three different CAMs have been isolated and described (1, 4, 7, 8, 12, 20, 25, 26, 28, 31, 32, 34). On the basis of their description, previously recognized molecules whose functions had been unknown (20, 26, 31) were identified as CAMs. Particular CAMs have pivotal roles in neuron-neuron, neuron-muscle, and neuron-glial binding, and from the earliest stages in the development of the nervous system, each appears in neural tissues in characteristic dynamic patterns and spatiotemporal distributions (12).

417

0066-4278/86/0315-0417$02.00

The detailed chemical properties of CAMs have been reviewed elsewhere (2, 9, 12, 13, 24); in this briefer survey I shall interpretively emphasize certain observations that bear upon their role in the formation of neural networks as these CAMs are expressed on neurons during development. No attempt has been made to be exhaustive in this short account; the attempt rather is to bring certain aspects up to date and correlate them. Moreover, this account must be preliminary: the exact interaction of CAM expression sequences with electrical activity and neuropharmacologic processes remain to be worked out. Nevertheless, several important generalizations have emerged in studying CAMs, and we have begun to glimpse several of the principles by which they regulate the formation of high-order neural structures from individual cells.

So far, two CAMs have been found in neural tissue (12): N-CAM (neural CAM) and Ng-CAM (neuron-glia CAM). Both molecules are found on neurons, but as implied by their names, they appear at different times, in different sequences, and they carry out different functions. These molecules have been partially characterized; they have different structures and binding specificities. N-CAM mediates the homotypic binding of neuron to neuron and the heterotypic binding of neuron to striated muscle, in both cases by a homophilic (N-CAM to N-CAM) binding mechanism. Ng-CAM mediates the heterotypic binding of neurons to glia, presumably by a heterophilic mechanism inasmuch as Ng-CAM is not present on glia in appreciable amounts. Correlation of the known structures, binding mechanisms, and sequences of expression of these molecules reveals the enormous dynamism and versatility of cell surface CAM systems as they come under different regulatory controls during neural histogenesis.

Chemical Structures

A structural comparison of N-CAM and Ng-CAM is shown in Figure 1. Fractions containing N-CAM have been shown to consist of polypeptide chains closely similar in general structure but of different molecular weights (130,000 and 160,000); only the higher Mr chain is shown in the diagram. N-CAM chains consist of three domains (Figure 1A): an amino terminal domain containing a region mediating homophilic binding; a middle domain containing the three attachment sites for the bulk of the carbohydrate, which is unusual for its high content of polysialic acid; and a carboxyl terminal domain, part of which spans the plasma membrane.

Less is known of Ng-CAM structure, but a comparison of this protein with N-CAM shows they are different (Figure 1B). Ng-CAM appears as three components of Mr 200,000, 135,000, and 80,000 (19). Chemical and immunochemical analyses suggest that the two lower molecular weight components are structurally related to that of highest molecular weight. Antisera exist that show cross-reactions between the Mr 200,000 component and both

CELL ADHESION MOLECULES   419

the Mr 135,000 component and Mr 80,000 component. At present there is no
evidence that the two lower molecular weight components are related. Pulse
chase experiments suggest a precursor-product relation between the Mr
200,000 and 135,000 polypeptides. It is not clear yet whether the two components of lower molecular weight are separately synthesized or are proteolytic
products of the Mr 200,000 component. The state of Ng-CAM at the neuronal
cell surface as a complex of these components or as separate polypeptides is not
yet established.

The two neuronal CAMs also have very different detailed chemical structures. For example, N-CAM and the Mr 135,000 component of Ng-CAM show
great differences (18) in their peptide maps (see Figure 1B). There is also a
clear-cut difference in the carbohydrate structures of N-CAM and Ng-CAM:
Unlike N-CAM, Ng-CAM does not contain large amounts of sialic acid present

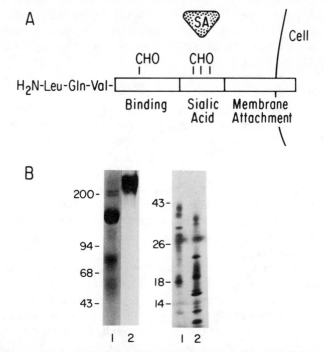

Figure 1   Structural features of N-CAM and Ng-CAM. (a) linear model of N-CAM (embryonic or
E form), which consists of three domains: an NH₂ terminal binding domain, a middle domain
containing large amounts (30 g/100 g polypeptide) of polysialic acid (SA) present on at least three
attachment sites (6), and a cell membrane–associated domain for the integral protein CHO-
carbohydrate. (b) Left panel: SDS gel electrophoretic comparison of (1) specific im-
munoprecipitated chick Ng-CAM and (2) E form of chick N-CAM. Right panel: One-dimensional
peptide maps (SDS gels) using S. aureus V8 protease (Cleveland procedure) comparing peptides of
(1) chick Ng-CAM and (2) chick N-CAM.

as polysialic acid. Two different monoclonal antibodies have been found, however, that show cross reactivity between the two CAMs, one between determinants on the polypeptide chains and one between saccharide determinants (18, 19) in the two molecules. It remains an open question whether the two CAMs are evolutionarily related.

Consistent with the differences in carbohydrate, Ng-CAM shows no evidence of the radical change in carbohydrate composition of the kind seen in N-CAM during development. This so-called E to A conversion is a diminution in polysialic acid from higher values (30 g/100 gm polypeptide) on embryonic or E forms to lower values (10 g/100 g polypeptide) on adult or A forms. Conversion occurs in N-CAM during the perinatal period (5), with a concurrent increase in the efficacy of homophilic binding. Although the sialic acid is not directly involved in binding, it modulates the binding, presumably through its high negative charge (13, 23). Finally, unlike N-CAM whose binding is homophilic, there is no evidence that Ng-CAM binding to glia is homophilic. Glia show no evidence of the significant amounts of the molecule, therefore the binding is presumed to be heterophilic, and to involve an as yet unidentified glial CAM (18, 19).

Histologic Appearance

A single neuron can display both N-CAM and Ng-CAM. However, it is important to note that this is seen only in postmitotic neurons, and that the expression sequence of the two proteins is different, with N-CAM preceding Ng-CAM throughout the nervous system (8a, 15, 33). As shown in Figure 2, N-CAM is a primary CAM: It appears in the early embryo in blastoderm, then in derivatives of more than one germ layer (6a, 12). It is seen in neural ectoderm, somites, heart, and kidney in a conjugate relationship to L-CAM (the liver cell adhesion molecule), particularly in areas of embryonic induction (15). In the chick, Ng-CAM appears later only in neural tissues during histogenesis; it is thus a secondary CAM.

Consistent with the major differences in their binding specificities, the expression sequences and histologic distributions of N-CAM and Ng-CAM are strikingly different both during early embryogenesis and in the histogenesis of local regions of brain and peripheral nerve (Figure 2). As mentioned above, in early development Ng-CAM is expressed only in neural ectodermal derivatives, whereas N-CAM is found in ectodermal and mesodermal derivatives, and transiently in endodermal derivatives (6a). Moreover, in later histogenesis the microscopic distribution of the two molecules differs both at the cellular level and the tissue level. N-CAM is found on all parts of neuronal surfaces (although in different amounts), and in all portions of a given neural tissue. In the central nervous system (CNS) Ng-CAM appears only transiently on cell somata, mainly on axons in a polar distribution (33). This is known as polarity

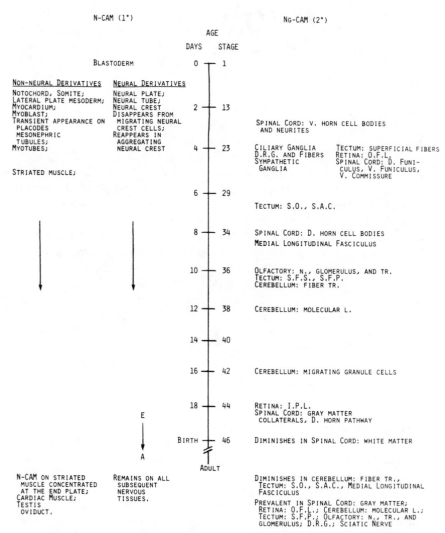

N-CAM (1°)   NG-CAM (2°)

AGE

DAYS   STAGE

BLASTODERM   0 ─┬─ 1

NON-NEURAL DERIVATIVES   NEURAL DERIVATIVES
NOTOCHORD, SOMITE;   NEURAL PLATE;
LATERAL PLATE MESODERM;   NEURAL TUBE;
MYOCARDIUM;   NEURAL CREST
MYOBLAST;   DISAPPEARS FROM   2 ─┼─ 13
TRANSIENT APPEARANCE ON   MIGRATING NEURAL   SPINAL CORD: V. HORN CELL BODIES
 PLACODES   CREST CELLS;   AND NEURITES
 MESONEPHRIC   REAPPEARS IN
 TUBULES;   AGGREGATING
MYOTUBES;   NEURAL CREST   4 ─┼─ 23   CILIARY GANGLIA   TECTUM: SUPERFICIAL FIBERS
                                                              D.R.G. AND FIBERS RETINA: O.F.L.
                                                              SYMPATHETIC   SPINAL CORD: D. FUNI-
STRIATED MUSCLE;   GANGLIA   CULUS, V. FUNICULUS,
                                                                                  V. COMMISSURE

                                                 6 ─┼─ 29

                                                              TECTUM: S.O., S.A.C.

                                                 8 ─┼─ 34   SPINAL CORD: D. HORN CELL BODIES
                                                              MEDIAL LONGITUDINAL FASCICULUS

                                                10 ─┼─ 36   OLFACTORY: N., GLOMERULUS, AND TR.
                                                              TECTUM: S.F.S., S.F.P.
                                                              CEREBELLUM: FIBER TR.

                                                12 ─┼─ 38   CEREBELLUM: MOLECULAR L.

                                                14 ─┼─ 40

                                                16 ─┼─ 42   CEREBELLUM: MIGRATING GRANULE CELLS

                                                18 ─┼─ 44   RETINA: I.P.L.
                                    E   SPINAL CORD: GRAY MATTER
                                                               COLLATERALS, D. HORN PATHWAY
                                    ↓
                              BIRTH ─┼─ 46   DIMINISHES IN SPINAL CORD: WHITE MATTER
                                  A   ╪

                                      ADULT

N-CAM ON STRIATED   REMAINS ON ALL   DIMINISHES IN CEREBELLUM: FIBER TR.,
 MUSCLE CONCENTRATED   SUBSEQUENT   TECTUM: S.O., S.A.C., MEDIAL LONGITUDINAL
 AT THE END PLATE;   NERVOUS   FASCICULUS
CARDIAC MUSCLE;   TISSUES.
TESTIS   PREVALENT IN SPINAL CORD: GRAY MATTER;
OVIDUCT.   RETINA: O.F.L.; CEREBELLUM: MOLECULAR L.;
                                                 TECTUM: S.F.P.; OLFACTORY: N., TR., AND
                                                 GLOMERULUS; D.R.G.; SCIATIC NERVE

Figure 2   Expression sequences of the two neuronal CAMs in the developing chick. The entries represent times of first appearance or sites of disappearance. Note that there is a macrosequence (N-CAM followed by Ng-CAM) as well as a microsequence for each CAM. E to A conversion of N-CAM occurs mainly in the perinatal period.

modulation (12). At various tissue locales Ng-CAM appears on axons and axon bundles of neural derivatives in a definite set of temporal sequences (8a, 33). It appears first in precursors of motor neurons and then in precursors of sensory neurons. A definite sequence of appearance is also seen in the laminae of areas like the optic tectum and the cerebellum (Figure 2). N-CAM is also found in these areas but in different relative amounts in different layers at different times. It is particularly intriguing that Ng-CAM is not polarity modulated on external granule cells of the embryonic cerebellum as they are migrating on guide glia, and that addition of anti-Ng-CAM antibodies to cerebellar slices in vitro blocks their movement (18).

The significance of these differential dynamic distributions is not yet clear, but it is tempting to suggest that the polarity modulation of Ng-CAM on each cell and the temporally variant modulations in its prevalence in different fiber tract layers are related to cyto-architecturally important neural-glial interactions, particularly those involved in the extension of fibers and migration of cell bodies during development. It is significant that both N-CAM and Ng-CAM are present on growth cones, and a study of their differential modulation on these specialized neural structures may be of particular importance in understanding events pertinent to neural guidance.

Recent studies (30) suggest that N-CAM is present at neuromuscular synapses, particularly in the synaptic cleft of the neuromuscular junction, although it is too early to specify the exact molecular disposition of the N-CAM. The most striking observation is that N-CAM is coincident in its distribution with that of the acetylcholine receptor in developing muscle; it is localized later at the mature neuromuscular junction. Moreover, N-CAM in muscle undergoes E to A conversion. After denervation, N-CAM decreases at the end plate, but is found in increased amounts in the cytoplasm and surface of the muscle (30). The detailed relation of Ng-CAM to the synapse is not yet known.

Modulation and Binding Mechanisms

All of these observations reinforce the idea that CAMs exercise their binding functions selectively by means of various mechanisms of cell surface modulation (12, 13). Such mechanisms include changes in the amounts of CAM at the surface (prevalence modulation), changes in distribution at different locations on an individual cell (polarity modulation), and changes in chemical properties of the CAM itself (chemical modulation such as E to A conversion). The functional significance of such modulation events is that they change the binding or adhesion behavior of CAMs in a graded but nonlinear fashion. The various modulation events are likely to alter the interactions of cell-cell adhesion with other primary developmental processes such as movement and changes in cell shape. Differential effects of modulation upon neurite extension, retraction, and growth cone movement would be expected to have particularly strong influences on histogenetic patterns.

Any attempt to understand such modulation events at the cellular level depends upon an understanding of the binding mechanisms of specific CAM molecules. N-CAM binding is *trans*-homophilic, i.e. N-CAM to N-CAM on apposing cells. The rate of this binding has been shown by kinetic assays (22,

23) of binding of CAM-bearing lipid vesicles to be strongly dependent upon the surface density of the molecule. In addition, chemical modulation, such as E to A conversion, has been shown separately to increase the rate of binding, despite the fact that the polysialic acid moieties of the N-CAM are not directly involved in binding. This suggests that the charge perturbation model originally proposed (13) is probably correct (Figure 3A). In view of the high-order dependence of binding rates on surface density (22, 23), one may speculate that N-CAM monomers interact to form multivalent complexes at the cell surface (Figure 3b). Formation of such complexes may be enhanced by the reduction in amount of polysialic acid during E to A conversion because this would tend to reduce intermolecular repulsion.

Less is known about the binding mechanisms of Ng-CAM, because neither the detailed location of its binding region nor its putative glial ligand (Gn-

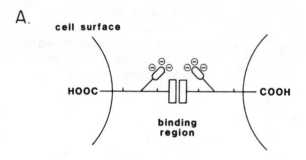

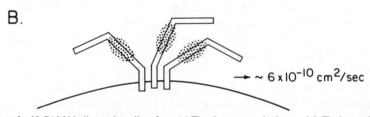

Figure 3   N-CAM binding at the cell surface. (*a*) The charge perturbation model. The homophilic binding via the NH$_2$ terminal domain can be perturbed by the net negative charge of polysialic acid on the middle domain (see Figure 1). The perturbation may result from alteration of conformation of the binding domain or from direct repulsion of bound CAMs from apposing cells. E to A conversion would be expected to result in increased efficacy of binding. (*b*) Schematic model of three N-CAM chains with their domains interacting to form a *cis* trivalent complex in the membrane. This can occur because the molecule is mobile in the plane of the membrane, with an apparent diffusion constant as shown in the figure. Dots represent polysialic acid, which by repulsion and excluded volume effects may serve two additional functions: regulation of molecular spacing and of the angle of the terminal binding domain, and maintenance of intercellular distance.

CAM) have been isolated. In view of the absence of Ng-CAM on glia, the evidence nevertheless strongly favors heterophilic interaction. An additional complication exists in understanding the differential mechanism of N-CAM and Ng-CAM binding: Fab fragments of antibodies to Ng-CAM can inhibit neuron-neuron interactions to a limited extent (19). Addition of specific Fab fragments of anti-N-CAM antibodies to those against Ng-CAM leads to greater degrees of inhibition of aggregation than are found with the anti-Ng-CAM fragments alone. This observation might be explained by two possible mechanisms: (1) In *trans* binding between neurons, Ng-CAM has a counter ligand on the neuronal surface (either N-CAM or a new molecule) that is the same as, or different from, that of the putative Gn-CAM on glia; (2) Ng-CAM and N-CAM interact on the same neuronal membrane. This *cis* interaction would lead to complexes of the two CAMs and to mutual modulation of binding. Specific attachment of Fab fragments either to N-CAM or Ng-CAM within such complexes would then be expected sterically to inhibit *trans* homophilic N-CAM binding. Neither mechanism has been excluded, but some preliminary evidence suggests that after isolation, N-CAM and Ng-CAM can interact, making the second mechanism a plausible one. These observations and the existence of different distributions of N-CAM and Ng-CAM occurring in definite sequences on cells and tissues (Figure 2) indicate the potential richness of surface modulation effects in altering cellular adhesion mechanisms.

Regulatory Events

Given this evidence for modulation and its potential effects on cell adhesion and motion it is natural to ask what regulatory mechanisms initiate the expression of CAM genes, the transport of CAMs to the cell surface, their metabolic turnover, and alterations of carbohydrate enzymes responsible for E to A conversion. An examination of the expression sequence for the two CAMs indicates that there must be at least three kinds of regulatory signals responsible for modulation: (1) signals for N-CAM and Ng-CAM gene expression; (2) signals for alteration of surface expression; (3) signals for E to A conversion.

At present, nothing is known of the nature of the signals responsible for activation of the various CAM genes in the expression sequence. It has been proposed (11) that CAMs act as regulators of morphogenetic movements, and that the evolutionary covariance of the timing of CAM regulatory genes and of factors underlying cell and tissue sheet movement leads to appropriate inductive sequences in ontogeny. One may embed this idea and the data on surface modulation into a diagram representing a CAM regulatory cycle, as shown in Figure 4. While the data reviewed here are consistent with the main elements of this cycle, the signals for CAM gene expression during development are still unknown. Two attractive candidates are (1) the release of morphogens following cell contact (presumably these morphogens would act at

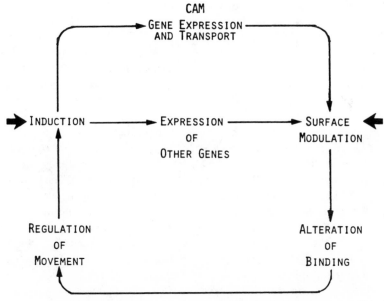

Figure 4   Proposed CAM regulatory cycle. Early induction signals (heavy arrow at *left*) lead to CAM gene expression. Surface modulation (by prevalence changes, polar redistribution on the cell, or chemical change such as E to A conversion) alters binding rates of cells. This regulates morphogenetic movements, which in turn affect embryonic induction or milieu-dependent differentiation. These changes can again affect CAM gene expression as well as expression of other genes for specific tissues. The heavy arrows at *left* and *right* indicate possible signals for initiation of induction that are still unknown. These signals could result from global surface modulation as a result of CAM binding *(right)* or from release of morphogens affecting induction *(left)*. This cycle is a representation of the regulator hypothesis (11) that expressly proposes that regulatory genes for CAMs and those for tissue-specific proteins are under separate temporal schedules of control. This is equivalent to saying that the outer loop of the cycle must be traversed at least once before engaging the inner loop. Successive courses through this cycle would lead to epigenetic changes during morphogenesis and histogenesis.

the sites of embryonic induction); and (2) the asymmetric interaction at the cell surface of CAMs themselves, leading to global cell surface modulation that would directly effect induction through cytoskeletal changes (14), which would in turn alter CAM gene expression and CAM surface transport by propagation through the cycle. One other alternative, not yet demonstrated, is a cellular interaction with substrate adhesion molecules (SAMs), such as laminin and fibronectin, followed by global surface modulations and alterations in CAM expression. Whatever the nature of the signals, there is little doubt that cyclic appearances of N-CAM and L-CAM occur in embryogenesis. This has been dramatically demonstrated in the morphogenesis of chicken feathers in which N-CAM and L-CAM expression occurs coordinately at three successive levels of feather formation, the first of which (initial induction) definitely involves arrest of movement of mesenchymal cells expressing N-CAM (5a, b).

Recent experiments in vitro demonstrate that N-CAM turns over at the cell surface, and that the E form is replaced at least in part by the A form (15a). When combined with the structural work showing that sialic acid is modulated, and not the carbohydrate attachment sites (6), these observations indicate that an intracellular sialyl transferase or sialidase is being regulated along with the transport of the molecule to the cell surface.

One particularly convincing demonstration of the action of CAM regulating signals is given by the alteration of N-CAM expression at the surface of cells transformed by Rous sarcoma virus (RSV) in both primary cultures of chick brain cells and in rat cerebellar cell lines (3, 17, for review see 2). The evidence on primary lines indicates that after transformation by RSV there is a series of differentiation events accompanied by loss of N-CAM at the cell surface, loss of adhesion, increased mobility, changes in cell shape, and expression of 34kDa pp60^{src} substrate. All of these changes occur in neuroepithelial cells that are definitely N-CAM positive before transformation. In rat cell lines infected with temperature-sensitive mutants, this cycle of events can be reversed once by return to the nonpermissive temperature. The cells aggregate with return of both surface N-CAM and of their morphology; subsequent attempts at reversal fail after one cycle. These observations dramatically illustrate the role of the control of surface N-CAM in maintaining cell-cell interactions, and they have obvious implications for a possible permissive role of N-CAM modulation in metastasis. They may also serve as a model system for studies of epithelial-mesenchymal transitions.

All of these experimental findings are consistent with the idea that it is a combination of the dynamics of expression, the regulatory loops, and various modulation mechanisms acting on a relatively few CAMs[1] of different specificity (10) that epigenetically yields the various patterns in neural histogenesis. CAM modulation mechanisms probably evolved early: N-CAM has been found in all vertebrate species tested (as far back in ancestry as elasmobranchs), which suggests that its functions were selected long ago, and that its structure has been strongly conserved (21). It is particularly striking that N-CAMs from widely divergent species cross-bind in a homophilic fashion as efficaciously as they do within a species. Thus N-CAM binding specificity has also been strongly conserved. Although this places additional emphasis on the idea that the differential effects of CAM action in morphogenesis and histogenesis depend

---

[1]The issue of the number of CAMs that actually exists is an empirical one. As discussed at length in Reference 10, the evidence indicates that CAMs are necessary for these histogenic events, and are not specified cell by cell as local addresses, which if it were true would require thousands or millions of CAMs of different specificity.

mainly upon differences in modulatory effects and in expression sequences rather than on multiple specificities, it does not imply that differences in CAM specificity are not required. The contrast between N-CAM and Ng-CAM indicates that both modulation and specificity differences are critical in histogenesis.

Future Directions

Although we are far from a full understanding of the means by which CAMs alter or determine morphogenetic and histogenetic pathways, a number of impressions can be gained from the data accumulated so far. First, CAMs exist at the cell surface in a dynamic state that reflects the multiplicity and regularity of the sequences of expression of their different modularity mechanisms. Second, the graded, nonlinear interactions that may be provided by *cis* and *trans* binding of CAMs, might lead to further refinement of the mechanisms of modulation and control. Third, CAM expression sequences must act covariantly with other key developmental processes, such as movement and process outgrowth, in order to lead to histologic structures and functioning neural networks. Fourth, there is a conservation principle: the same CAM specificity can be used early and late in development by switching modulation mechanisms. Indeed, CAMs persist in CNS tracts even in adult life, probably because of the absence in general of SAMs and of cell junctions in such tracts. Fifth, in specific histogenetic events, the expression of secondary CAMs carrying additional specificities (e.g. Ng-CAM) is apparently necessary—both modulation and the appearance of new specificity are required for rich histogenetic patterns. This is reflected clearly in the differential spatiotemporal patterns of N-CAM and Ng-CAM distribution. The combination of these principles acting in a CAM regulatory cycle (Figure 4) would lead to epigenetic sequences in histogenesis. Each traverse of such a cycle would be in a new context, leading to new structural possibilities.

While these impressions represent a change in our view of neural development (10), they also serve to point up the gaps in our knowledge of the genetic and epigenetic regulatory mechanisms for CAMs. The mechanisms of both *cis* and *trans* CAM-CAM interactions, their biochemical synthetic pathways and transport to the cell surface, and the relationship of CAM expression to other cytodifferentiation events remain to be detailed. The exact spatiotemporal sequences of development of defined structures containing N-CAM (for example, neuromuscular junctions) also remain to be worked out. It is too early even to state that the complete function of any CAM is established: there remain to be investigated the intriguing possibilities of ion binding, neurotransmitter binding, and interactions of these molecules with cellular cytoskeletal elements. Other CAMs may be uncovered; a Ca^{++}-dependent adhesion can be observed when N-CAM is down modulated by cellular transformation of neurons (3, 17), and a recent report of Ca^{++}-dependent molecules in neural precursors has appeared (19a). Above all, the nature of the signals regulating CAM gene expression (Figure 4) remains as the central issue to be resolved. Although it is difficult to explore this issue, the recent cloning of gene probes for N-CAM (27) and L-CAM (16) should facilitate investigation of many of the questions surrounding CAM regulation.

CAMs provide a unique opportunity to study a set of cell surface molecules that are essential in regulating the social interactions of cells, cell movements, the merger of tissue sheets, and the formation of neural networks. N-CAM serves as one of the first examples in which the carbohydrate of a glycoprotein may be assigned a definite function at the cell surface, at the same time confirming the existence of local cell surface modulation (13, 14). CAM expression sequences (Figure 2) provide a reference point for analyzing the relative roles of SAMs and cell junctional molecules as they appear in developmental sequences during histogenesis (13). Studies of CAMs have deep significance for examining certain problems of metazoan evolution, and particularly for relating developmental genetic events of morphogenesis to the evolutionary determination of organ structure and animal form (9, 11, 29). Their modulation during transforming events may shed light on the connection of neoplasia with embryonic states.

Most pertinent to the main subject of this brief survey, CAMs are key structural determinants of anatomical constancy and variation in neural networks. The relation of CAM function to dynamic neuroanatomy in terms of interactive events at molecular, cellular, and tissue levels should provide one of the fundamental bases for further developments within the emerging sciences of molecular embryology and molecular histology. Clearly, a further understanding of these levels should provide important biochemical clues that will help us relate morphology and tissue structure to physiological function.

Literature Cited

1. Bertolotti, R., Rutishauser, U., Edelman, G. M. 1980. A cell surface molecule involved in aggregation of embryonic liver cells. *Proc. Natl. Acad. Sci. USA* 77:4831–35
2. Brackenbury, R. 1985. Molecular mechanisms of cell adhesion in normal and transformed cells. *Cancer Metastasis Rev.* 4:41–58
3. Brackenbury, R., Greenberg, M. E., Edelman, G. M. 1984. Phenotypic changes and loss of N-CAM mediated adhesion in transformed embryonic chicken retinal cells. *J. Cell Biol.* 99:1944–54
4. Brackenbury, R., Thiery, J.-P., Rutishauser, U., Edelman, G. M. 1977. Adhesion among neural cells of the chick embryo. I. An immunological assay for molecules involved in cell-cell binding. *J. Biol. Chem.* 252:6835–40
5. Chuong, C.-M., Edelman, G. M. 1984. Alterations in neural cell adhesion molecules during development of different regions of the nervous system. *J. Neurosci.* 4:2354–68
5a. Chuong, C.-M., Edelman, G. M. 1985. Expression of cell adhesion molecules in embryonic induction: I. Morphogenesis of nestling feathers. *J. Cell Biol.* 101:1009–26
5b. Chuong, C.-M., Edelman, G. M. 1985. Expression of cell adhesion molecules in embryonic induction: II. Morphogenesis of adult feathers. *J. Cell Biol.* 101:1027–43

6. Crossin, K. L., Edelman, G. M., Cunningham, B. A. 1984. Mapping of three carbohydrate attachment sites in embryonic and adult forms of the neural cell adhesion molecule (N-CAM). *J. Cell Biol.* 99:1848–55

6a. Crossin, K. L., Chuong, C.-M., Edelman, G. M. 1985. Expression sequences of cell adhesion molecules. *Proc. Natl. Acad. Sci. USA* 82:6942–46

7. Damsky, C. H., Richa, J., Solter, D., Buck, C. A. 1983. Cell CAM 120/80-A cell-cell adhesion molecule present in the early embryo and adult epithelia. *J. Cell Biol.* 97:251a

8. Damsky, C. H., Richa, J., Solter, D., Knudsen, K., Buck, C. A. 1983. Identification and purification of a cell surface glycoprotein mediating intercellular adhesion in embryonic and adult tissue. *Cell* 34:455–66

8a. Daniloff, J. K., Chuong, C.-M., Levi, G., Edelman, G. M. 1985. Differential distribution of cell adhesion molecules during histogenesis of the chick nervous system. *J. Neurosci.* In press

9. Edelman, G. M. 1985. Cell adhesion and the molecular processes of morphogenesis. *Ann. Rev. Biochem.* 54:135–69

10. Edelman, G. M. 1984. Cell surface modulation and marker multiplicity in neural patterning. *Trends Neurosci.* 7:78–84

11. Edelman, G. M. 1984. Cell adhesion and morphogenesis: The regulator hypothesis. *Proc. Natl. Acad. Sci. USA* 81:1460–64

12. Edelman, G. M. 1984. Modulation of cell adhesion during induction, histogenesis, and perinatal development of the nervous system. *Ann. Rev. Neurosci.* 7:339–77

13. Edelman, G. M. 1983. Cell adhesion molecules. *Science* 219:450–57

14. Edelman, G. M. 1976. Surface modulation in cell recognition and cell growth. *Science.* 192:218–26

15. Edelman, G. M., Gallin, W. J., Delouvee, A., Cunningham, B. A., Thiery, J.-P. 1983. Early epochal maps of two different cell adhesion molecules. *Proc. Natl. Acad. Sci. USA* 80:4384–88

15a. Friedlander, D. R., Brackenbury, R., Edelman, G. M. 1985. Conversion of embryonic form to adult forms of N-CAM *in vitro* results from *de novo* synthesis of adult forms. *J. Cell Biol.* 101:412–19

16. Gallin, W. J., Prediger, E. A., Edelman, G. M., Cunningham, B. A. 1985. Isolation of a cDNA clone for the liver cell adhesion molecule (L-CAM). *Proc. Natl. Acad. Sci. USA* 82:2809–13

17. Greenberg, M. E., Brackenbury, R., Edelman, G. M. 1984. Alteration of neural cell adhesion molecule (N-CAM) expression after neuronal cell transformation by Rous sarcoma virus. *Proc. Natl. Acad. Sci. USA* 81:969–73

18. Grumet, M., Hoffman, S., Chuong, C.-M., Edelman, G. M. 1984. Polypeptide components and binding functions of neuron-glia adhesion molecules. *Proc. Natl. Acad. Sci. USA,* 81:7989–93

19. Grumet, M., Hoffman, S., Edelman, G. M. 1984. Two antigenically related neuronal CAM's of different specificities mediate neuron-neuron and neuron-glia adhesion. *Proc. Natl. Acad. Sci. USA* 81:267–71

19a. Hatta, K., Okada, T. S., Takeichi, M. 1985. A monoclonal antibody disrupting calcium-dependent cell-cell adhesion of brain tissues: Possible role of its target antigen in animal pattern formation. *Proc. Natl. Acad. Sci. USA* 82:2789–93

20. Hirn, M., Ghandour, M. S., Deagostini-Bazin, H., Goridis, C. 1983. Molecular heterogeneity and structural evolution during cerebellar ontogeny detected by monoclonal antibody of the mouse cell surface antigen BSP-2. *Brain Res.* 265:87–100

21. Hoffman, S., Chuong, C.-M., Edelman, G. M. 1984. Evolutionary conservation of key structures and binding functions of neural cell adhesion molecules. *Proc. Natl. Acad. Sci. USA* 81:6881–85

22. Hoffman, S., Edelman, G. M. 1984. The mechanism of binding of neural cell adhesion molecules. In *Gene Expression and Cell-Cell Interactions in the Developing Nervous System,* ed. J. M. Lauder, P. Nelson, pp. 147–60. New York: Plenum

23. Hoffman, S., Edelman, G. M. 1983. Kinetics of homophilic binding by E and A forms of the neural cell adhesion molecule. *Proc. Natl. Acad. Sci. USA* 80:5762–66

24. Horwitz, A. F., Knudsen, K. A., Damsky, C. H., Decker, C., Buck, C. A., Neff, N. T. 1984. Adhesion-related integral membrane glycoproteins identified by monoclonal antibodies. In *Monoclonal Antibodies and Functional Cell Lines,* ed. R. H. Kennet, K. B. Bechtol, T. J. McKearn, pp. 103–18. New York: Plenum

25. Hyafil, F., Morello, D., Babinet, C., Jacob, F. 1980. A cell surface glycoprotein involved in the compaction of embryonal carcinoma cells and cleavage stage embryos. *Cell* 21:927–34

26. Jorgensen, O. S., Delouvee, A., Thiery, J.-P., Edelman, G. M. 1980. The nervous system specific protein D2 is in-

volved in adhesion among neurites from cultured rat ganglia. *FEBS Lett.* 111:39–42

27. Murray, B. A., Hemperly, J. J., Gallin, W. J., MacGregor, J. S., Edelman, G. M., Cunningham, B. A. 1984. Isolation of clones for the chicken neural cell adhesion molecule (N-CAM). *Proc. Natl. Acad. Sci. USA* 81:5584–88

28. Nielsen, L. D., Pitts, M., Grady, S. R., McGuire, E. J. 1981. Cell-cell adhesion in the embryonic chick: partial purification of liver cell adhesion molecules from liver membranes. *Dev. Biol.* 186:315–26

29. Raff, R. A., Kaufman, T. C. 1983. *Embryos, Genes and Evolution.* New York: Macmillan. 395 pp.

30. Rieger, F., Grumet, M., Edelman, G. M. 1984. N-CAM at the vertebrate neuromuscular junction. *J. Cell Biol.* 101: 285–93

31. Schachner, M., Faissner, A., Kruse, J., Lindner, J., Meier, D. H., et al. 1983. Cell-type specificity and developmental expression of neural cell-surface components involved in cell interactions and of structurally related molecules. *Cold Spring Harbor Symp. Quant. Biol.* 68: 557–68

32. Thiery, J.-P., Brackenbury, R., Rutishauser, U., Edelman, G. M. 1977. Adhesion among neural cells of the chick embryo. II. Purification and characterization of a cell adhesion molecule from neural retina. *J. Biol. Chem.* 252:6841–45

33. Thiery, J.-P., Delouvee, A., Grumet, M., Edelman, G. M. 1985. Initial appearance and regional distribution of the neuron-glia cell adhesion molecule. *J. Cell Biol.* 100:442–56

34. Yoshida-Noro, C., Suzuki, N., Takeichi, M. 1984. Molecular nature of the calcium-dependent cell-cell adhesion system in mouse teratocarcinoma and embryonic cells studied with a monoclonal antibody. *Dev. Biol.* 101:19–27

Ann. Rev. Physiol. 1986. 48:431–46

GENES ENCODING MAMMALIAN NEUROENDOCRINE PEPTIDES: Strategies Toward Their Identification and Analysis

Kelly E. Mayo[1] and Ronald M. Evans

Molecular Biology and Virology Laboratory, The Salk Institute for Biological Studies, Post Office Box 85800; and Howard Hughes Medical Institute, San Diego, California 92138

Geoffrey M. Rosenfeld

Eukaryotic Regulatory Biology Program, School of Medicine, University of California; and Howard Hughes Medical Institute, San Diego, California 92093

INTRODUCTION

Small peptides are important mediators in the transfer of information throughout and between the endocrine and nervous systems, where they act to maintain homeostasis and participate in the control of behaviors necessary to deal with an ever changing environment. Many of these peptides serve multiple and complex roles as both classical hormones in the endocrine system and neurotransmitters or neuromodulators in the nervous system (see References 27, 37, and 64 for recent reviews).

The initial members of this loose grouping of "neuroendocrine peptides" were identified and characterized by classical biochemical approaches. In an attempt to understand something of the mode and regulation of biosynthesis of these peptides, researchers turned to the emerging techniques of recombinant DNA. Molecular biology has indeed had several major impacts on the neuroendocrine peptide field. Firstly, molecular cloning of cDNAs that encode these

[1]Present address: Department of Biochemistry, Molecular Biology and Cell Biology, Northwestern University, Evanston, IL 60201

431

0066-4278/86/0315-0431$02.00

peptides led to the realization that most are synthesized as larger precursor proteins, which are proteolytically processed to liberate the mature peptide, and that in many cases these precursors include multiple bioactive peptides. Sequence analysis of numerous precursor proteins led to the establishment of a set of "rules" for predicting the processing and subsequent modification of these peptides from their respective precursors. Secondly, cDNA clones encoding neuroendocrine peptides have served as probes for determining sites of precursor synthesis, for analyzing the regulation of precursor biosynthesis, and for isolating and characterizing the genes encoding these precursors. Lastly, molecular cloning has led to the identification of an increasing number of novel neuroendocrine peptides encoded by new genes related to known peptide-encoding genes, encoded by new mRNAs generated from known peptide-encoding genes, or included within precursor proteins containing known peptides.

Our knowledge concerning the structure of the precursors and genes for both established and novel neuroendocrine peptides has expanded so rapidly that it has surpassed our ability to determine the physiological correlates of this information (52). It seems clear that new technologies and approaches will be required to correct this deficit, and that these will draw heavily upon the fields of not only molecular biology, but physiology, immunology, and neurobiology. In this short review we attempt to explore new methodologies that promise to be useful for the identification and analysis of genes encoding neuroendocrine peptides. Although we will attempt to review the field in general terms, specific illustrative examples will be drawn using those genes currently being analyzed in our own laboratories. In order to establish a common working background, we first briefly consider the basic structural characteristics common to those neuroendocrine genes thus far analyzed (see also 15, 35, 47).

STRUCTURAL FEATURES OF NEUROENDOCRINE PEPTIDE PRECURSORS AND GENES

Although antibodies were initially used to indicate that peptides were synthesized as part of larger precursor molecules, these studies could provide only limited insight into the mechanisms used to process these precursors. A complete determination of the amino acid sequence of peptide precursors was only possible through the application of molecular biological techniques. Beginning with pre-proopiomelanocortin in 1979 (49), a large number of cDNA clones that predict the complete primary structures of their respective peptide precursors have been isolated. To synthesize cDNAs, mRNA from a tissue source expected to produce the appropriate peptide is converted into double-stranded DNA by the sequential actions of the enzymes reverse transcriptase and DNA polymerase. Restriction endonucleases are then utilized to insert the cDNA into an appropriate vector for its propagation, usually a bacterial plasmid or a bacteriophage. Because the desired recombinant will generally represent only a small percentage of those generated, various screening procedures must be employed to identify the correct cDNA clone. Once identified, the cDNA clone is propagated and isolated for DNA sequence analysis. A more complete description of recombinant DNA techniques for the uninitiated can be found in several excellent sources (41, 57, 77).

Although a summary of neuroendocrine peptide precursors that have been analyzed by recombinant DNA techniques is beyond the scope of this review, a perusal of the literature indicates that cDNAs encoding more than twenty small (less than 50 amino acids), single-chain bioactive peptides have been characterized from mammalian species. Because the peptides under consideration must be secreted to function as mediators of intercellular communication, all are synthesized in a pre-propeptide form that includes an amino-terminal hydrophobic signal sequence that directs their transport across membranes (39). Following removal of the signal sequence, the propeptide can then be further processed by proteolytic enzymes to generate the mature peptide. Many of these precursors are probably processed to yield multiple peptides, but in most cases biological actions have thus far been attributed to one or a few peptides. Analysis of the amino acid sequence surrounding the cleavage sites at which peptides are processed from their precursors indicates that peptides are generally flanked by paired basic amino acid residues which presumably serve as a substrate for a trypsin-like processing enzyme (14, 40); however, single basic recognition sites are occasionally used. Many bioactive peptides are further posttranslationally modified; the most common of these modifications is carboxy-terminal amidation. Sequence analysis suggests that a single glycine residue following the peptide sequence signals the amidation, and may serve as the amide donor (5).

It is becoming increasingly clear that a multitude of mechanisms exist to increase the diversity of neuroendocrine peptides needed for efficient intercellular communication in complex multicellular organisms. Many neuroendocrine peptides are members of gene families that have evolved from common ancestral genes following gene duplication (47, 53). For example, preprovasopressin and pre-prooxytocin share considerable sequence homology and have very similar structures (32). Alternative RNA processing is used to generate multiple mRNAs that encode distinct neuropeptide precursors from a single common gene; examples include the calcitonin/CGRP gene and the pre-protachykinin gene (19, 20, 51). As previously discussed, the most obvious mechanism for increasing diversity is the generation of multiple bioactive peptides from a single precursor protein, which can best be appreciated by considering the opioid peptide precursors pre-proopiomelanocortin, preproenkephalin, and pre-prodynorphin. This diversity is further amplified by tissue-specific processing of precursors, such as those encoding the opioid peptides (10, 72).

cDNA clones encoding many of the neuroendocrine peptides have been used as probes to identify and isolate their respective genes from genomic libraries constructed in bacteriophage λ. These genes appear to be structurally very similar to nonneuroendocrine genes, in that they all contain introns that must be processed from the primary RNA transcript, and they all have consensus DNA sequences thought to be involved in the initiation of transcription, in mRNA processing, and in polyadenylation (6, 12, 58). Figure 1 serves to illustrate the structural features of eukaryotic genes, and to review the process by which the gene is transcribed into mRNA, translated to generate the pre-propeptide, and proteolytically processed to yield a mature peptide. Two genes are considered: rat growth hormone-releasing factor (GRF), which serves as an example of a "simple" gene that encodes a single mRNA and peptide product, and rat calcitonin/CGRP, which serves as an example of a "complex" gene that encodes two mRNAs and multiple bioactive peptides in a tissue-specific manner.

STRATEGIES FOR CLONING NEUROENDOCRINE PEPTIDE GENES

The first genes amenable to recombinant DNA analysis were those expressed at high levels in distinct tissue distributions, such as globin and ovalbumin. This has been true in the neuroendocrine system as well; pre-proopiomelanocortin, the first peptide-encoding cDNA isolated, represents nearly one third of the mRNA in the neurointermediate pituitary (68). Enriched mRNAs of this type can be identified by screening cDNA libraries with cDNA probes isolated from tissues either expressing or not expressing the desired gene, a procedure that has been termed plus-minus, or differential, screening (66). The identity of the isolated clone has often been confirmed by some form of hybrid-select translation, where the cDNA clone is used to select by hybridization a specific mRNA whose identity can be determined by in vitro translation and immunoprecipitation (24). Unfortunately, many interesting peptides are produced from rare mRNA transcripts, and therefore do not easily lend themselves to these rather straightforward approaches. This has necessitated the development of new approaches to cDNA cloning and screening.

One especially fruitful approach to cloning peptide cDNAs has been to take advantage of "fortuitous" sources that express high levels of a particular peptide. Thus, somatostatin, a fairly low abundance brain and pancreatic mRNA, was cloned early on when it was recognized that anglerfish islets represented a greatly enriched source of this mRNA (25). Likewise, frog skin was found to contain high levels of peptides either identical to or related to

A.   A "SIMPLE" NEUROENDOCRINE GENE: RAT GRF

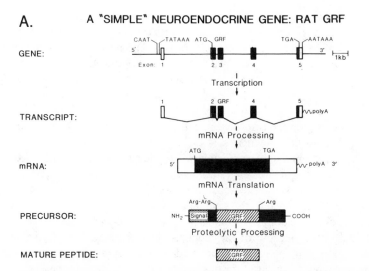

B.   A "COMPLEX" NEUROENDOCRINE GENE: RAT CALCITONIN/CGRP

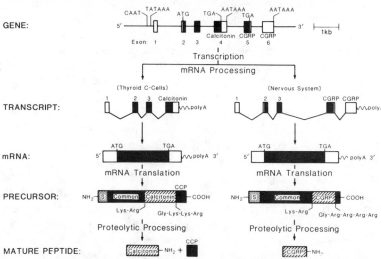

Figure 1   Schematic structures and processing routes of two mammalian genes encoding neuroendocrine peptides. Panel *A* shows the rat GRF gene (43), panel *B* the rat calcitonin/CGRP gene (1). Exons are indicated by boxes, coding regions by shading, cross-hatching, or stippling. Exons that contain the major bioactive peptides are labeled GRF, calcitonin, and CGRP. The gene is drawn to the indicated scale; the remainder of the diagram is not scaled. CAAT, TATAA, and AATAAA indicate consensus sequences involved in transcription initiation and polyadenylation (6, 12, 58). ATG and TGA are transcription initiation and termination codons. PolyA indicates a site for eventual polyadenylation, and does not imply a temporal order of polyadenylation versus splicing. Only the mature peptides with known bioactivity are shown.

known mammalian peptides, and it has served as a source for the isolation of cDNAs encoding thyrotropin-releasing hormone, caerulein (cholecystokinin-like), and xenopsin (neurotensin-like) (26, 59, 67). Another enriched source of peptide mRNAs are tumors of neuronal or endocrine origin, such as neuroblastomas, medullary thyroid carcinomas, pheochromocytomas, and pancreatic islet tumors. In fact, nearly half of the cloned cDNAs encoding neuroendocrine peptides have been isolated from tumor tissue.

An enormously powerful approach to the identification of recombinant clones encoding peptide precursors is the use of synthetic oligonucleotide probes (31). This technique is applicable where the full or partial amino acid sequence of the peptide under study is known. Using this knowledge, one can predict from the universal genetic code the possible combinations of mRNA sequences that would encode the peptide or a portion of the peptide, and synthesize an oligonucleotide complementary to this sequence for use as a hybridization probe. Because of the redundancy of the genetic code, some peptide sequences lend themselves more readily to this approach than others.

Two basic strategies are used for oligonucleotide screening. In the first, a subset of the peptide (often 4–6 amino acids) whose sequence generates the fewest redundancies is used to predict a "pool" of oligonucleotides to be used as probe. This pool will include the correct sequence as well as several others, and therefore usually results in the identification of both the desired clone and numerous false positives. Secondary screening procedures, such as hybrid selection or the use of a second oligonucleotide pool predicted from another portion of the peptide sequence, are then utilized to distinguish the correct clones. In the second general strategy, a single, long, unique oligonucleotide probe is predicted based upon known codon usage preferences. Codon usage charts have been compiled for several species based upon DNA sequence analysis of a large number of cloned genes (22). An alternative use of oligonucleotides is as specific primers for reverse transcription of mRNA into cDNA, which generates a library that is greatly enriched for the desired clone (28, 54). Oligonucleotide screening protocols of some type have been used to identify the majority of the peptide cDNAs thus far cloned. The utility of this technique has been greatly increased by the advent of microsequencing procedures (76), which allow amino acid sequences to be determined for small amounts of purified peptide, and by the introduction of automated oligonucleotide synthesis, which allows for the rapid and cost-effective production of the desired probes.

Another productive approach that is currently being applied to the cloning of cDNAs, including those of neuroendocrine origin, is immunological screening of cDNA expression libraries. A series of cloning vectors have been developed that include sequences adjacent to the cDNA insertion site that will promote transcription and translation of the insert in either eukaryotic or bacterial cells (65, 74, 80). If the orientation and translational reading frame of the insert are appropriate, the portion of the protein represented in the cDNA will be produced in the host cell. If antibody probes against the desired peptide exist, these can be used to screen the cDNA library immunologically by a technique very much akin to "Western" protein blotting (71). One potential drawback to this technique is that if the protein product is being expressed in a bacterial cell, it is unlikely to be appropriately posttranslationally modified (for example glycosylated), and antibodies that recognize such modification will not be useful. In the case of small peptides that are synthesized as parts of larger proteins, antibodies against the mature peptide might not recognize the unprocessed precursor. The utility of this technique is rapidly increasing with the development of improved expression vectors, screening, and detection reagents. Monoclonal antibody technologies that allow probes to be generated against small amounts of purified peptide will also have a major impact in this area (73, 78).

An alternative use of cDNA expression vectors that has not yet been widely applied to the cloning of neuroendocrine peptide cDNAs is the use of various bioassay and selection schemes. If the desired product has a bioassayable activity (as many peptides do), it should be feasible to screen recombinant clones that express the product using this bioassay. This approach has already been used to isolate a growth factor cDNA (69). Likewise, if the desired product can be selected for or easily scored for, schemes for identification of recombinant clones can often be devised. Examples include the identification of oncogenes based upon the transformed phenotype (62, 63), and identification of cell surface molecules based upon cell sorting using an appropriate tag (36). For these approaches to be applicable to the cloning of neuropeptides, it will be necessary to develop vectors and host cell lines in which the precursor will not only be expressed, but will be appropriately processed and modified. The screening procedures themselves also must be advanced to the position where the analysis of large numbers of recombinants is feasible.

In parallel with these advances in cDNA screening strategies and methods, the last several years have seen major progress in techniques for the construction of cDNA libraries. Perhaps the most notable of these is the development of bacteriophage vectors for cDNA cloning and expression (30, 79). These vectors allow for the construction of extremely large libraries (greater than 10^7 recombinants) from as little as one microgram of poly(A)$^+$ mRNA. This makes feasible the creation of region-specific cDNA libraries from very defined anatomical domains, for example, particular brain nuclei. In invertebrates, this technology has been used to make cDNA libraries specific for single, large neurons of defined physiological function (50, 70).

STRATEGIES FOR THE ANALYSIS OF
NEUROENDOCRINE PEPTIDE GENE EXPRESSION

Cloned cDNAs specific for neuroendocrine peptides can be utilized as hybridization probes for the quantitative determination of their respective mRNAs. A variety of techniques are commonly used to measure mRNA abundance, including "Northern" RNA blotting, dot or slot RNA immobilization, solution hybridization, and S_1 nuclease mapping (3, 16, 45). RNA hybridization can be used to determine the tissue and cellular distribution of an mRNA in the organism, to measure relative mRNA abundance in various tissues, and to quantitate changes in mRNA abundance either during development or in response to various physiological perturbations. In considering the regulation of peptide precursor mRNAs, it must be appreciated that numerous potential control steps exist. These include transcription rate, RNA processing and transport to the cytoplasm, translational utilization of the mRNA, and the rate of degradation of the mRNA (13). Although it is convenient and informative to simply measure steady state mRNA levels by the aforementioned techniques, cDNA hybridization probes can also be used to determine transcription rates and mRNA half-lives.

It is perhaps surprising that RNA hybridization techniques have not been widely applied as tools for studying the regulation of neuroendocrine peptide genes, but there are probably several reasons for this. Firstly, peptide mRNAs are generally of relatively low abundance, and often have a very limited tissue distribution. Although a particular peptide may be present in the brain, it is often present in a defined and limited subset of neurons, a distribution that makes isolation of the appropriate tissue for RNA analysis difficult at best. Secondly, it is often difficult to culture and establish permanent lines of cells that make particular peptides (for example hypothalamic neurons), which precludes the possibility of performing simple regulation experiments in vitro. Even when such cells can be cultured, they often lose differentiated functions, such as receptors that allow them to respond to appropriate stimuli.

Immunocytochemical techniques have been developed that circumvent most of these problems and allow for the exquisitely sensitive localization of peptides in neural and endocrine tissues (17). However, these techniques suffer from an inability to differentiate sites of final peptide localization from sites of precursor synthesis. They are also not generally applicable for monitoring changes in peptide biosynthesis, because it is difficult to differentiate changes in synthesis from changes in secretion. A logical extension of immunohistochemistry for the analysis of peptide-encoding mRNAs is the development of in situ hybridization, often referred to as hybridization histochemistry (29). For this technique, a labeled probe complementary to the mRNA of interest is incubated with fixed and sectioned tissue mounted on microscope slides, and the labeled hybrids are detected by exposure to X-ray film or by liquid emulsion auto-radiography. A variety of probes have been utilized including cDNAs, RNAs, and oligonucleotides labeled with either ^{32}P (for rapid determination of tissue distribution) or ^{3}H (for cellular localization). Figure 2 shows schematically the process of in situ hybridization as applied to the detection of GRF mRNA in rat brain. Other peptide mRNAs that have been detected by this technique include pre-proopiomelanocortin mRNA (60), pre-proenkephalin mRNA (4), pre-procalcitonin mRNA (11), and pre-prooxytocin mRNA (44). Hybridization histochemistry is already being widely used to localize sites of mRNA synthesis. However, the full potential of the technique will only be realized when methods for the quantitative measurement of hybridization at the cellular level are fully developed.

One important aspect of neuroendocrine peptides already mentioned is the discrete tissue specificity of their expression. A molecular explanation of the factors that control this tissue-specificity is germane to an understanding of peptide function in the neuroendocrine system. Recently, the first DNA sequences that promote tissue-specific gene expression have been described; these are the tissue-specific enhancers. Enhancers are short DNA sequences that act in an unknown manner to stimulate transcription of a linked gene (61). Tissue-specific enhancers have been defined by DNA transfection studies in which the cloned enhancer element is active only in cells that normally express the gene that the enhancer was derived from. Examples include enhancers within the immunoglobulin genes that are active only in lymphoid cells (2, 21), and enhancers near the insulin and chymotrypsin genes that are active only in pancreatic cells (75). It is presumed that the tissue-specificity of these elements can be explained by the existence of enhancer-binding proteins that would be present only in the appropriate cell lineage. Consistent with this notion, the first such factors have now been observed in lymphoid cells (9, 18). It will obviously be necessary to attempt to localize such enhancers within genes that encode neuroendocrine peptides, and to define the proteins that they interact with in a tissue-specific manner. In this regard, it is interesting to note that a small DNA element termed "ID" has recently been found within many genes that are expressed in the brain (48); however, this element does not seem to function as a classical enhancer.

One drawback to mammalian cell transfection studies of neuroendocrine gene products is the lack of appropriate cell types that can be grown in culture. A promising alternative approach is the use of transgenic animals for localization of DNA sequences important not only for tissue-specific expression, but also for developmental control and for appropriate regulation. This strategy entails introducing a cloned gene construct into the germ line of an animal (usually a mouse), either by microinjection into fertilized eggs (7, 56) or by retroviral infection of early-stage embryos (33, 34). Animals that develop

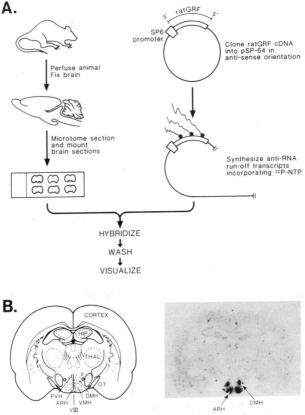

Figure 2 Localization of rat GRF mRNA in the brain by hybridization in situ. Panel *A* shows a schematic representation of the process of preparing tissue and GRF probe. The SP6-promoter system for generating labeled RNA as probe has been described in detail (46). Panel *B* shows a schematic diagram of the structural features of the brain region being analyzed *(left)*, and an autoradiogram showing the localization of rat GRF mRNA *(right)*. Abbreviations: CORTEX = cerebral cortex, HIP = hippocampal formation, THAL = thalamus, F = fornix, OT = optic tract, VIII=third ventricle, ARH = arcuate hypothalamus, VMH = ventromedial hypothalamus, DMH = dorsal-medial hypothalamus, PVH = periventricular hypothalamus.

following these manipulations stably integrate the cloned DNA into their germ line with an appreciable frequency. These animals and their offspring can then be used to assay features of transgene expression, such as developmental control, tissue-specificity, and regulation by physiological agents. Because transgene integration into the host genome is not site-specific, this approach assumes that DNA sequences important for correct regulation and expression will be resident in the cloned gene construct. If so, they can be mapped by testing multiple variant constructs in the transgenic animal system. This approach has recently been used to demonstrate a functional lymphoid-specific enhancer within an immunoglobulin gene (8), and holds great promise for the analysis of neuroendocrine genes.

An alternative use of transgenic animals is for the determination of developmental and physiological roles for peptides. Although much information can be obtained by simply testing synthetic peptides in bioassays or in animals, these approaches cannot guarantee that the peptide will reach its appropriate target or that it will be present at the correct developmental time to elicit an observable effect. Expression or overexpression of the peptide precursor in transgenic animals holds great potential for addressing these issues. Figure 3 demonstrates such an approach, in which we overproduced human pre-proGRF in transgenic mice using a heterologous promoter. Animals expressing this fusion gene grew to be significantly larger than controls, which strongly implicates this peptide in growth control. An additional physiological finding in these animals was massive enlargement and hyperplasia of the pituitary. These observations suggest that GRF or another peptide processed from the precursor may act as a pituitary growth factor (23). Because this is presumably a developmental effect, it might well have escaped detection using more conventional assays for peptide function. This approach, used in concert with established technologies, is especially promising for the assignment of functions to the many novel peptides recently identified by cDNA cloning methods.

A notable aspect of genes encoding neuroendocrine peptides is their ability to generate diverse products by tissue-specific RNA processing or tissue-specific precursor processing. Elucidation of the mechanisms that generate this diversity clearly requires the establishment of faithful in vitro processing systems that can be manipulated to mimic particular processing pathways. Such systems could be utilized to biochemically define cellular factors important for processing, and would form the basis for a mutational analysis to define sequences within the gene, RNA, or precursor that signal correct processing. Cell extracts that splice RNA transcripts have recently been described (38, 55), and should provide a starting point for the analysis of tissue-specific RNA processing. Biochemical evidence for involvement of particular classes of enzymes in the processing of peptide precursors has been obtained (14, 40), but little is known about tissue-specific precursor processing. A particularly exciting approach to protein processing is the cloning and analysis of genes that encode processing enzymes. Recently, a large family of genes encoding the kallikreins, proteases thought to be involved in the processing of biologically active peptides, has been cloned (42). The many enzymes of this family appear to differ in substrate specificity, and it is tempting to speculate that they might direct tissue-specific processing of some peptides.

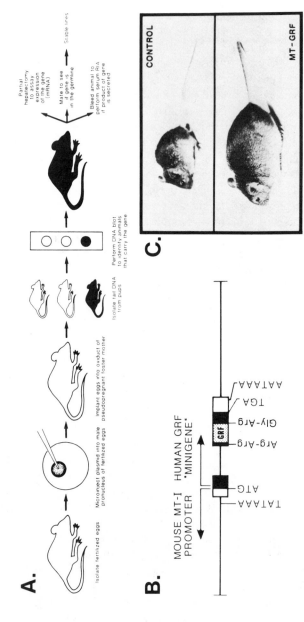

Figure 3   Expression of human GRF in transgenic mice. Panel A shows schematically the process by which lines of transgenic mice are generated by DNA microinjection. Panel B shows the structure of the injected DNA, which is a fusion between a mouse metallothionein-I promoter and a human GRF "minigene" (23). Panel C compares a MT-GRF transgenic mouse with an age and sex-matched control animal. The transgenic animal weighs 46 grams, the control animal 23 grams.

SUMMARY

During the last five years, cDNAs and genes encoding more than 20 neuroendocrine peptides have been cloned. The information gleaned from these genes has been largely structural to this point, and illustrates the great versatility of neuroendocrine genes in generating diverse sets of bioactive peptides. An ongoing contribution of the application of recombinant DNA techniques to the neuroendocrine system promises to be the identification of novel peptides; it will require a concerted effort to determine their physiological functions. The application of recombinant DNA to the study of expression and regulation of neuroendocrine genes is still in its infancy, but a variety of newly emerging techniques promise to be useful for these approaches. Although we have considered the application of recombinant DNA only to the cloning and analysis of neuroendocrine peptide genes, molecular biology will clearly also have a major future impact in investigating aspects of other molecules involved in neuropeptide action, such as processing enzymes and peptide receptors.

Literature Cited

1. Amara, S. G., Evans, R. M., Rosenfeld, M. G. 1984. Calcitonin/calcitonin gene-related peptide transcription unit: Tissue-specific expression involves selective use of alternative polyadenylation sites. *Mol. Cell. Biol.* 4:2151–60
2. Banerji, J., Olson, L., Schaffner, W. 1983. A lymphocyte-specific celluler enhancer is located downstream of the joining region in immunoglobulin heavy chain genes. *Cell* 33:729–40
3. Berk, A. J., Sharp, P. A. 1977. Sizing and mapping of early adenovirus mRNAs by gel electrophoresis of S1 endonuclease-digested hybrids. *Cell* 12:721–32
4. Bloch, B., Milner, R. J., Baird, A., Gubler, V., Reymond, C., et al. 1984. Detection of the messenger RNA coding for preproenkephalin A in bovine adrenal by *in situ* hybridization. *Regul. Peptides* 8:345–54
5. Bradbury, A. F., Finnie, M. D. A., Smyth, D. G. 1982. Mechanism of C-terminal amide formation by pituitary enzymes. *Nature* 298:686–88
6. Breathnach, R., Chambon, P. 1981. Organization and expression of eukaryotic split genes coding for proteins. *Ann. Rev. Biochem.* 50:349–83
7. Brinster, R. L., Chen, H. Y., Trumbauer, M., Senear, A. W., Warren, R., Palmiter, R. D. 1981. Somatic expression of herpes thymidine kinase in mice following injection of a fusion gene into eggs. *Cell* 27:223–31
8. Brinster, R. L., Ritchie, K. A., Hammer,

R. E., O'Brien, R. L., Arp, B., Storb, U. 1983. Expression of a microinjected immunoglobulin gene in the spleen of transgenic mice. *Nature* 306:332–36
9. Church, G. M., Ephuissi, A., Gilbert, W., Tonegawa, S. 1985. Cell-type-specific contacts to immunoglobulin enhancers in nuclei. *Nature* 313:798–801
10. Civelli, O., Douglass, J., Herbert, E. 1984. Pro-opiomelanocortin: A polyprotein at the interface of the endocrine and nervous systems. *Peptides* 6:69–94
11. Coghlan, J. D., Penschow, J. D., Hudson, P. J., Niall, H. D. 1984. Hybridization histochemistry: Use of recombinant DNA for tissue localizations of specific mRNA populations. *Clin. Exper. Hyper.-Theory Practice* A6:63–78
12. Corden, J., Wasylyk, B., Buchwalder, A., Sassone-Corsi, P., Kedinger, C., Chambon, P. 1980. Promoter sequences of eukaryotic protein-coding genes. *Science* 209:1406–14
13. Darnell, J. E. Jr. 1982. Variety in the level of gene control in eukaryotic cells. *Nature* 297:365–71
14. Docherty, K., Steiner, D. F. 1982. Post translational proteolysis in polypeptide hormone biosynthesis. *Ann. Rev. Physiol.* 44:625–38
15. Douglass, J., Civelli, O., Herbert, E. 1984. Polyprotein gene expression: Generation of diversity of neuroendocrine peptides. *Ann. Rev. Biochem.* 53:665–715
16. Durnam, D. M., Palmiter, R. D. 1983. A

444   MAYO, EVANS & ROSENFELD

practical approach for quantitating specific mRNAs by solution hybridization. *Anal. Biochem.* 131:385–93

17. Elde, R. 1983. Immunocytochemistry. In *Brain Peptides*, ed. D. T. Krieger, M. J. Brownstein, J. B. Martin, pp. 485–94. New York: Wiley

18. Ephrussi, A., Church, G. M., Tonegawa, S., Gilbert, W. 1985. B-lineage-specific interactions of an immunoglobulin enhancer with cellular factors *in vivo. Science* 227:134–40

19. Evans, R. M., Amara, S. G., Rosenfeld, M. G. 1982. RNA processing regulation of neuroendocrine gene expression. *DNA* 1:323–28

20. Evans, R. M., Amara, S., Rosenfeld, M. G. 1983. Molecular events in developmental regulation of neuroendocrine genes: Characterization of the novel neuropeptide CGRP. *Cold Spring Harbor Symp. Quant. Biol.* 48:413–17

21. Gillies, S. D., Morrison, S. L., Oi, V. T., Tonegawa, S. 1983. A tissue-specific transcription enhancer element is located in the major intron of a rearranged immunoglobulin heavy chain gene. *Cell* 33:717–28

22. Grantham, R., Gauthier, M., Jacobzone, M., Mercier, R. 1981. Codon catalog usage is a genome strategy modulated for gene expressivity. *Nucl. Acids Res.* 9:R43–R74

23. Hammer, R. E., Brinster, R. L., Rosenfeld, M. G., Evans, R. M., Mayo, K. E. 1985. Expression of human growth hormone-releasing factor in transgenic mice results in increased somatic growth. *Nature* 315:413–16

24. Harpold, M. M., Dobner, P. R., Evans, R. M., Bancroft, F. C. 1978. Construction and identification by positive hybridization-translation of a bacterial plasmid containing a rat growth hormone structural gene sequence. *Nucl. Acids Res.* 5:2039–53

25. Hobart, P., Crawford, R., Shen, L., Pictet, R., Rutter, W. J. 1980. Cloning and sequence analysis of cDNAs encoding two distinct somatostatin precursors found in the endocrine pancreas of anglerfish. *Nature* 288:137–41

26. Hoffman, W., Bach, T. C., Seliger, H., Kriel, G. 1983. Biosynthesis of caerulein in the skin of *Xenopus laevis:* Partial sequences of precursors as deduced from cDNA clones. *EMBO* J. 2:111–14

27. Hökfelt, T., Johansson, O., Ljungdahl, A., Lundberg, J. M., Schultzberg, M. 1980. Peptidergic neurons. *Nature* 284: 515–21

28. Hudson, P., Haley, J., Cronk, M., Shine, J., Niall, H. 1981. Molecular cloning and characterization of cDNA sequences coding for rat relaxin. *Nature* 281:127–31

29. Hudson, P., Penschow, J., Shine, J., Ryan G., Niall, H., Coghlan, J. 1981. Hybridization histochemistry: Use of recombinant DNA as a "homing probe" for tissue localization of specific mRNA populations. *Endocrinology* 108:353–56

30. Huynh, T. V., Young, R. A., Davis, R. W. 1985. Constructing and screening cDNA libraries in λgt10 and λgt11. In *DNA Cloning Techniques: A Practical Approach*, pp. 48–78, ed. D. Glover. Oxford: IRL

31. Itakura, K., Rossi, J. J., Wallace, R. B. 1984. Synthesis and use of synthetic oligonucleotides. *Ann. Rev. Biochem.* 53: 323–56

32. Ivell, R., Richter, D. 1984. Structure and comparison of the oxytocin and vasopressin genes from rat. *Proc. Natl. Acad. Sci. USA* 81:2006–10

33. Jaenisch, R. 1980. Retroviruses and embryogenesis: Microinjection of moloney leukemia virus into midgestation mouse embryos. *Cell* 19:181–88

34. Jaenisch, R., Jähner, D., Nobis, P., Simon, I., Lóhler, J., et al. 1981. Chromosomal position and activation of retroviral genomes inserted into the germline of mice. *Cell* 24:519–29

35. Kaldany, R.-R. J., Nambu, J. R., Scheller, R. H. 1985. Neuropeptides in identified *Aplysia* neurons. *Ann. Rev. Neurosci.* 8:431–55

36. Kavathas, P., Herzenberg, L. A. 1983. Stable transformation of mouse L cells for human membrane T-cell differentiation antigens, HLA and β_2-microglobulin: Selection by fluorescence-activated cell sorting. *Proc. Natl. Acad. Sci. USA* 80:524–28

37. Krieger, D. T. 1982. Brain Peptides. In *Physiopathology of Hypophysial Disturbances and Diseases of Reproduction,* pp. 1–18. New York: Liss

38. Kroiner, A. R., Maniatis, T., Ruskin, B., Green, M. R. 1984. Normal and mutant human β-globin pre-mRNAs are faithfully and efficiently spliced *in vitro. Cell* 36:993–1005

39. Lingappa, V. R., Blobel, G. 1980. Early events in the biosynthesis of secreted and membrane proteins: The signal hypothesis. *Rec. Progr. Hormone Res.* 36:451–75

40. Loh, Y. P., Gainer, H. 1983. Biosynthesis and processing of neuropeptides. In *Brain Peptides*, ed. D. T. Krieger, M. J. Brownstein, J. B. Martin. pp. 79–116 New York: Wiley

41. Maniatis, T., Fritsch, E. F., Sambrook,

J. 1982. *Molecular Cloning: A Laboratory Manual.* Cold Spring Harbor, NY: Cold Spring Harbor Lab. 545 pp.

42. Mason, A. J., Evans, B. A., Cox, D. R., Shine, J., Richards, R. I. 1983. Structure of mouse kallikrein gene family suggests a role in specific processing of biologically active peptides. *Nature* 303:300–7

43. Mayo, K. E., Cerelli, G. M., Rosenfeld, M. G., Evans, R. M. 1985. Characterization of cDNA and genomic clones encoding the precursor to rat hypothalamic growth hormone-releasing factor. *Nature* 314:464–67

44. McEwen, B. S., Pfaff, D. W. 1985. Hormone effects on hypothalamic neurons: Analyzing gene expression and neuromodulator action. *Trends Neurosci.* 8:105–10

45. Meinkoth, J., Wahl, G. 1984. Hybridization of nucleic acids immobilized on solid supports. *Anal. Biochem.* 138:267–84

46. Melton, D. A., Krieg, P. A., Rebagliati, M. R., Maniatis, T., Zinn, K., Green, M. R. 1984. Efficient *in vitro* synthesis of biologically active RNA and RNA hybridization probes from plasmids containing a bacteriophage SP6 promoter. *Nucl. Acids Res.* 12:7035–56

47. Miller, W. L., Baxter, J. D., Eberhardt, N. L. 1983. Peptide hormone genes: Structure and evolution. In *Brain Peptides,* ed. D. T. Krieger, M. J. Brownstein, J. B. Martin, pp. 15–78. New York: Wiley

48. Milner, R. J., Bloom, F. E., Lai, C., Lerner, R. A., Sutcliffe, J. G. 1984. Brain-specific genes have identifier sequences in their introns. *Proc. Natl. Acad. Sci. USA* 81:713–17

49. Nakanishi, S., Inoue, A., Kita, T., Nakamura, M., Chang, A. C. Y., et al. 1979. Nucleotide sequence of cloned cDNA for bovine corticotropin-β-lipotropin precursor. *Nature* 278:423–27

50. Nambu, J. R., Taussig, R., Mahon, A. C., Scheller, R. H. 1983. Gene isolation with cDNA probes from identified *Aplysia* neurons: Neuropeptide modulators of cardiovascular physiology. *Cell* 35:47–56

51. Nawa, H., Kotani, H., Nakanishi, S. 1984. Tissue-specific generation of two preprotachykinin mRNAs from one gene by alternative RNA splicing. *Nature* 312:729–34

52. Newmark, P. 1983. An embarrassment of peptides. *Nature* 303:655

53. Niall, H. D. 1982. The evolution of peptide hormones. *Ann. Rev. Physiol.* 44:615–24

54. Noyes, B. E., Mevarech, M., Stein, R.,

Agarwal, K. L. 1979. Detection and partial sequence analysis of gastrin mRNA by using an oligonucleotide probe. *Proc. Natl. Acad. Sci. USA* 76:1770–74

55. Padgett, R. A., Hardy, S. F., Sharp, P. A. 1983. Splicing of adenovirus RNA in a cell-free transcription system. *Proc. Natl. Acad. Sci. USA* 80:5230–34

56. Palmiter, R. D., Brinster, R. L., Hammer, R. E., Trumbauer, M. E., Rosenfeld, M. G., et al. 1982. Dramatic growth of mice that develop from eggs microinjected with metallothionein-growth hormone fusion genes. *Nature* 300:611–15

57. Perbal, B. V. 1984. *A Practical Guide to Molecular Cloning.* New York: Wiley. 554 pp.

58. Proudfoot, N. J., Brownlee, G. G. 1976. 3' non-coding region sequences in eukaryotic messenger RNA. *Nature* 263: 211–14

59. Richter, K., Kawashima, E., Egger, R., Kreil, G. 1984. Biosynthesis of tyrotropin releasing hormone in the skin of *Xenopus laevis:* Partial sequence of the precursor deduced from cloned cDNA. *EMBO J.* 3:617–21

60. Roberts, J. L., Chen, C.-L. C., Dionne, F. T., Gee, C. E. 1982. Peptide hormone gene expression in heterogeneous tissues: the pro-opiomelanocortin system. *Trends Neurosci.* 5:314–17

61. Schaffner, W., Lübbe, A. 1985. Tissue-specific gene expression. *Trends Neurosci.* 8:100–4

62. Shih, C., Shilo, B.-Z., Goldfarb, M. P., Dannenberg, A., Weinberg, R. A. 1979. Passage of phenotypes of chemically transformed cells via transfection of DNA and chromatin. *Proc. Natl. Acad. Sci. USA* 76:5714–18

63. Shimizu, K., Goldfarb, M., Perucho, M., Wigler, M. 1983. Isolation and preliminary characterization of the transforming gene of a human neuroblastoma cell line. *Proc. Natl. Acad. Sci. USA* 80:383–87

64. Snyder, S. H., Innis, R. B. 1979. Peptide neurotransmitters. *Ann. Rev. Biochem.* 48:755–82

65. Stanley, K. K., Luzio, J. P. 1984. Construction of a new family of high efficiency bacterial expression vectors: Identification of cDNA clones coding for human liver proteins. *EMBO J.* 3:1429–34

66. St. John, T. P., Davis, R. W. 1979. Isolation of galactose-inducible DNA sequences from *Saccharomyces cerevisiae* by differential plaque filter hybridization. *Cell* 16:443–52

67. Sures, I., Crippa, M. 1984. Xenopsin: The neurotensin-like octapeptide from

Xenopus skin at the carboxyl terminus of its precursor. *Proc. Natl. Acad. Sci. USA* 81:380–84

68. Taii, S., Nakanishi, S., Numa, S. 1979. Distribution of the messager RNA coding for the common precursor to corticotropin and β-lipotropin within bovine brain. *Eur. J. Biochem.* 93:205–12

69. Taniguchi, T., Matsui, H., Fujita, T., Takaoka, C., Kashima, N., et al. 1983. Structure and expression of a cloned cDNA for human interleukin-2. *Nature* 302:305–10

70. Taussig, R., Kaldany, R.-R., Scheller, R. H. 1984. A cDNA clone encoding neuropeptides isolated fom *Aplisia* neuron L11. *Proc. Natl. Acad. Sci. USA* 81:4988–92

71. Towbin, H., Staehelin, T., Gordon, J. 1979. Electrophoretic transfer of proteins from polyacrylamide gels to nitrocellulose sheets: Procedures and some applications. *Proc. Natl. Acad. Sci. USA* 76:4350–54

72. Udenfriend, S., Kilpatrick, D. L. 1983. Biochemistry of the enkephalins and enkephalin-containing peptides. *Arch. Biochem. Biophys.* 221:309–23

73. Valentino, K. L., Winter, J., Reichardt, L. F. 1985. Applications of monoclonal

antibodies to neuroscience research. *Ann. Rev. Neurosci.* 8:199–232

74. Viera, J., Messing, J. 1982. The pUC plasmids, an M13mp7-derived system for insertion mutagenesis and sequencing with synthetic universal primers. *Gene* 19:259–68

75. Walker, M. D., Edlund, T., Boulet, A. M., Rutter, W. J. 1983. Cell specific expression controlled by the 5' flanking region of insulin and chymotrypsin genes. *Nature* 306:557–61

76. Walsh, K. A., Ericsson, L. H., Parmelee, D. C., Titani, K. 1981. Advances in protein sequencing. *Ann. Rev. Biochem.* 50:261–84

77. Watson, J. D., Tooze, J., Kurtz, D. T. 1983. *Recombinant DNA: A short course.* New York: Freeman. 260 pp.

78. Yelton, D. E., Scharff, M. D. 1981. Monoclonal antibodies: A powerful new tool in biology and medicine. *Ann. Rev. Biochem.* 50:657–80

79. Young, R. A. 1985. Immunoscreening λgt11 recombinant DNA expression libraries. *Genet. Eng.* 7:29–42

80. Young, R. A., Davis, R. W. 1983. Efficient isolation of genes by using antibody probes. *Proc. Natl. Acad. Sci. USA* 80:1194–98

Ann. Rev. Physiol. 1986. 48:447–59

NEURAL GRAFTING IN THE AGED RAT BRAIN

Fred H. Gage

Department of Neurosciences, University of California, San Diego, California 92093

Anders Björklund

Department of Histology, University of Lund, S-22362 Lund, Sweden

INTRODUCTION

Aging can result in severe neurological impairments which are manifest prior to physical deterioration. In certain age-related neurodegenerative diseases, such as Parkinson's disease and Alzheimer's disease, functional impairments have been associated with specific biochemical and morphological changes in identified brain regions (for review see 5, 13, 17, 37, 38, 51, 65). Though the cause and nature of these diseases are not known, enough neuropathological and neurochemical knowledge has been accumulated to allow the development of hypotheses concerning the relationships between functional decrement in, or degeneration of, specific neuronal subsystems and the development of neurological symptoms in the diseased patients. Such hypotheses have also played an important role in the development of experimental animal models of these age-related diseases.

A standard paradigm for the development of animal models of age-dependent neurodegenerative diseases has been to investigate the behavioral consequences of selective brain damage in young animals (usually rodents) with the brain region chosen based on clinical evidence, e.g. lesions of the nigrostriatal dopamine system as a model of Parkinson's disease (12, 21, 45, 66), or lesions of the nucleus basalis as a model of Alzheimer's disease (22, 69). This approach has as its objective the identification of physiological mechanisms and neurotransmitter systems that are necessary for normal as well as specific abnormal functional activity. Such lesion models have the drawback that they require quite specific hypotheses concerning the particular brain

447

0066-4278/86/0315-0447$02.00

structure or transmitter system responsible for the observed symptoms, and the complexity of the aging process in relation to the disease is thus obviated. The alternative to this approach is to use aged animals as a model (4, 5, 14, 39, 40, 42, 44, 48, 68). Aged rats, like aged humans, are known to develop behavioral impairments that may be quite specific and yet profound. In particular, the severe age-dependent decrements in motor functions and cognitive behavior have been widely adopted as experimental models of extrapyramidal and dementing disorders in man. There is no evidence to date that aged animals develop neurodegenerative diseases homologous to those observed in humans, such as Alzheimer's disease or Parkinson's disease. However, the deficits measured and the correlated physiological changes are sufficiently similar to make them interesting in the perspective of the changes that occur with age in humans.

Intracerebral grafting has recently been introduced as a new experimental approach for the study of functional recovery after experimental or age-dependent brain damage. There is emerging evidence from studies in young adult animals with selective brain lesions that grafts of selected nuclei or brain regions, implanted into identified brain regions, may be used to identify the neural substrates sufficient for recovery of normal function (6, 62). In aged animals, grafting of defined populations of neurons into discrete areas of the host brain may therefore have the potential to identify both the neurochemical systems and neuroanatomical circuits associated with various components of the behavioral deficits seen in aged animals. In the present review we will deal with some technical aspects of grafting and graft survival in the aged rat brain, and summarize the studies published thus far on the functional effects of intracerebral grafts in rats with age-dependent decline in cerebral functions.

GRAFT PROCEDURES APPLICABLE TO STUDIES IN AGED RATS

Most of the information that is available concerning the applicability of grafting procedures to the aged brain arises from experiments directed at developing young or adult hosts, since no systematic efforts along these lines have so far been directed at the aged brain. The summary below is thus based primarily on experience obtained from studies in young rats.

Donor Tissue

For central nervous tissue the optimal donor age for grafting is the fetal or early neonatal period (18, 43, 54, 64). For implantation of suspensions of dissociated neurons in particular, special emphasis has been placed on obtaining donor cells close to their birth date, since older cells show poor or no survival (9). When using peripheral tissue, such as sympathetic cervical ganglion, peripheral nerve, or adrenal medulla, as a donor tissue the age of the donor is less critical, and even adult donors can be used with good results (20, 25, 55, 57, 58, 64).

Some evidence supports the possibility that cultured cells or cultured cell lines may survive at least to some extent when grafted to young adult rats (11, 35, 46, 53). Several advantages could be achieved if cultured cells could be used in intracerebral grafting. Specifically, the donor tissue could be prepared well before surgery, and the donor tissue could be manipulated easily prior to grafting. In addition, specific cell lines could be identified with characterized neurotransmitter types, and large quantities of the cells could be manufactured and used as a consistent and reliable source of donor tissue. To date, however, too little information is available to judge the potential of this application.

Cryoprotection is another variation in the graft procedure that has been used to increase its utility, efficiency, and applicability. Though several laboratories have demonstrated that grafts can survive freezing in a cryoprotecting medium for up to several months, the number and size of the surviving grafts are greatly reduced (19, 41). We recently demonstrated that freshly dissected fetal forebrain tissue can be stored in a refrigerator ($+4°C$) in preservative medium for at least 5 days prior to 100% successful grafting, although the size of the surviving grafts is reduced (30). This may provide a considerable logistic advancement in the grafting methodology, allowing for a convenient time interval between tissue dissection and grafting.

Immunology

Though the brain has been considered immunologically privileged, the extent of this privileged status is limited (see 3, 49 for review). Several experiments have demonstrated that intracerebral grafting across major histocompatibility barriers is possible, but the overall results are clearly less successful than when grafting is performed between immunologically related animals (7, 10, 23, 47, 49, 67). Recently we tested the degree of rejection of grafts of fetal mouse substantia nigra to rat striatum of young adult rats, in the presence or absence of the immunosuppressant drug Cyclosporin A (10). Our results demonstrate that all animals treated with the immunosuppressant had large, functionally active grafts similar to those seen in grafting between individuals of the same rat strain. The untreated animals had considerably fewer surviving grafts, and those that did survive (about 15%) were smaller, contained fewer viable cells, and had little or no functional effects. To what extent these results are also valid for aged recipient rats is not yet known.

Methods of Implantation

Two principal procedures have so far been applied for functional grafting in the brain of aged rats. One involves the placement of pieces of fetal central nervous system (CNS) tissue into one of the cerebral ventricles (57, 36). This procedure does not result in extensive damage to the host brain, but the number of implantation sites, and hence the regions of the host brain that can be reached by the graft, are limited. An alternative technique is the cell suspension method (8, 9). In this procedure the tissue is mechanically dissociated, with or without prior incubation in trypsin, into a cell suspension which is injected in small aliquots (usually 1–3 μl) with a microsyringe under stereotaxic control. Such cell suspension grafts can be implanted into the depth of any lesioned brain or spinal cord site with good survival. This procedure allows pregraft determination of cell viability, as well as control over the number of cells per injection site. A disadvantage of the cell suspension technique is that if the size and location of the graft are not properly controlled the grafts can result in damage or distortion of intrinsic circuitry of the host.

GRAFTING TO THE AGED BRAIN OF RODENTS

To date six papers and four congress abstracts have been published directly addressing the issue of intracerebral grafting in the aged brain. All these papers demonstrate that fetal CNS tissue will survive and extend axons when grafted to the aged rat or mouse brain, and several of them report that fetal grafts can reverse age-related functional deficits in the aged hosts.

Graft Survival and Fiber Outgrowth

Azmitia et al (2) examined the outgrowth of serotonergic fibers from fetal grafts obtained from the brain stem raphe region implanted in the hippocampus of adult and aged (24-month-old) mice. The raphe grafts survived and extended immunocytochemically positive serotonergic processes into the host hippocampus both in the young adult and aged recipients, although the density of innervation was greater in the young than in the aged host hippocampus. Sladek et al (61) grafted fetal hypothalamic neurons to the third ventricle of middle-aged (12-month-old) and aged (25-month-old) Brattleboro rats. No major differences were observed between grafts in the young and middle-aged host brains, though few neurophysin-containing processes were identified as passing through the graft-host border. Matsumoto et al (50) have reported that grafts of newborn medial basal hypothalamus survive grafting to the third ventricle of Wistar rats 21–30 months of age. Similarly, Rogers et al (56) have reported that fetal medial preoptic area grafts will survive in middle-aged (13- to 15-month-old) Long Evans rats. Sladek et al (63) have also reported that fetal grafts of the locus coeruleus regions survive and extend noradrenergic axons when grafted to the third ventricle in aged rats.

We have reported the successful grafting of neuronal cell suspensions prepared from the ventral mesencephalon and septal-diagonal band area of rat fetuses into the depths of intact neostriatum and hippocampus of 21- to 23-

month-old female Sprague-Dawley rats of the same strain (32). Graft survival assessed 3–4 months after grafting was comparable to that seen in our previous studies of young adult recipients. Fiber outgrowth into the host brain was evaluated in animals that were subjected to lesions of the intrinsic nigro-striatal or septo-hippocampal pathways 6–10 days before killing. Dense dopaminergic fiber outgrowth was seen within a zone of up to about 1 mm radius around the nigral implants, and the dense outgrowth of acetylcholine esterase (AChE)-positive fibers occurred up to 2 mm away for the septal implants. In an ongoing electron microscopic investigation of the ingrowing cholinergic fibers, using choline acetyltransferase immunocytochemistry, we obtained evidence that the grafts are capable of forming mature synaptic contacts with neurons in the aged host hippocampus (15). The overall magnitude of fiber outgrowth was less than that generally seen in previously *denervated* targets in young adult recipients. The outgrowth seen in the aged rats with intact afferents, however, appeared to be as extensive as in young recipients when the grafts were placed in *non-denervated* targets. In addition, the distribution of the AChE-positive fibers from the septal implants in the host hippocampus suggested that the pattern found in the nondenervated target tissue of the aged recipients was more diffuse than and partly different from normal. Thus, an interesting possibility is that synapse loss in the intrinsic connections of the hippocampus, may influence the pattern of the graft-derived innervation, and even improve the implant's ability to terminate in the otherwise intact target of the aged host brain.

Functional Effects

Two of the studies previously cited investigated the ability of hypothalamic grafts to reverse symptoms of reduced reproductive function in aging female rodents. In the study by Matsumoto et al (50) the recipients of the grafts of newborn medial basal hypothalamic tissue showed a significant increase in ovarian and uterine weight as compared to age-matched controls that did not receive grafts. This finding suggests that the grafts were secreting gonadotrophin releasing hormone. In addition, the appearance of corpora lutea in the grafted (but not in the control) ovaries indicated that the transplants had reinstated ovulation in the senescent rats. Rogers et al (56) showed that the cardinal signs of reproductive senescence (as evaluated by vaginal cytology) were halted and partially reversed in the aged hosts that received fetal medial preoptic area grafts. In a recent abstract Sladek et al (63) reported that locus coeruleus grafts from rat fetuses to the third ventricle of old Fischer 344 rats improved retention of a passive avoidance task six weeks after the procedure.

As stated previously, we have focused our attention on whether selective intracerebral grafting could ameliorate any of the motor coordination (33) or learning deficits (27, 29) observed in aged rats prior to grafting.

MOTOR COORDINATION SKILLS   Motor coordination skills were assessed by three measures adapted from the battery described by Campbell et al (14): (*a*) the ability to maintain balance on, and successfully reach a safety platform at either end of, a narrow bridge of round or square cross section; (*b*) the period of time that the animal could sustain its own weight clinging suspended from a taut wire; and (*c*) the ability to descend in a coordinated manner on a vertical pole covered with wire mesh. Prior to transplantation the aged rats were significantly impaired with respect to the young controls on the three measures. On the square and round bridges, young rats had no difficulty walking and exploring along the rod, and they generally reached the platform within 30–60 seconds. The aged rats before transplantation had greater difficulties maintaining balance. Most animals fell off the bridges or lay on the bridges without attempting to walk and clung tightly with all four paws or with the forepaws while the hind paws hung freely. Twelve weeks following transplantation the aged rats with nigral grafts, but not the aged control or the septal-grafted rats, showed marked and significant improvement in their balance and limb coordination on both the square and round bridges. Typically they could walk along the bridge without falling, displayed gait posture similar to the young rats, and fell less frequently than the other aged rats. On the wire mesh–covered pole the aged rats descended more rapidly before transplantation than did the young controls, frequently falling, slipping, or sliding down backwards. Although the aged rats with nigral transplants had a tendency to descend in a more controlled and coordinated manner, with head-down orientation as seen in the young controls, the differences from the other aged rats did not reach significance on this measure. The aged rats showed no difference between groups in either body weight or in latency to fall from the taut wire; this suggests that enhanced motor coordination in the aged rats with nigral grafts was not attributable to nonspecific differences in weight or strength of these animals.

LEARNING AND MEMORY   Learning and memory were assessed in the Morris' water maze task (52) 1 week prior to transplantation and 2 1/2 to 3 months after transplantation (29). This test requires that the rat use spatial cues in the environment to find a platform hidden below the surface of a pool of opaque water. Normal young rats have no trouble learning this task with speed and accuracy. Since our previous studies using this task (31, 34) showed that only a portion (1/4 to 1/3) of our rats were markedly impaired, a pretransplant test served to identify those impaired individuals in the aged rat group. Based on the performance of the young controls, we set the criterion for impaired performance in the aged rats such that the mean escape latency (i.e. swim time to find the submerged platform) should be above an upper 99% confidence limit of the escape latencies recorded in the young control group (29). A subgroup of old rats showed mean swim times greater than the criterion, and were thus allocated to the "old impaired" group, which was used for subsequent transplantation. The remaining subgroup of aged rats constituted the "old nonimpaired" group. This latter group and a young control group served as reference groups. A portion of the "old impaired" group received bilateral suspension grafts prepared from the septal-diagonal band area obtained from 14- to 16-day-old embryos of the same rat strain. Three implant deposits were made stereotaxically into the hippocampal formation on each side. The remaining "old impaired" rats were left unoperated and served as the "old impaired" control group. On the posttransplantation test, 2 1/2 to 3 months after grafting, the nongrafted groups remained impaired, while the grafted animals, as a group, showed a significant improvement in performance as indicated by escape latency. This improvement of the grafted group was demonstrated by comparisons to its pretransplantation performance as well as to the performance of the nongrafted old controls in the second test.

The ability of the rats to use spatial cues for the location of the platform in the pool was assessed by analyzing their search behavior after removal of the platform on the fifth day of testing. While the young rats and rats in the old nonimpaired groups focused their search on the fourth quadrant, where the platform had previously been placed, the "old-impaired" rats failed to do so in the pretransplant test. In the posttransplantation test the grafted rats, but not the nongrafted "old-impaired" group, showed significantly improved performance. Swim distance in the fourth quadrant was increased by 83%, and they swam significantly more in the fourth quadrant than in other quadrants of the pool. In contrast, the nongrafted controls showed no significant change over their pretransplant performance.

MECHANISMS OF ACTION OF INTRACEREBRAL NEURAL IMPLANTS: A WORKING MODEL

These results demonstrate the ability of intracerebral grafts to ameliorate age-related impairments in motoric and complex cognitive behaviors. To what extent this effect is dependent on the dopaminergic and cholinergic neurons in the nigral and septal grafts, respectively, is not clear at present. It is interesting to note, however, that intrahippocampal septal grafts, identical to the ones used here, had no effect on the motor coordination disabilities described above, while the fetal substantia nigra implanted into the striatum was effective in reducing these motor disabilities. This suggests that the behavioral effects of the grafts are regionally specific, and may be mediated through a direct action on elements in the surrounding region of the host brain.

In a follow-up study now in preparation (27) we have made some initial attempts to analyze the septal graft effects pharmacologically. In these experiments we used a modified water-maze protocol in which the platform was visible ("cue" trials) and invisible ("place" trials) on alternating trials. In this test it was clear that the "old impaired" rats were severely impaired not only when the platform was hidden (i.e. spatial reference memory), but also in the acquisition of the task when the platform was visible (which can be taken as a measure of nonspatial reference memory). The nongrafted impaired rats remained as impaired on both the "cue" and the "place" tasks when retested 2 1/2 months after the first test, while the impaired rats with septal suspension implants in the hippocampal formation were significantly improved on both components of the tasks. Moreover, while the nongrafted animals showed worse performance during the first two days of the second test session, as compared to the last days of the first test session, the grafted animals retained their level of performance from the end of the first test session. This indicates that the septal grafts can have an effect not only on acquisition but also on retention of the learned performance.

In the pharmacological test, atropine (50 mg/kg, i.p.) abolished completely the ability to find the platform in the grafted animals, both with visible and invisible platforms. Consistent with this, the ability to locate the platform site after platform removal was eliminated. In contrast, atropine had no significant effect in the "old-impaired" rats without grafts, and only marginal effect in the young control rats. Physostigmine (0.05 mg/kg, i.p.) had no significant effect on either grafted or nongrafted animals when administered during a single day of trials. These observations seem consistent with the idea that the graft-mediated improvements in both spatial and nonspatial learning and memory in the water-maze test were dependent on intact cholinergic neurotransmission.

In studies of young adult rats it appears that implanted embryonic nerve cells in some cases can substitute quite well for a lost intrinsic neuronal system. The intracerebral implants can probably exert their effects in several ways. The functional effects seen with grafts of nigral, hypothalamic, or adrenal medullary tissue placed into one of the cerebral ventricles, such as in the studies of Perlow et al (55), Freed et al (24, 25), and Gash et al (36), can probably be explained on the basis of a diffuse release of an active amine or peptide into the host cerebrospinal fluid (CSF) and adjacent brain tissue. In other instances, such as in animals with dopamine-rich grafts reinnervating the previously denervated neostriatum or acetylcholine-rich grafts reinnervating the previously denervated hippocampus (see 21, 28 for reviews), we believe that the available data provide quite substantial evidence that behavioral recovery is caused by the ability of the grafted neurons to reinnervate relevant parts of the host brain. This is illustrated, for example, by studies in young rats with lesions of the nigrostriatal dopamine pathway that show that the degree of functional recovery induced by nigral transplants is well correlated with the extent of striatal dopamine reinnervation, and that the "profile" of functional recovery is dependent on which area of the striatal complex is reinnervated by the graft.

Moreover, recent electron microscopic studies (15, 16, 26) on nigral grafts reinnervating the caudate-putamen and septal grafts reinnervating the hippocampus have demonstrated that the ingrowing dopaminergic and cholinergic fibers, respectively, establish abundant mature synaptic contacts with the initially denervated host target neurons.

To what extent the intracerebral implants can be functionally integrated with the host brain is, however, still poorly known, and remains an interesting question for further investigation. The chances for extensive integration may be greatest for neuronal suspension grafts implanted as deposits directly into the depth of the brain, but even solid grafts inserted as whole pieces into the brain have in several cases been seen to become reinnervated from the host brain, both in adult and developing recipients. Indeed, Arbuthnott et al (1) have in an electrophysiological study obtained evidence that neurons within solid nigral grafts transplanted into a cortical cavity overlying the striatum can be influenced by the host brain. Nevertheless, a recent horseradish peroxidase (HRP) study (26) failed to detect any host afferents to intracortical solid nigral grafts, despite the fact that these grafts had themselves formed extensive dopaminergic (DA) connections in the host striatum and had produced behavioral recovery. This suggests that implanted neurons can also function well in the absence of some, or perhaps even all, of their normal afferent inputs.

To what extent these observations on grafts in young adult rats with denervating lesions are also valid for the interpretation of the graft-induced functional effects in aged rats (without any preceding experimentally induced brain damage) is unclear. The observations of fiber outgrowth from the graft into the surrounding host brain region seem to support the possibility that also in the nondenervated aged host brain target the implanted dopaminergic and cholinergic neurons may act via specific efferent connections with the host. Preliminary observations, using electron microscopic immunocytochemistry (15), indicate that the graft-derived cholinergic fibers, growing into the dentate gyrus in the aged hosts, indeed are capable of forming normal synaptic contacts with neuronal elements in the host. Also, there is some evidence (see above) that the transplant-induced functional effects, as in the experiments in young adult rats, are graft-specific. Thus, the effects of grafts placed in the striatum on motor coordination impairments were seen only with dopamine-rich tissue and not with acetylcholine-rich septal tissue.

As a working hypothesis we propose, therefore, that the functional effects of the implanted neural tissue in aged rats are exerted by a specific action of selective neuronal elements in the graft on a dysfunctioning surrounding brain region of the host, and that this influence is mediated via the fiber connections established by the implanted neurons. On the assumption that impaired dopaminergic (in the striatum) and cholinergic (in the hippocampus) neurotransmissions contribute to the age-dependent motoric and cognitive impairments, we also propose that the ameliorative action of the nigral and septal grafts is at least partly due to a restoration of neurotransmission in the area. However, our results in the hippocampal formation in particular suggest that although cholinergic reinnervation of the target may be necessary for the effects of septal grafts in the water-maze task, this may not be sufficient for graft function. Several neuronal cell types may participate, and afferent connections to the grafts may also be involved.

Neuronal replacement by neural implants in aged and brain-damaged young rats is a striking example of how the brain can allow new elements to be inserted and linked into its own functional subsystems. Obviously there must be definite limitations as to which types of neurons or functional subsystems can successfully be manipulated in this way. Neural implants would seem most likely to have behaviorally meaningful functional effects with types of neurons that normally do not convey or link specific or patterned messages, e.g. in sensory or motor input and output systems. Indeed, functional or behavioral recovery in the neuronal replacement paradigm has so far been demonstrated primarily for neurons of the types that normally appear to act as tonic regulatory or level-setting systems.

Both the mesencephalic dopamine neurons and the basal forebrain acetylcholine neurons are commonly conceived of as modulatory or level-setting systems that tonically regulate the activity of the neostriatal and hippocampal neuronal machineries. Removal of the dopaminergic or cholinergic control mechanisms seems to result in severe inhibition or impairment of neostriatal and hippocampal functions, respectively. Functional recovery seen after reinstatement of impaired dopaminergic or cholinergic transmission by drugs or by neural implants can thus be interpreted as a reactivation of an inhibited, but otherwise intact, neuronal machinery.

An interesting implication of this model is that it may be sufficient for the nigral and septal grafts to reinstate dopaminergic and cholinergic transmission in the reinnervated target in a tonic and relatively nonspecific manner to compensate for at least some lesion-induced or age-dependent behavioral impairments. Temporally or spatially patterned inputs to the grafted neurons may not be necessary for the maintenance of such tonic activity. This mode of action would allow for behavioral recovery to occur even in the absence of afferent connections from the host. Indeed, our studies on nigral grafts reinnervating the neostriatum in young animals with nigro-striatal bundle lesions, using biochemical analyses of dopamine synthesis and metabolism (59, 60) or in vivo brain dialysis (70), indicate that grafted DA neurons can maintain a sufficiently high spontaneous activity even in the absence of any major afferents from the host brain. The reason for this may be that even in the intact situation local regulation at the terminal level (e.g. through local transmitter interactions or presynaptic autoreceptors) may play an important role in the maintenance of tonic, baseline transmission in the aminergic systems.

ACKNOWLEDGMENT

We thank Siv Carlson for generous assistance in the preparation of the manuscript. Research leading to this review was supported by the Swedish Medical Research Council and the National Institutes of Aging (AG06088).

Literature Cited

1. Arbuthnott, G., Dunnett, S. B., Mac-Leod, N. 1984. Electrophysiological recording from nigral transplants in the rat. *J. Physiol.* 360:32
2. Azmitia, E. C., Perlow, M. J., Brennan, M. J., Lauder, J. M. 1981. Fetal raphe and hippocampal transplants into adult and aged C57BL/6N mice: A preliminary immunocytochemical study. *Brain Res. Bull.* 7:703–10
3. Barker, C. F., Billingham, R. E. 1981. Immunologically privileged sites. *Adv. Immunol.* 25:1–54
4. Barnes, C. A., McNaughton, B. L. 1980. Physiological compensation for loss of afferent synapses in rat hippocampal granule cells during senescence. *J. Physiol.* 309:473–85
5. Bartus, R. T., Dean, R. L., Beer, B., Lippa, A. S. 1982. The cholinergic hypothesis of geriatric memory dysfunction. *Science* 217:408–16
6. Björklund, A., Stenevi, U., eds. 1985. *Neural Grafting in the Mammalian CNS.* Amsterdam: Elsevier. 709 pp.
7. Björklund, A., Stenevi, U., Dunnett, S. B., Gage, F. H. 1982. Cross-species neural grafting in a rat model of Parkinson's disease. *Nature* 298:652–54
8. Björklund, A., Stenevi, U., Schmidt, R. H., Dunnett, S. B., Gage, F. H. 1983. Intracerebral grafting of neuronal cell suspensions: I. Introduction and general methods of preparation. *Acta Physiol. Scand. Suppl.* 522:1–7
9. Brundin, P., Isacson, O., Gage, F. H., Stenevi, U., Björklund, A. 1985a. Intracerebral grafts of neuronal cell suspensions. See Ref. 6, p. 52
10. Brundin, P., Nilsson, O. G., Gage, F. H., Björklund, A. 1985b. Cyclosporin A increases survival of cross-species intrastriatal grafts of embryonic dopamine-containing neurons. *Exp. Brain Res.* 60:204–8
11. Brundin, P., Isacson, O., Prochiantz, A., Barbin, G., Mallart, M., et al. 1985c. Survival of grafted dopamine neurons previously cultured in vitro. *Neurosci. Lett.* In press
12. Burns, R. S., Markey, S. P., Phillips, J. M., Chiueh, C. C. 1984. The neurotoxicity of 1-methyl-4-phenyl-1,2,3,6-tetrahydropyridine in the monkey and man. *Can. J. Neurol. Sci.* 11:166–68
13. Calne, D. B., Langston, J. W. 1975. Aetiology of Parkinson's disease. *Lancet* 2:1457–59
14. Campbell, B. A., Krauter, E. E., Wallace, J. E. 1980. Animal models of aging: Sensory-motor and cognitive function in the aging rat. In *Psychology of Aging: Problems and Prospectives,* ed. D. G. Stein, pp. 201–13. Amsterdam: Elsevier–North-Holland
15. Clarke, D. J., Gage, F. H., Björklund, A. 1985. Formation of cholinergic synapses in the dentate gyrus of behaviorally-impaired young and aged rats by grafted basal forebrain neurons. *Soc. Neurosci. Abstr.* 11:730
16. Clarke, D. J., Gage, F. H., Björklund, A. 1986. Formation of cholinergic synapses by intra-hippocampal septal grafts as revealed by choline acetyl-transferase immunocytochemistry. *Brain Res.* In press
17. Coyle, J. T., Price, D. L., DeLong, M. R. 1983. Alzheimer's disease: A disorder of cortical cholinergic innervation. *Science* 219:1184–89
18. Das, G. D., Hallas, P., Das, K. G. 1979. Transplantation of neural tissues in the brains of laboratory mammals: Technical details and comments. *Experientia* 35:143–53
19. Das, G. D., Houle, J. D., Brasko, J., Das, K. G. 1982. Freezing of neural tissues and their transplantation in the brain of rats: Technical details and histological observations. *J. Neurosci. Methods* 8:1–15
20. David, S., Aguayo, A. J. 1985. Peripheral nerve transplantation techniques to study regeneration from the CNS of adult mammals. See Ref. 6, pp. 61–69
21. Dunnett, S. B., Björklund, A., Stenevi, U. 1983. Dopamine-rich transplants in experimental Parkinsonism. *Trends Neurosci.* 6:266–70
22. Flicker, C., Dean, R. L., Watkins, D. L., Fisher, S. K., Bartus, R. T. 1983. Behavioral and neurochemical effects following neurotoxic lesions of a major cholinergic input to the cerebral cortex in

the rat. *Pharmacol. Biochem. Behav.*
18:973–81
23. Freed, W. J. 1983. Functional brain tissue transplantation: reversal of lesion-induced rotation by intraventricular substantia nigra and adrenal medulla grafts, with a note on intracranial retinal grafts. *Biol. Psychiatry* 18:1205–66
24. Freed, W. J., Ko, G. N., Niehoff, D. L., Kuher, M. J., Hoffer, B. J., et al. 1983. Normalization of spiroperidol binding in the denervated rat striatum by homologous grafts of substantia nigra. *Science* 222:937–39
25. Freed, W. J., Morihisa, E., Spoor, E., Hoffer, B. J., Olson, L., et al. 1981. Transplanted adrenal chromaffin cells in rat brain reduce lesion-induced rotational behavior. *Nature* 292:351–52
26. Freund, T. F., Bolam, J. P., Björklund, A., Stenevi, U., Dunnett, S. B., Smith, A. D. 1985. Efferent synaptic connections of grafted dopaminergic neurons reinnervating the host neostriatum: A tyrosine hydroxylase immunocytochemical study. *J. Neurosci.* 3:603–16
27. Gage, F. H., Björklund, A. 1985. Specificity of intrahippocampal graft-induced improvements of cognitive performance in aged rats. *Soc. Neurosci. Abstr.*
28. Gage, F. H., Björklund, A., Stenevi, U., Dunnett, S. B. 1985a. Grafting of embryonic CNS tissue to the damaged adult hippocampal formation. See Ref. 6, pp. 559–73
29. Gage, F. H., Björklund, A., Stenevi, U., Dunnett, S. B., Kelly, P. A. T. 1984a. Intrahippocampal septal grafts ameliorate learning impairments in aged rats. *Science* 225:533–36
30. Gage, F. H., Brundin, P., Isacson, O., Björklund, A. 1985b. Fetal brain tissue can survive grafting and reinnervate denervated host brain following a five day pre-graft preservation period. *Neurosci. Lett.* 60:133–37
31. Gage, F. H., Dunnett, S. B., Björklund, A. 1984b. Spatial learning and motor deficits in aged rats. *Neurobiol. Aging* 5:43–48
32. Gage, F. H., Dunnett, S. B., Stenevi, U., Björklund, A. 1983a. Intracerebral grafting of neuronal cell suspensions VIII. Survival and growth of implants of nigral and septal cell suspensions in intact brains of aged rats. *Acta Physiol. Scand. Suppl.* 522:67–75
33. Gage, F. H., Dunnett, S. B., Stenevi, U., Björklund, A. 1983b. Aged rats: Recovery of motor impairments by intrastriatal nigral grafts. *Science* 221:966–69

34. Gage, F. H., Kelly, P. A. T., Björklund, A. 1984c. Regional changes in brain glucose metabolism reflect cognitive impairments in aged rats. *J. Neurosci.* 4:2856–66
35. Gash, D. M., Notter, M. F. D., Dick, L. B., Kraus, A. L., Okawara, S. H., et al. 1985. Cholinergic neurons transplanted into the neocortex and hippocampus of primates: Studies on African Green monkeys. See Ref. 6, pp. 595–603
36. Gash, D. M., Sladek, J. R. Jr., Sladek, C. D. 1980. Functional development of grafted vasopressin neurons. *Science* 210:1367–69
37. Greenwald, B. S., Mohs, R. C., Davies, K. L. 1983. Neurotransmitter deficits in Alzheimer's disease: Criteria for significance. *J. Am. Geriatr. Soc.* 31,5:310–16.
38. Hornykiewics, O. 1982. Brain neurotransmitter changes in Parkinson's disease. In *Movement Disorders*, ed. C. D. Marsden, S. Fahn, pp. 41–63. London: Butterworth
39. Ingram, D. K., Brennan, M. J. 1984. Animal behavior models in biogerontology. *Neurobiol. Aging* 5:63–66
40. Ingram, D. K., London, E. D., Goodrick, C. L. 1981. Age and neurochemical correlates of radial maze performance in rats. *Neurobiol. Aging* 2:41–47
41. Jensen, S., Sörensen, T., Möller, A. G., Zimmer, J. 1984. Intraocular grafts of fresh and freeze-stored rat hippocampal tissue: A comparison of survivability and histological and connective organization. *J. Comp. Neurol.* 227:558–68
42. Joseph, J. A., Berger, R. E., Engel, B. T., Roth, G. S. 1978. Age-related changes in the nigrostriatum: A behavioral and biochemical analysis. *J. Gerontol.* 33:643–49
43. Kromer, L. F., Björklund, A., Stenevi, U. 1983. Intracephalic embryonic neural implants in the adult rat brain. I. Growth and mature organization of brain stem, cerebellar and hippocampal implants. *J. Comp. Neurol.* 218:433–59
44. Kubanis, P., Zornetzer, S. F. 1981. Age-related behavioral and neurobiological changes: A review with an emphasis on memory. *Behav. Neural. Biol.* 31:115–72
45. Langston, J. W., Irwin, I., Langston, E. B., Forno, L. S. 1983. 1-Methyl-4-phenylpyridinium ion (MPP+): Identification of a metabolite of MPTP, a toxin selective to the substantia nigra. *Neurosci. Lett.* 48:87–92
46. Lindsay, R. M., Raisman, G. 1984. An autoradiographic study of neuronal development, vascularization and glial cell

migration from hippocampal transplants labelled in intermediate explant culture. *Neuroscience* 12:513–30

47. Low, W. C., Lewis, P. R., Bunch, S. T. 1983. Embryonic neural transplants across a major histocompatibility barrier: Survival and specificity of innervation. *Brain Res.* 262:328–33

48. Marshall, J. F. 1982. Sensorimotor disturbances in the aging rodent. *J. Gerontol.* 37:548–54

49. Mason, D. W., Charlton, H. M., Jones, A., Parry, D. M., Simmonds, S. J. 1985. Immunology of allograft rejection in mammals. See Ref. 6, pp. 91–98

50. Matsumoto, A., Kobayashi, S., Muralsami, S., Arai, Y. 1984. Recovery of declined ovarian function in aged female rats by transplantation of newborn hypothalamic tissue. *Proc. Jpn Acad.* 60:73–76

51. McGeer, E. G. 1981. Neurotransmitter systems in aging and senile dementia. *Prog. Neuro-Psychopharmacol. Biol. Psychiatry* 5:435–45

52. Morris, R. G. M. 1981. Spatial localization does not require the presence of local cues. *Learn. Motiv.* 12:239–60

53. Olson, L., Ebendal, T., Seiger, Å. 1984. Intraocular grafting of cultured brain tissue: Growth, vascularization and neuron survival in locus coeruleus and cortex cerebri. *Neurosci. Lett.* 47:139–44

54. Olsson, L., Seiger, Å., Strömberg, I. 1983. Intraocular transplantation in rodents. A detailed account of the procedure and examples of its use in neurobiology with special reference to brain tissue grafting. In *Advances in Cellular Neurobiology,* Vol. 4, ed. S. Fedoroff. New York: Academic. 407 pp.

55. Perlow, M. J., Kumakura, K., Guidotti, A. 1980. Prolonged survival of bovine adrenal chromaffin cells in rat cerebral ventricle. *Proc. Natl. Acad. Sci. USA* 77:5278–81

56. Rogers, J., Hoffman, G. E., Zornetzer, S. F., Vale, W. W. 1984. Hypothalamic grafts and neuroendocrine cascade theories of aging. In *Neural Transplants: Development and Function,* ed. J. R. Sladek, D. M. Gash, pp. 205–22. New York: Plenum

57. Rosenstein, J. M., Brightman, M. W. 1978. Intact cerebral ventricle as a site for tissue transplantation. *Nature* 275:83–85

58. Rosenstein, J. M., Brightman, M. W. 1979. Regeneration and myelination in autonomic ganglia transplanted to intact brain surfaces. *J. Neurocytol.* 8:359–79

59. Schmidt, R. H., Ingvar, M., Lindvall, O., Stenevi, U., Björklund, A. 1982. Functional activity of substantia nigra grafts reinnervating the striatum: Neurotransmitter metabolism and (^{14}C)-2-deoxy-D-glucose autoradiography. *J. Neurochem.* 38:737–48

60. Schmidt, R. H., Björklund, A., Stenevi, U., Dunnett, S. B., Gage, F. H. 1983. Intracerebral grafting of neuronal cell suspension. III. Activity of intrastriatal nigral suspension implants as assessed by measurements of dopamine synthesis and metabolism. *Acta Physiol. Scand. Suppl.* 522:23–32

61. Sladek, J. R., Gash, D. M. 1982. The use of neural grafts as a means of restoring neuronal loss associated with aging. *Anat. Rec.* 202:178A

62. Sladek, J. R., Gash, D. M., eds. 1984. *Neural Transplants, Development and Function.* New York: Plenum. 454 pp.

63. Sladek, J. R., Gash, D. M., Collier, T. J. 1984. Noradrenergic neuron transplants into the third ventricle of aged F344 rats improve inhibitory avoidance memory performance. *Soc. Neurosci. Abstr.* 10:772

64. Stenevi, U., Björklund, A., Svendgaard, N.-Aa. 1976. Transplantation of central and peripheral monoamine neurons to the adult rat brain: Techniques and conditions for survival. *Brain Res.* 114:1–20

65. Terry, R. D., Katzman, R. 1983. Senile dementia of the Alzheimer type. 1983. *Ann. Neurol.* 14:497–506

66. Ungerstedt, U., Arbuthnott, G. W. 1970. Quantitative recording of rotational behavior in rats after 6-hydroxydopamine lesions of the nigrostriatal dopamine system. *Brain Res.* 24:485–93

67. Vinogradova, O. S., Bragin, A. G., Kitchigina, V. F. 1985. Spontaneous and evoked activity of neurons in intrabrain allo- and xenografts of the hippocampus and septum. See Ref. 6, pp. 409–19

68. Walker, R. F. 1984. Impact of age-related changes in serotonin and norepinephrine metabolism on reproductive function in female rats: An analytical review. *Neurobiol. Aging* 5:121–39

69. Wenk, G. L., Olton, D. S. 1984. Recovery of neocortical choline acetyltransferase activity following ibotenic acid injection into the nucleus basalis Meynert in rats. *Brain Res.* 293:184–86

70. Zetterström, T., Brundin, P., Gage, F. H., Sharp, T., Isacons, O., et al. 1985. In vivo measurement of spontaneous release and metabolism of dopamine from intrastriatal nigral grafts using intracerebral dialysis. *Brain Res.* In press

Ann. Rev. Physiol. 1986. 48:461–71

NEURONAL RECEPTORS

Solomon H. Snyder

Departments of Neuroscience, Pharmacology and Experimental Therapeutics, Psychiatry and Behavioral Sciences, The Johns Hopkins University School of Medicine, 725 North Wolfe Street, Baltimore, Maryland 21205

INTRODUCTION

Many reviews have discussed neurotransmitter receptors. This essay is titled *Neuronal Receptors* to highlight neuronal drug binding sites, which may or may not represent neurotransmitter receptors. The term receptor conventionally includes the recognition site for the hormone or neurotransmitter as well as second messenger systems. This review focuses upon recognition sites, labeled by ligand binding techniques, which can clarify subtle aspects of synaptic function, such as the multiple subtypes of receptors, links between recognition sites and second messenger functions, autoradiographic localization of receptors, endogenous neurotransmitter ligands for drug receptors, and receptor binding techniques as strategies to characterize enzymes.

Opiate Receptors

The first well-characterized neurotransmitter receptor was the nicotinic acetylcholine receptor in the electric organs of fish. The success in labeling these receptors stemmed from the availability of potent and pseudo-irreversible selective toxins from snake venoms, such as alpha-bungarotoxin or *Naja naja* toxin. More importantly, in the electric organs of fish such as *Torpedo,* the acetylcholine receptor represents as much as 20% of the membrane protein. By contrast, most neurotransmitter receptors in the brain are only one-millionth by weight of brain tissue.

Thus, it was surprising that opiate receptors could be labeled by the binding of reversibly acting opiate drugs using crude brain homogenates. Success in this endeavor stemmed from several factors. One was the use of low concentrations of [^{3}H] ligands with nanomolar affinities for receptor sites. At low concentrations such ligands are more likely to bind to specific receptors than to

461

nonspecific sites. By extensive but very rapid washing techniques nonspecifically bound ligand can be removed while the receptor-bound drug is preserved.

One of the first important principles to arise from opiate receptor research was the distinction between agonists and antagonists. Sodium ions in low concentration selectively reduce the affinity of agonists but not antagonists for opiate receptors (45), and guanine nucleotides elicit the same effect (4, 11). Both sodium and guanine nucleotides act upon a GTP-binding protein that links the receptor to adenylate cyclase or other second messengers and allosterically regulates agonist binding. In intact organisms presumably the system works in reverse, i.e. opiate receptor binding alters the interactions of the GTP-binding proteins with sodium and guanine nucleotides. Agonists link receptors and GTP-binding proteins, while antagonists fail to produce such interactions and therefore do not bring about cellular alterations. Opiate agonists and corresponding antagonists generally differ only by the existence of an N-methyl group in the agonist and an N-allyl or N-cyclopropyl group in the antagonist. How such a small chemical change alters receptor-associated events remains a mystery. Nonetheless, sodium and GTP reliably differentiate pure agonists, pure antagonists, and compounds with mixed agonist-antagonist effects (4, 11). Mixed agonist-antagonist opiates offer the greatest potential as relatively nonaddicting analgesics; thus sodium and GTP effects upon receptor binding have provided a widely utilized screening device for potential analgesics.

With the introduction of numerous opiate [^{3}H] ligands, differences in drug specificity became evident that implied receptor subtypes. For example, mu binding sites have uniquely high affinity for morphine, while delta-receptors have less affinity for morphine and greater affinity for the opioid peptide enkephalins (35). Based on clinical and intact animal studies, Martin et al (37) predicted discrete mu- and kappa-receptors prior to their biochemical characterization. Kappa binding sites have very little affinity for the enkephalins and morphine, but have substantially higher affinity for the opioid peptide dynorphin as well as certain "kappa-like" opiate drugs (10, 29). Most opiate [^{3}H] ligands bind to discrete high and (relatively) low affinity sites, designated mu_1 and mu_2, respectively (31). The long-acting naloxone derivative naloxonazine (31) selectively abolishes mu_1 receptors and opiate analgesia, but does not prevent respiratory depression, a potentially therapeutic receptor distinction. Functional relevance has been shown for other opiate binding sites. The differential contractile effects of opiates in guinea pig intestine and mouse vas deferens distinguish mu and delta opiate receptors (35). The rabbit vas deferens responds selectively to kappa drugs (42). Beta-endorphin selectively affects the rat vas deferens (65) via epsilon receptors, which correspond to a binding site for benzomorphan opiates (8).

The existence of multiple opiate receptors raises theoretical questions. Do the various receptor subtypes physiologically interact with the same opioid neurotransmitters, like norepinephrine with alpha- and beta-adrenergic receptors, or are certain receptors selective for specific transmitters? The neuronal localizations of mu- and delta-receptors correspond somewhat to those of met- and leu-enkephalin, respectively, which suggests that these interactions are selective (21). The very high affinity of kappa receptors for dynorphin may indicate a functional interaction (10), though kappa-receptor localization differs markedly from that of endogenous dynorphin (22).

Autoradiographic studies permit the microscopic localization of receptors. Selective localizations of opiate receptors clarify their pharmacological actions (44). Analgesic effects may derive from discrete receptors in the substantia gelatinosa of the spinal cord and trigeminal nucleus, the medial thalamus, and the periaqueductal grey. Euphoric actions may involve the high densities of receptors in various structures of the limbic system and in the norepinephrine-containing locus coeruleus. Opiates potently constrict the pupil of the eye, which may reflect the response of receptors concentrated in the pretectal nuclei, which regulate pupillary diameter. The lethal effect of opiate overdose is generally associated with respiratory depression. Opiate receptors are highly localized to vagal nuclei, such as the nucleus of the solitary tract, which regulate respiration.

Localization of subtypes of opiate receptors may indicate function. Mu-receptors that are confined largely to areas associated with pain perception, such as the medial thalamus and periaqueductal grey, may account for the analgesic effects of opiates (21). Delta-receptors, which are more concentrated in limbic areas, may mediate euphoric effects (21). Kappa-receptors are highly localized to deep layers of the cerebral cortex (22), where cells that project to the thalamus modulate sensory input to cortex. Thus, kappa-receptors may influence sensory integration, which would explain the unique sedation as well as analgesia elicited by kappa drugs.

Benzodiazepine Receptors

Paradigms that have been used successfully with opiate receptors have been applied to other drug classes. [^{3}H]Diazepam binding labels benzodiazepine receptors, whose drug specificity parallels its pharmacologic actions (38, 52). GABA, the major inhibitory neurotransmitter in the brain, increases benzodiazepine receptor binding (57). The relative potencies of GABA and various amino acids in stimulating benzodiazepine binding mimic their affinities for GABA receptors identified by direct binding studies (69). This allosteric interaction indicates that benzodiazepine receptors are a subunit of GABA receptors.

The exact function of the benzodiazepine recognition site on the GABA receptor complex is unclear. Whether or not another endogenous ligand, such as a recently isolated protein that competes potently with benzodiazepine binding, functions physiologically is also unclear (15). Conceivably, the benzodiazepine receptor is a recognition site for interactions among the several subunits of the GABA receptor.

GABA hyperpolarizes neurons and inhibits their firing by increasing membrane permeability to chloride. Accordingly, the selective regulation of GABA and benzodiazepine receptor binding by chloride ions suggests that the chloride ion channel protein is also part of the GABA receptor complex (12). Convulsants such as picrotoxin block GABA synaptic effects by competing with chloride ions rather than GABA. The binding of ligands such as dihydropicrotoxinin or the structurally similar cage convulsant TBPS (*tert*-butylbicyclophosphorothionate) is regulated by chloride ions and may represent the direct labeling of the chloride ion channel or a closely associated protein (53, 59). Barbiturate drugs and ethanol seem to act fairly selectively at binding sites labeled by the cage convulsants, which explains the similarity of their pharmacological effects and those of benzodiazepines. The intimate relatedness of these binding sites is reflected by findings that purification to apparent homogeneity of a benzodiazepine binding receptor protein results in a copurification of GABA binding sites and preservation of chloride effects (47).

As with the opiate receptor, subtypes of benzodiazepine receptors have been identified, Type I and Type II. One of the subtypes may be responsible for the sedating actions of benzodiazepines while the other elicits antianxiety effects, though this differentiation is controversial (32). The two receptor subtypes can be physically separated based on their differential solubility in detergents (34). In at least one neuronal system, the striatonigral pathway, Type I receptors occur postsynaptically, while Type II receptors are localized to terminals of the striatonigral neurons (33). A postsynaptic localization for Type I receptors is consistent with their selective association with postsynaptic densities purified by subcellular fractionation (60).

Phencyclidine (PCP) Receptors

To clarify the psychotomimetic effects of PCP, binding sites for this substance were identified in brain membranes (63, 70). Whereas most opiate and benzodiazepine ligands have affinities in the low nanomolar range for their receptors, [^{3}H]PCP binds with a dissociation constant of about 0.1–0.3 μM. Accordingly, it has proved difficult to differentiate specific and nonspecific binding interactions, though careful drug specificity studies have established the pharmacological relevance of PCP receptor binding (64, 68). At the pharmacologically meaningful sites the relative potencies of various PCP derivatives in competing for binding parallel their behavioral effects. Moreover, recently a thienyl derivative of PCP, [^{3}H]TCP ([^{3}H]N-(1-[2-thienyl]cyclohexyl)3,4-piperidine), with a tenfold higher binding affinity than PCP, has facilitated an unequivocal characterization of the receptor (62).

Though PCP receptors have been less extensively characterized than benzodiazepine and opiate receptors, certain similar themes are apparent. Evidence has been presented for endogenous ligands of the PCP receptor (46). Blockade by PCP of potassium channels in synaptosomes and the neuromuscular junction (3) suggests that the action of PCP is associated with a specific ion channel. [^{3}H]PCP may bind directly to a protein linked to potassium channels (3).

Sigma Receptors

Certain opiates are psychotomimetic. Martin suggested that these effects involve a subtype of opiate receptor designated sigma (37). However, these effects are not blocked by naloxone, and (+) isomers of drugs frequently elicit more sigma-like behavioral actions than (−) isomers; this stereoselectivity is opposite that evidenced at conventional opiate receptors (48). Thus, sigma sites are distinct from classic opiate receptors. The psychotomimetic opiate N-allylnormetazocine (SKF-10,047) binds to sites with the drug specificity of sigma receptors (56), as does [^{3}H]ethylketocyclazocine (58). The neuroleptic haloperidol is almost as potent at sigma binding sites as at dopamine receptors and so is a useful ligand (30, 58), as is the dopamine-related agent 3-PPP [(3-hydroxyphenyl)-N-(1-propyl)-piperidine)] (30). Since PCP can interact with sigma receptors, the psychotomimetic effects of PCP may involve actions at sigma sites. On the other hand, certain sigma opiates have reasonable affinity for PCP receptors, which could mediate some of their behavioral effects. It has even been suggested that PCP and sigma receptor binding sites are the same membrane protein (67). [^{3}H]N-Allylnormetazocine labels two sites (26). The high affinity site is the sigma receptor, and the low affinity site appears to be identical with the PCP receptor. Though the extent to which the subjective effects of PCP and of psychotomimetic opiates resemble each other is not clear, their molecular actions may overlap.

Autoradiographic localizations of sigma receptors are extremely discrete (30). Receptors are highly concentrated in a series of motor nuclei in the brainstem, such as the oculomotor, facial, motor trigeminal, and hypoglossal nuclei, and some are also concentrated in the sensory nuclei, such as the vestibular and cochlear nuclei. Sigma receptors are also concentrated in limbic brain regions, which may explain their psychotomimetic actions. Receptors are especially abundant on large neuronal cells, such as the motor neurons of the spinal cord and the Purkinje cells of the cerebellum as well as the pyramidal cells of the hippocampus. The differentiation of sigma sites from opiate receptors suggests the existence of an endogenous ligand associated with emotional and motor behavior.

Calcium Antagonist Receptors

Calcium antagonist drugs have major clinical importance in treating angina and cardiac arrhythmias. Three distinct receptor classes appear to be responsible for the actions of the three distinct types of calcium antagonist drugs, the di-hydropyridines, the verapamil-like drugs, and diltiazem (18, 20, 39). These three receptors appear to be linked to each other allosterically, in a way reminiscent of the multiple subunits of benzodiazepine receptors. A link to calcium ion channels is apparent in the absolute requirement of calcium ions for dihydropyridine receptor binding (23). Inorganic calcium agonists and antagonists can be distinguished at receptor binding sites by the ability of ions to stimulate dihydropyridine binding or to block stimulatory effects of calcium. Receptor binding techniques have not differentiated between the agonist and antagonist effects of dihydropyridine drugs themselves. While a role for these drugs and associated voltage-dependent calcium channels in cardiac and smooth muscle is well accepted, their exact function in the brain is not clear. Autoradiographic studies have localized calcium antagonist receptors to specific synaptic regions in a variety of areas, which suggests a link to neurotransmitter function (25). It is conceivable that the receptors interact with an endogenous neurotransmitter whose synaptic effects are mediated via calcium. A behavioral role for these receptor sites is suggested by evidence that di-phenylbutylpiperidine neuroleptics, which are unique for their ability to relieve the "negative" symptoms of schizophrenia, such as emotional withdrawal, have potent verapamil-like calcium antagonist action in addition to blocking dopamine receptors (24).

Conventional Neurotransmitter Receptors

In contrast to the puzzles posed by "drug" receptors, receptors associated with well-known neurotransmitters are somewhat more straightforward. Space limitations preclude a detailed review of the extensive literature. Binding techniques have identified receptor sites for virtually all of the known biogenic amine, amino acid, and peptide neurotransmitters (50). It has been possible to differentiate multiple receptor subtypes. As many as four subtypes of alpha-adrenergic (7) and of serotonin receptors (16) can be differentiated by binding techniques. Histamine H_1 and H_2 receptors can be differentially labeled (9, 19, 27). At least two subtypes of dopamine receptors, D_1 and D_2, have been well characterized (13). As with opiate receptors, biogenic amine receptor binding sites that are linked to adenylate cyclase are regulated by guanine nucleotides with appropriate differentiation of agonists and antagonists.

Receptors for amino acid neurotransmitters, such as glutamate, glycine, aspartate, and GABA, can be readily detected. Glycine receptors were labeled with the convulsant glycine antagonist [^{3}H]strychnine shortly after the identification of opiate receptors (66). Several subtypes of glutamate receptors can be labeled utilizing a variety of glutamate derivatives or the excitotoxin kainic acid (17). Conventional postsynaptic GABA receptors were first labeled with [^{3}H]GABA itself (69). A different type of GABA receptor, designated

GABA$_B$, that regulates neurotransmitter release via inhibitory effects upon adenylate cyclase (5) occurs on nerve terminals. GABA$_B$ receptors can be labeled with [^{3}H]GABA provided that calcium ions are added to amplify GABA$_B$ interactions. The crucial role of calcium for GABA$_B$ receptors may relate to the importance of calcium in regulating neurotransmitter release. GABA$_B$ receptors can also be labeled by the muscle relaxant drug baclofen.

Many peptide receptors have been characterized by high affinity binding sites. Examples include receptors for vasoactive intestinal polypeptide (VIP), cholecystokinin (CCK), thyrotropin releasing hormone (TRH), somatostatin, substance P, neuropeptide Y, angiotensin, and bradykinin (49). Progress in characterizing the physiological functions of these peptides and their receptors has been hampered by the lack of potent and selective drugs that are agonists or antagonists at the receptors.

As more diverse properties of neurotransmitters are reported, criteria for their identification become less clear-cut. The purines ATP and adenosine have been suggested as neurotransmitters or neuromodulators. ATP may well be a cotransmitter in sensory and sympathetic nerves (6). Molecular elucidation of its receptors is very limited. Adenosine receptors have been well characterized, exist in at least two subtypes (both linked to adenylate cyclase), and appear to be responsible for the behavioral actions of xanthine stimulants such as caffeine (51).

Receptor-Like Binding Sites Linked to Enzymes

The distinction between hormonal or neurotransmitter receptors and enzymes is becoming increasingly fuzzy. For instance, epidermal growth factor (EGF) (14) and insulin receptors (61) have protein kinase activities. Receptor binding sites for the potently tumor-promoting phorbol esters are identical to protein kinase C (41). Studies in smooth muscle and by single unit recording implicate protein kinase C in synaptic activity (1, 2).

In other instances drug binding sites may reflect specific enzymes. For instance, the high affinity receptor-like binding sites for the Parkinsonian neurotoxin MPTP (1-methyl-4-phenyltetrahydropyridine) represent binding of MPTP to monoamine oxidase Type B (28, 43). One can also directly label enzymes using binding techniques. Monoamine oxidase Type A can be labeled with the monoamine oxidase inhibitor [^{3}H]harmaline (40).

In some instances ligand binding to enzymes clarifies enzyme properties better than conventional catalytic assays. Angiotensin-converting enzyme can be labeled with the inhibitor [^{3}H]captopril (54), while the enkephalin-forming carboxypeptidase enkephalin convertase can be labeled with the inhibitor [^{3}H]GEMSA ([^{3}H]guanidinoethylmercaptosuccinic acid) (55). In both instances ligand binding provides a simple and sensitive technique for measuring the number of enzyme molecules even in crude tissue extracts. When combined with catalytic assays, one can measure the turnover number of the enzyme in multiple samples, something which would be extremely difficult to do using conventional techniques. Autoradiography of [³H]captopril and [³H]GEMSA binding sites provides an efficient means of localizing these enzymes at the microscopic level. [³H]Captopril autoradiography has localized angiotensin-converting enzyme to a prominent striatonigral pathway in the brain (54). Since no endogenous angiotensin occurs in this pathway, the findings suggest a novel peptide substrate. The selective association of enkephalin convertase-containing neurons labeled by [³H]GEMSA with endogenous enkephalin provides strong evidence that this enzyme is physiologically associated with the biosynthesis of enkephalin (36).

ACKNOWLEDGMENT

This work was supported by USPHS grants DA-00266, MH-18501, and Research Scientist Award DA-00074.

Literature Cited

1. Baraban, J. M., Gould, R. J., Peroutka, S. J., Snyder, S. H. 1985. Phorbol ester effects on neurotransmission: Interaction with neurotransmitters and calcium in smooth muscle. *Proc. Natl. Acad. Sci. USA* 82:604–7
2. Baraban, J. M., Snyder, S. H., Alger, B. E. 1985. Protein kinase C regulates ionic conductance in hippocampal pyramidal neurons: Electrophysiological effects of phorbol esters. *Proc. Natl. Acad. Sci. USA.* 82:2538–42
3. Blaustein, M. P., Ickowicz, R. K. 1983. Phencyclidine in nanomolar concentrations binds to synaptosomes and blocks certain potassium channels. *Proc. Natl. Acad. Sci. USA* 80:3855–59
4. Blume, A. J. 1978. Interactions of ligands with opiate receptors of brain membranes: Regulation by ions and nucleotides. *Proc. Natl. Acad. Sci. USA* 75:1713–17
5. Bowery, N. G. 1983. Classification of GABA receptors. In *The GABA Receptors,* ed. S. J. Enna, pp. 178–213. New Jersey: Humana
6. Burnstock, G. 1985. Purinergic mechanisms broaden their sphere of influence. *Trends Neurosci.* 8:5–6
7. Bylund, D. B., U'Prichard, D. C. 1983. Characterization of alpha₁ and alpha₂ adrenergic receptors. *Int. Rev. Neurobiol.* 24:344–433
8. Chang, K.-J., Blanchard, S. G., Cuatrecasas, P. 1984. Benzomorphan sites are ligand recognition sites of putative epsilon receptors. *Mol. Pharmacol.* 26:484–88

9. Chang, R. S. L., Tran, V. T., Snyder, S. H. 1979. Heterogeneity of histamine H₁-receptors: Species variations in [³H]-mepyramine binding of brain membranes. *J. Neurochem.* 32:1653–63
10. Chavkin, C., James, I., Goldstein, A. 1982. Dynorphin is a specific endogenous ligand of the kappa opioid receptor. *Science* 215:413–15
11. Childers, S. R., Snyder, S. H. 1980. Differential regulation by guanine nucleotides of opiate agonist and antagonist receptor interactions. *J. Neurochem.* 34:583–93
12. Costa, T., Rodbard, D., Pert, C. B. 1979. Is the benzodiazepine receptor coupled to a chloride anion channel? *Nature* 277:315–16
13. Creese, I., Sibley, D. R., Hamblin, M. W., Leff, S. E. 1983. The classification of dopamine receptors: Relationship to radioligand binding. *Ann. Rev. Neurosci.* 6:43–71
14. Downward, J., Yarden, Y., Mayes, E., Scrace, G., Totty, N., et al. 1984. Close similarity of epidermal growth factor receptor and V-erb-B oncogene protein sequences. *Nature* 307:521–27
15. Ferrero, P., Guidotti, A., Conti-Tronconi, B., Costa, E. 1985. A brain octadecaneuropeptide generated by tryptic digestion of DBI (diazepam binding inhibitor) functions as a proconflict ligand of benzodiazepine recognition site. *Neuropharmacol.* 23:1359–62
16. Fillion, G. 1983. 5-Hydroxytryptamine receptors in brain. In *Handbook of Psychopharmacology,* ed. L. L. Iversen, S.

D. Iversen, S. H. Snyder, 17:139–66. New York: Plenum

17. Foster, A. C., Fagg, G. E. 1984. Acidic amino acid binding sites in mammalian neuronal membranes: Their characteristics and relationship to synaptic receptors. *Brain Res. Rev.* 7:103–64

18. Galizzi, J. P., Fosset, M., Lazdunski, M. 1984. [^{3}H]Verapamil binding sites in skeletal muscle transverse tubule membranes. *Biochem. Biophys. Res. Commun.* 118:239–45

19. Gillian, A., Gajtkowski, D. B., Norris, D. B., Rising, T. J., Wood, T. P. 1983. Specific binding of ^{3}H-tiotidine to histamine H_2 receptors in guinea pig cerebral cortex. *Nature* 304:65–67

20. Goll, A., Ferry, D. R., Striessnig, J., Schober, M., Glossmann, H. 1984. (–)-[^{3}H]Desmethoxyverapamil, a novel Ca^{2+} channel probe. *FEBS Lett.* 176:371–77

21. Goodman, R. R., Snyder, S. H., Kuhar, M. J., Young, W. S. III. 1980. Differentiation of delta and mu opiate receptor localization by light microscopic autoradiography. *Proc. Natl. Acad. Sci. USA* 77:6239–43

22. Goodman, R. R., Snyder, S. H. 1982. Kappa opiate receptors localized by autoradiography to deep layers of cerebral cortex: Relation to sedative effects. *Proc. Natl. Acad. Sci. USA* 79:5703–7

23. Gould, R. J., Murphy, K. M. M., Snyder, S. H. 1982. [^{3}H]Nitrendipine labeled calcium channels discriminate inorganic calcium agonists and antagonists. *Proc. Natl. Acad. Sci. USA* 79:3656–60

24. Gould, R. J., Murphy, K. M. M., Reynolds, I. J., Snyder, S. H. 1983. Antischizophrenic drugs of the diphenylbutylpiperidine type act as calcium channel antagonists. *Proc. Natl. Acad. Sci. USA* 80:5122–25

25. Gould, R., Murphy, K. M. M., Snyder, S. H. 1985. Autoradiographic localization of calcium channel antagonist receptors in rat brain with [^{3}H]nitrendipine. *Brain Res.* 330:217–23

26. Gundlach, A. L., Largent, B. L., Snyder, S. H. 1985. Phencyclidine and sigma opiate receptors in brain: biochemical autoradiographic differentiation. *Eur. J. Pharmacol.* 113:465–66

27. Hill, S. J., Emson, P. C., Young, J. M. 1978. The binding of [^{3}H]mepyramine to histamine H_1 receptors in guinea pig brain. *J. Neurochem.* 31:997–1004

28. Javitch, J. A., Uhl, G. R., Snyder, S. H. 1984. Parkinsonism-inducing neurotoxin, N-methyl-4-phenyl-1,2,3,6-tetrahydropyridine: Characterization and localization of receptor binding sites in rat and human brain. *Proc. Natl. Acad. Sci. USA* 81:4591–95

29. Kosterlitz, H. W., Paterson, S. J. 1980. Characterization of opioid receptors in nervous tissue. *Philos. Trans. R. Soc. London Ser. B* 210:113–22

30. Largent, B. L., Gundlach, A. L., Snyder, S. H. 1984. Psychotomimetic opiate receptors labeled and visualized with (+)-[^{3}H]3-(3-hydroxyphenyl)-N-(1-propyl)piperidine. *Proc. Natl. Acad. Sci. USA* 81:4983–87

31. Ling, G. S. F., MacLeod, J. M., Lee, S., Lockhart, S. H., Pasternak, G. 1984. Separation of morphine analgesia from physical dependence. *Science* 226:462–64

32. Lippa, A. S., Meyerson, L. R., Beer, B. 1982. Molecular substrates of anxiety: Clues from the heterogeneity of benzodiazepine receptors. *Life Sci.* 31:1409–1417

33. Lo, M. M. S., Niehoff, D. L., Kuhar, M. J., Snyder, S. H. 1983. Differential localization of Type I and Type II benzodiazepine binding sites in substantia nigra. *Nature* 306:57–60

34. Lo, M. M. S., Strittmatter, S. M., Snyder, S. H. 1982. Physical separation and characterization of two types of benzodiazepine receptors. *Proc. Natl. Acad. Sci. USA* 79:680–84

35. Lord, J. A. H., Waterfield, A. A., Hughes, J., Kosterlitz, H. W. 1977. Endogenous opioid peptides: Multiple agonists and receptors. *Nature* 267:495–99

36. Lynch, D. R., Strittmatter, S. M., Snyder, S. H. 1984. Enkephalin convertase localization by [^{3}H]guanidinoethyl-mercaptosuccinic acid autoradiography: Selective association with enkephalin-containing neurons. *Proc. Natl. Acad. Sci. USA* 81:6543–47

37. Martin, W. R., Eades, C. G., Thompson, J. A., Huppler, R. E., Gilbert, P. E. 1976. The effects of morphine- and nalorphine-like drugs in the nondependent and morphine dependent chronic spinal dog. *J. Pharmacol. Exp. Ther.* 197:517–22

38. Mohler, H., Okada, T. 1977. Benzodiazepine receptor: Demonstration in the central nervous system. *Science* 198:849–51

39. Murphy, K. M. M., Gould, R. J., Largent, B. L., Snyder, S. H. 1983. A unitary mechanism of calcium antagonist drug action. *Proc. Natl. Acad. Sci. USA* 80:860–64

40. Nelson, D. L., Herbet, A., Petillot, Y., Pichat, L., Glowinski, J., Hamon, M. 1979. ^{3}H-Harmaline as a specific ligand of MAO A I. Properties of the active site

of MAO A from rat and bovine brains. *J. Neurochem.* 32:1817–27

41. Nishizuka, Y. 1984. Turnover of inositol phospholipids and signal transduction. *Science* 225:1365–70

42. Oka, T., Negishi, K., Suda, M., Matsumiya, T., Inazu, T., Ueki, M. 1981. Rabbit vas deferens: A specific bioassay for opioid kappa receptor agonists. *Eur. J. Pharmacol.* 73:235–36

43. Parsons, B., Rainbow, T. C. 1984. High affinity binding sites for [³H]MPTP may correspond to monoamine oxidase. *Eur. J. Pharmacol.* 102:375–77

44. Pert, C. B., Kuhar, M. J., Snyder, S. H. 1976. Opiate receptor: Autoradiographic localization in rat brain. *Proc. Natl. Acad. Sci. USA* 73:3729–33

45. Pert, C. B., Pasternak, G., Snyder, S. H. 1973. Opiate agonists and antagonists discriminated by receptor binding in brain. *Science* 182:1359–61

46. Quirion, R., Dimaggio, D. A., French, E. D., Contreras, P. C., Shiloach, J., et al. 1984. Evidence for an endogenous peptide ligand for the phencyclidine receptor. *Peptides* 5:967–73

47. Sigel, E., Barnard, E. A. 1984. A gamma aminobutyric acid/benzodiazepine receptor complex from bovine cerebral cortex: improved purification with preservation of regulatory sites and their interactions. *J. Biol. Chem.* 259:7219–23

48. Slifer, B. L., Balster, R. L. 1983. Reinforcing properties of stereoisomers of the putative sigma agonists. *N*-Allylnormetazocine and cyclazocine in Rhesus monkeys. *J. Pharmacol. Exp. Ther.* 225:522–28

49. Snyder, S. H. 1980. Brain peptides as neurotransmitters. *Science* 209:976–83

50. Snyder, S. H. 1984. Drug and neurotransmitter receptors in the brain. *Science* 224:22–31

51. Snyder, S. H. 1985. Adenosine as a neuromodulator. *Ann. Rev. Neurosci.* 8:103–24

52. Squires, R. F., Braestrup, C. 1977. Benzodiazepine receptors in rat brain. *Nature* 266:732–34

53. Squires, R. F., Casida, S. E., Richardson, M., Saedrup, E. 1983. [³⁵S]*tert*-butylbicyclophosphorothionate binds with high affinity to specific sites coupled to gamma-aminobutyric acid-A and ion recognition sites. *Mol. Pharmacol.* 23: 326–36

54. Strittmatter, S. M., Lo, M. M. S., Javitch, J. A., Snyder, S. H. 1984. Autoradiographic visualization of angiotensin-converting enzyme in rat brain with [³H]captopril: Localization to a

striatonigral pathway. *Proc. Natl. Acad. Sci. USA* 81:1599–1603

55. Strittmatter, S. M., Lynch, D. R., Snyder, S. H. 1984. [³H]Guanidinoethylmercaptosuccinic acid binding to tissue homogenates: Selective labeling of enkephalin convertase. *J. Biol. Chem.* 259:11812–17

56. Su, T.-P. 1982. Evidence for sigma opioid receptor: Binding of [³H]SKF-10047 to etorphine-inaccessible sites in guinea pig brain. *J. Pharmacol. Exp. Ther.* 223:284–90

57. Tallman, J., Thomas, J. W., Gallager, D. W. 1978. GABAergic modulation of benzodiazepine binding site sensitivity. *Nature* 274:383–85

58. Tam, S. W. 1983. Naloxone-inaccessible sigma receptor in rat central nervous system. *Proc. Natl. Acad. Sci. USA* 80:6703–7

59. Ticku, M. K., Ban, M., Olsen, R. W. 1978. Binding of [³H]alpha-dihydropicrotoxinin, a gamma-aminobutyric acid antagonist, to rat brain membranes. *Mol. Pharmacol.* 14:391–402

60. Trifiletti, R. R., Snyder, S. H. 1985. Localization of Type I benzodiazepine receptors to postsynaptic densities in bovine brain. *J. Neurosci.* 5:1049–57

61. Ullrich, A., Bell, J. R., Chen, E. Y., Herrara, R., Petruzzelli, L. M., et al. 1985. Human insulin receptor and its relationship to the tyrosine kinase family of oncogenes. *Nature* 313:756–61

62. Vignon, J., Chicheportiche, R., Chicheportiche, M., Kamenka, J.-M., Geneste, P., Lazdunski, M. 1983. [³H]TCP: A new tool with high affinity for the PCP receptor in rat brain. *Brain Res.* 280:194–97

63. Vincent, J. P., Kartalovski, B., Geneste, P., Kamenka, J. M., Lazdunski, M. 1979. Interaction of phencyclidine ("angel dust") with a specific receptor in rat brain membranes. *Proc. Natl. Acad. Sci. USA* 76:4678–82

64. Vincent, J. P., Vignon, J., Kartalovski, B., Lazdunski, M. 1980. Binding of phencyclidine to rat brain membranes: technical aspects. *Eur. J. Pharmacol.* 68:73–77

65. Wuster, M., Schulz, R., Herz, A. 1981. Multiple opiate receptors in peripheral-tissue preparations. *Biochem. Pharmacol.* 30:1883–87

66. Young, A. B., Snyder, S. H. 1973. Strychnine binding associated with glycine receptors of the central nervous system. *Proc. Natl. Acad. Sci. USA* 70:2832–36

67. Zukin, R. S., Zukin, S. R. 1981. Demonstration of [³H]cyclazocine binding to

multiple opiate receptor sites. *Mol. Pharmacol.* 20:246–54

68. Zukin, S. R., Fitz-Syage, M. L., Nichtenhauser, R., Zukin, R. S. 1983. Specific binding of [^{3}H]phencyclidine in rat central nervous tissue: further characterized and technical consideration. *Brain Res.* 258:277–84

69. Zukin, S. R., Young, A. B., Snyder, S. H. 1974. Gamma-aminobutyric acid binding to receptor sites in rat central nervous system. *Proc. Natl. Acad. Sci. USA* 71:4802–7

70. Zukin, S. R., Zukin, R. S. 1979. Specific [^{3}H]phencyclidine binding in rat central nervous system. *Proc. Natl. Acad. Sci. USA* 76:5372–76

ENDOCRINOLOGY

CNS PEPTIDES THAT REGULATE PITUITARY FUNCTION

Introduction, Jack L. Kostyo, *Section Editor*

It has been several decades since Geoffrey Harris and others made the pioneering observations suggesting that the central nervous system regulates the secretion of the anterior pituitary hormones by producing stimulatory or inhibitory chemical messengers that are delivered to the pituitary via the hypophyseal portal circulation. In the intervening years, a host of investigators became involved in the search for these elusive messengers or releasing factors, as they came to be called. Extensive efforts were made to isolate and chemically characterize these substances, determine their sites of production, storage, and release into the hypophyseal portal circulation, and to study the nature of the neural events governing their release. The intensity and scope of this work has been of such magnitude that it has spawned a major subdiscipline of endocrinology, namely neuroendocrinology.

Because of the minute quantities of these substances present in the central nervous system and the state of the art of peptide chemistry, the isolation and chemical characterization of the peptide releasing factors proved to be a herculean task. Indeed, it has only been in the last several years that corticotropin releasing factor and growth hormone releasing factor have been isolated and characterized. In all likelihood, other releasing factors for which there is presently only presumptive evidence will be discovered and characterized in the near future. Because the characterized peptide releasing factors have proven to be small to medium sized molecules, it has been possible to produce them synthetically, which has conferred an enormous advantage in investigations of their origin in the brain, their mechanisms of action, their pharmacology, and ultimately their potential usefulness as therapeutic agents in humans.

Research on central nervous system peptides that regulate anterior pituitary function continues at an intense pace, continually providing new insights into their nature and actions. Because these substances are of such current interest, this year's section on Endocrinology consists of seven chapters devoted to recent work on some of the well-established peptide releasing factors, as well as on endogenous opioid peptides, substance P, and neurotensin, which may also prove to be physiological regulators of anterior pituitary hormone secretion.

Ann. Rev. Physiol. 1986. 48:475–94

MEDIATION BY CORTICOTROPIN RELEASING FACTOR (CRF) OF ADENOHYPOPHYSIAL HORMONE SECRETION

Catherine L. Rivier and Paul M. Plotsky

The Clayton Foundation Laboratories for Peptide Biology, The Salk Institute, 10010 N. Torrey Pines Road, La Jolla, California 92037

INTRODUCTION

The key role played by the hypothalamus in the regulation of adrenocorticotropic hormone (ACTH) is well established (for review see 5). In 1981 our laboratory isolated and characterized a 41-residue peptide from ovine hypothalami that met the criteria expected of a physiologic corticotropin releasing factor (CRF) (124, 132). Subsequently, the structures of rat (109, 125), caprine (66), and bovine (26) CRFs have also been established, and a structure has been proposed for human CRF on the basis of the DNA sequence of the human CRF genome (32). Ovine and rat CRFs differ by seven residues, while rat and human CRFs are identical. Additionally, two other peptides share homologies with ovine CRF: sauvagine, a 40-residue peptide found in frog skin (27, 76), and urotensin, a 41-residue peptide isolated from teleost urophyses (64).

The availability of synthetic replicates of ovine CRF (oCRF) and rat/human CRF (r/hCRF) and the production of antisera or antagonists directed against these entities have allowed experiments that have increased our understanding of the mechanisms that regulate the function of the corticotroph, and have established CRF as a major physiologic regulator of ACTH secretion. The present article deals primarily with studies carried out since the isolation of oCRF, and the literature search was completed in March 1985; for earlier work the reader is referred to some excellent reviews which have appeared over the last few years (5, 147).

475

0066-4278/86/0315-0475$02.00

ACTIVITY OF CRF IN VITRO

Response to a CRF Challenge

ACUTE ADMINISTRATION   As shown by our laboratory (96, 133) and others (2, 43), the addition of increasing doses of ovine CRF (oCRF) to rat primary anterior pituitary cell cultures causes a dose-related increase in ACTH secretion. oCRF also increases ACTH secretion by human (39, 42) and fish (30, 31) adenohypophysis, as well as by some tumor lines like the AtT-20 mouse pituitary tumor cells (52). The minimal effective concentration of oCRF that evokes release of ACTH in rat cells is in the range of 1–10 pM, and the plateau response is reached at 1–10 nM (133). At these doses CRF also stimulates cyclic AMP accumulation (45, 62), but is devoid of effect on the basal secretion of other anterior pituitary hormones (133), and shows no significant interaction with other releasing factors on anterior pituitary hormone secretion (133, 139). However, since β-endorphin and ACTH are secreted concomitantly by the pituitary gland under a variety of circumstances (48), it is not surprising that oCRF also stimulates the release of proopiomelanocortin (POMC)-derived peptides from the anterior pituitary (39, 133). Additionally, cultured neurointermediate lobe cells respond to CRF by the release of cyclic AMP (cAMP) (43, 45) and adenylate cyclase (62), and by POMC-like peptide activity (69, 133); however, significantly larger doses of CRF are usually necessary to elicit a response by this cell type than by anterior lobe corticotropic cells (133).

Because of the similarities between oCRF, r/hCRF, sauvagine, and urotensin (83, 132, 133), the respective ability of these peptides to release ACTH has been extensively investigated. These comparative studies have indicated that oCRF, r/hCRF, sauvagine, and urotensin exhibit statistically equivalent potencies on the rat corticotrophs (96).

LONG-TERM ADMINISTRATION   Exposure of cultured rat anterior pituitary cells to oCRF for 24 hr causes a marked decrease in intracellular ACTH levels, but cellular ACTH content is virtually replenished after 8 days of CRF treatment (133). ACTH secretion rates remain elevated during this time; these results indicate that CRF increases the total (cellular plus medium) ACTH content of the cultures, and suggest that CRF can elevate the rate of ACTH synthesis (133). In addition, the finding that long-term treatment with oCRF increases POMC mRNA levels both in vitro (128) and in vivo (9) supports the hypothesis that CRF may regulate the expression of the gene coding for POMC.

Prolonged exposure to a secretagogue had been demonstrated to result in some degree of desensitization in many endocrine systems examined. Thus it was of interest to investigate the effects of long-term administration of CRF. Prior exposure of pituitary cells to CRF results in partial desensitization to CRF itself (93, 122), but not to forskolin (93), vasopressin, or 8-BrcAMP (122). This observation suggests that there is no defect in the cAMP-mediated steps leading to ACTH release from the corticotrophs (93, 122). Several investigators have proposed that the decreased responsiveness to CRF during prolonged exposure to the peptide may be due to a temporary, reversible inability of CRF to stimulate cAMP production. In contrast to the effect of long-term administration of CRF, CRF delivered in a pulsatile manner maintains pituitary sensitivity (122), as is true in the case of the hypothalamic peptide GnRH (121).

Interaction Between CRF and Other Secretagogues

A variety of studies have indicated that the action of CRF on ACTH release could be modulated by glucocorticoids, catecholamines, neurohypophysial peptides, and other substances (2, 23, 42–44, 47, 52, 133, 141).

The stimulatory action of CRF on the corticotrophs in vitro is inhibited by glucocorticoids. This effect appears to be near maximum if cells are pre-incubated with dexamethasone for 4 hr, but is only partial if dexamethasone is added at the same time as oCRF (133). Increasing doses of steroids shift the dose-response curves to CRF to the right and reduce maximum stimulated ACTH release (133). This steroid-induced inhibition is noncompetitive in that the plateau ACTH response to CRF is reduced by pretreatment with dexamethasone (133). It should be noted that in vitro, CRF can still elicit some ACTH secretion even at maximally effective concentrations of glucocorticoids (133); this observation correlates with in vivo studies showing that stress [which presumably induces the release of endogenous CRF (92)] is capable of increasing plasma ACTH levels even in the presence of high circulating corticosterone levels (5).

The ability of arginine-vasopressin (AVP) and oxytocin (OT), which are themselves weak ACTH secretagogues, to potentiate the effect of CRF at the pituitary level has been observed by a number of investigators (2, 42, 43, 47, 133). AVP and OT each exhibit effect additivity with CRF, as evidenced by the further elevation of ACTH secretion at plateau concentrations of CRF following coaddition of AVP or OT. This additivity is observed at concentrations of AVP and OT that are in the range of those found in portal blood (53, 148), thus it is quite possible that the interaction between AVP or OT and CRF may play a physiological role. The exact mechanisms involved in this potentiation are not completely understood at the present time, but it may be relevant that this synergism is accompanied by parallel changes in intracellular cyclic AMP levels (43).

The catecholamines, epinephrine and norepinephrine, also show an effect additivity with CRF (44, 106, 133). In the case of epinephrine, this interaction takes place at concentrations of catecholamines reached in portal blood during stress (37) and may represent a physiologic mechanism of ACTH regulation. Finally, angiotensin II, a very weak ACTH secretagogue (99, 126), also modestly enhances the ACTH response to CRF (99).

Somatostatin (SS) is present in rat hypophysial portal blood in significant concentrations (13). This fact led to the investigation of a possible effect of interaction between SS and CRF on ACTH secretion. Indeed, Richardson has observed that SS significantly inhibits CRF-induced ACTH release from mouse pituitary tumor cells (94). The doses necessary to achieve this inhibition, however, are higher than those reported to be present in portal blood.

In conclusion, both ovine and rat/human CRF represent potent specific stimulators of ACTH secretion by anterior pituitary cells. This action is inhibited by glucocorticoids and high doses of SS, and is potentiated by a variety of secretagogues such as neurohypophysial peptides and catecholamines.

ACTIVITY OF CRF IN VIVO

Profile of ACTH Release in Response to Exogenous CRF Administration

ACUTE ADMINISTRATION   Studies carried out in our laboratory have indicated that blockade of endogenous CRF activity by immunoneutralization with anti-CRF serum (97, 102) or CRF antagonists (108), as well as by hypothalamic lesions that destroy CRF-containing neurons (8), significantly lowers baseline ACTH secretion in adrenalectomized rats, and inhibits stress-induced ACTH release in intact animals. These results, which have been confirmed by other investigators (14, 67), strongly suggest that CRF plays a physiologic role in regulating ACTH secretion. The availability of synthetic CRF has allowed extensive investigation of the biological activity of this peptide. The animal model used to study CRF-induced ACTH and POMC-related peptides secretion in vivo have included nonanesthetized rats (95), sheep (21, 58), and monkeys (54, 59a, 115a) bearing indwelling venous catheters, pharmacologically blocked rats (95), and rats with hypothalamic deafferentiations (95). In all these preparations, as well as in awake human subjects (70, 77, 81, 114, 116, 117), the intravenous (iv) administration of oCRF elicits dose-related increases in plasma levels of ACTH and POMC-related peptides. These increases occur within 1–2 min of oCRF injection, and the duration of the response is proportional to the dose of CRF administered (81; C. Rivier & W. Vale, unpublished). In the rat, oCRF and r/hCRF are equipotent stimulators of ACTH secretion, and do not appear to have statistically different durations of action (C. Rivier & W. Vale, unpublished). By contrast, in man and primates oCRF exhibits an extended duration of action (79b) and induces a biphasic response (81), which is not observed following the administration of r/hCRF (116). These marked differences between the time-course of action of these two peptides are probably due to the long half-life and low MRC of oCRF as compared to r/hCRF (81).

The ability of oCRF to act on the sympathetic nervous system and metabolism depends on its route of administration (7, 29). In rats and sheep the ACTH releasing effect of oCRF is comparable whether it is injected in the jugular vein or in the lateral ventricle of the brain (21, 106); in the rat, the dose-related elevations of plasma ACTH levels measured after peripheral or central administration of oCRF are similar in magnitude (106). Although the pituitary responsiveness to GRF diminishes with age (119), CRF activates the pituitary-adrenal axis during gestation (39, 143) in neonate rats (138) and in adult rats of various ages (C. Rivier, unpublished).

In addition to the extensive characterization of the profile of ACTH and corticosteroid responses to oCRF or r/hCRF administration that has been carried out in normal men (see above), the responses of patients with pathological disorders such as Cushing's, Addison's, or Nelson's disease have also been studied. Several investigators have reported that pituitary adenomas associated with Cushing's disease are responsive to oCRF, but there appear to be marked variations in the magnitude of such responses (70, 78, 85, 118). Similarly, patients with Nelson's or Addison's syndrome also respond to oCRF with increases in plasma ACTH levels (78, 114, 118).

LONG-TERM ADMINISTRATION   In intact rats the ability of the pituitary to respond to some prolonged stresses becomes blunted with time (113; C. Rivier & W. Vale, unpublished), and a similar desensitization is also observed during the long-term administration of oCRF. In the intact rat previous exposure to CRF causes a blunting of the ACTH response when CRF is again injected 0.5–6.0 hr later, but this blunting is significantly less pronounced in adrenalectomized animals (100). These results indicate that part, but not all, of the diminished ability of CRF to repeatedly stimulate ACTH release is due to glucocorticoid feedback (100). Similarly, iv infusion of oCRF into intact rats over a 24-hr or a 7-day period is accompanied by a peak of ACTH secretion, followed by a decrease to lower values (104). This pattern is similar to that observed in intact rats exposed to long-lasting stress (113). Such results suggest that in the rat continuous stimulation of the pituitary-adrenal axis by peripherally administered CRF causes some degree of desensitization of the pituitary-adrenal axis, but is still accompanied by persistent elevations of the circulating levels of both ACTH and corticosteroids. By contrast, the continuous infusion of oCRF into man is accompanied by a significant desensitization of the pituitary (115b). Whether or not this represents a species difference in the modulating effect of circulating corticosteroids on pituitary responsiveness to CRF remains open to question.

Interaction Between CRF and Other Secretagogues

In agreement with in vitro results, in vivo experiments indicate that glucocorticoids, neurohypophysial peptides, and catecholamines modulate the activity of CRF in both laboratory animals and humans. Pretreatment with dexamethasone or corticosterone markedly inhibits CRF-induced ACTH release (95), while the addition of vasopressin, oxytocin, or catecholamines potentiates it (16, 68, 101, 105). Studies of the interaction of CRF and AVP in the rat have indicated that while AVP is a potent releasor of ACTH in the nonanesthetized rats, it elicits a significantly lower maximum ACTH response in pharmacologically blocked animals and in rats whose endogenous CRF has been immunoneutralized (101). These results suggest that at least part of the AVP-induced ACTH secretion observed in nonanesthetized animals may be due to a potentiation of endogenous CRF by exogenously administered AVP. Similarly, the ACTH releasing activity of oxytocin (105), catecholamines (105), and angiotensin II (99) is markedly decreased in the presence of anti-CRF serum, which also supports the hypothesis that these factors interact with endogenous CRF to stimulate corticotrophs.

Neuroanatomical Evidence of Multifactor Regulation: Pathways to the primary plexus of the portal capillaries

CRF   The parvocellular region of the paraventricular nucleus is the primary source of immunoreactive (ir) CRF input to the external zone of the median eminence in most species studied (60, 71, 73, 129). Approximately 2000 irCRF-stained neurons are found within the paraventricular nucleus, with the densest distribution in the medial parvocellular region. The trajectory of CRF to the median eminence (73, 82, 129) explains the difficulty encountered in blocking ACTH secretion following electrolytic lesions (8, 55) and knife cuts (49, 71). Both irCRF immunostaining and hypothalamic content are sensitive to glucocorticoid feedback: They show a decrease within 12–24 hr following bilateral adrenalectomy and a gradual return to preadrenalectomy levels within 5–7 days (127). Many CRF-stained perikarya also costain for a variety of other peptides, including AVP (111, 130), OT (129), dynorphin (112), and enkephalin (51). The pattern of CRF immunostaining throughout the central nervous system is the subject of several excellent studies (73, 129, 149) and is beyond the scope of this review.

AVP AND OT   A specialized AVP neurosecretory system that projects to the external zone of the median eminence has been identified by immunostaining and lesion methods (142, 149). AVP-positive perikarya found in the anterior and medial periventricular nucleus have been labeled following injection of tracers into the median eminence (137). These cells are smaller than the so-called magnocellular AVP-positive neurons found in other portions of the paraventricular nucleus and in the supraoptic and suprachiasmatic nuclei (11, 142). Terminals and fibers within this pathway are characterized by secretory vesicles of smaller diameter than those found in magnocellular fibers (11, 142). Bilateral electrolytic lesions of the paraventricular, but not the suprachiasmatic, nuclei cause disappearance of median eminence AVP-positive fibers (53). Immunostaining of median eminence AVP is initially decreased within 12–24 hr of bilateral adrenalectomy, and then increases above basal levels within a week (149). These changes and patterns of afferent input suggest that parvo- and magnocellular AVP pathways may be differentially regulated. Immunohistochemical staining has revealed few OT-positive fibers in the external zone of the median eminence (137, 142). Colocalization of irCRF and irOT within secretory granules of median eminence fibers has been reported (22, 129); however, it appears that these fibers project to the posterior lobe, not to the external zone of the median eminence.

Secretion of CRF and Other Putative ACTH Regulatory Peptides into the Hypophysial Portal Circulation

Stimuli that elicit adenohypophysial secretion of ACTH must be encoded within the central nervous system, processed, and then transformed into hypophysiotropic signals recognized by corticotropes. Numerous in vitro and in vivo studies have identified a constellation of putative ACTH regulatory factors, including CRF (46, 95, 133), AVP (2, 33, 46, 47), OT (2, 42, 63), angiotensin II (99, 123, 126), and epinephrine (37, 56, 89). The presence of irCRF (38, 40, 89, 92), irAVP (38, 53, 89, 148), irOT (35, 53, 89), and epinephrine (37, 56, 89) has been confirmed in the hypophysial portal plasma of the rat at concentrations that exceed those found in the systemic circulation and that are within a range capable of directly stimulating ACTH secretion. Hypophysial portal irCRF appears to be derived from perikarya within the paraventricular nuclei, as demonstrated immunohistochemically (73, 129). It has also been shown that bilateral stereotaxic microinjection of procaine hydrochloride reversably decreases portal irCRF levels below assay detection limits (87).

Several groups have attempted to ascertain which of these factors participate in the regulation of ACTH secretion in response to various stimulus paradigms by direct measurement of their secretion into the portal circulation. Despite the inherent limitations of these anesthetized, nonbasal-state animal models, useful information regarding regulatory processes may be inferred from these observations.

HEMODYNAMIC STIMULI   Hypovolemic, hypotensive (15% of estimated blood volume) hemorrhage is associated with increased hypophysial portal concentrations of irCRF, irAVP, irOT, and epinephrine (89, 92), as well as elevated systemic ACTH levels. The ACTH secretory response to hemorrhage is attenuated in a dose-dependent fashion by systemic pretreatment with antiserum to synthetic rat CRF (87, 89), and systemic pretreatment with the ganglionic blocking agent chlorisondamine or the vasopressin pressor antagonist [1-deaminopenicillame, 2-(O-methyl)tyrosine]-AVP attenuates the ACTH secretory response (87, 89) to hemorrhage. These observations suggest that regulation of hemorrhage-induced ACTH secretion is multifactorial in nature, and that CRF acts as the predominant dynamic regulatory agent. Observation of significant portal-to-systemic concentration gradients suggests a central origin for irCRF, irAVP, irOT, and epinephrine.

Pretreatment of rats with dexamethasone is without effect on basal secretion of ACTH or irCRF, but abolishes the secretory responses of both substances to hemorrhage (92). Thus it appears that dexamethasone feedback acts at the central level at a site or sites proximal to CRF-secreting cells. However, corticosterone at physiological stress levels attenuates both basal and hypotension-induced irCRF secretion (P. M. Plotsky, unpublished). An excellent review of glucocorticoid feedback recently appeared (61).

Systemic ACTH concentration is substantially reduced by atrial pulsation in the rat (87, 89); however, this is not paralleled by reduction of hypophysial portal irCRF, irOT, or epinephrine concentrations (89). A significant decline of portal irAVP accompanies the reduction of systemic ACTH in response to atrial pulsation. Under these conditions irAVP appears to act in a dynamic role, while irCRF acts in a permissive fashion.

INSULIN-INDUCED HYPOGLYCEMIA   Insulin-induced hypoglycemia is associated with activation of the adrenocortical axis and is frequently used as a provocative test of hypothalamic-pituitary function. The ACTH secretory response to insulin administration in the urethanized, fasted rat is abolished by prior treatment with antiserum to synthetic rat CRF, attenuated by pretreatment with a vasopressin pressor antagonist, and is only moderately reduced by ganglionic blockade (91). These observations suggest that CRF may be the primary driving force for ACTH secretion in response to hypoglycemia. However, measurement of hypophysial portal plasma concentrations of irCRF, irAVP, and irOT after insulin-induced hypoglycemia reveals a significant elevation of irAVP levels without a concomitant rise of irCRF or irOT levels (91). These observations led Plotsky et al (87, 91) to propose that CRF functions in a permissive role, maintaining sufficient gain in the system to allow expression of the weaker ACTH releasing activity of AVP, and possibly epinephrine, by effect additivity with the constant levels of CRF.

HYPOTHERMIA   Gibbs (36, 38) observed inhibition of ACTH secretion in hypothermic rats. Hypophysial portal plasma concentrations of irAVP and irOT, but not irCRF, are significantly decreased in hypothermic rats as compared to euthermic controls. The hypothermic rats are less sensitive to challenge with exogenous CRF than are euthermic animals, although a similar loss of sensitivity to CRF challenge is not apparent between hemipituitaries maintained at 37°C and 31°C in vitro. This observation led Gibbs to propose that the inhibition of ACTH secretion in hypothermic rats is mediated by reduced hypothalamic secretion of irAVP and irOT, which in turn decreases pituitary responsiveness to the constant portal irCRF concentration.

CENTRALLY MEDIATED ACTIONS OF CRF

CRF-Induced Secretion of Hypothalamic Factors

The administration of CRF to cultured anterior pituitary cells stimulates the secretion of ACTH and POMC-related peptides, but does not alter the levels of luteinizing hormone (LH), follicle stimulating hormone (FSH), growth hormone (GH), or prolactin (PRL) (133, 139). However, in vivo CRF has been shown to influence the release of pituitary hormones other than ACTH through interactions with various transmitters at the hypothalamic level. Indeed, accumulating evidence suggests that CRF may function as a central neurotransmitter/neuromodulator in addition to its established role as a hypophysiotropic factor (reviewed in 131, 135). This concept is supported by the central distribution of irCRF in the brain (71, 129), the presence of specific high-affinity receptors for CRF in the central nervous system (CNS) (17, 146), the electrophysiological actions of CRF (1, 24, 25, 120, 136), and the physiological effects of centrally administered CRF (6, 29, 108).

In the rat, exposure to stress results in increased plasma ACTH (reviewed in 5, 15) and PRL (27, 79a) levels, decreased secretion of GH (review in 72) and, if the stress is prolonged and severe, a lowering of LH release (4, 12). Since exposure to stress may be accompanied by changes in CRF secretion within the CNS (75), it is feasible that CRF may also mediate some stress-induced alteration of pituitary hormones other than POMC-related peptides. Consequently, several investigators have studied possible central effects of CRF on pituitary hormones other than ACTH using intracerebroventricular injection of synthetic CRF with subsequent measurement of hypophysial portal plasma concentrations of selected substances.

GONADOTROPIN RELEASING HORMONE (GnRH)   As mentioned above, the acute administration of oCRF to normal anterior pituitary cells in culture (133, 139) or peripherally to intact rats (105) does not significantly alter the secretion of LH, FSH, PRL, or GH. In contrast, the central injection of CRF results in a marked decrease in plasma LH, but not FSH (80, 105, 106), levels in gonadectomized rats. In steroid-primed (98), but in non-pretreated rats, CRF can also increase PRL release following administration into the lateral ventricle (C. Rivier & W. Vale, unpublished).

Study of the possible pathways mediating the effects of CRF on LH secretion has indicated that they do not appear to involve either opiate or catecholaminergic pathways, nor increased levels of circulating β-endorphin (106). P. Plotsky and W. Vale (unpublished) have observed that the intracerebroventricular infusion of oCRF administered on the morning of proestrus attenuates the afternoon LH and irGnRH surge. It is quite possible that this mechanism may account for CRF-induced inhibition of LH secretion. Furthermore, our finding that a CRF antagonist administered centrally can at least partially reverse stress-induced inhibition of LH release (107a) supports the hypothesis that an inhibitory effect of CRF on central release of GnRH may mediate the deleterious action of stress on reproductive functions.

SOMATOSTATIN (SS)   Secretion of growth hormone, which is regulated by hypothalamic growth hormone releasing factor (GRF) and SS, is attenuated in the rat following activation of the pituitary-adrenal axis (72). Since this activation is most probably accompanied by increased CRF secretion (92), our laboratory and others have examined the possibility of a central action of CRF on GH secretion. It was found that in the rat CRF acts centrally to inhibit the spontaneous pulses of GH release (80, 103). This effect could be mediated through at least two mechanisms: a CRF-induced stimulation of SS release, or a CRF-mediated inhibition of GRF secretion. The finding that CRF stimulates the release of irSS from cultured brain cells (84) suggests that such a mechanism may modulate the inhibitory action of CRF on GH secretion in vivo and mediate stress-induced inhibition of GH secretion. Indeed, immunoneutralization of endogenous SS has been shown to reverse the decrease in plasma GH levels of rats receiving CRF intracerebroventricularly (59b, 107b). This supports the hypothesis that hypothalamic SS mediates the inhibitory action of centrally administered CRF on GH secretion.

AVP AND OT   Injection of 1–100 pmol rCRF attenuates the secretion of both irAVP and irOT into the hypophysial portal plasma of urethane-anesthetized male rats (88). Administration of antiserum directed against rat CRF is without significant effect on the portal levels of either irAVP or irOT. This latter result is difficult to interpret since it is unknown whether or not the antiserum had diffusional access to target cells.

Autoregulation of CRF Secretion

The concept of autoregulation is applicable to a wide range of physiological systems and may be a component of the hypothalamic-pituitary-adrenal axis (34, 141). It may be mediated in one of two ways: (a) presynaptic inhibition of CRF release from hypothalamic nerve terminals within the external zone of the median eminence by CRF, or (b) inhibition of CRF release by a factor cosecreted from the same terminal. Indirect evidence favors the existence of CRF-mediated autofeedback (141). However, direct measurement of irCRF in the hypophysial portal plasma following intracerebroventricular injection of oCRF (100 pmol) does not support these observations (87, 88). Ovine CRF retains full biological activity in the rat (P. M. Plotsky, unpublished observation), but does not exhibit cross-reactivity with the antiserum to rCRF used for radioimmunoassay. Thus CRF does not appear to mediate autoregulation of its own secretion in time periods of < 120 min. Neither longer time periods nor effects on CRF synthesis have been examined at this time.

Electrophysiological Actions of CRF

One important criterion for identification of a substance as a putative neurotransmitter involves demonstration of an electrophysiological effect following its application. The electrical activity may be measured in the form of EEG activity, single unit firing rate in the anesthetized or the awake preparation, or intra- and extracellular recording from cell-slice preparations. All of these methods have been applied to the investigation of CRF. Ehlers et al (25) observed EEG activation in the hippocampus (increased 6–8 Hz activity) and the cortex (desynchronization of < 15 Hz activity). Delayed effects include amygdaloid after-discharges that were associated with behavioral symptoms such as motionlessness (2 hr) and motor seizures (4–7 hr). Pressure ejection of CRF into the locus ceruleus, an area innervated by descending irCRF-containing fibers (129), and the parabrachial nucleus results in the activation of approximately 65% of the cells tested (136). No changes in unit activity are observed following CRF application in the region of cerebellar Purkinje cells.

Forebrain areas of the rat have been mapped by Eberly and colleagues for sensitivity to iontophoretically applied CRF (24). They found CRF-induced excitation of 50% of the cortical cells tested, and 59% of cells tested in the preoptic, anterior, and ventromedial regions of the hypothalamus. Intracellular recordings have been obtained from hippocampal and hypothalamic slice preparations. Hippocampal CA1 and CA3 pyramidal cells are depolarized by CRF (1). The reduction of after-hyperpolarizations in CA3 cells by CRF may be the result of decreased calcium-dependent potassium conductance (1). A predominantly inhibitory action of CRF upon unit activity is observed on parvocellular neurons of the paraventricular region of the hypothalamic slice (120). This action may be mediated via axon collaterals from paraventricular cells to magnocellular cells, and thus may provide the substrate for CRF-mediated attenuation of AVP/OT secretion into the portal circulation (88).

NEURAL CONTROL OF CRF SECRETION:
Neurotransmitter Effects

Unraveling the neurochemistry of pathways controlling hypothalamic secretion of CRF into the hypophysial portal circulation remains a formidable undertaking. Considerable effort has been expended in measuring the effects of lesions (8, 55), knife-cuts (49, 71), and pharmacological interventions on adenohypophysial ACTH secretion, from which hypothalamic secretion of CRF is then inferred (see Activity of CRF In Vivo). Such an approach is less than rigorous in the case of ACTH, the secretion of which appears to be regulated by multiple hypothalamic factors (38, 87, 99, 101, 106, 133). Unfortunately, earlier bioassay of CRF activity often did not discriminate between CRF and AVP, which yielded confounded results. Development of a sensitive radioimmunoassay for CRF has ameliorated this problem (134). This literature has been adequately reviewed by many investigators (5, 147). A concise summary of the relevant findings follows: (*a*) acetylcholine facilitates secretion of bioactive CRF from hypothalamic tissue in vitro through a mixed population of muscarinic and nicotinic receptors (10, 57); (*b*) serotonin may facilitate release of bioactive CRF from hypothalamic tissue by direct activation of these perikarya (10) or via activation of cholinergic pathways impinging upon them (57); (*c*) norepinephrine is generally thought to play an inhibitory role in regulation of bioactive CRF secretion via α-adrenergic mechanisms (3, 57); however, limited evidence has been advanced in support of a facilitatory role for norepinephrine (28, 140); general consensus suggests only a minor role of dopamine in regulation of CRF secretion (28, 140), and an inhibitory role for epinephrine (74, 110); thus the role of the catecholamines remains controversial; (*d*) γ-aminobutyric acid has been demonstrated to inhibit release of bioactive CRF from hypothalamic tissue in vitro, and this action is prevented following treatment with bicuculline (10, 57); (*e*) opiates such as morphine and β-endorphin inhibit ACTH secretion and are assumed to act via inhibition of hypothalamic CRF secretion (86).

Gibbs & Vale (41) report that blockade of serotonin reuptake into presynaptic terminals with fluoxetine (10 mg/kgBW, ip) was associated with large increases of irCRF and irAVP concentrations in the hypophysial portal plasma of pentobarbital-anesthetized rats. In a separate group of rats, it was found that fluoxetine treatment resulted in ten- and four-fold increases in systemic ACTH and AVP concentrations, respectively. P. M. Plotsky (unpublished) has infused neurotransmitters into the third ventricle of urethane-anesthetized rats. Preliminary results indicate that acetylcholine administration is associated with a 3.1-fold elevation of irCRF levels in the hypophysial portal plasma, while norepinephrine causes a decrease in nonstimulated portal irCRF concentration. β-endorphin was associated with significant reduction of portal irCRF levels from a mean preinjection concentration of 478 ± 44 pg/ml to less than 56 pg/ml. Alternatively, intracerebroventricular injection of naloxone, an opiate antagonist, evoked a 2.6-fold increase in mean portal irCRF concentration, which suggests that opiates may act as autoregulatory agents to limit CRF secretion.

Administration of AVP (0.5–100.0 pmol, icv), which has been postulated to facilitate CRF secretion (50), is found to attenuate secretion of irCRF into the hypophysial portal circulation in a dose-dependent fashion (90). Furthermore, irCRF levels are elevated 53% following administration of antiserum to AVP (2.0 μl, icv) and 30% following injection of the pressor antagonist [1-deaminopenicillamine,2-(O-methyl)tyrosine]-AVP (100 pmol, icv). It appears that endogenous AVP acts as a tonic inhibitory influence at the central level, while it acts to potentiate the ACTH releasing activity of CRF at the pituitary level.

CRF RECEPTORS

Specific, high-affinity receptors for CRF have been localized in the anterior and intermediate lobes of the rat pituitary gland (19, 65), the human anterior pituitary gland (20), and in the rat CNS (17, 146). Adenohypophysial receptors parallel the distribution of corticotrophs in the anterior lobe, whereas receptors in the intermediate lobe are distributed homogeneously. Radioreceptor assay of anterior pituitary homogenates yields an affinity constant of CRF for this receptor of approximately 10^{-9} M (19, 144). The CRF receptor appears to be coupled to the adenylate cyclase system (43, 45, 62).

Adrenalectomy is followed by a decrease in the number of CRF receptors within the anterior, but not intermediate, lobe of the pituitary gland (18, 146). Administration of glucocorticoids reverses this phenomenon (18, 144, 145). Down-regulation of adenohypophysial CRF receptors may occur after adrenalectomy; however, this remains controversial because of possible artifacts associated with occupancy of the receptors (145). Central nervous system CRF receptors appear to be unaffected by adrenalectomy (18, 146), but additional work will be required to confirm this observation for regional populations of receptors.

ACKNOWLEDGMENT

Work in the authors' laboratory was supported by NIH grants AM26741, HD13527, AM33093, and AA06420-02. Research conducted in part by the Clayton Foundation, California Division. Catherine Rivier is a Clayton Foundation Investigator; Paul Plotsky is a Mellon Foundation Assistant Professor. The authors thank Rebecca B. Hensley for her assistance in the preparation of the manuscript.

Literature Cited

1. Aldenhoff, J. B., Gruol, D. L., Rivier, J., Vale, W., Siggins, G. R. 1983. Corticotropin-releasing factor decreases post-burst hyperpolarizations and excites hippocampal pyramidal neurons *in vitro*. *Science* 221:875–77

2. Antoni, F. A., Holmes, M. C., Jones, M. T. 1983. Oxytocin as well as vasopressin potentiate ovine CRF *in vitro*. *Peptides* 4:411–15

3. Berkenbosch, F., Vermes, I., Binnekade, R., Tilders, F. J. H. 1981. α-Adrenergic stimulation induces an increase of the plasma levels of immunoreactive α-MSH, β-endorphin, ACTH and corticosterone. *Life Sci.* 29:2249–56

4. Blake, C. A. 1975. Effects of "stress" on pulsatile luteinizing hormone release in ovariectomized rats. *Proc. Soc. Exp. Biol. Med.* 148:813

5. Brodish, A. 1979. Control of ACTH secretion by corticotropin-releasing factor(s). *Vitam. Horm.* 37:111–53

6. Brown, M. R., Fisher, L. A. 1983. Central nervous system effects of corticotropin releasing factor in the dog. *Brain Res.* 280:75–79

7. Brown, M. R., Fisher, L. A., Spiess, J., Rivier, J., Rivier, C., et al. 1982. Comparison of the biologic actions of corticotropin-releasing factor and sauvagine. *Regul. Peptides* 4:107–14

8. Bruhn, T. O., Plotsky, P. M., Vale, W. W. 1984. Effect of paraventricular lesions on corticotropin-releasing factor-like immunoreactivity into the stalk-median eminence: Studies on the adrenocorticotropin response to ether stress and exogenous CRF. *Endocrinology* 114:57–62

9. Bruhn, T. O., Sutton, R. E., Rivier, C. L., Vale, W. W. 1984. Corticotropin-releasing factor regulates proopiomelanocortin messenger ribonucleic acid levels *in vivo*. *Neuroendocrinology* 39:170–75

10. Buckingham, J. C., Hodges, J. R. 1979. Hypothalamic receptors influencing secretion of corticotropin releasing hormone in the rat. *J. Physiol.* 290:421–31

11. Burlet, A., Chateau-Chapleur, M., Dreyfuss, F. 1982. The vasopressinergic infundibular fibers: collaterals from the hypothalamo-neurohypophseal tract? In *Neuroendocrinology of Vasopressin, Corticoliberin, and Opiomelanocortins*, ed. A. J. Baertschi, J. J. Dreifuss, pp. 95–105. New York: Academic

12. Charpenet, G., Tache, Y., Forest, M.

G., Haour, F., Saez, J. M., et al. 1981. Effects of chronic intermittent immobilization stress on rat testicular androgenic function. *Endocrinology* 109:1254

13. Chihara, K., Arimura, A., Schally, A. V. 1979. Immunoreactive somatostatin in rat hypophysial portal blood: effects of anesthetics. *Endocrinology* 104:1434–41

14. Conte-Devolx, B., Rey, M., Boudouresque, F., Giraud, P., Castanas, E., et al. 1983. Effect of 41-CRF antiserum on the secretion of ACTH, β-endorphin and α-MSH in the rat. *Peptides* 4:301–4

15. Cook, D. M., Kendall, J. W., Greer, M. A., Kramer, R. M. 1973. The effect of acute or chronic ether stress on plasma ACTH concentration in the rat. *Endocrinology* 93:1019

16. DeBold, C. R., Sheldon, W. R., DeCherney, G. S., Jackson, R. V., Alexander, A. N., et al. 1984. Arginine vasopressin potentiates adrenocorticotropin release induced by ovine corticotropin-releasing factor. *J. Clin. Invest.* 73:533–38

17. De Souza, E. B., Perrin, M. H., Insel, T. R., Rivier, J., Vale, W., *et al.* 1985. Corticotropin-releasing factor receptors are widely distributed within the rat central nervous system: an autoradiographic study. *J. Neurosci.* In press

18. De Souza, E. B., Perrin, M. H., Insel, T. R., Rivier, J., Vale, W., et al. 1985. Differential regulation of corticotropin-releasing factor receptors in anterior and intermediate lobes of pituitary and in brain following adrenalectomy in rats. *Neurosci. Lett.* 56:121–28

19. De Souza, E. B., Perrin, M. H., Rivier, J., Vale, W. W., Kuhar, M. J. 1984. Corticotropin-releasing factor receptors in rat pituitary gland: autoradiographic localization. *Brain Res.* 296:202–7

20. De Souza, E. B., Perrin, M. H., Whitehouse, P. J., Rivier, J., Vale, W. 1985. Corticotropin-releasing factor receptors in human pituitary gland: autoradiographic localization. *Neuroendocrinology* 40:419–22

21. Donald, R. A., Redekopp, C., Cameron, V., Nicolls, M. G., Bolton, J., et al. 1983. The hormonal actions of corticotropin releasing factor in sheep: Effect of intravenous and intracerebroventricular injection. *Endocrinology* 113:866–70

22. Dreyfuss, F., Burlet, A., Tonon, M. C., Vaudry, H. 1984. Comparative immunoelectron microscopic localization of corticotropin-releasing factor (CRF-

41) and oxytocin in the rat median eminence. *Neuroendocrinology* 39:284–87

23. Dupouy, J. P., Chatelain, A. 1983. *In vitro* effects of corticosterone, synthetic ovine corticotrophin releasing factor and arginine vasopressin on the release of adrenocorticotrophin by fetal rat pituitary glands. *J. Endocrinol.* 101:339–44

24. Eberly, L. B., Dudley, C. A., Moss, R. L. 1983. Iontophoretic mapping of corticotropin-releasing factor (CRF) sensitive neurons in the rat forebrain. *Peptides* 4:837–41

25. Ehlers, C. L., Henriksen, S. J., Wang, M., Rivier, J., Vale, W., et al. 1983. Corticotropin releasing factor produces increases in brain excitability and convulsive seizures in rats. *Brain Res.* 278:332–36

26. Esch, F., Ling, N., Bohlen, P., Baird, A., Benoit, R., et al. 1984. Isolation and characterization of the bovine hypothalamic corticotropin-releasing factor. *Biochem. Biophys. Res. Commun.* 122:899–905

27. Euker, J. S., Meites, J., Riegle, G. D. 1973. Effects of acute stress on serum LH and prolactin in intact, castrated and dexamethasone-treated rats. *Endocrinology* 96:85

28. Fehm, H. L., Voigt, K. H., Lang, R. E., Pfeiffer, E. F. 1980. Effects of neurotransmitters on the release of corticotropin releasing hormone (CRH) by rat hypothalamic tissue *in vitro*. *Exp. Brain Res.* 39:229–34

29. Fisher, L. A., Rivier, J., Rivier, C., Spiess, J., Vale, W., et al. 1982. Corticotropin-releasing factor (CRF): Central effects on mean arterial pressure and heart rate in rats. *Endocrinology* 110:2222–24

30. Fryer, J., Lederis, K., Rivier, J. 1983. Urotensin I, a CRF-like neuropeptide, stimulates ACTH release from the teleost pituitary. *Endocrinology* 113:2308–10

31. Fryer, J., Lederis, K., Rivier, J. 1984. Cortisol inhibits the ACTH-releasing activity of Urotensin I, CRF and sauvagine observed with superfused goldfish pituitary cells. *Peptides* 5:925–30

32. Furutani, Y., Morimoto, Y., Shibahara, S., Noda, M., Takahashi, H., et al. 1983. Cloning and sequence analysis of cDNA for ovine corticotropin-releasing factor precursor. *Nature* 301:537

33. Gann, D. S., Carlson, D. E. 1982. Role of AVP in the control of ACTH secretion *in vivo*. In *Neuroendocrinology of Vasopressin, Corticoliberin and Opiomelanocortins*, ed. A. J. Baertschi, J. J. Dreifuss, pp. 281–96. New York: Academic

34. Gann, D. S., Ward, D. G., Carlson, D. E. 1978. Neural control of ACTH: a homeostatic reflex. *Recent Prog. Horm. Res.* 34:357–400

35. Gibbs, D. M. 1984. High concentrations of oxytocin in hypophysial portal plasma. *Endocrinology* 114:1216

36. Gibbs, D. M. 1985. Inhibition of corticotropin release during hypothermia: the role of corticotropin-releasing factor, vasopressin, and oxytocin. *Endocrinology* 116:723–27

37. Gibbs, D. M. 1985. Hypothalamic epinephrine is released into portal blood during stress. *Brain Res.* 335:360–64

38. Gibbs, D. M. 1985. Measurement of hypothalamic corticotropin-releasing factors in hypophysial portal blood. *Fed. Proc.* 44:203–6

39. Gibbs, D. M., Stewart, R. D., Vale, W., Rivier, J., Yen, S. S. C. 1983. Synthetic corticotropin-releasing factor stimulates secretion of immunore-active β-endorphin/β-lipotropin and ACTH by human fetal pituitaries *in vitro*. *Life Sci.* 32:547–50

40. Gibbs, D. M., Vale, W. 1982. Presence of corticotropin releasing factor-like immunoreactivity in hypophysial portal blood. *Endocrinology* 111:1418–20

41. Gibbs, D. M., Vale, W. 1983. Effect of the serotonin reuptake inhibitor fluoxetine on corticotropin releasing factor and vasopressin secretion into hypophysial portal blood. *Brain Res.* 280:176

42. Gibbs, D. M., Vale, W., Rivier, J., Yen, S. S. C. 1984. Oxytocin potentiates the ACTH-releasing activity of CRF(41) but not vasopressin. *Life Sci.* 34:2245–49

43. Giguere, V., Labrie, F. 1982. Vasopressin potentiates cyclic AMP accumulation and ACTH release induced by corticotropin-releasing factor (CRF) in rat anterior pituitary cells in culture. *Endocrinology* 111:1752–54

44. Giguere, V., Labrie, F. 1983. Additive effects of epinephrine and corticotropin-releasing factor (CRF) on adrenocorticotropin release in rat anterior pituitary cells. *Biochem. Biophys. Res. Commun.* 110:456–62

45. Giguere, V., Labrie, F., Cote, J., Coy, D. H., Sueiras-Diaz, J., et al. 1982. Stimulation of cyclic AMP accumulation and corticotropin release by synthetic ovine corticotropin-releasing factor in rat anterior pituitary cells: Site of glucocorticoid action. *Proc. Natl. Acad. Sci. USA* 79:3466–69

46. Gillies, G., Puri, A., Hodgkinson, S., Lowry, P. J. 1984. Involvement of rat corticotrophin-releasing factor-41 related peptide and vasopressin in adrenocorti-

cotrophin-releasing activity from super-fused rat hypothalami *in vitro*. *J. Endocrinol.* 103:25–29

47. Gillies, G. E., Linton, E. A., Lowry, P. J. 1982. Corticotropin releasing activity of the new CRF is potentiated several times by vasopressin. *Nature* 299:355–57

48. Guillemin, R., Vargo, T., Rossier, J., Minick, S., Ling, N., et al. 1977. β-endorphin and adrenocorticotropin are secreted concomitantly by the pituitary gland. *Science* 197:1267–1369

49. Halasz, B., Slusher, M., Gorski, R. A. 1967. Adrenocorticotrophic hormone secretion in rats after partial or total deafferentation of the medial basal hypothalamus. *Neuroendocrinology*. 2:43–55

50. Hedge, G. A., Yates, M. B., Marcus, R., Yates, F. E. 1966. Site of action of vasopressin in causing corticotropin release. *Endocrinology* 79:328–40

51. Hokfelt, T., Fahrenkrug, J., Tatemoto, K., Mutt, V., Werner, S., et al. 1983. The PH1 (PH1-27)/corticotropin-releasing factor/enkephalin immunoreactive hypothalamic neuron: Possible morphological basis for integrated control of prolactin, corticotropin, and growth hormone secretion. *Proc. Natl. Acad. Sci. USA* 80:895–98

52. Hook, V. Y. H., Heisler, S., Sabol, S. L., Axelrod, J. 1982. Corticotropin releasing factor stimulates adrenocorticotropin and β-endorphin release from AtT-20 mouse pituitary tumor cells. *Biochem. Biophys. Res. Commun.* 106:1364–71

53. Horn, A. M., Robinson, I. C. A. F., Fink, G. 1985. Oxytocin and vasopressin in rat hypophysial portal blood: experimental studies in normal and Brattleboro rats. *J. Endocrinol.* 104:211–24

54. Insel, T. R., Aloi, J. A., Goldstein, D., Wood, J. H., Jimerson, D. C. 1984. Plasma cortisol and catecholamine responses to intracerebroventricular administration of CRF to rhesus monkeys. *Life Sci.* 34:1873–78

55. Ixart, G., Alonso, G., Szafarczyka, A., Malaval, F., Nouguier-Soule, J., Assenmacher, I. 1982. Adrenocorticotropic regulations after bilateral lesions of the paraventricular or supraoptic nuclei and in Brattleboro rats. *Neuroendocrinology* 35:270–76

56. Johnston, C. A., Gibbs, D. M., Negro-Vilar, A. 1983. High concentrations of epinephrine derived from a central source and of 5-hydroxyindole 3-acetic acid in hypophysial portal plasma. *Endocrinology* 113:819–21

57. Jones, M. T., Hillhouse, E. W. 1977. Neurotransmitters regulation of corticotropin-release factor *in vitro*. In *ACTH and Related Peptides: Structure, Regulation and Action*, ed. D. T. Krieger, W. F. Ganong, pp. 536–60. New York: NY Acad. Sci.

58. Kalin, N. H., Gonder, J. C., Shelton, S. E. 1983. Effects of synthetic ovine CRF on ACTH, cortisol and blood pressure in sheep. *Peptides* 4:221–23

59a. Kalin, N. H., Shelton, S. E., Kraemer, G. W., McKinney, W. T. 1983. Associated endocrine, physiological and behavioral changes in rhesus monkeys after intravenous corticotropin-releasing factor administration. *Peptides* 4:211–15

59b. Katakami, H., Arimura, A., Frohman, L. A. 1985. Involvement of hypothalamic somatostatin in the suppression of growth hormone secretion by central corticotropin-releasing factor in conscious male rats. *Neuroendocrinology* 41:390–93

60. Kawata, M., Hashimoto, K., Takhara, J., Sano, Y. 1983. Differences in the distributional pattern of CRF-, oxytocin-, and vasopressin-immunoreactive nerve fibers in the median eminence of the rat. *Cell Tissue Res.* 230:47

61. Keller-Wood, M. E., Dallman, M. F. 1984. Corticosteroid inhibition of ACTH secretion. *Endocrine Rev.* 5:1–24

62. Labrie, F., Gagne, B., Lefevre, G., Meunier, H. 1983. CRF stimulates adenylate cyclase activity in the intermediate lobe of the pituitary gland. *Mol. Cell. Endocrinol.* 30:347–51

63. Lang, R. E., Heil, J. W. E., Ganten, D., Hermann, K., Unger, T., et al. 1983. Oxytocin unlike vasopressin is a stress hormone in the rat. *Neuroendocrinology* 37:314–16

64. Lederis, K., McMaster, D., Ichikawa, T., MacCannell, K. L., Rivier, J. 1983. Isolation, analysis of structure, synthesis and biological actions of urotensin I neuropeptides. *Can. J. Biochem.* 61:602–14

65. Lerout, P., Pelletier, G. 1984. Radioautographic study of binding and internalization of corticotropin-releasing factor by rat anterior pituitary corticotrophs. *Endocrinology* 114:14

66. Ling, N., Esch, F., Bohlen, P., Baird, A., Guillemin, R. 1984. Isolation and characterization of caprine corticotropin-releasing factor. *Biochem. Biophys. Res. Commun.* 122:1218–24

67. Linton, E. A., Tilders, F. J. H., Hodgkinson, S., Berkenbosch, F., Vermes, I., et al. 1985. Stress-induced secretion of adrenocorticotropin in rats is inhibited by

NEUROENDOCRINE ROLE OF CRF   491

administration of antisera to ovine corticotropin-releasing factor and vasopressin. *Endocrinology* 116:966–70
68. Liu, J. H., Muse, K., Contreras, P., Gibbs, D., Vale, W., et al. 1983. Augmentation of ACTH-releasing activity of synthetic corticotropin releasing factor (CRF) by vasopressin in women. *J. Clin. Endocrinol. Metab.* 57:1087–89
69. Lutz-Bucher, B., Koch, B. 1983. Failure of vasopressin to potentiate the effect of synthetic CRF on ACTH output from intermediate pituitary. *Neuroendocrinology* 5:111–15
70. Lytras, N., Grossman, A., Perry, L., Tomlin, S., Wass, J. A. H., et al. 1984. Corticotropin-releasing factor: responses in normal subjects and patients with disorders of the hypothalamus and pituitary. *Clin. Endocrinol.* 20:71–84
71. Makara, G. B., Antoni, F. A., Stark, E., Karteszi, M. 1984. Hypothalamic organization of corticotropin releasing factor (CRF) producing structures. In *Neuroendocrine Perspectives*, ed. E. E. Muller, R. M. MacLeod, 4:71–119. New York: Elsevier
72. Martin, J. B. 1976. Brain regulation of growth hormone secretion. In *Frontiers in Neuroendocrinology*, L. Martini, W. F. Ganong, 4:129–68. New York: Raven
73. Merchenthaler, I., Vigh, S., Petrusz, P., Schally, A. V. 1983. The paraventricular-infundibular corticotropin-releasing factor (CRF) pathway as revealed by immunocytochemistry in long-term hypophysectomized or adrenalectomized rats. *Regul. Peptides* 5:295–306
74. Mezey, E., Kiss, J. Z., Skirboll, L. R., Goldstein, M., Axelrod, J. 1984. Increase of corticotropin-releasing factor staining in rat paraventricular nucleus neurones by depletion of hypothalamic adrenaline. *Nature* 310:140–41
75. Moldow, R. L., Fishman, A. T. 1982. Physiological changes in rat hypothalamic CRF: circadian, stress and steroid suppression. *Peptides* 3:837–40
76. Montecucchi, P. C., Anastasi, A., de Castiglione, R., Erspamer, V. 1980. Isolation and amino acid composition of sauvagine. *Int. J. Peptide Protein Res.* 16:191
77. Motomatsu, T., Takahashi, H., Ibayashi, H., Nobunaga, M. 1984. Human plasma proopiomelanocortin N-terminal peptide and adrenocorticotropin: circadian rhythm, dexamethasone suppression, and corticotropin-releasing hormone stimulation. *Endocrinology* 59:495–98
78. Nakahara, M., Shibasaki, T., Shizume, K., Kiyosawa, Y., Odagiri, E., et al.

1983. Corticotropin-releasing factor test in normal subjects and patients with hypothalamic-pituitary-adrenal disorders. *J. Clin. Endocrinol. Metab.* 57:963–68
79a. Neill, J. D. 1970. Effect of "stress" on serum prolactin and luteinizing hormone levels during the estrous cycle of the rat. *Endocrinology* 87:1192–97
79b. Nicholson, W. E., DeCherney, S., Jackson, R. V., DeBold, C. R., Uderman, H., et al. 1983. Plasma distribution, disappearance half-time, metabolic clearance rate, and degradation of synthetic ovine corticotropin-releasing factor in man. *J. Clin. Endocrinol. Metab.* 57:1263–69
80. Ono, N., Lumpkin, M. D., Samson, W. K., McDonald, J. K., McCann, S. M. 1984. Intrahypothalamic action of corticotrophin-releasing factor (CRF) to inhibit growth hormone and LH release in the rat. *Life Sci.* 35:1117–23
81. Orth, D. N., DeBold, C. R., DeCherney, G. S., Jackson, R. V., Sheldon, W. R., et al. 1985. Clinical studies with synthetic ovine corticotropin-releasing factor. *Fed. Proc.* 44:197–202
82. Palkovits, M. 1984. Neuropeptides in the hypothalamo-hypophyseal system: lateral retrochiasmatic area as a common gate for neuronal fibers towards the median eminence. *Peptides* 5:35–39
83. Pallai, P. V., Mabilia, M., Goodman, M., Vale, W., Rivier, J. 1983. Structural homology of corticotropin-releasing factor, sauvagine, and urotensin I: Circular dichroism and prediction studies. *Proc. Natl. Acad. Sci. USA* 30:6770–74
84. Peterfreund, R. A., Vale, W. W. 1983. Ovine corticotropin-releasing factor stimulates somatostatin secretion from cultured brain cells. *Endocrinology* 112:1275–78
85. Pieters, G. F. F. M., Hermus, A. R. M. M., Smals, A. G. H., Bartelink, A. K. M., Benraad, T. J., Kloppenborg, P. W. C. 1983. Responsiveness of the hypophyseal-adrenocortical axis to corticotropin-releasing factor in pituitary-dependent Cushing's disease. *J. Clin. Endocrinol.* 57:513–16
86. Pittman, Q. J., Hatton, J. D., Bloom, F. E. 1980. Morphine and opioid peptides reduce paraventricular neuronal activity: studies on the rat hypothalamic slice preparation. *Proc. Natl. Acad. Sci. USA* 77:5527–31
87. Plotsky, P. M. 1985. Hypophysiotropic regulation of adenohypophysial ACTH secretion. *Fed. Proc.* 44:207–13
88. Plotsky, P. M., Bruhn, T. O., Otto, S. 1985. Central modulation of im-

munoreactive arginine vasopressin and oxytocin secretion into the hypophysial-portal circulation by corticotropin-releasing factor. *Endocrinology* 116:1669–71

89. Plotsky, P. M., Bruhn, T. O., Vale, W. 1985. Evidence for multifactor regulation of the adrenocorticotropin secretory response to hemodynamic stimuli. *Endocrinology* 116:633–39

90. Plotsky, P. M., Bruhn, T. O., Vale, W. 1985. Central modulation of immunoreactive corticotropin-releasing factor secretion by arginine vasopressin. *Endocrinology* 115:1639–41

91. Plotsky, P. M., Bruhn, T. O., Vale, W. 1985. Hypophysiotropic regulation of ACTH secretion in response to insulin-induced hypoglycemia. *Endocrinology* 117:323–29

92. Plotsky, P. M., Vale, W. 1984. Hemorrhage-induced secretion of corticotropin-releasing factor-like immunoreactivity into the rat hypophysial portal circulation and its inhibition by glucocorticoids. *Endocrinology* 114:164–69

93. Reisine, T., Hoffman, A. 1983. Desensitization of corticotropin-releasing factor receptors. *Biochem. Biophys. Res. Commun.* 111:919–25

94. Richardson, U. I. 1983. ACTH secretion in mouse pituitary tumor cells in culture: inhibition of CRF-stimulated hormone release by somatostatin. *Life Sci.* 33:1981–88

95. Rivier, C., Brownstein, M., Spiess, J., Rivier, J., Vale, W. 1982. *In vivo* CRF-induced secretion of ACTH, β-endorphin and corticosterone. *Endocrinology* 110:272–78

96. Rivier, C., Rivier, J., Lederis, K., Vale, W. 1983. *In vitro* and *in vivo* ACTH-releasing activity of ovine CRF, sauvagine and urotensin I. *Regul. Peptides* 5:139–43

97. Rivier, C., Rivier, J., Vale, W. 1982. Inhibition of adrenocorticotropic hormone secretion in the rat by immunoneutralization of corticotropin-releasing factor (CRF). *Science* 218:377–79

98. Rivier, C., Vale, W. 1974. *In vivo* stimulation of prolactin secretion in the rat by thyrotropin releasing factor, related peptides and hypothalamic extracts. *Endocrinology* 95:978–83

99. Rivier, C., Vale, W. 1983. Effect of angiotensin II on ACTH release *in vivo:* Role of corticotropin-releasing factor (CRF). *Regul. Peptides* 7:253–58

100. Rivier, C., Vale, W. 1983. Influence of the frequency of ovine corticotropin-releasing factor (CRF) administration on ACTH and corticosterone secretion in the rat. *Endocrinology* 113:1422–26

101. Rivier, C., Vale, W. 1983. Interaction of corticotropin-releasing factor (CRF) and arginine vasopressin (AVP) on ACTH secretion *in vivo*. *Endocrinology* 113:939–42

102. Rivier, C., Vale, W. 1983. Modulation of stress-induced ACTH release by corticotropin-releasing factor, catecholamines and vasopressin. *Nature* 305:325–27

103. Rivier, C., Vale, W. 1984. Corticotropin-releasing factor (CRF) acts centrally to inhibit growth hormone secretion in the rat. *Endocrinology* 114:2409–11

104. Rivier, C., Vale, W. 1984. Effect of the long-term administration of CRF on the pituitary-adrenal and pituitary-gonadal axis in the male rat. *J. Clin. Invest.* 75:689–94

105. Rivier, C., Vale, W. 1984. Influence of corticotropin-releasing factor (CRF) on reproductive functions in the rat. *Endocrinology* 114:914–21

106. Rivier, C., Vale, W. 1985. Effects of CRF, neurohypophysial peptides and catecholamines on pituitary function. *Fed. Proc.* 44:189–95

107a. Rivier, C., Vale, W. 1985. Involvement of endogenous corticotropin-releasing factor in mediating stress-induced inhibition of LH release in the castrated rat. *Science* In press

107b. Rivier, C., Vale, W. 1985. Involvement of corticotropin-releasing factor (CRF) and somatostatin (SS) in stress-induced inhibition of GH secretion in the rat. *Endocrinology* 117:2478–82

108. Rivier, J., Rivier, C., Vale, W. 1984. Synthetic competitive antagonists of corticotropin releasing factor: effect on ACTH secretion in the rat. *Science* 224:889–91

109. Rivier, J., Spiess, J., Vale, W. 1983. Characterization of rat hypothalamic corticotropin-releasing factor. *Proc. Natl. Acad. Sci. USA* 80:4851–55

110. Roth, K. A., Katz, R. J., Sibel, M., Mefford, I. N., Barchas, J. D., et al. 1981. Central epinergic inhibition of corticosterone release in rat. *Life Sci.* 128:2389–94

111. Roth, K. A., Weber, E., Barchas, J. D. 1982. Immunoreactive corticotropin releasing factor (CRF) and vasopressin colocalized in a subpopulation of the immunoreactive vasopressin cells in the paraventricular nucleus of the hypothalamus. *Life Sci.* 31:1857–60

112. Roth, K. A., Weber, E., Barchas, J. D., Chang, D., Chang, J.-K. 1982. Immunoreactive dynorphin-(1–8) and corticotropin-releasing factor in a subpopulation of hypothalamic neurons. *Science* 219:189–91

113. Ruhmann-Wenbold, A., Nelson, D. H. 1977. Plasma ACTH in stressed and non-stressed adrenalectomized rats. *Ann. NY Acad. Sci.* 297:498

114. Schulte, H. M., Chrousos, G. P., Avgerinos, P., Oldfield, E. H., Gold, P. W., et al. 1984. The corticotropin-releasing hormone stimulation test: a possible aid in the evaluation of patients with adrenal insufficiency. *J. Clin. Endocrinol. Metab.* 58:1064–67

115a. Schulte, H. M., Chrousos, G. P., Gold, P. W., Oldfield, E. H., Phillips, J. M., et al. 1982. Metabolic clearance rate and plasma half-life of radioiodinated corticotropin-releasing factor in a primate. *J. Clin. Endocrinol.* 55:1023–25

115b. Schulte, H. M., Chrousos, G. P., Gold, P. W., Booth, J. D., Oldfield, E. H., et al. 1985. Continuous administration of synthetic ovine corticotropin-releasing factor in man. *J. Clin. Invest.* 75:1781–85

116. Schurmeyer, T. H., Avgerinos, P. C., Gold, P. W., Gallucci, W. T., Tomai, T. P. et al. 1984. Human corticotropin-releasing factor in man: pharmacokinetic properties and dose-response of plasma adrenocorticotropin and cortisol secretion. *Endocrinology* 59:2203–8

117. Sheldon, W. R., DeBold, C. R., Evans, W. S., DeCherney, G. S., Jackson, R. V., et al. 1985. Rapid sequential intravenous administration of four hypothalamic releasing hormones as a combined anterior pituitary function test in normal subjects. *J. Clin. Endocrinol. Metab.* 60:623

118. Shibasaki, T., Nakahara, M., Shizume, K., Kiyosawa, Y., Suda, T., et al. 1983. Pituitary adenomas that caused Cushing's disease or Nelson's syndrome are not responsive to ovine corticotropin-releasing factor *in vitro*. *J. Clin. Endocrinol. Metab.* 56:414–16

119. Shibasaki, T., Shizume, K., Nakahara, M., Masuda, A., Jibiki, K., et al. 1984. Age-related changes in plasma growth hormone response to growth hormone-releasing factor in man. *J. Clin. Endocrinol. Metab.* 58:212–14

120. Siggins, G. R., Gruol, D., Aldenhoff, J., Pittman, Q. 1985. Electrophysiological actions of corticotropin-releasing factor in the central nervous system. *Fed. Proc.* 44:237–42

121. Smith, M. A., Vale, W. W. 1981. Desensitization to gonadotropin-releasing hormone observed in superfused pituitary cells on cytodex beads. *Endocrinology* 108:752–59

122. Smith, M. A., Vale, W. W. 1985. Partial desensitization to corticotropin-releasing factor in superfused rat anterior pituitary cells. *Neuroendocrinology*. In press

123. Sobel, D., Vagnucci, A. 1982. Angiotensin II mediated ACTH release in rat pituitary cell culture. *Life Sci.* 30:1281–86

124. Spiess, J., Rivier, J., Rivier, C., Vale, W. 1981. Primary structure of corticotropin-releasing factor from ovine hypothalamus. *Proc. Natl. Acad. Sci. USA* 78:6517–21

125. Spiess, J., Rivier, J., Vale, W. 1983. Sequence analysis of rat hypothalamic corticotropin-releasing factor with the orthophthalaldehyde strategy. *Biochemistry* 22:4341–46

126. Spinedi, E., Negro-Vilar, A. 1984. Angiotensin II increases ACTH release in the absence of endogenous arginine vasopressin. *Life Sci.* 34:721–29

127. Stillman, M. A., Recht, L. D., Rosario, S. L., Seif, S. M., Robinson, A. G., et al. 1977. The effects of adrenalectomy and glucocorticoid replacement on vasopressin and vasopressin-neurophysin in the zona externa of the median eminence of rat. *Endocrinology* 101:42–49

128. Sutton, R., Birnberg, N., Evans, R., Rosenfield, M. G., Rivier, J., et al. 1985. Corticotropin releasing factor and other ACTH secretagogues increase proopiomelanocortin mRNA levels in cultured pituitary cells. *J. Biol. Chem.* In press

129. Swanson, L. W., Sawchenko, P. E., Rivier, J., Vale, W. W. 1983. Organization of ovine corticotropin-releasing factor immunoreactive cells and fibers in the rat brain: an immunohistochemical study. *Neuroendocrinology* 36:165–86

130. Tramu, G., Croix, C., Pillez, A. 1983. Ability of the CRF immunoreactive neurons of the paraventricular nucleus to produce a vasopressin-like material. *Neuroendocrinology* 37:467–69

131. Vale, W., Rivier, C., Brown, M. R., Spiess, J., Koob, G., et al. 1983. Chemical and biological characterization of corticotropin-releasing factor. *Recent Prog. Horm. Res.* 39:245–70

132. Vale, W., Spiess, J., Rivier, C., Rivier, J. 1981. Characterization of a 41 residue ovine hypothalamic peptide that stimulates the secretion of corticotropin and β-endorphin. *Science* 213:1394–97

133. Vale, W., Vaughan, J., Smith, M., Yamamoto, G., Rivier, J., et al. 1983. Effects of synthetic ovine CRF, glucocorticoids, catecholamines, neurophypophysial peptides and other substances on cultured corticotropic cells. *Endocrinology* 113:657–62

134. Vale, W., Vaughan, J., Yamamoto, G., Bruhn, T., Douglas, C., et al. 1983. Assay of corticotropin releasing factor. *Methods Enzymol.* 103:565–77

135. Vale, W. W., Rivier, C., Spiess, J., Brown, M., Rivier, J. 1983. Corticotropin releasing factor. In *Brain Peptides*, ed. D. Krieger, M. Brownstein, J. Martin, pp. 961–74. New York: Wiley

136. Valentino, R. J., Foote, S. L., Asten-Jones, G. 1983. Corticotropin-releasing factor activates noradrenergic neurons of the locus coeruleus. *Brain Res.* 270:363–67

137. Vandesande, F., Dierickx, K., DeMey, J. 1977. The origin of the vasopressinergic and oxytocinergic fibers of the external region of the median eminence of the rat hypophysis. *Cell Tissue Res.* 180:443–52

138. Walker, C-D., Perrin, M., Rivier, C. 1985. Maturation of the hypothalamic-pituitary-adrenal axis in the neonatal rat. *Endocrine Soc. Proc. 67th Ann. Meet.*, p. 18

139. Wehrenberg, W. B., Baird, A., Ying, L., Rivier, C., Ling, N. 1984. Multiple stimulation of the adenohypophysis by combinations of the hypothalamic releasing factors. *Endocrinology* 114:1995–2001

140. Weiner, R. I., Ganong, W. F. 1978. Role of brain monamines and histamine in regulation of anterior pituitary secretion. *Physiol. Rev.* 58:905–76

141. Widmaier, E. P., Dallman, M. F. 1984. The effects of corticotropin-releasing factor on adrenocorticotropin secretion from perifused pituitaries *in vitro*: rapid inhibition by glucocorticoids. *Endocrinology* 115:2368–74

142. Wiegand, S. J., Price, J. L. 1980. Cells of origin of the afferent fibers to the median eminence in the rat. *J. Comp. Neurol.* 192:1–9

143. Wintour, E. M., Bell, R. J., Fei, D. T., Southwell, C., Tregear, G. W., et al. 1984. Synthetic ovine corticotropin-releasing factor stimulates adrenocorticotropin release in the ovine fetus over the last fifth of gestation. *Neuroendocrinology* 38:86–87

144. Wynn, P. C., Aguilera, G., Morell, J., Catt, K. J. 1982. Properties and regulation of high-affinity pituitary receptors for corticotropin-releasing factor. *Biochem. Biophys. Res. Commun.* 110:602–8

145. Wynn, P. C., Harwood, J. P., Catt, K. J., Aguilera, G. 1985. Regulation of corticotropin-releasing factor (CRF) receptors in the rat pituitary gland: effects of adrenalectomy on CRF receptors and corticotroph responses. *Endocrinology* 116:1653–59

146. Wynn, P. C., Hauger, R. L., Holmes, M. C., Millan, M. A., Catt, K. J., et al. 1984. Brain and pituitary receptors for corticotropin releasing factor: localization and differential regulation after adrenalectomy. *Peptides* 5:1077–84

147. Yasuda, N., Greer, M. A., Aizawa, T. 1982. Corticotropin-releasing factor. *Endocrine Rev.* 3:123–40

148. Zimmerman, E. A., Carmel, P. W., Husain, M. K., Ferin, M., Tannenbaum, M., et al. 1973. Vasopressin and neurophysin: high concentrations in monkey hypophyseal portal blood. *Science* 182:925–27

149. Zimmerman, E. A., Stillman, M. A., Recht, L. D., Antunes, J. L., Carmel, P. W. 1977. Vasopressin and corticotropin-releasing factor: an axonal pathway to portal capillaries in the zona externa of the median eminence containing vasopressin and its interaction with adrenal corticoids. *Ann. NY Acad. Sci.* 297:405–17

Ann. Rev. Physiol. 1986. 48:495–513

MECHANISM OF ACTION OF GONADOTROPIN RELEASING HORMONE

P. Michael Conn, Daphne Staley, Cynthia Harris, William V. Andrews, William C. Gorospe, Craig A. McArdle, William R. Huckle, and James Hansen

Department of Pharmacology, University of Iowa College of Medicine, Iowa City, Iowa 52242

INTRODUCTION

Gonadotropin releasing hormone (GnRH) stimulates release of the pituitary gonadotropins. These hormones, luteinizing hormone (LH) and follicle stimulating hormone (FSH), regulate sperm and ovum maturation as well as steroidogenesis in the gonads. The mechanism by which GnRH evokes release of LH and FSH has attracted the attention of physiologists because clinical studies indicate that the releasing hormone can be utilized as a potent regulator of conception and of steroidogenesis (2, 21, 72). Accordingly, GnRH and its analogs have great potential for treatment of human disease and as contraceptives.

CHEMICAL FEATURES AND CONFIGURATION OF THE GnRH MOLECULE

While scientific interest has stimulated much of the activity in this field, a number of chemical features of the GnRH decapeptide have aided the productivity. The structure of GnRH is pyroGlu[1]His[2]Trp[3]Ser[4]Tyr[5]Gly[6]Leu[7]Arg[8]-Pro[9]Gly[10]amide. Accordingly, the molecule is small enough that it has been possible to synthesize thousands of active (agonistic and antagonistic) chemical analogs (4, 52). It has also been possible to subject the molecules to analysis by physical means in order to learn something of their structure (61). The

495

0066-4278/86/0315-0495$02.00

best evidence suggests that the biologically active releasing hormone analogs exist in a least-energy state in which the amino and carboxyl termini are in close proximity. We suspect, from structure-activity relations obtained with these analogs, that amino and carboxyl terminal amino acids are involved in formation of a region recognized by the receptor. The structure-activity relations also suggest that D-amino acid substitutions in the first three amino acids result in the production of pure antagonists. Such molecules bind to the receptor, but do not activate the effector system. Accordingly, it appears that the first three amino acids are involved in effector activation.

The remaining amino acids may well be present only for the convenience of the investigator! They allow preparation of radiolabeled (^{125}I-Tyr^5-GnRH) derivatives of the natural releasing hormone (and most of its analogs) without perturbation of the structure essential for binding by, and activation of, the receptor. Other useful information became available when it was noted that one preferred site for proteolytic attack is adjacent to the Gly^6 position (40). Accordingly, substitution of D-amino acids at this locus results in metabolically stable compounds. Dextrorotary Ala, Lys, (tert)butyl-Ser, and others have been used successfully at this site. The presence of D-amino acids in the sixth position also stabilizes a beta turn in the molecule and, when combined with the substitution of an ethylamide group for the Gly^{10}amide, results in a ten-fold enhancement in the affinity for the receptor. Accordingly, it has been possible to design antagonists, agonists, "superagonists," and inactive analogs. The ability to insert D-Lys^6 in place of Gly^6 (and thereby introduce a unique epsilon amino group without loss of activity) has allowed further derivatization, including the preparation of fluorescent derivatives, and derivatives that may be "fixed" for microscopic studies, or chemically altered for other purposes. Thus, the rapidity of the progress on the molecular mechanism of GnRH action is largely due to the character of the molecule itself. In contrast, similar studies of other hypothalamic releasing hormones are more difficult because the hormones are either so small that virtually any chemical modification leads to destruction of the biological activity (i.e. TRH, a tripeptide), or so large that they are difficult to use for chemical work (i.e. CRF, GHRF, each of which contain 40 or more amino acids).

RADIOLIGAND ASSAYS: Pituitary and Extrapituitary Binding Sites

Early studies directed toward understanding the nature of the interaction of GnRH with its receptor utilized tritiated (69) or radio-iodinated GnRH (77), and suffered from a number of problems of interpretion. First, the tritiated probes were relatively low in specific activity, and it was therefore not possible to get accurate measures of the number of receptors per cell (N) or of the binding affinity (K_a). Even the use of the ^{125}I-GnRH probe did not solve all of the problems since the molecule was still susceptible to proteolysis. Under the conditions of the assay, GnRH was degraded during the incubation period, and it was not possible to accurately set (or even determine in retrospect) the concentration of GnRH added at each point. Further, the degradation might be expected to occur to differing degrees at different concentrations, and so might result in curved Scatchard plots, giving the illusion of multiple receptor classes.

For these reasons, the observation by Marshall's group (12) that GnRH "superagonists," which were protected against degradation, could be radioiodinated (10) and utilized as radioligands for the GnRH receptor set several different laboratories to examining the GnRH receptor. Two general observations were made and rapidly confirmed in many laboratories (13). First, the number of GnRH receptors per pituitary cell was quite flexible in different endocrine states of the animals, but the K_a was constant (58). Second, the GnRH receptor was not a unique feature of the pituitary but could also be found in gonadal and placental tissue (51). This second observation correlates well with the observation of biologically significant actions of GnRH in the gonads (45, 46), and the presence of GnRH-like substances in the placenta (73). Because hypothalamic GnRH does not reach a sufficient concentration in the peripheral circulation to occupy the gonadal receptor, it has been speculated that there is a gonadal GnRH-like substance ("gonadocrinin"), which would explain both the presence of the receptor and its apparent coupling to a biological response system. Interest in this area has been diminished by the inability of workers to find this receptor in some mammals examined. Because extrapituitary receptors have been reviewed in detail in this series (47) they will not be treated further here.

The pituitary GnRH receptor has been shown to consist of a single class of binding site, one that is of high affinity and is saturable (11, 58, 59). The functional receptor is a plasma membrane protein (57). The relation between the affinity and concentration of GnRH needed to stimulate LH release in a half-maximal fashion suggests the presence of spare receptors in the system (15). Structure-binding relations can be predicted with some accuracy from structure-activity relations, allowing further for degradation and solubility. Except as noted above, it appears that the GnRH receptor is predominantly in the pituitary.

STRUCTURE OF THE GnRH RECEPTOR

GnRH (analog) binding assays have been available for five years; they have been useful for characterizing the relationship between GnRH receptor frequency and physiological states. Little information is available about the physical nature of the receptor, even though two laboratories have reported solubilization of this molecule (68, 80). A number of indirect methodologies have proved useful in studying the receptor. For example, Hazum's group (43) has used the technique of affinity labeling of the GnRH receptor (with a radioactive probe) followed by (denaturing and reducing) gel electrophoresis in order to determine the molecular weight of the component of the GnRH receptor molecule that binds the releasing hormone. In these studies a component was labeled with a molecular weight of approximately 60,000. A minor component of smaller molecular weight was also labeled. This component was believed to be a degradation product.

Our laboratory (35) has taken advantage of a newly appreciated technique, radiation inactivation (target size analysis), to measure the functional molecular weight of the GnRH receptor while it is still a component of the plasma membrane. This technique is based on the observation that an inverse relationship exists between the dose-dependent inactivation of a macromolecule by ionizing radiation and the size of that macromolecule. A purified fraction of rat pituitary membranes was frozen with liquid nitrogen and placed in aluminum trays. The trays, maintained at $-45°C$, were then irradiated with a 0.5 mA beam of 1.5 MeV electrons produced by a Van der Graaf electron generator. Following varying exposure times, the plates were removed and kept on dry ice until a radioligand assay could be performed using a metabolically stable superagonist. Numbers of receptors and binding affinity were determined by Scatchard analysis. We selected releasing hormone incubation concentrations above and below the K_d value so as to obtain the best possible line from which the slope and x intercept might be calculated. Five different tracer concentrations were used for each Scatchard plot.

As molecular weight standards, horse liver alcohol dehydrogenase (84,000), yeast alcohol dehydrogenase (160,000), pyruvate kinase (224,000), and E. coli beta-galactosidase (464,000) were also inactivated. These enzymes all have two or more subunits, but under the conditions described inactivate as the oligomeric structure and are therefore useful marker proteins. The muscarinic cholinergic receptor (80,000) was also used for calibrations. An arithmetic method was used for comparison of the inactivation of the standards to the GnRH receptor. This method provides a molecular weight of $136,346 \pm 8,120$ for this moiety. This estimate is approximately twice that obtained (60,000) by Hazum's group in reduced and denatured samples, and thus presents the possibility that the functional receptor consists of a high molecular weight complex in its native state. The radiation inactivation studies indicate that the GnRH receptor is either a single weight class of protein or several closely related weight classes, such as might occur due to protein glycosylation.

THE GnRH RECEPTOR IN DEVELOPMENT AND IN VARYING ENDOCRINE STATES

Since interaction of GnRH with its receptor was presumably a requisite for stimulation of gonadotropin release, an early question asked was whether changes in the N or K_a of the receptor for its ligands, and concomitant changes in sensitivity, accompanied physiological states in which LH or FSH was altered. Several states were examined in the rat (37, 39, 58, 71), including various times throughout the ovarian cycle (LH is released on the afternoon of proestrus), during lactation (LH is depressed), following castration (LH is elevated, a state that can be reversed by administration of steroids), and old age (LH is decreased). In all of these cases it was possible to measure changes in the numbers of GnRH receptors (per pituitary) without alterations in the binding affinity. In the case of the ovarian cycle, the peak of GnRH receptors precedes the LH surge by a few hours, which suggests that other factors are involved in promoting release. In other cases, the number of GnRH receptors was an accurate predictor of the relative circulating levels of LH. Since the changes were measured in purified membrane fractions or crude homogenates derived from pituitary tissue, it is not certain whether the changes in the GnRH receptor numbers reflect changes in frequency (receptors per cell) or changes in gonadotrope prevalence (gonadotropes per tissue mass).

MOLECULAR BIOLOGY OF THE GnRH-RECEPTOR: Mobility and Potential Interactions

Probably the most challenging area for the molecular physiologist has been understanding the molecular basis of GnRH action. Clearly, the interaction of GnRH with its receptor can be established as the first step in the series of events that leads to release of the gonadotropins. The first insights into this area came from use of fluorescent derivatives of GnRH analogs. These analogs were incubated with living pituitary cell cultures; the microscopic image was enhanced and amplified ("image intensified microscopy") to view the result (44). Initially, it was possible to view a diffuse pattern of labeling, which corresponded to interaction of the fluorescent analog with receptors distributed generally on the surface of the cell. Since (unlabeled) GnRH competed for binding (measured by fluorescence), and the fluorescent analog competed with radiolabeled GnRH analogs for binding, it was possible to conclude that the fluorescent image was allowing us to view the interaction with the receptors. The limited resolution of this technique, however, did not allow us to view *single* receptor-ligand interactions. Rather, each "spot" of fluorescence probably corresponds to 50–100 receptors.

At 37°C the pattern of diffuse labeling gave way to formation of discrete patches at 10–15 minutes. The patches were internalized. This immediately presented a question: Was the patching, capping, and internalization process needed for GnRH stimulated release, or was this simply associated with degradation (or some other process)? Three experiments were designed in order to determine the role of patching, capping, and internalization in the release process. First, release was examined under conditions in which internalization did not occur (20, 33). When releasing hormone was attached to an immobile support larger than the cell, it could be shown that release continued in a fashion that suggested that internalization was not necessary for release. It was possible to show that the covalent attachment of the GnRH analog to the support was sufficiently stable under the conditions of the incubation to rule out dissociated hormone as a stimulator of the cells. The attachment was also stable to detergents and soaps, proteases, and chaotropic agents. Second, blockade of patching and internalization of the GnRH receptor with vinblastin did not block LH release, which also suggests that these events were uncoupled. Third, it could be shown that internalized GnRH would not support continued gonadotropin release. To do so, cells were incubated in GnRH long enough to allow considerable internalization. Extracellular GnRH was then removed, and the ongoing release rapidly terminated. Accordingly, internalization is not required for LH release and, in fact, is not a sufficient condition to support it.

Support for the contention that internalization is associated with degradation comes from electron microscopic studies (49, 50). In such studies a metabolically stable gonadotropin releasing hormone agonist (e.g. D-Lys^6-GnRH) is coupled to electron opaque markers (e.g. colloidal gold and ferritin). This approach has the advantage of increasing the resolution of localization to a "circle of uncertainty" about 10–20 times smaller than that obtained by autoradiography. After an initial uniform distribution on the cell surface the derivatives were taken up individually, as well as in small clusters, in coated and uncoated membrane invaginations, and moved to the lysosomal compartment either directly or after passage through the Golgi apparatus. The results suggest that labeled GnRH or GnRH-receptor complex may be routed to two distinct intracellular compartments: the lysosome and the Golgi cisternae.

RECEPTOR-RECEPTOR INTERACTIONS AND EFFECTOR COUPLING

It is clear that the interaction of the releasing hormone with the plasma membrane receptor (59) is the primary event in the molecular mechanism of GnRH action. This interaction provokes a number of changes in the cell, including the formation of the patch. It was apparent from the studies described above that the formation of the patch was not involved in the mechanism of gonadotropin release; the resolution of the technique by which we observed the interaction of (fluorescent) GnRH analog with the receptor, however, was limited to 50–100 molecules. Formation of these relatively large scale aggregates, as noted above, can be inhibited by vinblastin, and therefore appears to involve contractile elements of the cytoskeleton. Since the interaction between the GnRH-receptor complex and the effector system likely did not involve interactions with the contractile element system (20, 70), we sought to examine the role of molecular interactions in the lateral plane of the plasma membrane. Such interactions might occur between small numbers of receptors, and was therefore termed "microaggregation," to distinguish it from patching and capping. We were aware at the time of descriptions in the clinical literature of autoimmune disorders in which the patient showed antibodies directed against receptors. In association with disorders such as Grave's disease, acanthosis nigricans, and others, receptors were present which bound receptors, sometimes producing activation of the response system (5). To us, this suggested that the ability to bring receptors together might be associated with the activation of the system.

Accordingly, we sought to develop molecular probes that could perturb the movement of the receptor molecule in the lateral plane of the plasma membrane. If microaggregation of the receptors (that is, the formation of receptor dimers, trimers, tetramers, and so on) is actually involved in the mechanism of GnRH action, then an antagonist might occupy the active site of the molecule and prevent microaggregation. To perturb this state, we designed an antagonist dimer (14), reasoning that such a molecule might compel microaggregates to form and therefore transform an antagonist into an agonist (34).

For this experiment we wanted a molecule with the following characteristics: (a) metabolic stability (i.e. a D-amino acid in the sixth position); (b) pure antagonist activity (i.e. no measurable agonist activity; antagonists are formed from placement of D-amino acid with hydrophobic character in the first through third positions); and (c) a single epsilon amino group in which substitutions could be made without altering the biological activity of the analog. The molecule selected was D-p-Glu^1-D-Phe^2-D-Trp^3-D-Lys^6-GnRH, which fulfilled all the criteria. The molecule was dimerized through the lysyl amino group with ethyleneglycol bis succinimydyl succinate (EGS, a bifunctional cross-linker). EGS is about 12 angstroms long and binds a lysyl amino at each terminus. Thus, the final product could be described as ANTAG—EGS—ANTAG; "ANTAG" indicates the antagonist described above. This "dimer" retained antagonist activity, which is not surprising since the cross-linker was scarcely longer than a couple of water molecules; a much greater distance would most likely be necessary to bridge the active sites on adjacent proteins (of the molecular weight expected for receptors) in the lateral plane of the plasma membrane. Presumably, the dimer was bound to the receptor through one of the ANT moieties, with the remainder of the molecule extending out into space. In order to bridge this distance we elected to use an antibody that cross-reacts with the antagonist, thus forming a complex:

Antibody $\Big\langle$ ANTAG——EGS——ANTAG

ANTAG——EGS——ANTAG.

This molecule behaved as an *agonist*. Interestingly, when the antibody was cleaved with pepsin and reduced, the (monofunctional) antibody reverted to antagonistic behavior. These experiments demonstrated that an antagonist could be converted to an agonist by conferring on it the ability to stimulate microaggregation. Thus, they suggest a role for microaggregation in the molecular mechanism of GnRH action. A mathematic model was constructed based on the assumption that the antibody conjugate bridged two receptors and, as a result, activated the effector and caused release of LH. This model accurately predicted the data (an unusual curve showing agonist activity then a reversion to antagonism at high concentration) within 5% over four-logarithms of antibody conjugate concentration (6).

In related studies (27), it was possible to demonstrate that the potency of a GnRH *agonist* could be enhanced by conferring on it the ability to bring receptors together. In other studies, it has been possible to demonstrate that other actions of the releasing hormone (desensitization, receptor up- and down-regulation) also can be stimulated by provoking microaggregation of the receptors (31, 75).

Recently, preliminary studies have been published using polycations (the GnRH receptor contains considerable negatively charged sialic acid). Such compounds stimulate LH release in a manner that requires (*a*) the presence of the positive charge, and (*b*) a minimum size of about 120 Å (30), which corresponds well to the size predicted for the separation of GnRH molecules on an antibody. It is attractive to speculate that the potency observed for this molecule is due to its ability to provoke microaggregation, or at least establish domains in the plasma membrane that are enriched in receptors, and thus are more likely to interact.

GnRH-EFFECTOR SYSTEM: Utility of Primary Cell Cultures

Much as the structure of GnRH facilitated the study of its receptor, so cell cultures of pituitaries have been helpful in elucidating the molecular mechanism that couples the receptor and the LH release process. Preparation of primary cultures is a relatively simple procedure (this is fortunate since to date no continuous culture that releases gonadotropins in response to GnRH has been reported). Pituitaries are removed and minced, treated with enzymes (collagenase and hyaluronidase) in order to break down intracellular connections, and then subjected to mechanical disruption. The clumps of cells (10–50 cells per clump) are collected by centrifugation. More harsh enzymatic treatment (trypsin or pancreatin), double dispersion, or more enthusiastic mechanical disruption of the tissue, results in dispersion of the tissue to single cells. Usually it is preferable to use clumps, since this procedure results in higher viability, however, if a nonspecific cellular phenomena is being studied and the cells must be purified, single cell dispersions are necessary.

Pituitary cultures offer a number of advantages: First, drugs that would be toxic in vivo, due to actions on other tissues, can be used in vitro. It is always wise, of course, to use independent tests of cell viability, such as release of soluble enzymes, ability to maintain normal cell function and morphology, and exclusion of trypan blue. In addition, radioactive substances can be incubated with cells at much higher specific activities than can be achieved in vivo. Second, the reproducibility of gonadotropin release is much higher in cell cultures than in pituitary tissue cultures. Typically, cell cultures are prepared from a large number of pituitaries and individual differences tend to be damped out. Third, studies can be conducted in purified cell preparations.

In addition, we note that pituitary cell cultures maintain many of the characteristics of the animal from which they were prepared. Pituitary cells obtained from female rats in estrus, for example, show a different LH release pattern than those from animals in proestrus. By controlling the contents of the cell culture medium it is possible to show actions of steroids on the cells following culture periods of 48 hr or more. For these reasons, pituitary cells in culture have been valuable for studies on the second messenger of GnRH.

Studies with hemipituitaries (7) initially implicated cyclic AMP as the second messenger for GnRH, although subsequent studies with cell cultures clearly indicated that cyclic AMP and gonadotropin release could be uncoupled (18). For example, neither dibutyryl cyclic AMP, methylisobutylxanthine (which inhibits the breakdown of cyclic AMP), cholera toxin, nor prostaglandin E_1 (both of which stimulate intra- and extracellular levels of cyclic AMP) either stimulate LH release or potentiate the ability of GnRH to do so. Likewise cyclic AMP does not markedly stimulate LH release, and treatment of cells with GnRH does not stimulate production of cyclic AMP nor enhance the occupancy of the regulatory subunit of the cyclic AMP–dependent protein kinase. It has also been possible to show that GnRH does not stimulate the activity of adenylate cyclase (79).

CALCIUM AS A SECOND MESSENGER FOR GnRH

Pituitary cell cultures have also been useful in studies of the possible role of Ca^{2+} as a second messenger for GnRH. In 1978 we developed criteria this ion would have to fulfill to be identified as a second messenger for GnRH (55). First, removal of Ca^{2+} should result in prompt extinction of LH release. Second, treatments that resulted in the elevation of intracellular Ca^{2+} should result in gonadotropin release, even in the absence of the releasing hormone. And third, it should be possible to measure movement of Ca^{2+} into an active site.

In the intervening years each of these criteria have been fulfilled. The sophistication with which such studies have been conducted has increased with advances in methodology. For example, the first studies using chemically pure releasing hormone showed an absolute dependence of LH release on extracellular Ca^{2+} (55, 56, 78). Inhibition of LH release by removal of Ca^{2+} was reversible (25). It could also be shown that the binding of GnRH to its receptor was not a Ca^{2+}-dependent step. The availability of specific Ca^{2+} ion channel blockers implicated the presence of such channels since these drugs also inhibited gonadotropin release (26). As the number of chemically different Ca^{2+} ion channel blockers increased it was possible to show that the pituitary channel appeared to differ in structure-activity relationships to that observed for muscle and nervous tissue. This finding suggests that the channel is different in secretory tissue (29). Similar relations have been observed for the pituitary gonadotrope and for another secretory cell (the chromaffin cell of the adrenal). In addition to demonstrating that extracellular Ca^{2+} was required to initiate or maintain gonadotropin release (1) and that removal of access to the extracellular Ca^{2+} pool resulted in prompt extinction of responses (1), it has been possible to show that buffering intracellular Ca^{2+} also inhibits the release mechanism (9). Inhibition by this means can be overcome by treating the cells so as to increase the concentration of intracellular Ca^{2+}.

The second criteria, that elevation of intracellular Ca^{2+} by whatever means should also provoke release of LH, has likewise been demonstrated by a number of different means. Ca^{2+} ionophores, which allow extracellular Ca^{2+} to move down its concentration gradient and enter cells, stimulate LH release in a Ca^{2+}-dependent fashion. Significantly, release occurs with the same efficacy and time course as that in response to GnRH, and appears to occur from the same pool (22, 28). Similarly, insertion of Ca^{2+} via Ca^{2+}-loaded lipid vesicles (liposomes) also stimulates the release of LH, while those loaded with Mg^{2+} or monovalent cations do not (28). Veratridine (or depolarizing concentrations of KCl) also stimulates LH release (14, 26). In the case of veratridine, it was possible to show that, as in neural tissue, this drug opened the Na^+ channel (a step inhibited by the drug tetrodotoxin), caused cell depolarization, and allowed Ca^{2+} to enter the cell through its own channel. Thus, LH release in response to veratridine and similar drugs requires both extracellular Na^+ and Ca^{2+} (26). In contrast, release of gonadotropin in response to GnRH requires only Ca^{2+}. It appears that occupancy of the GnRH receptor by the releasing hormone or depolarization of the gonadotrope by veratridine both allow Ca^{2+} to enter the cell by an ion-specific channel. Inhibition studies with Ca^{2+} channel inhibitors suggest that these channels may be identical. Thus, elevation of the intracellular Ca^{2+} concentrations by a large number of different agents provoke LH release.

The third criteria, demonstration of the movement of Ca^{2+} into an active site in response to GnRH has been the most difficult to show. Our early attempts, and those of other laboratories, to show the movement of Ca^{2+} in response to GnRH relied on the use of $^{45}Ca^{2+}$ (24). While it is possible to show Ca^{2+} flux in response to GnRH, the techniques require the use of preloading periods in the absence of Ca^{2+} or the use of La^{3+} wash protocols to diminish the amount of Ca^{2+} sticking nonspecifically to the outside of cells. These procedures subject the cells to conditions known to inhibit the release of LH. Recently, a number of Ca^{2+}-sensing molecules have been described that can be loaded into cells without being manually injected. Quin 2 is a fluorescent analog of the Ca^{2+} specific chelator, EGTA, and freely diffuses into cells as the uncharged acetoxymethyl ester (Quin 2/AM). Once inside, the action of nonspecific esterases produce free Quin 2, which is charged and impermeant. Such intracellularly trapped quin 2 can be used to measure intracellular Ca^{2+} levels. The addition of GnRH (but not the very low affinity analog, des^{1}GnRH, or an antagonist) produced an immediate (< 10 sec) increase in measurable intracellular Ca^{2+} (9). Accordingly, it has been possible to demonstrate intracellular movement of Ca^{2+} in response to GnRH.

CALMODULIN AS AN INTRACELLULAR RECEPTOR FOR CALCIUM MOBILIZED IN RESPONSE TO GnRH

It is clear that treatment of pituitaries results in a net increase in intracellular Ca^{2+}. Because the value obtained by Quin 2 analysis provides a mean increase for the entire cell population, changes that are compartmentalized or limited to a single cell type would be larger than estimated by this method. Thus it seems likely that the increase in intracellular Ca^{2+} would be sufficient to occupy calmodulin, the multifunctional protein that appears to mediate many of the intracellular actions of Ca^{2+} (8, 60).

In vivo administration of GnRH provokes a redistribution of calmodulin within the cell. Radioimmunoassayable calmodulin in the plasma membrane fraction increases rapidly (min) and in a dose-dependent manner, following administration of GnRH (17). Similar amounts disappear from the soluble fraction under the same conditions. It is an attractive possibility that this observation may reflect a translocation of the protein. Such a step would likely lead to altered regulation of enzymatic activities regulated by calmodulin. Such activities include those regulating the metabolism of cyclic nucleotides, lipids, and protein phosphorylation.

Recently, it has been possible to show that one site in the plasma membrane where calmodulin accumulates in response to GnRH is the GnRH-receptor patch described above (48). Such an observation suggests that a close association exists between GnRH, its receptor, the effector molecule (presumably a Ca^{2+} ion channel), and calmodulin. As noted above, the formation of the patch as such does not appear to be involved in the steps provoking LH release, but the intimate association between these moieties may have functional significance.

In addition, it is conceivable that such a complex may be associated with the mechanism governing extinction of the response system.

Supporting a role for calmodulin in the mechanism of action of GnRH action is the observation that drugs that inhibit calmodulin also inhibit GnRH-stimulated gonadotropin release in a similar potency order. These drugs include Pimozide, Penfluridol, trifluoperazine, and (relatively inactive) trifluoperazine sulfoxide (32). Most recently we have successfully synthesized naphthalene sulfonamide calmodulin inhibitors ("W compounds"), which also inhibit stimulation of LH release in the same potency series with which they inhibit calmodulin (16, 42).

POTENTIAL MODULATORY ROLE OF LIPIDS IN THE MECHANISM OF GnRH ACTION

Recently, an increased appreciation of lipids as informational molecules in biological systems has occurred (3, 66). Gonadotropin release in response to GnRH appears to be perturbed by, or to perturb the metabolism of, many lipids, including phosphatidylinositol and its metabolites, prostaglandins, HETE compounds, phosphatidic acid, arachidonic acid, and others (36, 54, 62, 63, 67). Even in the face of such demonstrations no specific role has yet been assigned to these agents in the molecular mechanism of GnRH action.

Interest in our own laboratory has revolved around diacylglycerols (DAGs). These compounds are metabolites of phoshatidylinositides, and have been implicated as activators of protein kinase C (the calcium/lipid-dependent kinase). Our interest in this area evolved from an observation made in 1984, that phorbol esters (PMA) stimulated LH release (in the absence of measurable desensitization) following short term exposure to GnRH (76). A similar treatment with the releasing hormone resulted in desensitization. Smith & Vale (62) made a similar observation following long term exposure of pituitary cells to phorbol esters; even when cells became refractory to phorbol esters (following 9 hr continuous exposure) they still remained responsive to GnRH. Observations from several groups (64, 65) suggested that the intracellular target for phorbol esters was protein kinase C (PKC). Other evidence indicated that phorbol esters binding to protein kinase C were competitive with diacylglycerols, which were synthesized endogenously and therefore were potential regulators of protein kinase C. In order to test the theory that DAGs might stimulate LH release by an action on protein kinase C we sought to synthesize DAGs that could enter living cells. The complete synthesis of these compounds has been described (19).

A series of diacylglycerols were synthesized with varying lengths and substituents in order to establish the structure-activity relationship between each with activation of protein kinase C and stimulation of pituitary luteinizing hormone release. This approach enabled us to distinguish between actions mediated by direct activation of protein kinase C and those due to other, presumably nonspecific, actions. sn-1,2 diacylglycerols were synthesized that contained fatty acids of 4–10 carbons; in some of these the 3' hydroxyl was replaced with a chlorohydryl or sulfhydryl moiety. Several diacylglycerols stimulated LH release in a saturable, time- and dose-dependent manner that was independent of extracellular calcium. Dioctanoylglycerol (diC$_8$) was the most effective of the diacylglycerols tested; 3' analogs lacking the hydroxyl were inactive. The diacylglycerols activated protein kinase C in vitro, whereas the 3' analogs did not. Accordingly, it was possible to show (19) a correlation between protein kinase C activation and gonadotropin release, even though it had not yet been possible to show that activation of protein kinase C is related to the physiological mechanism of GnRH action.

In order to examine the interaction of protein kinase C activation by lipids and calcium we sought to determine the combined interactions of these on LH release (41). At the same time, we hoped to identify the sites of action of protein kinase C activators with respect to the mechanism of calcium action in the gonadotrope (23, 24).

LH release from cultured pituitary cells was examined in response to GnRH, diC$_8$, and PMA (41). We found that diC$_8$ and PMA stimulate LH release with approximately 75% and 50% of the efficacy of GnRH, respectively. The time course of LH release for these secretagogues was qualitatively similar for concentrations that stimulated similar amounts of LH release (41). A nearly linear rate of release was observed for the first hour. Maximal release was measured at 3 hr.

In order to compare the release requirements for the three secretagogues, LH release was measured in the presence of either a GnRH receptor antagonist, a calcium ion channel inhibitor (D600), or a calmodulin inhibitor (Pimozide). These inhibitors were selected because the site of action of each has been characterized in this system, and each is among the most potent inhibitors known at each site. The GnRH antagonist, Ac[D-pC1-Phe[1,2]-D-Trp[3]-D-Lys[6]-D-Ala[10]]-GnRH, at 0.5 ng/ml was 50% effective at inhibiting GnRH stimulated LH release. In contrast, LH release in response to either diC$_8$ or PMA was not inhibited at any concentration of the GnRH receptor antagonist examined (range=0–1000 ng/ml).

In order to determine whether LH release in response to PKC activators requires either activation of calcium ion channels or calmodulin, agents that specifically block these actions were used. The calcium ion channel blocker D600 was an effective inhibitor of GnRH-stimulated LH release at the lowest concentration used (10^{-6} M). Inhibition was dose dependent, and was greater than 70% for 10^{-4} M D600. There was no significant change in the amount of LH released in the presence of D600 when cells were stimulated with either diC$_8$ (75 or 150 μM) or PMA (1, 3, or 10 ng/ml).

The effect of the calmodulin inhibitor Pimozide on cultured pituitary cells stimulated with GnRH (2 nM), diC_8 (75 or 150 μM), or PMA (1, 3, or 10 ng/ml) was also examined. Significant inhibition of LH release was observed when the cells were stimulated with GnRH; the concentration that inhibited 50% of the maximum response to GnRH for Pimozide was approximately 1 μM. Such inhibition was not observed with LH release in response to diC_8 and PMA.

It appeared from the studies above that LH release in response to PKC activators is not mediated by the GnRH receptor, and does not require activation of either the receptor-regulated calcium ion channel or calmodulin. In order to study the relationship between activation of LH release by calcium and by PKC activators, the ability of these secretagogues to synergize in their actions was examined. A dose dependent stimulation of LH release with the ionophore was observed. Concentrations of PMA and diC_8 that are minimally active in stimulating LH release showed substantially more than an additive effect when combined with the ionophore. Accordingly, activators of PKC appear to synergize with the calcium ionophore A23187.

Such studies provide evidence that activators of protein kinase C (PMA, diC_8) (19, 74, 76) stimulate LH release by a mechanism that is not inhibited by antagonists of GnRH (Ac[D-pC1-Phe^{1,2}-D-Trp^3-D-Lys^6-D-Ala^{10}]-GnRH), Ca^{2+} ion channels (D600), or calmodulin (Pimozide) at concentrations that inhibit LH release in response to the releasing hormone. While no action of the PKC activators at the receptor was expected because of their structural dissimilarity to GnRH, the GnRH receptor antagonist study was undertaken because some molecules, such as cyclic AMP, that appear dissimilar to GnRH activate the receptor by a poorly understood mechanism, which can be inhibited by GnRH antagonists. D600 and Pimozide were also not inhibitory to the actions of the PKC activators.

The data described above also demonstrate that PKC activators synergize with the actions of the Ca^{2+} ionophore, A23187. Despite the three hour incubations used in the present study, desensitization is not likely to be involved since gonadotrope cells take more than six hours to become markedly refractory to PMA (74), and even at that time remain fully responsive to stimuli that depend on Ca^{2+} mobilization to stimulate LH release (74). A similar lack of cross-desensitization has been noted in short-pulse desensitization studies (76). In addition, the three hour data presented could be qualitatively reproduced at a one hour time.

Previous studies have shown an absolute requirement for extracellular Ca^{2+} for GnRH stimulation or maintenance of LH release (1, 55). Indeed, the more current of these studies (1) shows that stimulated LH release has a minute-to-minute dependance on extracellular Ca^{2+} and access to that pool. More recently (9) it has been possible to show, using the fluorescent probe Quin 2, that Ca^{2+} flux following gonadotrope receptor activation is extremely rapid. These studies, taken with the observations that A23187, but not PKC activators, can stimulate LH release with the same efficacy as GnRH, support a primary role for Ca^{2+} in the mechanism of GnRH action.

In numerous systems PKC appears to be regulated by both Ca^{2+} and DAGs (66), although PKC activators do not appear to be able to cause Ca^{2+} mobilization (38). A recent study (59) also implicated DAGs as stimulators of prolactin release from a clonal line. It is notable that the concentrations of various DAGs needed to stimulate LH release compares to that required to maximally stimulate PKC. Thus, the lack of dependence on Ca^{2+} shown in the present work and suggested previously may reflect the ability of high levels of these lipids to synergize with small yet measurable concentrations of intracellular Ca^{2+} in the gonadotrope that has not been exposed to GnRH. Moreover, such synergy could allow low levels of Ca^{2+} to be functionally significant; this is especially important since the measured concentration of Ca^{2+} in GnRH cells is lower than would have been predicted from the relatively high concentration of ionophore A23187 needed to provoke release. The recent observation (24) that increases in intracellular Ca^{2+} at levels too low to provoke LH release effectively up-regulates the GnRH receptor, suggests the biological efficacy of such small increases.

In order to demonstrate a role for PKC in GnRH action it will be necessary to show that the releasing hormone activates the enzyme, that specific inhibition of the enzyme blocks GnRH action, and that enzymatic activation by any means leads to GnRH-like actions. While only the third of these criteria has been met (in two GnRH-dependent systems; 19, 53), the present data indicate a potential role for PKC since activators of the enzyme show synergism with drugs that elevate cellular Ca^{2+}. Accordingly, the possibility is presented that such lipids may serve an amplification role of the GnRH receptor–mediated Ca^{2+} signal.

ADDITIONAL ACTIONS OF CALCIUM IN MEDIATION OF OTHER ACTIONS OF GnRH

It is clear that Ca^{2+} fulfills the requirements of a second messenger molecule for GnRH stimulated gonadotropin release. The releasing hormone also regulates the frequency of its own receptor and the responsiveness of the cells to GnRH. Accordingly, it was of interest to determine whether Ca^{2+} was required for these events.

In the case of desensitization it was clear that Ca^{2+} was not required for its occurrence. It was possible to show (75) that desensitization occured normally in the absence of extracellular Ca^{2+}; under these conditions LH release and desensitization could also be uncoupled since the latter condition could be demonstrated in the absence of the former. In addition, significant LH release could be provoked in response to Ca^{2+} ionophore without measurable desensitization.

510   CONN ET AL

Likewise, GnRH receptor down-regulation (1–2 hr after exposure to GnRH or its agonists) occurred normally in the absence of extracellular Ca^{2+} or blockade of accessibility to this ion, and was not inhibited by inhibitors of protein synthesis (31). Down regulation was not measured in response to a GnRH antagonist.

In marked contrast, receptor up-regulation (4–8 hr after exposure to GnRH or its agonists) had an absolute requirement for extracellular Ca^{2+}, and was blocked by inhibitors of protein synthesis. Treatments (veratridine, A23187) that allow Ca^{2+} to enter the cells were effective even at concentrations that were too low to evoke LH release. Indeed, this observation suggests that Ca^{2+} may have different actions at high and low intracellular concentrations (31, 55).

SUMMARY

GnRH interacts with a plasma membrane receptor to provoke gonadotropin release, as well as regulate numbers of its own receptor and target cell responsiveness. Receptor numbers are altered in different physiological states of the animal. Microaggregation of the GnRH receptor mimics all known actions of the releasing hormone, and therefore is viewed as an early step in the molecular mechanism of hormone action. Internalized hormone is neither necessary nor sufficient for stimulation of known releasing hormone actions. Evidence summarized in the present work suggests that Ca^{2+} serves a role as a second messenger for GnRH-stimulated gonadotropin release, and that it may be involved in receptor up-regulation in response to the releasing hormone. In the former role, diacylglycerols by their action on protein kinase C, in a fashion independent of the Ca^{2+}-calmodulin system, may act as a signal amplifier.

ACKNOWLEDGMENT
Work from the authors' laboratory was supported by NIH HD 19899 (HD13220). We thank Ms. Connie Kunkel for her editorial assistance.

NOTE ADDED IN PROOF   Since submission of this manuscript we have demonstrated that GnRH stimulates production of endogenous diacylglycerols in pituitary cell cultures (81). This supports the contention that these compounds, acting as PKC regulators, may serve to amplify the GnRH-mediated Ca^{2+} signal.

Literature Cited

1. Bates, M. D., Conn, P. M. 1984. Calcium mobilization in the pituitary gonadotrope: Relative roles of intra- and extracellular sources. *Endocrinology* 115: 1380–85
2. Beling, C. G., Wentz, A. C. 1978. *The LH-Releasing Hormone.* New York: Masson. 542 pp.
3. Berridge, M. J. 1980. Receptors and calcium signalling. *Trends Pharmacol. Sci.* Nov:419–24
4. Bex, F., Corbin, A. 1982. Luteinizing hormone releasing hormone analogs as antihormones. In *Hormone Antagonists,* ed. M. K. Agarwal, pp. 609–22. Berlin, New York: de Gruyter

5. Blecher, M., Bar, R. 1981. *Receptors and Human Disease*. Baltimore: Williams and Wilkins

6. Blum, J. J., Conn, P. M. 1982. Gonadotropin releasing hormone stimulation of luteinizing hormone: A ligand-receptor-effect model for receptor mediated responses. *Proc. Natl. Acad. Sci. USA* 79:7307–11

7. Borgeat, P., Chavancy, G., Dupont, A., Labrie, F., Arimura, A., Schally, A. V. 1972. Stimulation of adenosine 3':5'-cyclic monophosphate accumulation in anterior pituitary gland in vitro by synthetic luteinizing hormone releasing hormone. *Proc. Natl. Acad. Sci. USA* 69: 2677–81

8. Cheung, W. Y. 1980. Calmodulin plays a pivotal role in cellular regulation. *Science* 207:19–27

9. Clapper, D., Conn, P. M. 1985. GnRH stimulation of pituitary gonadotrope cells produces an increase in intracellular calcium. *Biol. Reprod.* 32:269–78

10. Clayton, R. N. 1983. Preparation of radiolabeled neuroendocrine peptides. *Methods Enzymol.* 103:32–48

11. Clayton, R. N., Catt, K. J. 1981. Gonadotropin-releasing hormone receptors: Characterization, physiological regulation and relationship to reproductive function. *Endocrine Rev.* 2:186–209

12. Clayton, R. N., Shakespear, R. A., Duncan, J. A., Marshall, J. C. 1979. Radioiodinated nondegradable GnRH analogs: New probes for the investigation of pituitary GnRH receptors. *Endocrinology* 105:1369–76

13. Conn, P. M. 1982. Gonadotropin releasing hormone stimulation of pituitary gonadotropin release: A model system for receptor-mediated calcium dependent secretion. In *Cellular Regulation of Secretion and Release*, ed. P. M. Conn, pp. 460–87. New York: Academic

14. Conn, P. M. 1983. Use of specific ion channel activating and inhibiting drugs in neuroendocrine tissue. *Methods Enzymol.* 103:401–5

15. Conn, P. M. 1983. Ligand dimerization: A technique for assessing receptor-receptor interactions. *Methods Enzymol.* 103:49–58

16. Conn, P. M., Bates, M. D., Rogers, D. C., Seay, S. G., Smith W. A. 1984. GnRH-receptor-effector-response coupling in the pituitary gonadotrope: A Ca²⁺ mediated system. In *Role of Drugs and Electrolytes in Hormonogenesis*, ed. K. Fotherby, S. B. Pal, pp. 85–103. New York: de Gruyter

17. Conn, P. M., Chafouleas, J., Rogers, D., Means, A. R. 1981. Gonadotropin releasing hormone stimulates calmodulin redistribution in the rat pituitary. *Nature* 292:264–65

18. Conn, P. M., Dufau, M. L., Catt, K. J. 1979. GnRH-stimulated release of LH from rat pituicytes does not require production of cyclic AMP. *Endocrinology* 104:448–53

19. Conn, P. M., Ganong, B. R., Ebeling, J., Staley, D., Neidel, J., Bell, R. M. 1985. Diacylglycerols release LH: structure-activity relations and protein kinase C. *Biochem. Biophys. Res. Commun.* 126:532–39

20. Conn, P. M., Hazum, E. 1981. LH release and GnRH-receptor internalization: Independent actions of GnRH. *Endocrinology* 109:2040–45

21. Conn, P. M., Hsueh, A. J. W., Crowley, W. F. 1984. The gonadotropin releasing hormone: Molecular and cell biology, physiology, and clinical applications. *Fed. Proc.* 43:2351–61

22. Conn, P. M., Kilpatrick, D., Kirshner, N. 1980. Ionophoretic Ca²⁺ mobilization in rat gonadotropes and bovine adrenomedullary cells. *Cell Calcium*, 1:129–33

23. Conn, P. M., Marian, J., McMillian, M., Rogers, D. 1980. Evidence for calcium mediation of gonadotropin releasing hormone action in the pituitary. *Cell Calcium* 1:7–20

24. Conn, P. M., Marian, J., McMillian, M., Stern, J. E., Rogers, D. C., et al. 1981. Gonadotropin releasing hormone action in the pituitary: A three step mechanism. *Endocrine Rev.* 2:174–84

25. Conn, P. M., Rogers, D. C. 1979. Restoration of responsiveness of gonadotropin releasing hormone (GnRH) in calcium depleted rat pituitary cells. *Life Sci.* 24:2461–66

26. Conn, P. M., Rogers, D. C. 1980. Gonadotropin release from pituitary cultures following activation of endogenous ion channels. *Endocrinology* 107:2133–34

27. Conn, P. M., Rogers, D. C., McNeil, R. 1982. Potency enhancement of a GnRH agonist: GnRH-receptor microaggregation stimulates gonadotropin release. *Endocrinology* 111:335–37

28. Conn, P. M., Rogers, D. C., Sandhu, F. S. 1979. Alteration of intracellular calcium level stimulates gonadotropin release from cultured rat pituitary cells. *Endocrinology* 105:1122–27

29. Conn, P. M., Rogers, D. C., Seay, S. G. 1983. Structure-function relationships of calcium ion channel antagonists at the pituitary gonadotrope. *Endocrinology* 113:1592–95

30. Conn, P. M., Rogers, D. C., Seay, S. G., Staley, D. 1984. Activation of luteinizing hormone release from pituitary cells

by polycations. *Endocrinology* 115: 1913–17

31. Conn, P. M., Rogers, D. C., Seay, S. G. 1984. Biphasic regulation of the GnRH receptor by receptor microaggregation and intracellular calcium levels. *Mol. Pharmacol.* 25:51–55

32. Conn, P. M., Rogers, D. C., Sheffield, T. 1981. Inhibition of gonadotropin releasing hormone stimulated luteinizing hormone release by Pimozide: Evidence for a site of action after calcium mobilization. *Endocrinology* 109:1122–26

33. Conn, P. M., Smith, R. G., Rogers, D. C. 1981. Stimulation of pituitary gonadotropin release does not require internalization of gonadotropin releasing hormone. *J. Biol. Chem.* 256:1098–1100

34. Conn, P. M., Rogers, D. C., Stewart, J. M., Neidel, J., Sheffield, T. 1982. Conversion of a gonadotropin releasing hormone antagonist to an agonist: Implication for a receptor microaggregate as the functional unit for signal transduction. *Nature* 296:653–55

35. Conn, P. M., Venter, J. C. 1985. Radiation inactivation (target size analysis) of the gonadotropin releasing hormone receptor. *Endocrinology* 116:1324–26

36. Conn, P. M., Whorton, R., Lazar, J. 1980. An inhibitor of arachidonic acid metabolism stimulates luteinizing hormone (LH) release from cultured cells. *Prostaglandins* 19:873

37. Dalkin, A. C., Bourne, G. A., Pieper, D. R., Regiani, S., Marshall, J. C. 1981. Pituitary and gonadal GnRH receptors during sexual maturation in the rat. *Endocrinology* 108:1658–63

38. Di Virgilio, F., Lew, D. P., Pozzan, T. 1984. Protein kinase C activation of physiological processes in human neutrophils at vanishingly small cytosolic Ca^{2+} levels. *Nature* 310:691–93

39. Frager, M. S., Pieper, D. R., Tonetta, J. A., Marshall, J. C. 1981. Pituitary GnRH receptors: Effects of castration, steroid replacement, and the role of GnRH in modulating receptors in the rat. *J. Clin. Invest.* 67:615–21

40. Griffiths, E. C., Kelly, J. A. 1979. Mechanism of inactivation of hypothalamic regulatory hormones. *Mol. Cell. Endocrinol.* 14:317–23

41. Harris, C. E., Conn, P. M. 1984. Diacylglycerols and protein kinase C: potential amplifying mechanism for Ca^{2+}-mediated GnRH stimulated LH release. *Mol. Pharmacol.* 27:532–36

42. Hart, R., Bates, M. D., Cormier, M. J., Rosen, G. M., Conn, P. M. 1983. Synthesis and characterization of calmodulin antagonistic drugs. *Methods Enzymol.* 102:195–204

43. Hazum, E. 1981. Photoaffinity labelling of luteinizing hormone releasing hormone receptor of rat pituitary membrane preparations. *Endocrinology* 109:1281–83

44. Hazum, E., Cuatrecasas, P., Marian, J., Conn, P. M. 1980. Receptor-mediated internalization of fluorescent gonadotropin releasing hormone by pituitary gonadotropes. *Proc. Natl. Acad. Sci. USA* 77:6692–95

45. Hsueh, A., Erickson, G. 1979. Extrapituitary action of GnRH: direct inhibition of ovarian steroidogenesis. *Science* 204:854–55

46. Hsueh, A., Erickson, G. 1979. Extrapituitary inhibition of testicular function by LHRH. *Nature* 281:66–67

47. Hsueh, A. J. W., Jones, P. B. C. 1983. Gonadotropin releasing hormone: extrapituitary actions and paracrine control mechanisms. *Ann. Rev. Physiol.* 45:83–94

48. Jennes, L., Bronson, D., Stumpf, W. E., Conn, P. M. 1985. Evidence for an association between calmodulin and membrane patches containing GnRH-receptor in cultured pituitary gonadotropes. *Cell Tissue Res.* 239:311–15

49. Jennes, L., Stumpf, W. E., Conn, P. M. 1983. Intracellular pathways of electron opaque GnRH-derivatives bound by cultured gonadotropes. *Endocrinology* 113: 1683–89

50. Jennes, L., Stumpf, W. E., Conn, P. M. 1984. Receptor-mediated binding and uptake of GnRH agonist and antagonist in cultured pituitary cells. *Peptides* 5:215–20

51. Jones, P. B. C., Conn, P. M., Marian, J. M., Hsueh, A. J. W. 1980. Binding of GnRH agonist to rat ovarian granulosa cells. *Life Sci.* 27:2125–32

52. Karten, M., Rivier, J. 1986. Overview of GnRH analog development. *Endocrine Rev.* In press

53. Kasson, B. G., Conn, P. M., Hsueh, A. J. W. 1985. Inhibition of granulosa cell differentiation by dioctanoylglycerol—A novel activator of protein kinase C. *Mol. Cell. Endocrinol.* 42:29–37

54. Kiesel, L., Catt, K. J. 1984. Phosphatidic acid and the calcium dependent actions of GnRH in pituitary gonadotrophs. *Arch. Biochem. Biophys.* 231: 202–10

55. Marian, J., Conn, P. M. 1979. GnRH stimulation of cultured pituitary cells requires calcium. *Mol. Pharmacol.* 16: 196–201

56. Marian, J., Conn, P. M. 1980. The calcium requirement in GnRH-stimulated LH release is not mediated through a specific action on the receptor. *Life Sci.* 27:87–92

57. Marian, J., Conn, P. M. 1983. Subcellular localization of the receptor for gonadotropin-releasing hormone in pituitary and ovarian tissue. *Endocrinology* 112:104–12

58. Marian, J., Cooper, R., Conn, P. M. 1981. Regulation of the rat pituitary GnRH-receptor. *Mol. Pharmacol.* 19:399–405

59. Martin, T. F. J., Kowalchyk, J. A. 1984. Evidence for the role of calcium and diacylglycerol as dual second messengers in thyrotropin-releasing hormone action: Involvement of diacylglycerol. *Endocrinology* 115:1517–26

60. Means, A. R., Dedman, J. R. 1980. Calmodulin: An intracellular calcium receptor. *Nature* 285:73–77

61. Momany, F. A. 1978. Conformational analysis of the molecular luteinizing hormone-releasing hormone 3. Analogue inhibitors and antagonists. *J. Med. Chem.* 21:63–68

62. Naor, Z., Catt, K. J. 1981. Mechanism of action of GnRH, involvement of phospholipid turnover in LH release. *J. Biol. Chem.* 256:2226–29

63. Naor, Z., Vanderhoek, J. Y., Linder, H. R., Catt, K. J. 1983. Arachidonic acid products as possible mediators of the action of GnRH. *Adv. Prost. Res.* 12:259–63

64. Niedel, J. E., Kuhn, L. J., Vandenbark, G. R. 1983. Phorbol receptor co-purifies with protein kinase C. *Proc. Natl. Acad. Sci. USA* 80:36–40

65. Shoyab, M. 1984. Isolation and characterization of a specific receptor for biologically active phorbol and ingenol esters. *Cancer Cells*, pp. 253–62. Cold Spring Harbor, New York: Cold Spring Harbor Lab.

66. Nishizuka, T. 1984. The role of protein kinase C in cell surface transduction and tumor promotion. *Nature* 308:693–98

67. Ojeda, S. R., Naor, Z., Negro-Villar, A. 1979. The role of prostaglandins in the control of gonadotropin and prolactin release. *Prost. Med.* 5:249–59

68. Perrin, M. H., Haas, Y., Rivier, J., Vale, W. 1982. Solubilization of the GnRH receptor from bovine pituitary plasma membranes. *Endocrinology* 112:1538–41

69. Perrin, M., Rivier, J., Vale, W. 1980. Radioligand assay for GnRH: relative potency of agonists and antagonists. *Endocrinology* 106:1289–96

70. Phillips, J. H., Burridge, K., Conn, P. M. 1983. Cytoskeletal proteins in cultured secretory cells from rat pituitary. *Exp. Cell Biology* 148:235–42

71. Savoy-Moore, R. T., Schwartz, N. B., Duncan, J. A., Marshall, J. C. 1980. Pituitary gonadotropin-releasing hormone receptors during the rat estrous cycle. *Science* 209:924–44

72. Schally, A. V., Kastin, A. J., Coy, D. H. 1976. LH-releasing hormone and its analogues: Recent basic and clinical investigations. *Int. J. Fertil.* 21:1–30

73. Siler-Khodr, T. M., Khodr, G. S. 1978. Content of luteinizing hormone-releasing factor in the human placenta. *Am. J. Obstet. Gynecol.* 130:216–19

74. Smith, M. A., Vale, W. W. 1981. Desensitization to gonadotropin-releasing hormone observed in superfused pituitary cells on cytodex beads. *Endocrinology* 108:752–59

75. Smith, W. A., Conn, P. M. 1983. GnRH-mediated desensitization of the pituitary gonadotrope is not calcium dependent. *Endocrinology* 112:408–10

76. Smith, W. A., Conn, P. M. 1984. Microaggregation of the GnRH-receptor stimulates gonadotrope desensitization. *Endocrinology* 114:553–59

77. Spona, J. 1973. LHRH stimulated gonadotropin release mediated by two distinct pituitary receptors. *FEBS Lett.* 35:59–62

78. Stern, J. E., Conn, P. M. 1981. Requirements for GnRH stimulated LH release from perifused rat hemipituitaries. *Am. J. Physiol.* 240:504–11

79. Theolyre, M., Berault, A., Garnier, J., Jutisz, M. 1976. Binding of GnRH to the pituitary plasma membrane and the problem of adenylate cyclase stimulation. *Mol. Cell. Endocrinol.* 5:365–72

80. Winiger, B. P., Birabeau, M. A., Lang, U., Capponi, A. M., Sizonenko, P. C., Aubert, J. 1983. Solubilization of pituitary GnRH binding sites by means of a zwitterionic detergent. *Mol. Cell. Endocrinol.* 31:77–83

81. Andrews, W. V., Conn, P. M. 1986. GnRH stimulates mass changes in phosphoinositides and diacylglycerol accumulation in purified gonadotrope cell cultures. *Endocrinology* In press

Ann. Rev. Physiol. 1986. 48:515–26

MECHANISM OF THYROTROPIN RELEASING HORMONE STIMULATION OF PITUITARY HORMONE SECRETION

Marvin C. Gershengorn

Division of Endocrinology and Metabolism, Department of Medicine, Cornell University Medical College and The New York Hospital, New York, New York 10021

INTRODUCTION

During the past several years, the mechanism of action of thyrotropin-releasing hormone (TRH; thyroliberin) has been studied intensively in GH cells, cloned rat mammotropic tumor cell lines that appear to be valid models for in vitro study of mammotroph function (30, 34, 48). In this article I review the recent findings (see 26 for previous review) that form the basis for a detailed hypothesis to explain the transduction of the TRH signal at the cell surface into stimulation of prolactin secretion.

It is generally agreed that an elevation of cytoplasmic free calcium ion concentration ($[Ca^{2+}]_i$) serves to couple, at least in part, the binding of many hormones and neurotransmitters to plasma membrane receptors with the stimulation of a variety of cellular processes (51). The elevation of $[Ca^{2+}]_i$ induced by these stimulants may be caused by mobilization (or redistribution) of intracellular calcium, or by enhancement of influx of extracellular Ca^{2+}, or both (17). It has been demonstrated that in some of these cells a very rapid effect after stimulant-receptor interaction is enhanced hydrolysis of phosphatidylinositol 4,5-bisphosphate [PtdIns(4,5)P_2] by a phospholipase C (or phosphodiesterase) to yield 1,2-diacylglycerol (DG) and inositoltrisphosphate (InsP$_3$) (18). Furthermore, it has been proposed that both DG (50) and InsP$_3$ (11) may serve as intracellular mediators (or second messengers) to transduce and amplify the signal, leading to stimulation of the physiologic response(s). DG appears to

515

exert its effects by enhancing the activity of a Ca^{2+}- and phospholipid-dependent protein kinase (protein kinase C) by an action that does not depend on an elevation of $[Ca^{2+}]_i$. $InsP_3$ appears to act to mobilize calcium from an intracellular pool to elevate $[Ca^{2+}]_i$. In addition, influx of extracellular calcium may be enhanced by hormones and neurotransmitters to elevate $[Ca^{2+}]_i$. The elevation of $[Ca^{2+}]_i$ may activate a Ca^{2+}- and calmodulin-dependent protein kinase(s) and, perhaps, other processes. It appears that this generalized schema of signal transduction by separate but converging pathways involving Ca^{2+} and lipid messengers may describe the mechanism of TRH stimulation of prolactin secretion.

TRH AND PHOSPHOINOSITIDES

In this section I present evidence that strongly supports the concept that in GH cells TRH acts to stimulate the hydrolysis of $PtdIns(4,5)P_2$ by a phospholipase C to yield $InsP_3$ and DG, and that this action may be the initial step in the sequence of intracellular events leading to prolactin secretion. The studies I emphasize have been performed in cells prelabeled with precursors to isotopic equilibrium in order to facilitate measurement of changes in the cellular content of even minor substances, such as $PtdIns(4,5)P_2$ and $InsP_3$. Hence, the earlier studies in which the polyphosphoinositides, $PtdIns(4,5)P_2$ and phosphatidyl-inositol 4-phosphate ($PtdIns4P$), were measured in cells labeled briefly with [^{32}P]phosphate will not be described (15, 54, 57, 64).

The effects of TRH on phosphoinositides and on inositol sugars have been determined in cells labeled to isotopic steady state with [^{3}H]inositol (5–7, 14, 15, 39, 44, 45, 52, 53, 58). The findings reported in most of these studies are very similar. We (52) found that the relative content of the phosphoinositides was: $PtdIns(4,5)P_2$, 2.5%; $PtdIns4P$, 2.8%; lysophosphatidylinositol, 6.2%; and phosphatidylinositol ($PtdIns$), 88%. Because $PtdIns$ comprises only 9% of total cell phospholipids (53), it is evident that the polyphosphoinositides, $PtdIns(4,5)P_2$ and $PtdIns4P$, are very minor lipids that make up less than 0.5% of the total cellular phospholipids. TRH was shown to cause a rapid (within 5 sec) decrease in the content of $PtdIns(4,5)P_2$ and $PtdIns4P$, and a slower decrease in $PtdIns$. Simultaneously, there was a rapid increase in the levels of $InsP_3$ and inositolbisphosphate ($InsP_2$) (peak levels were attained at between 15 and 30 sec), and a slower but more prolonged increase in inositolmonophosphate ($InsP$) and inositol (Ins). In cells labeled to equilibrium with [^{3}H]arachidonic acid, we (53) showed that TRH stimulated a transient increase in the content of DG that peaked at between 15 and 30 sec; similar increments in DG were found in cells labeled with [^{3}H]glycerol (44) and [^{3}H]oleic acid (45). Because $InsP_3$ can only be formed in mammalian cells by hydrolysis of $PtdIns(4,5)P_2$, it can be concluded that a proximate event in TRH action is the phospholipase C–mediated hydrolysis of PtdIns(4,5)P$_2$. Hence, the decrease in PtdIns(4,5)P$_2$ and the increments in InsP$_3$ and DG may be accounted for, at least in part, by this mechanism. However, the enzymic reactions involved in the decrements in PtdIns4P and PtdIns and the increases in InsP$_2$, InsP, and Ins can not be definitively determined because these changes can be caused either by phospholipase C–mediated hydrolysis of PtdIns4P and PtdIns, or by conversion of PtdIns to PtdIns4P and to PtdIns(4,5)P$_2$ by specific kinases coupled with sequential dephosphorylation of InsP$_3$ to InsP$_2$ to InsP to Ins by phosphatases. In fact, at least part of the decrease in PtdIns4P and PtdIns is caused by conversion to PtdIns(4,5)P$_2$, because the amount of InsP$_3$ that is formed during stimulation by TRH exceeds the total cell content of PtdIns(4,5)P$_2$ (14, 52).

An important question regarding TRH-stimulated, phospholipase C–mediated hydrolysis of PtdIns(4,5)P$_2$ is whether this reaction is dependent on an elevation of $[Ca^{2+}]_i$, in which case PtdIns(4,5)P$_2$ hydrolysis could not be the initial event after TRH-receptor interaction. Two general approaches have been taken to address this issue. It was shown that elevation of $[Ca^{2+}]_i$ by Ca^{2+} ionophores (14, 39, 52) and by membrane depolarization with high extracellular K^+ (7, 52, 58) did not simulate the effect of TRH to hydrolyze PtdIns(4,5)P$_2$. Conversely, lowering extracellular Ca^{2+} by deleting Ca^{2+} from the medium or by adding a Ca^{2+} chelating agent, which is known also to deplete intracellular stores of Ca^{2+} in GH cells (26), did not inhibit TRH-induced hydrolysis of PtdIns(4,5)P$_2$ (45, 52, but see 7). Hence, these findings support the hypothesis that phospholipase C–mediated hydrolysis of PtdIns(4,5)P$_2$ induced by TRH is not a consequence of an elevation of $[Ca^{2+}]_i$, but rather may be an early event in the sequence leading to an elevation of $[Ca^{2+}]_i$. The molecular details of the mechanism by which the TRH-receptor complex may be coupled to the phospholipase C enzyme are not known; however, there is some evidence that a guanine nucleotide binding protein may be involved (35, 36).

INSP$_3$ AS MEDIATOR OF CELLULAR Ca^{2+} MOBILIZATION

Berridge (11) proposed that InsP$_3$ may function as an intracellular messenger to mobilize Ca^{2+} from pools within cells. To determine whether InsP$_3$ may serve as a mediator of the TRH-induced release of Ca^{2+} (27, 55, 65) (see TRH AND $[Ca^{2+}]_i$), we developed a preparation of saponin-permeabilized GH cells in order to allow InsP$_3$ access to intracellular Ca^{2+} pools (27). Permeabilized cells sequestered Ca^{2+} in an ATP-dependent manner into two functionally distinct sites, tentatively identified as mitochondrial and nonmitochondrial pools based on their sensitivity to agents that release Ca^{2+} from mitochondria. The nonmitochondrial pool had a high affinity for Ca^{2+} and could be saturated when permeabilized cells were incubated in buffer with as little as 200 nM $[Ca^{2+}]_{free}$. By contrast, the mitochondrial pool exhibited a lower affinity for Ca^{2+} but a greater capacity for accumulation, which was not fully saturated even at $[Ca^{2+}]_{free}$ up to 1000 nM. When permeabilized cells were incubated in buffer with a $[Ca^{2+}]_{free}$ initially between 200 and 1000 nM, $[Ca^{2+}]_{free}$ was buffered to 130 nM, a level identical with that maintained in intact cells (see TRH AND $[Ca^{2+}]_i$). In permeabilized cells that had accumulated $^{45}Ca^{2+}$ to a steady state level, InsP$_3$ caused a very rapid loss of $^{45}Ca^{2+}$ followed by a slow re-uptake, even when mitochondrial Ca^{2+} accumulation was blocked. InsP$_3$-induced release of Ca^{2+} from a nonmitochondrial pool within permeabilized cells was concentration-dependent; half-maximal effect was at 1 μM. The effect of InsP$_3$ was specific as there was no effect of InsP$_2$, InsP, or Ins at similar or even higher concentrations. The concentration of InsP$_3$ that caused half-maximal release of nonmitochondrial calcium was lower than the estimated concentration of InsP$_3$ (30–50 μM) in intact GH cells after TRH addition (14, 52). However, such an estimate is very rough, and the biologically active fraction within the cell is unknown. Hence, it is not yet possible to make precise quantitative comparisons of InsP$_3$ action in intact and permeabilized cells. Nevertheless, these data are compatible with the hypothesis that InsP$_3$ is the signal generated by TRH-receptor interaction that mobilizes Ca^{2+} from an intracellular pool(s), perhaps within the endoplasmic reticulum (27, 55).

TRH AND $[Ca^{2+}]_i$

Based upon many previous observations (see 26 for review), it was suggested that an elevation of $[Ca^{2+}]_i$ served to couple stimulation by TRH to secretion of prolactin. This hypothesis has now been supported by direct evidence, derived from experiments employing an intracellularly trapped fluorescent probe of Ca^{2+}, Quin 2, and an intracellularly trapped photoprotein, aequorin, that TRH stimulates a rapid elevation of $[Ca^{2+}]_i$ in GH cells (3, 4, 27–29, 43, 59–61). In these studies, basal (or resting) $[Ca^{2+}]_i$ was reported to be as low as 37 nM (43) and as high as 350 nM (3, 4). The majority of reports, however, have found basal $[Ca^{2+}]_i$ in GH cells to be about 120 nM (27–29, 59–61).

TRH stimulates an immediate severalfold elevation of $[Ca^{2+}]_i$, followed by a more prolonged secondary increase, i.e. a biphasic elevation of $[Ca^{2+}]_i$. In our experiments, basal $[Ca^{2+}]_i$ was 120 $\pm$ 18 nM, and TRH stimulated a rapid increase in $[Ca^{2+}]_i$, which reached a peak of 520 $\pm$ 29 nM at less than 10 sec, followed by a decline over 1.5 min. This was followed by a sustained elevation of $[Ca^{2+}]_i$ to 260 $\pm$ 14 nM, which lasted for at least 12 min ("second phase"). Several groups of investigators have concluded that the first phase elevation of $[Ca^{2+}]_i$ is caused in large part, if not completely, by mobilization of cellular Ca^{2+}, and that the second phase is due to enhanced influx of extracellular Ca^{2+}. These conclusions are based on the following observations: (a) In cells incubated in medium depleted of Ca^{2+} or in the presence of EGTA, a Ca^{2+} chelating agent, the first phase elevation was not affected but the second phase was abolished (3, 28, 29, 59, 61). (b) In cells exposed to organic Ca^{2+} channel blocking agents, such as verapamil or nifedipine, the first phase elevation was only minimally inhibited but the second phase elevation was inhibited by greater than 50% (4, 29, 59). (c) The first phase elevation, but not the sustained second phase, was abolished by pretreating cells with a low dose of a Ca^{2+} ionophore to deplete intracellular Ca^{2+} stores (4). Furthermore, because the first phase elevation of $[Ca^{2+}]_i$ was not affected in cells in which the mitochondrial pool was depleted, it appears that the TRH-responsive pool was nonmitochondrial, perhaps within the endoplasmic reticulum (27). The enhanced influx of extracellular Ca^{2+} appears to occur through voltage-dependent Ca^{2+} channels (32, 33, 65–67).

Studies that complement the findings of direct measurement of $[Ca^{2+}]_i$ have been performed. Electrophysiological experiments have extended the initial observation that TRH stimulates an increase in the frequency of Ca^{2+}-dependent action potentials in GH cells (compiled in 26). TRH initially causes a transient hyperpolarization of GH cells that is apparently secondary to an increase in K^+ conductance through the plasma membrane; this may last for up to 60 sec, during which the cells are electrically silent (8, 10, 22, 38, 56). The increase in K^+ conductance may be due to "opening" of K^+ channels caused by the elevation of $[Ca^{2+}]_i$. This is followed by an increase in plasma membrane resistance, which leads to a decrease in K^+ conductance, a return toward the resting level of polarization, followed by an increase in the frequency of Ca^{2+}-dependent action potentials. It is the period of increased Ca^{2+} spiking activity that correlates with the second phase elevation of $[Ca^{2+}]_i$. It has been speculated that the TRH receptor may be intimately associated with a K^+ channel (38). Other studies have shown that there is a Ca^{2+}-transporting ATPase (9) and a Na^+-Ca^{2+} exchange mechanism (37) within the plasma membrane of GH cells, and it was suggested that these two processes may serve to limit the elevation of $[Ca^{2+}]_i$.

TRH AND PROTEIN PHOSPHORYLATION

Protein phosphorylation-dephosphorylation is a common regulatory mechanism in many cell types. TRH has been shown to stimulate the phosphorylation of proteins found in cytosolic (19–21, 62, 63), microsomal (19, 21), and nuclear fractions (49) from GH cells. Although neither the biologic functions nor identities of any of these proteins are known, some understanding of the mechanisms involved in these phosphorylations has been gained, and some tentative correlations with secretory or synthetic responses to TRH have been shown.

Drust, Martin, and their colleagues (19–21), Sobel & Tashjian (63), and

Sobel & Boutterin (62) demonstrated that TRH stimulates the phosphorylation of a set of proteins in GH cell cytosol. Drust & Martin (19) concluded that a major subset of these proteins was phosphorylated by a protein kinase(s) that was activated by a presumed elevation of $[Ca^{2+}]_i$ in intact cells. This was based on their findings that several agents that elevate $[Ca^{2+}]_i$, such as a Ca^{2+} ionophore and depolarization by high extracellular K^+ or tetraethylammonium ion, also stimulated the phosphorylation of these same proteins, and that at least one of these proteins was phosphorylated in a Ca^{2+}-dependent manner in vitro. Sobel & Tashjian (63) and Drust & Martin (20) showed that another set of proteins phosphorylated during TRH stimulation of intact cells appeared to be acted upon by protein kinase C (50). This suggestion is based on their findings that phorbol esters (20, 63) and exogenous phospholipase C (20) stimulated the phosphorylation of a set of proteins in intact cells that were also phosphorylated during TRH action, and that phorbol esters and DG caused phosphorylation of these same proteins in vitro (20). In contrast, these same investigators showed that agents that raised intracellular levels of cyclic AMP, such as cyclic AMP analogs, cholera toxin, and vasoactive intestinal peptide, stimulated phosphorylation of a set of proteins distinct from those stimulated by TRH. However, a small number of proteins were affected by both TRH and cyclic AMP, but perhaps at different sites. [This is some of the recent evidence against a role for cyclic AMP as a second messenger in TRH action (see 26 for review of previous data, 12, 31, but see 24, 25).] Hence, TRH stimulation of protein phosphorylation appears to be mediated, at least in part, by Ca^{2+}-, (calmodulin?)-dependent protein kinase(s) and protein kinase C, but not by cyclic AMP–dependent protein kinase(s).

Sobel & Tashjian (63) also categorized cytosolic phosphoproteins as to whether they were phosphorylated in response to agents, other than TRH, that stimulate secretion or synthesis of prolactin. They were thereby able to tentatively categorize certain phosphoproteins affected by TRH as being associated with stimulation of secretion or with synthesis. In this regard, Murdoch et al (49) described a temporal correlation between TRH stimulation of transcription of the prolactin gene and the phosphorylation of a specific nuclear protein. However, as stated above, the role of any of these protein phosphorylations in the mechanism of stimulation by TRH of prolactin secretion or synthesis is undefined.

TRH STIMULATION OF BIPHASIC PROLACTIN SECRETION

Although it is well established that TRH stimulates prolactin secretion, the detailed kinetics of the response have only recently been determined. Several groups of investigators have shown that the effect of TRH is biphasic with a "burst" phase of secretion at a higher rate that lasts for approximately two minutes followed by a sustained phase at a lower rate (1, 2, 4, 13, 29, 41, 46, 47). Based on the effects of cycloheximide, Aizawa & Hinkle (1) concluded that the burst phase consisted primarily of release of preformed prolactin, whereas the sustained phase included secretion of newly synthesized prolactin.

It was proposed, based on the findings summarized in previous sections, that two pathways, one initiated by an elevation of $[Ca^{2+}]_i$ and the other by DG activation of protein kinase C, may act in concert to mediate stimulated secretion. In the initial series of reports, several groups of investigators used pharmacological agents to stimulate specifically one or the other of these pathways. For example, Delbeke et al (13) showed that a calcium ionophore, presumably by elevating $[Ca^{2+}]_i$, stimulated only a burst of secretion, whereas a phorbol ester, used to mimic DG activation of protein kinase C, caused a sustained secretory response. Similar stimulation of isolated burst phase secretion caused by a presumed elevation of $[Ca^{2+}]_i$ was obtained by others with calcium ionophores (1, 47, but see 4), with depolarization by high extracellular K^+ (2, 41, 47), with agents that release intracellular Ca^{2+} (47), and with the Ca^{2+} channel agonist, BayK8644 (23). In contrast, stimulation of sustained secretion in the absence of a burst was found by other investigators with phorbol esters (2, 4, 46) and with exposure to phospholipase C (46), presumably via activation of protein kinase C. From these data, the majority of workers suggested that the burst phase of secretion stimulated by TRH may be mediated by an elevation of $[Ca^{2+}]_i$, and the sustained phase may be mediated by DG activation of protein kinase C (see below).

More direct evidence regarding the role of elevation of $[Ca^{2+}]_i$ as the mediator of the first and second phases of secretion has been obtained (4, 41). Albert & Tashjian (4) found that if they depleted the TRH-responsive intracellular pool of Ca^{2+} by pretreatment of GH cells with low doses of ionophore (so as to abolish the spike increase in $[Ca^{2+}]_i$) the burst phase but not the sustained phase of secretion was abolished. Moreover, when they blocked influx of extracellular Ca^{2+} with the organic channel blocking agent, nifedipine, they partially inhibited the secondary elevation of $[Ca^{2+}]_i$, and partially inhibited sustained secretion of growth hormone. (It is not clear why prolactin secretion was not measured in these experiments.) From these data and their inability to stimulate prolactin secretion with a Ca^{2+} ionophore, Albert & Tashjian (4) concluded that rapid elevation of $[Ca^{2+}]_i$ was necessary but not sufficient to cause burst secretion, and that the sustained phase of secretion was directly related to the $[Ca^{2+}]_i$. We used a different experimental approach to address the same questions. We pretreated GH cells with arachidonic acid to prevent the elevation of $[Ca^{2+}]_i$ usually caused by TRH (40), and found that the burst phase of prolactin secretion was abolished (41). In parallel experiments we showed that abolition of the burst phase of secretion in arachidonic acid-pretreated cells was not caused by depletion of preformed prolactin, and that K^+ depolarization, which induces an elevation of $[Ca^{2+}]_i$ but does not affect phosphoinositide metabolism (53), still caused a burst secretion (41, 42). Recent experiments have shown that TRH-stimulated hydrolysis of $PtdIns(4,5)P_2$ to yield $InsP_3$ and DG was not affected by arachidonic acid pretreatment (unpublished observations), which supports the notion that neither $InsP_3$ or DG is capable of causing burst secretion in the absence of an elevation of $[Ca^{2+}]_i$. In contrast, the sustained phase of secretion stimulated by TRH was not inhibited even though the secondary elevation of $[Ca^{2+}]_i$ usually caused by enhanced influx of extracellular Ca^{2+} was abolished. Based on these findings, we proposed that an elevation of $[Ca^{2+}]_i$ is necessary and sufficient to cause burst phase secretion, but is not necessary for sustained secretion. Hence, it may be that the partial inhibition of sustained secretion reportedly caused by organic channel blocking agents (4, 47) is not due to inhibition of an increase in $[Ca^{2+}]_i$, but is secondary to a decrease in $[Ca^{2+}]_i$ to a level below that which is usually found in resting cells and which is required for DG activation of protein kinase C (50).

In summary, it appears that the burst phase of prolactin secretion is caused by the rapid elevation of $[Ca^{2+}]_i$, and that the sustained phase of prolactin secretion can be independent of an elevation of $[Ca^{2+}]_i$, and may be mediated by DG activation of protein kinase C.

MODEL OF TRH ACTION

Based on the observations reviewed here, I propose the following as the sequence of intracellular events involved in the mechanism of TRH stimulation of prolactin secretion from GH cells. The binding of TRH to its plasma membrane receptor stimulates the hydrolysis of $PtdIns(4,5)P_2$ to yield $InsP_3$ and DG. There is a concomitant enhancement of conversion of PtdIns to PtdIns4P to $PtdIns(4,5)P_2$, and these three phosphoinositides contribute to the formation of $InsP_3$ and DG, both of which serve subsequent mediator functions. $InsP_3$, the water-soluble product of $PtdIns(4,5)P_2$ hydrolysis, diffuses from the plasma membrane to a nonmitochondrial pool of calcium, perhaps the endoplasmic reticulum, and causes the release of Ca^{2+}. The movement of Ca^{2+} from a sequestered pool(s) into the cytoplasm results in the rapid elevation of $[Ca^{2+}]_i$, which couples stimulus to burst secretion. The elevation of $[Ca^{2+}]_i$ may activate exocytosis directly, or through phosphorylation of proteins involved in the exocytotic process via activation of a Ca^{2+}- and calmodulin-dependent protein kinase(s), or both. The elevation of $[Ca^{2+}]_i$ is extended by a delayed but prolonged TRH-induced enhancement of influx of extracellular Ca^{2+}. Concomitant with the effects of $InsP_3$ and of elevation of $[Ca^{2+}]_i$, phosphorylation of proteins involved in the exocytotic process may be stimulated through DG activation of protein kinase C, leading to the sustained phase of secretion. As noted above, this phase of secretion does not require an elevation of $[Ca^{2+}]_i$, but the effect of submaximal increases in DG content may be enhanced by simultaneous elevation of $[Ca^{2+}]_i$.

Although the model I have proposed appears well founded, many of the essential features remain undefined. Neither the molecular events that underlie the coupling of the TRH-receptor complex to hydrolysis of $PtdIns(4,5)P_2$ nor the mechanism by which $InsP_3$ mobilizes calcium are known. In fact, the localization of the hormone-sensitive pool(s) of phosphoinositides to the cell surface can only be inferred from very indirect evidence. Furthermore, the link between TRH-stimulated phosphoinositide metabolism and elevation of $[Ca^{2+}]_i$ has only been superficially explored, and the molecular events that mediate enhanced Ca^{2+} influx are not known, though phosphorylation of channel proteins or a membrane potential effect caused by a decrease in K^+ conductance may be involved. The role of protein phosphorylation in activation of exocytosis is speculative, and none of the proteins that are phosphorylated during TRH action have been identified or shown to be involved in secretion. Hence, it must be emphasized that the model I propose is intended to serve mainly to guide further investigation into the molecular events that couple TRH-receptor interaction at the cell surface to the transduction and amplification of intracellular signals. Although this model was developed to explain the mechanism of TRH stimulation of prolactin secretion from GH cells, it is consistent with some observations that have been made with TRH in thyrotropin (thyroid-stimulating hormone)-secreting cells and in a variety of other cells. I believe this schema is generally applicable to stimulus-response coupling in many cell types.

ACKNOWLEDGMENTS

Several laboratories have made significant contributions to our understanding of the mechanism of TRH action during the last three years, as evidenced by the large number of investigators whose reports I have cited. I apologize for any omissions from this compilation and for any imbalance in my presentation of the data in this review, in particular, for the necessarily brief treatment afforded the electrophysiological studies. I gratefully thank my colleagues, especially E. Geras, R. N. Kolesnick, M. J. Rebecchi, and C. Thaw, for their contributions to this work. I also thank L. Brenner-Gati, E. Geras, R. N. Kolesnick, and P. Sherline for their thoughtful criticisms of this manuscript. My research was supported by grants AM33468 and AM33469 from the National Institutes of Health.

Literature Cited

1. Aizawa, T., Hinkle, P. M. 1985. Thyrotropin-releasing hormone rapidly stimulates a biphasic secretion of prolactin and growth hormone in GH_4C_1 rat pituitary tumor cells. *Endocrinology* 116: 73–82

2. Aizawa, T., Hinkle, P. M. 1985. Differential effects of thyrotropin-releasing hormone, vasoactive intestinal peptide, phorbol ester, and depolarization in GH_4C_1 rat pituitary cells. *Endocrinology* 116:909–19

3. Albert, P. R., Tashjian, A. H. Jr. 1984. Thyrotropin-releasing hormone-induced spike and plateau in cytosolic free Ca^{2+} concentrations in pituitary cells. *J. Biol. Chem.* 259:5827–32

4. Albert, P. R., Tashjian, A. H. Jr. 1984. Relationship of thyrotropin-releasing hormone-induced spike and plateau phases in cytosolic free Ca^{2+} concentrations to hormone secretion. *J. Biol. Chem.* 259:15350–63

5. Baird, J. G., Brown, B. L. 1985. The effects of divalent cations on thyrotropin releasing hormone (TRH) stimulated inositol phosphate accumulation and prolactin secretion in GH_3 cells. *Biochem. Soc. Trans.* In press

6. Baird, J. G., Dobson, P. R. M., Wojcikiewicz, R. J. H., Brown, B. L. 1983. Thyrotropin-releasing hormone stimulates inositol phosphate production in normal anterior pituitary cells and GH_3 tumour cells in the presence of lithium. *Biosci. Rep.* 3:1091–99

7. Baird, J. G., Wojcikiewicz, R. J. H., Dobson, P. R. M., Brown, B. L. 1984. The involvement of calcium ions in phosphatidylinositol hydrolysis in the anterior pituitary. *Biochem. Soc. Trans.* 12:327–28

8. Barker, J. L., Dufy, B., Owen, D. G., Segal, M. 1983. Excitable membrane properties of cultured central nervous system neurons and clonal pituitary cells. *Cold Spring Harbor Symp.* 68:259–68

9. Barros, F., Kaczorowski, G. J. 1984. Mechanisms of Ca^{2+} transport in plasma membrane vesicles prepared from cultured pituitary cells. *J. Biol. Chem.* 259:9404–10

10. Barros, F., Katz, G. M., Kaczorowski, G. J., Vandlen, R. L., Reuben, J. P. 1985. Calcium currents in GH_3 cultured pituitary cells under whole-cell voltage-clamp: inhibition by voltage-dependent potassium currents. *Proc. Natl. Acad. Sci. USA.* 82:1108–12

11. Berridge, M. J. 1984. Inositol trisphosphate and diacylglycerol as second messengers. *Biochem. J.* 220:345–60

12. Brostrom, M. A., Brostrom, C. O., Brotman, L. A., Green, S. S. 1982. Regulation of Ca^{2+}-dependent cyclic AMP accumulation and Ca^{2+} metabolism in intact pituitary tumor cells by modulators of prolactin production. *Mol. Pharmacol.* 23:399–408

13. Delbeke, D., Kojima, I., Dannies, P. S., Rasmussen, H. 1984. Synergistic stimulation of prolactin release by phorbol ester, A23187 and forskolin. *Biochem. Biophys. Res. Commun.* 123:735–41

14. Drummond, A. H., Bushfield, M., MacPhee, C. H. 1984. Thyrotropin-releasing hormone-stimulated [^{3}H]inositol metabolism in GH_3 pituitary tumor cells. *Mol. Pharmacol.* 25:201–8

15. Drummond, A. H., MacPhee, C. H. 1981. Phosphatidylinositol metabolism in GH_3 pituitary tumour cells stimulated by TRH. *Brit. J. Pharmacol.* 74:967P–68P

16. Drummond, A. H., Raeburn, C. A. 1984. The interaction of lithium with thyrotropin-releasing hormone-stimulated lipid metabolism in GH_3 pituitary tumour cells. *Biochem. J.* 224:129–36

17. Douglas, W. W. 1978. Stimulus-secretion coupling: variations on the theme of calcium-activated exocytosis involving cellular and extracellular sources of calcium. *Ciba Found. Symp.* 54:61–90

18. Downes, P., Michell, R. H. 1982. Phosphatidylinositol 4-phosphate and phosphatidylinositol 4,5-bisphosphate: Lipids in search of a function. *Cell Calcium* 3:467–502

19. Drust, D. S., Martin, T. F. J. 1982. Thyrotropin-releasing hormone rapidly and transiently stimulates cytosolic calcium-dependent protein phosphorylation in GH_3 pituitary cells. *J. Biol. Chem.* 257:7566–73

20. Drust, D. S., Martin, T. F. J. 1984. Thyrotropin-releasing hormone rapidly activates protein phosphorylation in GH_3 pituitary cells by a lipid-linked, protein kinase C-mediated pathway. *J. Biol. Chem.* 259:14520–30

21. Drust, D. S., Sutton, C. A., Martin, T. F. J. 1982. Thyrotropin-releasing hormone and cyclic AMP activate distinctive pathways of protein phosphorylation in GH pituitary cells. *J. Biol. Chem.* 257:3306–12

22. Dufy, B., Israel, J. M., Zyzek, E., Gourdji, D. 1982. Differential effects of

K+, TRH and VIP on the electrophysiological properties of pituitary cells in culture. *Neuroendocrinol. Lett.* 4:245–52

23. Enyeart, J. J., Hinkle, P. M. 1984. The calcium agonist Bay K 8644 stimulates secretion from a pituitary cell line. *Biochem. Biophys. Res. Commun.* 122:991–96

24. Gautvik, K. M., Gordeladze, J. O., Jahnsen, T., Haug, E., Hansson, V., Lystad, E. 1983. Thyroliberin receptor binding and adenylyl cyclase activation in cultured prolactin-producing rat pituitary tumor cells (GH cells). *J. Biol. Chem.* 258:10304–11

25. Gautvik, K. M., Kriz, M., Jahnsen, T., Haug, E., Hansson, V. 1982. Relationship between stimulated prolactin release from GH cells and cyclic AMP degradation and formation. *Mol. Cell. Endocrinol.* 26:295–308

26. Gershengorn, M. C. 1982. Thyrotropin releasing hormone. A review of the mechanisms of acute stimulation of pituitary hormone release. *Mol. Cell. Biochem.* 45:163–79

27. Gershengorn, M. C., Geras, E., Purrello, V. S., Rebecchi, M. J. 1984. Inositol trisphosphate mediates thyrotropin-releasing hormone mobilization of nonmitochondrial calcium in rat mammotropic pituitary cells. *J. Biol. Chem.* 259:10675–81

28. Gershengorn, M. C., Thaw, C. 1983. Calcium influx is not required for TRH to elevate free cytoplasmic calcium in GH3 cells. *Endocrinology* 113:1522–24

29. Gershengorn, M. C., Thaw, C. 1985. Thyrotropin-releasing hormone (TRH) stimulates biphasic elevation of cytoplasmic free calcium in GH3 cells. Further evidence that TRH mobilizes cellular and extracellular Ca^{2+}. *Endocrinology* 116:591–96

30. Gourdji, D., Tougard, C., Tixier-Vidal, A. 1982. Clonal prolactin strains as a tool in neuroendocrinology. In *Frontiers in Neuroendocrinology*, ed. W. F. Ganong, L. Martini, 7:317–57. New York: Raven.

31. Guild, S., Drummond, A. H. 1983. Adenosine 3',5'-cyclic monophosphate-dependent release of prolactin from GH3 pituitary tumour cells. *Biochem. J.* 216:551–57

32. Hagiwara, S., Ohmori, H. 1982. Studies of calcium channels in rat clonal pituitary cells with patch electrode voltage clamp. *J. Physiol.* 331:231–52

33. Hagiwara, S., Ohmori, H. 1983. Studies of single calcium channel currents in rat clonal pituitary cells. *J. Physiol.* 336:649–61

34. Hinkle, P. M. 1984. Interaction of peptide hormones with rat pituitary tumor cells in culture. In *Secretory Tumors of the Pituitary Gland*, ed. P. McL. Black, N. T. Zervas, E. C. Ridgway, J. B. Martin, et al, 1:25–43. New York: Raven.

35. Hinkle, P. M., Kinsella, P. A. 1984. Regulation of thyrotropin-releasing hormone binding by monovalent cations and guanyl nucleotides. *J. Biol. Chem.* 259:3445–49

36. Hinkle, P. M., Phillips, W. J. 1984. Thyrotropin-releasing hormone stimulates GTP hydrolysis by membranes from GH4C1 rat pituitary tumor cells. *Proc. Natl. Acad. Sci. USA* 81:6183–87

37. Kaczorowski, G. J., Costello, L., Dethmers, J., Trumble, M. J., Vandlen, R. L. 1984. Mechanisms of Ca^{2+} transport in plasma membrane vesicles prepared from cultured pituitary cells. *J. Biol. Chem.* 259:9395–9403

38. Kaczorowski, G. J., Vandlen, R. L., Katz, G. M., Reuben, J. P. 1983. Regulation of excitation-secretion coupling by thyrotropin-releasing hormone (TRH): Evidence for TRH receptor-ion channel coupling in cultured pituitary cells. *J. Membr. Biol.* 71:109–18

39. Kolesnick, R. N., Gershengorn, M. C. 1984. Ca^{2+} ionophores affect phosphoinositide metabolism differently than thyrotropin-releasing hormone in GH3 pituitary cells. *J. Biol. Chem.* 259:9514–19

40. Kolesnick, R. N., Gershengorn, M. C. 1985. Arachidonic acid inhibits thyrotropin-releasing hormone-induced elevation of cytoplasmic free calcium in GH3 pituitary cells. *J. Biol. Chem.* 260:707–13

41. Kolesnick, R. N., Gershengorn, M. C. 1985. Direct evidence that burst but not sustained secretion of prolactin stimulated by thyrotropin-releasing hormone is dependent on elevation of cytoplasmic calcium. *J. Biol. Chem.* 260:5217–20

42. Kolesnick, R. N., Musacchio, I., Thaw, C., Gershengorn, M. C. 1984. Arachidonic acid mobilizes calcium and stimulates prolactin secretion from GH3 cells. *Am. J. Physiol.* 246:E458–62

43. Kruskal, B. A., Keith, C. H., Maxfield, F. R. 1984. Thyrotropin-releasing hormone-induced changes in intracellular [Ca^{2+}] measured by microspectrofluorometry on individual quin2-loaded cells. *J. Cell Biol.* 99:1167–72

44. MacPhee, C. H., Drummond, A. H. 1984. Thyrotropin-releasing hormone stimulates rapid breakdown of phospha-

tidylinositol 4,5-bisphosphate and phosphatidylinositol 4-phosphate in GH_3 pituitary tumor cells. *Mol. Pharmacol.* 25:193–200

45. Martin, T. F. J. 1983. Thyrotropin-releasing hormone rapidly activates the phosphodiester hydrolysis of polyphosphoinositides in GH_3 pituitary cells. *J. Biol. Chem.* 258:14816–22

46. Martin, T. F. J., Kowalchyk, J. A. 1984. Evidence for the role of calcium and diacylglycerol as dual second messengers in thyrotropin-releasing hormone action: Involvement of diacylglycerol. *Endocrinology* 115:1517–26

47. Martin, T. F. J., Kowalchyk, J. A. 1984. Evidence for the role of calcium and diacylglycerol as dual second messengers in thyrotropin-releasing hormone action: Involvement of Ca^{2+}. *Endocrinology* 115:1527–36

48. Martin, T. F. J., Tashjian, A. H. Jr. 1977. Cell culture studies of thyrotropin-releasing hormone action. In *Biochemical Actions of Hormones*, ed. G. Litwack, 4:269–312. New York: Academic

49. Murdoch, G. H., Franco, R., Evans, R. M., Rosenfeld, M. G. 1983. Polypeptide hormone regulation of gene expression. Thyrotropin-releasing hormone rapidly stimulates both transcription of the prolactin gene and the phosphorylation of a specific nuclear protein. *J. Biol. Chem.* 258:15329–35

50. Nishizuka, Y. 1984. The role of protein kinase C in cell surface signal transduction and tumour promotion. *Nature* 308:693–98

51. Rasmussen, H., Barrett, P. Q. 1984. Calcium messenger system: An integrated view. *Physiol. Rev.* 64:938–84

52. Rebecchi, M. J., Gershengorn, M. C. 1983. Thyroliberin stimulates rapid hydrolysis of phosphatidylinositol 4,5-bisphosphate by a phosphodiesterase in rat mammotropic pituitary cells. *Biochem. J.* 216:287–94

53. Rebecchi, M. J., Kolesnick, R. N., Gershengorn, M. C. 1983. Thyrotropin-releasing hormone stimulates rapid loss of phosphatidylinositol and its conversion to 1,2-diacylglycerol and phosphatidic acid in rat mammotropic pituitary cells. *J. Biol. Chem.* 258:227–34

54. Rebecchi, M. J., Monaco, M. E., Gershengorn, M. C. 1981. Thyrotropin releasing hormone rapidly enhances [^{32}P]orthophosphate incorporation into phosphatidic acid in cloned GH_3 cells. *Biochem. Biophys. Res. Commun.* 101:124–30

55. Ronning, S. A., Heatley, G. A., Martin, T. F. J. 1982. Thyrotropin-releasing hormone mobilizes Ca^{2+} from endoplasmic reticulum and mitochondria of GH_3

pituitary cells: Characterization of cellular Ca^{2+} pools by a method based on digitonin permeabilization. *Proc. Natl. Acad. Sci. USA* 79:6294–98

56. Sand, O., Sletholt, K., Gautvik, K. M., Haug, E. 1983. Trifluoperazine blocks calcium-dependent action potentials and inhibits hormone release from rat pituitary tumour cells. *Eur. J. Pharmacol.* 86:177–84

57. Schlegel, W., Roduit, C., Zahnd, G. 1981. Thyrotropin releasing hormone stimulates metabolism of phosphatidylinositol in GH_3 cells. *FEBS Lett.* 134:47–49

58. Schlegel, W., Roduit, C., Zahnd, G. 1984. Polyphosphoinositide hydrolysis by phospholipase C is accelerated by thyrotropin releasing hormone (TRH) in clonal rat pituitary cells (GH_3 cells). *FEBS Lett.* 168:54–60

59. Schlegel, W., Wollheim, C. B. 1984. Thyrotropin-releasing hormone increases cytosolic free Ca^{2+} in clonal pituitary cells (GH_3 cells): Direct evidence for the mobilization of cellular calcium. *J. Cell Biol.* 99:83–87

60. Snowdowne, K. W. 1984. Estimates for cytosolic calcium concentration. *Am. J. Physiol.* 247:E837

61. Snowdowne, K. W., Borle, A. B. 1984. Changes in cytosolic ionized calcium induced by activators of secretion in GH_3 cells. *Am. J. Physiol.* 246:E198–E201

62. Sobel, A., Boutterin, M. C. 1985. Cytoplasmic protein phosphorylation related to multihormonal regulation of prolactin in pituitary cells. *Neurochem. Int.* In press

63. Sobel, A., Tashjian, A. H. Jr. 1983. Distinct patterns of cytoplasmic protein phosphorylation related to regulation of synthesis and release of prolactin by GH cells. *J. Biol. Chem.* 258:10312–24

64. Sutton, C. A., Martin, T. F. J. 1982. Thyrotropin-releasing hormone (TRH) selectively and rapidly stimulates phosphatidylinositol turnover in GH pituitary cells: A possible second step of TRH action. *Endocrinology* 110:1273–80

65. Tan, K.-N., Tashjian, A. H. Jr. 1981. Receptor-mediated release of plasma membrane-associated calcium and stimulation of calcium uptake by thyrotropin-releasing hormone in pituitary cells in culture. *J. Biol. Chem.* 256:8994–9002

66. Tan, K.-N., Tashjian, A. H. Jr. 1984. Voltage-dependent calcium channels in pituitary cells in culture. *J. Biol. Chem.* 259:418–26

67. Tan, K.-N., Tashjian, A. H. Jr. 1984. Voltage-dependent calcium channels in pituitary cells in culture. *J. Biol. Chem.* 259:427–34

Ann. Rev. Physiol. 1986. 48:527–36

ENDOGENOUS OPIOID PEPTIDES AND HYPOTHALAMO-PITUITARY FUNCTION

Trevor A. Howlett and Lesley H. Rees

Departments of Endocrinology and Chemical Endocrinology, St. Bartholomew's Hospital, London, EC1A 7BE, United Kingdom

INTRODUCTION

Since the isolation of the first endogenous opioid peptides over ten years ago (46) research has expanded exponentially. Many different opioid peptides, their precursors, and their receptors have been characterized (12, 68, 79). Physiological roles for opioids have been described in such diverse areas as nociception, behavior and psychiatry, appetite, stress and shock. Much interest has centered, particularly in man, on the role of opioids in neuroendocrine regulation, which is the subject of this review. As always, differences exist between man and other animals, e.g. the much-studied rat. For brevity this review will therefore concentrate on the human data, mentioning other species only if important differences exist or if no comparable data are available in man. Unless otherwise stated all effects appear to occur at the hypothalamic rather than pituitary level. For clarity we use the term *opioid* to refer to endogenous peptides, and *opiate* to refer to morphine-like alkaloids (45).

OPIOID PEPTIDES AND RECEPTORS

All opioids firmly established to exist in man derive from one of three precursor peptides, whose structure has been elucidated from DNA analysis (79). The pentapeptides met- and leu-enkephalin were the first isolated (46); they share the N-terminal sequence Tyr-Gly-Gly-Phe, which appears to be the opioid active sequence, and differ in their C-terminal residues, methionine and leucine, respectively. All other opioids are essentially C-terminal extended

527

enkephalins; these extensions often endow greater potency (29) and different receptor specificity (68, 107). Pro-opiomelanocortin (POMC), the adrenocorticotropic hormone (ACTH) precursor, is the source of β-endorphin, a 31-residue extended met-enkephalin. Pro-enkephalin contains one copy of leu-enkephalin and six copies of the met-enkephalin sequence (two of which are extended: met-enkephalin-Arg-Phe and -Arg-Gly-Leu), flanked by dibasic residues. Pro-dynorphin (pro-enkephalin B) is the source of the extended leu-enkephalins α- and β-neoendorphin, dynorphin, rimorphin (dynorphin B), and leumorphin.

Multiple opioid receptors have been characterized by the behavioral effects of opiates (58), by their bioactivity in isolated tissue preparations (107), and by competitive displacement binding (41, 54). The μ-receptor, the original morphine receptor, is highly sensitive to antagonism by naloxone; no specific ligand has been isolated, but β-endorphin (also active at δ- and ε-receptors) probably fulfils this role. Met- and leu-enkephalin interact with the δ-receptor, which is resistant to naloxone. Pro-dynorphin-derived peptides interact with the κ-receptor, which is also relatively resistant to naloxone. Finally, a separate, naloxone-sensitive ε-receptor has been described for β-endorphin. Since specific δ, κ, and ε antagonists are not yet available, the opioid peptide or receptor involved in a particular neuroendocrine effect is usually inferred, in man, from the dose of naloxone required to antagonize or produce the hormonal change (low dose = μ/ε; high dose = δ/κ). In other animals injection of opioid antisera also yields valuable information (73, 82).

Opioids are distributed throughout the brain and spinal cord in specific neurone tracts, and opioidergic neurones of the three precursor types are generally separate (13). High concentrations of all opioids as well as their receptors (41) are present in the hypothalamus and median eminence. β-endorphinergic neurones originate largely in the arcuate nucleus, and project to the median eminence and elsewhere within the brain, whereas large numbers of enkephalinergic neurones are found in many hypothalamic nuclei (13). Pro-dynorphin opioids are largely localized in the magnocellular neurones of the supraoptic and paraventricular nuclei and project to the posterior pituitary, but they are also found in the arcuate nucleus and posterior hypothalamus (102). In addition, the anterior pituitary contains β-endorphin in the corticotrophs, and met-enkephalin, possibly in the somatotrophs (103).

ANTERIOR PITUITARY HORMONES

Prolactin

Administration of morphine and other opiates (18, 89), enkephalin analogues (19, 37, 88, 99), and β-endorphin (75, 76) causes release of prolactin (PRL) in man, which is easily antagonized by low doses of naloxone. The effect is potentiated by dopamine antagonists and blocked by dopamine agonists (16), which suggests that it is mediated by inhibition of dopamine secretion from the median eminence, a concept supported by much experimental evidence in the rat (39, 40, 91, 106). In the rat, β-endorphin is a more potent secretagogue then met-enkephalin (23) or dynorphin (94), and intraventricular administration of antiserum to β-endorphin lowers both basal and stress-induced PRL secretion (73). This finding suggests that β-endorphin is the opioid involved. Most studies have found no effect of opioids on isolated pituitary cells in vitro, but recent preliminary evidence suggests that α-neo-endorphin (59) and leumorphin (Imura H., personal communication) may be able to stimulate PRL release directly. In the rat, naloxone lowers basal and stimulated PRL levels (6, 62, 84, 93), which suggests an important physiological role for opioids; however, the situation is less clear in man. Most studies have reported no effect of naloxone (up to 16 mg) on basal (37, 56, 66, 70), stress-induced (37, 66, 87, 100), or puerperal (38, 56) levels of PRL, nor on secretion by prolactinomas (5, 36, 70, 90). However, naloxone inhibition of basal or stress-related PRL release has been reported by some (69, 80, 81). Naloxone (15 mg) may abolish the exercise-induced PRL release in highly trained athletes (64), but this has not been confirmed using untrained subjects (32, 60, 87). Conversely, naloxone may stimulate pulsatile PRL release in normal women in the late follicular and mid luteal phase (11) or on an oral contraceptive (9), but not in early follicular or late luteal phase or in hypogonadal women. This pulsatile release of PRL coincides with that of luteinizing hormone (LH), and may therefore be mediated via luteinizing hormone releasing hormone (LHRH) (see below), which may stimulate PRL release (10) and possibly involves paracrine gonadotroph/lactotroph interaction (11, 20).

Growth Hormone

In man, growth hormone (GH) release is stimulated by an enkephalin analogue (19, 88, 99) and some opiates (18), but not by morphine (18, 89) or β-endorphin (75). Low doses of naloxone antagonize this effect, which suggests that μ- or ε-receptors are involved, but the opioid involved is unclear. Opioid stimulation in man involves cholinergic (17) but not dopaminergic (16) interactions; other neurotransmitters have been implicated in the rat (62). Modulation of both somatostatin (22) and growth hormone releasing factor (GRF) (104) may be involved. In man, in contrast to the rat, naloxone does not alter basal (37, 66, 87), sleep-related (56), or stress-related (66, 87, 100) release of GH. Attenuation of exercise-induced GH release was inhibited in some studies (64, 87), but not others (32, 60). Neither opioids nor naloxone alter GH secretion in acromegaly (5, 19, 66, 90).

TSH

Opioids inhibit thyroid stimulating hormone (TSH) release in the rat (62), but stimulate TSH release in man (18, 88). Naloxone may slightly lower TSH in normal subjects (37), but has no effect on TSH in primary hypothyroidism (38, 66). A major physiological role is therefore unlikely.

ACTH

In the rat, opioids acutely stimulate release of CRF (7) and therefore ACTH (62); in contrast, opioids are inhibitory in man. Enkephalin analogues and opiates suppress (18, 19, 88), and naloxone stimulates (34, 66, 98), cortisol release in normal subjects. The high dose of naloxone required suggests involvement of δ- or κ-selective opioids (33), which appear to inhibit a stimulatory noradrenergic pathway (30). Opioid stimulation is independent of the circadian rhythm of ACTH secretion, but of similar magnitude and not additive to the stress-induced response (34). These observations suggest that removal of opioid inhibitory tone may mediate at least some ACTH-cortisol stress responses. Peripheral effects are also possible since naloxone potentiates ACTH-stimulated corticosterone release from rat adrenal in vitro (55). Opioids inhibit ACTH secretion in Addison's disease (27), but in Cushing's disease and Nelson's syndrome responses appear heterogenous: both opioids and naloxone may be inhibitory or have no effect (1, 21, 27, 90).

Gonadotropins

Chronic opiate addiction produces hypogonadism in both sexes (65), and opioids and opiates promptly suppress LH and FSH in both animals (6, 62) and man (18, 35, 75, 88). Naloxone acutely increases serum LH, and possibly FSH, levels in both sexes (25, 35, 51, 66, 67) which indicates chronic inhibitory opioid control. Infusion of naloxone for 24 hr also increases serum testosterone in the male (15). Opioid effects are mediated via LHRH: Opioids have no effect on LH response to LHRH (35); LHRH antagonists block naloxone stimulation in the rat (4); naloxone stimulates LHRH release from human (74) and rat (22) hypothalami in vitro; and morphine decreases hypothalamic LHRH content (49). In the rat there is ample evidence that adrenergic pathways are involved (24, 48, 49, 92), but neither adrenergic (97) nor dopaminergic (16) mechanisms appear to be involved in man. The relative naloxone-sensitivity of gonadotropin responses suggests μ- or ε-receptor involvement (33). However, in the rat, intrahypothalamic injection of antisera to both β-endorphin and dynorphin (but not met-enkephalin) stimulates LH release (82), which suggests that both opioids may be involved, although β-endorphin is more potent.

Naloxone increases both the frequency and amplitude of pulsatile LH release in both sexes (25, 35, 67, 72, 78). In females the effect is most marked in the late follicular and mid-luteal phases (72), and it is thus possible that opioids mediate the slower LH pulses seen at this time. Indeed, in animals hypothalamic (47) and hypophyseal portal (105) concentrations of β-endorphin rise after ovulation.

Opioids are intimately involved in the feedback of gonadal steroids on LHRH secretion. Thus most studies agree that naloxone is unable to further elevate LH in postmenopausal or ovariectomized women, and that naloxone sensitivity is restored by replacement with estrogens and/or progesterone (8, 63, 76, 85). Endogenous levels of gonadal steroids and naloxone sensitivity are both maximal in the mid luteal phase. Feedback of gonadal steroids may thus be mediated via opioidergic pathways; however, the evidence on whether or not opioids can inhibit LH in postmenopausal women is contradictory (35, 76), so this is not yet certain. Gonadal steroids do raise hypophyseal portal β-endorphin concentrations in ovariectomized monkeys (101).

Changes in opioid inhibitory tone are unlikely to initiate puberty since, unlike the rat (3), man's responsiveness to naloxone is absent before puberty, and does not develop until near maturity (26, 96). A number of pathological hypogonadotrophic conditions may be mediated by changes in opioid tone: Naloxone restores LH pulsatility in patients with hyperprolactinemia (36, 51, 70), in some patients with so-called hypothalamic amenorrhea (71), and in amenorrheic athletes (61). These findings suggest that opioids mediate amenorrhea, and indicate a possible therapeutic role for oral opioid antagonist therapy in the future. The majority of patients with anorexia nervosa show no LH response to naloxone (2, 36), and patients who do respond may have another preexisting cause for amenorrhea (2).

β-endorphin is coreleased into plasma with ACTH in response to stressful stimuli (86). β-endorphin and met-enkephalin rise during exercise in the female (43); however, the plasma levels achieved are in the picomolar range, and are insufficient to stimulate known opiate receptors. Thus the observed changes in opioid neuroendocrine control in such circumstances are unlikely to be mediated by these plasma changes. Decreased opioid tone (and naloxone nonresponse) has been implicated in the pathophysiology of polycystic ovary syndrome (14), although normal naloxone response is also reported (51). Peripheral effects are also possible: intratesticular naloxone inhibits testosterone secretion in the rat (28).

POSTERIOR PITUITARY

Prodynorphin-derived opioids and met-enkephalin are localized with vasopressin (VP) and oxytocin, respectively, in the magnocellular neurones of the supra-optic and paraventricular nuclei projecting to the posterior pituitary (57, 102).

In the rat, neurohypophyseal dynorphin varies in parallel with VP in response to osmotic stimuli in vivo (42), and is released in vitro (83), although plasma dynorphin is not elevated after dehydration in man (44).

Although administration of opiates may have an antidiuretic effect, this is probably not mediated by VP (95). In man, opioids appear to inhibit VP release in response to osmotic stimuli (31, 52, 77) and nicotine stimulation (53). Conversely, naloxone inhibits VP response to orthostatic stimuli (50), so more than one pathway may be operative. Whether this inhibition represents ultra-short loop feedback by dynorphin is unknown. No data are available on oxytocin release in man, but in the rat opioids inhibit secretion (95).

CONCLUSIONS

Opioidergic neurones are thus able to modulate secretion of every pituitary hormone, but physiological effects (as judged by naloxone) only appear important with regard to ACTH, LH, FSH, and possibly vasopressin. Pathological changes in opioid control are to date only apparent on LH. Further elucidation of the precise role of each opioid in man awaits the availability of specific μ-, δ-, κ-, and ε-receptor antagonists. In the future, clinical availability of orally active opiate antagonists will allow further exploration of the pathological effects of changes in opioid regulation. Interactions with other classical and peptide neurotransmitters is clearly important and as yet incompletely explored.

Literature Cited

1. Allolio, B., Winklemann, W., Hipp, F. X., Kaulen, D., Mies, R. 1982. Effects of a met-enkephalin analog on adrenocorticotropin (ACTH), growth hormone and prolactin in patients with ACTH hypersecretion. *J. Clin. Endocrinol. Metab.* 55:1–7
2. Baranowska, B., Rozbicka, G., Jeske, W., Abdel-Fattah, M. H. 1984. The role of endogenous opiates in the mechanism of inhibited luteinizing hormone (LH) secretion in women with anorexia nervosa: The effect of naloxone on LH, follicle-stimulating hormone, prolactin and β-endorphin secretion. *J. Clin. Endocrinol. Metab.* 59:412–16
3. Bhanot, R., Wilkinson, M. 1983. Opiatergic control of gonadotrophin secretion during puberty in the rat: A neurochemical basis for the hypothalamic "gonadostat". *Endocrinology* 113:596–603
4. Blank, M. S., Roberts, D. L. 1982. Antagonist of gonadotrophin-releasing hormone blocks naloxone-induced elevations in serum luteinizing hormone. *Neuroendocrinology* 35:309–12
5. Blankstein, J., Reyes, F., Winter, J., Faiman, C. 1979. Failure of naloxone to alter growth hormone and prolactin levels in acromegalic and in hyperprolactinaemic patients. *Clin. Endocrinol.* 11:474–79
6. Bruni, J. F., VanVugt, D., Marshall, S., Meites, J. 1977. Effects of naloxone morphine and methionine enkephalin on serum prolactin, luteinizing hormone, follicle stimulating hormone, thyroid stimulating hormone and growth hormone. *Life Sci.* 21:461–66
7. Buckingham, J. C. 1982. Secretion of corticotrophin and its hypothalamic releasing factor in response to morphine and opioid peptides. *Neuroendocrinology* 35:111–16
8. Casper, R. F., Alapin-Rubillovitz, S. 1985. Progestins increase endogenous opioid peptide activity in postmenopausal women. *J. Clin. Endocrinol. Metab.* 60:34–6
9. Casper, R. F., Bhanot, R., Wilkinson, M. 1984. Prolonged elevation of hypothalamic opioid peptide activity in women taking oral contraceptives. *J. Clin. Endocrinol. Metab.* 58:582–84
10. Casper, R. F., Yen, S. S. C. 1981. Simultaneous pulsatile release of prolactin and luteinizing hormone induced by luteinizing hormone-releasing factor. *J. Clin. Endocrinol. Metab.* 52:934–36

11. Cetel, N. S., Quigley, M. E., Yen, S. S. C. 1985. Naloxone-induced prolactin secretion in women: evidence against a direct prolactin stimulatory effect of endogenous opioids. *J. Clin. Endocrinol. Metab.* 60:191–96

12. Cox, B. M. 1982. Endogenous opioid peptides: A guide to structures and terminology. *Life Sci.* 31:1645–58

13. Cuello, A. C. 1983. Central distribution of opioid peptides. *Br. Med. Bull.* 39:11–16

14. Cumming, D. C., Reid, R. L., Quigley, M. E., Rebar, R. W., Yen, S. S. C. 1984. Evidence for decreased endogenous dopamine and opioid inhibitory influences on LH secretion in polycystic ovary syndrome. *Clin. Endocrinol.* 20:643–48

15. Delitala, G., Giusti, M., Mazzocchi, G., Granziera, L., Tarditi, W., Giordano, G. 1983. Participation of endogenous opiates in regulation of the hypothalamic-pituitary-testicular axis in normal men. *J. Clin. Endocrinol. Metab.* 57:1277–81

16. Delitala, G., Grossman, A., Besser, G. M. 1981. Changes in pituitary hormone levels induced by met-enkephalin in man—the role of dopamine. *Life Sci.* 29:1537–44

17. Delitala, G., Grossman, A., Besser, G. M. 1983. Opiate peptides control growth hormone through a cholinergic mechanism in man. *Clin. Endocrinol.* 18: 401–5

18. Delitala, G., Grossman, A., Besser, M. 1983. Differential effects of opiate peptides and alkaloids on anterior pituitary hormone secretion. *Neuroendocrinology* 37:275–79

19. Demura, R., Suda, T., Wakabayashi, I., Yoshimura, M., Jibiki, K., et al. 1981. Plasma pituitary hormone responses to the synthetic enkephalin analog (FK33-824) in normal subjects and patients with pituitary diseases. *J. Clin. Endocrinol. Metab.* 52:263–66

20. Denef, C., Andries, M. 1983. Evidence for paracrine interaction between gonadotrophs and lactotrophs in pituitary cell aggregates. *J. Endocrinol. Metab.* 112: 813–22

21. Deuss, U., Allolio, B., Kaulen, D., Fischer, H., Winklemann, W. 1985. Effects of high dose and low dose naloxone on plasma ACTH in patients with ACTH hypersecretion. *Clin. Endocrinol.* 22:273–79

22. Drouva, S. V., Epelbaum, J., Tapia-Arancibia, L., Laplante, E., Kordon, C. 1981. Opiate receptors modulate LHRH and SRIF release from mediobasal hypothalamic neurones. *Neuroendo-*

crinology 32:163–67

23. Dupont, A., Barden, N., Cusan, L., Merand, Y., Labrie, F., Vaudry, H. 1980. β-endorphin and met-enkephalins: Their distribution, modulation by estrogens and haloperidol, and role in neuroendocrine control. *Fed. Proc.* 39: 2544–50

24. Dyer, R. G., Mansfield, S., Corbet, H., Dean, A. D. P. 1985. Fasting impairs LH secretion in female rats by activating an inhibitory opioid pathway. *J. Endocrinol.* 105:91–97

25. Ellinboe, J., Veldhuis, J. D., Mendelson, J. H., Kuehnle, J. C., Mello, N. K., Holbrook, P. G. 1982. Effect of endogenous opioid blockade on the amplitude and frequency of pulsatile luteinizing hormone secretion in normal men. *J. Clin. Endocrinol. Metab.* 54: 854–57

26. Fraioli, F., Cappa, M., Fabbri, A., Gnessi, L., Moretti, C., et al. 1984. Lack of endogenous opioid inhibitory tone in early puberty. *Clin. Endocrinol.* 20:299–305

27. Gaillard, R. C., Grossman, A., Smith, R., Rees, L. H., Besser, G. M. 1981. The effects of a met-enkephalin analogue on ACTH, β-LPH, β-endorphin and met-enkephalin in patients with adrenocortical disease. *Clin. Endocrinol.* 14:471–78

28. Gerendai, I., Shaha, C., Thau, R., Bardin, C. W. 1984. Do testicular opiates regulate leydig cell function? *Endocrinology* 115:1645–47

29. Goldstein, A., Tachibana, S., Lowney, L. I., Hunkapiller, M., Hood, L. 1980. Dynorphin (1–13), an extraordinarily potent opioid peptide. *Proc. Nat. Acad. Sci. USA* 76:6666–70

30. Grossman, A., Besser, G. M. 1982. Opiates control ACTH through a noradrenergic mechanism. *Clin. Endocrinol.* 17:287–90

31. Grossman, A., Besser, G. M., Milles, J. J., Baylis, P. H. 1980. Inhibition of vasopressin release in man by an opiate peptide. *Lancet* 2:1108–10

32. Grossman, A., Bouloux, P., Price, P., Drury, P. L., Lam, K. S. L., et al. 1984. The role of opioid peptides in the hormonal responses to acute exercise in man. *Clin. Sci.* 67:483–91

33. Grossman, A., Bouloux, P. M. G., Moult, P. J. A., Perry, L., Delitala, G., Besser, G. M. 1985. The opioid modulation of circulating cortisol LH and FSH—Analysis of receptors involved. *J. Endocrinol.* 104, Suppl. P68, Abstr. 103

34. Grossman, A., Gaillard, R. C., McCartney, P., Rees, L. H., Besser, G. M. 1982. Opiate modulation of the pituitary-adrenal axis: effects of stress and circa-

dian rhythm. *Clin. Endocrinol.* 17:279–86

35. Grossman, A., Moult, P. J. A., Gaillard, R. C., Delitala, G., Toff, W. D., et al. 1981. The opioid control of LH and FSH release: effects of a met-enkephalin analogue and naloxone. *Clin. Endocrinol.* 14:41–47

36. Grossman, A., Moult, P. J. A., Mcintyre, H., Evans, J., Silverstone, T., et al. 1982. Opiate mediation of amenorrhoea in hyperprolactinaemia and in weight-loss related amenorrhoea. *Clin. Endocrinol.* 17:379–88

37. Grossman, A., Stubbs, W. A., Gaillard, R. C., Delitalia, G., Rees, L. H., Besser, G. M. 1981. Studies of the opiate control of prolactin, GH and TSH. *Clin. Endocrinol.* 14:381–86

38. Grossman, A., West, S., Williams, J., Evans, J., Rees, L. H., Besser, G. M. 1982. The role of opiate peptides in the control of prolactin in the puerperium, and TSH in primary hypothyroidism. *Clin. Endocrinol.* 16:317–20

39. Gudelsky, G. A., Porter, J. C. 1979. Morphine and opioid peptide-induced inhibition of the release of dopamine from tuberoinfundibular neurons. *Life Sci.* 25:1697–1702

40. Haskins, J. T., Gudelsky, G. A., Moss, R. L., Porter, J. C. 1981. Iontophoresis of morphine into the arcuate nucleus: effects on dopamine concentrations in hypophysial portal plasma and serum prolactin concentrations. *Endocrinology* 108:767–71

41. Herz, A. 1984. Multiple opioid receptors. In *Opioid Modulation of Endocrine Function*, ed. G. Delitala, et al. pp. 11–19. New York: Raven

42. Hollt, V., Haarman, I., Seizinger, B. R., Herz, A. 1981. Levels of dynorphin (1–13) immunoreactivity in rat neurointermediate pituitaries are concomitantly altered with those of leucine enkephalin and vasopressin in response to various endocrine manipulations. *Neuroendocrinology* 33:333–39

43. Howlett, T. A., Tomlin, S., Ngahfoong, L., Rees, L. H., Bullen, B. A., et al. 1984. Release of β-endorphin and met-enkephalin during exercise in normal women: Response to training. *Br. Med. J.* 288:1950–52

44. Howlett, T. A., Walker, J., Besser, G. M., Rees, L. H. 1984. "Dynorphin" in plasma: Enzymatic artifact and authentic immunoreactivity. *Reg. Pept.* 8:131–40

45. Hughes, J., Kosterlitz, H. W. 1983. Opioid peptides: Introduction. *Br. Med. Bull.* 39:1–13

46. Hughes, J., Smith, T. W., Kosterlitz, H.

W., Fothergill, L. A., Morgan, B. A., Morris, H. R. 1975. Identification of two related pentapeptides from the brain with potent opiate agonist activity. *Nature* 258:577–79

47. Hulse, G. K., Coleman, G. J., Copolou, D. L., Clements, J. A. 1984. Relationship between endogenous opioids and the oestrus cycle in the rat. *J. Endocrinol.* 100:271–75

48. Kalra, S. P., Crowley, W. R. 1982. Epinephrine synthesis inhibitors block naloxone-induced LH release. *Endocrinology* 111:1403–5

49. Kalra, S. P., Simpkins, J. W. 1981. Evidence for noradrenergic mediation of opioid effects on luteinizing hormone secretion. *Endocrinology* 109:776–82

50. Lightman, S. L., Forsling, M. L. 1980. Evidence for endogenous opioid control of vasopressin release in man. *J. Clin. Endocrinol. Metab.* 50:569–71

51. Lightman, S. L., Jacobs, H. S., Maguire, A. K., McGarrick, G., Jeffcoate, S. L. 1981. Constancy of opioid control of luteinizing hormone in different pathophysiological states. *J. Clin. Endocrinol. Metab.* 52:1260–63

52. Lightman, S. L., Langdon, N., Forsling, M. L. 1980. Effects of the opiate antagonist naloxone and the enkephalin analog DAMME on the vasopressin response to a hypertonic stimulus in man. *J. Clin. Endocrinol. Metab.* 51:1447–49

53. Lightman, S., Langdon, N., Todd, K., Forsling, M. 1982. Naloxone increases the nicotine-stimulated rise of vasopressin secretion in man. *Clin. Endocrinol.* 16:353–58

54. Lord, J. A. H., Waterfield, A. A., Hughes, J., Korsterlitz, H. W. 1977. Endogenous opioid peptides—Multiple agonists and receptors. *Nature* 267:495–99

55. Lymangrover, J. R., Dokas, L. A., Kong, A., Martin, R., Saffran, M. 1981. Naloxone has a direct effect on the adrenal cortex. *Endocrinology* 109:1132–37

56. Martin, J. B., Tolis, G., Wood, I., Guyda, H. 1979. Failure of naloxone to influence physiological growth hormone and prolactin secretion. *Brain Res.* 168:210–15

57. Martin, R., Voigt, K. H. 1981. Enkephalins coexist with oxytocin and vasopressin in nerve terminal of rat neurohypophysis. *Nature* 289:502–4

58. Martin, W. R., Eades, C. G., Thompson, J. A., Huppler, R. E., Gilbert, P. E. 1976. The effects of morphine- and nalorphine-like drugs in the nondependent and morphine dependent

chronic spinal dog. *J. Pharmacol. Exp. Ther.* 197:517–32

59. Matsushita, N., Kato, Y., Shimatsu, A., Katakami, H., Fujino, M., Matsuo, H., Imura, H. 1982. Stimulation of prolactin secretion in the rat by α-neo-endorphin, β-neo-endorphin and dynorphin. *Biochem. Biophys. Res. Commun.* 107:735–41

60. Mayer, G., Wessel, J., Kobberling, J. 1980. Failure of naloxone to alter exercise-induced growth hormone and prolactin release in normal men. *Clin. Endocrinol.* 13:413–16

61. McArthur, J. W., Bullen, B. A., Betting, I. Z., Pagane, M., Badger, T. M., Klibanski, A. 1980. Hypothalamic amenorrhoea in runners of normal body distribution. *Endocr. Res. Commun.* 7:13–25

62. Meites, J., Bruni, J. F., Van Vugt, D. A., Smith, A. F. 1979. Relation of endogenous opioid peptides and morphine to neuroendocrine function. *Life Sci.* 24:1325–36

63. Melis, G. B., Paoletti, A. M., Gambacciani, M., Mais, V., Fioretti, P. 1984. Evidence that estrogens inhibit LH secretion through opioids in postmenopausal women using naloxone. *Neuroendocrinology* 39:60–63

64. Moretti, C., Fabbri, A., Gnessi, L., Cappa, M., Calzolari, A., et al. 1983. Naloxone inhibits exercise-induced release of PRL and GH in athletes. *Clin. Endocrinol.* 18:135–38

65. Morley, J. E. 1981. The endocrinology of the opiates and opioid peptides. *Metabolism* 30:195–209

66. Morley, J. E., Baranetsky, N. G., Wingert, T. D., Carlson, H. E., Hershman, J. M., et al. 1980. Endocrine effects of naloxone-induced opiate receptor blockade. *J. Clin. Endocrinol. Metab.* 50: 251–57

67. Moult, P. J. A., Grossman, A., Evans, J. M., Rees, L. H., Besser, G. M. 1981. The effect of naloxone on pulsatile gonadotrophin release in normal subjects. *Clin. Endocrinol.* 14:321–24

68. Paterson, S. J., Robson, L. E., Kosterlitz, H. W. 1983. Classification of opioid receptors. *Br. Med. Bull.* 39:31–36

69. Pontiroli, A. E., Baio, G., Stella, L., Crescenti, A., Girardi, A. M. 1982. Effects of naloxone on prolactin, luteinizing hormone and cortisol responses to surgical stress in humans. *J. Clin. Endocrinol. Metab.* 55:378–80

70. Quigley, M. E., Sheehan, K. L., Casper, R. F., Yen, S. S. C. 1980. Evidence for increased opioid inhibition of luteinizing hormone secretion in hyperprolactinaemic patients with pituitary microadenoma.

J. Clin. Endocrinol. Metab. 50, 427–430

71. Quigley, M. E., Sheehan, K. L., Casper, R. F., Yen, S. S. C. 1980. Evidence for increased dopaminergic and opioid activity in patients with hypothalamic hypogonadotropic amenorrhea. *J. Clin. Endocrinol. Metab.* 50:949–54

72. Quigley, M. E., Yen, S. S. C. 1980. The role of endogenous opiates on LH secretion during the menstrual cycle. *J. Clin. Endocrinol.* 51:179–81

73. Ragavan, V. V., Frantz, A. G. 1981. Opioid regulation of prolactin secretion: evidence for a specific role of β-endorphin. *Endocrinology* 109:1769–71

74. Rasmussen, D. D., Liu, J. H., Wolf, P. L., Yen, S. S. C. 1983. Endogenous opioid regulation of gonadotrophin-releasing hormone release from the human fetal hypothalamus in vitro. *J. Clin. Endocrinol. Metab.* 57:881–84

75. Reid, R. L., Hoff, J. D., Yen, S. S. C., Li, C. H. 1981. Effects of exogenous β-endorphin on pituitary hormone secretion and its disappearance rate in normal human subjects. *J. Clin. Endocrinol. Metab.* 52:1179–84

76. Reid, R. L., Quigley, M. E., Yen, S. S. C. 1983. The disappearance of opioidergic regulation of gonadotropin secretion in postmenopausal women. *J. Clin. Endocrinol. Metab.* 57:1107–10

77. Reid, R. L., Yen, S. S. C., Artman, H., Fisher, D. A. 1981. Effects of synthetic β-endorphin on release of neurohypophyseal hormones. *Lancet* 2:1167–70

78. Ropert, J. F., Quigley, M. E., Yen, S. S. C. 1981. Endogenous opiates modulate pulsatile luteinizing hormone release in humans. *J. Clin. Endocrinol. Metab.* 52:583–85

79. Rossier, J. 1982. Opioid peptides have found their roots. *Nature* 298:221–22

80. Rubin, P., Swezey, S., Blaschke, T. 1979. Naloxone lowers plasma prolactin in man. *Lancet* i:1293

81. Saltiel, H., Passa, P. H., Kuhn, J. M., Fiet, J., Canivet, J. 1982. Mediation par les peptides opioides de la response antehypophysaire a l'hypoglycemie insulinique. *Nouv. Presse Med.* 11:847–50

82. Schulz, R., Wilhelm, A., Pirke, K. M., Gramsch, C., Herz, A. 1981. β-endorphin and dynorphin control serum luteinizing hormone level in immature female rats. *Nature* 294:757–59

83. Seizinger, B. R., Maysinger, D., Hollt, V., Grimm, C., Herz, A. 1982. Concomitant neonatal development and in vitro release of dynorphin and α neo-endorphin. *Life Sci.* 31:1757–60

84. Shaar, C. J., Frederickson, C. A., Dinin-

ger, N. B., Jackson, L. 1977. Enkephalin analogues and naloxone modulate the release of growth hormone and prolactin: Evidence for regulation by an endogenous opioid peptide in brain. *Life Sci.* 21:853–60

85. Shoupe, D., Montz, F. J., Lobo, R. A. 1985. The effects of estrogen and progestin on endogenous opioid activity in oophorectomized women. *J. Clin. Endocrinol. Metab.* 30:178–83

86. Smith, R., Grossman, A., Gaillard, R., Clement-Jones, V., Ratter, S., et al. 1981. Studies on circulating met-enkephalin and β-endorphin: normal subjects and patients with renal and adrenal disease. *Clin. Endocrinol.* 15:291–300

87. Spiler, I. J., Molitch, M. E. 1980. Lack of modulation of pituitary hormone stress response by neural pathways involving opiate receptors. *J. Clin. Endocrinol. Metab.* 50:516–20

88. Stubbs, W. A., Delitala, G., Jones, A., Jeffocate, W. J., Edwards, C. R. W., et al. 1978. Hormonal and metabolic responses to an enkephalin analogue in normal man. *Lancet* ii:1225–27

89. Tolis, G., Hickey, J., Guyda, H., 1975. Effects of morphine on serum growth hormone, cortisol, prolactin and thyroid stimulating hormone in man. *J. Endocrinol. Metab.* 41:797–800

90. Tolis, G., Jukier, L., Wiesen, M., Krieger, D. T. 1982. Effect of naloxone on pituitary hypersecretory syndromes. *J. Clin. Endocrinol. Metab.* 54:780–84

91. Van Loon, G. R., Ho, D., Kim, C. 1980. β-endorphin induced decrease in hypothalamic dopamine turnover. *Endocrinology* 106:76–80

92. Van Vugt, D. A., Aylsworth, C. F., Sylvester, P. W., Leung, F. C., Meites, J. 1981. Evidence for hypothalamic noradrenergic involvement in naloxone-induced stimulation of luteinizing hormone release. *Neuroendocrinology* 33:261–64

93. Van Vugt, D. A., Bruni, J. F., Meites, J. 1978. Naloxone inhibition of stress-induced increase in prolactin secretion. *Life Sci.* 22:85–90

94. Van Vugt, D., Sylvester, P. W., Aylsworth, C. F., Meites, J. 1981. Comparison of acute effects of dynorphin and β-endorphin on prolactin release in the rat. *Endocrinology* 109:2017–18

95. Greidanus, T. B. V., ten Haaf, J. A. 1984. Opioids and the posterior pituitary. In *Opioid Modulation of Endocrine Function*, ed. G. Delitala, et al. pp. 125–36. New York: Raven

96. Veldhuis, J. D., Kulin, H. E., Warner, B. A., Santner, S. J. 1982. Responsiveness of gonadotropin secretion to infusion of an opiate-receptor antagonist in hypogonadotropic individuals. *J. Clin. Endocrinol. Metab.* 55:649–53

97. Veldhuis, J. D., Rogol, A. D., Williams, F. A., Johnson, M. L. 1983. Do α-adrenergic mechanisms regulate spontaneous or opiate-modulated pulsatile luteinizing hormone secretion in man? *J. Clin. Endocrinol. Metab.* 57:1292–96

98. Volavka, J., Cho, D., Mallya, A., Bauman, L. 1979. Naloxone increases ACTH and cortisol levels in man. *N. Engl. J. Med.* 300:1056–57

99. Von Graffenreid, B., Del Pozo, E., Roubicek, J., Krebs, E., Poldinger, W., et al. 1978. Effects of the synthetic enkephalin analogue FK 33–824 in man. *Nature* 272:729–30

100. Wakabayashi, I., Demura, R., Miki, N., Ohmura, E., Miyoshi, H., Shimuze, K. 1980. Failure of naloxone to influence plasma growth hormone, prolactin, and cortisol secretions induced by insulin hypoglycaemia. *J. Clin. Endocrinol. Metab.* 50:597–99

101. Wardlaw, S. L., Wehrenberg, W. B., Ferin, M., Antunes, J. L., Frantz, A. G. 1982. Effect of sex steroids on β-endorphin in hypophyseal portal blood. *J. Clin. Endocrinol. Metab.* 55:877–81

102. Watson, S. J., Khachaturian, H., Coy, D., Taylor, L., Akil, H. 1982. Dynorphin is located throughout the CNS and is often localised with α-neo-endorphin. *Life Sci.* 31:1773–76

103. Weber, E., Voigt, K. H., Martin, R. 1978. Pituitary somatotrophs contain met-enkephalin-like immunoreactivity. *Proc. Nat. Acad. Sci. USA* 75:6134–38

104. Wehrenberg, W. B., Brazeau, P., Luben, R., Ling, N., Guillemin, R. 1983. A non-invasive functional lesion of the hypothalamo-pituitary axis for the study of growth hormone-releasing factor. *Neuroendocrinology* 36:489–91

105. Wehrenberg, W. B., Wardlaw, S. L., Frantz, A. G., Ferin, M. 1982. β-endorphin in hypophyseal portal blood—variations throughout the menstrual cycle. *Endocrinology* 111:879–81

106. Wilkes, M. M., Yen, S. S. C. 1980. Reduction by β-endorphin of efflux of dopamine and dopac from superfused medial basal hypothalamus. *Life Sci.* 27:1387–91

107. Wuster, M., Schulz, R., Herz, A. 1981. Multiple opiate receptors in peripheral tissue preparations. *Biochem. Pharmacol.* 30:1883–87

Ann. Rev. Physiol. 1986. 48:537–49

SUBSTANCE P AND NEUROTENSIN: Their Roles in the Regulation of Anterior Pituitary Function

Neil Aronin, Rafael Coslovsky, and Susan E. Leeman

Departments of Medicine and Physiology, University of Massachusetts Medical School, Worcester, Massachusetts 01605

INTRODUCTION

Substance P and neurotensin are both peptides that were first isolated and chemically characterized from extracts of bovine hypothalamus (7, 8, 56). As with many other neuropeptides, these peptides have diverse functions, in keeping with their widespread distribution throughout the nervous system, the gastrointestinal tract, and several endocrine glands. There is considerable evidence that substance P and neurotensin contribute to the regulation of anterior pituitary function. Access to the regulation of anterior pituitary function can occur at many sites, including neural afferent inputs to the hypothalamus, the neuroendocrine cells, hypothalamic interneurons, the neural-capillary interface of the median eminence, and the anterior pituitary gland. A potentially important source of anterior pituitary regulation by substance P and neurotensin is within the anterior pituitary itself. There, these peptides may serve as local, or paracrine, agents. For each peptide we will review the morphological basis for its presence in the hypothalamus and anterior pituitary, the consequences of the administration of each into the central nervous system and anterior pituitary, and finally, their responsiveness in the anterior pituitary to hormonal regulation.

SUBSTANCE P

Cellular Localization of Substance P–Like Immunoreactivity

AFFERENT INPUTS TO THE HYPOTHALAMUS   There are multiple afferent systems to the hypothalamus. Immunohistochemical findings indicate that

537

fibers from the amygdala-fugal pathway, probably via the stria terminalis, contain substance P, and enter the bed nucleus of the stria terminalis (47) and lateral hypothalamus (46). The stria terminalis also projects to regions containing neuroendocrine cells (42), which suggests that substance P released from these afferent terminals may interact with these cells.

INTRINSIC HYPOTHALAMIC NEURONAL ELEMENTS   The distribution of neuronal elements labeled for substance P by immunohistochemistry varies among mammalian species. Cell bodies with substance P–like immunoreactivity have been observed in the arcuate nucleus, the medial preoptic area, and less commonly in the periventricular zone in the rat (37, 43), whereas in the monkey numerous cells have been found in the arcuate nucleus, the region lateral to the arcuate nucleus, and the periventricular area of the dorsal tuberal region (45). In the rat neuronal staining for substance P is distributed in cells of the ventromedial nucleus, dorsomedial nucleus, lateral hypothalamus, lateral preoptic area, and dorsal and ventral premammillary nuclei (43). These cells lack a projection to the median eminence but probably subserve important roles in integrating information from within the limbic system, including neuroendocrine regulation. Immunoreactive substance P fibers are distributed in the same regions that contain substance P–positive cells (37, 43). These labeled fibers are especially prominent in the medial preoptic area. The source of substance P fibers, whether extrahypothalamic or hypothalamic (collaterals from projecting neurons to other central nervous system regions, or neuroendocrine cells, or interneurons), is not known. An important ultrastructural observation is that terminals containing substance P form axodendritic synapses in the rat tubero-infundibular region (53). Whether the postsynaptic element is a neuroendocrine cell is unknown.

Neurons in the hypothalamus and other brain regions often contain more than one neuropeptide or candidate transmitter. In the mouse injected with colchicine, some vasopressinergic cells of the supraoptic and paraventricular nuclei also contain substance P–like immunoreactivity (51). Coexistence of substance P and oxytocin was not found. The functional importance of colocalization of transmitters in neurons is not known.

MEDIAN EMINENCE   The external lamina of the median eminence, the site of termination of neuroendocrine axons onto capillaries of the hypothalamic-portal system, has a dense plexus of substance P–positive fibers in the monkey (23). On the other hand, the external lamina of the median eminence in the rat appears to contain fewer labeled terminals: both sparse (37) and moderate (53) staining has been reported. Smaller concentrations of radioimmunoassayable substance P also are measured in the external layer of the median eminence compared to other hypothalamic regions (4). In the primate, fibers are present in the internal layer of the median eminence (45), consistent with detection of substance P–containing fibers in the posterior pituitary. Electron microscopic examination of the substance P axons in the rat median eminence demonstrates that some immunoreactive boutons in the external layer contact the basal lamina of capillaries in the hypophyseal-portal system (53). This finding provides morphological evidence that substance P may be secreted from neuroendocrine cells directly into the portal circulation to reach the anterior pituitary. Alternatively, substance P fibers strategically adjoining capillaries may have other roles, for example, affecting flow characteristics of the portal system.

ANTERIOR PITUITARY   Substance P–like immunoreactivity has been demonstrated in the rodent anterior pituitary, but there is disagreement on the particular cell type(s) in which the peptide is localized. Both in prepubertal and adult rats, Morel and coworkers (40) found that immunoreactive substance P is present in the lactotroph and in the gonadotroph. In the guinea pig, using a different immunocytochemical technique, De Palatis and colleagues found that substance P–like immunoreactivity is localized in a subpopulation of thyrotrophs (13). More work is clearly needed to establish the distribution and subcellular localization of substance P in the anterior pituitary.

Responses to the Administration of Substance P

INTRAVENTRICULAR INJECTION   In the hypothalamus, in situ demonstration of effects of a peptide has been explored using intraventricular and intracerebral injections. In both cases determining whether the action of the peptide is directly on the neuroendocrine cell or indirectly through regulation of a nearby neuron(s) is difficult. With intraventricular injection, diffusion of the peptide is necessary for the administered substance to reach neuronal systems. The depth to which the substance diffuses into the brain is generally not reported, but since the paraventricular, arcuate, and periventricular neuroendocrine neurons are near the third ventricle, penetration of substances to these areas is likely. Intracerebral injection would seem to improve the opportunity of the peptide to reach the brain region to be studied, but the likelihood remains that the substance spreads and may affect several types of neurons in the area of diffusion. Differences in findings among studies may be explained by differences in the site and dose of injected substances, the state of consciousness of the experimental animal (i.e. anesthesia), its level of stress, its gender, general hormonal status, and biorhythms. Keeping in mind these many potential pitfalls, we believe that the following studies indicate that substance P can, under particular conditions, affect anterior pituitary hormone release, but how and under what circumstances these effects are physiological largely remains uncertain.

Growth hormone and prolactin   Chihara and coworkers (9) injected substance P (10 nM in 10 μl saline) into the lateral ventricle of urethane-anesthetized male rats that had been pretreated intravenously with normal sheep serum, sheep anti-somatostatin antiserum, or rabbit anti–substance P antiserum. Substance P administration suppressed serum growth hormone concentrations in animals given normal sheep serum or anti–substance P antiserum. However, pretreatment with anti-somatostatin antiserum abolished the suppressive effect of the intraventricular substance P injection. Prolactin levels were unaffected by any of these manipulations (9). This study suggests that substance P can decrease growth hormone release through a somatostatin-dependent mechanism. However, Abe and coworkers (1) found no change in somatostatin concentrations in hypothalamic portal blood after intraventricular injection of substance P (0.016–2.0 μg) in urethane or pentobarbital anesthetized rats. In conscious, ovariectomized rats, Vijayan & McCann found that substance P (0.5–2.0 μg) injected into the third ventricle increased serum growth hormone and prolactin levels (54, 55). Following administration of substance P (100 μg) into the lateral ventricle of female rhesus monkeys, an increase in prolactin and a small decrease in growth hormone serum concentrations have been reported (17).

Thyrotropin and luteinizing hormone   In urethane-anesthetized, estrogen-primed rats, injection of substance P (5 μg) into the lateral ventricle did not change serum thyrotropin concentrations (38). The same lack of effect has been observed in conscious, ovariectomized rats (55) following substance P administration into the third ventricle. In the identical experimental paradigm, serum luteinizing hormone concentrations increased after intraventricular substance P injection. In the conscious female rhesus monkey, however, administration of substance P (100 μg) into the lateral ventricle did not result in a change in serum gonadotropin levels (17).

INTRAVENOUS INJECTION   The site of action of peptides injected peripherally is most likely the anterior pituitary, as peptides so administered do not ordinarily gain entrance to the central nervous system. Differences in experimental designs sometimes may explain apparently contradictory results.

Growth hormone   Intravenous administration of substance P (5–50 μg) to urethane-anesthetized male rats caused an increase in serum growth hormone concentrations at 10 min post-injection (32). This increase was suppressed by concomitant injection of L-DOPA or nicotine. In urethane-anesthetized normal and estrogen/progesterone-primed male rats, intravenous injection of substance P (20 μg) increased growth hormone release 5 min after injection (44). In this study the histamine antagonist diphenhydramine partially abolished the growth hormone response. No change in growth hormone concentrations was found in ovariectomized rats given a smaller intravenous dose of substance P (1 μg).

Prolactin In two studies in urethane-anesthetized male rats, substance P injection (5–50 μg and 20 μg) was associated with an increase in serum prolactin after 10 min (32, 44). L-DOPA blocked the prolactin response (32), whereas diphenhydramine blunted the prolactin increase (44). Intravenous administration of substance P (1 μg) to freely mobile ovariectomized rats also caused an increase in prolactin secretion at 5, 15, and 30 min post-injection (54). However, immunoneutralization of circulating substance P by administration of anti–substance P antiserum to proestrus rats did not alter serum prolactin levels 6, 7, and 8 hr after injection (35).

Thyrotropin and luteinizing hormone Intravenous injection of substance P (1 μg) to conscious, ovariectomized rats did not change thyrotropin serum concentrations (55).

The effects of intravenous injection of substance P on gonadotropin release may be inhibitory. Intravenous administration of substance P (1 μg) to conscious ovariectomized rats caused a decline in serum luteinizing hormone 15 and 30 min post-injection (54). Inhibiting substance P activity by immunoneutralization with anti–substance P antiserum was associated with an increase in serum gonadotropin concentrations (35).

Corticotropin and β-endorphin Plasma β-endorphin concentrations increased after intravenous administration of substance P (5 μg/100 g BW) in pentobarbital-anesthetized rats (39). In female rhesus monkeys, no change in serum cortisol values followed intramuscular injection of substance P (17).

IN VITRO Incubation of hemipituitaries obtained from ovariectomized rats in medium containing substance P (150, 250, and 500 ng/ml) resulted in enhanced release of prolactin, but no change in growth hormone secretion (54, 55). No similar in vitro studies on prolactin or growth hormone release have been reported in non-ovariectomized female animals, or in males. Substance P failed to alter the release of both gonadotropins (54) and thyrotropin (55) from hemipituitaries of ovariectomized rats. Incubation of quartered anterior pituitaries from male rats with corticotropin releasing hormone or arginine vasopressin caused release of corticotropin into the medium; this release was inhibited by addition of substance P (10 μM) into the incubation medium (41). Substance P did not affect basal secretion of corticotropin. Inhibition by substance P of the corticotropin release caused by hypothalamic extract or lysine-vasopressin also has been found (29). On the other hand, substance P (10 nM to 10 μM) stimulated the release of β-endorphin-like immunoreactivity from dispersed rat anterior pituitary cells in a dose-dependent fashion, and this release was prevented by the addition of verapamil to the incubation medium (39). How substance P stimulates the corticotroph to secrete β-endorphin but has an inhibitory effect on the same cell for corticotropin release is unclear.

There is some preliminary data indicating that rat anterior pituitary membranes possess a single class of binding site for substance P, with a dissociation constant in the range of 7–13 nM, and a maximal number of binding sites of 20–40 fmol/mg protein (34). These binding sites require further characterization in order to be defined as true receptors, but their existence supports the possibility of a direct action of substance P on anterior pituitary cells.

Responsiveness of Substance P in the Anterior Pituitary to Hormonal Manipulations

The anterior pituitary contains radioimmunoassayable substance P (2, 14) that is releasable in a K^+-stimulated, Ca^{2+}-dependent manner (2, 13) and can be regulated by both thyroid hormone and gonadal steroids (2, 11). Thyroidectomy increases and thyroid hormone administration decreases concentrations of radioimmunoassayable substance P in extracts of anterior pituitary (2). Additionally, there is evidence that substance P content in the anterior pituitary undergoes a maturational process, possibly involving gonadal steroids. The anterior pituitaries of neonatal, infantile, and juvenile male and female rats have the same concentrations of substance P. By the time of puberty (between 40 and 50 days of age), substance P content in the anterior pituitary is greater in males than in females (10), a difference that persists in adulthood. Yoshikawa & Hong (57) have evidence that testosterone alters the concentrations of substance P in the anterior pituitary of adult rats by actions of this androgen in a critical period of anterior pituitary development. Neonatal orchiectomy resulted in a marked decrease in substance P levels in the anterior pituitary of the adult animal. Neonatal female rats treated with testosterone had higher concentrations of substance P in the anterior pituitary than did their untreated littermates (57). Furthermore, whereas in the adult rat estradiol decreases and dihydrotestosterone increases substance P content in the anterior pituitary, prepubertal rats do not respond to these gonadal hormones until the juvenile period of development (10). In contrast to the effects of gonadal steroids, infantile and juvenile pups made hypothyroid by giving methimazole to the mother had increased levels of substance P in the anterior pituitary gland (10). Whether thyroid and gonadal hormones act directly on the anterior pituitary or on the hypothalamus to alter substance P content in the anterior pituitary is unclear. Whether substance P in the anterior pituitary gland is synthesized or taken up there is not certain. Nonetheless, its presence, its releasability from hemipituitaries, and the evidence that this peptide in anterior pituitary can be regulated by the hormonal status of the rat, raise the possibility that some of the effects of substance P on anterior pituitary hormone release may be local, or paracrine.

NEUROTENSIN

Cellular Localization of Neurotensin-Like Immunoreactivity

INTRINSIC HYPOTHALAMIC NEURONAL ELEMENTS   Immunohistochemical studies of neurotensin-like immunoreactivity in the hypothalamus have been carried out primarily in the rat. Numerous cells containing neurotensin have been found in the paraventricular and periventricular cell groups, and the lateral hypothalamus (28, 30, 31). Both magno- and parvocellular neurons are labeled with neurotensin in the paraventricular nucleus, which may indicate that neurotensin-stained cells are components of the hypothalamic–anterior pituitary axis and the neurohypophyseal tract. Scattered neurotensin-positive cells have been observed in other hypothalamic regions, with the exception of the supraoptic, suprachiasmatic, and ventromedial nuclei. Dense fiber labeling is located in the paraventricular and periventricular zones and, importantly, in the median eminence (28, 30).

Some hypothalamic neurons that are positive for neurotensin may also contain catecholamines, as demonstrated using the Falk-Hillarp fluorescence method to identify catecholaminergic elements and immunohistochemistry. These cells were distributed in the periventricular and arcuate regions (25). In another immunohistochemical study some cells in the arcuate nucleus contained both neurotensin and tyrosine-hydroxylase immunoreactivities (22). These findings strengthen the argument that neurotensin and a catecholamine, probably dopamine, coexist in some hypothalamic neurons. Additionally, the distribution of neurotensin and dopamine fibers overlap in the median eminence (22, 25). Furthermore, colocalization of neurotensin immunoreactivity in paraventricular cells that also contain corticotropin-releasing factor has been demonstrated in the rat (49). It is not known whether these substances are released together into the hypophyseal-portal system, or whether they interact in the regulation of the anterior pituitary function.

Noradrenergic input from the brain stem may have a trophic effect on neurotensin-containing cells in the paraventricular area. Injection of 6-hydroxydopamine into the locus coeruleus, which destroys the norepinephrinergic cells and their projections from this brain stem site, results in a decrease in staining of neurotensin-labeled cell bodies in the ipsilateral paraventricular nucleus (33). This study suggests the possibility that extrahypothalamic inputs to the hypothalamus may regulate the content of peptides in some neuroendocrine neurons.

MEDIAN EMINENCE   The origin of much of the dense plexus of im-munoreactive neurotensin terminals in the median eminence is the arcuate nucleus. Treatment of neonatal rats with monosodium glutamate, which destroys arcuate cells, abolishes nearly all of the neurotensin-positive immunoreactivity in the median eminence, particularly its lateral aspects (27). At the electron microscopic level, neurotensin-labeled terminals have been observed near capillaries (26). This finding provides morphological evidence that neurotensin can be secreted into the hypophyseal-pituitary portal system.

ANTERIOR PITUITARY   Like substance P, neurotensin immunoreactivity has been located by immunohistochemistry in anterior pituitary cells (21). To date, however, there is no information on the possible colocalization of neurotensin with anterior pituitary hormones.

Responses to the Administration of Neurotensin

INTRAVENTRICULAR OR INTRACEREBRAL INJECTION

Growth hormone   Following intraventricular injection, growth hormone secretion has been found to be decreased in anesthetized male rats, but is enhanced in freely mobile female rats. In studies by Maeda & Frohman (38), placement of neurotensin (2 or 5 μg) into the lateral ventricle of anesthetized estrogen-primed adult male rats resulted in a decrease in serum growth hormone concentrations. The chlorpromazine-stimulated increase in growth hormone was abolished by neurotensin administration (38). It has been suggested that the reduction in growth hormone by intraventricular neurotensin is mediated in part by somatostatin. Injection of neurotensin (0.016–2.0 μg) into the lateral ventricle of anesthetized male rats was associated with dose-related increases in radioimmunoassayable somatostatin concentrations in the hypothalamic-pituitary portal circulation (1). Vijayan & McCann injected neurotensin (2 or 5 μg) into the third ventricle of conscious, freely mobile, ovariectomized rats, and found that growth hormone release was enhanced at 5 min (55). The reasons for these apparent discrepancies are unclear, but may be related to differences in experimental design.

Prolactin   In anesthetized male rats, administration of neurotensin into the lateral ventricle decreased basal and TRH-stimulated prolactin secretion (38). In conscious male rats, neurotensin (5 μg) injection into the third ventricle decreased basal serum prolactin levels (36). Impairment of dopamine activity by treatment of the animals with α-methyl-p-tyrosine or spiroperidol limited the reduction in prolactin. This finding raises the possibility that the neurotensin effect may be mediated in part by dopamine. However, administration of neurotensin (5 μg) into the lateral ventricle of conscious male rats restrained and exposed to cold, caused a decrease in prolactin, which was not affected by the dopamine antagonist haloperidol (52). Consistent with the above findings, Vijayan & McCann found reduced prolactin secretion at 5, 15, and 30 min following neurotensin (2 or 5 μg) injection into the third ventricle of conscious, freely mobile ovariectomized rats (55).

Luteinizing hormone   Intraventricular injection of neurotensin (2 or 5 μg) into conscious, ovariectomized rats decreased luteinizing hormone at 5, 15, 30 min (54). Intracerebral microinjection of neurotensin (40 ng) directly into the medial preoptic area of the anesthetized, ovariectomized or proestrus rat resulted in an increase in serum luteinizing hormone concentrations at 15, 30, and 60 min (19). These two studies again point out that the site of injection, as well as other experimental variables, promote different effects.

INTRAVENOUS INJECTION

Growth hormone   Growth hormone secretion increased following intravenous injection of neurotensin in anesthetized male rats (38), but Vijayan & McCann (55) reported no change in growth hormone release in conscious female rats that received intravenous neurotensin.

Prolactin   In estrogen/progesterone-primed and untreated urethane-anesthetized male rats (38, 44), and in ovariectomized, freely mobile rats (54), an increase in serum prolactin has been observed soon after injection of neurotensin (0.5–10.0 μg).

Thyrotropin   Intravenous injection of neurotensin at doses that promoted an increase in prolactin levels also enhanced serum thyrotropin secretion, both in estrogen-primed, anesthetized male rats and ovariectomized, conscious rats (38, 55).

IN VITRO   Possible direct effects of neurotensin on anterior pituitary hormone release have been studied in vitro. As with in vivo reports, these studies vary in experimental designs and results. Incubation of dispersed anterior pituitary cells from female rats with neurotensin (54 nM) caused a decrease in basal secretion of prolactin and thyrotropin into the medium (3). The responsiveness of thyrotropin to thyrotropin releasing hormone (TRH) treatment was blunted in this system. A stimulatory effect of neurotensin (50–500 ng/ml medium) on prolactin secretion has been observed on incubated hemipituitaries taken from ovariectomized rats (54). In this study, thyrotropin secretion was enhanced, whereas no effect on luteinizing hormone secretion was demonstrated. Addition of neurotensin (5–100 nM) to anterior pituitaries from male rats resulted in an increase in prolactin secretion, but not that of growth hormone or gonadotropins (18). The increase in prolactin following neurotensin treatment was additive to that of TRH. Canonico et al (6) have provided evidence that the neurotensin-induced release of prolactin occurs via an increase in the level of hypophyseal arachidonic acid. Incubation of neurotensin with rat anterior pituitary fragments had no effect on basal corticotropin release or corticotropin releasing hormone mediated corticotropin release (41).

Responsiveness of Neurotensin in the Anterior Pituitary to Hormonal Manipulation

The anterior pituitary contains radioimmunoassayable and immunohistochemically detectable (21) neurotensin. Release of neurotensin from the anterior pituitary is stimulated by K^+ and is Ca^{++} dependent (21). Neurotensin levels in the anterior pituitary essentially remained unchanged following transection of the pituitary stalk (20), evidence that the anterior pituitary gland may be the source of at least some of the immunoreactive neurotensin found there.

Neurotensin in the anterior pituitary of the rat is regulated in part by the thyroid status of the animal. Adult animals made hypothyroid by treatment with propylthiouracil show a marked reduction in the neurotensin content in the anterior pituitary (21). Hypothyroidism in the adult rat results in a modest increase in the hypothalamic concentration of neurotensin (20). Neurotensin content in extrahypothalamic regions and the ileum appears to be unaffected by the hypothyroid state. Hyperthyroidism decreases radioimmunoassayable neurotensin in the rat hypothalamus, and incubation of hypothalamic fragments with tri-iodothyronine enhances the release of neurotensin in a dose-dependent manner (50).

Neurotensin, like substance P, is found at several sites in the hypothalamus and in the anterior pituitary. Both peptides may interact with neuroendocrine cells, are present in neuroendocrine neurons that contact the hypophyseal portal system, and are located in the anterior pituitary gland, where their contents can be regulated by the hormonal environment of the animal. Enkephalinergic neurons also are widely distributed in the mammalian hypothalamus (15, 48) and are found in high density in neuroendocrine cell groups; intraventricular or intravenous administration of enkephalin may affect the release of anterior pituitary hormones (5, 12, 16). Met-enkephalin is also measurable in the anterior pituitary, where the content of this opioid peptide is regulated in part by estrogen or haloperidol administration (24). Thus, the same peptide may have multiple roles at different sites, as neurotransmitters, neuromodulators, and paracrine agents. Study of the actions of peptides on secretion of anterior pituitary hormones may provide insight into the more subtle ways that the neuroendocrine system is regulated.

ACKNOWLEDGMENT

Studies from our laboratories were supported in part by NIH Grants AM 01126-4 and AM 29876.

Literature Cited

1. Abe, H., Chihara, K., Chiba, T., Matsu-kura, S., Fujita, T. 1981. Effect of intraventricular injection of neurotensin and other various bioactive peptides on plasma immunoreactive somatostatin levels in rat hypophysial portal blood. *Endocrinology* 105:64–68
2. Aronin, N., Morency, K., Leeman, S. E., Braverman, L. E., Coslovsky, R. 1984. Regulation by thyroid hormone of the concentration of substance P in the rat anterior pituitary. *Endocrinology* 114: 2138–42
3. Askew, R. D., Ramsden, D. B., Sheppard, M. C. 1984. The effect of neurotensin on pituitary secretion of thyrotrophin and prolactin in vitro. *Acta Endocrinol.* 105:156–60
4. Brownstein, M., Mroz, E., Kizer, J., Palkovits, M., Leeman, S. 1976. Regional distribution of substance P in the brain of the rat. *Brain Res.* 116:299–305
5. Bruni, J. F., Vugt, D. V., Marshall, S., Meites, J. 1977. Effects of naloxone, morphine and methionine enkephalin on serum prolactin, luteinizing hormone, follicle stimulating hormone, thyroid stimulating hormone and growth hormone. *Life Sci.* 21:461–66
6. Canonico, P. L., Speciale, C., Sortino, M. A., Scapagnini, U. 1985. Involvement of arachidonate metabolism in neurotensin-induced prolactin release *in vitro*. *Amer. J. Physiol.* 12:257–63
7. Carraway, R. E., Leeman, S. E. 1973. The isolation of a new hypotensive peptide, neurotensin, from bovine hypothalami. *J. Biol. Chem.* 248:6854–61
8. Chang, M. M., Leeman, S. E. 1970 Isolation of a sialogogic peptide from bovine hypothalamic tissue and its characterization as substance P. *J. Biol. Chem.* 245:4784–90
9. Chihira, K., Arimura, A., Coy, D. H., Schally, A. V. 1978. Studies on the interaction of endorphins, substance P, and endogenous somatostatin in growth hormone and prolactin release in rats. *Endocrinology* 102:281–90
10. Coslovsky, R., Braverman, L. E., Lee-

man, S. E., Aronin, N. 1985. The differential effects of thyroid and gonadal hormones on substance P in the anterior pituitary of the prepubertal rat. *Endocrinology* 47:2198–2202
11. Coslovsky, R., Evans, R. W., Leeman, S. E., Braverman, L. E., Aronin, N. 1984. The effects of gonadal steroids on the content of substance P in the rat anterior pituitary. *Endocrinology* 115: 2285–89
12. del Pozo, E., Martin-Perez, J., Stadelmann, A., Girard, J., Brownell, J. 1980. Inhibiting action of a met-enkephalin on ACTH release in man. *J. Clin. Invest.* 65:1531–34
13. DePalatis, L. R., Fiorindo, R. P., Ho, R. H. 1982. Substance P immunoreactivity in the anterior pituitary gland of the guinea pig. *Endocrinology* 110:282–84
14. DePalatis, L. R., Khorram, O., Ho, R. H., Negro-Vilar, A., McCann, S. M. 1984. Partial characterization of immunoreactive substance P in the rat pituitary gland. *Life Sci.* 34:225–38
15. DiFiglia, M., Aronin, N. 1984. Immunoreactive Leu-enkephalin in the monkey hypothalamus including observations on its ultrastructural localization in the paraventricular nucleus. *J. Comp. Neurol.* 225:313–26
16. Dupont, A., Cusan, L., Labrie, F., Coy, D. H., Li, C. H. 1977. Stimulation of prolactin release in the rat by intraventricular injection of β-endorphin and methionine enkephalin. *Biochem. Biophys. Res. Commun.* 75:76–82
17. Eckstein, N., Wehrenberg, W. B., Louis, K., Carmel, P. W., Zimmerman, E. A., et al. 1980. Effects of substance P on anterior pituitary secretion in the female rhesus monkey. *Neuroendocrinology* 31:338–42
18. Enjalbert, A., Arancibia, S., Priam, M., Bluet-Pajot, M. T., Kordon, C. 1982. Neurotensin stimulation of prolactin secretion in vitro. *Neuroendocrinology* 34:95–98
19. Ferris, C. F., Pan, J. X., Singer, E. A., Boyd, N. D., Carraway, R. E., Leeman,

548   ARONIN, COSLOVSKY & LEEMAN

S. E. 1984. Stimulation of luteinizing hormone release after stereotaxic microinjection of neurotensin into the medial preoptic area of rats. Neuroendocrinology 38:145–51
20. Goedert, M., Lightman, S. L., Emson, P. C. 1984. Neurotensin in the rat anterior pituitary gland: effects of endocrinological manipulations. Brain Res. 299: 160–63
21. Goedert, M., Lightman, S. L., Nagy, J. I., Marley, P. D., Emson, P. C. 1982 Neurotensin in the rat anterior pituitary gland. Nature 298:163–65
22. Hokfelt, T., Everitt, B.-J., Theodorsson-Norheim, E., Goldstein, M. 1984. Occurrence of neurotensinlike immunoreactivity in subpopulations of hypothalamic, mesenchephalic, and medullary catecholamine neurons. J. Comp. Neurol. 222:543–59
23. Hokfelt, T., Pernow, B., Nilsson, G., Wetterberg, L., Goldstein, M., Jeffcoate, S. 1978. Dense plexus of substance P immunoreactive nerve terminals in eminentia medialis of the primate hypothalamus. Proc. Natl. Acad. Sci. USA 75:1013–15
24. Hong, J. S., Yoshikawa, K., Hudson, P. M., Uphouse, L. L. 1982. Regulation of pituitary and brain enkephalin systems by estrogen. Life Sci. 31:2181–84
25. Ibata, Y., Fukui, K., Okamura, H., Kawakami, T., Tanaka, M., et al. 1983. Coexistence of dopamine and neurotensin in hypothalamic arcuate and periventricular neurons. Brain Res. 269:177–79
26. Ibata, Y., Kawakamu, F., Fukui, K., Obata-Tsuto, H. L., Tanaka, M., et al. 1984. Light and electron microscopic immunocytochemistry of neurotensin-like immunoreactive neurons in the rat hypothalamus. Brain Res. 302:221–30
27. Jennes, L., Stumpf, W. E., Bissette, G., Nemeroff, C. B. 1984. Monosodium glutamate lesions in rat hypothalamus studied by immunohistochemistry for gonadotropin releasing hormone, neurotensin, tyrosine hydroxylase, and glutamic acid decarboxylase and by autoradiography for [3H]estradiol. Brain Res. 308:245–53
28. Jennes, L., Stumpf, W. E., Kalivas, P. W. 1982. Neurotensin: topographical distribution in rat brain by immunohistochemistry. J. Comp. Neurol. 210:211–24
29. Jones, M. T., Gillham, B., Holmes, M. C., Hodges, J. R., Buckingham, J. C. 1978. Influence of substance P on hypothalamo-pituitary-adrenocortical

activity in the rat. J. Endocrinol. 76:183–84
30. Kahn, D., Abrams, G. M., Zimmerman, E. A., Carraway, R., Leeman, S. E. 1980 Neurotensin neurons in the rat hypothalamus: an immunocytochemical study. Endocrinology 107:47–54
31. Kahn, D., Hou-You, A., Zimmerman, E. A. 1982. Localization of neurotensin in the hypothalamus. Ann. NY Acad. Sci. 400:117–31
32. Kato, Y., Chihara, K., Ohgo, S., Iwasaki, Y., Abe, H., Imura, H. 1976. Growth hormone and prolactin secretion in rats. Life Sci. 19:441–46
33. Kawakami, F., Fukui, K., Okamura, H., Nakajima, T., Yanaihara, N., Ibata, Y. 1984. Influence of ascending noradrenergic fibers on the neurotensin-like immunoreactive neurons in the rat paraventricular nucleus. Neurosci. Lett. 44:149–54
34. Kerdelhue, B., Lenoir, V., Hubleau, P., Tartar, A. 1984. Substance P receptors in rat anterior pituitary membranes. 7th Int. Congr. Endocrinol. Quebec, Canada, p. 877. Amsterdam: Excerpta Medica. (Abstr.)
35. Kerdelhue, B., Valens, M., Langlois, Y. 1978. Stimulation de la secretion de la LH et de la FSH hypophysaires après immunoneutralisation de la substance P endogene, chez la ratte cyclique. C. R. Acad. Sci. Paris 286:977–79
36. Koenig, J. I., Mayfield, M. A., McCann, S. M., Krulich, L. 1982. On the prolactin-inhibiting effect of neurotensin. Neuroendocrinology 35:277–81
37. Ljungdahl, A., Hokfelt, T., Nilsson, G. 1978. Distribution of substance P-like immunoreactivity in the central nervous system of the rat. I. Cell bodies and nerve terminals. Neuroscience 3:861–943
38. Maeda, K., Frohman, L. A. 1978. Dissociation of systemic and central effects of neurotensin on the secretion of growth hormone, prolactin, and thyrotropin. Endocrinology 103:1903–9
39. Matsumura, M., Yamanoi, A., Yamamoto, S., Saito, S. 1982. In vivo and in vitro effects of substance P on the release of β-endorphin-like immunoreactivity. Neuroendocrinology 35:163–68
40. Morel, G., Chayvialle, J. A., Kerdelhue, B., Dubois, P. M. 1982. Ultrastructural evidence for endogenous substance P-like immunoreactivity in the rat pituitary gland. Neuroendocrinology 35:86–92
41. Nicholson, S. A., Adrian, T. E., Gillham, B., Jones, M. T., Bloom, S. R. 1984. Effect of hypothalamic neu-

SUBSTANCE P AND NEUROTENSIN 549

ropeptides on corticotrophin release from
quarters of rat anterior pituitary gland in
vitro. *J. Endocrinol.* 100:219–26
42. Palkovits, M., Zaborszky, L. 1979. Neural connections of the hypothalamus. In
Anatomy of the Hypothalamus, ed. P. J.
Morgane, J. Panksepp, 6:379–510. New
York: Dekker. 729 pp.
43. Panula, P., Hsiu-Ying, T. Y., Costa, E.
1984. Comparative distribution of bom-
besin/GRP- and substance P-like immunoreactivities in rat hypothalamus. *J.
Comp. Neurol.* 224:606–18
44. Rivier, C., Brown, M., Vale, W. 1977.
Effects of neurotensin, substance P and
morphine sulfate on the secretion of prolactin and growth hormone in the rat.
Endocrinology 100:751–54
45. Ronnekleiv, O. K., Kelly, M. J., Eskay,
R. L. 1984. Distribution of immunoreactive substance P neurons in the hypothalamus and pituitary of the rhesus monkey. *J. Comp. Neurol.* 224:51–59
46. Sakanaka, M., Shiosaka, S., Takatsuki,
K., Inagaki, S., Hara, Y., et al. 1982.
Origins of substance P-containing fibers
in the lateral septal area of young rats:
immunohistochemical analysis of experimental manipulations. *J. Comp.
Neurol.* 212:268–77
47. Sakanaka, M., Shiosaka, S., Takatsuki,
K., Inagaki, S., Takagi, H., et al. 1981.
Experimental immunohistochemical
studies on the amygdalofugal peptidergic
(substance P and somatostatin) fibers in
the stria terminalis of the rat. *Brain Res.*
221:231–42
48. Sar, M., Stumpf, W. E., Miller, R. J.,
Chang, K.-J., Cuatrecasas, P. 1978. Immunohistochemical localization of enkephalin in rat brain and spinal cord. *J.
Comp. Neurol.* 182:17–38
49. Sawchenko, P. E., Swanson, L. W.,
Vale, W. W. 1984. Corticotropin-
releasing factor: co-expression within

distinct subsets of oxytocin-, vasopres-
sin-, and neurotensin-immunoreactive
neurons in the hypothalamus of the male
rat. *J. Neurosci.* 4:1118–29
50. Sheppard, M. C., Shennan, K. I. J.
1983. The effect of thyroid hormones in
vitro and in vivo on hypothalamic
neurotensin release and content. *Endocrinology* 112:1996–98
51. Stoeckel, M. E., Porte, A., Klein, M. J.,
Cuello, A. C. 1982. Immunohistochemical localization of substance P in the
neurohypophysis and hypothalamus of
the mouse compared with the distribution
of other neuropeptides. *Cell Tissue Res.*
223:533–44
52. Tache, Y., Brown, M., Collu, R. 1979.
Effects of neuropeptide on adenohy-
pophyseal hormone response to acute
stress in male rats. *Endocrinology*
105:220–24
53. Tsuruo, Y., Kawano, H., Nishimaya,
T., Hisano, S., Daikoku, S. 1983 Substance P-like immunoreactive neurons in
the tuberoinfundibular area of rat
hypothalamus. Light and electron microscopy. *Brain Res.* 289:1–9
54. Vijayan, E., McCann, S. M. 1979. In
vivo and in vitro effects of substance P
and neurotensin on gonadotropin and
prolactin release. *Endocrinology* 105:
64–68
55. Vijayan, E., McCann, S. M. 1980.
Effects of substance P and neurotensin on
growth hormone and thyrotropin release
in vivo and in vitro. *Life Sci.* 26:321–27
56. von Euler, U. S., Gaddum, J. H. 1931.
An unidentified depressor substance in
certain tissue extracts. *J. Physiol.* 72:74–
87
57. Yoshikawa, K., Hong, J. S. 1983. Sex-
related difference in substance P level in
rat anterior pituitary: a model of neonatal
imprinting by testosterone. *Brain Res.*
273:362–65

Ann. Rev. Physiol. 1986. 48:551–67

SOMATOSTATIN MEDIATION OF ADENOHYPOPHYSIAL SECRETION[1]

Yogesh C. Patel and Coimbatore B. Srikant

Fraser Laboratories, Royal Victoria Hospital, McGill University, Departments of Medicine, and Neurology and Neurosurgery, Montreal, Quebec H3A 1A1, Canada

INTRODUCTION

The cyclic tetradecapeptide somatostatin (somatostatin-14, S-14) was originally isolated from the hypothalamus as a GH inhibitory factor. Subsequent studies revealed that this peptide's immunoreactivity is heterogeneous and is distributed in many tissues of the body in mammalian and submammalian species. Somatostatin-containing cells consist typically of nerve cells or endocrine-like cells (D-cells), and are found in highest density in the hypothalamus, cerebral cortex, gut, and endocrine pancreas. The biological effects of the peptide have been extensively investigated with the finding that its wide anatomical distribution is paralleled by an equally broad spectrum of actions. Today, S-14 is best regarded as one, and perhaps the most important, member of a family of somatostatin-like peptides that are widely distributed in neural and nonneural tissues. This peptide family subserves important physiological functions, both locally as a neurotransmitter, neuromodulator, or paracrine regulator, and distally as a hypophysiotropic substance or a classical hormone. The full scope of the somatostatin system has been explored in a comprehensive recent review (64) and in a monograph (53). This chapter will focus on hypothalamic somatostatin, its neural localization, regulation of secretion, physiological role in GH and TSH regulation, and mechanism of action on the anterior pituitary.

[1] Work from the authors' laboratory referred to in this review was supported by grants from the Canadian Medical Research Council (MT-6196, MT-6832) and the NIH (AM213-73).

551

MOLECULAR HETEROGENEITY OF SOMATOSTATIN

Four separate pre-prosomatostatin peptides have now been identified in the fish; they represent products of four closely related somatostatin genes (23, 79). In mammals, current evidence points to a single pre-prosomatostatin, which at least in the rat appears to be the product of a single somatostatin gene (32). This precursor is processed enzymatically to yield four peptides, which have now been fully characterized as normal products of mammalian somatostatin cells (9, 57). These include S-14, somatostatin-28 (S-28), $S-28_{(1-12)}$, and pro-somatostatin (pro-S), a 92–amino acid peptide containing the S-28 sequence at the C-terminus. S-14 and S-28 are the two principal bioactive forms; their actions are qualitatively similar but quantitatively different. Pro-S exhibits weak S-14-like biological activity (57). Extracts of the normal rat hypothalamus or median eminence contain S-14, S-28, and pro-S in the approximate molar ratio 15:4:1 (16, 55). All three forms are released from the median eminence in vitro in amounts comparable to their tissue content and have been identified in hypothalamo-hypophysial portal blood (16, 18). Little is currently known about the biological actions of $S-28_{(1-12)}$, which is found in concentrations equivalent to those of S-14 in most mammalian somatostatin-producing tissues (9). It is localized in and released from the median eminence, but no evidence of S-14-like activity has been found yet (9, 16).

LOCALIZATION IN THE HYPOTHALAMUS

Within the hypothalamus the most prominent collection of somatostatin-positive nerve cell bodies is in the anterior periventricular region (5, 29, 38, 42). Somatostatin perikarya in somewhat lower densities are found in several other hypothalamic nuclei, including the paraventricular, arcuate, ventromedial, medial forebrain bundle area, suprachiasmatic, retrochiasmatic areas, and supramammillary region (29, 38, 42). The periventricular somatostatin cells are located close to the third ventricle in three to four layers that run parallel to the ventricular wall within an ovoid area that extends from the preoptic nucleus to the rostral margin of the ventromedial nucleus (29, 42). The cells are small to medium in size (12–16 μm in diameter), and in frontal or parasagittal sections appear to be predominantly bipolar (5, 38, 42). Axons from these cells sweep laterally from the periventricular region and run caudally through the hypothalamus to form a discrete pathway towards the midline that enters the median eminence at the level of the ventromedial nucleus. Within the median eminence, somatostatinergic nerve endings extend in a compact band throughout the zona externa (5, 29, 38). A proportion of the fibers from this pathway course through the neural stalk and terminate in the neural lobe (52). The anterior hypothalamic periventricular somatostatin pathway to the median eminence accounts for ~ 80% of somatostatin immunoreactivity in the hypothalamus (21, 52). A homologous somatostatin pathway has been reported for primates, guinea pigs, dogs, reptiles, frogs, and fish (38). Other hypothalamic nuclei known to contain somatostatin perikarya do not appear to make significant contributions to median eminence somatostatin (43).

In addition to those in the median eminence, axons from the periventricular neurons project widely both within the hypothalamus and via long extensions to extrahypothalamic structures, notably in the limbic system (42). Projections over short distances result in inputs to the organum vasculosum lamina terminalis and to the following hypothalamic nuclei: preoptic, suprachiasmatic, ventromedial, arcuate, and ventral premammillary nucleus (42). Long distance projections innervate the olfactory tubercle, the septum, the habenula, the hippocampus, and possibly the amygdala (42, 49). The intimate association of the hypothalamic periventricular nucleus with the limbic system, which is itself endowed with a rich network of somatostatin-positive cell bodies and fibers, suggests an important role of somatostatin in limbic function.

FACTORS CONTROLLING SOMATOSTATIN SECRETION FROM THE HYPOTHALAMUS

The regulation of hypothalamic somatostatin secretion has been extensively investigated in recent years, both directly and indirectly, using a variety of in vivo and in vitro model systems. These have included in vivo measurement of somatostatin concentration in hypothalamic tissue, hypothalamic perfusate, and portal blood, in vivo immunoneutralization experiments with anti-somatostatin serum (anti-S), static incubation systems with hypothalamic fragments or slices, and dispersed cell cultures. A wide array of secretagogues have been tested in these systems with results that show reasonable reproducibility as well as some inconsistency. These data can only be broadly summarized here; for a detailed bibliography the reader is referred to References 61 and 64. Much of the discordance can be attributed to inherent differences in the model systems and experimental design or conditions. Despite their individual limitations, collectively these methods have provided a reasonably comprehensive profile of the regulation of hypothalamic somatostatin secretion.

Membrane depolarization–induced release of somatostatin from hypothalamic nerve endings was the first and most important physiological stimulus to be identified. A dramatic increase in somatostatin release occurs in response to electrical stimulation of neural lobes and median eminence fragments, or to chemical depolarization with high K^+, ouabain, or veratridine (12, 24, 61, 80). The release in both instances is Ca^{2+}-dependent, and is blocked by withdrawal of Ca^{2+} from the incubation medium and by agents that interfere with Ca^{2+} entry, including Co^{2+}, Mn^{2+}, and verapamil (24, 61). High K^+–

induced release of somatostatin by a Ca^{2+}-sensitive mechanism also occurs from islet and gastric D-cells. This finding suggests that depolarization-mediated somatostatin release is a fundamental property of neural and nonneural somatostatin cells.

Of the transmitters studied, dopamine (12, 19, 47), acetylcholine (19, 58), and norepinephrine (19, 47, 61) all appear to enhance somatostatin release with some degree of reproducibility both in vivo and in vitro. In contrast, gamma amino butyric acid (GABA) (58) and serotonin (58, 68) are reliable inhibitors of hypothalamic somatostatin secretion. Among the peptides investigated, glucagon (80), neurotensin (1, 11, 45, 78, 80), CRF (59), and bombesin (2) appear to be potent stimulators of somatostatin release, and opiates (25), VIP (25, 27, 80), and secretin (27) are weak inhibitors of secretion. Insulin (10) and GRF (6) have been reported to stimulate somatostatin release while substance P (1, 27, 78), CCK (80), and TRH (80) exhibit no consistent effect. Analogs of somatostatin that are biologically active but immunologically inactive are capable of inhibiting endogenous somatostatin secretion from cultured hypothalamic cells. This observation suggests that an ultrashort loop feedback mechanism may operate within the hypothalamus for autoregulation of somatostatinergic neurons by released somatostatin (60, 61). Of the hormones tested, GH (11, 20, 71), somatomedin (13), T4, and T3 (12) reportedly enhance somatostatin secretion, while glucocorticoids (61) are without effect.

PHYSIOLOGICAL ROLE OF SOMATOSTATIN IN ANTERIOR PITUITARY REGULATION

The anterior hypothalamic periventricular somatostatinergic neurons with their projections to the median eminence constitute the final common pathway for GH inhibition. Disruption of this pathway by appropriately placed lesions or surgical cuts augments GH and TSH secretion in the rat (21, 22, 100). Conversely, electrical stimulation of this neuronal system potentiates release of somatostatin into the portal vessels and inhibits GH release (17). Although hypothalamic secretion via the median eminence undoubtedly constitutes the main source of somatostatin reaching the pituitary under normal conditions, two other routes for delivery of somatostatin to the pituitary exist. The first one of these is via cerebrospinal fluid (csf) transported from the third ventricle across the median eminence to the portal vessels. Leakage of somatostatin from csf into the portal circulation is suggested by data showing significant transfer of synthetic S-14 or S-28 into the peripheral circulation within 1–2 min of application of the peptides into the cerebral ventricles (93). Secondly, somatostatin produced peripherally is capable of reaching the anterior pituitary. This may occur physiologically, for instance in man, in whom somatostatin levels in the systemic circulation rise following mixed meal ingestion to values that have been shown to be capable of inhibiting GH secretion (81). Since peripheral blood somatostatin is largely a reflection of gut somatostatin production (55), a potential influence of gut somatostatin on pituitary GH and TSH regulation must be entertained.

Role of Somatostatin in the Generation of the Normal Ultradian Rhythm of GH Secretion

The secretion of GH from the anterior pituitary occurs in a pulsatile manner in all species that have been examined (88). In the rat in particular, GH secretion is characterized by an endogenous ultradian rhythm with high amplitude GH secretory bursts, which are believed to be mediated by episodic release of GRF occurring at 3.3 hr intervals throughout the 24 hr period. In the intervening trough periods, plasma GH levels are undetectable. Somatostatin has been implicated as a physiological regulator of these GH trough periods by two lines of evidence: (a) Immunoneutralization with anti-S augments trough GH secretion (88, 90, 95), and (b) synthetic GRF administered during trough periods produces a weak GH response that is normalized when the peptide is administered together with anti-S serum. The latter finding suggests that circulating somatostatin has an antagonistic effect on the GRF-induced GH response during trough periods (90). Intermittent surges of somatostatin secretion may also account for trough GH levels in man, as indicated by recent studies showing preservation of pulsatile GH secretion during constant infusion with GRF (98). Somatostatin secretion appears to continue at a low basal rate during peak periods, since immunoneutralization with anti-S further augments the magnitude of the GH response to synthetic GRF during peak GH secretion (90). Based on these findings, Tannenbaum has postulated that somatostatin is secreted tonically from the hypothalamus, and that superimposed upon this steady state release is an additional rhythmic surge with a periodicity of 3–4 hr (90). A similar pattern of GRF secretion that is 180° out of phase with somatostatin secretion then generates the typical ultradian pattern of GH secretion. Direct sampling of portal blood has recently been attempted to confirm such a pattern of somatostatin and GRF secretion from the hypothalamus in vivo (62). Using an anaesthetic that permits episodic GH secretion, Plotsky & Vale studied somatostatin and GRF levels in sequential 20 min collections of rat portal blood. Massive surges of GRF were observed, during which portal somatostatin concentrations declined by 37% from the mean trough value of 112 pg/ml. Although a biphasic pattern of somatostatin release is implied, these findings have to be interpreted in the light of the fact that the rats employed in this study exhibited mean peak GH levels that were significantly lower than those found in the conscious rat, and were presumably stressed.

Stress and Somatostatin

Acute or chronic exposure to stressful stimuli, e.g. exercise, immobilization, or ether inhalation consistently suppresses GH secretion in the rat, as demonstrated by a reduction in mean plasma GH levels and abolition of the ultradian rhythm (8, 21, 96). A great deal of evidence has now been marshalled to suggest that somatostatin release from the median eminence plays a key role in this process. Involvement of the hypothalamus was initially suggested by studies showing that stress-induced GH inhibition was prevented by complete surgical isolation of the medial basal hypothalamus (22). The site of inhibition was subsequently localized by lesion experiments to the periventricular somatostatinergic cells (21, 22). Destruction of these neurons or their axonal projections results in 80–90% depletion of median eminence somatostatin and is accompanied by blockade of the GH response to stress (21, 22). In rats subjected to exercise stress, somatostatin in the median eminence is significantly depleted, which presumably reflects augmented release into the portal vessels (94). Passive immunization experiments have provided definitive proof of a role for somatostatin in stress-mediated GH suppression. Treatment with anti-S augments GH secretion and partially restores the GH secretory pulses in rats subjected to exercise (96) or ether stress (8). These experiments, however, did not analyze the separate effects of anti-S on trough and peak GH levels to characterize the pattern of hypothalamic somatostatin release in response to stress. In view of the prolonged suppression of GH (several hours) following an acute stressful episode, the proposed pulsatile manner in which somatostatin is normally secreted is presumably converted to a pattern of sustained hypersecretion, which during peak periods is sufficient to block GRF-induced GH secretion. Such a possibility will hopefully be confirmed by additional passive immunization experiments.

Role of Somatostatin in GH Autoregulation

There is now considerable evidence to suggest that GH is capable of inhibiting its own secretion by means of a feedback mechanism operating on the hypothalamus (see 63 for review). Thus, rats bearing somatotropic tumors have reduced pituitary GH content, and the pituitaries of such animals synthesize GH in vitro at a reduced rate. In the human and the rhesus monkey, infusion of GH has been shown to interfere with subsequent hypoglycemia-, arginine-, and vasopressin-induced GH release (3). In 1973 Root and coworkers, and subsequently others, made the observation that GH treatment of GH-deficient children led to a reversible inhibition of the TSH response to injections of TRH (72). The subsequent isolation of somatostatin from the hypothalamus and the demonstration that injections of the peptide inhibited both GH and TSH secretion provided the first major clues to the possible mechanism of GH-induced inhibition of GH secretion. It was suggested that GH treatment might stimulate hypothalamic somatostatin secretion, which would then inhibit GH and TSH secretion. This hypothesis has been confirmed and expanded by a variety of studies from different laboratories. Hypothalamic somatostatin concentration is increased in normal rats treated with exogenous GH (11, 50). Furthermore, the in vitro release of somatostatin from hypothalami obtained from such GH-treated rats is increased (11). Conversely, somatostatin content and release from the median eminence is reduced in hypophysectomized rats, but is restored to normal following GH administration (11, 50). Exposure of normal rat hypothalamic blocks to r GH in physiological concentrations results in a dose-dependent stimulation of somatostatin release (11). Exogenous GH also enhances somatostatin release from cultures of dispersed neonatal hypothalamic cells, but at considerably higher concentrations (71). Injection of r GH into the cerebral ventricles of rats results in significant suppression of GH secretory pulses, which lasts up to 6 hr (88). Intraventricularly administered r GH evokes dose-dependent stimulation of somatostatin release from the median eminence, as determined by direct sampling of hypophysial portal blood, which provides further evidence of a stimulatory effect of GH on hypothalamic somatostatin (20). In terms of the physiological significance of the GH-induced somatostatin release on GH secretion, immunoneutralization with anti-S only partially restores the amplitude of the GH secretory pulses (33). Only a combination of anti-S and GRF both administered intravenously (iv) is capable of completely normalizing the high amplitude GH secretory bursts in rats given r GH centrally (33). These findings firmly establish hypothalamic somatostatin as a physiological mediator of GH autofeedback. This role, however, appears to be partial and is now believed to be shared with GRF, the secretion of which seems to be inhibited by GH.

GH exerts an effect on hypothalamic somatostatin output both directly, as discussed above, and indirectly via somatomedins. Intracerebroventricular administration of somatomedin preparations suppresses GH secretory pulses in a manner analogous to that observed with centrally delivered GH (89). As in the case of GH, this effect may be due in part to release of somatostatin, since somatomedin-C has been shown to directly stimulate somatostatin release from normal rat hypothalamic fragments in vitro (13).

Somatostatin Mediation of Neuropharmacological Effects on GH and TSH Secretion

Attempts have been made to relate the effects of transmitter and neuropeptide substances on somatostatin release and their ability to alter GH and TSH secretion. Such comparisons, when restricted to the same animal species (to allow for the marked species differences in GH regulation), have yielded some interesting insights into the potential physiological role of somatostatin in mediating these effects. For instance, in the rat, release of somatostatin by dopamine may explain dopaminergic inhibition of GH and TSH secretion (40, 97). Likewise, serotonin-induced inhibition of somatostatin release may account in part for enhanced GH and TSH secretion following intraventricularly administered serotonin in the rat (36, 58). The inhibitory effect of GABA on hypothalamic somatostatin release may be physiologically relevant since intraventricular GABA has been shown to stimulate GH secretion (87). GABA, however, inhibits TSH secretion, which suggests that other GABAergic mechanisms, probably mediated via TRH, may overshadow any somatostatin effects on the thyrotroph (99). The recently demonstrated ability of centrally administered CRF to inhibit GH secretion in the rat is consistent with the reported finding of augmented hypothalamic somatostatin release induced by CRF in vitro (70). The effect of neurotensin on somatostatin secretion is remarkably consistent. This peptide is localized in the anterior hypothalamus in close anatomical proximity to the periventricular somatostatin pathway. Since centrally administered neurotensin suppresses GH and TSH secretion in the rat (45), the stimulatory effect of this peptide on somatostatin release may be physiologically important with respect to GH and TSH modulation. Glucagon and bombesin both exist in the hypothalamus, stimulate hypothalamic somatostatin release, and when injected intraventricularly appropriately inhibit GH secretion (2, 39). Although the effect of central glucagon on TSH release has not been adequately examined, bombesin certainly is known to inhibit TSH secretion as well (15).

In all these instances, the appropriately matched somatostatin and GH/TSH responses provide presumptive evidence of neural mediation by somatostatin. The possibility that simultaneous suppression of GRF and TRH is evoked by these monoamines and peptides, however, cannot be overlooked as an additional or alternative mechanism to explain the changes in GH and TSH secretion. This is particularly the case with agents such as acetylcholine that produce a unidirectional change in both somatostatin and GH release (58). Cholinergic stimulation of hypothalamic somatostatin is clearly dwarfed in this instance by other cholinergic mechanisms that produce overall augmentation of GH secretion. The precise physiological role of somatostatin in the neurotransmitter- and neuropeptide-mediated changes in GH and TSH secretion will hopefully be illuminated through more direct means such as in vivo immunoneutralization experiments.

Somatostatin-Mediated Effects of Nutrients

Hypothalamic somatostatin release in the rat is modulated by local glucose concentration. Basal and K^+-induced somatostatin release from hypothalamic fragments is inversely related to medium glucose concentration (10, 44). When 5% glucose solution is injected into the third ventricle of rats, there is a significant decrease in somatostatin concentration in the hypophysial portal blood (19). Conversely, intracellular glucopenia induced by 2-deoxyglucose (2-DG) results in dose-dependent stimulation of somatostatin release from hypothalamic fragments (10, 44). Modulation of hypothalamic somatostatin release by glucose is physiologically significant in terms of GH secretion, at least in the rat, in which insulin-induced hypoglycemia or centrally administered 2-DG inhibits pulsatile GH secretion (48, 91). The in vivo administration of anti-S to 2-DG-treated rats augments trough GH secretion, which suggests that somatostatin released endogenously in response to neuronal glucopenia plays a physiological role in the ensuing GH suppression (48). Antiserum to somatostatin, however, does not restore GH pulsatility. This implies that 2-DG may also act on GH by inhibiting GRF secretion (48). These in vivo responses may not be glucose-specific, but rather may result from stress. Nonspecificity of the glucose effect on somatostatin would explain the marked species difference in the response of GH to glucose between rat and man; in man a fall in blood glucose stimulates GH release.

Prolonged food deprivation in the rat results in profound inhibition of GH secretion with virtual obliteration of the normal ultradian rhythm (92). Passive immunization with anti-S fully restores the normal GH secretory pattern, which suggests that circulating somatostatin is mediating the GH suppression of starvation (92). The increased somatostatin that reaches the pituitary under these circumstances could originate from the hypothalamus in response to a stress mechanism, or from the pancreas and gut. The latter is more likely in view of the marked alterations in somatostatin concentration noted in these tissues under starvation conditions (92).

Role of Peripheral Somatostatin in Disease States

A pronounced effect of systemically produced somatostatin on anterior pituitary function occurs in disease states, such as somatostatin-producing tumors and experimental insulinopenic diabetes. Human somatostatinomas are associated with strikingly elevated peripheral blood levels of somatostatin sufficient to block GH and TSH secretion (41). In insulin-deficient diabetic rats pulsatile GH secretion is markedly attenuated (88) and TSH secretion is impaired (31) concomitant with hypersomatostatinemia, which results from augmented somatostatin output from the pancreas and gut (54, 56). Antiserum to somatostatin normalizes GH secretion, which clearly implicates peripherally produced somatostatin in mediating pituitary GH and TSH suppression (88).

Role of Somatostatin in TSH Regulation

Somatostatin is capable of inhibiting TSH secretion both directly via action on the thyrotrophs and indirectly by inhibiting TRH release at the hypothalamic level (35). Exogenous S-14 is a potent inhibitor of basal and TRH-stimulated TSH release. For a given concentration of S-14, the thyrotrophs are probably less sensitive to inhibition than the somatotrophs (81). This may explain the fact that the normal circadian pattern of TSH secretion does not exhibit the very low TSH levels that typify the GH trough periods, believed to be produced by episodic somatostatin secretion (95). Lesions of the anterior periventricular nucleus lead to elevated basal TSH levels and blockade of the normal stress-induced inhibition of TSH secretion (21). A physiological role for somatostatin in regulating TSH secretion has been clearly implied by passive immunization studies with anti-S. Anti-S increases basal plasma TSH levels and potentiates the TSH responses to acute cold exposure (28) and to TRH administration (7).

Hypothalamic somatostatin function appears to be modulated by thyroid hormones and possibly TSH (12, 71). Berelowitz et al reported a reduction in hypothalamic somatostatin content and in vitro release from hypothalami of hypothyroid rats and normalization of both with T3 treatment (12). T3 stimulates the in vitro release of somatostatin from hypothalamic fragments (12). Thus, the elevated TSH levels of primary hypothyroidism may result in part from a decrease in the inhibitory effect of hypothalamic somatostatin. Preliminary evidence suggests that TSH may be capable of stimulating somatostatin release from hypothalamic neurons and, like GH, may be subject to autoregulation through activation of hypothalamic somatostatin release (71). Additional experiments will be necessary to document the physiological significance of this control mechanism.

ACTIONS OF SOMATOSTATIN ON THE PITUITARY GLAND

Somatostatin exerts multiple effects on the pituitary gland. It inhibits basal and stimulated GH and TSH secretion and basal prolactin secretion from the normal gland, GH and prolactin secretion from adenomatous glands in humans, GH and prolactin secretion from GH_4C_1 tumor cells, and ACTH secretion from human and mouse (AtT-20) ACTH-producing tumors (64, 69). The normal somatotrophs are exquisitely sensitive to suppression by S-14 (IC_{50} of 65 pM for GH suppression from dissociated rat pituitary cells in culture) (73), and relatively more sensitive to inhibition by S-14 than the thyrotrophs (81). The potency of S-14 is approximately equal for inhibition of GH and prolactin secretion from GH_4C_1 cells (75) and for inhibition of ACTH secretion from AtT-20 cells (69, 82). The tumor cells, however, appear to be 10–100 times less sensitive to S-14 than normal pituitary cells. S-28 is relatively more potent than S-14 for normal GH inhibition in vivo and in vitro and for ACTH inhibition in AtT-20 cells (14, 82). Its in vitro potency for GH suppression has been reported to be 3–8 times greater than that of S-14 (14). The comparative effects of these two peptides on normal TSH secretion or on secretion from tumor cells have not been adequately analyzed.

The pituitary actions of somatostatin are receptor-mediated. By ultrastructural in vitro autoradiography, these receptors have been localized in the normal rat pituitary on somatotrophs, thyrotrophs, and lactotrophs, the three known targets for normal somatostatin actions in the pituitary (46). Biochemically, these receptors were first demonstrated in GH_4C_1 cells (76) and have subsequently been localized to plasma membrane fractions in the normal rat pituitary (4, 83, 84). S-14 receptors exhibit high affinity ($K_d = 1$ nM) with a B_{max} of 305 fmol/mg protein. The binding affinity of pituitary S-14 receptors is comparable to that observed for brain and adrenocortical S-14 receptors but lower than that of pancreatic acinar cell S-14 receptors (86). Similar high affinity receptors have also been described in the AtT-20 tumor cells (69, 82) and in human somatotroph tumors (66). Structure-activity relationship studies have revealed that the cyclic structure of S-14 is essential and that amino acid residues 7–11 constitute the ligand recognition site for S-14 receptor binding, the same structural region that constitutes the active site for biological activity (86).

Normal rat pituitary S-14 receptors differ from those in other tissues in several ways. First, pituitary binding of S-14 is not sensitive to Ca^{2+} as is the case in pancreatic acinar cells (86). Second, the binding affinities of S-28 and of a number of structural analogs of S-14 for the pituitary differ from those observed in other tissues. For instance, S-14 receptors in the normal pituitary bind S-28 with equal or greater affinity than S-14 (4, 83), whereas S-14 receptors in the brain and pancreatic acinar cells bind S-14 with greater affinity than S-28 (86). S-28 also exhibits greater affinity than S-14 for receptor binding in the AtT-20 cells, which is in keeping with its more potent inhibition of ACTH secretion (82). Conversely, S-28 has reduced binding potency and GH inhibitory activity in the GH_4C_1 cells when compared to S-14 (75). The binding affinities of a number of structural analogs of S-14 and S-28 in the pituitary correlate well with their biopotencies (4, 75, 84). As in the case of S-28, however, a comparison of the binding affinity and actions of some of these analogs in the pituitary and in other somatostatin-responsive tissues reveals major inconsistencies. For instance, [D-Br_5-Trp^8]-S-14 binds to S-14 receptors in the pituitary with an affinity three times greater than in brain and adrenal cortex, while [L-Br_5-Trp^8]-S-14 exhibits a threefold greater affinity for S-14 receptors in the brain and pituitary than for those in the adrenal cortex (85). These data highlight the heterogeneity of S-14 receptors in different tissues and point to the possible existence of separate populations of S-14 and S-28 receptors. Using radioligands prepared from S-14 and S-28 analogs, some (67) but not all laboratories have been able to distinguish distinct receptors for the two somatostatin moieties in direct binding studies using normal tissues or AtT-20 cells (82, 86). Using a totally different approach, that of in vivo autoradiography, the same radioligands have definitely revealed the existence of separate binding sites in the median eminence and other circumventricular organs (51). The existence of distinct S-14 and S-28 receptors appears to be highly likely, but further technical refinements, such as more selective radioligands or specific antagonists for S-14 and S-28, will be necessary to establish this with certainty.

Alterations in peptide hormone levels are known to result, in general, in reciprocal changes in receptor number and/or affinity and concomitant changes in the extent of the biological response. That S-14 acts in this manner was first shown in AtT-20 cells, which following pretreatment with S-14 exhibited an enhanced response to forskolin stimulation of ACTH secretion (65). This was found to be a consequence of S-14 receptor down-regulation, due mainly to decreased binding capacity following preincubation of the cells with S-14 or S-28 (82). Whether the normal pituitary S-14 receptors are capable of such down-regulation is not known, but such a mechanism seems highly likely since S-14 receptor concentrations in other normal tissues, e.g. brain, are known to be reciprocally related to endogenous somatostatin levels (86). In GH_4C_1 cells, S-14 receptors have been reported to be down-regulated by glucocorticoids (74) and TRH (77). S-14 receptor regulation by these agents has not been demonstrated in normal pituitary tissue.

Peptides such as GRF and VIP that exert stimulatory effects on pituitary hormone secretion also promote intracellular cAMP accumulation (75) and stimulate adenylate cyclase activity in anterior pituitary plasma membranes (34). The receptors for these peptides appear to be coupled to adenylate cyclase via the stimulatory component of guanine nucleotide binding protein (N_s). The S-14-mediated decrease in VIP-stimulated cAMP accumulation could result from a direct action on adenylate cyclase via the inhibitory component of the guanine nucleotide binding protein (N_i) and/or by stimulation of phosphodiesterase. The failure of 3-isobutyl-1-methylxanthine (a potent inhibitor of phosphodiesterase) to block the S-14-induced decrease of stimulated cAMP formation suggests that S-14 does not influence cAMP degradation. Islets activating protein (IAP, pertussis toxin), which catalyzes ADP ribosylation of N_i and thereby blocks the inhibition of adenylate cyclase by certain hormones and neurotransmitters, has been shown to decrease the S-14 inhibition of VIP-stimulated adenylate cyclase activity (75). Furthermore, pretreatment of GH_4C_1 cells with IAP completely abolishes the inhibition by S-14 of VIP-stimulated adenylate cyclase activity (75). The involvement of N_i in the inhibition of adenylate cyclase by S-14 has also been demonstrated in cyc^- S-49 lymphoma cells (37). The inhibition of basal hormone secretion by S-14 is not accompanied by a decrease in basal cAMP and appears to be mediated by a different mechanism (75, 82). The inhibition of basal prolactin secretion by S-14, however, is blocked by IAP. This finding suggests that the various pathways of S-14 action are all connected to N_i (75). S-14 has been shown to block membrane depolarization in anterior pituitary cells (26) and to reduce the influx of Ca^{2+} into the cell. This, combined with the recent finding that guanine nucleotides regulate Ca^{2+} channels (30), raises the intriguing possibility that N_i coupled to S-14 receptors can also regulate the intracellular Ca^{2+} pool. It is not known whether a direct link between N_i and Ca^{2+} flux exists. Evidence available to date clearly indicates the involvement of adenylate cyclase and the Ca^{2+} channel in the expression of the actions of S-14. The dissociated effects of preincubation of AtT-20 cells with S-14 or S-28 on the responsiveness to forskolin stimulation of ACTH secretion and cAMP accumulation suggest that Ca^{2+}-dependent and -independent mechanisms could be differentially sensitive to S-14 and S-28 (82). Further studies should resolve the extent of interdependency, if any, of the actions of somatostatin on membrane potential, Ca^{2+} influx, and adenylate cyclase.

Literature Cited

1. Abe, H., Chihara, K., Chiba, T., Matsukura, S., Fujita, T. 1981. Effect of intraventricular injection of neurotensin and other various bioactive peptides on plasma immunoreactive somatostatin levels in rat hypophysial portal blood. *Endocrinology* 108:1939–43
2. Abe, H., Chihara, K., Minamitani, N., Iwasaki, J., Chiba, T., et al. 1981. Stimulation by bombesin of immunoreactive somatostatin release into rat hypophysial portal blood. *Endocrinology* 109:229–34
3. Abrams, R. L., Kaplan, S., Grumbach, M. 1971. The effect of human growth hormone on the plasma growth hormone, cortisol, glucose and free fatty acid response to insulin: Evidence for growth hormone autoregulation in man. *J. Clin. Invest.* 50:940–50
4. Aguilera, G., Parker, D. S. 1982. Pituitary somatostatin receptors: Characterization by binding with a non-degradable peptide analogue. *J. Biol. Chem.* 257:1134–37
5. Alpert, L. C., Brawer, J. R., Patel, Y. C., Reichlin, S. 1976. Somatostatinergic neurons in anterior hypothalamus: Immunohistochemical localization. *Endocrinology* 98:255–58
6. Arimura, A., Merchenthaler, I., Culler, M. D., Iswasaki, K. Distribution and release of GRF. 1984. In *Endocrinology, Proc. 7th Int. Congr. Endocrinol. July 1–7, 1984,* ed. F. Labrie, L. Proulx, 42:827–30. Amsterdam: Excerpta Medica
7. Arimura, A., Schally, A. V. 1976. Increase in basal and thyrotropin releasing hormone (TRH)-stimulated secretion of

thyrotropin (TSH) by passive immunization with antiserum to somatostatin in rats. *Endocrinology* 98:1069–72
8. Arimura, A., Smith, W. D., Schally, A. V. 1976. Blockade of the stress-induced decrease in blood GH by antisomatostatin serum in rats. *Endocrinology* 98:540–43
9. Benoit, R., Bohlen, P., Ling, N., Esch, F., Baird, A., et al. 1985. Somatostatin-$28_{(1–12)}$-like peptides. See Reference 53, 6:89–107
10. Berelowitz, M., Dudlak, D., Frohman, L. A. 1982. Release of somatostatin-like immunoreactivity from incubated rat hypothalamus and cerebral cortex. *J. Clin. Invest.* 69:1293–1301
11. Berelowitz, M., Firestone, S., Frohman, L. A. 1981. Effects of growth hormone excess and deficiency on hypothalamic somatostatin content and release and on tissue somatostatin distribution. *Endocrinology* 109:714–19
12. Berelowitz, M., Maeda, K., Harris, S., Frohman, L. A. 1980. The effect of alterations in the pituitary-thyroid axis on hypothalamic content and in vitro release of somatostatin-like immunoreactivity. *Endocrinology* 107:24–29
13. Berelowitz, M., Szabo, M., Frohman, L. A., Firestone, S., Chu, L. 1981. Somatomedin-C mediates growth hormone negative feedback by effects on both the hypothalamus and the pituitary. *Science* 212:1279–81
14. Bohlen, P., Brazeau, P., Benoit, R., Ling, N., Esch, F., Guillemin, R. 1980. Isolation and amino acid composition of two somatostatin-like peptides from ovine hypothalamus: somatostatin-28

and somatostatin-25. *Biochem. Biophys. Res. Commun.* 96:725–34

15. Brown, M., Rivier, J., Vale, W. 1977. Actions of bombesin, thyrotropin releasing factor, prostaglandin E_2 and naloxone on thermoregulation in the rat. *Life Sci.* 20:1681–88

16. Charpenet, G., Patel, Y. C. 1985. Characterization of tissue and releasable molecular forms of somatostatin-$28_{(1–12)}$-like immunoreactivity in rat median eminence. *Endocrinology* 116: 1863–68

17. Chihara, K., Arimura, A., Kubli-Garfias, C., Schally, A. V. 1979. Enhancement of immunoreactive somatostatin release into hypophysial portal blood by electrical stimulation of the preoptic area in the rat. *Endocrinology* 105:1416–18

18. Chihara, K., Arimura, A., Schally, A. V. 1979. Immunoreactive somatostatin in rat hypophyseal portal blood: Effects of anesthetics. *Endocrinology* 104:1434–41

19. Chihara, K., Arimura, A., Schally, A. V. 1979. Effect of intraventricular injection of dopamine, norepinephrine, acetylcholine, and 5-hydroxytryptamine on immunoreactive somatostatin release into rat hypophyseal portal blood. *Endocrinology* 104:1656–62

20. Chihara, K., Minamitani, N., Kaji, H., Arimura, A., Fujita, T. 1981. Intraventricularly injected growth hormone stimulates somatostatin release into rat hypophyseal portal blood. *Endocrinology* 109:2279–81

21. Critchlow, V., Abe, S., Urman, S., Vale, W. 1981. Effects of lesions of the periventricular nucleus of the preoptic-anterior hypothalamus on growth hormone and thyrotropin secretion and brain somatostatin. *Brain Res.* 222:267–76

22. Critchlow, V., Rice, R. W., Abe, K., Vale, W. 1978. Somatostatin content of the median eminence in female rats with lesion-induced disruption of the inhibitory control of growth hormone secretion. *Endocrinology* 103:817–25

23. Dixon, J. E., Andrews, P. C. 1985. Somatostatins of the channel catfish. See Reference 53, 2:19–29

24. Drouva, S. V., Epelbaum, J., Hery, M., Tapia-Arancibia, L., Laplante, E., Kordon, C. 1981. Ionic channels involved in the LHRH and SRIF release from rat mediobasal hypothalamus. *Neuroendocrinology* 32:155–62

25. Drouva, S. V., Epelbaum, J., Tapia-Arancibia, L., Laplante, E., Kordon, C. 1981. Opiate receptors modulate LHRH and SRIF release from mediobasal hypothalamic neurons. *Neuroendocrinology* 32:163–67

26. Dufy, B., Barker, J. 1984. Peptide hormones regulate ionic conductances in clonal pituitary cells. *Progr. 7th Int. Endocrine Congr., Quebec City, 1984*, p. 633, Abstr. #746

27. Epelbaum, J., Tapia-Arancibia, L., Besson, J., Rotsztejn, W. H., Kordon, C. 1979. Vasoactive intestinal peptide inhibits release of somatostatin from hypothalamus in vitro. *Eur. J. Pharmacol.* 58:493–95

28. Ferland, L., Labrie, F., Jolin, M., Arimura, A., Schally, A. V. 1976. Physiological role of somatostatin in the control of growth hormone and thyrotropin secretion. *Biochem. Biophys. Res. Commun.* 68:149–56

29. Finley, J. C. W., Maderdrut, J. L., Roger, L. J., Petrusz, P. 1981. The immunocytochemical localization of somatostatin-containing neurons in the rat central nervous system. *Neuroscience* 6:2173–92

30. Gomperts, B. D. 1983. Involvement of guanine nucleotide-binding protein in the gating of Ca^{2+} by receptors. *Nature* 306:64–66

31. Gonzales, C., Montoya, E., Jolin, T. 1980. Effect of streptozotocin diabetes on the hypothalamic-pituitary thyroid axis in the rat. *Endocrinology* 107:2099–2103

32. Goodman, R. H., Montminy, M. R., Low, M. J., Habener, J. F. 1985. Biosynthesis of rat preprosomatostatin. See Reference 53, 3:31–47

33. Gurd, W., Barrett, S. J., Tannenbaum, G. S. 1985. The interrelationship of somatostatin (SRIF) and growth hormone releasing factor (GRF) in mediation of growth hormone autofeedback. *Progr. 67th Ann. Meet. Endocrine Soc., Baltimore*, p. 58, Abstr.

34. Harwood, J. P., Grewe, C., Aguilera, G. 1984. Actions of growth hormone releasing factor and somatostatin on adenylate cyclase and growth hormone release in rat anterior pituitary. *Mol. Cell. Endocrinol.* 37:277–84

35. Hirooka, Y., Hollander, C. S., Suzuki, S., Ferdinand, P., Juan, S.-I. 1978. Somatostatin inhibits release of thyrotropin releasing factor from organ cultures of rat hypothalamus. *Proc. Natl. Acad. Sci. USA* 75:4509–13

36. Holak, H., Baldys, A., Jarzab, B., Wystrychowski, A., Slirzypek, J. 1978. Changes in serum TSH level after intraventricular injection of various neu-

romediators in rats. *Acta Endocrinol.* 87:279–82

37. Jacobs, K. H., Schultz, G. 1983. Occurrence of a hormone-sensitive inhibitory coupling component of the adenylate cyclase in S49 lymphoma cyc⁻ variants. *Proc. Natl. Acad. Sci. USA* 80:3899–3902

38. Johansson, O., Hokfelt, T., Elde, R. P. 1984. Immunohistochemical distribution of somatostatin-like immunoreactivity in the central nervous system of the adult rat. *Neuroscience* 13:265–339

39. Katakami, H., Kato, Y., Matsushita, N., Shimatsu, A., Waseda, N., Imura, H. 1984. Interrelation between somatostatin output from the mediobasal hypothalamus and plasma growth hormone levels in conscious rats: effects of glucagon administration. *Endocrinology* 115:1598–1604

40. Kato, Y., Dupre, J., Beck, J. C. 1973. Plasma growth hormone in the anesthetized rat: Effect of dibutyryl cyclic AMP, prostaglandin E₁, adrenergic agents, vasopressin, chlorpromazine, amphetamine and L-dopa. *Endocrinology* 93:135–46

41. Krejs, G. J., Orci, L., Conlon, J. M., Ravazzola, M., Davis, G. R., et al. 1979. Somatostatinoma syndrome—Biochemical morphological and clinical features. *N. Engl. J. Med.* 301:285–92

42. Krisch, B. 1979. Immunohistochemical results on the distribution of somatostatin in the hypothalamus and in limbic structures of the rat. *J. Histochem. Cytochem.* 27:1389–90

43. Lechan, R. M., Nestler, J. L., Jacobson, S. 1982. The tuberoin-fundibular system of the rat as demonstrated by immunohistochemical localization of retrogradely transported wheat germ agglutinin (WGA) from the median eminence. *Brain Res.* 245:1–15

44. Lengyel, A.-M., Grossman, A., Nieuwenhuyzen-Kruseman, A. C., Ackland, J., Rees, L. H., Besser, M. 1984. Glucose modulation of somatostatin and LHRH release from rat hypothalamic fragments in vitro. *Neuroendocrinology* 39:31–38

45. Maeda, K., Frohman, L. A. 1978. Dissociation of systemic and central effects of neurotensin on the secretion of growth hormone, prolactin and thyrotropin. *Endocrinology* 103:1903–9

46. Morel, G., Leroux, P., Pelletier, G. 1985. Ultrastructural autoradiographic localization of somatostatin-28 in the rat pituitary gland. *Endocrinology* 116: 1615–20

47. Negro-Vilar, A., Ojeda, S. R., Arimura, A., McCann, S. M. 1978. Dopamine and norepinephrine stimulate somatostatin release by median eminence fragments in vitro. *Life Sci.* 23:1493–98

48. Painson, J.-C., Tannenbaum, G. S. 1985. Effects of intracellular glucopenia on pulsatile growth hormone secretion: Mediation in part by somatostatin. *Endocrinology* 117:1132–38

49. Palkovits, M., Tapia-Arancibia, L., Kordon, C., Epelbaum, J. 1982. Somatostatin connections between the hypothalamus and the limbic system of the rat brain. *Brain Res.* 250:223–28

50. Patel, Y. C. 1979. Growth hormone stimulates hypothalamic somatostatin. *Life Sci.* 24:1589–94

51. Patel, Y. C., Baquiran, G., Srikant, C. B., Posner, B. I. 1985. Quantitative in vivo autoradiographic localization of [¹²⁵I-Tyr¹¹] somatostatin-14 and [Leu⁸, D-Trp²², ¹²⁵I-Tyr²⁵] somatostatin-28 binding sites in rat brain. *J. Clin. Invest.* Submitted for publication

52. Patel, Y. C., Hoyte, K., Martin, J. B. 1979. Effect of anterior hypothalamic lesions on neurohypophysial and peripheral tissue concentrations of somatostatin in the rat. *Endocrinology* 105:712–15

53. *Somatostatin*, ed. Y. C. Patel, G. S. Tannenbaum. New York: Plenum. 510 pp.

54. Patel, Y. C., Wheatley, T., Malaisse-Lagae, F., Orci, L. 1980. Elevated portal and peripheral blood concentration of immunoreactive somatostatin in spontaneously diabetic (BBL) Wistar rat: Suppression with insulin. *Diabetes* 29:757–61

55. Patel, Y. C., Wheatley, T., Ning, C. 1981. Multiple forms of immunoreactive somatostatin: comparison of distribution in neural and nonneural tissues and portal plasma of the rat. *Endocrinology* 109: 1943–49

56. Patel, Y. C., Wheatley, T., Zingg, H. H. 1980. Increased blood somatostatin concentration in streptozotocin diabetic rats. *Life Sci.* 27:1563–70

57. Patel, Y. C., Zingg, H. H., Srikant, C. B. 1985. Somatostatin-14 immunoreactive forms in the rat: characterization, distribution and biosynthesis. See Reference 53, 5:71–87

58. Peterfreund, R. A., Vale, W. W. 1983. Muscarinic cholinergic stimulation of somatostatin secretion from long term dispersed cell cultures of fetal rat hypothalamus: inhibition by γ aminobutyric acid and serotonin. *Endocrinology* 112:526–34

59. Peterfreund, R. A., Vale, W. W. 1983.

Ovine corticotropin-releasing factor stimulates somatostatin secretion from cultured brain cells. *Endocrinology* 112: 1275–78

60. Peterfreund, R. A., Vale, W. W. 1984. Somatostatin analogs inhibit somatostatin secretion from cultured hypothalamus cells. *Neuroendocrinology* 39:397–402

61. Peterfreund, R. A., Vale, W. W. 1985. Somatostatin secretion from the hypothalamus. See Reference 53, 11:183–200

62. Plotsky, P. M., Vale, W. 1985. Patterns of growth hormone releasing factor and somatostatin secretion into the hypophysial portal circulation of the rat. *Prog. 67th Ann. Meet. Endocrine Soc., Baltimore, June,* p. 57 Abstr. #228

63. Reichlin, S. 1974. Regulation of somatotropic hormone secretion. In *Handbook of Physiology: Endocrinology IV,* Part 2, pp. 405–47. Washington, D.C.: Am. Physiol. Soc.

64. Reichlin, S. 1983. Somatostatin. In *Brain Peptides,* ed. D. T. Krieger, M. Brownstein, J. B. Martin, pp. 711–52. New York: Wiley

65. Reisine, T., Axelrod, J. 1983. Prolonged somatostatin pretreatment desensitizes somatostatin's inhibition of receptor-mediated release of adrenocorticotropin hormone and sensitizes adenylate cyclase. *Endocrinology* 113:811–13

66. Reubi, J. C., Landolt, A. M. 1984. High density of somatostatin receptors in pituitary tumors from acromegalic patients. *J. Clin. Endocrinol. Metab.* 59:1148–51

67. Reubi, J. C., Perrin, M., Rivier, J., Vale, W. 1982. High affinity binding sites for somatostatin in rat pituitary. *Biochem. Biophys. Res. Commun.* 105: 1538–45

68. Richardson, S. B., Hollander, C. S., Prasad, J. A., Hirooka, Y. 1981. Somatostatin release from rat hypothalamus in vitro: effects of melatonin and serotonin. *Endocrinology* 109:602–6

69. Richardson, U. I., Schonbrunn, A. 1981. Inhibition of adrenocorticotropin secretion by somatostatin in pituitary cells in culture. *Endocrinology* 108:281–90

70. Rivier, C., Vale, W. 1984. Corticotropin releasing factor (CRF) acts centrally to inhibit growth hormone secretion in the rat. *Endocrinology* 114:2409–11

71. Robbins, R. J., Leidy, J. W., Landon, R. M. 1985. The effects of growth hormone, corticotropin and TSH on the production and secretion of somatostatin by hypothalamic cells in vitro. *Endocrinology* 117:538–43

72. Root, A. W., Snyder, S. J., Rivani, I.,

Di George, A. M., Utiger, R. D. 1973. Inhibition of thyrotropin-releasing hormone mediated secretion of thyrotropin by human growth hormone. *J. Clin. Endocrinol. Metab.* 36:103–7

73. Rorstad, O. P., Epelbaum, J., Brazeau, P., Martin, J. B. 1979. Chromatographic and biological properties of immunoreactive somatostatin in hypothalamic and extrahypothalamic brain regions of the rat. *Endocrinology* 105:1083–92

74. Schonbrunn, A. 1982. Glucocorticoids down-regulate somatostatin receptors in pituitary cells in culture. *Endocrinology* 110:1147–54

75. Schonbrunn, A., Dorflinger, L. J., Koch, B. D. 1985. Mechanisms of SRIF action in pituitary cells. See Reference 53, 17:305–24

76. Schonbrunn, A., Tashjian, A. 1978. Characterization of functional receptors for somatostatin in rat pituitary cells in culture. *J. Biol. Chem.* 253:6473–83

77. Schonbrunn, A., Tashjian, A. 1980. Modulation of somatostatin receptors by thyrotropin releasing hormone in a clonal pituitary cell strain. *J. Biol. Chem.* 255:190–98

78. Sheppard, M. C., Kronheim, S., Pimstone, B. L. 1979. Effect of substance P, neurotensin and the enkephalins on somatostatin release from the rat hypothalamus in vitro. *J. Neurochem.* 32:647–49

79. Shields, D., Warren, T. G., Green, R. F. 1985. Expression of angler-fish preprosomatostatin genes in mammalian cells: Studies on the synthesis and posttranslational processing of somatostatin precursors. See Reference 53, 1:3–18

80. Shimatsu, A., Kato, Y., Matsushita, N., Katakami, H., Yanaihara, N., Imura, H. 1982. Effects of glucagon, neurotensin, and vasoactive intestinal polypeptide on somatostatin release from perifused rat hypothalamus. *Endocrinology* 110: 2113–17

81. Skamene, A., Patel, Y. C. 1984. Infusion of graded concentrations of somatostatin-14 in man: Pharmacokinetics and differential inhibitory effects on pituitary and islet hormones. *Clin. Endocrinol.* 20:555–64

82. Srikant, C. B., Heisler, S. 1985. Relationship between receptor binding and biopotency of somatostatin-14 and somatostatin-28 in mouse pituitary tumor cells. *Endocrinology* 117:271–78

83. Srikant, C. B., Patel, Y. C. 1981. Receptor binding of somatostatin-28 is tissue specific. *Nature* 294:259–60

84. Srikant, C. B., Patel, Y. C. 1982. Characterization of pituitary membrane receptors for somatostatin in the rat. *Endocrinology* 110:2138–44
85. Srikant, C. B., Patel, Y. C. 1985. Somatostatin receptors in the rat adrenal cortex: Characterization and comparison with brain and pituitary receptors. *Endocrinology* 116:1717–23
86. Srikant, C. B., Patel, Y. C. 1985. Somatostatin receptors. See Reference 53, 16:291–304
87. Takahara, J. O., Yunoki, S., Hosogi, H., Yakushiji, W., Kageyama, F., Ofuji, T. 1980. Concomitant increases in serum growth hormone and hypothalamic somatostatin in rats after injection of gamma aminobutyric acid, aminooxyacetic acid, or hydroxybutyric acid. *Endocrinology* 106:343–47
88. Tannenbaum, G. S. 1985. Physiological role of somatostatin in regulation of pulsatile growth hormone secretion. See Reference 53, 14:229–59
89. Tannenbaum, G. S., Guyda, H. J., Posner, B. I. 1983. Insulin-like growth factors: a role in growth hormone negative feedback and body weight regulation via brain. *Science* 220:77–79
90. Tannenbaum, G. S., Ling, N. 1984. The interrelationship of growth hormone (GH)-releasing factor and somatostatin in generation of the ultradian rhythm of GH secretion. *Endocrinology* 115:1952–57
91. Tannenbaum, G. S., Martin, J. B., Colle, E. 1978. Ultradian growth hormone rhythm in the rat: Effects of feeding, hyperglycemia and insulin induced hypoglycemia. *Endocrinology* 99:720–27
92. Tannenbaum, G. S., Rorstad, O., Brazeau, P. 1979. Effects of prolonged food deprivation on the ultradian growth hormone rhythm and immunoreactive somatostatin tissue levels in the rat. *Endocrinology* 104:1733–38
93. Tannenbaum, G. S., Patel, Y. C. 1985. On the fate of intracerebroventricularly administered somatostatin in the rat. Massive hypersomatostatinemia resulting from leakage into the peripheral circulation has effects on GH secretion and glucoregulation. *Endocrinology* Submitted for publication
94. Terry, L. C., Crowley, W. R. 1980. The effects of exercise stress on somatostatin concentrations in discrete brain nuclei. *Brain Res.* 197:543–46
95. Terry, L. C., Martin, J. B. 1981. The effects of lateral hypothalamic-medial forebrain stimulation and somatostatin antiserum on pulsatile growth hormone secretion in freely behaving rats: Evidence for a dual regulatory mechanism. *Endocrinology* 109:622–27
96. Terry, L. C., Willoughby, J. O., Brazeau, P., Martin, J. B., Patel, Y. C. 1976. Antiserum to somatostatin prevents stress induced inhibition of growth hormone secretion in the rat. *Science* 192:565–67
97. Tumisto, J., Ranta, T., Pekka, M., Saarinen, A., Leppaluoto, J. 1975. Neurotransmitter control of thyrotropin secretion in the rat. *Eur. J. Pharmacol.* 30:221–29
98. Vance, M. L., Kaiser, D. L., Evans, W. L., Furlanetto, R., Vale, W., et al. 1985. Pulsatile growth hormone secretion in normal man during a continuous 24-hour infusion of human growth hormone releasing factor (1–40). *J. Clin. Invest.* 75:1584–90
99. Vijayan, E., McCann, S. 1978. Effects of intraventricular injection of γ-aminobutyric acid on plasma growth hormone and thyrotropin in conscious ovariectomized rats. *Endocrinology* 103:1883–93
100. Willoughby, J. O., Martin, J. B. 1978. Pulsatile growth hormone secretion: inhibitory role of medial preoptic area. *Brain Res.* 148:240–44

Ann. Rev. Physiol. 1986. 48:569–91

GROWTH HORMONE RELEASING HORMONE[1]

Marie C. Gelato and George R. Merriam

Developmental Endocrinology Branch, NICHHD, National Institutes of Health, Bethesda, Maryland 20892

INTRODUCTION

The role of a growth hormone releasing hormone (GHRH) in the regulation of GH secretion has been recognized since the late 1950s, and was reviewed in this series by Reichlin et al in 1976 (93) and by Vale and colleagues in 1977 (120). These authors outlined the several lines of evidence that led to the postulation of the existence of a GHRH: that interruption of the connection between hypothalamus and pituitary leads to a decrease in GH secretion; that electrical stimulation of the ventromedial nucleus and basal hypothalamus stimulates GH secretion; that crude hypothalamic extracts stimulate GH release from anterior pituitaries in culture; that passive immunization with antibodies against somatostatin elevates GH basal levels, but pulsatile release of GH continues; and that a factor present in both plasma and CSF of some patients with acromegaly stimulates release of GH from pituitaries in vitro. All of these results appeared to support the existence of a hypothalamic GHRH, but identification and characterization of this hormone proved an elusive goal.

The abnormal production of factors with growth hormone–releasing activity by tumors such as bronchial carcinoids and pancreatic islet cell tumors had long been recognized. These factors produce all the clinical features of acromegaly (98), and Frohman & Szabo suggested that these tumor growth hormone–releasing factors (GRF's) might be similar to the GHRH of hypothalamic origin

---

(38). In November 1982, two articles published nearly simultaneously described the primary sequence of GRF's from patients with pancreatic islet cell tumors. One, described by Guillemin and colleagues (51), was a 44–amino acid amide, hpGRF(1–44)-NH$_2$, and the other, isolated by Rivier and coworkers (95), was the free acid hpGRF(1–40)-OH of the first 40 amino acids in the same sequence. Studies in rats (15, 110) and humans (13, 62) soon indicated that these factors are highly similar to those present in the hypothalamus. In the brief period since those discoveries, the availability of synthetic GHRH's has stimulated an avalanche of reports on the effects, regulation, and applications of GHRH in man and other animals. The focus of the present review will therefore be on the newly synthesized GHRH and studies using it as a physiologic probe and a potential clinical tool.

As is the case for other releasing factors, differences in nomenclature persist. When tumoral growth hormone–releasing factor was first identified, the acronyms GRF and GHRF were used (38). Currently the abbreviations GHRH and GRH are in widest use for the hypothalamic growth hormone–releasing hormone (45); the French literature tends to follow the preference of Guillemin for the term somatocrinin, by analogy to somatostatin (19, 22). In this review we use the abbreviation GRF for factors of tumoral origin, and GHRH for the hypothalamic peptides.

IDENTIFICATION AND SEQUENCING OF GHRH

The identification and sequencing of GRF in 1982 was made possible by the availability of tissue extracts from two patients who presented with clinical features of acromegaly and were found to have pancreatic islet cell tumors (98, 117). The removal of these tumors resulted in a reduction of serum GH and somatomedin C levels and resolution of symptoms. In both tumors several peptides with GH releasing activity were identified. Guillemin and colleagues (51) reported the main structure to be a 44–amino acid amide (hpGRF(1–44)-NH$_2$) and the other fragments to have the subsequences (1–37)-OH and (1–40)-OH. In the tumor characterized by Rivier and coworkers (95) the most abundant fraction was a 40–amino acid peptide, which proved to be the free acid hpGRF(1–40)-OH; the other fragments identified were hpGRF(1–40)-NH$_2$ and hpGRF(1–29)-NH$_2$.

Immunohistochemical studies in several species, including rat (70), monkey (9, 57), and human (10, 30), using antibodies directed against the 30–44 terminus of tumoral GRF, showed the presence of strongly cross-reacting material in specific nuclei of the hypothalamus, which indicates similarity to hypothalamic GHRH. In other studies injection of neutralizing antibodies against tumor-derived GRF blocked the GH response to hypothalamic extracts with GHRH activity (130); this also suggests that hpGRF and GHRH are very similar. Human hypothalamic GHRH was subsequently purified from brain fragments by gel filtration and reverse-phase HPLC (13). Two major peaks of GHRH activity were present, which coeluted with hpGRF-44-NH$_2$ and hpGRF-40-OH. A cDNA for a GRF precursor hybridized with only one human genomic region, which contains the full 1–44 sequence, a glycine amidation signal, and additional flanking residues (50, 67). Recently the structure of human hypothalamic GHRH has been determined by Ling and colleagues; it contains 44 amino acids and is identical to tumor-derived hpGRF(1–44)-NH$_2$ (62).

GHRH peptides have been identified and sequenced from several other species, including pig, cow, sheep (21), goat (21), and rat. Porcine (14) and bovine (34) GHRH closely resemble human GHRH, with a three-residue difference between porcine and human GHRH and a five-residue difference between bovine and human GHRH; the differences are located primarily at the C terminus. Rat GHRH differs more extensively and has 43 amino acids (15, 110). In general there is a marked structural homology among the GHRH's sequenced from a variety of mammalian species, particularly at the N terminus. This may explain why most antisera raised against the full GHRH sequence identify the more variable C terminal region.

The greater conservation of the N terminus of GHRH suggests that this region contains the active site of the molecule. Initial reports of the activity of the different tumor fragments hpGRF(1–40)-OH, hpGRF(1–44)-NH$_2$, hpGRF(1–37)-OH, and hpGRF(1–29)-NH$_2$ indicated that they all had similar potencies for the release of GH in vitro. Ling et al (61) synthesized a series of C-terminal deleted fragments of human GHRH and tested their ability to release GH from rat anterior pituitary cells in culture. Fragments as small as 1–34 retained 23% of the activity of hGHRH, and further deletions down to (1–29)-NH$_2$ yielded no further decrease in bioactivity. Only with deletion to GHRH(1–19)-NH$_2$ did activity completely disappear. They concluded that the minimal sequence with full intrinsic activity lies in the 1–21 fragment. Earlier work from these authors (60) demonstrated that an aromatic residue at position 1 is necessary for potent biological activity. They compared ten different position-1-substituted analogs to hGHRH(1–40)-OH and concluded that a hydrogen bond formed with the first residue may be required for receptor-ligand interaction. Manipulations of this region can result in the enhancement of activity. Analogs based upon the (1–29)-NH$_2$ sequence, with substitutions in the first three positions, include peptides that are 7–50 times more potent than native hGHRH(1–29)-NH$_2$ in stimulating GH release in the rat (55, 60).

Since GRF has repeatedly been found in pancreatic islet cell tumors, there has been much speculation as to whether its production there is strictly ectopic, or whether it might be a gut peptide as well as a hypothalamic hormone. GHRH is structurally a member of the secretin-glucagon family of peptides, which includes VIP, glucagon, secretin, gastric inhibitory peptide, and PHI-27; this last peptide has the greatest homology with GHRH (27, 115). Porcine PHI and its human equivalent PHM share many biological activities with VIP, and PHI and VIP are subsequences of a common precursor molecule (27, 87). Immunohistochemical studies have identified material with GHRH-like immunoreactivity in the upper intestinal tract in both rat and human (18, 30). A preliminary report suggests that GHRH is able to stimulate exocrine pancreatic enzyme secretion in vitro (82). Tannenbaum (113) reported that intrathecal administration of GHRH in the rat elevated plasma glucose concentrations, although this effect probably reflects central rather than peripheral activities, since peripherally administered GHRH generally has no such effect (42, 119). These reports are suggestive, but it is still uncertain whether GHRH has physiological functions outside the brain.

Momany and colleagues have described the design and synthesis of a family of synthetic peptides, originally derived from enkephalins, that also have GH-releasing activity (75). These small peptides, of which the most potent, called GH-releasing peptide (GHRP), has the structure His-DTrp-Ala-Trp-DPhe-Lys-NH$_2$, have no primary sequence homology with GHRH, but there has been speculation that they might mimic the conformation of its active site. Their GH-releasing potency is about 1% that of GHRH in vitro. Badger and colleagues compared the activities of GHRH and GHRP and found both similarities and differences in their actions (3, 68). Nonparallelism of their dose-response curves suggests that they may act by different mechanisms; alternatively, GHRP may be a partial agonist. Substances that cross-react with antibodies directed against GHRP have not yet been found to occur naturally.

DISTRIBUTION AND ONTOGENY OF GHRH

Distribution

Even prior to the characterization of GHRH, studies using electrical stimulation or ablation of areas within the hypothalamus predicted that the arcuate and ventromedial nuclei were the two main sites of GHRH production. Monosodium glutamate treatment of rats produces a specific lesion in the arcuate nucleus (11, 74), and this results in a significant reduction of GH secretion. This finding suggests that this defect results in GHRH deficiency. With the availability of antisera raised against synthetic GHRH, many investigators employing immunocytochemical and immunohistochemical techniques have reported on the distribution and localization of GHRH. Bloch and colleagues demonstrated that C-terminally directed antisera against hpGRF(1–40) revealed immunoreactive fibers in the median eminence in human and monkey hypothalami, but immunoreactive cell bodies were found only in the arcuate nucleus (9, 10). Lechan et al, using an antiserum that recognizes GRF(23–44)-NH$_2$, demonstrated GHRH immunoreactive cell bodies in both ventromedial and arcuate nuclei of primate brain (57). Shibasaki et al found immunoreactive GHRH in extracts from human pituitary stalk, hypothalamus, optic chiasm, and pancreas (106). The material from pituitary stalk and hypothalamus coeluted with GHRH(1–44)-NH$_2$ on gel permeation chromatography, while the pancreatic extracts also contained a peak that eluted as a higher molecular weight species. Although the structure of rat GHRH differs from that of other mammals, its distribution is similar, with immunoreactive cell bodies in the arcuate and ventromedial nuclei (70). These fibers project to the median eminence and make contact with portal vessels.

There are a few reports demonstrating GHRH immunoreactivity in extrahypothalamic sites, including placenta (138), the upper intestinal tract in human and rat (18, 30), and pituitary somatotrophs in primates (76). In the gastric antrum of humans immunoreactive GHRH colocalizes with gastrin.

Thus, while somatostatin (24, 92) and the releasing factors TRH (33) and CRH (12, 81) have wide distribution in the brain, GHRH is found only in a small number of nuclei. In this limited distribution it more closely resembles LHRH (32), but the distribution of brain GHRH is even more restricted than that of LHRH.

Ontogeny

Studies of the development of the GHRH neuronal system are still few. Using an indirect immunofluorescence technique with an antiserum directed against the C-terminal of GRF(1–44)-NH$_2$, Bresson et al detected staining in the infundibular nucleus as early as 18 weeks of human fetal development (23). Bloch et al were not able to demonstrate immunoreactive staining in the arcuate nucleus until the 29th week of gestation (10). These two studies suggest that hypothalamic GHRH may not be necessary for the control of GH until mid or late gestation. Postnatal studies in the cat also show a delayed rise in GHRH concentrations: At 15 days of age only slight GHRH-like immunoreactivity is observed in the median eminence, but this increases markedly by age 1 month (25).

In the ovine fetus, GHRH is able to stimulate GH release between 71 and 135 days of gestation, and the response decreases with advancing age (48, 80). The magnitude of the response to GHRH parallels the levels of endogenous GH observed; thus circulating levels of GH are higher in the fetal period than postnatally. This suggests that GHRH may be involved in maintaining GH levels in this species as early as mid gestation. The physiological role of placental GHRH-like material is still uncertain.

MECHANISM OF ACTION

Most peptide hormones act through binding to a specific receptor on the surface of target cells. The activated receptor then stimulates a series of intracellular events that differ from hormone to hormone. The cell surface receptor for GHRH has been only incompletely characterized; more is known about the postreceptor events triggered by GHRH. Seifert et al have reported the demonstration of specific high affinity binding sites for GHRH on rat anterior pituitary cells (103). They used a GHRH analog, [His[1],Nle[27]]-hGHRH(1–32)-NH$_2$, as ligand in order to avoid iodination of the amino-terminal tyrosine[1] in native GHRH, which abolishes binding affinity. The dissociation constant based on competition studies was 41×10^{-12} M, and receptor concentration averaged 11 fmol per pituitary equivalent. The in vitro biological potencies of several GHRH analogs were highly correlated with their binding affinities. Rat GHRH was more potent than hGHRH(1–40) in releasing GH from rat anterior pituitary cells, and had a higher binding affinity. Biological potency and binding affinity were increased in parallel in a group of C-terminally amidated fragments such as the [His[1],Nle[27]]-hGRF(1–32)-NH$_2$ analog used as a radioligand, while removal of the amino-terminal residue markedly decreased both biological potency and binding activity. The radioligand was not displaced from the binding sites by either PHI or VIP. These authors also found that glucocorticoids appear to be necessary to maintain an adequate number of GHRH receptor binding sites. Adrenalectomy significantly reduced the binding capacity of the rat anterior pituitary cells, although the binding affinity remained constant.

Binding of GHRH to its receptors stimulates formation of cyclic AMP (6, 53). Brazeau and colleagues (22) demonstrated that increasing the cellular content of cAMP stimulates GH release and that the dose-response curve parallels that seen with either GHRH(1–40) or GHRH(1–44). Both calmodulin and GTP are involved in the stimulation of adenylate cyclase by GHRH (53, 99). Lewin et al suggest that GHRH stimulates a cAMP-dependent protein kinase located on pituitary secretory granules, which increases granule exocytosis and causes acute release of preformed GH (59). The release of GH also appears to be dependent on calcium, since the addition of CoCl$_2$, a blocker of calcium uptake, rendered GHRH ineffective in stimulating GH release (6, 22). Cyclic AMP may not be the sole effector of GHRH-stimulated GH release, as GHRH also stimulates ^{32}P incorporation into phosphatidylinositol (26), an early postreceptor event when the second messenger is calcium (5). Whether these changes are obligatory mediators of GHRH action is uncertain, however; Raymond et al (90) showed that, in contrast to the rapid effect of LHRH on ^{32}P incorporation into phosphatidylcholine, the effect of GHRH was a slow event seen only after 60 minutes. This observation suggests that phospholipid metabolism may not be critical to the early steps of GHRH action.

GHRH also stimulates GH synthesis. Barinaga et al have shown that GHRH can alter transcription of the GH gene both in vitro and in vivo, with a 2.5-fold increase 30 min after injection of GHRH (4). Later work by Gick et al demonstrated a similar increase in GH mRNA in rat pituitary cell cultures after addition of GHRH, with no effect on prolactin release or levels of prolactin mRNA (47). These studies indicate that GHRH is a potent and specific stimulator of GH synthesis as well as release.

Human GHRH is active in a wide range of species, but its effects are highly selective. It has been shown to stimulate GH secretion in mammals, birds, and fish (42, 58, 78, 86, 119). In all these species no other pituitary hormone was affected, with the exception of prolactin at high doses in humans (43) and primates (2) in vivo, and in sheep pituitary cells in vitro (56).

One report demonstrated stimulation of amylase secretion from dispersed guinea pig pancreatic acini (82). These authors found that rGHRH was 100 times more potent a stimulus than hGHRH. As noted above, several studies have shown GHRH immunoreactivity in the GI tract in rodents and humans. However, it remains to be determined whether GHRH has any physiological role in normal pancreatic function. GHRH has some binding affinity for the VIP receptor (82), and the observed effects may reflect this cross-reactivity rather than a specific role for GHRH.

In normal pituitary there appears to be no synergy or antagonism between GHRH and the other hypothalamic releasing hormones (127). This may have a practical clinical application, as the results of administering a single bolus of all the releasing factors together may be the same as the responses to a lengthy series of tests of each factor separately (105), which would simplify the process of pituitary function testing.

PHARMACOKINETICS AND PHYSIOLOGIC ACTIONS

Pharmacokinetics

There is limited information on the turnover, metabolism, or metabolic clearance rate (MCR) of GHRH. Frohman et al used both the single bolus and continuous infusion techniques to determine the MCR of GHRH(1–40) in normal men (39). The calculated MCR's were 194 ± 17.5 L/m^2/day with single injection techniques, and 202 ± 16 L/m^2/day with continuous infusions. Following single injections the disappearance rate could be divided into two phases: an equilibration phase of 7.6 ± 1.2 min, followed by an elimination phase of 51.8 ± 5.4 min. The half-time for the disappearance of GHRH from circulation after continuous infusions was 41.3 ± 3 min. These figures are similar to our own results following continuous administration of GHRH-44 to normal men; we observed an equilibration half-time of approximately 45 min. By contrast, Losa et al (65) reported the half-time of disappearance to be 7.6 $\pm$

1.7 min following a single injection of 200 μg GHRH-44, and could detect no GHRH in plasma after 30 min. This $T_{1/2}$ is very similar to the equilibration phase reported by Frohman et al. The factors responsible for the difference in results are not clear, but they may be related to assay technique, since the sensitivities of the two assay systems were very different. The MCR reported by Frohman et al is slower than that of other human releasing hormones, but similar to that reported for ovine CRH (79). Human CRH (102), TRH (77), LHRH (91), and somatostatin (83) are all cleared from peripheral plasma much more quickly. This does not necessarily imply that endogenous GHRH has a long duration of action, since clearance from hypothalamic portal blood is dominated by other mechanisms, such as dilution, but it does explain the prolonged effect of administered GHRH on GH release (39, 121) and may have more relevance in determining the effects of ectopic GHRH production.

Potency and Specificity

As described above, the core unit for biological activity of the GHRH molecule appears to be the 1–21 N-terminal fragment. Thus one would expect that the forms of GHRH in widest use for in vitro and in vivo studies—GHRH(1–44)-NH₂, GHRH(1–40)-OH, and GHRH(1–29)-NH₂—would have qualitatively similar effects, but might differ in potency. An initial report of Guillemin and colleagues suggested that hpGRF-44 might be more potent in vitro than GHRH-40 or GHRH-37 (51). Wehrenberg & Ling (132) compared the in vivo potency of several human GHRH peptides in cannulated rats pretreated with antibodies to both somatostatin and rat hypothalamic GHRH. In this system hGHRH-37, hpGHRH-40, and hpGHRH-44 were equipotent. GHRH(1–28) had significantly lower activity than GHRH-44, and GHRH(1–24) was not active in vivo. These authors also found GHRH-44 and rGHRH to be equipotent for the release of GH in the rat.

In clinical studies, Grossman et al compared the effects of a maximal dose of GHRH(1–40) and GHRH(1–29) in normal men and in patients with growth hormone deficiency, and found that these two preparations resulted in a similar stimulation of GH release (49). Comparing a 50 μg bolus dose of GHRH(1–44), GHRH(1–40), and GHRH(1–29) in normal men, Losa et al showed that the maximal effects of these three GHRH's are indistinguishable (64).

The dose-response relationship for the effects of GHRH in man was initially obscured by the marked heterogeneity in response, which may be due to variations in endogenous somatostatin secretion. Subsequently, we and other groups have determined dose-response curves for the effects of GHRH in both primates and adult men and women (2, 43, 65, 121). For GHRH-44, the half-maximally effective doses (ED_{50}) for women and men were 0.2 and 0.4 μg/kg, respectively (43). A dose of 1 μg/kg had maximal effect. Higher doses produced no higher peak responses, but had a longer duration of action (121).

We also found a slight but significant rise in prolactin at the highest dose used (> 10 μg/kg) in both rhesus monkeys and normal adults. In our studies, this effect was observed in vivo (43) but not in vitro (2); however, Law et al (56) reported slight elevations in prolactin release from ovine pituitary cells in vitro. It is not clear whether this effect on prolactin, observed only at high doses of GHRH, has physiological significance. Thus GHRH stimulates the prompt release of GH in a dose-dependent manner, and its action is highly specific for GH release. The maximally effective dose in man appears to be approximately 1 μg/kg, and all three peptides, GHRH(1–44), GHRH(1–40), and GHRH(1–29), appear to be comparable in potency.

Physiological Differences in Response

In several species there is a sexual dimorphism in the pattern of GH secretion; however, we did not find any significant differences between the GH responses to GHRH in men as compared with women studied during the mid-follicular and mid-luteal phases of the menstrual cycle (43). Evans et al tested women in the early follicular, late follicular, and mid-luteal phases of the menstrual cycle, using a dose of 3.3 μg/kg (35), and also found no changes in the response of GH to GHRH. In our study the women did have a slightly, but significantly, lower ED_{50} than the men. This is consistent with earlier findings that estrogen can enhance the effects of a variety of indirect stimuli of GH release (71); however, the effect is not large, and it is more likely that this enhancement is due to an effect of estrogen on GHRH release rather than on its pituitary effects.

There is still controversy as to whether the response of GH to GHRH decreases with age. In rats, Wehrenberg & Ling found no age-related change in the GH response to either a submaximal or a maximal dose of GHRH (131). Sonntag et al (109), however, reported that the in vivo response in old rats (over 20 months) was decreased by more than 50% as compared with young rats (age 3–4 months). However, the responses of cultured anterior pituitary cells taken from the two groups of animals were not significantly different. They inferred from this that the hypothalamus was the source of the age-related difference, not a change in the sensitivity of the pituitary gland.

Data in human subjects are also in disagreement. Shibasaki et al (108) reported a marked decline in the GH response to GHRH of men older than 40. The mean peak plasma GH levels after GHRH administration to men in their twenties and thirties was 30 ng/ml, falling to less than 10 ng/ml for men in their forties and older. In a study of men in the Baltimore Longitudinal Study of Aging, however, we saw no age-related decline in the GH responses to a 1μg/kg dose of GHRH in subjects through their eighties (84).

We have also studied whether the response to GHRH changes during normal childhood development. We studied 85 normal children, 40 boys ages 7–17 and 45 girls ages 5–17, at different pubertal stages. The responses in the girls were nearly uniform throughout puberty and did not differ from those of adult women. There was a slight decrease in response observed in mid-pubertal boys, but otherwise their responses were similar to those of adult men (40). Thus, although full agreement is still lacking, the majority of the data support the view that the responsiveness of the anterior pituitary gland to GHRH remains relatively constant throughout life after early childhood. Therefore, it seems likely that changes in GHRH secretion, rather than in GHRH responses, account for the known decrease in GH secretion seen with advancing age (89, 137).

Hormonal Modulation of Response

A variety of factors, including thyroid hormones, glucocorticoids, somato-medins, and sex steroids, can alter spontaneous GH secretion and the GH response to provocative stimuli (37). With the availability of synthetic GHRH it has been possible to explore how these hormones affect GH release, whether through altering GHRH secretion or altering the responsiveness of the pituitary gland to GHRH.

The effect of glucocorticoids on the GH response to GHRH has been studied both in vivo and in vitro. Wehrenberg et al showed that both intact and adrenalectomized rats treated with dexamethasone had an enhanced GH response to GHRH (126). Adrenalectomized animals had significantly lower GH responses to a submaximal dose of GHRH than intact animals, and this response was restored with dexamethasone treatment. However, a maximal dose of GHRH resulted in a similar GH response in adrenalectomized and intact animals. From these data the authors concluded that glucocorticoids increase the sensitivity of the pituitary gland to GHRH. Thus, while hypercorticolism is known to inhibit growth, and may do so in part by interfering with GH release, this decrease appears not to be due to a reduction in responsiveness to GHRH. Michel et al (73) have shown similar results in vitro in primary cultures of rat anterior pituitary cells. Pre-incubation of the cells with dexamethasone resulted in a fourfold increase in both GH release following GHRH stimulation and in the sensitivity of the pituitary cells to GHRH. They further demonstrated that dexamethasone enhanced the cAMP response to GHRH; thus the effect prob-ably occurs at an early step in GHRH action.

GH secretion is also reduced in hypothyroidism (133), and propylthiouracil-induced hypothyroidism blunts the response to GHRH both in vivo and in vitro (97).

There is still relatively little information on the effect of sex steroids on the GH response to GHRH. As noted earlier, prepubertal boys and girls (40) and young and old adult men and women (43, 84) show similar responses to maximal doses of GHRH. There also appears to be no obvious change in the responses of women during the menstrual cycle (35, 43). McCormick and colleagues examined the effects of testosterone and estrogen on GHRH responses in castrated animals. In both sexes, testosterone increased and estrogen decreased the GH response to GHRH (69). This is in contrast to the in vivo effects of estrogen on GH release in the human, where estrogens appear to sensitize the pituitary gland to stimulators of GH release (37, 71).

Insulin-like growth factors (IGF-I and IGF-II) are known to suppress GH release in the rat (1, 123). This appears to involve both suppression of GHRH release and blunting of GHRH effects. Small quantities of IGF applied intraventricularly suppress GH secretion, an effect probably mediated through decreased GHRH release (1). Brazeau et al reported that both IGF-I and IGF-II inhibit the GH response to GHRH in rat pituitary cell cultures; IGF-II was less potent (19). A similar inhibition is seen in human pituitary adenomas taken from patients with acromegaly. Ceda and colleagues showed that pituitary cells from all tumors tested had specific receptors for IGF-I, IGF-II, and insulin; however, the ability of IGF's to inhibit GHRH-stimulated GH release was very variable (28). It is not yet clear whether these results can be extrapolated to normal human pituitary cells.

Somatostatin, the GH release-inhibiting hormone, is a potent noncompetitive inhibitor of GHRH action in vitro. Stimulation of GH release from rat anterior pituitary cells in vitro was completely antagonized by somatostatin (20). In cultured pituitary tumor cells from patients with acromegaly, Lamberts et al (54) showed that somatostatin blocked the GH rise following GHRH. Changes in endogenous somatostatin secretion may be responsible for the marked variability in the amplitude of GH responses to GHRH in vivo. Tannenbaum & Ling (114) demonstrated the interrelationship between GHRH and somatostatin in the rat, in which GH secretion varies in a predictable diurnal rhythm. During periods of low GH secretion ("troughs"), GHRH had very little ability to stimulate further GH release, while during periods of higher GH release its GH-stimulating effect was markedly greater. When the animals were passively immunized with antisera to somatostatin, the reduction in GHRH responsivity during trough periods was abolished. These data indicate that somatostatin is a potent modulator of the action of GHRH directly at the level of the anterior pituitary gland.

Glucose suppresses GH levels in normal subjects, and can modulate the effects of GHRH. Normal adult men and women given GHRH following a loading dose of intravenous 50% dextrose had significantly depressed GH responses as compared to their responses while fasting (104). While both insulin and glucose levels rose after the glucose infusions there was no correlation between the change in insulin levels and the decrease in response of GH to GHRH. The suppressive effect of hyperglycemia is not sustained indefinitely; however, a group of hyperglycemic, poorly controlled diabetic patients showed no change in responsiveness to GHRH (88). It is not clear at what level glucose acts to inhibit the GH response to GHRH; it may trigger a reflex elevation in hypothalamic somatostatin secretion.

Imaki et al (52) studied the effects of free fatty acids (FFA's) on the GH response to GHRH. It has been shown that FFA's inhibit the GH rise following various indirect stimuli, such as insulin and L-dopa (8, 36). Imaki and colleagues found that FFA's also decrease the GH response to GHRH. Whether FFA's act directly on the anterior pituitary gland or through other central mechanisms such as somatostatin is not yet clear.

One other parameter that can alter GHRH response is body mass. Williams et al showed that the GH response to GHRH was severely blunted in morbidly obese patients (134). Following weight loss the GH response increased but was still lower than that of normal subjects. In their subjects the GH response to GHRH was inversely correlated with body weight, a correlation also seen in our study of aging men (84), none of whom were severely obese. The mechanism of this effect of body weight on the response to GHRH is not known.

CLINICAL APPLICATIONS

Syndromes of GH Hypersecretion

GH secretion is increased in a variety of disorders, including acromegaly, poorly controlled diabetes mellitus, anorexia nervosa, and malnutrition. In most of these conditions the alterations in GH secretion reflect alterations in feedback regulation; in acromegaly, overproduction of GH by a pituitary tumor is the primary abnormality, although a subset of these patients have tumoral hypersecretion of GHRH.

ACROMEGALY   Overproduction of GH by pituitary tumors does not necessarily imply autonomy. Several reports have demonstrated that most patients with acromegaly remain responsive to GHRH. Two early studies by Wood et al (136) and Shibasaki et al (107) suggested that the magnitude of the GH response to GHRH correlated with the GH responses to other stimuli, or with suppression of GH following oral glucose. In two larger series these have not been consistent findings. We (41) and Chiodini et al (29) found no correlation between the GH response to GHRH and basal GH levels, somatomedin-C levels, the GH response to TRH, age, sex, or the size of the tumor. In our series, patients previously treated with radiation, surgery, or bromocriptine had a significantly lower mean response than normal controls, and some of the patients who had received radiation therapy had no GH response at all. Chiodini and colleagues reported that those patients who responded to bromocriptine with decreased GH levels had lower responses to GHRH than patients refractory to bromocriptine. Such a correlation was not evident in our series.

From these studies it would appear that GHRH testing has limited diagnostic usefulness in the evaluation of acromegaly and adds little to other currently available tests, with one possible exception, the differentiation of patients with ectopic production of GHRH from those with pituitary tumors. Only a few patients with ectopic GHRH production have been tested with GHRH (66, 101); in contrast to other untreated acromegalics, most of these patients show no rise in GH following the exogenous administration of GHRH. Thus, an untreated patient with acromegaly who fails to respond to GHRH may have the ectopic GRF syndrome.

The measurement of GHRH levels in peripheral plasma in these patients is a simpler and even more direct test for this condition. Two studies have used radioimmunoassay of GHRH levels in peripheral plasma of acromegalic patients to attempt to determine how frequently this condition occurs. Penny et al (85) measured levels in 80 patients with acromegaly; of these, 4 patients had elevated GHRH levels. The elevation was marked in only one of the 4; this patient had ectopic production of GHRH by a carcinoid tumor. In the other series 177 acromegalic patients were screened (116). GHRH levels were not elevated, except in 3 patients already known to have tumors secreting GHRH. All of these had markedly elevated levels, above 1 ng/ml; the highest level seen in normals was 82 pg/ml. These data suggest that ectopic GHRH production is an uncommon cause of acromegaly, accounting for less than 1% of all cases.

Since most acromegalics respond to GHRH, it is of interest to know whether desensitization of the response to GHRH occurs after continuous GHRH exposure, as has been demonstrated for LHRH. If so, GH levels might even be driven below baseline values, and long-acting GHRH preparations could be used therapeutically, as has been employed to good effect with LHRH analogs. The presence of acromegaly in patients with ectopic production of GHRH suggests that this degree of desensitization may not occur, but the question remains an open one. Bilezikjian & Vale (7) showed that 24 hr exposure of pituitary cells to GHRH in vitro resulted in loss of responsiveness of these cells to subsequent stimulation with GHRH. There was a partial depletion of GHRH stores, but the effect was more complex. The concentration-response curve was shifted to the right, with a fivefold increase in EC_{50}; an attenuation of adenyl cyclase activity was also noted. A study of Badger et al using perifused pituitary cells yielded findings consistent with these results (3). Thus there may be two mechanisms involved in the decrease: pool depletion and desensitization related to receptor occupancy.

In vivo data in both animals and man also suggest that there may be more than one mechanism. Wehrenberg et al (129) showed that rats treated continuously for 24 hr with GHRH had significantly lower pituitary GH content than rats treated with saline. This suggests that depletion of pituitary stores is at least a partial cause of the blunted GHRH responses observed. We (44), Losa et al (63), and Webb et al (125) demonstrated that after several hours of exposure to

GHRH the response to a subsequent GHRH bolus was blunted. During continuous infusion of GHRH there is first a sharp rise in GH, GH levels then fall, and the response to an additional bolus of GHRH at the end of the infusion period is markedly attenuated. Vance et al (122) reported that when infusions of either saline or graded doses of GHRH were followed by a supramaximal GHRH bolus, there was a reciprocal relationship between the quantity of GH released during the infusion and during the bolus periods. This finding also suggests that the pool of GH that can be released over a period of a few hours is finite.

To determine whether this desensitization might reduce GH levels even below basal values in acromegaly, we have performed prolonged (24 hr) infusions of GHRH. Some patients continue to secrete GH at high levels and are still responsive to further stimulation with GHRH, while in others GH falls off in a manner similar to that seen in short infusions in normals, i.e. there is wide inter-tumor variability. In no case, however, did GH fall below baseline levels. Whether a more complete desensitization could be produced by more prolonged exposure is uncertain; it is known from studies with LHRH that receptor down-regulation may take 72 hr or longer. In normal subjects infused with 1 μg/kg/hr GHRH for 24 hr the most striking effect is that GH secretion is increased over basal rates but episodic secretion of GH persists. This may reflect the episodic secretion of hypothalamic somatostatin.

Because somatostatin inhibits GH secretion through a class of receptors separate from those for GHRH, we used it to assist in distinguishing the possible mechanisms of desensitization. When pituitary cells were coperifused with 10 nM of both GHRH and somatostatin, GH release was prevented, but the response to a subsequent dose of GHRH was still blunted compared to that following perifusion with somatostatin alone (94). This suggests that desensitization can occur during GHRH receptor occupancy, independent of GH pool depletion.

OTHER GH HYPERSECRETING CONDITIONS   Basal GH levels are also elevated in patients with poorly controlled diabetes mellitus. In this condition, the magnitude of the GH response to GHRH is similar to that seen in controls, although GH rises from higher basal values (88). Thus the responsiveness of the pituitary gland does not appear to be altered, in contrast to the response seen in normal individuals made acutely hyperglycemic, in whom the GH response to GHRH is markedly decreased (104). It has been suggested that increases in somatostatin tone may mediate these blunted responses. Whether the difference between the results of these two situations indicates a decrease in somatostatin secretion in poorly controlled diabetics or the participation of hyperinsulinemia in the acute blunting is not presently known.

In children with protein-calorie malnutrition and in adults with anorexia nervosa, basal GH levels are also markedly elevated and somatomedin-C levels are usually low or undetectable, but the GH elevation after GHRH is indistinguishable from that of normal subjects (72, 135). The elevated basal level of GH resembles that seen in animals in which somatostatin has been immunoneutralized (14, 124). It is interesting to speculate that both in poorly controlled diabetes mellitus and in malnutrition there might be a similar decrease in somatostatin tone.

GH Deficiency

Probably the greatest potential for clinical application of GHRH lies in the evaluation and treatment of GH deficiency (GHD). The first question addressed was what portion of patients with this disorder are GHRH deficient rather than GHRH resistant, and so would respond to GHRH. Rodents treated with monosodium glutamate (MSG) develop GH deficiency and lesions of the arcuate nucleus, which suggests that the growth failure results from decreased secretion of GHRH (74). Their GH secretion can be restored with GHRH administration (128). In the human, GH deficiency could either similarly be due to a hypothalamic defect, or could result from an intrinsic pituitary disorder. The results of indirect tests suggested that the majority of GH deficient patients have hypothalamic disease, but until GHRH became available there was no way to test this hypothesis directly.

Initial GHRH studies were conducted in adults with GHD. Borges et al (17) and Wood et al (136) demonstrated that some adult patients with GHD are responsive to GHRH. We studied two groups of adult patients with GHD, one group with Hand-Schüller-Christian disease (HSC), an infiltrative process known to affect the hypothalamus selectively, and another group with idiopathic GHD. All the HSC patients had a measurable GH response to GHRH, while only three of seven patients with idiopathic GHD responded to GHRH. When GHD is due to a hypothalamic disorder GHRH can provoke a GH response; the lower proportion of responses among patients with idiopathic GHD may reflect the greater heterogeneity of this condition, which could include some patients with pituitary lesions.

In GHD children, Takano et al (111) reported that approximately 40% of the patients had a GH response of greater than 5 ng/ml after GHRH. In two larger series reported by Schriock et al (100) and Rogol et al (96), an even greater proportion of children, 70–80%, were responsive to GHRH. In our own series of 35 children with GHD, 80% responded to a single iv bolus of GHRH, and approximately half of these responses overlapped with those of normal prepubertal children (40). Schriock et al noted that the GHRH responses of patients with GHD decreased after age 16, in contrast to results in normals (84) in whom we saw no age-related decrement in GH responses. This may reflect the effect of a more prolonged period of atrophy of chronically unstimulated somatotrophs.

The GH responses to GHRH and to other ("indirect") provocative tests for GH deficiency are not strongly correlated. In our series we found no significant correlation between the GH responses to GHRH and those to insulin or L-dopa stimulation tests. Patients who respond to either L-dopa or insulin also respond to GHRH, but the converse is not necessarily true; many GHD patients have entirely normal responses to GHRH. Thus, it would seem that while GHRH may help to distinguish between hypothalamic and pituitary causes of GH deficiency, it is not useful in establishing the diagnosis.

Failure to respond to a single bolus of GHRH does not necessarily rule out the possibility of a hypothalamic defect and a responsive pituitary. We, and Borges et al (16), working with adult patients, found that some who failed to respond initially converted to a positive response, after repeated GHRH stimulation. We (45) and Takano and colleagues (112) have shown similar results in GHD children.

These observations have important therapeutic implications. Since the majority of patients with GHD have a GH response to GHRH, it would seem that GHRH could become the basis of an alternative form of therapy for children with GHD.

In a first such study, in 1984, we reported the effects of repeated administration of GHRH on short term linear growth in three children with GHD (46). Subsequently, we extended our observations to seven children with GHD, in a placebo-controlled trial. GHRH was administered at 3 hr intervals over 9–12 days. Even with this brief treatment period four of seven children had a significant increase in linear growth velocity (45). All four of these children had restoration of episodic GH secretion, but the somatomedin C (SMC) responses varied. The remaining three children failed to grow. Two of the three had no rise in either GH or SMC, and one child was an initial nonresponder who acquired a GH response during treatment. Thorner et al (118) reported two children with GHD who were treated for 6 months with GHRH, also at 3 hr intervals. One child had a marked increase in growth rate; the other child responded initially, but growth then declined. This second child came from an environment where psychosocial deprivation may have been part of the cause of growth failure. Recently we have also found an acceleration of growth in children treated with chronic subcutaneous GHRH therapy.

Thus, GHRH appears to have great promise for the treatment of GHD. Experience is still very limited, however, and much further work needs to be done to optimize and then simplify its use.

Because of the wide range of species (42, 58, 78, 86) in which GHRH is active, treatment with GHRH could potentially be used to accelerate the growth of animals of commercial importance. Preliminary data indicate that it can have this effect in normal animals as well as those with GH deficiency (31). If effective, this use may find even wider application than GHRH therapy in man.

Literature Cited

1. Abe, H., Molitch, M. E., Van Wyk, J. J., Underwood, L. E. 1983. Human growth hormone and somatomedin C suppress the spontaneous release of growth hormone in unanesthetized rats. *Endocrinology* 113:1319–24

2. Almeida, O. F. X., Schulte, H. M., Rittmaster, R. J., Chrousos, G. P., Loriaux, D. L., Merriam, G. R. 1984. Potency and specificity of a growth hormone-releasing factor in a primate and in vitro. *J. Clin. Endocrinol. Metab.* 58:309–12

3. Badger, T. M., Millard, W. J., McCormick, G. F., Bowers, C. Y., Martin, J. B. 1984. The effects of growth hormone (GH)-releasing peptides on GH secretion in perifused pituitary cells of adult male rats. *Endocrinology* 115:1432–38

4. Barinaga, M., Yamomoto, G., Rivier, C., Vale, W., Evans, R., Rosenfeld, M. G. 1983. Transcriptional regulation of growth hormone gene expression by growth hormone-releasing factor. *Nature* 306:84–85

5. Berridge, M. J. 1981. Phosphatidylinositol hydrolysis: a multifunctional transducing mechanism. *Mol. Cell. Endocrinol.* 24:115–40

6. Bilezikjian, L. M., Vale, W. 1983. Stimulation of adenosine 3',5'-monophosphate production by growth hormone-releasing factor and its inhibition by somatostatin in anterior pituitary cells in vitro. *Endocrinology* 113:1726–31

7. Bilezikjian, L. M., Vale, W. W. 1984. Chronic exposure of cultured rat anterior pituitary cells to GRF causes partial loss of responsiveness to GRF. *Endocrinology* 115:2032–34

8. Blackard, W. G., Hull, E. W., Lopez, S. A. 1971. Effects of lipids on growth hormone secretion in humans. *J. Clin. Invest.* 50:1439–43

9. Bloch, B., Brazeau, P., Ling, N., Bohlen, P., Esch, F., et al. 1983. Immunohistochemical detection of growth hormone-releasing factor in brain. *Nature* 301:607–8

10. Bloch, B., Gaillard, R. C., Brazeau, P., Lin, H. D., Ling, N. 1984. Topographical and ontogenetic study of the neurons producing growth hormone-releasing factor in human hypothalamus. *Regul. Peptides* 8:21–31

11. Bloch, B., Ling, N., Benoit, R., Wehrenberg, W. B., Guillemin, R. 1984. Specific depletion of immunoreactive growth hormone-releasing factor by

monosodium glutamate in rat median eminence. *Nature* 307:272–73

12. Bloom, F. E., Battenberg, E. L. F., Rivier, J., Vale, W. 1982. Corticotropin releasing factor (CRF): immunoreactive neurones and fibers in rat hypothalamus. *Regul. Peptides* 4:43–48

13. Bohlen, P., Brazeau, P., Bloch, B., Ling, N., Gaillard, R., Guillemin, R. 1983. Human hypothalamic growth hormone releasing factor (GRF): evidence for two forms identical to tumor derived GRF-44-NH$_2$ and GRF-40. *Biochem. Biophys. Res. Commun.* 114:930–36

14. Bohlen, P., Esch, F., Brazeau, P., Ling, N., Guillemin, R. 1983. Isolation and characterization of the porcine hypothalamic growth hormone releasing factor. *Biochem. Biophys. Res. Commun.* 116: 726–34

15. Bohlen, P., Wehrenberg, W. B., Esch, F., Ling, N., Brazeau, P., Guillemin, R. 1984. Rat hypothalamic growth hormone-releasing factor: isolation, sequence analysis and total synthesis. *Biochem. Biophys. Res. Commun.* 125: 1005–12

16. Borges, J. L., Blizzard, R. M., Evans, W. D., Furlanetto, R., Rogol, A. D., et al. 1984. Stimulation of growth hormone (GH) and somatomedin C in idiopathic GH-deficient subjects by intermittent pulsatile administration of synthetic human pancreatic tumor GH-releasing factor. *J. Clin. Endocrinol. Metab.* 59:1–6

17. Borges, J. L., Blizzard, R. M., Gelato, M. C., Furlanetto, R., Rogol, A. D., et al. 1983. Effects of human pancreatic tumor growth hormone releasing factor on growth hormone and somatomedin C levels in patients with idiopathic growth hormone deficiency. *Lancet* 1:119–24

18. Bosman, F. T., Van Assche, C., Nieuwenhuyzen Kruseman, A. C., Jackson, S., Lowry, P. J. 1984. Growth hormone releasing factor (GRF) immunoreactivity in human and rat gastrointestinal tract and pancreas. *J. Histochem. Cytochem.* 32:1139–44

19. Brazeau, P., Guillemin, R., Ling, N., Van Wyk, J., Humbel, R. 1982. Inhibition par les somatomédines de la sécrétion de l'hormone de croissance stimulée par le facteur hypothalamique somatocrinine (GRF) ou le peptide de synthèse hpGRF. *C. R. Acad. Sci. Ser. III* 295: 651–54

20. Brazeau, P., Ling, N., Bohlen, P., Esch, F., Ying, S. Y., Guillemin, R. 1982. Growth hormone releasing factor, so-

matocrinin, releases pituitary growth hormone in vitro. *Proc. Natl. Acad. Sci. USA* 79:7909–13

21. Brazeau, P., Bohlen, P., Esch, F., Ling, N., Wehrenberg, W. B., Guillemin, R. 1984. Growth hormone-releasing factor from ovine and caprine hypothalamus: isolation, sequence analysis and total synthesis. *Biochem. Biophys. Res. Commun.* 125:606–14

22. Brazeau, P., Ling, N., Esch, F., Bohlen, P., Mougin, C., Guillemin, R. 1982. Somatocrinin (growth hormone releasing factor) in vitro bioactivity: Ca^{++} involvement, cAMP mediated action and additivity of effect with PGE2. *Biochem. Biophys. Res. Commun.* 109:588–94

23. Bresson, J. L., Clavequin, M. C., Fellman, D., Bugnon, C. 1984. Ontogeny of the neuroglandular system revealed with hpGRF-44 antibodies in human hypothalamus. *Neuroendocrinology* 39:68–73

24. Brownstein, M., Arimura, A., Sato, H., Schally, A. V., Kizer, J. S. 1975. The regional distribution of somatostatin in the rat brain. *Endocrinology* 96:1456–61

25. Bugnon, C., Gouget, A., Fellmann, D., Clavequin, M. C. 1983. Immunocytochemical demonstration of a novel peptidergic neurone system in the cat brain with an anti-growth hormone-releasing factor serum. *Neurosci. Lett.* 38:131–37

26. Canonico, P. L., Cronin, M. J., Thorner, M. O., MacLeod, R. M. 1983. Human pancreatic GRF stimulates phosphatidylinositol labeling in cultured anterior pituitary cells. *Am. J. Physiol.* 245: E587–90

27. Carlquist, M., Kaiser, R., Tatemato, K., Jornvall, H., Mutt, V. 1984. A novel form of the polypeptide PHI isolated in high yield from bovine upper intestine. Relationships to other peptides of the glucagon-secretin family. *Eur. J. Biochem.* 144:243–47

28. Ceda, F. P., Hoffman, A. R., Silverberg, G. D., Wilson, D. M., Rosenfeld, R. G. 1985. Regulation of growth hormone release from cultured human pituitary adenomas by somatomedins and insulin. *J. Clin. Endocrinol. Metab.* 60:1204–9

29. Chiodini, P. G., Liuzzi, A., Dallabonzana, D., Oppizzi, G., Verde, G. G. 1985. Changes in growth hormone (GH) secretion induced by human pancreatic GH releasing hormone-44 in acromegaly: a comparison with thyrotropin-releasing hormone and bromocriptine. *J. Clin. Endocrinol. Metab.* 60:48–52

30. Christofides, N. D., Stephanou, A., Suzuki, H., Yiangou, Y., Bloom, S. J. 1984. Distribution of immunoreactive growth hormone-releasing hormone in the human brain and intestine and its production by tumors. *J. Clin. Endocrinol. Metab.* 59:747–51

31. Clark, R. G., Robinson, I. C. A. F. 1985. Growth induced by pulsatile infusion of an amidated fragment of human growth hormone releasing factor in normal and GHRH deficient rats. *Nature* 314:281–83

32. Dupont, A., Labrie, F., Pelletier, G., Puviani, R., Coy, D. H., et al. 1974. Organ distribution of radioactivity and disappearance of radioactivity from plasma after administration of [^{3}H] luteinizing hormone-releasing hormone to mice and rats. *Neuroendocrinology* 16:65–73

33. Dupont, A., Labrie, F., Pelletier, G., Puviani, R. 1972. Organ distribution of thyrotropin-releasing hormone. *Gen. Comp. Endocrinol.* 19:522–26

34. Esch, F., Bohlen, P., Ling, N., Brazeau, P., Guillemin, R. 1983. Isolation and characterization of the bovine hypothalamic growth hormone releasing factor. *Biochem. Biophys. Res. Commun.* 117:772–79

35. Evans, W. S., Borges, J. L., Vance, M. L., Kaiser, D. L., Rogol, A. D., et al. 1984. Effects of human pancreatic growth hormone-releasing factor-40 on serum growth hormone, prolactin, luteinizing hormone, follicle-stimulating hormone, and somatomedin-C concentrations in normal woman through the menstrual cycle. *J. Clin. Endocrinol. Metab.* 59:1006–10

36. Fraser, W. M., Blackard, W. G. 1977. The effect of lipid on prolactin and growth hormone secretion. *Horm. Metab. Res.* 9:389–93

37. Frohman, L. A. 1981. Diseases of the anterior pituitary. In *Endocrinology and Metabolism*, ed. P. Felig, J. D. Baxter, A. E. Broadus, L. A. Frohman, Ch. 7, pp. 169–72. New York: McGraw Hill

38. Frohman, L. A., Szabo, M. 1981. Ectopic production of growth hormone-releasing factor by carcinoid and pancreatic islet tumors associated with acromegaly. *Prog. Clin. Biol. Res.* 74: 259–71

39. Frohman, L. A., Thominet, J. L., Webb, C. B., Vance, M. L., Uderman, H., et al. 1984. Metabolic clearance and plasma disappearance rates of human pancreatic tumor growth hormone releasing factor in man. *J. Clin. Invest.* 73:1304–11

40. Gelato, M. C., Malozowski, S., Nicoletti, M., Levine Ross, J., Pescovitz, O. H. et al. 1985. Responses to growth hormone-releasing hormone (GHRH) during development and pu-

berty in normal boys and girls. *28th Journees Int. Henri-Pierre Klotz d'Endocrinol. Clin., Paris, May, 1985.* Paris: Soc. Endocrinol. (Abstr.)

41. Gelato, M. C., Merriam, G. R., Vance, M. L., Goldman, J. A., Webb, C., et al. 1985. Effects of growth hormone-releasing factor upon growth hormone secretion in acromegaly. *J. Clin. Endocrinol. Metab.* 60:251–57

42. Gelato, M. C., Pescovitz, O., Cassorla, F., Loriaux, D. L., Merriam, G. R. 1983. Effects of a growth hormone releasing factor in man. *J. Clin. Endocrinol. Metab.* 57:674–76

43. Gelato, M. C., Pescovitz, O. H., Cassorla, F., Loriaux, D. L., Merriam, G. R. 1984. Dose-response relationships for the effects of growth hormone-releasing factor-(1–44)-NH$_2$ in young adult men and women. *J. Clin. Endocrinol. Metab.* 59:197–201

44. Gelato, M. C., Rittmaster, R. S., Pescovitz, O. H., Caruso Nicoletti, M., Nixon, W. E., et al. 1985. Growth hormone responses to continuous infusions of growth hormone-releasing hormone. *J. Clin. Endocrinol. Metab.* 61:223–28

45. Gelato, M. C., Ross, J. L., Malozowski, S., Pescovitz, O. H., Skerda, M., et al. 1985. Effects of pulsatile administration of growth hormone (GH)-releasing hormone on short term linear growth in children with GH deficiency. *J. Clin. Endocrinol. Metab.* 61:444–50

46. Gelato, M. C., Ross, J. L., Pescovitz, O., Cassorla, F., Skerda, M., Merriam, G. R. 1984. Acceleration of linear growth after repeated doses of growth hormone-releasing hormone. *Pediat. Res.* 18:167A (Abstr. 430).

47. Gick, G. G., Zeytin, F. N., Brazeau, P., Ling, N. C., Esch, F. S., Bancroft, F. C. 1984. Growth hormone-releasing factor regulates growth hormone mRNA in primary cultures of rat pituitary cells. *Proc. Natl. Acad. Sci. USA* 81:1553–55

48. Gluckman, P. D. 1984. Functional maturation of the neuroendocrine system in the perinatal period: studies of the somatotropic axis in the ovine fetus. *J. Dev. Physiol.* 6:301–12

49. Grossman, A., Savage, M. O., Lytras, N., Preece, M. A., Sueiras-Diaz, J., et al. 1984. Responses to analogues of growth hormone-releasing hormone in normal subjects and in growth-hormone deficient children and young adults. *Clin. Endocrinol.* 21:321–30

50. Gubler, U., Monahan, J. J., Lomedico, P. T., Bhatt, R. S., Collier, K. J., et al. 1983. Cloning and sequence analysis of cDNA for the precursor of human growth hormone-releasing factor somatocrinin. *Proc. Natl. Acad. Sci. USA* 80:4311–14

51. Guillemin, R., Brazeau, P., Bohlen, P., Esch, F., Ling, N., Wehrenberg, W. B. 1982. Growth hormone-releasing factor from a human pancreatic tumor that caused acromegaly. *Science* 218:585–87

52. Imaki, T., Shibasaki, T., Shizume, K., Masuda, A., Nakahara, M., et al. 1985. The effect of free fatty acids on growth hormone (GH)-releasing hormone-mediated GH secretion in man. *J. Clin. Endocrinol. Metab.* 60:290–93

53. Labrie, F., Gagne, B., Lefevre, G. 1983. Growth hormone-releasing factor stimulates adenylate cyclase activity in the anterior pituitary gland. *Life Sci.* 33:2229–33

54. Lamberts, S. W., Verleun, T., Oosterom, R. 1984. The interrelationship between the effects of somatostatin and human pancreatic growth hormone-releasing factor on growth hormone release by cultured pituitary tumor cells from patients with acromegaly. *J. Clin. Endocrinol. Metab.* 58:250–54

55. Lance, V. A., Murphy, N. A., Sueiras-Diaz, J., Coy, D. H. 1984. Superactive analogs of growth hormone-releasing factor (1–29)-amide. *Biochem. Biophys. Res. Commun.* 119:265–72

56. Law, G. J., Ray, K. P., Wallis, M. 1984. Effects of growth hormone-releasing factor, somatostatin, and dopamine on growth hormone and prolactin secretion from cultured ovine pituitary cells. *FEBS Lett.* 166:189–93

57. Lechan, R. M., Lin, H. D., Ling, N., Jackson, I. M., Jacobson, S., Reichlin, S. 1984. Distribution of immunoreactive growth hormone releasing factor (1–44) NH$_2$ in the tuberoinfundibular system of the rhesus monkey. *Brain Res.* 309:55–61

58. Leung, F. C., Taylor, J. E. 1983. In vivo and in vitro stimulation of growth hormone-release in chickens by synthetic human pancreatic growth hormone releasing factor (hpGRFs). *Endocrinology* 113:1913–15

59. Lewin, M. J., Reyl-Desmars, F., Ling, N. 1983. Somatocrinin receptor coupled with cAMP-dependent protein kinase on anterior pituitary granules. *Proc. Natl. Acad. Sci. USA* 80:6538–41

60. Ling, N., Baird, A., Wehrenberg, W. B., Ueno, N., Munegumi, T., et al. 1984. Synthesis and in vitro bioactivity of human growth hormone-releasing factor analogs substituted at position-1. *Biochem. Biophys. Res. Commun.* 122:304–10

61. Ling, N., Baird, A., Wehrenberg, W.

B., Ueno, H., Munegumi, T., Brazeau, P. 1984. Synthesis and in vitro bioactivity of C-terminal deleted analogs of human growth hormone-releasing factor. *Biochem. Biophys. Res. Commun.* 123: 854–61

62. Ling, N., Esch, F., Bohlen, P., Brazeau, P., Wehrenberg, W. B., Guillemin, R. 1984. Isolation, primary structure, and synthesis of human hypothalamic somatocrinin: growth hormone-releasing factor. *Proc. Natl. Acad. Sci. USA* 81: 4302–6

63. Losa, M., Bock, L., Schopohl, J., Stalla, G. K., Muller, O. A., von Werder, K. 1984. Growth hormone releasing factor infusion does not sustain elevated GH-levels in normal subjects. *Acta Endocrinol.* 107:462–70

64. Losa, M., Schopohl, J., Muller, O. A., Von Werder, K. 1984. Stimulation of growth hormone secretion with human growth hormone releasing factors (GRF$^{1-44}$, GRF$^{1-40}$, GRF$^{1-29}$) in normal subjects. *Klin. Wochenschr.* 62:1140–43

65. Losa, M., Stalla, G. K., Muller, O. A., von Werder, K. 1983. Human pancreatic growth hormone-releasing factor (hpGRF): dose-response of GRF- and GH-levels. *Klin. Wochenschr.* 61:1249–53

66. Lytras, N., Grossman, A., Wass, J. A. H., Coy, D. H., Rees, L. J., Besser, G. M. 1984. Growth hormone-releasing hormone test in patients with hypothalamic disease, Cushing's syndrome, and acromegaly. *Prog. VII Int. Cong. Endocrinology, Quebec, July 1984,* p. 982. Amsterdam: Excerpta Medica. (Abstr. No. 1444)

67. Mayo, K. E., Vale, W., Rivier, J., Rosenfeld, M. G., Evans, R. M. 1983. Expression-cloning and sequence of a cDNA encoding human growth hormone-releasing factor. *Nature* 306:86–88

68. McCormick, G. F., Millard, W. J., Badger, T. M., Bowers, C. Y., Martin, J. B. 1985. Dose-response characteristics of various peptides with GH-releasing activity in the unanesthetized male rat. *Endocrinology* 117:97–105

69. McCormick, G. F., Millard, W. J., Badger, T. M., Martin, J. B. 1984. Gonadal steroid modulation of growth hormone-releasing factor-stimulated growth hormone secretion. *Prog. 14th Ann. Meet. Soc. Neurosci., Oct. 1984,* p. 1214 (Abstr. no. 348.17)

70. Merchenthaler, I., Vigh, S., Schally, A. V., Petrusz, P. 1984. Immunocytochemical localization of growth hormone-

releasing factor in the rat hypothalamus. *Endocrinology* 114:1082–85

71. Merimee, T. J., Fineberg, S. E., Tyson, J. R. 1969. Fluctuations of human growth hormone secretion during the menstrual cycle: response to arginine. *Metabolism* 18:606–10

72. Merriam, G. R., Gelato, M. C., Avgerinos, P., Blackman, M., Cassorla, F., et al. 1985. Applications of growth hormone-releasing hormone in diagnosis and therapy. *Neuroendocrinol. Lett.* 7:102

73. Michel, D., Lefevre, G., Labrie, F. 1984. Dexamethasone is a potent stimulator of growth hormone-releasing factor-induced cyclic AMP accumulation in the adenohypophysis. *Life Sci.* 35:597–602

74. Millard, W. J., Martin, J. B. Jr., Audet, J., Sagai, S. M., Martin, J. B. 1982. Evidence that reduced growth hormone secretion observed in monosodium glutamate-treated rats is the result of a deficiency in growth hormone-releasing factor. *Endocrinology* 110:540–50

75. Momany, F. A., Bowers, C. Y., Reynolds, G. A., Hong, A., Newlander, K. 1984. Conformational energy studies and *in vitro* and *in vivo* activity data on growth hormone-releasing peptides. *Endocrinology* 114:1531–36

76. Morel, G., Mesguick, P., Dubois, M. P., Dubois, P. M. 1984. Ultrastructural evidence for endogenous growth hormone-releasing factor-like immunoreactivity in the monkey pituitary gland. *Neuroendocrinology* 38:123–33

77. Morley, J. E., Gavin, T. J., Pekany, A. E., Utiger, R. D., Nair, M. G., et al. 1979. Plasma clearance and plasma half-disappearance time of exogenous thyrotropin-releasing hormone and pyroglutamyl-N 3 im-methylhistidyl prolineamide. *J. Clin. Endocrinol. Metab.* 48: 377–80

78. Moseley, W. M., Krabill, L. F., Friedman, A. R., Olsen, R. F. 1984. Growth hormone response of steers injected with synthetic human pancreatic growth hormone-releasing factors. *J. Anim. Sci.* 58:430–35

79. Nicholson, W. E., DeCherney, G. S., Jackson, R. V., DeBold, C. R., Uderman, H., et al. 1983. Plasma distribution, disappearance half-time, metabolic clearance rate, and degradation of synthetic ovine corticotropin releasing factor in man. *J. Clin. Endocrinol. Metab.* 57:1263–69

80. Ohmura, E., Jansen, A., Chernick, V., Winter, J., Friesen, H. G., et al. 1984. Human pancreatic growth hormone

releasing factor (hpGRF-1–40) stimulates GH release in the ovine fetus. *Endocrinology* 114:299–301

81. Olschowha, J. A., O'Donahue, T. L., Mueller, G. P., Jacobowitz, D. M. 1982. The distribution of corticotropin releasing factor-like immunoreactive neurons in rat brain. *Peptides* 3:995–1015

82. Pandol, S. J., Seifert, H., Thomas, M. W., Rivier, J., Vale, W. 1984. Growth hormone-releasing factor stimulates pancreatic enzyme secretion. *Science* 225: 326–28

83. Patel, Y. C., Wheatley, T., Fitz-Patrick, D., Brock, G. 1980. A sensitive radioimmunoassay for immunoreactive somatostatin in extracted plasma: measurement and characterization of portal and peripheral plasma in the rat. *Endocrinology* 107:306–13

84. Pavlov, E. P., Merriam, G. R., Harman, S. M., Gelato, M. C., Blackman, M. R. 1984. Responses of growth hormone (GH) and somatomedin-C (SM-C) to growth hormone releasing hormone (GHRH) in healthy aging men. *Clin. Res.* 32:689A (Abstr.)

85. Penny, E. S., Penman, E., Price, J., Rees, L. H., Sopwith, A. M., et al. 1984. Circulating growth hormone releasing factor concentrations in normal subjects and patients with acromegaly. *Br. Med. J.* 289:453–55

86. Peter, R. E., Nahorniak, C. S., Vale, W. W., Rivier, J. E. 1984. Human pancreatic growth hormone-releasing factor (hpGRF) stimulates growth hormone release in goldfish. *J. Exp. Zool.* 231:161–63

87. Polak, J. M., Bloom, S. R. 1984. Regulatory peptides—the distribution of two newly discovered peptides, PHI and NPY. *Peptides* 5 (Suppl. 1):79–89

88. Press, M., Tamborlane, N. V., Thorner, M. O., Vale, W., Rivier, J., et al. 1984. Pituitary response to growth hormone-releasing factor in diabetes. Failure of glucose-mediated suppression. *Diabetes* 33:804–6

89. Prinz, P. N., Weitzman, E. D., Cummingham, G. R., Karacan, I. 1983. Plasma growth hormone during sleep in young and aged men. *J. Gerontol.* 38:519–24

90. Raymond, V., Leung, P. C., Veilleux, R., Lefevre, G., Labrie, F. 1984. LHRH rapidly stimulates phosphatidylinositol metabolism in enriched gonadotropins. *Mol. Cell. Endocrinol.* 36:157–64

91. Redding, T. W., Kastin, A. J., Gonzalez-Barcena, D., Coy, D. H., Coy, E. J., et al. 1973. The half-life, metabolism

and excretion of tritiated luteinizing hormone-releasing hormone (LHRH) in men. *J. Clin. Endocrinol. Metab.* 37: 626–31

92. Reichlin, S. 1983. Somatostatin. *N. Engl. J. Med.* 309:1495–1501

93. Reichlin, S., Saperstein, R., Jackson, I. M. D., Boyd, A. E. III, Patel, Y. 1976. Hypothalamic hormones. *Ann. Rev. Physiol.* 38:389–424

94. Rittmaster, R. S., Merriam, G. R. 1985. Continuous growth hormone releasing hormone infusion decreases GH secretion by rat pituitary cells in the absence of significant GH pool depletion. *Endocrine Soc. Ann. Meet., Baltimore, June 1985. Endocrinology* 116:36A (Abstr. 142)

95. Rivier, J., Spiess, J., Thorner, M., Vale, W. 1982. Characterization of a growth hormone-releasing factor from a human pancreatic islet tumor. *Nature* 300:276–78

96. Rogol, A. D., Blizzard, R. M., Johanson, A. J., Furlanetto, R. W., Evans, W. S., et al. 1984. Growth hormone release in response to human pancreatic tumor growth hormone-releasing hormone-40 in children with short stature. *J. Clin. Endocrinol. Metab.* 59:580–86

97. Root, J. L., Duckett, G. E., Sweetland, M., Strezelecki, J. A., Root, A. W. 1985. Hypothyroidism blunts the GH releasing effect of human pancreatic GH releasing factor in the adult male rat *in vivo* and *in vitro*. *Endocrinology* 116:1703–6

98. Sassolas, G., Chayvialle, J. A., Partensky, C., Berger, G., Trouillas, J., et al. 1983. Acromegaly, clinical expression of the production of growth hormone releasing factor in pancreatic tumors. *Ann. Endocrinol.* 44:347–54

99. Schettini, G., Cronin, M. J., Hewlett, E. L., Thorner, M. O., MacLeod, R. M. 1984. Human pancreatic tumor growth hormone-releasing factor stimulates anterior pituitary adenylate cyclase activity, adenosine $3',5'$-monophosphate accumulation, and growth hormone release in a calmodulin-dependent manner. *Endocrinology* 115:1308–14

100. Schriock, E. A., Lustig, R. H., Rosenthal, S. M., Kaplan, S. L., Grumbach, M. M. 1984. Effect of growth hormone (GH)-releasing hormone (GRH) on plasma GH in relation to magnitude and duration of GH deficiency in 26 children and adults with isolated GH deficiency or multiple pituitary hormone deficiencies: evidence for hypothalamic GRH deficiency. *J. Clin. Endocrinol. Metab.* 58:1043–49

101. Schulte, H. M., Benker, G., Windeck, R., Olbricht, T., Reinwein, D. 1985. Failure to respond to growth hormone releasing hormone (GHRH) in acromegaly due to a GHRH secreting pancreatic tumor: dynamics of multiple endocrine testing. *J. Clin. Endocrinol. Metab.* 61:585–87

102. Schurmeyer, T. H., Avgerinos, P. C., Gold, P. W., Gallucci, W. T., Tomai, T. P., et al. 1984. Human corticotropin-releasing factor in man: pharmacokinetic properties and dose-response of plasma adrenocorticotropin and cortisol secretion. *J. Clin. Endocrinol. Metab.* 59: 1103–8

103. Seifert, H., Perrin, M., Rivier, J., Vale, W. 1985. Binding sites for growth hormone releasing factor on rat anterior pituitary cells. *Nature* 313:487–89

104. Sharp, P. S., Foley, K., Chahal, P., Kohner, E. M. 1984. The effect of plasma glucose on the growth hormone response to human pancreatic growth hormone releasing factor in normal subjects. *Clin. Endocrinol.* 20:497–501

105. Sheldon, W. R. Jr., DeBold, C. R., Evans, W. S., DeCherney, G. S., Jackson, R. V., et al. 1985. Rapid sequential intravenous administration of four hypothalamic releasing hormones as a combined anterior pituitary function test in normal subjects. *J. Clin. Endocrinol. Metab.* 60:623–30

106. Shibasaki, T., Kiyosawa, Y., Masuda, A., Nakahara, M., Imaki, T., et al. 1984. Distribution of growth hormone-releasing hormone-like immunoreactivity in human tissue extracts. *J. Clin. Endocrinol. Metab.* 59:263–68

107. Shibasaki, T., Shizume, K., Masuda, A., Nakahara, M., Hizuka, N., et al. 1984. Plasma growth hormone response to growth hormone-releasing factor in acromegalic patients. *J. Clin. Endocrinol. Metab.* 58:215–17

108. Shibasaki, T., Shizume, K., Nakahara, M., Masuda, A., Jibihi, K., et al. 1984. Age-related changes in plasma growth hormone response to growth hormone-releasing factor in man. *J. Clin. Endocrinol. Metab.* 58:212–14

109. Sonntag, W. E., Hylka, V. W., Meites, J. 1983. Impaired ability of old male rats to secrete growth hormone in vivo but not in vitro in response to hpGRF (1–44). *Endocrinology* 113:2305–7

110. Spiess, J., Rivier, J., Vale, W. 1983. Characterization of rat hypothalamic growth hormone-releasing factor. *Nature* 303:532–35

111. Takano, K., Hizuka, N., Shizume, K., Asakawa, K., Miyakawa, M., et al. 1984. Plasma growth hormone (GH) response to GH-releasing factor in normal children with short stature and patients with pituitary dwarfism. *J. Clin. Endocrinol. Metab.* 58:236–41

112. Takano, K., Hizuka, N., Shizume, K., Honda, N., Ling, N. C. 1985. Plasma growth hormone (GH) responses to single and repetitive subcutaneous administration of GH releasing factor (hpGRF-44) in normal and GH deficient children. *Acta Endocrinol.* 108:11–19

113. Tannenbaum, G. S. 1984. Growth hormone-releasing factor: direct effects on growth hormone, glucose, and behavior via the brain. *Science* 26:464–66

114. Tannenbaum, G. S., Ling, N. 1984. The interrelationship of growth hormone (GH)-releasing factor and somatostatin in generation of the ultradian rhythm of GH secretion. *Endocrinology* 115:1952–57

115. Tatemoto, K. 1984. PHI—a new brain-gut peptide. *Peptides* 5:151–54

116. Thorner, M. O., Frohman, L. A., Leong, D. A., Thominet, J., Downs, T., et al. 1984. Extrahypothalamic growth-hormone-releasing factor (GRF) secretion is a rare cause of acromegaly: plasma GRF levels in 177 acromegalic patients. *J. Clin. Endocrinol. Metab.* 59:846–49

117. Thorner, M. O., Perryman, R. L., Cronin, M. J., Rogol, A. D., Draznin, M., et al. 1982. Somatotroph hyperplasia. Successful treatment of acromegaly by removal of a pancreatic islet tumor secreting a growth hormone-releasing factor. *J. Clin. Invest.* 70:965–77

118. Thorner, M. O., Reschke, J., Chitwood, J., Rogol, A. D., Furlanetto, R. 1985. Acceleration of growth in two children treated with human growth hormone-releasing factor. *N. Engl. J. Med.* 312:4–9

119. Thorner, M. O., Rivier, J., Spiess, J., Borges, J. L., Vance, M. L., et al. 1983. Human pancreatic growth-hormone-releasing factor selectively stimulates growth hormone secretion in man. *Lancet* 1:24–28

120. Vale, W., Rivier, C., Brown, M. 1977. Regulatory peptides of the hypothalamus. *Ann. Rev. Physiol.* 39:473–527

121. Vance, M. L., Borges, J. L., Kaiser, D. L., Evans, W. J., Furlanetto, R., et al. 1984. Human pancreatic tumor growth hormone-releasing factor: dose-response relationships in normal man. *J. Clin. Endocrinol. Metab.* 58:838–44

122. Vance, M. L., Kaiser, D. L., Evans, W. S., Thorner, M. O., Furlanetto, R., et al.

1985. Evidence for a limited growth hormone (GH)-releasing hormone (GHRH)-releasable quantity of GH: effects of 6-hour infusions of GHRH on GH secretion in normal man. *J. Clin. Endocrinol. Metab.* 60:370–75

123. Van Wyk, J. J., Underwood, L. E. 1975. Relation between growth hormone and somatomedin. *Ann. Rev. Med.* 26:427–41

124. Varner, M. A., Davis, S. L., Reeves, J. J. 1980. Temporal serum concentrations of growth hormone, thyrotropin, insulin, and glucagon in sheep immunized against somatostatin. *Endocrinology* 106:1027–32

125. Webb, C. B., Vance, M. L., Thorner, M. O., Perisutti, G., Thominet, J., et al. 1984. Plasma growth hormone responses to constant infusions of human pancreatic growth hormone releasing factor. Intermittent secretion or response attenuation. *J. Clin. Invest.* 74:96–103

126. Wehrenberg, W. B., Baird, A., Ling, N. 1983. Potent interaction between glucocorticoids and growth hormone-releasing factor in vivo. *Science* 221:556–58

127. Wehrenberg, W. B., Baird, A., Ying, S. Y., Rivier, C., Ling, N., Guillemin, R. 1984. Multiple stimulation of the adenohypophyhsis by combinations of hypothalamic releasing factors. *Endocrinology* 114:1995–2001

128. Wehrenberg, W. B., Bloch, B., Chong-Li, Z., Brazeau, P., Ling, N., Guillemin, R. 1984. Pituitary response to growth hormone-releasing factor in rats with functional or anatomical lesions of the central neurons system that inhibit endogenous growth hormone secretion. *Regul. Peptides* 8:1–8

129. Wehrenberg, W. B., Brazeau, P., Ling, N., Textor, G., Guillemin, R. 1984. Pituitary growth hormone response in rats during a 24-hour infusion of growth hormone-releasing factor. *Endocrinology* 114:1613–16

130. Wehrenberg, W. B., Brazeau, P., Luben, R., Bohlen, P., Guillemin, R. 1984. Inhibition of the pulsatile secretion of growth hormone by monoclonal antibodies to the hypothalamic growth hor-

mone releasing factor (GRF). *Endocrinology* 111:2147–48

131. Wehrenberg, W. B., Ling, N. 1983. The absence of an age-related change in the pituitary response to growth hormone-releasing factor in rats. *Neuroendocrinology* 37:473–75

132. Wehrenberg, W. B., Ling, N. 1983. In vivo biological potency of rat and human growth hormone-releasing factor and fragments of human growth hormone-releasing factor. *Biochem. Biophys. Res. Commun.* 115:525–30

133. Williams, T., Maxon, H., Thorner, M. O., Frohman, L. A. 1985. Blunted growth hormone (GH) response to GH-releasing hormone in hypothyroidism resolves in the euthyroid state. *J. Clin. Endocrinol. Metab.* 61:454–56

134. Williams, T., Berelowitz, M., Joffe, S. N., Thorner, M. O., Rivier, J., et al. 1984. Impaired growth hormone responses to growth hormone-releasing factor in obesity. A pituitary defect reversed with weight reduction. *N. Engl. J. Med.* 311:1403–7

135. Winterer, J., Muzzo, S., Young, I., Malozowski, S., Gelato, M., et al. The growth hormone response to growth hormone-releasing hormone (GHRH) stimulation in infantile protein-calorie malnutrition and partial recovery. *28th Journees Int. Henri-Pierre Klotz d'Endocrinol. Clin., Paris, May, 1985* Paris: Soc. Endocrinol. (Abstr.)

136. Wood, S. M., Ch'ng, J. L., Adams, E. F., Webster, J. D., Joplin, G. F., et al. 1983. Abnormalities of growth hormone release in response to human pancreatic growth hormone releasing factor (GRF (1–44) in acromegaly and hypopituitarism. *Br. Med. J.* 286:1687–91

137. Zadik, Z., Chalew, S. A., McCarter, R. J., Meistas, M., Kowarski, A. A. 1985. The influence of age on the 24 hour integrated concentration of growth hormone in normal individuals. *J. Clin. Endocrinol. Metab.* 60:513–16

138. Baird, A., Wehrenberg, W. B., Böhlen, B., Ling, N. 1985. Immunoreactive and biologically active growth hormone-releasing factor in the rat placenta. *Endocrinology* 117:1598–1601

COMPARATIVE AND INTEGRATIVE PHYSIOLOGY

THERMOREGULATION IN VERTEBRATES

Introduction, James E. Heath, *Section Editor*

The four chapters in this section attempt to summarize what is known of the neural bases of thermoregulation. For convenience the topics are divided into central receptors, peripheral receptors, transmitters and modulators in thermoregulatory pathways, and central integration of thermal responses. However, within the central nervous system there is no such simple division of these functions. The authors have also brought together information on various animals to provide insight into the evolutionary and neurophysiological origins of thermoregulatory mechanisms.

At the outset researchers working on the thermosensitivity of neurons are plagued by the problem of distinguishing temperature reception from a direct effect of temperature on neurons in general. Nearly all mechanoreceptors show strong response to temperature, while many central neurons respond to changes in brain temperature but are not involved in thermoreception or thermoregulatory pathways. The chapters by Spray and Boulant provide guidance through these dangerous waters.

The explosion of information on chemical communication in the brain has profoundly affected our understanding of thermoregulation. The simplicity of early models has given way to more complex models that describe the many newly discovered peptides, opioids, catecholamines, etc, that have functions in one or another thermoregulatory pathway. As our awareness of the complexity of chemical communication has increased, the anatomical complexity of thermoregulatory responses has also been revealed. In addition to the involvement of the brainstem in these responses, increasing attention has been paid to the importance of spinal and forebrain involvement. The inherently behavioral and physiological basis for thermoregulation argues that these complexities will increase.

It may be time to search out vertebrates that are adaptational specialists to serve as models for a general understanding of thermoregulation. For example, perhaps shrews and small birds would be better choices for the study of the control and development of shivering responses than are the dog and the rabbit. Investigation of reptilian behavioral thermoregulation might yield information that would provide guidelines to approaching the study of the complexity of the mammalian brain. Dogs are among the most accomplished panters and remain an ideal model for studying respiratory involvement in thermoregulation. The enlarged pinnae of rabbits and the naked state of humans suggest that these mammals are specialists in vasomotor thermoregulatory mechanisms and are especially dependent on peripheral thermoreceptors for production of thermoregulatory responses. Brain slice and single-unit techniques in unanesthetized animals offer new approaches to sorting out the neural fabric underlying thermoregulation.

These reviews inspire appreciation for the robustness of thermoregulation as a paradigm for understanding whole animal integrative biology and for the richness of variety and adaptive strategies of the vertebrates.

Ann. Rev. Physiol. 1986. 48:595–612

INTEGRATION AND CENTRAL PROCESSING IN TEMPERATURE REGULATION[1]

Christopher J. Gordon

Experimental Biology Division, Health Effects Research Laboratory, US Environmental Protection Agency, Research Triangle Park, North Carolina 27711

James E. Heath

Department of Physiology and Biophysics, University of Illinois, Urbana, Illinois 61801

INTRODUCTION

Over the past ten years there has been a surge of papers on the integration and processing of thermal information at various levels of the mammalian central nervous system (CNS). Much of the work has centered on the integration of thermal stimuli from the scrotum and other anatomical sites in anesthetized and unanesthetized animals. These data have altered our view of the CNS mechanisms of temperature regulation.

In this paper our discussion is limited primarily to single neuronal studies in key CNS sites, including the spinal cord, trigeminal nuclei, thalamus, midbrain, hypothalamus, and preoptic area. A primary objective is to elucidate the processes by which the CNS integrates ascending thermal information into efferent signals for driving the variety of thermoregulatory motor systems.

[1]This manuscript has been reviewed by the Health Effects Research Laboratory, US Environmental Protection Agency and approved for publication. Mention of trade names or commercial products does not constitute endorsement or recommendation for use. The US Government has the right to retain a nonexclusive, royalty-free license in and to any copyright covering this paper.

Spinal Cord

There is substantial processing of afferent inputs from thermoafferent neurons, as well as from other neuronal types, at the spinal level. Primary thermoreceptors respond to a rapid temperature change with a dynamic overshoot of unit activity that eventually settles to a new steady state level (95). Dorsal horn neurons (DHNs), which receive thermoreceptor afferents, respond to a rapid change in skin temperature with either a typical dynamic/static response, a dynamic only response, or a static only response in unit activity (43, 92). Unlike the continuous change in firing rate with skin temperature found in thermoafferent neurons, many DHNs show an abrupt shift in activity over a very small change in temperature (92, 97). The integrative response of some DHN's to skin heating may be attributable to mechanosensitive inputs which exhibit a purely static or purely dynamic response to shifts in skin temperature (94).

With regard to scrotal thermal inputs, three major dissimilarities between the activity of thermoreceptors and that of DHNs suggest the existence of spinal integration (97): (*a*) in spite of the abundance of mechanosensitive afferent neurons of the scrotum, most temperature-responsive DHN's are not responsive to mechanical stimulation; (*b*) bursting activity, which is common in afferent neurons, is apparently absent in temperature-responsive DHN's; and (*c*) transient inhibition upon warming and cooling ("inverse" warm or cold reaction) found in some DHN's has not been recorded in afferent (pudendal) nerve fibers.

Integration in DHN's involves the spatial summation of converging warm and cold thermoafferents. Using a systemic injection of Ca^{2+} which excites warm thermoafferents and inhibits cold thermoafferents (50), it was found that warm-responsive DHN's were consistently excited, whereas cold-responsive units responded inconsistently (92). This implies that most warm-responsive DHN's receive relatively uniform input from warm thermoafferents, while cold-responsive DHN's have a greater convergence of warm and cold thermoafferents. This difference in spatial integration may explain the accelerated vasomotor response found in the activation of warm- but not cold-responsive DHN's (91).

The thermosensitive nature of spinal neurons to local temperature suggests that both skin and spinal temperature are integrated. Cold- and warm-sensitive ascending tract fibers have been reported for a multitude of species (117, 118). Spinal neurons sensitive to temperature receive inputs from peripheral thermoafferent neurons (97). There is apparently a high degree of integration of supraspinal input by spinal thermosensitive neurons (38). For example, in the nonspinalectomized cat, ascending cold-sensitive neurons in the spinal cord are relatively unaffected by changes in skin temperature. However, following a high level (C1/C2) spinalectomy the same units become increasingly sensitive to skin temperature. Interestingly, spinalectomy had little effect on neuron thermosensitivity per se but severely influenced the response of spinal neurons to skin temperature.

Trigeminal Nucleus

The secondary neurons at this level have a function similar to the DHN's of the spinal cord except that they receive synaptic input from primary thermoreceptors ascending from the facial areas rather than the trunk and scrotum. Spontaneously active neurons in the superficial layer of the medulla are immediately silenced when the face of the rat or rabbit is warmed (16). Thermoresponsive neurons are apparently more concentrated in the trigeminal region than in the lumbar region of the spinal cord, which may reflect a relatively high concentration of thermal receptors in the face. There appears to be a large innervation in the trigeminal nucleus of cold receptors from the lips, nose, and orbit of the rabbit (16) and cat (17). The lips and nose but not the orbit of the rat are highly innervated by cold receptors (16). Interestingly, the ears of the rabbit, which are known to be extremely thermal sensitive, are not represented in the trigeminal nucleus (16). This is probably attributable to the fact that 90% of the afferent neurons from the rabbit ear pass through the spinal cord, with only 10% entering the trigeminal system (124). Conversely, the cat has a relatively large innervation of cold receptors in the ear, which do pass through the trigeminal system (17).

The integration of facial thermal information by secondary neurons in the trigeminal nucleus is minimal compared to the extensive integration of scrotal temperature in the lumbar spinal cord. Except in the cat (99), the static and dynamic responses of trigeminal neurons are generally similar to those of peripheral receptors (17, 100). There appears to be some convergence of thermoafferents onto secondary neurons of the trigeminal nucleus, but it is nowhere near as extensive as that found in the spinal cord (16, 17, 100). There is little evidence of bursts of single unit activity of cold-responsive neurons in the trigeminal nucleus of the cat, rat, and rabbit, although they commonly occur in facial cold thermoreceptors (1). Some such bursts have been noted in monkey trigeminal neurons (100). Single unit activity is generally greater in the trigeminal nucleus than in the primary thermoreceptors (98). This observation may indicate some convergence from primary to secondary neurons.

Processing of thermal information in the trigeminal nucleus appears to be largely unaffected by other neural sites. It is well known that nociceptive neurons in the dorsal horn and trigeminal complex can be inhibited by stimulation of the nucleus raphe magnus (NRM) (e.g. 12). Electrical stimulation of the NRM selectively blocks nociceptive trigeminal inputs without influencing the activity of cold-responsive neurons in the same area (12). Moreover, the integration of warm and cold inputs in the trigeminal nucleus cannot be modified by extensive thermal acclimation during development (13). However, thalamic integration of thermal inputs can be modified by temperature acclimation (see below). Thus, thermal information from the facial areas appears to be transmitted to thalamic areas via the trigeminal nucleus in a relatively uninterrupted process.

Thalamus

At the level of the thalamus there is a tremendous increase in processing of thermal information, especially from the scrotal area. Many laboratories have found that neuron activity in the ventrobasal complex abruptly increases with a small (~0.5–2.0°C) change in scrotal temperature (44, 62, 114, 116). These warm-responsive units are termed switching neurons because of their on-off behavior. Below threshold scrotal temperatures of 33–38°C the unit displays a low basal activity; when the temperature is raised above a threshold zone it elicits a step-like increase in activity that is sustained throughout thermal stimulation. Since the scrotum is highly sensitive to temperature, it is thought that the switching response of thalamic neurons may serve as a warning signal when scrotal temperature reaches a critical level (113).

Primary thermoreceptors and thalamic thermoresponsive neurons are functionally similar with respect to their phasic and static responses to step changes in temperature. A rapid decrease in tongue temperature elicits a large increase in thalamic unit activity, which then settles to a lower steady-state level after 75 sec of stimulation (73). Application of a heat lamp to the face or forepaw of the cat causes a near instantaneous drop in activity of cold-response thalamic neurons. Removal of the heat source causes a rapid recovery of activity with an occasional overshoot (74). Thus, like thermoafferent neurons, some thalamic neurons show a very rapid change in activity with temperature that may overshoot the eventual steady-state level. In the rhesus and squirrel monkeys, thermoresponsive thalamic units have steady-state outputs similar to those of primary trigeminal units under a wide range of skin temperature (98, 99).

Thermoresponsive and nonthermoresponsive thalamic neurons show bursts of activity. Jahns (62) found that some units respond to decreasing scrotal temperature with changes from a relatively rapid rate of tonic activity to bursts of activity. About half of the neurons in the ventrobasal complex exhibited bursts of activity; however, the burst parameters were not correlated with a thermal stimulus, as was shown for primary thermoreceptors (115). Although bursts of neuron activity are thought to be critical for information processing of thermoafferent and preoptic neurons (see below), it is not clear if these bursts of activity play a role in the processing of thalamic information.

There is selective spatial integration of some inputs in the thalamus. In general, thalamic and preoptic neurons facilitated by scrotal heating are also excited by noxious stimulation, whereas units inhibited by scrotal warming are inhibited by noxious stimulation (67). There is little evidence of thalamic thermoresponsive neurons that respond to mechanical stimuli (73, 114).

Recent studies have shown interesting interactions between thermoresponsive thalamic neurons and other CNS sites. The switching response of thalamic neurons to scrotal heating can be abolished by blocking activity of the cerebral cortex (45) or by lesioning the NRM (121). Thus, the ability of thalamic thermoresponsive neurons to generate a switching response depends on an intact link with the cerebral cortex. It is hypothesized that the switching response of thalamic neurons to scrotal heating is dependent on positive feedback mediated through a thalamus-cortex-thalamus loop (45).

Cold acclimation does not affect the processing of thermal information in the trigeminal nuclei (13); however, it does influence the response of thalamic thermoresponsive cells to scrotal heating (127). Following five weeks of acclimation of adult rats to 3°C, warm-responsive thalamic and midbrain neurons switch to higher levels of activity at lower scrotal temperatures compared to nonacclimated rats. Thus, the effect of cold acclimation is to lower the threshold temperatures that activate heat dissipating responses, as reflected by shifts in the characteristics of some thalamic thermoresponsive neurons (127).

Midbrain

Many areas of the midbrain have been studied for thermoregulatory properties. It appears that the raphe nuclei are key sites for the integration of peripheral and central thermal stimuli, and in the processing of information ascending to the preoptic/anterior hypothalamic area (POAH) (7, 75). Many warm-sensitive neurons, but few or no cold-sensitive neurons, were recorded in the median and dorsal raphe nuclei during changes in midbrain temperature in the rat (54) and the cat (11). In the rabbit there are more warm-sensitive than cold-sensitive cells in the raphe nuclei (81). Furthermore, it was shown that many of the raphe neurons sensitive to midbrain temperature also respond to changes in temperature of the abdominal skin. In the raphe nuclei of the rat, 65% of the thermoresponsive neurons exhibited peak activity at a skin temperature of 37.7°C, while the remaining 35% exhibited peak activity at a skin temperature of 29.0°C (15). The majority of the thermoresponsive units were found in the nucleus raphe magnus; this may reflect the high degree of spinal input to the NRM. Many of the thermoresponsive raphe neuron units are serotonergic and project to the POAH (14, 15, 81).

Recent studies suggest that ascending thermal afferent information is processed in series through the raphe nuclei and then to the thalamus and the hypothalamus (46). Lesioning the raphe nuclei abolishes the switching response of thalamic and hypothalamic neurons to scrotal heating (121). However, extensive lesioning of the brainstem lemniscal pathways has no effect on the response of thalamic or hypothalamic neurons to scrotal heating. Switching responses to scrotal heating predominate in the NRM and are not dependent on cortical input (45). In addition to switching responses, it has been noted that scrotal heating evokes an increase in periodicity of single unit activity in the NRM and in warm-responsive hypothalamic neurons (63). In the processing of scrotal thermal information, it appears that switching responses are generated in the raphe nuclei as dictated by peripheral thermal inputs, then passed to the thalamus and hypothalamus (45, 46). The spinothalamic lemniscal pathways appear to have little significance in the processing of scrotal thermal information (128).

While switching responses have been observed in the raphe nuclei during scrotal thermal stimulation, bell-shaped responses of midbrain neurons to thermal stimulation have been seen in studies of other skin areas. Cold-responsive neurons predominate in the pontine dorsomedial reticular formation (subcoeruleus region) of the guinea pig, and they respond to skin cooling of the abdomen or leg (51). The peak activity of the cold-responsive neurons at skin temperatures of 22–29°C parallels that of peripheral cold receptors. Neurons responsive to abdominal skin cooling were also found in the rabbit raphe nuclei, but their activity was linear or biphasic, not bell shaped (81). Subcoeruleus cold-responsive neurons, which are noradrenergic, probably project directly to the hypothalamus (51). The current evidence suggests that thermal stimuli from the abdominal skin, and perhaps other skin areas, are processed through the pontine area, whereas distinct switching responses, which are apparently unique to scrotal heating, are generated and processed through the raphe nuclei.

Thermosensitive neurons in the midbrain appear to integrate thermal information from other key CNS sites (35). Many thermosensitive midbrain neurons are modulated by shifts in hypothalamic temperature (112). Similar patterns are achieved in midbrain thermosensitive neurons by local heating or cooling of the spinal cord (53). Thus, diffuse and discrete areas of the midbrain (e.g. raphe nuclei) are involved in the integration of local and peripheral thermal signals, as well as temperature shifts in principal thermal integrative CNS sites.

Hypothalamus

The anatomical complexities of the hypothalamus and preoptic area (POAH) have compounded the difficulty of neurophysiological study of their integrative role in thermoregulation. The success of studies on integration in the aforementioned CNS sites (spinal cord, thalamus, etc) may be attributed to a relatively clear understanding of the neuronal connectivity of these structures. However, the afferent and efferent pathways to the hypothalamus and preoptic area, which may be involved in thermoregulation, are complex and relatively numerous (5, 69, 85, 125). In view of the diverse inputs into the hypothalamus, it is not suprising to find an abundance of studies demonstrating thermointegrative responses of hypothalamic neurons by the stimulation of virtually any site in the CNS (10, 40, 48, 49, 105, 110). Three current areas of research on the thermointegrative properties of the hypothalamus will be discussed here: (a) the integration and processing of thermal information from the skin (excluding the scrotum); (b) the integration of scrotal thermal information; and (c) the integration of nonthermal inputs with thermoregulatory stimuli.

PERIPHERAL INPUTS EXCLUDING SCROTUM   Over the past two decades an array of studies demonstrated convergence of thermoafferent inputs from the skin onto thermosensitive neurons in the hypothalamus (e.g. 10, 48, 49, 61, 105). In general, a large percentage of warm-sensitive neurons in the hypothalamus, especially the POAH, are facilitated by skin warming, and cold-sensitive neurons are facilitated by skin cooling.

In analyzing integrative properties of hypothalamic neurons in response to skin and/or hypothalamic temperature stimulation, one is confronted with the problems of anesthetics. Until recently, most single unit studies were performed using anesthetized preparations. Since anesthetics severely reduce synaptic transmission, these studies are difficult to interpret at higher levels of the CNS, where thermal information may pass through several synapses before reaching the area under study (e.g. hypothalamus). The impact of anesthetics on thermointegrative properties of hypothalamic neurons can be assessed by comparing studies using the rabbit. In the anesthetized condition 7% (41) and 34% (6) of the POAH units responded to skin or ambient temperature, while in the unanesthetized condition approximately 75% of POAH units responded to changes in skin or ambient temperature (23, 27, 102). Moreover, various types of anesthetics may influence the responsiveness of primary thermoreceptors to dynamic temperature shifts (52). That anesthetics influence the processing of thermal information from the receptor level to motor output suggests that our future understanding of thermointegration will be altered as more research is performed using unanesthetized animals.

Purported thermointegrative neurons have been identified in many studies by using direct thermal stimulation of the POAH and other CNS sites (21, 22, 28, 77, 106). However, the changes in temperature necessary to activate neuron activity are usually much greater than the normal range of CNS temperature (42). Indeed, with the exceptions of hibernation, sleep, and exercise, the temperature of the hypothalamus is very stable in most homeotherms under relatively extreme environmental conditions. It seems appropriate, in most cases, to assess thermointegrative functions of CNS neurons by activating them naturally through changes in skin temperature.

Reaves (104) first assessed the effect of the interaction between peripheral and central thermal stimulation on POAH neuron activity in the unanesthetized, unrestrained rabbit. POAH units were ten times more sensitive (i.e. Δ firing rate/°C) to changes in POAH temperature than to changes in ambient temperature. POAH single units apparently have different response times to changes in skin temperature. In the unanesthetized rabbit exposed dorsally to radiant heat, some POAH neurons required several minutes to reach their maximal change in firing rate, whereas others exhibited a near-instantaneous response to skin temperature (23). The latter response appears similar to switching responses of single units in the midbrain, thalamus, and hypothalamus during scrotal heating (see above). Jahns (64) developed the notion of two fundamental reaction modes in the anesthetized rat: a slow, continuous change in neuron activity during peripheral thermal stimulation predominates in the midbrain and hypothalamus, while rapid, stepwise responses occur in the mesencephalon and ventrobasal complex. A recent study in the unanesthetized rabbit revealed POAH neurons responded differentially to warm air blown across the face, with either a relatively rapid time constant of ~10 sec or a slow time constant of ~60 sec (34). Rapid- and slow-responding POAH neurons may be necessary integrative components that drive respectively, rapid motor outputs such as behavior, and relatively slow motor outputs such as vasomotor tone and metabolic processes (23).

SCROTAL THERMAL INPUTS   The scrotum of the rat is similar to that in other species—raising its temperature to a critical level leads to vigorous heat dissipating responses (60, 91). The integration of scrotal thermal inputs in the hypothalamus influences the control of other motor outputs. For example, the threshold hypothalamic temperature for elevating tail skin temperature is reduced by elevating scrotal temperature (60).

Single unit studies support the convergence and integration of scrotal and hypothalamic thermal signals. A large proportion of warm-sensitive preoptic neurons are facilitated by scrotal heating, while cold-sensitive neurons are facilitated by scrotal cooling (86). Interestingly, heating either side of the scrotum evokes similar preoptic neural responses, which suggests that, at this level of the CNS, spatial discrimination of thermal stimuli is relatively unimportant in evoking thermoregulatory responses (86).

Switching or off-on type responses to scrotal heating, which occur in the raphe nuclei and thalamus, also predominate in the POAH (45, 86). Simultaneous recordings in the rat thalamus and hypothalamus demonstrated that neurons increased their firing rates from minimum to maximum with a ≤ 1°C change in scrotal temperature (66). The threshold temperature of some simultaneously recorded thalamic and hypothalamic neurons differed by less than 0.4°C. Moreover, the onset of switching responses was associated with desynchronization of the cortical EEG. It appears that threshold temperatures of switching neurons are generated in the raphe nuclei; this information passes through the thalamus, where it is integrated with inputs from the cerebral cortex, and is then passed to the hypothalamus and preoptic area (45, 66).

Dynamic responses to rapid changes in skin temperature that occur at the spinal, trigeminal, and thalamic levels are apparently not maintained at the hypothalamic level. Nakayama et al (86) found no evidence of dynamic hypothalamic neural response to scrotal heating. No dynamic responses were found in the POAH of the unanesthetized rabbit (23, 27) or anesthetized rat (70, 71) during rapid increases in skin temperature. On the other hand, a heating rate of only 2°C/min of the scrotum led to a dynamic facilitation or inhibition of some POAH neurons in the rat (88). However, such slow heating rates of the skin do not evoke dynamic responses in thermoafferent or dorsal horn neurons. Hence, these unusual dynamic neural responses to change in skin temperature are probably generated at supraspinal levels (88).

NONTHERMAL INPUTS   Other than sweat glands and brown adipose tissue, there are apparently no specific cells or organs used solely by the thermoregulatory system. Temperature regulation has evolved through the utilization of preexisting physiological systems, e.g. locomotor system for shivering, cardiovascular system for skin temperature control, and respiratory system for evaporative heat loss (90). Thus, it is not surprising to find that a wide variety of nonthermal stimuli, such as mechanostimulation (80), electrical stimulation of the CNS (18, 55, 56), and changes in vascular pressure (60), affect thermoregulatory function.

The acoustic startle response is a clear example of a nonthermal stimulus that leads to the activation of thermoregulatory effectors. Acoustic stimuli induce transient vasoconstriction and changes in skin evaporative water loss that last for tens of seconds (8). In the unanesthetized rabbit a loud tone (510 Hz at 89 dB for 0.5 sec) facilitates or inhibits neurons normally inhibited by skin heating but has no significant effect on heat-excited or thermally unresponsive units (26). The firing rate of some POAH units was affected for over 10 sec by a single 0.5 sec acoustic stimulus. Such long-term thermoregulatory unit responses to acoustic stimulation may be associated with activating thermoregulatory motor outputs, which also last for several seconds following a startle response.

Another interesting aspect of integration of nonthermal stimuli involves the control of caloric intake. Generally, food consumption is stimulated by central or peripheral cooling and is inhibited by heating. Neurons in the lateral hypothalamus (LH), which were facilitated by preoptic cooling, were also inhibited by iontophoretic application of glucose (129). In the ventromedial hypothalamus (VMH) a large percentage of neurons facilitated by glucose were also facilitated by preoptic heating (87). In a recent study it was found that nearly all VMH neurons facilitated by glucose also responded to scrotal warming (89). It is possible that peripheral thermal signals from the scrotum (and perhaps other areas) pass via thermosensitive POAH neurons to neurons of the VMH and LH, which control caloric intake (57).

MOTOR OUTPUTS

Origin

In spite of the innumerable studies on CNS control of body temperature, it is still not clear which site(s) contribute to motor control during normal thermoregulation. This is a difficult problem because thermoregulatory responses can be evoked in a coordinated manner by local thermal stimulation of virtually any CNS site from spinal cord to cortex (e.g. 40, 48, 49, 105). Another problem is the lack of anatomically clear efferent pathways for thermoregulation. There has been no demonstration of a distinct efferent pathway emanating from a key integrative site, such as the POAH, for sweating, pilloerection, vasomotor tone, etc; the existence of such a pathway for shivering is uncertain (47).

It was recently proposed that thermoregulation is achieved through a hierarchical set of integrators located at various levels of the CNS (110, 111). Basically, central or peripheral thermal information is thought to be integrated at various CNS sites, each of which can facilitate or inhibit a different site. Overall, there may be a connectivity of multiple thermostats, with a net result of a fine control over body temperature. The hierarchical concept is primarily based on CNS electrical stimulation and lesion experiments. It remains to be shown if such a hierarchy of control occurs under natural circumstances.

Using the 2-deoxy-D-[^{14}C] glucose (2-DG) technique it has been possible to generate a pictorial representation of possible integrative sites involved in thermoregulation (79, 82–84). In addition to the preoptic area and hypothalamus, other CNS sites, including the medial forebrain bundle, thalamus, and red nucleus, showed significant changes in 2-DG uptake during thermal stimulation. Interestingly, there were marked differences in 2-DG uptake by the various brain regions under conditions of central versus peripheral thermal stimulation. Further development of the 2-DG technique may lead to better characterization of integrative sites for thermoregulation.

Spatial Properties

Vasomotor and sudomotor control are mediated through the sympathetic nervous system. Blood flow is inversely related to neural activity in tissues innervated by vasoconstrictor noradrenergic fibers. Thermal stimulation alters sympathetic nervous system activity such that peripheral and deep body blood flow shifts in an appropriate way to accelerate heat loss in a hot environment and reduce heat loss in a cold environment. For example, sympathetic nerve activity decreases in fibers innervating cutaneous tissues and increases in fibers innervating splanchnic tissues during spinal, hypothalamic, or peripheral heating (36, 58, 93). The reciprocal pattern of sympathetic activity occurs during cooling. The changes in sympathetic tone of cutaneous and splanchnic vascular tissues during the onset of fever are similar to those elicited by cold exposure (107).

Sympathetically controlled vasodilator neurons that innervate skin and skeletal muscle are important in thermoregulation (3). Vasodilating nerves may be responsible for control of arteriovenous shunts and the induction of cold-induced vasodilation (3). In the heat-stressed dog, lingual blood flow is enhanced through facilitation of vasodilating fibers rather than suppression of vasoconstriction fiber activity (122).

Temporal Properties

Taking into account the number of synapses for passage and integration of thermal inputs, it is not suprising to find a major difference in the temporal response property at the final efferent level versus the primary afferent level. The highly active, tonic activity characteristic of thermoreceptors is not found in sympathetic motor outputs. For example, the highest mean firing rate of a postganglionic sympathetic fiber in unanesthetized humans is ~ 11 ips (4), compared with the 0–50 ips activity range of thermoreceptors (48, 49). Moreover, sympathetic activity at various levels, from brainstem to postganglionic fibers, is oscillatory, with rapid frequencies that parallel cardiac, respiratory, and cortical activity, as well as much slower frequencies similar to sudomotor and vasomotor rhythms (2, 4, 32, 59). One of the slowest thermoregulatory rhythms, the circadian oscillation of body temperature, may be controlled by several brainstem nuclei (101).

Are the reduced tonic activity and extensive frequency modulation of sympathetic activity necessary for the efficient transduction of neural signals to particular effector tissues or organs? Under certain thermal conditions, principal thermoregulatory effectors, such as sweating, vasomotor tone, and metabolism, oscillate with frequencies ranging from 0.0002 to 18 Hz (32). Slow, rhythmic efferent activity may enhance transduction at neuroeffector junctions (4). For example, pronounced changes in vascular resistance occur when postganglionic fiber activity is raised from 1 to 4 ips, whereas only minimal effects occur at frequencies of 10–15 ips (19). Vascular resistance vessels respond relatively slowly, with a cut-off stimulation frequency of ~4 Hz and a resonant frequency of 0.03 Hz (108). Postganglionic vasoconstrictor fibers undergo a prolonged activity shift lasting up to 60 min when the preganglionic fibers are stimulated for 2 sec at 25 Hz (65). Apparently, vasomotor sympathetic ganglia and neuroeffector junctions respond relatively slowly, with a low frequency response that is optimally coupled to the nervous system via slow rhythmic effector signals (32).

The POAH area may have a key role in generating rhythmic efferent signals. For example, 21% of the POAH units in the unanesthetized rabbit displayed slow bursts of activity during POAH cooling or monoamine stimulation (24).

The frequency of the bursts was 0.067 Hz, which correlates with the oscillatory frequency of vasomotor tone in the rabbit and other species (32). Other populations of POAH neurons exhibit much faster rhythms that are similar to the bursting pattern of primary cold thermoreceptors (25, 103). Temporal modulation of single unit activity at relatively fast and slow frequencies may be a principal mechanism for the transduction and integration of thermal information in the POAH as well as other CNS sites. Indeed, over forty years ago Burton & Taylor (9) stated that "integration with respect to time may be as important a property of nervous mechanisms as spatial integration, for it makes possible the effective regulation of a physiological phenomenon which is by nature continually fluctuating." In other words, regulation of body temperature under conditions of continually fluctuating ambient temperature necessitates that the CNS integrate the intrinsically rhythmic activity of thermoregulatory effectors (32).

Control

Many studies have shown that proportional control is the main feature of thermoregulation in mammals. The magnitude of effector activity, such as metabolism and evaporation, is proportional to the deviation of skin, deep body, and/or brain temperature from their respective set point temperatures (40, 76, 78).

Hypothalamic temperature has generally been considered a principal error signal in proportional control. However, the concept of hypothalamic temperature as a key input is complicated by the vascular mechanisms in the control of brain temperature in various species (105). Species with a carotid rete (e.g. cat, sheep, dog) are able to maintain hypothalamic temperature below aortic temperature under thermoneutral temperatures, ambient heat stress, and/or during exercise. Moreover, many species that lack a carotid rete, including some mammals, birds, and reptiles, are nevertheless capable of lowering brain temperature during exercise (e.g. 29, 68, 123), and also maintain brain temperature below body temperature under normal ambient conditions. These physiologic properties exemplify the complexity of hypothalamic temperature as a potential thermal input in thermoregulatory control. Clearly, the deviation of skin temperature from its preferred level is one of the most important variables of proportional control of body temperature.

Proportional control cannot account for all of the thermoregulatory responses. Rate or differential control is also critical to normal thermoregulatory processes. The rate of temperature change will supersede proportionally controlled shifts in activity of thermoregulatory effectors (126). Tail vasomotor control in mice is more dependent on the rate of heat absorption than on the total absorbed heat load (31). Rate sensitivity may act as a feed-forward or trigger mechanism, such that the thermoregulatory system can anticipate a potential thermal stress (30, 120). In other words, even though thermal receptors on the skin can respond within milliseconds to a change in the thermal environment, thermoregulatory effectors may require several minutes to reach the change in activity necessary to offset the environmental heat load. With such long response lags, a proportional system may not be sufficient for regulation in dynamic thermal environments.

On-off control is another key mechanism in some aspects of thermoregulation. As mentioned earlier, neurons in the pathways activated by scrotal heating, located in the raphe nuclei, thalamus, and hypothalamus, respond in an on-off (switching reponse) pattern to graded changes in scrotal temperature. However, it is not clear what motor response(s) an on-off thermoafferent and integrative pathway may control. One possibility is tail blood flow in rodents, which shows an on-off type response during ambient thermal stimulation (130). Periods of vasodilation and vasoconstriction are correlated with a 0.4°C cycle of hypothalamic temperature. Interestingly, the average frequency of tail blood flow of 0.0007 Hz in the rat is very near the cut-off frequency of skin temperature in the mouse during cyclic thermal stimulation (33). The temporal characteristics of on-off control may be related to the frequency characteristics of the control system.

SUMMARY

Our understanding of the neural control of body temperature has been clarified by research over the past ten years. Overall, ascending thermal inputs are integrated with other thermal and nonthermal inputs, which results in efferent signals with the spatial and temporal characteristics necessary for driving effector organs involved in thermal homeostasis. There is substantial support for the hypothesis that the afferent component of the thermoregulatory system integrates thermal stimuli into several neural patterns, the principal ones being a stepwise, switching response of neuron activity during scrotal thermal stimulation and a proportional response to other thermal inputs. Furthermore, some thermointegrative CNS neurons respond relatively rapidly or slowly during peripheral thermal stimulation, which may be critical in driving behavioral and autonomic motor outputs, respectively.

The control of thermoregulatory motor outputs is multifaceted and exhibits proportional, rate-sensitive, and/or on-off regulatory patterns during thermal stimulation. These complex motor patterns indicate the presence of extensive temporal and spatial integration of ascending thermal information. This is supported by the fact that the pattern of efferent nerve activity in various motor systems (e.g. vasomotor) is vastly different from that produced by recordings of primary thermoreceptor activity. Understanding the nature and mechanisms of the CNS transduction of peripheral thermal stimuli to efferent command signals for driving thermoregulatory motor outputs will be a challenging endeavor in the future.

ACKNOWLEDGMENTS

We thank Drs. Amir Rezvani, T. A. Reaves, and Steven Trautwein for their review of the manuscript. We also thank M. Long, K. Fehlner, L. Williams, and B. Crabtree for their assistance in the preparation of the manuscript for publication.

Literature Cited

1. Bade, H., Braun, H. A., Hensel, H. 1979. Parameters of the static burst discharge of lingual cold receptors in the cat. *Plügers Arch.* 382:1–5
2. Barman, S. M., Gebber, G. L. 1981. Brain stem neuronal types with activity patterns related to sympathetic nerve discharge. *Am. J. Physiol.* 240:R335–47
3. Bell, C. 1983. Vasodilator neurons supplying skin and skeletal muscle of the limbs. *J. Auton. Nerv. Sys.* 7:257–62
4. Bini, G., Hagbarth, K.-E., Hynninen, P., Wallin, B. G. 1980. Thermoregulatory and rhythm-generating mechanisms governing the sudomotor and vasoconstrictor outflow in human cutaneous nerves. *J. Physiol.* 306:537–52
5. Boulant, J. A. 1980. Hypothalamic control of thermoregulation. Neurophysiological basis. In *Handbook of the Hypothalamus,* Vol. 3, pp. 1–82, ed. P. J. Morgane, J. Panksepp. New York: Dekker
6. Boulant, J. A., Hardy, J. D. 1974. The effect of spinal cord skin temperatures on the firing rate and thermosensitivity of preoptic neurones. *J. Physiol.* 240:639–60
7. Brück, K., Hinckle, P. 1980. Thermoregulatory noradrenergic and serotonergic pathways to hypothalamic units. *J. Physiol.* 304:193–202
8. Burton, A. C. 1939. The range and variability of the blood flow in the human fingers and the vasomotor regulation of body temperature. *Am. J. Physiol.* 127:437–53
9. Burton, A. C., Taylor, R. M. 1940. A study of the adjustment of peripheral vascular tone to the requirements of the regulation of body temperature. *Am. J. Physiol.* 129:565–77
10. Cabanac, M. 1975. Temperature regulation. *Ann. Rev. Physiol.* 38:415–39
11. Cronin, M. J., Baker, M. A. 1976. Heat sensitive midbrain raphe neurons in the anesthetized cat. *Brain Res.* 110:175–81
12. Dawson, N. J., Dickenson, A. H., Hel-

lon, R. F., Woolf, C. J. 1981. Inhibitory controls on thermal neurones in the spinal trigeminal nucleus of cats and rats. *Brain Res.* 209:440–45
13. Dawson, N. J., Hellon, R. F., Herington, J. G., Young, A. A. 1982. Facial thermal input in the caudal trigeminal nucleus of rats reared at 30°C. *J. Physiol.* 33:545–54
14. Dickenson, A. H. 1977. Specific responses of rat raphe neurons to skin temperature. *J. Physiol.* 273:277–93
15. Dickenson, A. H. 1978. Serotonergic raphe neurones involved in an ascending thermal pathway. In *New Trends in Thermal Physiology,* ed. Y. Houdas, J. D. Guieu, pp. 50–52. Paris: Masson
16. Dickenson, A. H., Hellon, R. F., Taylor, D. C. M. 1979. Facial thermal input to the trigeminal spinal nucleus of rabbits and rats. *J. Comp. Neurol.* 185:203–10
17. Dostrovsky, J. O., Hellon, R. F. 1978. The representation of facial temperature in the caudal trigeminal nucleus of the cat. *J. Physiol.* 277:29–47
18. Eisenman, J. S. 1974. Unit studies of brainstem projections to the preoptic area and hypothalamus. In *Recent Studies of Hypothalamic Function, Int. Symp. Calgary, 1973,* pp. 328–40. Basel: Karger
19. Folkow, B. 1952. Impulse frequency in sympathetic vasomotor fibers correlated to the release and elimination of the transmitter. *Acta Physiol. Scand.* 25:49–76
20. Deleted in proof
21. Gerber, R. L., Klussmann, F. W., Heller, H. C. 1984. Preoptic/anterior hypothalamic neural responses to thermal stimulation of the hypothalamus and spinal cord in unanesthestized, unrestrained rabbits. In *Thermal Physiology,* ed. J. R. S. Hales, pp. 83–86. New York: Raven
22. Glotzbach, S. F., Heller, H. C. 1984. Changes in the thermal characteristics of

INTEGRATION AND TEMPERATURE REGULATION 609

hypothalamic neurons during sleep and
wakefulness. Brain Res. 309:17–26
23. Gordon, C. J. 1981. Effect of slow and
rapid skin heating on the activity of single
neurons in the preoptic area of unanesthetized rabbits. Brain Res. Bull.
6:371–76
24. Gordon, C. J., Heath J. E. 1980. Slow
bursting thermal sensitive neurons in the
preoptic area of the rabbit. Brain Res.
Bull. 5:515–18
25. Gordon, C. J., Heath, J. E. 1981. Temporal patterning of neuronal activity during thermal and neurochemical stimulation of the preoptic/anterior hypothalamus of the awake rabbit. Neuropharmacology 20:163–68
26. Gordon, C. J., Heath, J. E. 1981. Acoustically driven thermal-identified neurons
in the preoptic area of unanesthetized rabbits. Brain Res. 212:301–7
27. Gordon, C. J., Heath, J. E. 1981. Effect
of beta-endorphin on the thermal excitability of preoptic neurons in the unanesthetized rabbit. Peptides 2:397–401
28. Gordon, C. J., Heath, J. E. 1981. Effect
of monoamines on firing rate and thermal
sensitivity of neurons in the preoptic area
of awake rabbits. Exp. Neurol. 72:352–
65
29. Gordon, C. J., Rezvani, A. H., Fruin,
M. E., Trautwein, S., Heath, J. E. 1981.
Rapid brain cooling in the free-running
hamster Mesocricetus auratus. J. Appl.
Physiol. 51:1349–54
30. Gordon, C. J. 1982. Effect of heating rate
on evaporative heat loss in the micro-
wave-exposed mouse. J. Appl. Physiol.
53:316–23
31. Gordon, C. J. 1983. Influence of heating
rate on control of heat loss from the tail in
mice. Am. J. Physiol. 244:R778–84
32. Gordon, C. J., Heath, J. E. 1983.
Reassessment of the neural control of
body temperature: importance of oscillat-
ing neural and motor components. Comp.
Biochem. Physiol. 74A:479–89
33. Gordon, C. J. 1984. Frequency and transient analysis of skin temperature control
in the mouse. Physiol. Zool. 57:500–8
34. Gordon, C. J., White, E. C. 1985. Temporal response of neurons to ambient
heating in the preoptic and septal area of
the unanesthetized rabbit. Comp. Biochem. Physiol. 82A:879–84
35. Gottschlich, K.-W., Werner, J., Schingnitz, G. 1984. Thermoafferent signal
processing in rats: an electrophysiological analysis of midbrain influences on the
thermoresponsive neurons in the ventrobasal thalamus. Pflügers Arch. 401:91–
96
36. Gregor, M., Jänig, W., Riedel, W. 1976.

Response pattern of cutaneous postganglionic neurones to the hindlimb on spinal cord heating and cooling in the cat.
Pflügers Arch. 363:135–40
37. Deleted in proof
38. Hackman, E., Simon, E. 1975. Single
unit activity in spinal anterolateral tracts
influenced by cold stimulation of spinal
cord and skin. In Depressed Metabolism
and Cold Thermogenesis, ed. C. Jansky,
197–201. Prague: Charles Univ.
39. Deleted in proof
40. Hammel, H. T. 1968. Regulation of internal body temperature. Ann. Rev. Physiol. 30:641–710
41. Hellon, R. F. 1970. The stimulation of
hypothalamic neurons by changes in
ambient temperature. Pflügers Arch.
321:56–66
42. Hellon, R. F. 1981. Neurophysiology of
temperature regulation: problems and
perspectives. Fed. Proc. 40:2804–7
43. Hellon, R. F., Misra, N. K. 1973.
Neurones in the dorsal horn of the rat
responding to scrotal skin temperature
changes. J. Physiol. 232:375–388
44. Hellon, R. F., Misra, N. K. 1973.
Neurones in the ventrobasal complex of
the rat thalamus responding to scrotal
skin temperature changes. J. Physiol.
232:389–99
45. Hellon, R. F., Taylor, D. C. M. 1982.
An analysis of a thermal afferent pathway
in the rat. J. Physiol. 326:319–28
46. Hellon, R. F. 1983. Central projections
and projections and processing of skin-
temperature signals. J. Therm. Biol.
8:7–8
47. Hemmingway, A., Stuart, D. G. 1963.
Shivering in man and animals. In Temperature, Its Measurements and Control
in Science and Industry. 3:407–27
48. Hensel, H. 1973. Neural processes in
thermoregulation. Physiol. Rev. 53:948–
1017
49. Hensel, H. 1981. Thermoreception and
Temperature Regulation, Monographs of
the Physiological Society No. 38, London: Academic. 321 pp.
50. Hensel, H., Schäfer, K. 1974. Effects of
calcium on warm and cold receptors.
1974. Pflügers Arch. 352:87–90
51. Hinckel, P., Schröder-Rosenstock, K.
1981. Responses of pontine units to skin-
temperature changes in the guinea pig. J.
Physiol. 314:189–94
52. Hirata, H., Poulos, D. A., Molt, J. T.
1984. Differences in thermal responses
of cat trigeminal ganglion cold receptors
under urethane and pentobarbital anes-
thetization. Brain Res. 292:387–89
53. Hori, T., Harada, Y. 1976. Midbrain
neuronal responses to local and spinal

cord temperatures. *Am. J. Physiol.* 231:1573–78
54. Hori, T., Harada, Y. 1976. Responses of midbrain raphe neurons to local temperature. *Pflügers Arch.* 364:205–7
55. Hori, T., Kiyohara, T., Nakashima, T., Shibata, M. 1982. Responses of preoptic thermosensitive neurons to medial forebrain bundle stimulation. *Brain Res. Bull.* 8:667–75
56. Hori, T., Kiyohara, T., Osaka, T., Shibata, M., Nakashima, T. 1982. Responses of preoptic thermosensitive neurons to mediobasal hypothalamic stimulation. *Brain Res. Bull.* 8:677–83
57. Imai-Matsumura, K., Nakayama, T. 1983. Response of lateral hypothalamic neurons to scrotal and preoptic thermal stimulation in rats. *Neurosci. Lett.* 35:277–82
58. Iriki, M. 1983. Regional differentiation of sympathetic efferents during thermal stimulation. *J. Therm. Biol.* 8:225–28
59. Iriki, M., Hales, J. R. S. 1976. Spontaneous thermoregulatory oscillations in cutaneous efferent sympathetic activity. *Experientia* 32:879–80
60. Ishokawa, Y., Nakayama, T., Kanosue, K., Matsumura, K. 1984. Activation of central warm-sensitive neurons and the tail vasomotor response in rats during brain and scrotal thermal stimulation. *Pflügers Arch.* 400:222–27
61. Ivanov, K. P., Dymnikova, L. P., Khalilov, E. 1981. The convergence onto posterior hypothalamic neurons of signals from thermosensors at different skin areas. *J. Therm. Biol.* 6:37–41
62. Jahns, R. 1975. Types of neuronal responses in the rat thalamus to peripheral temperature changes. *Exp. Brain Res.* 23:157–66
63. Jahns, R. 1976. Different projections of cutaneous thermal inputs to single units of the midbrain raphe nuclei. *Brain Res.* 101:355–61
64. Jahns, R. 1977. Reaction modes of central neurons in the thermoafferent pathway. *Pflügers Arch.* 368:R29 (Abst.)
65. Jänig, W., Krauspe, R., Widersatz, G. 1982. Transmission of impulses from pre- to postganglionic vasoconstrictor and sudomotor neurons. *J. Auton. Nerv. Sys.* 6:95–106
66. Kanosue, K., Nakayama, T., Ishikawa, Y., Hosono, T. 1984. Threshold temperatures of diencephalic neurons responding to scrotal warming. *Pflügers Arch.* 400:418–23
67. Kanosue, K., Nakayama, T., Ishikawa, Y., Imai-Matsumura, K. 1984. Responses of hypothalamic and thalamic neurons to noxious and scrotal thermal

stimulations in rats. *J. Therm. Biol.* 9:11–13
68. Kilgore, D. L. Birehard, G. F., Boggs, D. F. 1981. Brain temperatures in running quail. *J. Appl. Physiol.* 50:1277–81
69. Kiyohara, T., Hori, T., Shibata, M., Nakashima, T., Osaka, T. 1984. Neural inputs to preoptic thermosensitive neurons—histological and electrophysiological mapping of central connections. *J. Therm. Biol.* 9:21–26
70. Knox, G. V., Campbell, C., Lomax, P. 1973. Cutaneous temperature and unit activity in the hypothalamic thermoregulatory centers. *Exp. Neurol.* 40:717–30
71. Knox, G. V., Campbell, C., Lomax, P. 1973. The effects of acetylcholine and nicotine on unit activity in the hypothalamic thermoregulatory centers of the rat. *Brain Res.* 51:215–23
72. Deleted in proof
73. Landgren, S. 1960. Thalamic neurones responding to cooling of the cat's tongue. *Acta Physiol. Scand.* 48:255–67
74. Martin, H. F. III, Manning, J. W. 1971. Thalamic "warming" and "cooling" units responding to cutaneous stimulation. *Brain Res.* 27:377–81
75. Matsumura, K., Nakayama, T., Ishikawa, Y. 1984. Effects of median raphe electrical stimulation on preoptic thermosensitive neurons in rats. In *Thermal Physiology*, ed. J. R. S. Hales, pp. 87–90. New York: Raven
76. McEwen, G. N., Heath, J. E. 1974. Thermoregulatory responses to preoptic cooling in unrestrained rabbits. *Am. J. Physiol.* 277:954–57
77. Mercer, J. B., Jessen, C., Pierau, F.-K. 1978. Thermal stimulation of neurons in the rostral brain stem of conscious goats. *J. Therm. Biol.* 3:5–10
78. Mercer, J. B., Simon, E. 1984. A comparison between total body thermosensitivity and local thermosensitivity in mammals and birds. *Pflügers Arch.* 400:228–34
79. Morimoto, A., Murakami, N. 1985. [14C]deoxyglucose incorporation into rat brain regions during hypothalamic or peripheral thermal stimulation. *Am. J. Physiol.* 248:R84–R92
80. Murakami, N., Stolwijk, J. A., Hardy, J. D. 1967. Responses of preoptic neurons to anesthetics and peripheral stimulation. *Am. J. Physiol.* 213:1015–24
81. Murakami, N., Sakata, Y. 1978. Temperature-responsive neurones in the midbrain raphe region of rabbits. *Neurosci. Lett.* 10:265–68
82. Murakami, N., Morimoto, A. 1982. Metabolic mapping of the rat brain involved in thermoregulatory responses us-

INTEGRATION AND TEMPERATURE REGULATION   611

ing the [^{14}C]2-deoxyglucose technique. *Brain Res.* 246:137–40

83. Murakami, N., Morimoto, A. 1984. Changes in metabolic activity of the brain stem during central and peripheral thermal stimulation. *J. Therm. Biol.* 9:33–38

84. Murakami, N., Morimoto, A., Watanabe, T. 1984. Radioactive deoxyglucose uptake in the rat CNS during thermoregulatory responses. In *Thermal Physiology*, ed. J. R. S. Hales, pp. 105–8. New York: Raven

85. Myers, R. D. 1980. Hypothalamic control of thermoregulation. Neurochemical mechanisms. In *Handbook of the Hypothalamus*, Vol. 3, pp. 83–209, ed. P. J. Morgane, J. Panksepp. New York: Dekker

86. Nakayama, T., Ishikawa, Y., Tsurutani, T. 1979. Projection of scrotal thermal afferents to the preoptic and hypothalamic neurons in rats. *Pflügers Arch.* 380:59–64

87. Nakayama, T., Yamamoto, K., Ishikawa, Y., Imai, K. 1981. Effects of preoptic thermal stimulation on the ventromedial hypothalamic neurons in rats. *Neurosci. Lett.* 26:177–81

88. Nakayama, T., Kanosue, K., Ishikawa, Y., Matsumura, K., Imai, K. 1983. Dynamic response of preoptic and hypothalamic neurons to scrotal thermal stimulation in rats. *Pflügers Arch.* 396: 23–26

89. Nakayama, T., Imai-Matsumura, K. 1984. Response of glucose-responsive ventromedial hypothalamic neurons to scrotal and preoptic thermal stimulation in rats. *Neurosci. Lett.* 45:129–34

90. Nelson, D. O., Heath, J. E., Prosser, C. L. 1984. Evolution of temperature regulatory mechanisms. *Am. Zool.* 24:791–807

91. Neya, T., Pierau, F.-K. 1976. Vasomotor response to thermal stimulation of the scrotal skin in rats. *Pflügers Arch.* 363:15–18

92. Neya, T., Pierau, F.-K. 1980. Activity patterns of temperature-reactive dorsal horn neurons and their reactions to peripheral receptor stimulation by Ca. *Jpn. J. Physiol.* 30:921–34

93. Ninomiya, I., Fujita, S. 1976. Reflex effects of thermal stimulation on sympathetic nerve activity to skin and kidney. *Am. J. Physiol.* 230:271–78

94. Pierau, F.-K., Carpenter, D. O. 1975. Discharge pattern of temperature sensitive afferents of the scrotal skin of the rat. In *Depressed Metabolism and Cold Thermogenesis*, ed. C. Jansky, 207–10. Prague: Charles Univ.

95. Pierau, F.-K., Wurster, R. D. 1981. Primary afferent input from cutaneous thermoreceptors. *Fed. Proc.* 40:2819–24

96. Deleted in proof

97. Pierau, F.-K., Yamasato, T., Cost, A., Berkes, S. 1984. Processing of afferent temperature signals in sensory ganglia and the spinal cord. *J. Therm. Biol.* 9:51–55

98. Poulos, D. A. 1975. Central processing of peripheral temperature information. In *The Somatosensory System*, ed. H. H. Kornhuber, pp. 78–93. Stuttgart: Thieme Edition/Publishing Sciences Group

99. Poulos, D. A. 1981. Central processing of cutaneous temperature information. *Fed. Proc.* 40:2825–29

100. Poulos, D. A., Molt, J. T. 1976. Response of central trigeminal neurons to cutaneous thermal stimulation. In *Sensory Functions of the Skin in Primates*, ed. Y. Zotterman, pp. 263–83. Oxford: Pergamon

101. Prosser, R., Kittrell, E., Satinoff, E. 1984. Circadian body temperature rhythms in rats with suprachiasmatic nuclear lesions. In *Thermal Physiology*, ed. J. R. S. Hales, pp. 67–70. New York: Raven

102. Reaves, T. A. 1976. *Thermosensitive Characteristics of Preoptic Area Neurons in the New Zealand White Rabbit, Oryctolagus cuniculus.* Ph.D. Dissertation, University of Illinois, Urbana.

103. Reaves, T. A., Heath, J. E. 1975. Interval coding of temperature by CNS neurones in thermoregulation. *Nature* 257:688–90

104. Reaves, T. A. Jr. 1977. Gain of thermosensitive neurons in the preoptic area of the rabbit, *Oryctolagus cuniculus. J. Therm. Biol.* 2:31–33

105. Reaves, T. A. Jr., Hayward, J. N. 1979. Hypothalamic and extrahypothalamic thermoregulatory centers. In *Body Temperature: Regulation, Drug Effects and Therapeutic Implications*, ed. P. Lomax, E. Schonbaum, pp. 39–70. New York: Dekker.

106. Reaves, T. A. Jr., Heath, J. E. 1983. Thermosensitive characteristics of a preoptic area neuron recorded over a 20 day period in the rabbit. *Brain Res. Bull.* 10:39–41

107. Riedel, W., Kozawa, E., Iriki, M. 1982. Renal and cutaneous vasomotor and respiratory rate adjustments to peripheral cold and warm stimuli and to bacterial endotoxin in conscious rabbits. *J. Auton. Nerv. Sys.* 5:177–194

108. Rosenbaum, M., Race, D. 1968. Frequency-response characteristics of vascular resistance vessels. *Am. J. Physiol.* 215:1397–1402

109. Deleted in proof
110. Satinoff, E. 1978. Neural organization and evolution of thermal regulation in mammals. *Science* 201:16–22
111. Satinoff, E. 1983. A reevaluation of the concept of the homeostatic organization of temperature regulation. In *Handbook of Behavioral Neurobiology*, eds. E. Satinoff, P. Teitelbaum, 6:443–72. New York: Plenum.
112. Sato, H. 1984. Midbrain neurons of rats responsive to hypothalamic temperature change and their local thermosensitivity. *J. Therm. Biol.* 9:39–45
113. Schingnitz, G. 1981. Neuronal responses in the rat's thalamus to scrotal heating. *Exp. Brain Res.* 43:419–21
114. Schingnitz, G., Werner, J. 1979. Responses of thalamic neurons to thermal stimulation of the limbs, scrotum and tongue in the rat. *J. Therm. Biol.* 5:53–61
115. Schingnitz, G., Werner, J. 1980. Thalamic burst firing—a neuronal code for temperature information? *Brain Res.* 195:467–70
116. Schingnitz, G., Werner, J. 1983. Thalamic neurons in the rat responding to thermal and noxious stimulation at various sites. *J. Therm. Biol.* 8:23–25
117. Simon, E., Iriki, M. 1970. Ascending neurons of the spinal cord activated by cold. *Experientia* 26:620–22
118. Simon, E., Iriki, M. 1971. Sensory transmission of spinal heat and cold sensitivity in ascending spinal neurons. *Pflügers Arch.* 328:103–20
119. Deleted in proof
120. Stolwijk, J. A., Hardy, J. D. 1974. Regulation and control in physiology. In *Medical Physiology*, ed. V. B. Mountcastle, pp. 1343–58. St. Louis: Mosby
121. Taylor, D. C. M. 1982. The effects of nucleus raphe magnus lesions on an ascending thermal pathway in the rat. *J. Physiol.* 326:309–18
122. Thomson, E. M., Pleschka, K. 1980. Vasodilatory mechanisms in the tongue and nose of the dog under heat load. *Pflügers Arch.* 387:161–66
123. Trautwein, S. N., Gordon, C. J., Heath, J. E. 1985. Changes in brain and body temperature of the lizard, *Sceloporous undulatus hyacinthinus* during rest and exercise. *Comp. Biochem. Physiol.* 80A:199–204
124. Weddell, G., Pallie, W., Palmer, E. 1955. Studies on the innervation of skin. I. The origin, course and number of sensory nerves supplying the rabbit ear. *J. Anat.* 89:162–74
125. Werner, J. 1980. The concept of regulation for human body temperature. *J. Therm. Biol.* 5:75–82
126. Werner, J. 1983. Influences of rate of temperature change on effector mechanisms in human thermoregulation. *J. Therm. Biol.* 8:51–54
127. Werner, J., Schingnitz, G., Hensel, H. 1981. Influence of cold adaptation on the activity of thermoresponsive neurons in thalamus and midbrain of the rat. *Pflügers Arch.* 391:327–30
128. Werner, J., Gottschlich, K.-W., Schingnitz, G., Bienek, A. 1984. Extralemniscal pathways to thermoresponsive units in thalamus and hypothalamus. In *Thermal Physiology*, ed. J. R. S. Hales, pp. 95–99. New York: Raven.
129. Yamamoto, K., Hakayama, T., Ishikawa, Y. 1981. Response of the lateral hypothalamic neurons to preoptic thermal stimulation in rats. *Neurosci. Lett.* 22:257–62
130. Young, A. A., Dawson, N. J. 1982. Evidence for on-off control of heat dissipation from the tail of the rat. *Can. J. Physiol. Pharmacol.* 60:392–98

Ann. Rev. Physiol. 1986. 48:613–23

NEUROTRANSMITTERS IN TEMPERATURE CONTROL

J. M. Lipton and Wesley G. Clark

Departments of Physiology, Anesthesiology, and Pharmacology, The University of Texas Health Science Center at Dallas, Dallas, Texas 75235

INTRODUCTION

Many neurotransmitters may be involved in central regulation of body temperature in normothermia, during heat and cold stress, in fever, and in exercise. Emphasis on amines and prostaglandins has declined somewhat, and a major focus in recent years has been upon the possibility that certain peptides participate in central nervous system (CNS) mediation of temperature control (9, 10). Several of these peptides were originally isolated from pituitary tissue or the alimentary canal, but they also occur in widespread regions of the CNS. While some, such as adrenocorticotropic hormone (ACTH), have well known functions in the periphery, the central roles of most peptides are much less understood.

ANTIPYRETIC PEPTIDES

Arginine Vasopressin

The concept that certain CNS peptides act as endogenous antipyretics to limit fever developed initially from research on arginine vasopressin (AVP) in sheep (63). A major finding was that septal concentrations of AVP varied inversely with temperature in fever (13). In the rat a hypothermic effect of AVP was demonstrated many years ago (45), and an antipyretic effect of AVP, but not of oxytocin, after intracerebroventricular (icv) injection was reported recently (32). However, there was no decrease in fever when AVP was injected intracerebroventricularly or into the septum of the rabbit (3). In afebrile rats injections of vasopressin into the primary temperature control in the preoptic/

0066-4278/86/0315-0613$02.00

anterior hypothalamus (PO/AH) increased their temperature in neutral, hot, and cold environments (37). In view of the variations in species, techniques, and responses, the generality of the antipyretic role of endogenous AVP remains an open question.

ACTH/α-Melanotropin

ACTH (1–24) and α-melanotropin (MSH), the 1–13 amino acid fragment of ACTH, were first shown to reduce temperature when given centrally to rabbits in a screen of several peptides (38). Subsequently, ACTH and MSH were found to be antipyretic when given centrally or peripherally in doses that had no effect on normal temperature. The parent molecule ACTH (1–39) was actually the first peptide with documented antipyretic activity, established with peripheral administration soon after the substance was described in 1949. Most of the recent research has focused on MSH. As an antipyretic this peptide is about 25,000 times more potent than acetaminophen on a molar basis (44). MSH reduces fever whether administered by icv or intravenous (iv) injection, or by administration into the stomach of rabbits (42). Its central site of action may be the septum; injections of MSH into this region are also antipyretic (19). Such injections may mimic a naturally occurring response since the septal concentration of MSH rises during fever (21, 56). In contrast, its concentration within the septum does not increase in rabbits made hyperthermic by exposure to heat (21). Icv administration of ACTH (1–24) reduces endotoxin-induced fever in squirrel monkeys (38), and MSH is likewise antipyretic when given intravenously to these primates (39). Corticotropin releasing factor (CRF), which releases ACTH/MSH from the pituitary, also lowers fever in a dose-related fashion when given intracerebroventricularly to rabbits (4). A decrease in CRF within the paraventricular region during fever has also been reported (21). Research on fragments indicates that ACTH/MSH (1–10), (4–9), (4–10), and (18–34, CLIP) are not antipyretic in the rabbit, whereas MSH (11–13, Lys-Pro-Val) given by icv or iv injection does inhibit fever (54; J. M. Lipton unpublished). A stable analog of MSH, [Nle^4, D-Phe^7]-MSH, is ten times more potent in reducing fever, making it the most potent antipyretic substance yet described (22).

The precise mechanism of action of MSH in reducing fever has not been determined. However, it is unlikely that antipyretic doses directly inhibit central heat production and conservation pathways, since MSH has no effect on the temperature of afebrile rabbits exposed to cold (53). The doses required to induce the antipyretic and hypothermic effects of the peptide differ. These effects appear to represent distinct actions within the CNS. Research on hyperthermic responses to arachidonate suggests that MSH and acetaminophen either differ in their central mechanisms of antipyresis, or that inhibition of arachidonic acid metabolism by acetaminophen is not essential to its antipyretic effect (8). In the latter case, central release of MSH could mediate the antipyretic effect of acetaminophen.

In guinea pigs, ACTH (1–24)- and MSH-induced hypothermia was enhanced in a cold environment (29). Lower, nonhypothermic doses reduced febrile responses to endotoxin. Hypothermic responses to MSH given peripherally to rats varied little with age but were enhanced in the dark phase of the daily cycle (65). ACTH given by icv injection or injected into the PO/AH of rats did not affect their temperature (61).

OTHER PEPTIDES

TRH

The thermal effects of TRH, which appears to act primarily on thermoeffector pathways, have been studied more than those of other endogenous peptides (see 9), in part due to the early discovery that it has CNS activity, including effects on temperature that are independent of its actions on the thyroid. Its possible clinical use for treatment of affective disorders, its ability to reduce hypothermic effects of a wide variety of agents, and perhaps the fact that its tendency to cause hyperthermia is consistent with, although apparently unrelated to, its role in thyroid function have added to the interest of temperature researchers.

The hyperthermic effect of injection of TRH into the PO/AH of rats was unaffected by pretreatment with aspirin, but was reduced by adrenergic antagonists (7). However, based on resistance to inhibition by adrenergic antagonists, others concluded that the noradrenergic system is not essential for this response in mice given TRH by intraperitoneal (ip) injection (49). In another study, TRH given intraperitoneally to mice caused hyperthermia that was associated with increased plasma norepinephrine and epinephrine (5). Simultaneous injection of these catecholamines was algebraically additive in inducing hyperthermia. Adrenal demedullation suppressed both the increase in plasma catecholamines and TRH-induced hyperthermia, but not the hyperthermic response to TRH plus catecholamine. Hypophysectomy also reduced TRH hyperthermia, in contrast to earlier reports, but not the increase of plasma catecholamines or the effect of combinations with exogenous catecholamines. These authors concluded that both the adrenal and pituitary have essential roles in TRH-induced hyperthermia. When injected into the hypothalamus of pigeons, TRH induced hyperthermia, shivering, and vasodilation that was probably compensatory (33).

Neurotensin

The primary temperature response to central administration of neurotensin (NT) in a variety of species is hypothermia, which is enhanced in cold environments. Injections of NT into 223 brain sites in rats (24) indicated that regions responsive to its hypothermic action are distinct from sites at which it inhibits nociception. Injections of NT into the periaqueductal gray, reported by others (64) to be sensitive to its hypothermic activity, had no clear effect on temperature (24). N-terminal fragments of NT were inactive, but a C-terminal fragment (8–13) did lower temperature (64).

Research on the mechanism of action of NT has been characterized by studies of its interactions with other substances. For example, NT increased the hypothermic response of rats to dopamine agonists (23). In contrast, icv pretreatment with amine or cholinergic antagonists did not reduce NT-induced hypothermia, whereas the calcium chelator EGTA did (34). Since chelators given centrally alone cause hyperthermia, a nonspecific antagonism between NT and EGTA may have been responsible. Similarly, in a 26°C environment intracisternal injection of prostaglandin E_2 in mice caused hyperthermia and prevented the hypothermic effect of NT, but prostaglandin synthesis inhibitors had no effect on the response to NT (40). In a cold environment, however, indomethacin did potentiate hypothermia after NT, which suggests that release of central prostaglandins may oppose the hypothermia.

NT caused hypothermia in rats in thermoneutral and cold environments but not in 34–40°C environments (35). Although the authors concluded that NT renders the animals poikilothermic and is unlikely to mediate normal thermoregulation, their data do not indicate poor regulation against heat because the mean temperature of NT-treated rats was always below that of controls. After failure to observe significant hypothermia in macaques after icv injection, it was concluded likewise that NT has no thermoregulatory role in this primate (41).

Opioid peptides

Although narcotic analgesics and opioid peptides clearly can greatly affect temperature (9, 10), no major role of endogenous opioid peptides in thermoregulation has yet been established. When β-endorphin is injected centrally with varied species, ambient temperature, and dose, it induces patterns of temperature change that closely resemble those associated with central or peripheral administration of morphine. Relatively low doses of morphine and β-endorphin raise the level about which temperature is regulated in the cat, rat, mouse, rabbit (51), primate (43), and fish (30). There is evidence from rabbits that this change in regulation may be due to impaired input from peripheral warmth sensors (52). Such an effect would be of greater significance the warmer the environment, and could account for the greater increase in body temperature at usual laboratory temperature than in the cold after injection of a given dose of β-endorphin to cats, rabbits, etc. In contrast to the above species, which have been used most often for the study of opioid-induced temperature changes, β-endorphin lowers the temperature of chickens and hamsters.

In those species in which small doses of β-endorphin induce hyperthermia, naloxone and similar antagonists ought to lower temperature if β-endorphin contributes to maintenance or elevation of body temperature. Naloxone, or naltrexone, prevented a rise in the temperature of rats secondary to restraint or handling, or lowered temperature when stress was minimized by habituation of the animals to the experimental procedures (9, 47). Aside from such reports, there is no convincing evidence that reasonable doses of opioid antagonists appreciably affect temperature, so it is unlikely that β-endorphin, which has been readily antagonized in most studies (9), plays a major role in normal thermoregulation, even in hot or cold environments (9, 11). Likewise, naloxone has not altered responses to pyrogen in the cat, rat (9), guinea pig (25), or sheep (16, 36), so a role of β-endorphin in fever is also unlikely. Neither are endogenous pyrogens or products of the arachidonic acid cascade likely to contribute to opioid-induced increases in temperature since antipyretics have not antagonized the hyperthermic action of opioid peptides in the cat, mouse (see 9), guinea pig (25), or rabbit (28, 51).

Even less is known of the potential thermoregulatory actions of the enkephalins. To obtain temperature changes, generally larger doses of the enkephalins have been necessary compared to β-endorphin, and central injections of 0.1– 1.0 mg have been common. The usual response at room temperature has been hyperthermia (9, 10), although there have been exceptions (55). In a study over a temperature range of 10–33°C in the desert rat (57), the temperature increase induced by Met-enkephalin varied inversely with ambient temperature. A major difference between Met-enkephalin and β-endorphin is that the hyperthermic response to the former is less readily antagonized by naloxone (9). Hence the lack of appreciable effect of naloxone on temperature does not rule out mediation of thermoregulation by enkephalins. Assessment of this possibility has been hampered by the lack of a selective enkephalin antagonist. A number of relatively stable and more potent enkephalin analogs have been tested (see 9, 26, 48, 57, 60 for examples). Unfortunately, these have generally been more readily antagonized by naloxone, and act more like β-endorphin than like the parent enkephalins because the structural modifications that increase stability tend to shift sensitivity away from naloxone-insensitive types of receptor.

Bombesin

Although enhancement of heat-escape behavior in an earlier study suggested that this peptide lowers the level of temperature regulation, it was found subsequently that injections of bombesin into the PO/AH of rats increased locomotor activity and enhanced both heat-reinforcement and heat-escape behavior (20). It was concluded that the effects on behavior are secondary to the change in activity, and do not demonstrate that bombesin lowers the regulated

618   LIPTON & CLARK

temperature. Other reports indicate that bombesin-induced hypothermia does not require the pituitary in the rat (50), whereas pinealectomy reduces the hypothermic effect, determined via thermal preference, in goldfish (31). Bombesin given by icv injection in a thermoneutral environment to food-deprived rats caused dose-related decreases in temperature and food intake (1). Hypothermia did not occur in satiated rats.

Cholecystokinin

Icv injections of cholecystokinin octapeptide (26–33) (CCK) lower the temperature of rats (9), increase the temperature of guinea pigs (27), and have little effect on core temperature in the chick (15). CCK as well as related caerulein analogs given subcutaneously (s.c.) caused dose-related hypothermias in mice (66); CCK was more potent in reducing temperature than chlorpromazine, haloperidol or morphine. In the pig iv CCK briefly inhibited heat reinforcement in the cold, but similar reductions in responding for food, water, and sucrose indicated that the effect of CCK was not specific for thermoregulation (2).

DOPAMINE

Evidence continues to mount for a role for dopamine (DA) in central control of temperature. The response of most species to administration of dopamine or related agonists is hypothermia (see 10), presumably due to stimulation of dopamine receptors in the PO/AH region, although apomorphine injections into the substantia nigra also lower temperature (6). In contrast, DA and apomorphine cause hyperthermia in the rabbit (10). Snow & Horita (59) reported that foot-shock had no appreciable thermal effect unless the animals were pretreated with apomorphine, and they concluded that apomorphine elicits hyperthermia by increasing sensitivity to stress and by decreasing the threshold for the response. From experiments in which DA agonists and antagonists were injected into the PO/AH of anesthetized rats, it was concluded (12) that stimulation of the D1 subtype of receptors, which is linked to adenylate cyclase, does not induce hypothermia. The temperature response to PO/AH injection of DA was found to be reversed in rats reared in a warm environment or acclimated to heat (17). This suggests that the thermal experience of an organism can alter temperature controls specifically within the PO/AH, although the authors cautioned that variation in injection sites or changes in peripheral thermoeffector mechanisms could also explain their data.

ARACHIDONIC ACID DERIVATIVES

Icv administration of inhibitors of phospholipase A_2, which releases arachidonic acid, inhibited the febrile response of rabbits to endogenous pyrogen (14). The essential arachidonate derivative remains unclear, with perhaps the greatest support for a derivative other than prostaglandin E_2 as a mediator. Leukotrienes C_4, D_4, and E_4, generated via lipoxygenases, have recently been shown not to increase temperature after icv injection in rats (46). Prostaglandin D_2 is also an unlikely mediator of fever since it causes hypothermia rather than hyperthermia in rats (18, 62). This autocoid may nevertheless have a role in central temperature control since its concentration within the PO/AH region increased significantly during endotoxin-induced hypothermia (62). Both the hypothermic response to endotoxin and the increase in prostaglandin D_2 concentration were prevented by pretreatment with indomethacin. In anesthetized rats, icv or iv injection of prostaglandin D_2 induced hyperthermia and was antagonized by pretreatment with antipyretics (58).

Concluding Remarks

This review of recent selected research underscores a shift in interest in the study of neurochemical control of body temperature. Inquiry into thermoregulatory functions of CNS amines and prostaglandins has decreased, perhaps as a result of controversy about their roles, and the low probability that any single new paper will dramatically resolve these issues. A new focus is upon the contributions of neuropeptides, many of which are found within neuroanatomical sites important to temperature control. Although there are presently few useful pharmacologic antagonists, the problem of determining the physiological relevance of a peptide to temperature control may be addressed by inactivation of the endogenous peptide by local treatment with specific antiserum.

As discussed in a previous review (9), there is evidence that certain peptides, such as bombesin which disrupts thermoregulation, have no physiological significance in temperature control. For most of the peptides the data is not yet adequate to rule them in or out as CNS mediators in thermoregulation. As noted above, the support is strongest for an antipyretic role for certain peptides, particularly ACTH/MSH.

To advance understanding of the contributions of central peptides in thermoregulation, several methodological points should be considered in future studies. (1) To define the effect of an injected peptide, it should be tested in animals exposed to hot and cold environments, as well as to a thermoneutral temperature. This allows assessment of the functional nature of the effect of the peptide (change in level of regulation or thermoeffector activity, etc). (2) Research on monamines has revealed definite species differences in temperature response to their central administration, and such differences may well become more evident in peptide studies. Such observations may reflect either real differences in the utilization of specific neurotransmitters in temperature control or artifactual differences due to physical factors, such as variation in spread of transmitter to active sites after intracerebral injection. (3) Because many systems of the brain are involved in thermoregulation, multiple contributions of a given neuropeptide to thermoregulatory control may lead to conflicting results when the peptide is injected into different brain regions. (4) Restraint has been shown to reverse the effects of opiates on thermoregulation, and various stresses are likely to affect responses to peptides as well, especially since several endogenous peptides are already known to be affected by stress. Stress may be reduced by avoiding restraint, by measures to habitutate the animals to the experimental situation, etc. In all studies, of course, appropriate use of control groups is essential to minimize misinterpretation since stress can never be totally eliminated from experiments with conscious subjects. (5) It is important to recall that the thermoregulatory apparatus utilizes other major systems of the body (respiratory, cardiovascular, etc). Thus a CNS peptide that acts primarily to affect, for instance, the distribution of peripheral blood flow could secondarily alter body temperature, and be thought erroneously to act directly on thermoregulatory controls. Direct actions on thermoeffector pathways can generally be discovered in experiments carried out in disparate thermal environments. These considerations underline one obvious conclusion: Only through triangulation of information from experiments using different methods can the importance of a neuropeptide to thermoregulation be established. Techniques that are relatively new in this field, such as assay of peptides in brain samples taken from febrile, hypothermic, and hyperthermic animals and immunoneutralization coupled with pyrogen administration or direct thermal challenge, can provide powerful evidence about the role of specific peptides in physiological control of temperature. There are technical difficulties and other problems with these approaches, but there is little doubt about the advantages they provide. Although important as a first step and in forming the basis of much of our present knowledge, simple measurement of the core temperature response to central injection of a peptide in a thermoneutral environment provides only limited information when considered alone.

ACKNOWLEDGMENT

Supported by National Institute of Neurological and Communicative Disorders and Stroke Grant NS 10046. The assistance of Denise Urbanski in preparing the manuscript is gratefully appreciated.

Literature Cited

1. Avery, D. D., Calisher, S. B. 1982. The effects of injections of bombesin into the cerebral ventricles on food intake and body temperature in food-deprived rats. *Neuropharmacology* 21:1059–63
2. Baldwin, B. A., Cooper, T. R., Parrott, R. F. 1983. Intravenous cholecystokinin octapeptide in pigs reduces operant responding for food, water, sucrose solution or radiant heat. *Physiol. Behav.* 30:399–403
3. Bernardini, G. L., Lipton, J. M., Clark, W. G. 1983. Intracerebroventricular and septal injections of arginine vasopressin are not antipyretic in the rabbit. *Peptides* 4:195–98
4. Bernardini, G. L., Richards, D. B., Lipton, J. M. 1984. Antipyretic effect of centrally administered CRF. *Peptides* 5:57–59
5. Boschi, G., Nomoto, T., Rips, R. 1983. Thyrotropin releasing hormone-induced

hyperthermia in mice: possible involvement of adrenal and pituitary glands. *Br. J. Pharmacol.* 80:229–33

6. Brown, S. J., Gisolfi, C. V., Mora, F. 1982. Temperature regulation and dopaminergic systems in the brain: does the substantia nigra play a role? *Brain Res.* 234:275–86

7. Chi, M. L., Lin, M. T. 1983. Involvement of adrenergic receptor mechanisms within hypothalamus in the fever induced by amphetamine and thyrotropin-releasing hormone in the rat. *J. Neural Transm.* 58:213–22

8. Clark, W. G., Holdeman, M., Lipton, J. M. 1985. Analysis of the antipyretic action of α-melanocyte-stimulating hormone in rabbits. *J. Physiol.* 359:459–65

9. Clark, W. G., Lipton, J. M. 1983. Brain and pituitary peptides in thermoregulation. *Pharmacol. Ther.* 22:249–97

10. Clark, W. G., Lipton, J. M. 1985. Changes in body temperature after administration of amino acids, peptides, dopamine, neuroleptics and related agents—II. *Neurosci. Biobehav. Rev.* 9:299–371

11. Clark, W. G., Pang, I.-H., Bernardini, G. L. 1983. Evidence against involvement of β-endorphin in thermoregulation in the cat. *Pharmacol. Biochem. Behav.* 18:741–45

12. Colboc, O., Protais, P., Costentin, J. 1983. Pharmacological evidence against the involvement of the D1 subtype of dopamine receptors in apomorphine-induced hypothermia. *Neurosci. Lett.* 39:211–16

13. Cooper, K. E., Kasting, N. W., Lederis, K., Veale, W. L. 1979. Evidence supporting a role for endogenous vasopressin in natural suppression of fever in the sheep. *J. Physiol.* 295:33–45

14. Cranston, W. I., Hellon, R. F., Mitchell, D., Townsend, Y. 1983. Intraventricular injections of drugs which inhibit phospholipase A_2 suppress fever in rabbits. *J. Physiol.* 339:97–105

15. Denbow, D. M., Myers, R. D. 1982. Eating, drinking and temperature responses to intracerebroventricular cholecystokinin in the chick. *Peptides* 3:739–43

16. Duranton, A., Buéno, L. 1984. Central opiate mechanism involved in gastrointestinal motor disturbances induced by E. coli endotoxin in sheep. *Life Sci.* 34:1795–99

17. Ferguson, A. V., Veale, W. L., Cooper, K. E. 1984. Changes in the hypothalamic mechanisms involved in the control of body temperature induced by the early

thermal environment. *Brain Res.* 290: 297–306

18. Förstermann, U., Heldt, R., Hertting, G. 1983. Effects of intracerebroventricular administration of prostaglandin D_2 on behaviour, blood pressure and body temperature as compared to prostaglandins E_2 and $F_{2\alpha}$. *Psychopharmacology* 80: 365–70

19. Glyn-Ballinger, J. R., Bernardini, G. L., Lipton, J. M. 1983. α-MSH injected into the septal region reduces fever in rabbits. *Peptides* 4:199–203

20. Hawkins, M. F., Avery, D. D. 1983. Effects of centrally-administered bombesin and adrenalectomy on behavioral thermoregulation and locomotor activity. *Neuropharmacology* 22:1249–55

21. Holdeman, M., Khorram, O., Samson, W. K., Lipton, J. M. 1985. Fever-specific changes in central MSH and CRF concentrations. *Am. J. Physiol.* 248: R125–29

22. Holdeman, M., Lipton, J. M. 1985. Antipyretic activity of a potent α-MSH analog. *Peptides* 6:273–75

23. Jolicoeur, F. B., De Michele, G., Barbeau, A., St-Pierre, S. 1983. Neurotensin affects hyperactivity but not stereotypy induced by pre and post synaptic dopaminergic stimulation. *Neurosci. Biobehav. Rev.* 7:385–90

24. Kalivas, P. W., Jennes, L., Nemeroff, C. B., Prange, A. J. Jr. 1982. Neurotensin: topographical distribution of brain sites involved in hypothermia and antinociception. *J. Comp. Neurol.* 210:225–38

25. Kandasamy, S. B., Williams, B. A. 1983. Hyperthermic responses to central injections of some peptide and non-peptide opioids in the guinea-pig. *Neuropharmacology* 22:621–28

26. Kandasamy, S. B., Williams, B. A. 1983. Hyperthermic effects of centrally injected (D-Ala^2, N-Met-Phe^4, Met-(O)^5-ol)-enkephalin (FK 33-824) in rabbits and guinea-pigs. *Neuropharmacology* 22:1177–81

27. Kandasamy, S. B., Williams, B. A. 1983. Cholecystokinin-octapeptide-induced hyperthermia in guinea-pigs. *Experientia* 39:1282–84

28. Kandasamy, S. B., Williams, B. A. 1983. Peptide and non-peptide opioid-induced hyperthermia in rabbits. *Brain Res.* 265:63–71

29. Kandasamy, S. B., Williams, B. A. 1984. Hypothermic and antipyretic effects of ACTH (1–24) and α-melanotropin in guinea-pigs. *Neuropharmacology* 23:49–53

30. Kavaliers, M. 1982. Pineal mediation of

the thermoregulatory and behavioral activating effects of β-endorphin. *Peptides* 3:679–85

31. Kavaliers, M. 1982. Pinealectomy modifies the thermoregulatory effects of bombesin in goldfish. *Neuropharmacology* 21:1169–73

32. Kovács, G. L., De Wied, D. 1983. Hormonally active arginine-vasopressin suppresses endotoxin-induced fever in rats: lack of effect of oxytocin and a behaviorally active vasopressin fragment. *Neuroendocrinology* 37:258–61

33. Lahti, H., Koskinen, M., Pyörnilä, A., Hissa, R. 1983. Hyperthermia after intrahypothalamic injections of thyrotropin releasing hormone (TRH) in the pigeon. *Experientia* 39:1338–40

34. Lee, T. F., Hepler, J. R., Myers, R. D. 1983. Evaluation of neurotensin's thermolytic action by ICV infusion with receptor antagonists and a Ca^{++} chelator. *Pharmacol. Biochem. Behav.* 19:477–81

35. Lee, T. F., Myers, R. D. 1983. Analysis of the thermolytic action of ICV neurotensin in the rat at different ambient temperatures. *Brain Res. Bull.* 10:661–65

36. Leshin, L. S., Malven, P. V. 1984. Bacteremia-induced changes in pituitary hormone release and effect of naloxone. *Am. J. Physiol.* 247:E585–91

37. Lin, M. T., Wang, T. I., Chan, H. K. 1983. A prostaglandin-adrenergic link occurs in the hypothalamic pathways which mediate the fever induced by vasopressin in the rat. *J. Neural Transm.* 56:21–31

38. Lipton, J. M., Glyn-Ballinger, J. R., Murphy, M. T., Zimmer, J. A., Bernardini, G., Samson, W. K. 1984. The central neuropeptides ACTH and α-MSH in fever control. *J. Therm. Biol.* 9:139–43

39. Lipton, J. M., Shih, S. 1985. Intravenous α-MSH reduces fever in squirrel monkeys. *Fed. Proc.* 44:1196

40. Mason, G. A., Hernandez, D. E., Nemeroff, C. B., Adcock, J. W., Hatley, O. L., Prange, A. J. Jr. 1982. Interaction of neurotensin with prostaglandin E$_2$ and prostaglandin synthesis inhibitors: effects on colonic temperature in mice. *Regulatory Peptides* 4:285–92

41. Mora, F., Lee, T. F., Myers, R. D. 1984. Is neurotensin in the brain involved in thermoregulation of the monkey? *Peptides* 5:125–28

42. Murphy, M. T., Lipton, J. M. 1982. Peripheral administration of α-MSH reduces fever in older and younger rabbits. *Peptides* 3:775–79

43. Murphy, M. T., Lipton, J. M. 1983. β-endorphin: effect on thermoregulation in aged monkeys. *Neurobiol. Aging* 4:187–90

44. Murphy, M. T., Richards, D. B., Lipton, J. M. 1983. Antipyretic potency of centrally administered α-melanocyte stimulating hormone. *Science* 221:192–93

45. Okuno, A., Yamamoto, M., Itoh, S. 1965. Lowering of the body temperature induced by vasopressin. *Jpn. J. Physiol.* 15:378–87

46. O'Rourke, S. T., Rudy, T. A. 1984. Intracerebroventricular and preoptic injections of leukotrienes C$_4$, D$_4$, and E$_4$ in the rat: lack of febrile effect. *Brain Res.* 295:283–88

47. Pae, Y.-S., Lai, H., Horita, A. 1985. Hyperthermia in the rat from handling stress blocked by naltrexone injected into the preoptic-anterior hypothalamus. *Pharmacol. Biochem. Behav.* 22:337–39

48. Pang, I.-H., Bernardini, G. L., Clark, W. G. 1984. Hyperthermic response of the cat to intraventricular injection of the opioid delta-receptor agonist D-Ala^2-D-Leu^5-enkephalin. *Brain Res. Bull.* 13:263–68

49. Pawłowski, L., Kwiatek, H. 1983. The effect of highly selective inhibitors of the uptake of noradrenaline or 5-hydroxytryptamine on TRH-induced hyperthermia in mice. *Psychopharmacology* 81:48–53

50. Rasler, F. E. 1983. Bombesin produces hypothermia in hypophysectomized rats. *Life Sci.* 32:2503–7

51. Rezvani, A. H., Gordon, C. J., Heath, J. E. 1982. Action of preoptic injections of β-endorphin on temperature regulation in rabbits. *Am. J. Physiol.* 243:R104–11

52. Rezvani, A. H., Heath, J. E. 1984. Reduced thermal sensitivity in the rabbit by β-endorphin injection into the preoptic/anterior hypothalamus. *Brain Res.* 292:297–302

53. Richards, D. B., Lipton, J. M. 1984. Antipyretic doses of α-MSH do not alter afebrile body temperature in the cold. *J. Therm. Biol.* 9:299–301

54. Richards, D. B., Lipton, J. M. 1984. Effect of α-MSH 11–13 (lysine-proline-valine) on fever in the rabbit. *Peptides* 5:815–17

55. Sakurada, T., Sakurada, S., Watanabe, S., Matsumura, H., Kisara, K., et al. 1983. Actions of intracerebroventricular administration of kyotorphin and an analog on thermoregulation in the mouse. *Peptides* 4:859–63

56. Samson, W. K., Lipton, J. M., Zimmer, J. A., Glyn, J. R. 1981. The effect of

fever on central α-MSH concentrations in the rabbit. *Peptides* 2:419–23

57. Shukla, R., Srimal, R. C., Dhawan, B. N. 1982. Centrally mediated effects of met-enkephalin and morphine on the body temperature of *Mastomys natalensis*. *Adv. Biosci.* 38:85–91

58. Sirén, A.-L. 1982. Central cardiovascular and thermal effects of prostaglandin D₂ in rats. *Prostaglandins Leukotrienes Med.* 8:349–59

59. Snow, A. E., Horita, A. 1982. Interaction of apomorphine and stressors in the production of hyperthermia in the rabbit. *J. Pharmacol. Exp. Ther.* 220:335–39

60. Szikszay, M., Benedek, G., Székely, J.-I. 1983. Thermoregulatory effects of D-met²-pro⁵-enkephalinamide. *Neuropeptides* 3:465–75

61. Thornhill, J. A., Wilfong, A. 1982. Lateral cerebral ventricle and preoptic-anterior hypothalamic area infusion and perfusion of β-endorphin and ACTH to unrestrained rats: core and surface temperature responses. *Can. J. Physiol. Pharmacol.* 60:1267–74

62. Ueno, R., Narumiya, S., Ogorochi, T., Nakayama, T., Ishikawa, Y., Hayaishi, O. 1982. Role of prostaglandin D₂ in the hypothermia of rats caused by bacterial lipopolysaccharide. *Proc. Natl. Acad. Sci. USA.* 79:6093–97

63. Veale, W. L., Cooper, K. E., Ruwe, W. D. 1984. Vasopressin: its role in antipyresis and febrile convulsion. *Brain Res. Bull.* 12:161–65

64. Widdowson, P. S., Griffiths, E. C., Slater, P., Yajima, H. 1983. Effects of mammalian and avian neurotensins and neurotensin fragments on wet-dog shaking and body temperature in the rat. *Regulatory Peptides* 7:357–65

65. Yehuda, S., Carasso, R. L. 1983. Changes in circadian rhythms of thermoregulation and motor activity in rats as a function of aging: effects of d-amphetamine and α-MSH. *Peptides* 4:865–69

66. Zetler, G. 1982. Cholecystokinin octapeptide, caerulein and caerulein analogues: effects on thermoregulation in the mouse. *Neuropharmacology* 21:795–801

Ann. Rev. Physiol. 1986. 48:625–38
Copyright © 1986 by Annual Reviews, Inc. All rights reserved

CUTANEOUS TEMPERATURE RECEPTORS

David C. Spray

Department of Neuroscience, Albert Einstein College of Medicine, Bronx, New York
10461

INTRODUCTION

Thermal stimulation of skin sensory surfaces elicits temperature sensations in
humans (cf 129), participates in the autonomic processes achieving endothermy
in mammals and birds, and is used by submammalian species that thermoregulate behaviorally (cf 125). First in the neural pathway responsible for detection
of localized skin temperature come the elements that transduce information on
steady-state and transient temperature. These receptors, defined by their excitation in response to cold or warm stimuli, pose several problems at the outset:
One is the nature of the stimulus, which for cold receptors is apparently the
withdrawal of energy from the end organ and for both warm and cold receptors
involves exchange of energy with surrounding tissues (cf. 7, 65, 68); another,
which has especially plagued the issue of transduction mechanism, is the
absence of very simple systems with response properties suitably similar to
those of thermoreceptors (cf 124). Thus we have based our hypotheses upon
extrapolation from temperature-dependent phenomena observed in structures
specialized for other purposes, such an elasmobranch electroreceptors, snail
neurons, and giant cephalopod axons.

The field of thermoreceptors has been reviewed repeatedly (cf 53, 56, 140).
Here I summarize studies characterizing the physiological and anatomical
properties of vertebrate temperature receptors; I present evidence relevant to the
mechanism by which thermal stimuli are transduced. In addition, I outline the
neural pathways involved in thermal sensation, mentioning possible loci of
descending control.

625

0066-4278/86/0315-0625$02.00

CHARACTERISTICS OF CUTANEOUS TEMPERATURE RECEPTORS

Studies on the neural basis of sensory perception awaited the development, in the late 1920s, of amplifiers with suitable gain and temporal response to resolve microvolt signals as brief as a millisecond. These studies, pioneered by Adrian and Zotterman, quickly revealed that impulses and impulse volleys with characteristic amplitudes and conduction velocities were evoked in peripheral nerves by heating or cooling the skin (cf 2, 3, 138).

Afferent nerve fibers satisfying the criteria of sensitivity and selectivity to cold (cf 52, 70) have been found in humans and other primates, and also in cat, dog, rat, hamster, and frog (Figure 1). At steady-state temperatures over at least the range from 20–30°C, a characteristic rate of activity is recorded in cold afferent fibers (68). During recordings lasting even as long as several hours, impulse activity is maintained at its characteristic rate, although slow frequency fluctuations have been reported in certain cases (cf 56). Cold receptors generally display unimodal curves relating impulse frequency to maintained skin temperature (Figure 1A). The range of temperatures to which fibers respond varies somewhat from one species or sensory surface to another, and individual fibers also show variability in peak response and range so that the integrated response of all thermoreceptor afferents spans a somewhat wider range (cf 9, 36). In many of the preparations studied, the impulses recorded at sustained skin temperatures show random temporal relations. For others, impulses occur as couplets or groups ("bursts"). This pattern generally appears as temperature is reduced below the temperature at which the peak static activity occurs (37, 69, 73, 105). The number of impulses within each burst increases as temperature is decreased, and this relation is linear for the preparations in which it has been quantified (cf 5, 34, 37, 74). The bell-shaped curve of temperature-receptor static response allows apparent redundancy in the neural code for individual temperatures. It has thus been argued that bursting, which only occurs at low temperatures, can resolve the ambiguity about where on the thermoreceptor response curve skin temperature actually lies (cf 39, 74). Alternatively, mean frequency and a burst parameter may be separately processed by the CNS (cf 10, 68, 115).

Peripheral nerves often contain afferents that respond to heating but not to cooling (Figure 1). Such receptors can be unresponsive to nonthermal stimuli, and thus satisfy the criteria for selective warm receptors. Warm-receptor discharge is initiated at constant temperatures above about 30°C. Activity increases as temperature rises, reaching maximum discharge at 41–47°C, and then decreases, often abruptly, as the skin is warmed further (Figure 1). The steady temperature at which impulse frequency is maximal may be a few degrees lower in some tissues or species than in others (Figure 1A), but the degree of variability from one study to another may be as large.

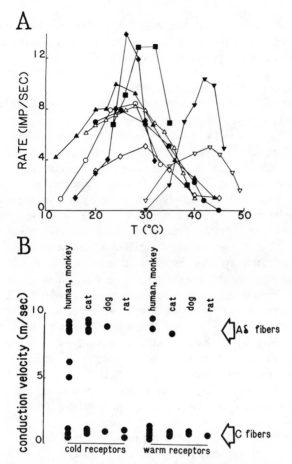

Figure 1 Response curves and conduction velocities for representative temperature receptors. A. Steady state activity for temperature receptors in a variety of representative preparations. Cold receptors (curves to the left) show peak responses at about 25–27°C. Data are on rat scrotum (72, open circles), cat nasal receptors (67, open triangles), monkey hand (24, filled circles), frog skin (121, filled diamonds), monkey hairy skin (182, open diamonds), dog lip (73, filled squares), and monkey hand (37, filled triangles). Warm receptors (two curves to the right) show peaks at or below 45°C; data are from monkey hairy skin (35, downward oriented triangles) and rat scrotum (47, filled downward oriented triangles). B. Distribution of conduction velocities reported for afferent fibers from mammalian cold (20, 24, 33, 34, 39, 46, 58, 60, 61, 67, 73, 75, 89, 90) and warm receptors (1, 26, 31, 35–37, 46, 51, 52, 59–62, 73, 75, 87–89, 130, 131, 139) indicate that both receptor populations include both A delta and C fibers (corresponding to arrows at right).

A comparison of the static response curves obtained for a number of warm and cold receptors shows that the static maxima are similar. [The warm receptors in the nasal area of cats comprise an exception, for which static activities are scaled up by a factor of about 4 or 5 (62).] The temperature range covered by the response of warm receptors is somewhat narrower than that for cold receptors, and responses overlap near 37°C. Not included in Figure 1 is an additional region of cold-receptor responsiveness starting above about 45°C. Because there is often a perception of cold in humans at such high temperatures [the paradoxical cold sensation (12, 29, 32)], this cold receptor discharge is believed to be its electrophysiological correlate.

Temperature receptors respond to thermal stimuli with a rapid change in impulse frequency (48, 49). A large increase in activity occurs in cold receptors when the skin is cooled, and activity is inhibited upon warming (Figure 1). Static and dynamic sensitivities can be compared by examining the response to small temperature steps over a range of steady temperatures; in cat nose and monkey skin, the ratio of dynamic to static responses is as high as -50 impulses/sec° (56). These dynamic responses are transient, the discharge rate thereafter relaxing to a level of activity appropriate for the steady temperature level. [With very rapid rates of cooling a phase of reduced activity may follow the initial peak discharge, the significance of which is unclear (24, 36, 107).] The kinetics of this dynamic response are apparently simple: In cat tongue, responses to temperature changes over a range of amplitudes and rates are well fit by single exponentials with time constants on the order of 2.2 sec (50); in monkey, (84) multiple time constants have been observed, the fastest of which was 15–30 sec (82). In the later experiments the fastest time constant was most rapid at the lowest adapting temperature but was not systematically affected by the temperature at which the skin was held over the range 25–35°C. The time constant for recovery from a prior cold stimulus is about 15 sec (24). Quantification of the temperature dependence of these rates, especially at lower temperatures, should provide additional information about the underlying mechanism.

The amplitude of the response to thermal transients is determined by the rate and magnitude of the temperature change. In cold receptors from frog, the maximum dynamic response is an approximately linear function of the magnitude of the temperature step and increases exponentially with rate of temperature change (121). In monkey skin and cat nose, the magnitude of the transient response is a linear function of stimulus intensity over a wide range of adapting temperatures (24, 31, 50); in cat, dynamic response was a curvilinear function of each stimulus parameter (82). In monkeys, the response becomes linear if the discharge rate is integrated over several seconds (24, 82). For most of the preparations studied so far, the temperature of greatest dynamic sensitivity corresponds to that of peak static sensitivity, and the amplitude of the enhanced activity parallels the shape of the static curve (24, 69, 73, 82). A striking exception is in the nose of the hibernating hamster, where the maximal dynamic response occurs at about 25°C and the static peak is at about 11°C (109).

Warm-receptor dynamic responses are also graded with the magnitude of the thermal stimulus (cf 35). Time constants of the decay are on the order of 5–12 sec (25, 26). The mean peak frequencies are curvilinearly related to the magnitude of the warm stimulus, becoming more sensitive to large stimuli as their temperature is increased to 40°C; beyond 45–50°C the response is depressed. Others (88, 131) have reported linear stimulus response relations for small temperature changes at adapting temperatures only to 35°C [above a 4°C warming pulse the response became nonlinear (131)]. In monkey skin and face, the relation becomes more linear if frequency is integrated over several seconds (26, 131).

For moderate rates of warming, initial frequency is an approximately linear function of rate of temperature change in human skin (88) and in monkey skin and face (8, 26). The decay time constant for the dynamic response is generally 5–12 sec for warm receptors (25, 35) and is apparently not very temperature dependent.

The psychophysical correlate of the dynamic response of temperature receptors is a heightened perception of changes in skin temperature (cf 86). Thermal sensation is a graded function of both magnitude and rate of thermal stimulation (79, 80, 84, 97, 98).

SPECIFICITY OF TEMPERATURE RECEPTORS

Another class of cutaneous receptors respond both to stable and transient temperatures and to light or moderate mechanical stimuli (70); they thus do not fulfill the thermoreceptor criterion of response specificity. Although rapidly adapting mechanoreceptors such as the Pacinian corpuscle (76) and hair follicle receptors (14) are only weakly excited by cooling, slowly adapting mechanoreceptors from a variety of preparations exhibit static and dynamic sensitivities comparable to those of specific receptors (e.g. 16, 18, 19, 92, 118, 132). In several such cases, bursting in response to cooling has also been reported (16, 105). Multimodal fibers, in particular the most slowly conducting C fibers, also fall within this nonspecific receptor class (33, 41).

Although psychophysical data suggest that cold objects may feel heavier than neutral ones (Weber's deception), implying that under some conditions thermal and mechanical sensations are not pure, the temperature sensitivity of slowly adapting mechanoreceptors has been regarded as irrelevant to sensation or physiological thermoregulation (cf 73). Nevertheless, evidence of spinal (42, 99), thalamic (43, 106), trigeminal (107), and cortical (44, 91) convergence of temperature and mechanoreceptor activity has prompted the assignment of some thermoregulatory importance to these receptors, especially at high stimulus strengths (16, 107). Thus the dynamic sensitivity of nonselective units might signal an increased change in temperature beyond the range of sensitivity of selective ones (107).

ANATOMICAL CORRELATES

A decade ago, attempts to associate the sensations of warmth and cold with specific cutaneous end organs were focussed by von Frey's (38) identification of Krause end bulbs and Ruffini endings in the sensory surfaces from which these experiences could be evoked. Repeated reexamination of this issue has clearly shown that Krause end bulbs and Ruffini endings are both specialized for mechanical and not thermal transduction, the latter being associated with the type II mechanoreceptor (cf 19). Free nerve endings, located in the dermal and epidermal skin layers, are the apparent terminations of the fibers from which specific thermal responses are elicited (cf 135). Structural studies of free nerve endings in glabrous and hairy skin of cat nasal area (54, 57) and frog dorsal skin (125, 136) demonstrate branching of small myelinated afferents (2.5–4 μm diameter) into unmyelinated processes that penetrate the basal lamina of the epithelium. Unmyelinated processes in both species possess vesicles of a variety of sizes of unknown function (cf. 57, 125, 137). In cat, cold receptor terminations are filled with mitochondria.

The afferents to which thermoreceptor end organs are connected are commonly dichotomized into the A delta category of myelinated axons for cold receptors and C fibers for warm receptors. As is apparent in Figure 1B, this separation is not absolute; a number of studies have demonstrated smaller fractions of cold receptors among afferents with C-fiber conduction velocities and warm receptors with myelinated axons. Nevertheless, that the populations of afferents show different sensitivities to anesthesia (39) supports separateness of fiber type.

The branching observed as the free nerve endings penetrate the dermis raises the issue of whether a single receptor might innervate multiple spots on the skin. Mapping studies with small thermal stimulators have generally demonstrated punctate or oblate receptive fields for single fibers, generally about 1 mm^2 in diameter (cf 35, 37, 82) or less (34, 73), although larger (82) and multiple fields have also been reported (e.g. 24, 35, 82, 83). Single-fiber recording from monkey skin afferents demonstrates that spatial and temporal summation can arise from the branching represented by the multiple fields (83); in this case the dynamic response was enhanced by stimulating multiple spots, and bursting within the response was initiated at lower changes in temperature when multiple fields were stimulated.

DESCENDING CONTROL OF THERMORECEPTORS

The most thoroughly characterized neural pathways for thermoreceptor processing are those from cat tongue and rat scrotum. Analogous pathways presumably mediate processing of receptor information from extremities. Afferents possess somata in representative sensory ganglia. Primary thermal afferents project to the marginal zone of the spinal cord (cf 22) to synapse upon rostral brain-stem and thalamic nuclei (cf 4, 45, 91, 96) and then project to somatosensory cortex (cf 47). Integration at the first level of synaptic interaction is apparently considerable; in the dorsal horn of the spinal column the representation of scrotal thermoreceptors is large and bilateral (45), and warm and cold thermoreceptor afferents may even converge (99). The brain-stem areas involve several midbrain raphe nuclei (47, 78, 133), and thalamic areas of thermoreceptor representation include VB and NPT (cf 77, 116). Relay to the hypothalamus is apparently from midbrain raphe nuclei in parallel to the thalamic projection (47).

Although positive feedback from somatosensory cortex to thermosensory thalamic neurons has been demonstrated (47), attempts to demonstrate descending control of the raphe nucleus on spinal processing have been unsuccessful (28), and stimulation of locus coeruleus or periaqueductal grey (either of which depresses activity of the afferent pain pathway) does not affect trigeminal cold receptors in rat (27). Central modulation of peripheral thermoreceptor activity is generally ineffective but modulation in primary afferents can be demonstrated. Mechanical stimuli decrease the response of both specific and nonspecific thermoreceptors, and the depression of activity by segmental stimulation is due to direct action on the afferent (e.g. 27, 28).

Sympathetic stimulation and application of adrenergic agonists have been shown to increase the thermal response of frog cutaneous thermoreceptors (cf 121, 124). The increased response is correlated with recruitment of larger fibers into the responsive population, presumably including those from temperature-sensitive mechanoreceptors. The intensity of the paradoxical cold response of mammalian cold receptors is enhanced by reducing sympathetic activity (94). Sympathetic enhancement of mechanoreceptor response has been demonstrated in mammalian and submammalian species (21, 93, 100).

An issue related to descending control is that of the end organ's possible adaptation to ambient temperature. Cold receptors from hibernating hamsters show a lower temperature of peak static response (109) than nonhibernating animals, and cold receptors from cold-acclimated frogs exhibit shifted static thermal response and enhanced dynamic discharge (123). In the first case, it is doubtful that the response reflects acclimation [and cats acclimated at cold temperatures show little change in responsivity (55)], whereas in the second the shift is attributable to elevated levels of circulating catecholamines.

TRANSDUCTION MECHANISM

Thermal sensitivity is a common feature of such neuronal characteristics as chemical and electrotonic synapses (cf 120, 126), ionic channels (cf 81), and ionic pumps (cf 127), and the main obstacle to determining the transduction mechanism of thermoreceptors has been satisfying the requirement of selectivity (cf hypotheses based on associated structures: 85, 112). An hypothesis that combines structural features of temperature receptors with thermal sensitivity of neuronal functions is that the cold receptor may transduce by virtue of the high surface-area:volume ratio of its terminal process together with the activity of ionic pumps in its terminal membranes (122). Operation of the highly temperature-sensitive Na/K pump would maintain the resting potential of the thermoreceptor membrane, so that a drop in temperature would decrease pump activity and thus depolarize the terminal, giving rise to receptor current.

Evidence in favor of this transduction mechanism includes the high temperature coefficients of thermoreceptors: Over the range 35–25°C, the static responses of a variety of cold receptors have Q_{10}s of about 3 (Figure 1). The temperature dependences of the two dynamic phases in the cold-receptor response to cooling and warming can be evaluated separately. Frog cold receptors exhibit a temperature coefficient of about 0.3 for turn on of the process (corresponding to a tripled rate for a 10°C temperature decrease) (124), and mammalian receptors are similarly sensitive (see the section on characteristics, above). In frog, the time constant of recovery of the initial discharge rate shows a Q_{10} of about 3.2 (cf 124); this parameter may be less temperature sensitive in mammals (25).

Further support for the role of pump inhibition in thermoreceptor response comes from experiments with K. Na-K pumps are characterized by remarkable sensitivity to external K (134), as are thermoreceptors. Increasing K in the bath gradually decreases static sensitivity and increases the dynamic response of cold receptors, whereas decreasing extracellular K increases static activity (103, 124). Another indication that cold receptors are activated by inhibition of the Na/K pump comes from application of the cardiac glycoside, ouabain. To this procedure the thermoreceptors of frog skin respond somewhat differently from those of rat scrotum. For frog cold receptors, addition of ouabain to the skin elicits a short-latency discharge that soon ceases. Thereafter, thermal stimuli are less effective; stronger concentrations of the drug render the receptors insensitive to thermal stimuli (122). In rat scrotum in situ, or in a nerve-skin preparation similar to that used in amphibia, receptors were not immediately excited; they were, however, rendered insensitive to cold stimuli, and their discharge rate increased in response to warming (102, 103).

Granted that transduction of thermal stimuli involves a metabolic step, the issue remains of whether other mechanisms contribute to the response. The bell-shaped temperature-response curves of elasmobranch electroreceptors led Sand to hypothesize interaction of underlying excitatory and inhibitory processes (113), a concept extended by Hensel (63) to explain the bell-shaped responses of thermoreceptors (Figure 1A). Such an inhibitory process could be the secondary result of prolonged depolarization (such as Na inactivation) or could be independent [such as the differential temperature sensitivities of Na and K permeability (40, 86, 101)]. The burst discharge seen in many cold receptors might result ultimately from an oscillation in generator potential which, by analogy to bursting neurons of molluscs, could depend upon a Ca-dependent K conductance (5, 13) [the transduction mechanism of the skate ampullary electroreceptor (which has been used as a model for thermoreceptor activation) involves a Ca-dependent outward current, presumably carried by K ions (23)]. Extracellular Ca and the divalent cation chelator EDTA affect thermoreceptors in opposite ways. Ca injection inhibits cat lingual afferents, stimulates warm receptors (64), and shifts the temperature of peak static discharge to lower temperatures (114), whereas EDTA increases the static activity of cold receptors, primarily at higher temperatures (114). Ca inhibits bursting of cold receptors (104, 114) while EDTA increases the number of impulses per burst (104) and can convert a nonbursting to a bursting cold receptor (114).

Other pharmacological stimuli that affect temperature receptors include menthol, which increases the activity of cold receptors (71); carbon dioxide, which decreases the static discharge of lingual cold receptors and increases warm receptor discharge (12); and cholinergic agonists, which extend the range of cat lingual afferents to higher temperatures (30) and decrease the threshold for frog cold receptors (128). It is unclear whether these agents exert specific actions providing additional information on the transduction mechanism or act nonspecifically.

Adequate description of warm-receptor transduction requires elucidation of an underlying process, perhaps involving the asymmetric temperature dependences of Na and K permeabilities that may participate in the transduction of cold thermal sensations. Alternatively, the membranes of warm receptors may be so leaky that the stimulation of the electrogenic pump would reactivate the ending.

SUMMARY AND CONCLUSIONS

Specific thermoreceptors comprise an electrophysiologically distinct class of cutaneous receptors with a morphological substrate (free nerve endings) and plausible transduction mechanism (electrogenic Na pump with or without auxillary temperature-dependent processes). Because responses to thermal and mechanical stimuli converge along the neural pathway, we have difficulty explaining the purity of cold and warm sensations; participation of dual-modality receptors in sensory discrimination cannot be ruled out.

The field is now at a point where a leap in understanding would be achieved (a) by intracellular recordings from the sensory receptor (for which patch clamp studies on isolated neuronal elements may provide the necessary technology) and (b) from continued analysis of what information is lost and what retained in passage from one synapse to the next along the thermal pathway.

ACKNOWLEDGMENTS

The invitation to contribute this review has encouraged the author to reconsider work done a decade ago in light of recent developments in this field and others. Current grant support includes a McKnight Foundation Development Award.

Literature Cited

1. Adriaensen, H., Gybels, J., Handwerker, H. O., Van Hees, J. 1983. Response properties of thin myelinated (A-δ) fibers in human skin nerves. J. Neurophysiol. 49:111–22
2. Adrian, E. D. 1928. The Basis of Sensation. London: Christophers
3. Adrian, E. D. 1932. The messages in sensory nerve fibres and their interpretation. Proc. R. Soc. London Ser. B 109:1–18
4. Auen, E. L., Poulos, D. A., Hirata, H., Molt, J. T. 1980. Location and organization of thalamic thermoreceptive neurons responding to cooling the cat oral-facial regions. Brain Res. 191:260–64
5. Bade, H., Braun, H. A., Hensel, H. 1979. Parameters of the static burst discharge of lingual cold receptors in the cat. Pflügers Arch. 382:1–5
6. Deleted in proof
7. Bazett, H. C., McGlone, B., Brocklehurst, R. J. 1930. The temperatures in the tissues which accompany temperature sensations. J. Physiol. 69:88–112
8. Beitel, R. E., Dubner, R. 1976. Response of unmyelinated (C) polymodal nociceptors to thermal stimuli applied to monkey's face. J. Neurophysiol. 39:1160–75
9. Benzing, H., Hensel, H., Wurster, R. 1969. Integrated static activity of lingual cold receptors. Pflügers Arch. 311:50–54
10. Benzinger, T. H. 1969. Heat regulation: homeostasis of central temperature in man. Physiol. Rev. 49:671–759
11. Deleted in proof
12. Boman, K. K. A. 1958. Elektrophysiologische Untersuchungen über die Thermoreceptoren der Gesichtshaut. Acta Physiol. Scand. 44(Suppl. 149):1–79
13. Braun, H. A., Bade, H., Hensel, H. 1980. Static and dynamic discharge patterns of bursting cold fibers related to hypothetical receptor mechanisms. Pflügers Arch. 386:1–9

14. Brown, A. G., Iggo, A. 1967. A quantitative study of cutaneous receptors and afferent fibres in the cat and rabbit. J. Physiol. 193:707–33
15. Deleted in proof
16. Burton, H., Terashima, S. I., Clark, J. 1972. Response properties of slowly adapting touch receptors to temperature stimulation in cats. Br. Res. 45:401–16
17. Deleted in proof
18. Casey, D. E., Hahn, J. F. 1970. Thermal effects on responses of cat touch corpuscle. Exp. Neurol. 28:35–45
19. Chambers, M. R., Andres, K. H., von During, M., Iggo, A. 1972. The structure and function of the slowly adapting type II mechanoreceptor in hairy skin. Q. J. Exp. Physiol. 57:417–45
20. Chatt, A. B., Kenshalo, D. R. 1979. The afferent fiber population mediating the thermal evoked response to skin cooling in man. Exp. Neurol. 64:146–54
21. Chernetski, K. E. 1964. Sympathetic enhancement of peripheral sensory input in the frog. J. Neurophysiol. 27:493–515
22. Christiansen, B. N., Perl, E. R. 1970. Spinal neurons specifically excited by noxious or thermal stimuli: marginal zone of the dorsal horn. J. Neurophysiol. 33:293–307
23. Clusin, W. T., Spray, D. C., Bennett, M. V. L. 1975. Activation of a voltage insensitive conductance by inward calcium current. Nature 256:425–27
24. Darian-Smith, I., Johnson, K. O., Dykes, R. 1973. "Cold" fiber population innervating palmar and digital skin of the monkey: responses to cooling pulses. J. Neurophysiol. 36:325–46
25. Darian-Smith, I., Johnson, K. O., LaMotte, C., Kenins, P., Shigenaga, Y., Ming, V. C. 1979. Coding of incremental changes in skin temperature by single warm fibers in the monkey. J. Neurophysiol. 42:1316–31

26. Darian-Smith, I., Johnson, K. O., LaMotte, C., Shigenaga, Y., Kenins, P., Champness, P. 1979. Warm fibers innervating palmar and digital skin of the monkey: responses to thermal stimuli. *J. Neurophysiol.* 42:1297–1315

27. Davies, S. N. 1984. Evidence for peripheral, but not central modulation of trigeminal cold receptive cells in the rat. *Brain Res.* 301:299–305

28. Dawson, N. J., Dickenson, A. H., Hellon, R. F., Woolf, C. J. 1982. Inhibitory controls on thermal neurons in the spinal trigeminal nucleus of cats and rats. *Brain Res.* 209:440–45

29. Dodt, E. 1953. The behaviour of thermoreceptors at low and high temperature with special reference to Ebbecke's temperature phenomena. *Acta Physiol. Scand.* 27:295–314

30. Dodt, E., Skouby, A. P., Zotterman, Y. 1953. The effect of cholinergic substances on the discharges from thermal receptors. *Acta Physiol. Scand.* 28:101–14

31. Dodt, E., Zotterman, Y. 1952. Mode of action of warm receptors. *Acta Physiol. Scand.* 26:345–57

32. Dodt, E., Zotterman, Y. 1952. The discharge of specific cold fibres at high temperatures. (The paradoxical cold.) *Acta Physiol. Scand.* 26:358–65

33. Douglas, W. W., Ritchie, J. M., Straub, R. W. 1960. The role of nonmyelinated fibres in signalling cooling of the skin. *J. Physiol.* 150:266–83

34. Dubner, R., Sumino, R., Wood, W. I. 1975. A peripheral "cold" fiber population responsive to innocuous and noxious thermal stimuli applied to monkey's face. *J. Neurophysiol.* 38:1373–89

35. Duclaux, R., Kenshalo, D. R. 1980. Response characteristics of cutaneous warm receptors in the monkey. *J. Neurophysiol.* 43:1–15

36. Duclaux, R., Schafer, K., Hensel, H. 1980. Response of cold receptors to low skin temperature in nose of the cat. *J. Neurophysiol.* 43:1571–77

37. Dykes, R. W. 1975. Coding of steady and transient temperatures by cutaneous "cold" fibers serving the hand of monkeys. *Br. Res.* 98:485–500

38. Frey, M. von. 1910. Physiologie der Sinnesorgane der menschlichen Haut. *Ergeb. Physiol. Biol. Chem. Exp. Pharmackol.* 9:351–68

39. Fruhstorfer, H., Zenz, M., Nolte, H., Hensel, H. 1974. Dissociated loss of cold and warm sensibility during regional anaesthesia. *Pflügers Arch.* 349:73–82

40. Gorman, A. L. F., Marmor, M. V. 1970. Temperature dependence of the sodium-potassium permeability ratio of a molluscan neurone. *J. Physiol.* 210:919–31

41. Hahn, J. F. 1971. Thermal-mechanical stimulus interactions in low-threshold C-fiber mechanoreceptors of cat. *Exp. Neurol.* 33:607–17

42. Hellon, R. F., Misra, N. K. 1973. Neurons in the dorsal horn of the rat responding to scrotal skin temperature changes. *J. Physiol.* 232:375–88

43. Hellon, R. F., Misra, N. K. 1973. Neurons in the ventrobasal complex of the rat thalamus responding to scrotal skin temperature changes. *J. Physiol.* 232:389–99

44. Hellon, R. F., Misra, N. K., Provins, K. A. 1973. Neurones in the somatosensory cortex of the rat responding to scrotal skin temperature changes. *J. Physiol.* 232:401–11

45. Hellon, R. F., Mitchell, D. 1975. Convergence in a thermal afferent pathway in the rat. *J. Physiol.* 248:359–76

46. Hellon, R. F., Hensel, H., Schafer, K. 1975. Thermal receptors in the scrotum of the rat. *J. Physiol.* 248:349–57

47. Hellon, R. F., Taylor, D. C. M. 1982. An analysis of a thermal afferent pathway in the rat. *J. Physiol.* 326:319–28

48. Hensel, H. 1952. Afferente Impulse aus den Kaltereceptoren der ausseren Haut. *Pflügers Arch. Gesamte Physiol. Menschen Tiere* 256:195–211

49. Hensel, H. 1953. The time factor in thermoreceptor excitation. *Acta Physiol. Scand.* 29:109–16

50. Hensel, H. 1953. Das Verhalten der Thermoreceptoren bei Temperatursprungen. *Pflügers Arch.* 256:470–78

51. Hensel, H. 1968. Spezifische Warmeimpulse aus der Nasenregion der Katze. *Pflügers Arch.* 302:374–376

52. Hensel, H. 1969. Cutane Warmereceptoren bei Primaten. *Pflügers Arch.* 313:150–52

53. Hensel, H. 1974. Thermoreceptors. *Ann. Rev. Physiol.* 36:233–49

54. Hensel, H. 1976. Functional and structural basis of thermoreception. *Prog. Brain Res.* 43:105–18

55. Hensel, H. 1981. Neural processes in long-term thermal adaptation. *Fed. Proc.* 40:2830–34

56. Hensel, H. 1982. Temperature receptors. *Prog. Brain Res.*

57. Hensel, H., Andres, K. H., von During, M. 1974. Structure and function of cold receptors. *Pflügers Arch.* 352:1–10

58. Hensel, H., Boman, K. K. A. 1960. Afferent impulses in cutaneous sensory nerves in human subjects. *J. Neurophysiol.* 23:564–78

59. Hensel, H., Huopaniemi, T. 1969. Static

and dynamic properties of warm fibres in the infraorbital nerve. *Pflügers Arch.* 309:1–10

60. Hensel, H., Iggo, A. 1971. Analysis of cutaneous warm and cold fibres in primates. *Pflügers Arch.* 329:1–8

61. Hensel, H., Iggo, A., Witt, I. 1960. A quantitative study of sensitive cutaneous thermoreceptors with C afferent fibers. *J. Physiol.* 153:113–26

62. Hensel, H., Kenshalo, D. R. 1969. Warm receptors in the nasal region of cats. *J. Physiol.* 204:99–112

63. Hensel, H., Nier, K. 1971. Integrated static activity of the ampullae of Lorenzini after longterm exposure to various temperatures. *Pflügers Arch.* 323:279–83

64. Hensel, H., Schafer, K. 1974. Effects of calcium on warm and cold receptors. *Pflügers Arch.* 352:87–90

65. Hensel, H., Strom, L., Zotterman, Y. 1951. Electrophysiological measurements of depth of thermoreceptors. *J. Neurophysiol.* 14:423–29

66. Deleted in proof

67. Hensel, H., Wurster, R. D. 1970. Static properties of cold receptors in nasal area of cats. *J. Neurophysiol.* 33:271–75

68. Hensel, H., Zotterman, Y. 1951. The response of the cold receptors to constant cooling. *Acta Physiol. Scand.* 22:96–113

69. Hensel, H., Zotterman, Y. 1951. Quantitative Beziehungen zwischen der Entladung einzelner Kaltefasern und der Temperatur. *Acta Physiol. Scand.* 23:291–319

70. Hensel, H., Zotterman, Y. 1951. The response of mechanoreceptors to thermal stimulation. *J. Physiol.* 115:16–24

71. Hensel, H., Zotterman, Y. 1951. The effect of menthol on the thermoreceptors. *Acta Physiol. Scand.* 24:27–34

72. Iggo, A. 1959. Cutaneous heat and cold receptors with slowly-conducting (C) afferent fibres. *Q. J. Exp. Physiol.* 44:362–70

73. Iggo, A. 1969. Cutaneous thermoreceptors in primates and sub-primates. *J. Physiol.* 200:403–30

74. Iggo, A., Iggo, B. J. 1971. Impulse coding in primate cutaneous thermoreceptors in dynamic thermal conditions. *J. Physiol.* 63:287–90

75. Iruchijima, J., Zotterman, Y. 1960. The specificity of afferent cutaneous C fibres in mammals. *Acta Physiol. Scand.* 49:267–78

76. Ishiko, N., Loewenstein, W. R. 1961. Effects of temperature on the generator and action potentials of a sense organ. *J. Gen. Physiol.* 45:105–24

77. Jahns, R. 1975. Types of neuronal re-

sponses in the rat thalamus to peripheral temperature changes. *Exp. Brain Res.* 23:157–66

78. Jahns, R. 1976. Different projections of cutaneous thermal inputs to single units of the midbrain raphe nuclei. *Brain Res.* 101:355–61

79. Johnson, K. O., Darian-Smith, I., LaMotte, C. 1973. Peripheral neural determinants of temperature discrimination in man: a correlative study of responses to cooling skin. *J. Neurophysiol.* 36:347–70

80. Johnson, K. O., Darian-Smith, I., LaMotte, C., Johnson, B., Oldfield, S. 1979. Coding of incremental changes in skin temperature by a population of warm fibers in the monkey: correlation with intensity discrimination in man. *J. Neurophysiol.* 42:1332–53

81. Joyner, R. W. 1981. Temperature effects on neuronal elements. *Fed. Proc.* 40:2814–8

82. Kenshalo, D. R., Duclaux, R. 1977. Response characteristics of cutaneous cold receptors in the monkey. *J. Neurophysiol.* 40:319–32

83. Kenshalo, D. R., Gallegos, E. S. 1967. Multiple temperature-sensitive spots innervated by single fibers. *Science* 158:1064–65

84. Kenshalo, D. R., Holmes, C. E., Wood, P. B. 1968. Warm and cool thresholds as a function of rate of stimulus temperature change. *Percept. Psychophys.* 3:81–84

85. Kenshalo, D. R., Nafe, J. P. 1963. Cutaneous vascular system as a model temperature receptor. *Percept. Mot. Skills* 17:257–58

86. Klee, M. R., Pierau, F. K., Faber, D. S. 1974. Temperature effects on resting potential and spike parameters of cat motoneurons. *Exp. Brain Res.* 19:478–92

87. Konietzny, F., Hensel, H. 1975. Warm fiber activity in human skin nerves. *Pflügers Arch.* 359:265–67

88. Konietzny, F., Hensel, H. 1977. The dynamic response of warm units in human skin nerves. *Pflügers Arch.* 370:111–14

89. Kumazawa, T., Perl, E. R. 1977. Primate cutaneous sensory units with unmyelinated (C) afferent fibers. *J. Neurophysiol.* 40:1325–38

90. LaMotte, R. H., Thalhammer, J. G. 1982. Response properties of high-threshold cutaneous cold receptors in the primate. *Brain Res.* 244:279–87

91. Landgren, S. 1960. Thalamic neurons responding to cooling of the cat's tongue. *Acta Physiol. Scand.* 48:255–67

92. Lippold, O. C. J., Nicholls, J. G., Red-

fearn, J. W. T. 1960. A study of the afferent discharge produced by cooling a mammalian muscle spindle. *J. Physiol.* 153:218–31

93. Loewenstein, W. R. 1956. Modulation of cutaneous mechanoreceptors by sympathetic stimulation. *J. Physiol.* 132:40–60

94. Long, R. R. 1977. Sensitivity of cutaneous cold fibers to noxious heat: Paradoxical cold discharge. *J. Neurophysiol.* 40:489–502

95. Deleted in proof

96. Martin, H. F., Manning, J. W. 1971. Thalamic "warming" and "cooling" units responding to cutaneous stimulation. *Brain Res.* 27:377–81

97. Molinari, H. H., Greenspan, J. D., Kenshalo, D. R. 1977. The effects of rate temperature change and adapting temperature on thermal sensitivity. *Sens. Process.* 1:354–62

98. Molinari, H. H., Kenshalo, D. R. 1977. Effect of cooling rate on the dynamic response of cat cold units. *Exp. Neurol.* 55:546–55

99. Neya, T., Pierau, F. K. 1980. Activity patterns of temperature-reactive dorsal horn neurons and their reactions to peripheral receptor stimulation by Ca. *Jpn. J. Physiol.* 30:921–34

100. Nilsson, B. Y. 1972. Effect of sympathetic stimulation on mechanoreceptors of cat vibrissae. *Acta Physiol. Scand.* 85:390–97

101. Pierau, F. K., Klee, M. R., Faber, D. S., Klussmann, F. W. 1971. Mechanism of cellular thermoreception in mammals. *Int. J. Biometeorol.* 15:134–40

102. Pierau, F. K., Torrey, P. J., Carpenter, D. O. 1974. Mammalian cold receptor afferents: Role of an electrogenic sodium pump in sensory transduction. *Brain Res.* 73:156–60

103. Pierau, F. K., Torrey, P., Carpenter, D. 1975. Effect of ouabain and potassium-free solution on mammalian thermosensitive afferents in vitro. *Pflügers Arch.* 359:349–56

104. Pierau, F. K., Ullrich, J., Wurster, R. D. 1977. Effect of Ca^{++} and EDTA on the bursting pattern of lingual cold receptors in cats. *Proc. Int. Union Physiol. Sci.* 13:597

105. Poulos, D. A. 1981. Central processing of cutaneous temperature information. *Fed. Proc.* 40:2830–34

106. Poulos, D. A., Benjamin, R. M. 1968. Response of thalamic neurons to thermal stimulation of the tongue. *J. Neurophysiol.* 31:28–43

107. Poulos, D. A., Lende, R. A. 1970. Response of trigeminal ganglion neurons to thermal stimulation of oral-facial regions. I. Steady state response. *J. Neurophysiol.* 33:508–17

108. Deleted in proof

109. Raths, P., Hensel, H. 1967. Cutane Thermorezeptoren bei Winterschlafen. *Pflügers Arch.* 293:281–302

110. Deleted in proof

111. Deleted in proof

112. Sams, W. M. Jr., Winkelmann, R. K. 1969. Temperature effects on isolated resistance vessels of skin and mesentery. *Am. J. Physiol.* 216:112–16

113. Sand, A. 1938. The function of the ampullae of Lorenzini, with some observations on the effect of temperature on sensory rhythms. *Proc. R. Soc. London Ser B.* 125:524–53

114. Schafer, K., Braun, H. A., Hensel, H. 1982. Static and dynamic activity of cold receptors at various calcium levels. *J. Neurophysiol.* 47:1017–28

115. Schingnitz, G., Werner, J. 1980. Thalamic burst firing–a neuronal code for temperature information? *Brain Res.* 195:467–70

116. Schingnitz, G., Werner, J. 1980. Responses of thalamic neurons to thermal stimulation of the limbs, scrotum and tongue in the rat. *J. Therm. Biol.* 5:53–61

117. Deleted in proof

118. Siminoff, R. 1965. Cutaneous nerve activity in response to temperature changes of the cat's skin. *Exp. Neurol.* 11:171–81

119. Sokolove, P. G., Cooke, I. M. 1971. Inhibition of impulse activity in a sensory neuron by an electrogenic pump. *J. Gen. Physiol.* 57:125–63

120. Sperelakis, N. 1970. Effects of temperature on membrane potentials of excitable cells. In *Physiological and Behavioral Temperature Regulation,* ed. J. D. Handy, A. P. Gagge, J. A. J. Stolwijk, pp. 408–41. Springfield, Ill: Thomas

121. Spray, D. C. 1974. Characteristics, specificity and efferent control of frog cutaneous cold receptors. *J. Physiol.* 237:15–38

122. Spray, D. C. 1974. Metabolic dependence of frog cold receptor sensitivity. *Brain Res.* 72:354–59

123. Spray, D. C. 1975. Effect of reduced acclimation temperature on responses of frog cold receptors. *Comp. Biochem. Physiol. A.* 50:391–95

124. Spray, D. C. 1975. Sympathetic interaction and transduction mechanism of frog cold receptors. In *Proc. Golgi Centennial Symp.,* ed. M. Santini, pp. 569–76. New York: Raven

125. Spray, D. C. 1976. Pain and temperature receptors in anuran skin. In *Handbook of*

Frog Neurobiology, ed. R. Llinas, pp. 607–28. New York: Springer-Verlag

126. Spray, D. C., Bennett, M. V. L. 1985. Physiology and pharmacology of gap junctions. *Ann. Rev. Physiol.* 47:281–303

127. Spray, D. C., Chronister, R. 1974. Composition of the dorsal cutaneous nerve in *Rana pipiens*. *Experientia* 30:44–45

128. Spray, D. C., Galansky, S. H. 1975. Effects of cholinergic agonists and antagonists on frog cold receptor activity. *Comp. Biochem. Physiol. C* 50:97–103

129. Stevens, J. C., Stevens, S. S. 1960. Warmth and cold: dynamics of sensory intensity. *J. Exp. Psychol.* 60:183–92

130. Stolwijk, J. A. J., Wexler, I. 1971. Peripheral nerve activity in response to heating the cat's skin. *J. Physiol.* 214:377–92

131. Sumino, R., Dubner, R., Starkman, S. 1973. Responses of small myelinated 'warm' fibers to noxious heat applied to the monkey's face. *Brain Res.* 62:260–63

132. Tapper, D. N. 1965. Stimulus-response relationships in the cutaneous slowly-adapting mechanoreceptor in hairy skin of the cat. *Exp. Neurol.* 13:364–85

133. Taylor, D. C. M. 1982. The effects of nucleus raphe magnus lesions on an ascending thermal pathway in the rat. *J. Physiol.* 326:309–18

134. Thomas, R. C. 1972. Electrogenic sodium pump in nerve and muscle cells. *Physiol. Rev.* 52:563–94

135. Weddell, G., Palmer, E., Pallie, W. 1955. Nerve endings in mammalian skin. *Biol. Rev.* 30:159–95

136. Whitear, M. 1955. Dermal nerve endings in *Rana* and *Bufo*. *Q. J. Microsc. Sci.* 96:343–49

137. Whitear, M. 1974. The vesicle population in frog skin nerves. *J. Neurocytol.* 3:49–58

138. Zotterman, Y. 1935. Action potentials in the glossopharyngeal nerve and in the chorda tympani. *Skand. Arch. Physiol.* 72:73–77

139. Zotterman, Y. 1936. Specific action potentials in the lingual nerve of cat. *Skand. Arch. Physiol.* 75:105–19

140. Zotterman, Y. 1953. Special senses: thermal receptors. *Ann. Rev. Physiol.* 15:357–72

Ann. Rev. Physiol. 1986. 48:639–54

TEMPERATURE RECEPTORS IN THE CENTRAL NERVOUS SYSTEM

Jack A. Boulant and Jay B. Dean

Department of Physiology, The Ohio State University, Columbus, Ohio 43210

INTRODUCTION

For half a century, it has been known that thermosensitive regions of the rostral brain stem are important in thermoregulation (61). Figure 1 indicates that a variety of thermoregulatory responses can be elicited by changing the temperature of the preoptic area and anterior hypothalamus (PO/AH). PO/AH warming evokes heat-loss responses, and PO/AH cooling evokes heat-production responses. If PO/AH temperature is changed slightly above or below normal, there are changes in heat-retention responses such as skin blood flow and thermoregulatory behavior. Figure 1 also describes the synaptic organization of PO/AH thermosensitive neurons (4). While most neurons are temperature insensitive, warm-sensitive neurons have firing rates that increase with warming or decrease with cooling. Conversely, the firing rates of cold-sensitive neurons increase with cooling or decrease with warming. Many central thermosensitive neurons also receive synaptic inputs from skin and spinal thermoreceptive pathways (4, 7). This indicates that such neurons are capable of thermal integration, and it increases the likelihood that these neurons function in thermoregulation. As summarized in Figure 1, the evidence for central thermosensitivity comes from thermoregulatory studies during thermal stimulation of discrete neural areas and from electrophysiological studies of temperature-sensitive neurons. In this review, these studies are presented first as an overview of the comparative aspects of central thermosensitivity in vertebrates. The second half of this review focuses on the properties and synaptic organization of PO/AH thermosensitive neurons.

639

0066-4278/86/0315-0639$02.00

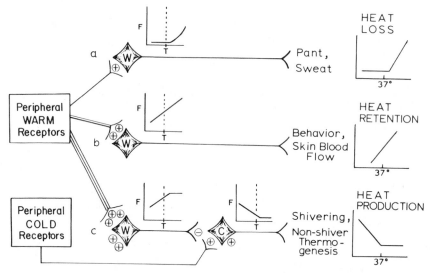

Figure 1   A model showing the hypothalamic neuronal control of various thermoregulatory responses. *W*=warm-sensitive neuron; *C*=cold-sensitive neuron; (+)=excitatory input; (−)=inhibitory input. Hypothalamic thermoresponse curves of different neurons and thermoregulatory responses are shown. *F*=neuronal firing rate; *T*=hypothalamic temperature; *dashed line*=thermoneutral temperature. (Redrawn from Boulant; Reference 4).

COMPARATIVE STUDIES OF CENTRAL THERMAL STIMULATION

Mammals

If local warming and cooling of a neural area induces appropriate thermoregulatory responses, then it is usually concluded that the neural area contains central thermoreceptors that function in thermoregulation (4, 6, 37, 93). The best example of such an area is the PO/AH in mammals. In the rabbit, for example, PO/AH cooling elicits a profound increase in metabolic heat production due to shivering. This response is quickly reversed during PO/AH warming, which also increases panting and skin blood flow. Cooling of the mammalian PO/AH may also elicit nonshivering thermogenesis, metabolic endocrine release, piloerection, and a host of behavioral thermoregulatory responses. During PO/AH warming certain mammals show sweating, saliva spreading (i.e. evaporative cooling), and other behavioral responses (4, 37).

In mammals, other neural areas have been shown to respond to thermal stimulation. The posterior hypothalamus differs from the PO/AH in that it lacks an appropriate thermosensitivity for autonomic responses (75); however, posterior hypothalamic thermal stimulation produces appropriate behavioral responses in squirrel monkeys (1). Local warming of the medulla (11) increases respiratory frequency, while thermal stimulation of the spinal cord sometimes elicits a variety of thermoregulatory responses comparable to those induced by manipulation of PO/AH temperature (93).

Birds

It has been suggested that birds display interspecies differences in terms of their predominant sites for central thermoreception (88). In some birds the spinal cord appears to be a primary thermoreceptive structure, especially in determining heat production. These species include the pigeon (28, 77), penguin (33, 97), quail (100), and duck (62, 96, 99). Even in these birds, appropriate heat loss and heat retention responses can be evoked by subtle changes in PO/AH temperature (97, 99, 100). During more drastic temperature changes, however, particularly during PO/AH cooling, thermoregulatory responses are often inappropriate or weak. In contrast, the hypothalami of other birds are highly thermosensitive and respond in a manner similar to that observed in mammals. Rostral brain stem thermal stimulation induces both appropriate heat-loss and heat-production in the emu (53), goose (36), and house sparrow (64). Moreover, spinal thermosensitivity was found to be of little significance in the goose (36). In the duck, thermal stimulation of the lower midbrain and upper pons produced effective thermoregulatory responses (62, 96, 98). It is important to emphasize that any divergence of avian thermoreception appears to exist only for physiological responses, not for behavioral responses. The avian rostral hypothalamus still remains highly thermosensitive in terms of controlling behavioral thermoregulatory responses (83–86).

Ectotherms (Reptiles, Amphibians, and Fishes)

Rostral brain stem thermal stimulation elicits appropriate behavioral thermoregulatory responses in lizards (32, 66), turtles (65), and fishes (13–15, 34) placed in thermal gradients. Brain stem warming causes these animals to exit from a warm environment at a lower body temperature than would normally elicit this response. Brain stem cooling produces the opposite response, with the exception of the brown bullhead, which apparently lacks appropriate central thermosensitivity in the hypothermic range (15). Amphibians have also been shown to behaviorally thermoregulate in response to extrahypothalamic thermal stimulation. In the frog, spinal cord (18) or intra-abdominal warming (9) causes behavioral selection of cooler environments. In some cases physiological responses are affected by rostral brain stem thermal stimulation. Evaporative heat-loss (panting) is directly related to brain temperature in turtles (65, 80) and lizards (12, 102). One study investigated brain thermosensitivity indirectly in the bullfrog by radiant heating of the head. It was found that head warming increased cutaneous mucus discharge, which impedes desiccation during basking (60).

Summary of Vertebrate Thermal Stimulation

The combined evidence from these studies supports the concept that the rostral brain stem serves a thermoregulatory function in all vertebrates. Behavioral thermoregulation predominates and is often recruited before physiological responses, even in species with well-developed autonomic thermoregulation (4). Satinoff (81) suggests that behavioral and autonomic thermoregulatory neuronal networks are functionally and anatomically distinct. Adair's (1) research on mammals and some avian studies (62, 83–86, 96, 98) support this concept. Caputa (10) further proposes that avian differences in the control of autonomic responses may be related to the development of flight. In some flying birds PO/AH thermosensitivity is apparently reduced such that brain temperature is maintained lower than body temperature. Since thermal fluctuations of the head could be great during flight, hypothalamic thermosensitivity might not be as appropriate as deep-body thermosensitivity (10, 100). Accordingly, in some species the neural control of autonomic thermoregulation may have shifted down the neuroaxis to the lower midbrain (62, 96, 98) and spinal cord (93).

ELECTROPHYSIOLOGY OF THERMOSENSITIVE NEURONS

Criteria for Neuronal Thermosensitivity

Table 1 shows the locations and proportions of thermosensitive neurons observed in many of the recent electrophysiological studies. Table 1 also indicates that there are no uniform criteria for classifying neuronal thermosensitivity. Earlier studies used either the neuronal Q_{10} or the slope of the thermoresponse curve as a criterion (4). Studies of neuronal integration have preferred slope because this criterion can be applied to a neuron's local temperature and to the peripheral temperature affecting the neuron's afferent input. Generally, minimum Q_{10} criteria include values significantly greater than 2.0 for warm-sensitive neurons and values less than 0.5 for cold-sensitive neurons. Minimum criteria for slopes or regression coefficients are 0.8 impulses/sec/°C for warm-sensitive neurons and -0.6 impulses/sec/°C for cold-sensitive neurons (4). It is also important that these values be determined over at least a 2–3°C temperature range. As evidenced by Table 1, recent publications show a disturbing trend towards classifying neurons based on values far below previously accepted minimums. Even more disturbing is the fact that many recent studies give no criteria at all. As a result, the proportions of thermosensitive neurons are probably overestimated in some recent studies.

Table 1   Recent single unit studies showing locations and proportions of neurons tested for local thermosensitivity.

Species	CNS location[a]	Warm (%)	Cold (%)	Insensitive (%)	n	Criteria warm[b]	Criteria cold[b]	Reference
cat	PO, AH	9	40	51	57	—	—	72
kangaroo rat	PO, AH	47	27	26	40	> 0	< 0	22
rabbit	PO, AH	43	11	46	28	> 0	< 0	21
rabbit	PO, AH	31	31	38	45	—	—	26
rabbit	PO, AH	38	24	38	53	—	—	25
rabbit	PO, AH	28	28	42	21	$+0.4$	—	23
rabbit	PO, AH	40	25	35	97	—	—	24
rat[c]	PO, AH	22	6	72	139	$+0.7^d$	-0.6	38
rat[c]	PO, AH	47	23	30	56	$+0.7^d$	-0.7^d	89
rat[c]	PO, AH	19	2	79	640	$+0.1^d$	-0.1^d	50
rat[c]	PO, AH	35	10	55	140	—	—	49
rat[c]	PO, AH	37	15	48	188	$+0.7$	-0.7	42
rat[c]	PO, AH	39	13	48	286	$+0.7$	-0.7	41
rat[c]	PO, AH	45	24	31	55	—	—	43
rat[c]	PO, AH	32	13	55	62	$Q_{10} > 2$	$Q_{10} < 0.5$	2
rat[c]	PO	33	12	55	112	—	—	56
rat[c]	PO	43	16	41	56	—	—	63
rat[c]	PO	34	10	56	145	$+0.7^d$	-0.7^d	57
rat[e]	PO, AH	32	6	62	117	$+0.8$	-0.6	87
rat[e]	PO, AH	73	0	27	22	$Q_{10} > 2$	$Q_{10} < 0.5$	47
rat[e]	PO, AH	30	10	60	138	$+0.8$	-0.5	55
rat[e]	PO, AH	17	15	68	48	$+0.8$	-0.6	54
rat[e]	PO, AH	17	8	75	86	$Q_{10} > 2$	—	44
rat[e]	PO	35	10	55	167	$+0.8$	-0.6	90
rat[e]	PO	37	8	55	180	$+0.8$	-0.6	91
rat[e]	PO	29	6	65	256	—	—	45
rat[e]	PO	61	7	32	60	—	—	67
rat[e]	AH	34	1	65	75	$+0.1^d$	-0.1^d	46
guinea pig[e]	PO, AH	43	13	44	53	$+0.8$	-0.6	8a
guinea pig[e]	PO	43	12	45	110	$+0.8$	-0.6	8b
rat[f]	PO	24	10	66	95	$Q_{10} > 2$	$Q_{10} < 0.5$	3
mouse[f]	PO, AH	28	4	68	54	—	—	51
cat[c]	PH	19	16	65	98	$Q_{10} > 2$	$Q_{10} < 0.5$	19
rabbit[c]	PH	15	2	83	155	—	—	104

Table 1   *(continued)*

Species	CNS loca-tion[a]	Neurons Warm (%)	Cold (%)	Insensitive (%)	n	Criteria warm[b]	Criteria cold[b]	Reference
cat[c]	rMB	10	8	82	99	$Q_{10} > 2$	—	16
cat[c]	cMB	72	11	17	72	$Q_{10} > 2$	—	16
rabbit[c]	MB	8	19	73	204	+0.8	−0.8	39
rabbit[c]	MB	10	27	63	51	—	—	48
rat[c]	MB	58	0	42	24	$Q_{10} > 2$	—	40
rabbit[c]	MD	21	26	53	187	—	—	52
duck	HY	49	14	37	35	$Q_{10} > 1$	$Q_{10} < 1$	94
sunfish[c]	PO	17	2	81	276	$+1.0^d$	-1.0^d	70
trout[c]	TH, MB	18	1	81	140	$Q_{10} > 4$	$Q_{10} < 0.25$	29

[a] HY = hypothalamus; PO = preoptic area; AH = anterior hypothalamus; PH = posterior hypothalamus; TH = thalamus; MB = midbrain; MD = medulla; r = rostral; c = caudal.
[b] Unless designated as Q_{10}, values are the minimum slope criterion in impulses/sec/°C used to access warm and cold thermosensitivity.
[c] Anesthetized preparation
[d] Also used $Q_{10} > 2$ or < 0.5 to access warm or cold sensitivity, respectively.
[e] Tissue slice preparation
[f] Tissue culture preparation

Neuronal Proportions and Locations

Thermosensitive neurons have been recorded in several species at various locations and in different types of preparations, including anesthetized and unanesthetized animals, and in vitro tissue slices (55) and tissue cultures (68). Only recent studies (primarily 1980–1985) that used local thermal stimulation to determine the proportions of warm-sensitive, cold-sensitive, and temperature-insensitive neurons are included in Table 1. Early single unit studies (1961–1980) (4, 37) indicate that in the mammalian PO/AH neuronal population approximately 30% of the neurons are warm sensitive, 10% are cold sensitive and 60% are temperature insensitive. A similar trend can be seen in Table 1, if one considers only recent studies with relatively large sample sizes (i.e. $n > 100$). The recent studies using anesthetized animals find that 31% of the PO/AH neurons are warm sensitive, 10% are cold sensitive, and 59% are temperature insensitive. Recent PO/AH tissue slice studies report that 34% of the neurons are warm sensitive, 9% are cold sensitive, and 57% are temperature insensitive. The two tissue culture studies found a slightly lower proportion of thermosensitive neurons: 26% warm sensitive, 7% cold sensitive, and 67% temperature insensitive. In Table 1, the studies using unanesthetized whole-animal preparations had smaller sample sizes (i.e. $n < 100$) and showed consistently higher percentages of cold-sensitive PO/AH neurons (26%). This may be due to the absence of any anesthetic suppression of synaptic activity impinging upon the cold-sensitive neurons, as depicted in Figure 1. It may also be attributable to the lack of any rigid cold-sensitivity criterion in these experiments, which could cause overestimation of this neuronal population.

Thermosensitive neurons are found in the PO/AH in all vertebrates studied (Table 1). In addition to those CNS locations indicated in Table 1, thermosensitive neurons have been identified in mammalian (92, 95, 103) and avian (27, 69, 76) spinal cords. Conversely, Gorke (27) explored the reptilian spinal cord and found no thermosensitive neurons. Recently, tissue slice studies have mapped the locations of temperature-sensitive neurons in the mammalian hypothalamus. Frontal preoptic slices show that warm-sensitive neurons are located primarily in the central and lateral portions of the medial and lateral preoptic areas and that cold-sensitive neurons are localized mainly in central portion of the medial preoptic area (90, 91). Horizontal slices passing through the entire hypothalamus show that cold-sensitive neurons are found in the preoptic area, lateral and posterior hypothalamus, mammillary nuclei, and nucleus reuniens. In addition to these regions, warm-sensitive neurons are found in the paraventricular, ventromedial, and anterior hypothalamic nuclei (17).

SYNAPTIC ORGANIZATION OF PREOPTIC THERMOSENSITIVE NEURONS

Neuronal Functional Specificity

Do both thermosensitive and temperature-insensitive neurons function in thermoregulation? In some neuronal models, synaptic inputs from temperature-insensitive neurons serve as steady-state reference signals to set-point interneurons (30, 31, 35). According to these models the interneurons simply compare synaptic inputs from warm-sensitive neurons with antagonistic synaptic inputs from temperature-insensitive neurons. Another model holds that while neurons may be temperature-insensitive in terms of their firing rates (i.e. impulses/sec), some are actually thermosensitive in terms of their interspike intervals (78). Thus, the coding of thermal information may not be limited to firing rate alone.

In describing the role of temperature-insensitive neurons we should consider other functional roles of a particular neural area. In addition to thermoregulation the PO/AH regulates body water, metabolite and hormonal levels, and sexual behavior; PO/AH neurons have been shown to be sensitive to osmotic pressure, blood glucose levels, and the levels of circulating reproductive steroids, testosterone and estrogen (90, 91). It has been suggested that the PO/AH neurons have functional specificity (4), i.e. that the thermosensitive neurons function in thermoregulation and the majority of the temperature-insensitive neurons constitute the osmosensitive, glucosensitive, and steroid-sensitive neurons, which control other regulatory systems. However, some studies suggest interrelationships between thermoregulation and these other regulatory systems (90, 91).

With the advent of tissue slice studies it is now possible to characterize individual neurons according to their sensitivities to a variety of endogenous factors. The evidence obtained from such studies belies any strong functional specificity among PO/AH neurons (90, 91). Figure 2 shows the proportions of preoptic temperature-sensitive and temperature-insensitive neurons that respond to various experimental perfusion media. Approximately half of the thermosensitive neurons are affected either by low glucose and hyperosmotic media or by testosterone and estradiol media. In contrast, these media affect a much smaller proportion of the temperature-insensitive neurons. Also, while most of the osmosensitive neurons are also affected by low glucose media, this is not the case with the testosterone- and the estradiol-sensitive neurons; these two steroids rarely affect the same neuron.

The important finding of these studies is that the population of temperature-insensitive PO/AH neurons does not contain the majority of the osmosensitive, glucosensitive, and steriod-sensitive neurons. Rather, most of these neurons constitute the population of thermosensitive neurons. This emphasizes that the observation of thermosensitivity in a neuron does not guarantee that it has a functional role in thermoregulation. However, these studies do indicate a neuronal basis for the interactions between different regulatory systems. For

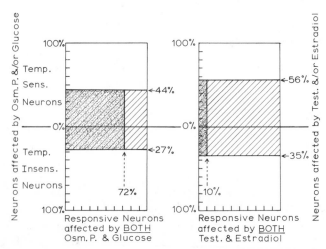

Figure 2 Proportions of temperature-sensitive and temperature-insensitive preoptic neurons affected either by hyperosmotic or hypoglucose media and by testosterone or estradiol media (hatched areas). Shaded areas show the proportions of osmosensitive neurons affected by glucose and the proportions of testosterone-sensitive neurons affected by estradiol. (Summarizes References 90 and 91.)

thermoregulation in particular the evidence shows that a central thermoreceptor can be affected by a variety of endogenous factors, in addition to synaptic inputs from afferent pathways. Moreover, it shows that temperature can affect the regulation of other homeostatic systems.

Influence of Afferent Input on Neuronal Thermosensitivity

Some studies make clear distinctions between "thermoreceptors" and set-point interneurons (20, 30, 35). Thermoreceptors are often defined as neurons whose thermoresponse curves are exponential or linear over wide temperature ranges. The thermoresponse curves of interneurons are thought by some to be nonlinear and limited to narrow temperature ranges. Under rigid definitions, thermoreceptors are viewed as neurons that are only sensitive to local temperature and that receive no afferent or local synaptic input (30, 35). These definitions of thermoreceptivity are not used in this review because there is nothing to preclude an inherently thermosensitive neuron from receiving synaptic input either from a nearby thermosensitive neuron or from a peripheral afferent pathway.

Warm-sensitive neurons may control several thermoregulatory responses. The model shown in Figure 1 proposes that a neuron's range of thermosensitivity indicates its most likely role in thermoregulation. It has been shown that low-firing warm-sensitive neurons are thermosensitive in the hyperthermic range but high-firing warm-sensitive neurons are thermosensitive in the hypothermic range (4). The higher-firing warm-sensitive neurons receive the greatest proportion of afferent input from peripheral thermoreceptor pathways (5, 7). Accordingly, this model (Figure 1) suggests that some warm-sensitive neurons (a) receive relatively little synaptic input, and therefore have low firing rates. Since these low-firing neurons are primarily thermosensitive above 37°C, they probably control heat-loss responses. Another group of warm-sensitive neurons (b) have medium firing rates and receive a moderate amount of afferent input. Since these neurons are equally thermosensitive both above and below 37°C, many are probably involved in heat-retention responses, such as changes in behavior and skin blood flow. A third group of warm-sensitive neurons (c) have high firing rates, presumably because they receive the greatest amount of afferent input. Since these neurons are primarily thermosensitive below 37°C, they probably control heat-production, possibly by inhibiting nearby interneurons that appear to be cold-sensitive. Figure 1 also suggests that these cold-sensitive neurons are synaptically driven by excitatory inputs, both from afferent pathways and from nearby neurons.

Neuronal Thermosensitivity in Tissue Slices

Recent tissue slice studies have improved our understanding of the synaptic organization of the preoptic neuronal network. Since tissue slices are devoid of afferent inputs, they provide a means to test predictions of the model in Figure 1.

Hypothalamic tissue slices contain the same proportions of warm-sensitive, cold-sensitive, and temperature-insensitive neurons as recorded in intact animals (Table 1). Most neurons in tissue slices, however, have low spontaneous firing rates, presumably due to the removal of afferent input (55). Figure 1 predicts that deafferentation will produce a homogeneous population of low-firing warm-sensitive neurons that are primarily thermosensitive above 37°C. Indeed, nearly all (87%) of the warm-sensitive neurons in tissue slices display their greatest thermosensitivity in the hyperthermic range (4, 54, 55). Cold-sensitive neurons in tissue slices also have low firing rates and are sensitive primarily to temperatures above 37°C. This finding suggests that the thermosensitivity of cold-sensitive neurons results from inhibitory input from nearby warm-sensitive neurons.

Synaptic Blockade of Thermosensitive Neurons

In addition to deafferentation, tissue slices offer certain advantages not afforded in whole-animal experiments. No anesthetic is used, and exact locations of recording sites are guaranteed. In addition, tissue slices can be alternately perfused with a normal nutrient medium and a medium containing an agent for synaptic blockade. In this way the firing rate and thermosensitivity of individual preoptic neurons can be determined before, during, and after synaptic blockade. One such study (54) found that synaptic blockade alters the firing rates of some warm-sensitive neurons but has no effect on other warm-sensitive neurons. Regardless of the firing rate effect, however, nearly all PO/AH warm-sensitive neurons retain their thermosensitivity during synaptic blockade, which suggests that warm-sensitive neurons possess an intrinsic thermosensitivity. In many cases, it appears that this sensitivity can be accentuated by local synaptic input, possibly from reverberating circuits of warm-sensitive neurons.

This same study (54) also showed that thermosensitivity is lost in cold-sensitive neurons during synaptic blockade. This observation supports the hypothesis that neuronal cold sensitivity is due to inhibition from nearby warm-sensitive neurons. This point remains controversial, however, since two other in vitro studies report the existence of cold sensitivity during synaptic blockade (3, 45). Unfortunately, the criteria used for cold sensitivity differ considerably, and it is likely that many of the cold-sensitive neurons in these later studies would be considered temperature-insensitive in the former study.

Intracellular Recordings of Thermosensitive Neurons

A study of the intracellular activity of preoptic neurons in fish has found two basic types of thermosensitive neurons (71). One type is warm sensitive, and displays pacemaker-like depolarizations with no evidence of synaptic input. It has firing rates that are exponentially thermosensitive. The other neuronal type includes both warm-sensitive and cold-sensitive neurons. This type of cell is strongly dependent on synaptic input, and the extent to which it is inherently thermosensitive is not known. As predicted in Figure 1, however, the cold-sensitive neurons in fish receive both inhibitory and excitatory synaptic potentials. This observation implies that cold sensitivity is synaptically derived. Another recent study (73) recorded the intracellular activity of preoptic thermosensitive neurons in the anesthetized rat. In this study the warm-sensitive neurons received much thermosensitive excitatory synaptic input, which appeared to accentuate an inherent thermosensitivity. This suggests that there are local networks of reverberating circuits among the warm-sensitive neurons. Again, the cold-sensitive neurons receive both inhibitory and excitatory synaptic potentials. In this rat study neuronal cold-sensitivity was directly dependent upon this synaptic input; local warming decreased the frequency of excitatory potentials and increased the frequency of inhibitory potentials.

Intracellular studies have been conducted on spinal motoneurons that increase their firing rates during cooling (58, 59, 74). Cooling increases membrane resistance, often followed by a slight depolarization. This depolarization appears to be due to decreases in the K:Na permeability ratio rather than decreases in the electrogenic pump (58). In addition, the increased membrane resistance causes an increase in the amplitude and duration of excitatory and inhibitory synaptic potentials (74). Both the decrease in membrane potential and the increase in the excitatory synaptic potential appear to contribute to the increased firing rate during cooling. While the thermal dependence of membrane resistance does provide a basis for neuronal cold-sensitivity, the cooling enhancement of firing rate appears to depend primarily on the postsynaptic membrane's response to excitatory synaptic input.

SUMMARY OF THERMORECEPTOR ELECTROPHYSIOLOGY

Although no uniform criteria exist for classifying neuronal thermosensitivity, various studies indicate that 40% of the PO/AH neurons are temperature-sensitive. Thermosensitivity per se does not guarantee that a neuron has a functional role in thermoregulation. In fact, many thermosensitive neurons are osmo-, gluco-, and steroid-sensitive, which suggests that there are interactions among various regulatory systems. PO/AH thermosensitive neurons also receive much thermal afferent input, indicating an integrative role in thermoregulation. Peripheral stimulation and tissue slice studies imply that this afferent input determines both neuronal firing rate and thermosensitivity range. Since the range of thermosensitivity suggests the function of a neuron, it is intriguing to speculate that the development of afferent input could determine a neuron's functional role in thermoregulation.

For warm-sensitive neurons, distinctions between thermoreceptors and synaptically driven interneurons remain debatable. Intracellular studies suggest that some warm-sensitive neurons receive much synaptic input, while others are independent of this input. Synaptic blockade shows that most synaptically driven PO/AH warm-sensitive neurons are inherently thermosensitive. This supports the concept that reverberating networks of warm-sensitive neurons reinforce neuronal thermosensitivity. The inherent thermosensitivity of cold-sensitive neurons is controversial. Intracellular studies of spinal motoneurons show that cold-sensitivity depends primarily on postsynaptic responses to excitatory input. Presumably, such thermosensitivity would disappear during synaptic blockade. While some studies suggest that PO/AH neuronal cold-sensitivity exists during synaptic blockade, other studies indicate that cold-sensitive neurons lose their thermosensitivity during blockade. These latter studies are supported by intracellular recordings which show that neuronal cold-sensitivity is due to synaptic rather than inherent activity.

ACKNOWLEDGMENT

Much of the authors' research cited in this chapter has been supported by grants from NIH, NSF, and the American Heart Association.

Literature Cited

1. Adair, E. 1974. Hypothalamic control of thermoregulatory behavior. In *Recent Studies of Hypothalamic Function,* eds. K. Lederis, K. E. Cooper, pp. 341–58. Basel: Karger
2. Baldino, F., Beckman, A. L., Adler, M. W. 1980. Actions of iontophoretically applied morphine on hypothalamic thermosensitive units. *Brain Res.* 196:199–208
3. Baldino, F., Geller, H. M. 1982. Electrophysiological analysis of neuronal thermosensitivity in rat preoptic and hypothalamic tissue cultures. *J. Physiol.* 327:173–84
4. Boulant, J. A. 1980. Hypothalamic control of thermoregulation. In *Handbook of the Hypothalamus,* ed. P. J. Morgane, J. Panksepp, pp. 1–82. New York: Dekker
5. Boulant, J. A., Demieville, H. N. 1974. Responses of thermosensitive preoptic and septal neurons to hippocampal and brain stem stimulation. *J. Neurophysiol.* 40:1356–68
6. Boulant, J. A., Gonzalez, R. R. 1977. The effect of skin temperature on the hypothalamic control of thermoregulation. *Brain Res.* 120:367–72
7. Boulant, J. A., Hardy, J. D. 1974. The effect of spinal and skin temperatures on

the firing rate and thermosensitivity of preoptic neurones. *J. Physiol.* 240:639–60
8a. Boulant, J. A., Scott, I. 1983. Effects of leukocytic pyrogen on hypothalamic neurons in tissue slices. In *Environment, Drugs and Thermoregulation,* ed. P. Lomax, E. Schonbaum, pp. 125–27. Basel: Karger
8b. Boulant, J. A., Scott, I. 1986. Comparison of prostaglandin E2 and leukocytic pyrogen on hypothalamic neurons in tissue slices. In *Proc. 6th Int. Symp. Pharmacol. Thermoregulation,* ed. P. Lomax, E. Schonbaum, Basel: Karger. In press
9. Cabanac, M., Jeddi, E. 1971. Thermopreferendum et thermoregulation comportementale chez trois poikilothermes. *Physiol. Behav.* 7:375–80
10. Caputa, M. 1984. Some differences in mammalian versus avian temperature regulation: Putative thermal adjustments to flight in birds. In *Thermal Physiology,* ed. J. R. S. Hales, pp. 413–17. New York: Raven
11. Chai, C. Y., Lin, M. T. 1973. Effects of thermal stimulation of medulla oblongata and spinal cord on decerebrate rabbits. *J. Physiol.* 234:409–19

12. Crawford, E. C., Barber, B. J. 1974. Effects of core, skin, and brain temperature on panting in the lizard *Sauromalus obesus*. *Am. J. Physiol.* 226:569–73

13. Crawshaw, L. I., Hammel, H. T. 1971. Behavioral thermoregulation in two species of Antarctic fish. *Life Sci.* 10:1009–20

14. Crawshaw, L. I., Hammel, H. T. 1973. Behavioral temperature regulation in the California horn shark, *Heterodontus francisci*. *Brain Behav. Evol.* 7:447–52

15. Crawshaw, L. I., Hammel, H. T. 1974. Behavioral regulation of internal temperature in the brown bullhead, *Ictalurus nebulosus*. *Comp. Biochem. Physiol. A* 47:51–60

16. Cronin, M. J., Baker, M. A. 1977. Thermosensitive midbrain neurons in the cat. *Brain Res.* 128:461–72

17. Dean, J. B., Boulant, J. A. 1985. Localization of diencephalic thermosensitive neurons in tissue slices. *Fed. Proc.* 44(4):1194 (Abstr.)

18. Duclaux, R., Fantino, M., Cabanac, M. 1973. Comportement thermorégulateur chez *Rana esculenta*. *Pflügers Arch.* 342:347–58

19. Edinger, H. M., Eisenman, J. S. 1970. Thermosensitive neurons in tuberal and posterior hypothalamus of cats. *Am. J. Physiol.* 219:1098–1103

20. Eisenman, J. S., Jackson, D. C. 1967. Thermal response patterns of septal and preoptic neurons in cats. *Exp. Neurol.* 19:33–45

21. Gerber, R. L., Klussmann, F. W., Heller, H. C. 1984. Preoptic/anterior hypothalamic neural responses to thermal stimulation of the hypothalamus and spinal cord in unanesthetized, unrestrained rabbits. See Ref. 10, pp. 83–86

22. Glotzbach, S. F., Heller, H. C. 1984. Changes in the thermal characteristics of hypothalamic neurons during sleep and wakefulness. *Brain Res.* 309:17–26

23. Gordon, C. J., Heath, J. E. 1980. Effects of prostaglandin E2 on the activity of thermosensitive and insensitive single units in the preoptic/anterior hypothalamus of unanesthetized rabbits. *Brain Res.* 183:113–21

24. Gordon, C. J., Heath, J. E. 1980. Slow bursting thermal sensitive neurons in the preoptic area of the rabbit. *Brain Res. Bull.* 5:515–18

25. Gordon, C. J., Heath, J. E. 1981. Effect of monoamines on firing rate and thermal sensitivity of neurons in the preoptic area of awake rabbits. *Exp. Neurol.* 72:352–65

26. Gordon, C. J., Heath, J. E. 1981. Acoustically driven thermal-identified neurons in the preoptic area of unanesthetized rabbits. *Brain Res.* 212:301–7

27. Gorke, K. 1980. Influences of spinal cord temperature changes on reflex discharge and spontaneous activity of spinal motoneurones in pigeons and leguans. *J. Comp. Physiol.* 139:251–59

28. Gorke, K., Pierau, F. K. 1979. Initiation of muscle activity in spinalized pigeons during spinal cord cooling and warming. *Pflügers Arch.* 381:47–52

29. Greer, G. L., Gardner, D. R. 1974. Characterization of responses from temperature-sensitive units in trout brain. *Comp. Biochem. Physiol. A* 48:189–203

30. Guieu, J. D., Hardy, J. D. 1971. Integrative activity of preoptic units I: Response to local and peripheral temperature changes. *J. Physiol.* 63:253–56

31. Hammel, H. T. 1965. Neurones and temperature regulation. In *Physiological Controls and Regulations*, ed. W. S. Yamamoto, J. R. Brobeck, pp. 71–97. Philadelphia/London: Saunders

32. Hammel, H. T., Caldwell, F. T., Abrams, R. M. 1967. Regulation of body temperature in the blue-tongued lizard. *Science* 156:1260–62

33. Hammel, H. T., Maggert, J., Kaul, R., Simon, E., Simon-Oppermann, C. 1976. Effects of altering spinal cord temperature on temperature regulation in the Adelie penguin, *Pygoscelis adeliae*. *Pflügers Arch.* 362:1–6

34. Hammel, H. T., Stromme, S. B., Myhre, K. 1969. Forebrain temperature activates behavioral thermoregulatory response in Arctic sculpins. *Science* 165:83–85

35. Hardy, J. D., Guieu, J. D. 1971. Integrative activity of preoptic units II: Hypothetical network. *J. Physiol.* 63:264–67

36. Helfmann, W., Jannes, P., Jessen, C. 1981. Total body thermosensitivity and its spinal and supraspinal fractions in the conscious goose. *Pflügers Arch.* 391:60–67

37. Hensel, H. 1981. *Thermoreception and Temperature Regulation*. London: Academic. 321 pp.

38. Hori, T. 1981. Thermosensitivity of preoptic and anterior hypothalamic neurons in the capsaicin-desensitized rat. *Pflügers Arch.* 389:297–99

39. Hori, T., Harada, Y. 1976. Midbrain neuronal responses to local and spinal cord temperatures. *Am. J. Physiol.* 231:1573–78

40. Hori, T., Harada, Y. 1976. Responses of midbrain raphe neurons to local temperature. *Pflügers Arch.* 364:205–7

41. Hori, T., Kiyohara, T., Nakashima, T.,

Shibata, M. 1982. Responses of preoptic thermosensitive neurons to medial forebrain bundle stimulation. *Brain Res. Bull.* 8:667–75

42. Hori, T., Kiyohara, T., Osaka, T., Shibata, M., Nakashima, T. 1982. Responses of preoptic thermosensitive neurons to mediobasal hypothalamic stimulation. *Brain Res. Bull.* 8:677–83

43. Hori, T., Kiyohara, T., Shibata, M., Nakashima, T. 1984. Involvement of prefrontal cortex in the central control of thermoregulation. See Ref. 10, pp. 71–74

44. Hori, T., Nakashima, T., Hori, N., Kiyohara, T. 1980. Thermo-sensitive neurons in hypothalamic tissue slices in vitro. *Brain Res.* 186:203–7

45. Hori, T., Nakashima, T., Kiyohara, T., Shibata, M., Hori, N. 1980. Effect of calcium removal on thermosensitivity of preoptic neurons in hypothalamic slices. *Neurosci. Lett.* 20:171–75

46. Hori, T., Nakashima, T., Kiyohara, T., Shibata, M. 1982. Comparison of anterior hypothalamic and preoptic thermosensitive neurons in vitro. *Neurosci. Lett.* 31:283–88

47. Hori, T., Nakashima, T., Kiyohara, T., Shibata, M. 1984. Effects of leukocytic pyrogen and sodium salicylate on hypothalamic thermosensitive neurons in vitro. *Neurosci. Lett.* 49:313–18

48. Hori, T., Nakayama, T. 1973. Effects of biogenic amines on central thermoresponsive neurones in the rabbit. *J. Physiol.* 232:71–85

49. Hori, T., Osaka, T., Kiyohara, T., Shibata, M., Nakashima, T. 1982. Hippocampal input to preoptic thermosensitive neurons in the rat. *Neurosci. Lett.* 32:155–58

50. Hori, T., Shinohara, K. 1979. Hypothalamic thermo-responsive neurones in the new-born rat. *J. Physiol.* 294:541–60

51. Hori, Y., Nakayama, T. 1982. Temperature sensitivity of the preoptic and anterior hypothalamic neurons in organ culture. *Tohoku J. Exp. Med.* 136:79–87

52. Inoue, S., Murakami, N. 1976. Unit responses in the medulla oblongata of rabbit to changes in local and cutaneous temperature. *J. Physiol.* 259:339–56

53. Jessen, C., Hales, J. R. S., Molyneux, G. S. 1982. Hypothalamic thermosensitivity in an emu, *Dromiceius novae-hollandiae. Pflügers Arch.* 393:278–80

54. Kelso, S. R., Boulant, J. A. 1982. Effect of synaptic blockade on thermosensitive neurons in hypothalamic tissue slices. *Am. J. Physiol.* 243:R480–90

55. Kelso, S. R., Perlmutter, M. N., Boulant, J. A. 1982. Thermosensitive single-unit activity of in vitro hypothalamic slices. *Am. J. Physiol.* 242:R77–R84

56. Kiyohara, T., Hori, T., Shibata, M., Nakashima, T. 1984. Effects of angiotensin II on preoptic thermosensitive neurones in the rat. See Ref. 10, pp. 141–44

57. Kiyohara, T., Hori, T., Shibata, M., Nakashima, T., Osaka, T. 1984. Neural inputs to preoptic thermosensitive neurons: Histological and electrophysiological mapping of central connection. *J. Therm. Biol.* 9:21–26

58. Klee, M. R., Pierau, F. K., Faber, D. S. 1974. Temperature effects on resting potential and spike parameters of cat motoneurons. *Exp. Brain Res.* 19:478–92

59. Klussmann, F. W., Stelter, W. J., Spaan, G. 1969. Temperature sensitivity of spinal motoneurones of the cat. *Fed. Proc.* 28:992–95

60. Lillywhite, H. B. 1971. Thermal modulation of cutaneous mucus discharge as a determinant of evaporative water loss in the frog, *Rana catesbeiana. Z. Vergl. Physiol.* 73:84–104

61. Magoun, H. W., Harrison, F., Brobeck, J. R., Ranson, S. W. 1938. Activation of heat loss mechanisms by local heating of the brain. *J. Neurophysiol.* 1:101–14

62. Martin, R., Simon, E., Simon-Oppermann, C. 1981. Brain stem sites mediating specific and non-specific temperature effects on thermoregulation in the Pekin duck. *J. Physiol.* 314:161–74

63. Matsumura, K., Nakayama, T., Ishikawa, Y. 1984. Effects of median raphe electrical stimulation on the preoptic thermosensitive neurons in rats. See Ref. 10, pp. 87–90

64. Mills, S. H., Heath, J. E. 1972. Responses to thermal stimulation of the preoptic area in the house sparrow, *Passer domesticus. Am. J. Physiol.* 222:914–19

65. Morgareidge, K. R., Hammel, H. T. 1975. Evaporative water loss in box turtles: Effects of rostral brainstem and other temperatures. *Science* 187:366–68

66. Myhre, K., Hammel, H. T. 1969. Behavioral regulation of internal temperature in the lizard *Tiliqua scincoides. Am. J. Physiol.* 217:1490–95

67. Nakashima, T., Hori, T., Kiyohara, T., Shibata, M. 1984. Effects of local osmolality changes on medial preoptic thermosensitive neurones in hypothalamic slices in vitro. See Ref. 10, pp. 133–36

68. Nakayama, T., Hori, Y., Suzuki, M., Yonezawa, T., Yamamoto, K. 1978.

Thermo-sensitive neurons in preoptic and anterior hypothalamic tissue cultures in vitro. *Neurosci. Lett.* 9:23–26

69. Necker, R. 1978. Temperature-sensitive ascending neurons in the spinal cord of pigeons. *Pflügers Arch.* 353:275–86

70. Nelson, D. O., Prosser, C. L. 1981. Temperature-sensitive neurons in the preoptic region of sunfish. *Am. J. Physiol.* 241:R259–63

71. Nelson, D. O., Prosser, C. L. 1981. Intracellular recordings from thermosensitive preoptic neurons. *Science* 213:787–89

72. Parmeggiani, P. L., Azzaroni, A., Cevolani, D., Ferrari, G. 1983. Responses of anterior hypothalamic-preoptic neurons to direct thermal stimulation during wakefulness and sleep. *Brain Res.* 269:382–85

73. Perlmutter, M. N., Boulant, J. A. 1983. Intracellular recordings from temperature-sensitive septal and hypothalamic neurons. *Soc. Neurosci.* 9(1):517 (Abstr.)

74. Pierau, F. K., Klee, M. R., Klussmann, F. W. 1976. Effect of temperature on postsynaptic potentials of cat spinal motoneurones. *Brain Res.* 114:21–34

75. Puschmann, S., Jessen, C. 1978. Anterior and posterior hypothalamus: effects of independent temperature displacements on heat production in conscious goats. *Pflügers Arch.* 373:59–68

76. Rautenberg, W., May, B., Necker, R., Rosner, G. 1978. Control of panting by thermosensitive spinal neurons in birds. In *Respiratory Function in Birds, Adult and Embryonic*, ed. J. Piiper, pp. 204–10. Berlin: Springer-Verlag

77. Rautenberg, W., Necker, R., May, B. 1972. Thermoregulatory responses of the pigeon to changes of the brain and the spinal cord temperatures. *Pflügers Arch.* 338:31–42

78. Reaves, T. A., Heath, J. E. 1975. Interval coding of temperature by CNS neurones in thermoregulation. *Nature* 257:688–90

79. Deleted in proof

80. Riedesel, M. L., Cloudsley-Thompson, J. L., Cloudsley-Thompson, J. A. 1971. Evaporative thermoregulation in turtles. *Physiol. Zool.* 44:28–32

81. Satinoff, E. 1978. Neural organization and evolution of thermal regulation in mammals. *Science* 201:16–22

82. Deleted in proof

83. Schmidt, I. 1976. Effect of central thermal stimulation on the thermoregulatory behavior of the pigeon. *Pflügers Arch.* 363:271–72

84. Schmidt, I. 1978. Behavioral and autonomic thermoregulation in heat stressed pigeons modified by central thermal stimulation. *J. Comp. Physiol.* 127:75–87

85. Schmidt, I. 1983. Weighting regional thermal inputs to explain autonomic and behavioral thermoregulation in the pigeon. *J. Therm. Biol.* 8:47–48

86. Schmidt, I., Simon, E. 1979. Interaction of behavioral and autonomic thermoregulation in cold exposed pigeons. *J. Comp. Physiol.* 133:151–57

87. Scott, I., Boulant, J. A. 1984. Dopamine effects on thermosensitive neurons in hypothalamic tissue slices. *Brain Res.* 306:157–63

88. Seller, T. J., Stephenson, J. D. 1983. Pharmacology of avian temperature regulation. In *Progress in Nonmammalian Brain Research*, ed. G. Nistico, L. Bolis, 2:105–35. Fla: CRC

89. Shibata, M., Hori, T., Kiyohara, T., Nakashima, T. 1984. Activity of hypothalamic thermosensitive neurons during cortical spreading depression in the rat. *Brain Res.* 308:255–62

90. Silva, N. L., Boulant, J. A. 1984. Effects of osmotic pressure, glucose, and temperature on neurons in preoptic tissue slices. *Am. J. Physiol.* 247:R335–45

91. Silva, N. L., Boulant, J. A. 1986. Effects of testosterone, estradiol, and temperature on neurons in preoptic tissue slices. *Am. J. Physiol.* In press

92. Simon, E. 1972. Temperature signals from skin and spinal cord converging on spinothalamic neurons. *Pflügers Arch.* 337:323–32

93. Simon, E. 1974. Temperature regulation: The spinal cord as a site of extrahypothalamic thermoregulatory functions. *Rev. Physiol. Biochem. Pharmacol.* 71:1–76

94. Simon, E., Hammel, H. T., Oksche, A. 1977. Thermosensitivity of single units in the hypothalamus of the conscious Pekin duck. *J. Neurobiol.* 8:523–35

95. Simon, E., Iriki, M. 1971. Sensory transmission of spinal heat and cold sensitivity in ascending spinal neurons. *Pflügers Arch.* 328:103–20

96. Simon, E., Martin, R., Simon-Oppermann, C. 1981. Central nervous versus total body thermosensitivity of the duck. *Int. J. Biometeor.* 25:249–56

97. Simon, E., Simon-Oppermann, C., Hammel, H. T., Kaul, R., Maggert, J. 1976. Effects of altering rostral brain stem temperature on temperature regulation in the Adelie penguin, *Pygoscelis adeliae*. *Pflügers Arch.* 362:7–13

98. Simon-Oppermann, C., Martin, R. 1979. Mammalian-like thermosensitivity

in the lower brainstem of the Pekin duck. *Pflügers Arch.* 379:291–93

99. Simon-Oppermann, C., Simon, E., Jessen, C., Hammel, H. T. 1978. Hypothalamic thermosensitivity in conscious Pekin ducks. *Am. J. Physiol.* 235:R130–40

100. Snapp, B. D., Heller, H. C., Gospe, S. M. Jr. 1977. Hypothalamic thermosensitivity in California quail, *Lophortyx californicus. J. Comp. Physiol.* 117:345–57

101. Deleted in proof

102. Templeton, J. R. 1971. Peripheral and central control of panting in the desert iguana, *Dipsosaurus dorsalis. J. Physiol.* 63:439–42

103. Wunnenberg, W., Bruck, K. 1970. Studies on the ascending pathways from the thermosensitive region of the spinal cord. *Pflügers Arch.* 321:233–41

104. Wunnenberg, W., Hardy, J. D. 1972. Response of single units of the posterior hypothalamus to thermal stimulation. *J. Appl. Physiol.* 33:547–52

COMPARATIVE PHYSIOLOGY

OXIDANTS AND ANTIOXIDANTS IN THE LUNG

Introduction, Robert E. Forster, II, *Section Editor*

We believe that life arose on this planet in a reducing atmosphere and that gaseous oxygen derived from photosynthesis. Oxygen is toxic to many life processes and is not always a life-sustaining inhalant. The lung is continuously exposed to a significant oxygen partial pressure and we would expect it to be especially vulnerable to toxic effects of the gas. We might also predict that protective measures against the toxicity of oxygen in cells would have arisen.

The theme of this section is the formation of free radical oxidants in the lung, their effects on its structure and function, and the importance of antioxidant mechanisms. The first article, by W. A. Pryor, provides background on the types of oxygen radicals and related oxidant species and discusses the mechanism of their formation, their lifetimes, and some pathological effects they produce in the lungs.

While oxygen radicals in the environment are generally destructive to the lung, exposed as it is to pollutants in the atmosphere, they are actually formed in cells as a defense against foreign organisms. H. J. Forman discusses in the second article the production of superoxide, hydrogen peroxide, and other possible oxidants by phagocytes in the lung. His article describes the stimulation and the mechanism of production of oxygen radicals and the source of their bactericidal activity. The next article, by L. L. Smith, describes the cellular and tissue damage caused by xenobiotics, such as paraquat, which when taken up in the lung are considered to release oxygen free radicals. The lung has three layers of defense against oxidants. One of these is made of metallo-enzymes called superoxide dismutases. These reduce superoxide to peroxide, which is then removed by the next layer of defense, the catalases and peroxidases. I. Fridovich and B. Freeman discuss these enzymes, their reactions and importance.

The actual mechanisms by which oxygen produces its toxic effects in the lung, and in particular the relation of hyperoxia to free radical production, are summarized by D. Jamieson, B. Chance, E. Cadenas, and A. Boveris. The lung sees the highest P_{O_2} of any organ. Breathing air under hyperbaric conditions or inspiring an increased oxygen concentration can produce toxic effects in the lung parenchyma. J. Crapo reviews the morphological changes seen in the lung during the development of this toxicity in the final article.

Ann. Rev. Physiol. 1986. 48:657–67

OXY-RADICALS AND RELATED SPECIES: Their Formation, Lifetimes, and Reactions

William A. Pryor

Thomas and David Boyd Professor in the Departments of Chemistry and Biochemistry, Louisiana State University, Baton Rouge, Louisiana 70803

INTRODUCTION

In this brief overview I will review some of the ways in which free radicals and related highly reactive species are produced in biological systems. I will discuss the reactivities and lifetimes of these species, and also will briefly list some pathological conditions and chronic diseases in which these species may be involved.

The rich variety of the species of interest in free radical biology is noteworthy. Table 1 lists species that have been implicated in various physiological and pathological processes; some of these are neutral radicals, some are radical ions, and some are molecules that contain an even number of electrons and, therefore, are not free radicals. As we shall see, radicals differ greatly in their stabilities; one of the radicals listed in Table 1, nitrogen dioxide, is sufficiently stable to reach ppm levels in polluted urban air.

What name can be used to encompass the species listed in Table 1? A phrase that is finding increased use in free radical biology is "partially reduced oxygen products." However, even this broad title is unsatisfactory since some of the species in Table 1 contain oxygen atoms at the same oxidation level as elemental oxygen (e.g. ozone and singlet oxygen). The property that these species share is that they have the *potential* to cause radical reactions to occur in biological systems. Some of these species are radicals and therefore react by radical processes; others react to produce molecules that can decompose to form radicals (e.g. singlet oxygen leads to hydroperoxides). However, these species need not always react via free radical pathways. For example, ozone, hydrogen

657

Table 1   Oxy-radicals and related species that have been implicated in cellular processes

Name	Symbol	Notes
Singlet oxygen	$^1O_2$	b
Ozone	O_3	b
Nitrogen dioxide	NO_2	a
Hydrogen peroxide	H_2O_2	b
Hydroxyl	HO·	a
Superoxide	O_2^-	a, c
Hydroperoxyl	HOO·	a, d
Alkoxyl	RO·	a
Peroxyl	ROO·	a
Acyloxyl	$R-\overset{\displaystyle O}{\overset{\|}{C}}-O·$	a
Acylperoxyl	$R-\overset{\displaystyle O}{\overset{\|}{C}}-OO·$	a
Aryloxyl	ArO·	a
Arylperoxyl	ArOO·	a
Hypochlorous acid	HOCl	b
Semiquinone radical	HQ·	a, e
Semiquinone radical anion	Q^-	a, f

[a]A radical (i.e. has an odd number of electrons)
[b]A nonradical
[c]Has pKa = 4.8
[d]The protonated form of superoxide
[e]For example, the benzene semiquinone radical is $HO-C_6H_4-O·$.
[f]For example, the benzene semiquinone radical is $^-O-C_6H_4-O·$.

peroxide, and hypochlorous acid can react by nonradical pathways as well as by radical-mediated routes, and distinguishing these two mechanisms is an important aspect of understanding the effects of these three species.

Nitrogen dioxide, like many radicals, has odd electron density on more than one atom; for NO_2 about 50% of the odd electron density is on the nitrogen (65). Other than NO_2, Table 1 does not list radicals for which the odd electron is not primarily localized on oxygen. However, radicals that have their odd electron density on other atoms often occur in biological systems. Carbon-centered radicals are formed from polyunsaturated fatty acids (PUFA), for example, by hydrogen atom abstraction in the propagation sequence of lipid autoxidation (41, 51) or by addition of radicals to one of the double bonds [e.g. NO_2 (58)]. Carbon-centered radicals also are formed when polynuclear aromatic hydrocarbons (PAH) are oxidized by one electron; these aromatic cation radicals are involved in the activation of PAH to carcinogenic forms (15). Hetero-atom-centered radicals (26, 35, 45) are quite commonly encountered. For example, hydrogen atom abstraction from thiols is very facile, so thiol radicals are readily formed from cysteine, GSH, etc. In addition, nitrogen-centered radicals and radical ions may occur, for example, when amines such as aminofluorene are oxidized by peroxidases (27).

HOW ARE RADICALS FORMED IN THE CELL?

Radicals are produced either by normal physiological processes, or because of the influence of exogenous species. These exogenous species may be compounds that occur naturally in the biosphere [e.g. ozone, NO_2, ethanol, or tetradecanoyl phorbol acetate (TPA)], industrial chemicals that are purposefully synthesized by man (e.g. carbon tetrachloride), or xenobiotics that are inadvertantly produced by man's activities (e.g. benzo[a]pyrene).

Of the radicals formed in biological systems, the greatest attention has been focused on superoxide, the species formed when oxygen is reduced by a single electron (29, 71):

$$O_2 + e^- \rightarrow O_2^{\cdot -} \qquad\qquad 1.$$

Superoxide undergoes a dismutation to form hydrogen peroxide,

$$2\,O_2^- + 2H^+ \rightarrow H_2O_2 + O_2 \qquad\qquad 2.$$

so H_2O_2 is also generally present in superoxide generating systems. In addition, superoxide can be protonated to form the hydroperoxyl radical (9):

$$O_2^- + H^+ \rightarrow HOO\cdot \qquad\qquad 3.$$

Separating effects observed in a given system into those caused by superoxide, $HOO\cdot$, and $HO\cdot$ (which can be produced from the decomposition of hydrogen peroxide) generally is not a trivial task.

The availability of superoxide dismutases (SOD), the enzymes that catalyze Equation 2 (29), has provided a tool that allows testing physiological processes for the involvement of superoxide. Unexpectedly, superoxide is found to be formed in all aerobically metabolizing cells (29). For example, superoxide appears to "leak" out of mitochondrial electron transport; these radicals may cause cooxidation of xenobiotics and/or initiate pathological changes (13). In addition, macrophages and certain other phagocytic cells produce superoxide during the oxidative burst that follows their activation (6, 66).

Superoxide is formed when electronegative compounds intercept electrons from normal cellular electron transport and then reduce oxygen, a process called redox cycling (5, 11, 17). This two-step process is a shunt in which

Equation 1 is the net change that occurs. This two-step redox cycle is illustrated in Equations 4 and 5 below for a quinone, Q.

$$Q + e^- \rightarrow Q^{\cdot -} \qquad\qquad 4.$$

$$Q^{\cdot -} + O_2 \rightarrow Q + O_2^{\cdot -} \qquad\qquad 5.$$

This type of redox cycle is extremely common; it is observed, for example, for certain anticancer drugs (5, 20, 21, 27) and some antiparasitic drugs (26).

It has become clear very recently that superoxide also is produced during the reperfusion of oxygenated blood into tissue that has briefly been anoxic (2, 46). Surgeons have observed that organs can be maintained in an anoxic state for some time with little or no damage; however, when arteries are unclamped and aerated blood is allowed to reperfuse the organ, tissue damage can be sudden and severe. A number of investigators have discovered that this damage can be mitigated or prevented if SOD or other protective species are added to the blood during reperfusion. The prevention of tissue injury during post-ischemic reperfusion is an extremely exciting development arising from the research in free radical biology. Although all the mechanisms by which superoxide is produced during reperfusion are not known, an interesting hypothesis has been suggested by McCord and his colleagues (46). These workers propose that xanthine dehydrogenase is converted to xanthine oxidase by a proteinase activated during anoxia.

A wide variety of drugs and xenobiotics can cause free radical production in the cell. Perhaps the earliest studied example is carbon tetrachloride; CCl_4 can accept an electron (from a P450 site in the liver in this case), causing the bond scission shown in Equation 6 below and producing the trichloromethyl radical. This radical then adds to the double bonds of PUFA in lipids, producing the familiar pattern of CCl_4-induced liver damage (62, 63).

$$CCl_4 + e^- \rightarrow Cl^- + Cl_3C\cdot \qquad\qquad 6.$$

The membrane-active TPA triggers a cascade of chemical effects from cells, one of which is superoxide production (16). TPA is a tumor promoter, i.e. when this compound is repeatedly applied to an organ following the application of an otherwise ineffective dose of a carcinogen, it causes the development of hyperplasia (22). It is now recognized that most promoters cause the production of superoxide; this in fact appears to be a necessary requirement. This is an extremely important subject, since many antioxidants and radical scavengers have anti-promoter effects (16, 22). The *initiation* of tumors is extremely common (1, 16); however, the infrequency of cancer and the long lag time between initial insult and tumor development are due to the requirement for continual, long-term exposure to *promoters* in order for cell transformation to be effected (22). Initiation by the carcinogen is irreversible; however, promotion is reversible (16, 22). Thus, a strategy for cancer prevention may lie in understanding the mechanism by which tumor promoters work and the ways in which certain radical scavengers exert protection.

When smoggy air is breathed, lung tissue is exposed to both ozone and the nitrogen oxides NO and NO_2 (collectively termed NOx). Ozone is an example of a nonradical that reacts with biological molecules to produce radicals (60). The two nitrogen oxides are both stable free radicals, and both react rapidly with heme compounds. However, nitric oxide (NO) is relatively unreactive toward simple organic molecules, whereas nitrogen dioxide is quite reactive. Since NO_2 is a free radical (with an odd number of electrons), it must react with molecules (which have an even number of electrons) to form free radicals. Thus, much of the pulmonary damage caused by breathing smoggy air results from radical-mediated reactions (48, 52, 58).

Nitric oxide and nitrogen dioxide also react with thiols (54). This appears important both in smog-induced inactivation of thiol-dependent enzymes and in cigarette-smoke toxicology (54). Fresh, undiluted gas phase cigarette smoke is remarkable in containing more than 10^{17} reactive oxy-radicals *per puff* (19, 59). Undiluted cigarette smoke also contains several hundred ppm NOx; in contrast, polluted air generally contains less than 1 ppm NOx. We have recently shown that some of the effects of cigarette smoke result from its very high NOx content (19). For example, the oxidative inactivation of the human anti-protease, alpha-1-proteinase inhibitor (a1PI), appears to be caused by species produced from the reactions of NO_2 with isoprene and other constituents of cigarette smoke. These reactions produce oxy-radicals and oxidants, such as per-oxynitrates, that can oxidize a critical methionine in a1PI, inactivating the protein (19, 41, 55, 56).

LIFETIMES OF FREE RADICALS AND RELATED SPECIES

It is generally recognized that small organic radicals are reactive and therefore short-lived, but there still is appreciable variation in their reactivities and lifetimes (53). Some radicals are sufficiently stable to diffuse some distance in the cell, whereas others (such as HO·) are so reactive that they react within 1 to 5 molecular diameters of their site of formation. Table 2 presents estimates of the lifetimes of radicals and some related species in tissue. For this table, radical lifetimes have been estimated in the following way: The rate constants for the reactions of most types of radicals with different types of substrates have been determined; thus, radical lifetimes can be calculated if the identities and concentrations of the reactive substrates in the vicinity of the radical are known.

In Table 2, a representative reactive substrate is chosen for each species, chosen to be typical of the type of substance with which the radical in question would preferentially react. The concentration of this substrate is then chosen to approximate the total reactivity profile that the radical would face in the cell. Thus, the model substrate concentration is taken as quite high if the radical is extremely reactive and unselective. For example, hydroxyl radicals react with rate constants that are nearly diffusion controlled, so their lifetimes have been estimated by assuming a nearby reaction shell consisting of 1 M linoleate, and a rate constant for the HO· + LH reaction of 10^9 M^{-1}s^{-1}. It should be noted that the HO· radical would react with any reactive species in its neighborhood with this rate constant, so the choice of substrate is not critical. (Water is present at an even higher concentration, but radicals do not, in general, react with water.) In contrast, the peroxyl radical is far more selective, so it is assumed to be surrounded by a medium with reactivity like that of linoleate at a concentration of 1 mM; that is to say, a peroxyl radical would not react with every molecule in its vicinity (as would the hydroxyl radical), but would only react when it collided with an activated molecule. Obviously this type of calculation can be criticized. However, the enormous differences in lifetimes that are obtained even by this simple calculation are highly suggestive and demonstrate that even small oxy-radicals differ from each other in very important ways, and some can probably diffuse some distance in the cell.

Table 2 Estimate of the half-lives of oxy-radicals and related species

Radical	Substrate[a]	Conc.[b]	Half-life (at 37°C)
HO·	LH[c]	1 M	10^{-9} sec
RO·	LH	100 mM	10^{-6} sec
ROO·	LH	1 mM	7 sec
L·[d]	O_2	20 μM	10^{-8} sec
H_2O_2	e	—	e
O_2^-	e	—	e
$^1O_2$	H_2O	Solvent	10^{-6} sec
Q$^-$	e, f	—	Days

[a]Substrate chosen as representative of typical reactive target molecules for the species in the first column
[b]A concentration of the substrate that is meant to approximate the sum of all reactive species in the vicinity of the radical and that is chosen to reflect the selectivity of the radical
[c]Linoleate
[d]L· is the linolenyl radical. The reversibility of the L· + O_2 reaction has been neglected. An oxygen concentration is used that is typical of moderately oxygenated tissue.
[e]See discussion in text.
[f]The cigarette tar free radical (57, 61).

The lifetimes of some of the species in Table 2 cannot be calculated in this way, and these species require some discussion. Hydrogen peroxide is a stable molecule; it is normally purchased in solutions up to 30% (9 moles/liter!) in water. However, hydrogen peroxide, like most peroxides, is very sensitive to decomposition caused by species that react with it. It is enzymatically decomposed by catalase and GSH peroxidase, and by extremely low concentrations of transition metals such as iron chelated with species such as EDTA and ADP (3, 51). Thus, the lifetime of H_2O_2 in the cell can only be calculated if the concentrations of all reactive species and protective enzymes in the immediate environment are known. However, it would be expected that H_2O_2 in most cellular environments would have a lifetime that would permit it to diffuse appreciable distances before reaction.

Similarly, the lifetime of superoxide cannot be calculated unless the concentrations of SOD and all reactive substrates are known. However, the lifetime of superoxide in a cellular environment in water would be expected to be very short, too short to permit diffusion for great distances. However, the lifetime of the hydroperoxyl (HOO·) radical in organic or lipophilic media could be longer (9).

PATHOLOGY THAT INVOLVES RADICAL REACTIONS

I will conclude this brief overview with a discussion of the effects that radicals can have in mammalian systems. Table 3 presents a list of diseases that recent evidence suggests involve, to some extent, radical reactions. A detailed discussion of each of these is not possible in the space available, but the cited references can be consulted for further discussion.

Table 3   Diseases and pathology that may to some extent involve radical-mediated reactions

Disease	Strength of the evidence for some radical involvement	References
Emphysema[a]	+++	41, 50, 55, 56, 69
Cancer[a]	+++	15, 16, 24, 27, 44, 50, 67, 68, 70
Arthritis[a]	++	25, 32
Atherosclerosis[a]	+	7, 33, 38
Cirrhosis[a]	+	37
Stroke[a]	+	38
Retrolental fibroplasia	+++	21
Cataract	++	8, 36
Adult respiratory distress syndrome	++	28, 66
Aging	+	4, 23, 53

[a] Critical, life-limiting diseases for humans (30).

The final process listed in the table is aging. The rate of aging of an animal appears primarily to be determined by genetic factors. Thus, the maximum lifespan of an animal is genetically determined, and it does not appear that significant manipulation of this maximum lifespan is possible utilizing the techniques of free radical biology (52, 53). For this reason, antioxidants do not affect maximum lifespan (34). However, the lifespan of individuals in the population varies as the stress on that individual is varied, and free radicals appear to play an important role in this stress. Therefore, antioxidants and radical scavengers extend the mean lifespan of various populations of organisms, including mammals (33, 52, 53).

Radicals increase aging both by influencing the rate of development of specific chronic diseases and by causing general "wear and tear" on biopolymer molecules. With regard to the influence of radical-mediated reactions on specific diseases, it is interesting that the evidence for radical involvement is becoming very much stronger for some chronic, life-limiting diseases that affect humans (30, 53) (see Table 3). The argument that free radicals cause general, nonspecific damage to biopolymer molecules is called the "free radical theory of aging" (34, 53). This theory was first suggested many years ago before there was evidence for it beyond the observation that ionizing radiation, which causes radicals to be formed in tissue, causes the increased appearance of certain diseases. In recent years, however, evidence that radicals attack PUFA, proteins, and nucleic acids *in vivo* has become quite persuasive. Perhaps the most interesting new data indicates that attack on proteins is common, which suggests that previous emphasis on PUFA as the primary or sole target for radical attack may be in error. Thus, some proteins become less functional with age (12, 43), and some enzymes lose activity (31). The time-dependent process in which enzymes lose fidelity, produce inaccurate DNA, leading to inaccurate enzymes, all repeated ad infinitum, is an expression of the classic error catastrophy theory (40, 64) which, with modifications, is still viable (72).

Literature Cited

1. Ames, B. N. 1984. Cancer and diet. *Science* 224:668–70
2. Aust, S. D. 1985. Iron in ischemic tissue injury. *Adv. Free Radical Biol. Med.* 1:1–19
3. Aust, S. D., Svingen, B. A. 1982. The role of iron in enzymatic lipid peroxidation. In *Free Radicals in Biology*, ed. W. A. Pryor, 5:1–25. New York: Academic. 283 pp.
4. Armstrong, D., Sohal, R. S., Cutler, R. G., Slater, T. F., eds. 1984. *Free Radicals in Molecular Biology, Aging, and Disease*, Vol. 27. New York: Raven. 416 pp.
5. Bachur, N. R., Gordon, S. L., Gee, M.

V. 1978. A general mechanism for microsomal activation of quinone anticancer agents to free radicals. *Cancer Res.* 38:1745–50
6. Baehner, R. L., Boxer, L. A., Ingraham, L. M. 1982. Reduced oxygen by-products and white blood cells. In *Free Radicals in Biology*, ed. W. A. Pryor, 5:91–108. New York: Academic. 283 pp.
7. Barrowcliffe, T. W., Gray, E., Kerry, P. J., Gutteridge, J. M. C. 1984. Triglyceride-rich lipoproteins are responsible for thrombin generation induced by lipid peroxides. *Thromb. Haem.* 52:7–10
8. Bhuyan, K. C., Bhuyan, D. K. 1984.

Molecular mechanism of cataractogenesis: III. Toxic metabolites of oxygen as initiators of lipid peroxidation and cataract. *Curr. Eye Res.* 3:67–81
9. Bielski, B. H. J., Arudi, R. L., Sutherland, M. W. 1983. A study of the reactivity of HO_2/O_2^- with unsaturated fatty acids. *J. Biol. Chem.* 258:4759–61
10. Bishop, C. T., Freeman, B. A., Crapo, J. D. 1984. Free radicals and lung injury. In *Free Radicals in Molecular Biology, Aging, and Disease,* ed. D. Armstrong, R. S. Sohal, R. G. Cutler, T. F. Slater, 27:381–90. New York: Raven. 416 pp.
11. Borg, D. C., Schaich, K. M. 1984. Cytotoxicity from coupled redox cycling of autoxidizing xenobiotics and metals. *Isr. J. Chem.* 24:38–53
12. Brot, N., Weissbach, H. 1983. Biochemistry and physiological role of methionine sulfoxide residues in proteins. *Arch. Biochem. Biophys.* 223:271–81
13. Cadenas, E., Boveris, A., Chance, B. 1984. Low-level chemiluminescence of biological systems. In *Free Radicals in Biology,* ed. W. A. Pryor, 6:212–38. Florida: Academic. 437 pp.
14. Cathcart, R., Schwiers, E., Saul, R. L., Ames, B. N. 1984. Thymine glycol and thymidine glycol in human and rat urine: A possible assay for oxidative DNA damage. *Proc. Natl. Acad. Sci. USA* 81: 5633–37
15. Cavalieri, E. L., Rogan, E. G. 1984. One-electron and two-electron oxidation in aromatic hydrocarbon carcinogenesis. In *Free Radicals in Biology,* ed. W. A. Pryor, 6:324–62. Florida: Academic. 437 pp.
16. Cerutti, P. A. 1985. Prooxidant states and tumor promotion. *Science* 227:375–80
17. Chesis, P. L., Levin, D. E., Smith, M. T., Ernster, L., Ames, B. N. 1984. Mutagenicity of quinones: Pathways of metabolic activation and detoxification. *Proc. Natl. Acad. Sci. USA* 81:1696–1700
18. Chiu, D., Lubin, B., Shohet, S. B. 1982. Peroxidative reactions in red cell biology. In *Free Radicals in Biology,* ed. W. A. Pryor, 5:115–54. New York: Academic 283 pp.
19. Church, D. F., Pryor, W. A. 1985. The free radical chemistry of cigarette smoke and its toxicological implications. *Environ. Health Perspect.* In press
20. Ciba Foundation. 1979. *Oxygen Free Radicals and Tissue Damage, Symp. 65.* New York: Excerpta Medica. 380 pp.
21. Ciba Foundation. 1983. *Biology of Vitamin E, Symp. 101.* London: Pitman. 248 pp.

22. Birnbaum, H. C., Borg, D. C., Cerutti, P., Floyd, R. A., Lesko, S. A., et. al. 1983. Free radicals in promotion. A chemical pathology study section workshop. *Cancer Res.* 43:5631–37
23. Cutler, R. G. 1984. Antioxidants, aging, and longevity. In *Free Radicals in Biology,* ed. W. A. Pryor, 6:371–423. Florida: Academic. 437 pp.
24. Cornwell, D. G., Morisaki, N. 1984. Fatty acid paradoxes in the control of cell proliferation: Prostaglandins, lipid peroxides, and cooxidation reactions. In *Free Radicals in Biology,* ed. W. A. Pryor, 6:96–133. Florida: Academic. 437 pp.
25. Del Maestro, R. F. 1984. Free radical injury during inflammation. In *Free Radicals in Molecular Biology, Aging, and Disease,* eds. D. Armstrong, R. S. Sohal, R. G. Cutler, T. F. Slater, 27:87–102. New York: Raven. 416 pp.
26. Docampo, R., Moreno, S. N. J. 1984. Free-radical intermediates in the antiparasitic action of drugs and phagocytic cells. In *Free Radicals in Biology,* ed. W. A. Pryor, 6:244–80. Florida: Academic. 437 pp.
27. Floyd, R. A., ed. 1982. *Free Radicals and Cancer.* New York: Dekker. 538 pp.
28. Freeman, B. A., Crapo, J. D. 1982. Biology of disease: Free radicals and tissue injury. *Lab. Invest.* 47:412–18
29. Fridovich, I. 1976. Oxygen radicals, hydrogen peroxide, and oxygen toxicity. In *Free Radicals in Biology,* ed. W. A. Pryor, 1:239–71. New York: Academic. 287 pp.
30. Fries, J. F., Crapo, L. M. 1981. *Vitality and Aging.* San Francisco: Freeman. 162 pp.
31. Fucci, L., Oliver, C. N., Coon, M. J., Stadtman, E. R. 1983. Inactivation of key metabolic enzymes by mixed-function oxidation reactions: Possible implication in protein turnover and aging. *Proc. Natl. Acad. Sci. USA* 80: 1521–25
32. Gutteridge, J. M. C., Hill, C., Blake, D. R. 1984. Copper stimulated phospholipid membrane peroxidation: antioxidant activity of serum and synovial fluid from patients with rheumatoid arthritis. *Clin. Chim. Acta* 139:85–90
33. Ham, E. A., Egan, R. W., Soderman, D. D., Gale, P. H., Kuehl, F. A. Jr. 1979. Peroxidase-dependent deactivation of prostacyclin synthetase. *J. Biol. Chem.* 254:2191–94
34. Harman, D. 1982. The free-radical theory of aging. In *Free Radicals in Biology,* ed. W. A. Pryor, 5:255–71. New York: Academic. 293 pp.

35. Kalyanaraman, B., Sivarajah, K. 1984. The electron spin resonance study of free radicals formed during the arachidonic acid cascade and cooxidation of xenobiotics by prostaglandin synthase. In *Free Radicals in Biology*, ed. W. A. Pryor, 6:150–92. Florida: Academic. 437 pp.

36. Katz, M. L., Robison, W. G. Jr., Dratz, E. A. 1984. Potential role of autoxidation in age changes of the retina and retinal pigment epithelium of the eye. In *Free Radicals in Molecular Biology, Aging, and Disease*, ed. D. Armstrong, R. S. Sohal, R. G. Cutler, T. F. Slater, 27:163–80. New York: Raven. 416 pp.

37. Klein, S. M., Cohen, G., Lieber, C. S., Cederbaum, A. I. 1983. Increased microsomal oxidation of hydroxyl radical scavenging agents and ethanol after chronic consumption of ethanol. *Arch. Biochem. Biophys.* 223:425–32

38. Koganemaru, S., Kuramoto, A. 1982. The effect of vitamin E on platelet kinetics of stroke-prone spontaneously hypertensive rats. *J. Nutr. Sci. Vitaminol.* 28:1–10

39. Lands, W. E. M., Kulmacz, R. J., Marshall, P. J. 1984. Lipid peroxide actions in the regulation of prostaglandin biosynthesis. In *Free Radicals in Biology*, ed. W. A. Pryor, 6:39–57. Florida: Academic. 437 pp.

40. Laughrea, M. 1982. On the error theories of aging: A review of the experimental data. *Exp. Gerontol.* 17:305–17

41. Laurent, P., Janoff, A., Kagan, H. M. 1983. Cigarette smoke blocks crosslinking of elastin in vitro. *Am. Rev. Respir. Dis.* 127:189–92

42. Lefer, A. M., Araki, H., Okamatsu, S. 1981. Beneficial actions of a free radical scavenger in traumatic shock and myocardial ischemia. *Circ. Shock* 8:273–82

43. Man, E. H., Sandhouse, M. E., Burg, J., Fisher, G. H. 1983. Accumulation of D-aspartic acid with age in the human brain. *Science* 220:1407–8

44. Marnett, L. J. 1984. Hydroperoxide-dependent oxidations during prostaglandin biosynthesis. In *Free Radicals in Biology*, ed. W. A. Pryor, 6:64–90. Florida: Academic. 437 pp.

45. Mason, R. 1982. Free-radical intermediates in the metabolism of toxic chemicals. In *Free Radicals in Biology*, ed. W. A. Pryor, 5:161–212. New York: Academic. 283 pp.

46. McCord, J. M. 1985. Oxygen-derived free radicals in postischemic tissue injury. *N. Eng. J. Med.* 312:159–63

47. Mead, J. F. 1976. Free radical mechanisms of lipid damage and consequences for cellular membranes. In *Free Radicals*

in Biology, ed. W. A. Pryor, 1:51–67. New York: Academic. 287 pp.

48. Menzel, D. B. 1976. The role of free radicals in the toxicity of air pollutants (nitrogen oxides and ozone). In *Free Radicals in Biology*, ed. W. A. Pryor, 2:181–200. New York: Academic. 303 pp.

49. Pollard, M., Luckert, P. H. 1981. Effect of indomethacin on intestinal tumors induced in rats by the acetate derivative of dimethylnitrosamine. *Science* 214:558–59

50. Powles, T. J., Bockman, R. S., Honn, K. V., Ramwell, P., eds. 1982. *Prostaglandins and Cancer: First International Conference*, Vol. 2. New York: Liss. 841 pp.

51. Pryor, W. A. 1976. The role of free radical reactions in biological systems. In *Free Radicals in Biology*, ed. W. A. Pryor, 1:1–43. New York: Academic. 287 pp.

52. Pryor, W. A. 1982. Free radical biology: Xenobiotics, cancer, and aging. *Ann. NY Acad. Sci.* 393:1–30

53. Pryor, W. A. 1984. Free radicals in autoxidation and in aging. Part I. Kinetics of the autoxidation of linoleic acid in SDS micelles: Calculations of radical concentrations, kinetic chain lengths, and the effects of vitamin E. Part II. The role of radicals in chronic human diseases and in aging. In *Free Radicals in Molecular Biology, Aging, and Disease*, ed. D. Armstrong, R. S. Sohal, R. G. Cutler, T. F. Slater, pp. 13–41. New York: Raven. 416 pp.

54. Pryor, W. A., Church, D. F., Govindan, C. K., Crank, G. 1982. Oxidation of thiols by nitric oxide and nitrogen dioxide: Synthetic utility and toxicological implications. *J. Org. Chem.* 47:156–59

55. Pryor, W. A., Dooley, M. M. 1985. Inactivation of human a-1-proteinase inhibitor by cigarette smoke: Effect of smoke phase and buffer. *Am. Rev. Resp. Dis.* 131:941–43

56. Pryor, W. A., Dooley, M. M., Church, D. F. 1984. Inactivation of human a-1-proteinase inhibitor by gas-phase cigarette smoke. *Biochem. Biophys. Res. Comm.* 122:676–81

57. Pryor, W. A., Hales, B. J., Premovic, P. I., Church, D. F. 1983. The radicals in cigarette tar: Their nature and suggested physiological implications. *Science* 220:425–27

58. Pryor, W. A., Lightsey, J. W. 1981. Mechanisms of nitrogen dioxide reactions: Initiation of lipid peroxidation and the production of nitrous acid. *Science* 214:435–37

59. Pryor, W. A., Prier, D. G., Church, D. F. 1983. An electron-spin resonance study of mainstream and sidestream cigarette smoke: The nature of the free radicals in gas-phase smoke and in cigarette tar. *Environ. Health Perspect.* 47:345–55

60. Pryor, W. A., Prier, D. G., Church, D. F. 1983. Detection of free radicals from low temperature ozone-olefin reactions by ESR spin trapping: Evidence that the radical precursor is a trioxide. *J. Am. Chem. Soc.* 105:2883–88

61. Pryor, W. A., Uehara, K., Church, D. F. 1984. The chemistry and biochemistry of the radicals in cigarette smoke: ESR evidence for the binding of the tar radical to DNA and polynucleotides. In *Oxygen Radicals in Chemistry and Biology*, ed. W. Bors, M. Saran, D. Tait, 193–201. Berlin: de Gruyter. 1058 pp.

62. Recknagel, R. O., Glende, E. A. Jr., Hruszkewycz, A. M. 1977. Chemical mechanisms in carbon tetrachloride toxicity. In *Free Radicals in Biology*, ed. W. A. Pryor, 3:97–130. New York: Academic. 311 pp.

63. Reynolds, E. S., Moslen, M. T. 1980. Free-radical damage in liver. In *Free Radicals in Biology*, ed. W. A. Pryor, 4:49–90. New York: Academic. 348 pp.

64. Strehler, B. L. 1962. *Time, Cells, and Aging.* New York: Academic. 270 pp.

65. Symons, M. 1978. *Electron-Spin Resonance Spectroscopy*, New York: Wiley. 190 pp.

66. Tate, R. M., Repine, J. E. 1984. Phagocytes, oxygen radicals, and lung injury. In *Free Radicals in Biology*, ed. W. A. Pryor, 6:199–207. Florida: Academic. 437 pp.

67. Thaler-Dao, H., de Paulet, A. C., Paoletti, R., eds. 1984. *Icosanoids and Cancer.* New York: Raven. 287 pp.

68. Ts'o, P. O. P., Caspary, W. J., Lorentzen, R. J. 1977. The involvement of free radicals in chemical carcinogenesis. In *Free Radicals in Biology*, ed. W. A. Pryor, 3:251–303. New York: Academic. 311 pp.

69. Weiss, S. J., Peppin, G., Ortiz, X., Ragsdale, C., Test, S. T. 1985. Oxidative autoactivation of latent collagenase by human neutrophils. *Science* 227:747–49

70. Weitzman, S. A., Weitberg, A. B., Clark, E. P., Stossel, T. P. 1985. Phagocytes as carcinogens: Malignant transformation produced by human neutrophils. *Science* 227:1231–33

71. Winston, G. W., Cederbaum, A. I. 1983. NADPH-dependent production of oxy-radicals by purified components of the rat liver mixed function oxidase system. *J. Biol. Chem.* 258:1508–13

72. Morley, A. A., Cox, S., Holliday, R. 1982. Human lymphocytes resistant to 6-thioguanine increase with age. *Mech. Ageing Devel.* 19:21–26

Ann. Rev. Physiol. 1986 48:669–80

OXIDANT PRODUCTION AND BACTERICIDAL ACTIVITY OF PHAGOCYTES

Henry Jay Forman

Department of Physiology, University of Pennsylvania, Philadelphia, Pennsylvania 19104, and Department of Medicine, Graduate Hospital Research Building, 415 South 19th Street, Philadelphia, Pennsylvania 19146

Michael J. Thomas

Department of Biochemistry, Bowman Gray School of Medicine, Wake Forest University, Winston-Salem, North Carolina 27103

INTRODUCTION

This review concerns recent progress in revealing mechanisms of production of activated oxygen species (the "respiratory burst"), and the chemistry of microbicidal action by phagocytes. For brevity, we have focused on representative studies since 1979. Several earlier reviews (7, 8, 21) can provide a more extensive background.

MECHANISMS OF PRODUCTION OF SUPEROXIDE AND HYDROGEN PEROXIDE

Stimulation of the Oxidase

Phagocytes, such as neutrophils and macrophages, produce superoxide (O_2^-) and H_2O_2 by an enzymatic process in which electrons are transferred from NADPH to O_2. This oxidase activity is low or nonexistent in resting cells. Stimulation of the oxidase is the process by which phagocytes transform this latent activity to an expressed activity. Another process, called "activation," involves transformation of phagocytes for greater phagocytic, secretory, and respiratory burst capacities before stimulation (81).

669

0066-4278/86/0315-0669$02.00

RECEPTORS   Production of activated oxygen species is a regulated process closely linked to phagocytosis and secretion of enzymes. These processes can be separated by selective interference with cellular stimulus-response mechanisms, cytoskeletal movement, or by granule depletion (8, 57, 58, 119). The first regulatory step in physiologic stimulation of phagocyte O_2^- production is specificity of receptor binding (102). The respiratory burst is similar to other receptor-mediated processes, which are characterized by a receptor occupancy requirement (61, 64, 94, 100, 105), inactivation and recycling of receptors (24, 97), and cross desensitization by stimuli (75). Although stimuli can produce differing amounts of O_2^- production, the same oxidase activity is apparently involved (75, 76).

MEMBRANE POTENTIAL CHANGES   One of the first events after binding appears to be depolarization of plasma membrane potential, as demonstrated by both a fluorescent dye technique (95, 116) and microelectrode impalement (19). Although hyperpolarization can occur in the plasma membrane of cultured macrophages (42), oxidation of fluorescent dye by neutrophils during the respiratory burst (117) has been misinterpreted as hyperpolarization. The importance of depolarization in respiratory burst stimulation was first suggested by failure of neutrophils from chronic granulomatous disease (CGD) patients to both depolarize and produce O_2^- (95, 116). CGD is a syndrome in which failure of O_2^- production upon stimulation can be due to a variety of defects, only one of which is the failure to depolarize (104 for review).

What accounts for the depolarization is not certain. Influx of Na^+ may trigger subsequent Ca^{2+} influx (60, 99) (see below). Blockage of anion channels, however, inhibits degranulation but may enhance O_2^- production (57, 106).

CALCIUM AND PROTEIN KINASE ACTIVITY   A transient increase in free cytosolic Ca^{2+} and binding to calmodulin appears to occur next in receptor-mediated respiratory burst stimulation (62, 67, 98). Both internal stores and extracellular Ca^{2+} could supply the increase in cytosolic Ca^{2+}. This may partially explain differences in the effect on activity by extracellular Ca^{2+} with different stimuli (37, 62, 98).

How the increase in Ca^{2+} mobilization and calmodulin binding is translated into stimulation is unknown. The rise in Ca^{2+} may initiate the inositol phosphate cycle (92) and be responsible for the phosphorylation of proteins (4) through protein kinase activation. Nevertheless, a transient increase in cytosolic Ca^+ may not be sufficient for stimulation, as demonstrated by a poor correlation between O_2^- production and the rise in free cytosolic Ca^{2+} stimulated by different agents (59, 84).

With phorbol myristate acetate (PMA) stimulation, the inositol phosphate cycle changes, followed by both Ca^{2+} mobilization and O_2^- production (96).

PMA directly activates protein kinase C by increasing the affinity of the enzyme for Ca^{2+} (20). The activation of protein kinase C, which can be accomplished through multiple routes, may be the common point for stimulation by various agents.

ADDITIONAL FACTORS   Several laboratories reported that peptide-protease inhibitors inhibit stimulation of O_2^- production (45, 50, 55). More recently, non-protease inhibiting impurities in the soybean preparation were shown to account for this inhibition (1). Non-peptide-protease inhibitors have multiple effects, including stimulation of the respiratory burst (29). Thus, a role for proteases in respiratory burst stimulation is uncertain.

Exogenous prostaglandin end products inhibit respiratory burst stimulation, possibly by interfering with Ca^{2+} mobilization through increased cAMP levels (30). With PMA stimulation, which does not require Ca^{2+} mobilization (see above), these prostaglandin derivatives did not inhibit O_2^- production (30). In contrast, inhibitors of endogenous prostaglandin or leukotriene synthesis both tend to suppress O_2^- production (50, 101, 110). The effect of cyclooxygenase inhibitors is not striking, perhaps because they simultaneously enhance endogenous leukotriene production, which has an opposing effect (110).

The Oxidase Mechanism

NADPH VERSUS NADH AS SUBSTRATE   Two distinct pyridine nucleotide oxidases in neutrophils have been suggested as responsible for the respiratory burst. One oxidase prefers NADPH but will oxidize NADH, and produces O_2^- (23, 41); the other is highly specific for NADH and produces both O_2^- and H_2O_2 (6). The former enzyme is found in phagosomal membranes, and is not expressed in resting cells nor in some CGD cells (40, 41, 51). In one variant of CGD the oxidase can be stimulated but has very low affinity for NADPH (66). In alveolar macrophages reversible depletion of NADPH (without decreased NADH) correlated with disappearance of the respiratory burst (38). Most current research concerns the NADPH oxidase, an FAD-binding flavoprotein (68). How electrons are transferred from this enzyme to O_2 is unresolved, but auxiliary redox components have been suggested.

CYTOCHROME b_{-245} Phagocytes contain a unique b type cytochrome, a role for which was first suggested by its absence from a CGD variant (93). This cytochrome has an unusual midpoint potential, -245 mV (27), binds CO (26), and is rapidly reoxidized by O_2 (26). There is controversy about whether cytochrome b_{-245} is a constituent component of the plasma membrane (70) or is translocated from specific (15) or tertiary (77) granules upon stimulation. While it is generally agreed that this cytochrome does interact with the oxidase, the connection with the flavoprotein is uncertain since NADPH could not reduce the cytochrome in anaerobic particulate oxidase preparations (26).

UBIQUINONE   Quinones added to neutrophils cause increased O_2^- production (25). NADPH oxidase also reduces dichlorophenolindophenol, a quinone analog (47). Thus, stimulated production could be similar to mitochondrial O_2^- production, in which ubisemiquinone reduces O_2 (36). Although ubiquinone was reported in tertiary granules in neutrophils (77), another study (70) failed to detect ubiquinone in either enucleated neutrophils, which were still capable of O_2^- production, or intact neutrophils. The extraction procedure and comparison of ubiquinone with mitochondrial cytochrome content need further study. Obviously, the mechanism and identity of the cofactors involved with the oxidase remain unresolved.

MECHANISM OF BACTERICIDAL ACTIVITY

Effect of Superoxide and Hydrogen Peroxide on Cellular Components

Superoxide is a weak oxidant and a fair reductant that undergoes spontaneous reaction with only a limited number of compounds (91). However, its production appears to be essential for bactericidal activity. Neutrophils that are unable to release superoxide (e.g. CGD) do not efficiently kill bacteria, even when other bactericidal systems are active. Rate constants for reactions of superoxide anion radical, O_2^- and its conjugate acid, $HO_2\cdot$, with several biologically important molecules have been measured (43), and $HO_2\cdot$ is manyfold more reactive than O_2^-. Examples of compounds that react with $HO_2\cdot/O_2^-$ include cysteine, ascorbic acid, enzyme-bound NADH, bilirubin (87), and polyunsaturated fatty acids (14, 43). Superoxide is also reported to disrupt erythrocyte membranes (88). Diffusion of O_2^- across membranes is reported to be slow (103), but $HO_2\cdot$ may be sufficiently lipophilic to diffuse into membranes. Superoxide disproportionates rapidly by Reactions 1 and 2 (below) with rate constants of 8.7×10^5 and $1 \times 10^8 \, M^{-1}s^{-1}$, respectively. The overall rate of disproportionation is pH dependent with a maximum at the pKa (4.69) of $HO_2\cdot$ (13).

$$HO_2\cdot + HO_2\cdot \rightarrow O_2 + H_2O_2 \qquad\qquad 1.$$

$$HO_2\cdot + O_2^- + H^+ \rightarrow O_2 + H_2O_2 \qquad\qquad 2.$$

Disproportionation may have a competitive advantage compared to other reactions in an acidic phagosome. The H_2O_2 formed can rapidly diffuse across lipid membranes, and it may be directly bactericidal or be converted into a stronger oxidant.

Active Oxygen Species in Bactericidal Activity

FORMATION AND PARTICIPATION OF HO·   Superoxide reacts slowly or not at all with H_2O_2 (86) and hydroperoxides (109) in aqueous solution. However, solutions of H_2O_2 and reduced iron undergo a Fenton reaction (oxidation of Fe^{2+} to Fe^{3+} by H_2O_2) yielding HO· (17). Reduction of iron (III) chelates (e.g. Fe-EDTA) by superoxide is reported to be sufficiently rapid (18) that it may be the reducing agent that drives the Fenton reaction. Solutions of iron-EDTA chelates and xanthine oxidase/xanthine cause the oxidation of tryptophan in a superoxide-dependent process (74); iron chelates play an essential role in microsomal lipid peroxidation (5). Iron-superoxide systems are reported to depolymerize proteins (28, 73) and to degrade DNA (16). Iron found in serum or in proteins, such as lactoferrin (3, 9) or transferrin (10, 71), may catalyze HO· formation in cells; however, involvement of lactoferrin in HO· formation by phagocytes is disputed (79). Kinetic evidence was reported for HO· formation by reaction of HOCl with H_2O_2 (69), but evidence for this pathway in neutrophils is lacking (10).

Evidence for participation of HO· during bactericidal activity was first proposed because of inhibition of bacterial killing afforded by radical scavengers, superoxide dismutase and/or catalase (53). In another study (72), however, radical scavengers were ineffective, and it was suggested that latex particles used in the earlier study (53) may have been in part responsible for inhibition of bactericidal activity. Ethylene evolution from methional and 4-(thiomethyl)-2-oxobutyric acid (KMB) has been used as a measure of HO· participation. However, a variety of radicals cause ethylene evolution from methional (85), and KMB is reported to be less selective than originally believed (118). One report describes (3) iron-augmented ethylene evolution, which implicates HO· participation via a Fenton reaction. It has been suggested (89) that ethylene evolution from methional and KMB is associated with myeloperoxidase activity rather than with radical formation. In the presence of the free radical trap, 5,5-dimethyl-1-pyrroline-N-oxide (DMPO), stimulated neutrophils yielded both hydroperoxy (HOO-) and hydroxy (HO-) DMPO adducts (46, 89). Solubilized NADPH oxidase, however, produces only HOO-DMPO (11). Since HOO-DMPO is reported to decompose, giving HO-DMPO (32), experiments employing spin traps to demonstrate HO· production must be interpreted with caution. Evolution of $[^{14}C]$-CO_2 from 1-$[^{14}C]$-benzoate has been cited as evidence for HO· generation in neutrophils (90). This process was strongly inhibited by azide, which suggests that a peroxidase may be involved. The involvement of HO· in bactericidal action therefore remains uncertain.

PARTICIPATION OF SINGLET OXYGEN ($^1O_2$)   Formation of $^1O_2$ by phagocytes is based on the unresolved luminescence observed during the oxidative burst and the oxidation of molecules that are known to react with $^1O_2$. Many of these probes may be susceptible to oxidation by other agents (49). Disproportionation of superoxide and reaction of H_2O_2 with HOCl are purported sources of $^1O_2$ in phagocytic cells (Reactions 3 and 4).

$$O_2^- + HO_2 \cdot \rightarrow {}^1O_2 + H_2O_2 \qquad\qquad 3.$$

$$H_2O_2 + {}^-OCl \rightarrow {}^1O_2 + H_2O + Cl^- \qquad\qquad 4.$$

However, the yield of ${}^1O_2$ from Reaction 4 is sharply diminished at pH < 8.5 (54), and experimental evidence shows that disproportionation does not yield a significant amount of ${}^1O_2$ (33). ${}^1O_2$-derived products were not found in xanthine oxidase/acetaldehyde-induced peroxidation of linoleic acid (108), nor were destinctive ${}^1O_2$ products found after stimulation of neutrophils by cholesterol-coated latex particles (35).

CHLORINE CONTAINING OXIDANTS   Myeloperoxidase is released from the azurophilic granules into phagosomes of stimulated neutrophils. Hypochlorous acid (HOC1) is believed to be generated from H_2O_2 and chloride through the action of this enzyme. HOC1 can degrade a wide variety of cell components (2). Chloramines produced by nonenzymatic reactions of HOC1 are bactericidal to *Escherichia coli,* and killing could be due to oxidation of SH moieties (107). Amines normally present in the serum, such as taurine (111), are rapidly chlorinated, and chloramines may act as long-lived bactericidal agents (112). In addition, degradation of alpha-1-protease inhibitor by HOC1 was suggested as a mechanism that allows neutrophil elastase to depolymerize proteins (115). Oxidation by HOC1 is reported to activate neutrophil collagenase (114). Other molecules have recently been shown to give stable, chlorinated products after phagocytosis (34, 52). The neutrophils from patients lacking myeloperoxidase kill bacteria more slowly than normal cells (65), and their candidacidal activity is reported to be absent (63); however, myeloperoxidase-deficient patients do not suffer from increased numbers or severity of infections (56).

PHYSIOLOGICAL IMPLICATIONS

The initiation of lipid peroxidation by free radicals has been proposed as a mechanism of cell damage in several oxidant injuries. Since bacteria do not contain appreciable quantities of polyunsaturated fatty acids (PUFA), lipid peroxidation is probably not directly bactericidal. Neutrophils and macrophages metabolize arachidonate to several hydroxylated eicosanoids (HETEs) (reviewed in 48). These enzymatically derived lipid peroxidation products can stimulate several responses in phagocytes, including chemotaxis, involved in the recruitment of additional phagocytes to infected areas (44, 82). Leukotriene B_4 and 5-HETE do not appear to stimulate superoxide generation (82), but may enhance O_2^- production stimulated by other agents (110). Autooxidation of arachidonic acid leads to formation of six different hydroperoxides (83) where the 5- and 15-HETEs predominate. Free radical derived

5- and 12-hydroperoxy eicosanoids and their hydroxy counterparts have been shown to have biological activities in neutrophils comparable to those of natural isomers (80). All PUFAs undergo free radical initiated autooxidation, which yields monohydroperoxy-PUFA. These hydroperoxides decompose to a variety of low molecular weight products including aldehydes (reviewed in 39). Continued oxidation gives polyperoxides, including dihydroperoxides and endoperoxides-hydroperoxides. NADPH-iron-induced peroxidation of microsomal lipids yields highly cytotoxic 4-hydroxynonenal (12). The production of chemotactic agents and secretion of lipid peroxidation-initiating radicals by active phagocytes into surrounding tissue could therefore contribute to inflammation coincident with microbicidal activity.

In addition to their microbicidal function, phagocytes have several other roles, for example, wound healing and disposal of aged or malignant cells. Unfortunately, normal tissue sometimes becomes the target for phagocytes. In inflammation and perhaps emphysema, activated oxygen species appear to be involved as agents of cell and matrix protein destruction and in chemoattractant production. The mechanisms involved in these processes are similar to those outlined above (22, 31, 78, 113 for reviews).

In conclusion, production of active oxygen species by phagocytes is an important part of their physiologic and pathologic roles. The past five years have produced some understanding of the mechanisms involved in regulation and chemistry of these processes, and have also opened new trails for investigation.

Literature Cited

1. Abramovitz, A. S., Yavelow, J., Randolph, V., Troll, W. 1983. Inhibition of superoxide production in human neutrophils by purified soybean polypeptides. Re-evaluation of the involvement of proteases. *J. Biol. Chem.* 258:15153–57

2. Albrich, J. M., McCarthy, C. A., Hurst, J. K. 1981. Biological reactivity of hypochlorous acid: implications for microbicidal mechanisms of leukocyte myeloperoxidase. *Proc. Natl. Acad. Sci. USA* 78:210–14

3. Ambruso, D. R., Johnston, R. B. 1981. Lactoferrin enhances hydroxyl radical production by human neutrophils, neutrophil particulate fractions, and an enzymatic generating system. *J. Clin. Invest.* 67:352–60

4. Andrews, P., Babior, B. 1983. Endogenous protein phosphorylation by resting and activated human neutrophils. *Blood* 61:333–40

5. Aust, S. D., Svingen, B. A. 1982. The role of iron in enzymatic lipid peroxidation. *In Free Radicals in Biology*, ed. W. A. Pryor, 5:1–28. New York: Academic. 283 pp.

6. Badwey, J. A., Karnovsky, M. L. 1979. Production of superoxide and hydrogen peroxide by an NADH-oxidase in guinea pig polymorphonuclear leukocytes. *J. Biol. Chem.* 254:11530–37

7. Badwey, J. A., Karnovsky, M. L. 1980. Active oxygen species and the functions of phagocytic leukocytes. *Ann. Rev. Biochem.* 49:695–726

8. Baehner, R. L., Boxer, L. A., Ingraham, L. M. 1982. Reduced oxygen by-products and white blood cells. See Ref. 5, pp. 91–113.

9. Bannister, J. V., Bannister, W. H., Hill, H. A. O., Thornalley, P. J. 1982. Enhanced production of hydroxyl radicals by the xanthine-xanthine oxidase reaction in the presence of lactoferrin. *Biochim. Biophys. Acta* 715:116–20

10. Bannister, J. V., Bellavite, P., Davoli, A., Thornalley, P. J., Rossi, F. 1982.

The generation of hydroxyl radicals following superoxide production by neutrophil NADPH oxidase. *FEBS Lett.* 150:300–2

11. Bannister, J. V., Bellavite, P., Serra, M. C., Thornalley, P. J., Rossi, F. 1982. An EPR study of the production of superoxide radicals by neutrophil NADPH oxidase. *FEBS Lett.* 145:323–26

12. Benedetti, A., Comporti, M., Esterbauer, H. 1980. Identification of 4-hydroxynonenal as a cytotoxic product originating from the peroxidation of liver microsomal lipids. *Biochim. Biophys. Acta* 620:281–96

13. Bielski, B. H. J. 1978. Reevaluation of the spectral and kinetic properties of HO_2 and O_2^- free radicals. *Photochem. Photobiol.* 28:645–49

14. Bielski, B. H. J., Arudi, R. L., Sutherland, M. W. 1983. A study of the reactivity of HO_2/O_2^- with unsaturated fatty acids. *J. Biol. Chem.* 258:4759–61

15. Borregaard, N., Heiple, J. M., Simons, E. R., Clark, R. A. 1983. Subcellular localization of the *b*-cytochrome component of the human neutrophil microbicidal oxidase: translocation during activation. *J. Cell Biol.* 97:52–61

16. Brown, K., Fridovich, I. 1981. DNA strand scission by enzymically generated oxygen radicals. *Arch. Biochem. Biophys.* 206:414–19

17. Buettner, G. R., Oberley, L. W., Leuthauser, S. W. H. C. 1978. The effect of iron on the distribution of superoxide and hydroxyl radicals as seen by spin trapping and on the superoxide dismutase assay. *Photochem. Photobiol.* 28:693–95

18. Butler, J., Halliwell, B. 1982. Reaction of iron-EDTA chelates with the superoxide radical. *Arch. Biochem. Biophys.* 218:174–78

19. Cameron, A. R., Nelson, J., Forman, H. J. 1983. Depolarization and increased conductance precede superoxide release by concanavalin A stimulated rat alveolar macrophages. *Proc. Natl. Acad. Sci. USA* 80:3726–28

20. Castagna, M., Takai, Y., Kaibuchi, K., Sano, K., Kikkawa, U., Nishizulas, Y. 1981. Direct activation of calcium-activated, phospholipid-dependent protein kinase by tumor-promoting phorbol esters. *J. Biol. Chem.* 257:7847–51

21. Cheson, B. D., Curnutte, J. T., Babior, B. M. 1977. The oxidative killing mechanisms of the neutrophil. In *Progress in Clinical Immunology*, ed. R. S. Schwartz 3:1–65. New York: Grune & Stratton

22. Cohen, A. B. 1979. Potential adverse effects of lung macrophages and neutrophils. *Fed. Proc.* 38:2644–47

23. Cohen, H. J., Chovaniec, M. E., Davies, W. A. 1980. Activation of the guinea pig granulocyte NAD(P)H-dependent superoxide generating enzyme: localization in a plasma membrane enriched particle and kinetics of activation. *Blood* 55:355–63

24. Cohen, H. J., Whitin, J. C., Chovaniec, M. E., Tape, E. J., Simons, E. R. 1984. Is activation of the granulocyte by concanavalin-A a reversible process. *Blood* 63:114–20

25. Crawford, D. R., Schneider, D. L. 1981. Evidence that a quinone may be required for the production of superoxide and hydrogen peroxide in neutrophils. *Biochem. Biophys. Res. Commun.* 99:1277–86

26. Cross, A. R., Higson, F. K., Jones, O. T. G., Harper, A. M., Segal, A. W. 1982. The enzymic reduction and kinetics of oxidation of cytochrome b_{-245} of neutrophils. *Biochem. J.* 204:479–85

27. Cross, A. R., Jones, O. T. G., Harper, A. M., Segal, A. W. 1982. The enzymic reduction and kinetics of oxidation of cytochrome b_{-245} of neutrophils. *Biochem. J.* 204:479–85

28. Curran, S. F., Amoruso, M. A., Goldstein, B. D., Berg, R. A. 1984. Degradation of soluble collagen by ozone or hydroxyl radicals. *FEBS Lett.* 176:155–60

29. Dri, P., Zabucchi, G., Bellavite, P. 1981. A dual effect of 1-1-tosylamide-2-phenylethyl chloromethyl ketone on the respiratory metabolism of guinea pig phagocytes. *Bull. Eur. Physiopath. Resp.* 17:175–85

30. Fantone, J. C., Marasco, W. A., Elgas, L. J., Ward, P. A. 1984. Stimulus specificity of prostaglandin inhibition of rabbit polymorphonuclear leukocyte lysosomal enzyme release and superoxide anion generation. *Am. J. Pathol.* 115:9–16

31. Fantone, J. C., Ward, P. A. 1982. Role of oxygen-derived free radicals and metabolites in leukocyte-dependent inflammatory reactions. *Am. J. Pathol.* 107:397–418

32. Finkelstein, E., Rosen, G. M., Rauckman, E. J. 1982. Production of hydroxyl radical by decomposition of superoxide spin-trapped adducts. *Mol. Pharmacol.* 21:262–65

33. Foote, C. S., Abakerli, R. B., Clough, R. L., Lehrer, R. I. 1981. On the question of singlet oxygen production in polymorphonuclear leukocytes. *Biolumin. Chem.* 2:81–88

34. Foote, C. S., Goyne, T. E., Lehrer, R. I. 1983. Assessment of chlorination by human neutrophils. *Nature* 301:715–16

35. Foote, C. S., Shook, F. C., Abakerli, R.

A. 1980. Chemistry of superoxide ion. 4. Singlet oxygen is not a major product of dismutation. *J. Am. Chem. Soc.* 102: 2503–4
36. Forman, H. J., Boveris, A. 1982. Superoxide radical and hydrogen peroxide in mitochondria. See Ref. 5, pp. 65–90.
37. Forman, H. J., Nelson, J. 1983. Effect of extracellular calcium on superoxide release by rat alveolar macrophages. *J. Appl. Physiol.* 54:1249–53
38. Forman, H. J., Nelson, J., Fisher, A. B. 1980. Rat alveolar macrophages require NADPH for superoxide production in the respiratory burst. *J. Biol. Chem.* 255: 9879–83
39. Frankel, E. N. 1982. Volatile lipid oxidation products. *Prog. Lipid Res.* 22:1–33
40. Gabig, T. G. 1983. The NADPH-dependent O_2^--generating oxidase from human neutrophils. Identification of a flavoprotein component that is deficient in a patient with chronic granulomatous disease. *J. Biol. Chem.* 258:6352–56
41. Gabig, T. G., Babior, B. M. 1979. The O_2^--forming oxidase responsible for the respiratory burst in human neutrophils. Properties of the solubilized enzyme. *J. Biol. Chem.* 254:9070–74
42. Gallin, E. K. 1984. Electrophysiological properties of macrophages. *Fed. Proc.* 43:2385–89
43. Gebicki, J. M., Bielski, B. H. J. 1981. Comparison of the capabilities of the perhydroxyl and the superoxide radicals to initiate chain oxidation of linoleic acid. *J. Am. Chem. Soc.* 103:7020–22
44. Goetzl, E. J., Brash, A. R., Tauber, A. I., Oates, J. A., Hubbard, W. C. 1980. Modulation of human neutrophil function by monohydroxyeicosatetraenoic acids. *Immunology* 39:491–501
45. Goldstein, B. D., Witz, G., Amoruso, M., Troll, W. 1979. Protease inhibitors antagonize the activation of polymorphonuclear leukocyte oxygen consumption. *Biochem. Biophys. Res. Commun.* 88: 854–60
46. Green, M. R., Hill, H. A. O., Okolow-Zubkowska, M. J., Segal, A. W. 1979. The production of hydroxyl and superoxide radicals by stimulated human neutrophils-measurements by EPR spectroscopy. *FEBS Lett.* 100:23–26
47. Green, T. R., Schaefer, R. E. 1981. Intrinsic dichlorophenolindophenol reductase activity associated with the superoxide-generating oxidoreductase of human granulocytes. *Biochemistry* 20:7483–87
48. Hansson, G., Malmsten, C., Radmark, O. 1983. The leukotrienes and other lipoxygenase products. In *New Com-*

prehensive *Biochemistry. Prostaglandins and Related Substances,* ed. C. Pace-Asciak, E. Granstrom, 5:127–69. Amsterdam/New York: Elsevier. 229 pp.
49. Held, A. M., Halko, D. J., Hurst, J. K. 1978. Mechanisms of chlorine oxidation of hydrogen peroxide. *J. Am. Chem. Soc.* 100:5732–40
50. Hoffman, M., Autor, A. P. 1982. Effect of cyclooxygenase inhibitors and protease inhibitors on phorbol-induced stimulation of oxygen consumption and superoxide production by rat alveolar macrophages. *Biochem. Pharmacol.* 31: 775–80
51. Hohn, D. C., Lehrer, R. I. 1975. NADPH oxidase deficiency in X-linked chronic granulomatous disease. *J. Clin. Invest.* 55:707–13
52. Hurst, J. K., Albrich, J. M., Green, T. R., Rosen, H., Klebanoff, S. 1984. Myeloperoxidase-dependent fluorescein chlorination by stimulated neutrophils. *J. Biol. Chem.* 259:4812–21
53. Johnston, R. B., Keele, B. B., Misra, H. P., Lehmeyer, J. E., Webb, L. S., et al. 1975. The role of superoxide anion generation in phagocytic bactericidal activity. *J. Clin. Invest.* 55:1357–72
54. Kajiwara, T., Kearns, D. R. 1973. Direct spectroscopic evidence for a deuterium solvent effect on the lifetimes of singlet oxygen in water. *J. Am. Chem. Soc.* 95:5886–90
55. Kitagawa, S., Takaku, F., Sakamoto, S. 1980. Serine protease inhibitors inhibit superoxide production by human basophils stimulated by anti-IgE. *Biochem. Biophys. Res. Commun.* 95:801–6
56. Klebanoff, S. J., Clark, R. A. 1978. *The Neutrophil: Functional and Clinical Disorders,* pp. 723–25. Amsterdam/New York: Elsevier. 810 pp.
57. Korchak, H. M., Eisenstat, B. A., Smolen, J. E., Rutherford, L. E., Dunham, P. B., Weissmann, G. 1982. Stimulus-response coupling in the human neutrophil. The role of anion fluxes in degranulation. *J. Biol. Chem.* 257:6916–22
58. Korchak, H. M., Roos, D., Giedd, K. N., Wynkoop, E. M., Vienne, K., et al. 1983. Granulocytes without degranulation: neutrophil function in granule-depleted cytoplasts. *Proc. Natl. Acad. Sci. USA* 80:4968–72
59. Korchak, H. M., Rutherford, L. E., Weissmann, G. 1984. Stimulus response coupling in the human neutrophil. I. Kinetic analysis of changes in calcium permeability. *J. Biol. Chem.* 259:4070–75

60. Korchak, H. M., Weissmann, G. 1980. Stimulus-response coupling in the human neutrophil transmembrane potential and the role of extracellular Na^+. *Biochim. Biophys. Acta* 601:180–94

61. Korchak, H. M., Wilkenfeld, C., Rich, A. M., Radin, A. R., Vienne, K., Rutherford, L. E. 1984. Stimulus response coupling in the human neutrophil. Differential requirements for receptor occupancy in neutrophil responses to a chemoattractant. *J. Biol. Chem.* 259:7439–45

62. Lehmeyer, J. E., Snyderman, R., Johnston, R. B. Jr. 1979. Stimulation of neutrophil oxidative metabolism by chemotactic peptides: Influence of calcium ion concentration and cytochalasin B and comparison with stimulation by phorbol myristate acetate. *Blood* 54:35–45

63. Lehrer, R. I., Cline, M. J. 1968. Absent myeloperoxidase and leukocyte candidacidal activity in a patient with systemic candidiasis. *Clin. Res.* 16:331

64. Lehrer, R. I., Cohen, L. 1981. Receptor-mediated regulation of superoxide production in human neutrophils stimulated by phorbol myristate acetate. *J. Clin. Invest.* 68:1314–20

65. Lehrer, R. I., Hanifin, J., Cline, M. J. 1969. Defective bactericidal activity in myeloperoxidase-deficient human neutrophils. *Nature* 223:78–79

66. Lew, P. D., Southwick, F. S., Stossel, T. P., Whitin, J. C., Simons, E., Cohen, H. J. 1981. A variant of chronic granulomatous disease: deficient oxidative metabolism due to a low affinity NADPH oxidase. *N. Engl. J. Med.* 305:1329–33

67. Lew, P. D., Stossel, T. P. 1981. Effect of calcium and superoxide production by phagocytic vesicles from rabbit alveolar macrophages. *J. Clin. Invest.* 67:1–9

68. Light, D. R., Walsh, C., O'Callaghan, A. M., Goetzl, E. J., Tauber, A. I. 1981. Characteristics of the cofactor requirements for the superoxide-generating NADPH oxidase of human polymorphonuclear leukocytes. *Biochemistry* 20:1468–76

69. Long, C. A., Bielski, B. H. J. 1980. Rate of reaction of superoxide radical with chloride-containing species. *J. Phys. Chem.* 84:555–57

70. Lutter, R., Van Zwieten, R., Weening, R. S., Hamers, M. N., Roos, D. 1984. Cytochrome *b*, flavins, and ubiquinone-50 in enucleated human neutrophils (polymorphonuclear leukocyte cytoplasts). *J. Biol. Chem.* 259:9603–6

71. Matohashi, N., Mori, I. 1983. Superoxide-dependent formation of hydroxyl radical catalyzed by transferrin. *FEBS Lett.* 157:197–99

72. McCay, P. B., Noguchi, T., Fong, K. L., Lai, E. K., Poyer, J. L. 1980. Production of radicals from enzyme systems and the use of spin traps. In *Free Radicals in Biology*, ed. W. A. Pryor, 4:155–86. New York: Academic. 348 pp.

73. McCord, J. M. 1974. Free radicals and inflammation: protection of synovial fluid by superoxide dismutase. *Science* 185:529–31

74. McCord, J. M., Day, E. D. 1978. Superoxide-dependent production of hydroxyl radical catalyzed by iron-EDTA complex. *FEBS Lett.* 86:139–42

75. McPhail, L. C., Clayton, C. C., Snyderman, R. 1984. The NADPH oxidase of human polymorphonuclear leukocytes. Evidence for regulation by multiple signals. *J. Biol. Chem.* 259:5768–75

76. McPhail, L. C., Snyderman, R. 1983. Activation of the respiratory burst enzyme in human polymorphonuclear leukocytes by chemoattractants and other soluble stimuli. Evidence that the same oxidase is activated by different transductional mechanisms. *J. Clin. Invest.* 72:192–200

77. Mollinedo, F., Schneider, D. L. 1984. Subcellular localization of cytochrome *b* and ubiquinone in a tertiary granule of resting human neutrophils and evidence for a proton pump ATPase. *J. Biol. Chem.* 259:7143–50

78. Nathan, C. F., Murray, H. W., Cohn, Z. A. 1980. The macrophage as an effector cell. *N. Engl. J. Med.* 303:602–26

79. Newburger, P. E., Tauber, A. I. 1982. Heterogeneous pathways of oxidizing radical production in human neutrophils and the HL-60 cell line. *Pediatr. Res.* 16:856–60

80. O'Flaherty, J. T., Thomas, M. J., Lees, C. J., McCall, C. E. 1981. Neutrophil-aggregating activity of monohydroxyeicosatetraenoic acids. *Am. J. Pathol.* 104:55–62

81. Pabst, M. J., Johnston, R. B. Jr. 1980. Increased production of superoxide anion by macrophages exposed in vitro to muramyl dipeptide or lipopolysaccharide. *J. Exp. Med.* 151:101–14

82. Palmblad, J., Malmsten, C. L., Uden, A. M., Radmark, O., Engstedt, L., Samuelsson, B. 1981. Leukotriene B_4 is a potent and stereospecific stimulator of neutrophil chemotaxis and adherence. *Blood* 58:658–61

83. Porter, N. A., Logan, J., Kontoyiannidou, V. 1979. Preparation and purification of arachidonic acid hydroperoxides

of biological importance. *J. Org. Chem.* 44:3177–81
84. Pozzan, T., Lew, D. P., Wollheim, C. B., Tsein, R. Y. 1983. Is cytosolic ionized calcium regulating neutrophil activation? *Science* 224:1413–15
85. Pryor, W. A., Tang, R. H. 1978. Ethylene formation from methional. *Biochem. Biophys. Res. Commun.* 81:498–503
86. Rigo, A., Stevanato, R., Finazzi-Agro, A., Rotilio, G. 1977. An attempt to evaluate the rate of the Haber-Weiss reaction by using ·OH radical scavengers. *FEBS Lett.* 80:130–32
87. Robertson, P., Fridovich, I. 1982. A reaction of the superoxide radical with tetrapyrroles. *Arch. Biochem. Biophys.* 213:353–57
88. Rosen, G. M., Barber, M. J., Rauckman, E. J. 1983. Disruption of erythrocyte membranal organization by superoxide. *J. Biol. Chem.* 258:2225–28
89. Rosen, H., Klebanoff, S. J. 1979. Hydroxyl radical generation by polymorphonuclear leukocytes measured by electron spin resonance spectroscopy. *J. Clin. Invest.* 64:1725–29
90. Sagone, A. L., Decker, M. A., Wells, R. M., Democko, C. 1980. A new method for detection of hydroxyl radical production by phagocytic cells. *Biochim. Biophys. Acta* 628:90–97
91. Sawyer, D. T., Valentine, J. S. 1981. How super is superoxide? *Acc. Chem. Res.* 14:393–400
92. Sbarra, A. J., Karnovsky, M. L. 1959. The biochemical basis of phagocytosis. I. Metabolic changes during the ingestion of particles by polymorphonuclear leukocytes. *J. Biol. Chem.* 234:1355–62
93. Segal, A. W., Jones, O. T. G., Webster, D., Allison, A. C. 1978. Absence of a newly described cytochrome *b* from neutrophils of patients with chronic granulomatous disease. *Lancet* 2:446–49
94. Seligmann, B. E., Fletcher, M. P., Gallin, J. I. 1982. Adaptation of human neutrophil responsiveness to the chemoattractant N-formylmethionylleucylphenylalanine. Heterogeneity and/or negative cooperative interaction of receptors. *J. Biol. Chem.* 257:6280–86
95. Seligmann, B. E., Gallin, J. I. 1980. Use of lipophilic probes of membrane potential to assess human neutrophil activation. Abnormality in chronic granulomatous disease. *J. Clin. Invest.* 66:493–503
96. Serhan, C. N., Broekman, M. J., Korchak, H. M., Smolen, J. E., Marcus, A. J., Weissmann, G. 1983. Changes in

phosphatidylinositol and phosphatidic acid in stimulated human neutrophils. Relationship to calcium mobilization, aggregation and superoxide radical generation. *Biochim. Biophys. Acta* 762:420–28
97. Sha'afi, R. I., Molski, T.-F.-P., Borgeat, P., Nacchache, P. H. 1981. Deactivation of the effects of f-met-leu-phe and leukotriene B_4 on calcium mobilization in rabbit neutrophils. *Biochem. Biophys. Res. Commun.* 103:766–73.
98. Simchowitz, L., Spilberg, I. 1978. Generation of superoxide radicals by human peripheral neutrophils activated by chemotactic factor. Evidence for the role of calcium. *J. Lab. Clin. Med.* 93:583–93
99. Simchowitz, L., Spilberg, I. 1979. Chemotactic factor-induced generation of superoxide radicals by human neutrophils: Evidence for the role of sodium. *J. Immunol.* 123:2428–35
100. Sklar, L. A., Jesaitis, A. J., Painter, R. G., Cochran, C. G. 1981. The kinetics of neutrophil activation. The response to chemotactic peptides depends upon whether ligand-receptor interaction is rate limiting. *J. Biol. Chem.* 256:9909–14
101. Smolen, J. E., Weissmann, G. 1980. Effects of indomethacin, 5, 8, 11, 14-eicosatetraynoic acid, and p-bromophenacyl bromide on lysosomal enzyme release and superoxide anion generation by human polymorphonuclear leukocytes. *Biochem. Pharmacol.* 29:533–38
102. Spilberg, I., Mehta, J., Daughaday, C., Simchowitz, L. 1981. Determination of a specific receptor for formyl-methionyl-leucyl-phenylalanine on the pulmonary alveolar macrophage and its relationship to chemotaxis and superoxide production. *J. Lab. Clin. Med.* 97:602–9
103. Takahashi, M. A., Asada, K. 1983. Superoxide anion permeability of phospholipid membranes and chloroplast thylakoids. *Arch. Biochem. Biophys.* 226:558–66
104. Tauber, A. I., Borregaard, N., Simons, E. R., Wright, J. 1983. Chronic granulomatous disease: A syndrome of phagocyte oxidase deficiencies. *Medicine* 62:286–309
105. Tauber, A. I., Brettler, D., Kennington, E., Blumberg, P. 1981. Relation of human neutrophils phorbol ester receptor occupancy and NADPH-oxidase activity. *Blood* 60:333–39
106. Tauber, A. I., Goetzl, E. J. 1981. Inhibition of complement-mediated function of human neutrophils by impermeant stil-

680   FORMAN & THOMAS

bene disulfonic acids. *J. Immunol.*
126:1786–89
107. Thomas, E. L. 1979. Myeloperoxidase,
hydrogen peroxide, chloride antimicro-
bial systems: nitrogen-chlorine derivatives of bacterial components in bactericidal action against Escherichia coli.
Infect. Immun. 23:522–31
108. Thomas, M. J., Mehl, K. S., Pryor, W.
A. 1982. The role of superoxide in xanthine oxidase-induced autooxidation of
linoleic acid. *J. Biol. Chem.* 257:8343–
47
109. Thomas, M. J., Sutherland, M. W., Arudi, R. L., Bielski, B. H. J. 1984. Studies
of the reactivity of HO_2/O_2^- with unsaturated hydroperoxides in ethanolic
solutions. *Arch. Biochem. Biophys.* 233:
772–75
110. Ward, P. A., Sulavik, M. C., Johnson,
K. J. 1984. Rat neutrophil activation and
effects of lypoxygenase and cyclooxygenase inhibitors. *Am. J. Pathol.* 116:
223–33
111. Weiss, S. J., Klein, R., Slivka, A., Wei,
M. 1982. Chlorination of taurine by human neutrophils. *J. Clin. Invest.* 70:598–
607
112. Weiss, S. J., Lampert, M. B., Test, S. T.
1983. Long-lived oxidants generated by
human neutrophils: characterization and
bioactivity. *Science* 222:625–28
113. Weiss, S. J., LoBuglio, A. F. 1982.
Phagocyte-generated oxygen metabolites
and cellular injury. *Lab. Invest.* 47:5–18
114. Weiss, S. J., Peppin, G., Ortiz, X.,

Ragsdale, C., Test, S. T. 1985. Oxidative autoactivation of latent collagenase
by human neutrophils. *Science* 227:747–
49
115. Weiss, S. J., Regiani, S. 1984. Neutrophils degrade subendothelial matrices in
the presence of alpha-1-proteinase inhibitor. Cooperative use of lysosomal
proteinases and oxygen metabolism. *J.
Clin. Invest.* 73:1297–1303
116. Whitin, J. C., Chapman, C. E., Simons,
E. R., Chovaniec, M. E., Cohen, H. J.
1980. Correlation between membrane
potential changes and superoxide production in human granulocytes stimulated by
phorbol myristate acetate. *J. Biol. Chem.*
255:1874–78
117. Whitin, J. C., Clark, R. A., Simons, E.
R., Cohen, H. 1981. Effects of the
myeloperoxidase system on fluorescent
probes of the granulocyte membrane
potential. *J. Biol. Chem.* 256:8904–6
118. Winston, G. W., Best, L., Cederbaum,
A. I. 1983. Fenton chemistry with
ferrous dipyridyl: potential use in assessing the relative specificity of chemical
probes for hydroxyl radicals. In *Oxy
Radicals and Their Scavenger Systems,*
ed. G. Cohen, R. A. Greenwald, 1:145–
50. New York: Elsevier. 399 pp.
119. Yamamoto, K., Johnston, R. B. Jr.
1984. Dissociation of phagocytosis from
stimulation of the oxidative metabolic
burst in macrophages. *J. Exp. Med.*
159:405–16

Ann. Rev. Physiol. 1986. 48:681–92

THE RESPONSE OF THE LUNG TO FOREIGN COMPOUNDS THAT PRODUCE FREE RADICALS

L. L. Smith

Imperial Chemical Industries, Central Toxicology Laboratory, Alderley Park, Macclesfield, Cheshire, SK10 4TJ, United Kingdom

INTRODUCTION

There can be little doubt that man is exposed to a large number of potentially harmful agents in the atmosphere as well as to the self-inflicted hazard of smoking tobacco. The lung is exposed to a variety of contaminating gases, vapors, and small particles present in the atmosphere. This is hardly surprising since an adult human inhales approximately 3000 kg of air per year (39). Thus even if the inhaled air contains only a small proportion of pollutants, the large respiratory volume means that over a period of time significant quantities of pollutant will reach the lung. In order to carry out its respiratory function, the lung requires a large surface area rich in capillaries to ensure an effective exchange of gases with the bloodstream. Since the total cardiac output passes through it, the lung can be exposed to toxic, xenobiotic compounds that have been absorbed from the gastrointestinal tract into the bloodstream or are present in the blood as toxic metabolites.

When considering the response of the lung to xenobiotics that form free radicals, the phenomenon of target cell toxicity must be addressed. Selective toxicity may result from the nature of exposure, for example, from gases that damage the epithelium of the respiratory airways and spare the epithelium in the parenchyma of the lung, or from particulates whose distribution is determined by their aerodynamic diameter. Foreign compounds may also be selectively accumulated from the blood by specific cells in the lung. Furthermore, despite the initial distribution of the compound in lung cells, metabolic activation of the

681

0066-4278/86/0315-0681$02.00

foreign compound may occur in particular cell types. Thus a combination of the disposition and activation of the chemical can be critical in determining the toxicity that occurs. This complexity is further compounded by two processes which are difficult to quantify. First, the intrinsic ability of individual cell types within the lung to cope with the consequences of free radical damage may be extremely variable. Second, when specific cells in the lung are damaged by chemical insult, other cell types that have not themselves been primarily damaged may be adversely affected or even destroyed. Put another way, the initial damage to lung cells may be followed by a secondary response, such as the development of an alveolitis. The consequent infiltration of inflammatory cells may then contribute to further lung cell damage.

A number of foreign compounds have been associated with free radical formation in the lung. These include carbon tetrachloride (4), bleomycin (40), silica-containing dust (59), thiourea (18), anthracyclin anticancer drugs (36), nitrofurantoin (30), paraquat (19), ozone (39), and nitrogen dioxide (NO_2) (39). A number of these xenobiotics, nitrofurantoin, adriamycin, bleomycin, and paraquat, are considered to exhibit their toxicity via the generation of radical species of oxygen. In many respects these may be considered chemical forms of oxygen toxicity, although as we shall see later, factors such as the disposition, localization, and activation of the compounds influence the lung to respond differently to each chemical.

This review examines a number of the factors important in chemically induced free radical damage in the lung. Particular consideration is given to the herbicide paraquat since this reflects the interest of the author.

PATHOLOGY IN THE LUNG

Paraquat

In the last twenty years there have been a number of human fatalities attributed to paraquat poisoning, largely as a consequence of the intentional ingestion of the commercial product for suicidal purpose (16). When paraquat is ingested the symptoms of poisoning depend largely on the amount consumed. However, the most characteristic feature is lung damage, which is usually the cause of death.

The effect of paraquat in the lung of various species of experimental animal has been investigated. The rat, mouse, dog, and monkey all develop lung damage with a pathology generally similar to that seen in man (7, 11, 37). The lesion that develops in the lung after paraquat exposure has two distinct phases (50). First, within one or two days of dosing, is a destructive phase in which the alveolar type I and type II epithelial cells are damaged. Consequently an alveolitis develops with the formation of edema and infiltration of inflammatory cells (56). The second phase of the lesion is a reparative phase characterized by an extensive fibrosis of the alveolar tissue (50). This leads to destruction of the normal architecture of the alveolar membranes, and the death of the experimental animal or patient from anoxia.

Other Free Radical Generators

The inhaled environmental pollutants NO_2 and ozone cause cellular injury that extends throughout the conducting airways (12). If the concentration of ozone in the atmosphere is sufficiently large the injury will extend to the alveolar epithelium. NO_2 is less chemically reactive than ozone, which in part explains why NO_2 produces deeper injury further into the lung than ozone (39).

Bleomycin is a mixture of glycopeptides used in cancer chemotherapy (55). A major side effect of bleomycin therapy is the development of pulmonary fibrosis (9), which limits the clinical use of the drug. Most of the early experimental animal models used intravenous or intraperitoneal administration of bleomycin (1, 15), and repeated injections were necessary to produce lung damage (1). More recently, the direct intratrachial instillation of a single dose of bleomycin has been widely used to produce acute pulmonary damage (51). The pathology observed with bleomycin is dependent on the dose and dosing regime used; a number of cell types in the parenchyma of the lung are damaged. Following the instillation of bleomycin into the lung the pathogenesis is similar to that seen with paraquat; an acute alveolitis forms and resolves as an extensive and ultimately lethal fibrosis.

With α-naphthylthiourea (ANTU) and other related thioureas toxic effects are predominately directed to the lung. ANTU was originally developed as a rat poison (42); in susceptible animals it produces severe pulmonary edema associated with minimal damage to the capillary endothelial cells (8, 35). In contrast to paraquat and bleomycin, ANTU does not severely damage the alveolar epithelial cells, although very high dose levels of ANTU in rats cause some injury to type I and type II epithelial cells.

Following the therapeutic use of nitrofurantoin in the treatment of urinary tract infections there have been occasional reports of acute or chronic lung injury (3). When rats are given large doses of nitrofurantoin acute lung injury develops, which is characterized by edema, hemorrhage, and cellular infiltration. Administration of the hepatotoxin CCl_4 does not generally result in severe lung damage, although areas of alveolar collapse, edema, and thickening of the alveolar walls have been observed (20). In rats, CCl_4 has been shown to cause extensive damage to the alveolar type II cells (20), whereas in the mouse lung, the Clara cells in the terminal bronchiole are severely damaged (29).

DISPOSITION AND LOCALIZATION IN THE LUNG

Paraquat

When paraquat is administered orally to rats the plasma concentration remains relatively constant over 30 hr, whereas the concentration in the lung rises progressively to several times that in the plasma (44). In no other organ studied is this time-dependent accumulation of paraquat seen (44). Following the intravenous dosing of paraquat to the rat, the greatest concentration is found in the lung because the initial half-life in the plasma and other organs (kidney, liver, muscle, adrenal, spleen, and testes) is shorter than that in the lung. This accumulation/retention of paraquat in the lung provides a convincing explanation for selective organ damage by paraquat following oral or intravenous dosing.

Rose et al showed that the time-dependent accumulation of paraquat into lung slices could be inhibited by the addition of metabolic inhibitors to the medium, and consequently the process has been described as energy-dependent (45). The uptake obeys saturation kinetics, and an apparent K_m and V_{max} for the process has been derived (45). The discovery that paraquat was actively taken up by the lung led to the search for endogenous compounds that would reduce this accumulation, since it was reasoned that the process responsible for the uptake of paraquat was present in order to accumulate an endogenous compound(s). A series of diamine and polyamine compounds (putrescine, spermidine, and spermine) were found to be effective inhibitors of the accumulation of paraquat, and were themselves accumulated into the lung. The process obeys saturation kinetics, and the accumulation is reduced by metabolic inhibitors, incubation under nitrogen, or cooling of the slice to 4°C (21, 47, 49). Thus it appears there is a receptor in the lung that is normally involved in the transport of diamine and polyamine compounds, which is capable of accumulating paraquat. The most probable reason for the pulmonary uptake of paraquat on this receptor is its structural similarity to these diamines and polyamines (21).

The fact that paraquat primarily damages the alveolar type I and type II epithelial cells indicates that these cell types may accumulate paraquat. Waddell & Marlowe (57) concluded that paraquat was present almost entirely in cells having the typical distribution of alveolar type II cells. There is also indirect evidence from lung slice studies that paraquat and the diamine putrescine are accumulated into these cell types (48).

The probability that paraquat is accumulated into only a few cell types in the lung is of considerable importance in attempting to understand its mechanism of toxicity. As there are more than forty different cell types in the lung (52), the accumulation of paraquat into only a small proportion of the total cell population may lead to a serious underestimate of the intracellular concentration in the target cells. The results describing the amount of paraquat in the lung are usually expressed on a per gram wet weight tissue basis, so the true intracellular concentration of paraquat may be underestimated by as much as two orders of magnitude.

Other Free Radical Generators

The pathology produced in the lung by the environmental pollutants ozone and NO_2 reflects the localization of these gases. The solubility, reactivity, and ease with which they are expelled from the lung determine how extensively they are distributed through the respiratory airways and into the alveolar regions (39). Therefore, inhaled toxins are localized in different cells of the lung depending on their particulate or gaseous nature.

There have been no reports of the selective disposition of bleomycin. However, it is apparent from the pathology that occurs following the instillation of bleomycin into the lung that a number of pulmonary cell types are damaged. Bleomycin has been shown to interact with the DNA of neoplastic cells, and if this occurs in pulmonary cells it may lead to the retention of the compound within the cell.

ANTU primarily damages the lung capillary endothelial cell. However, autoradiographic studies of the lungs of rats receiving the chemically related ^{14}C-thiourea indicate that the compound or its metabolites were distributed generally throughout the lung (24). If ANTU is distributed in a way similar to thiourea, then it appears that there is no selective uptake into the capillary endothelium. The specific damage to this cell type may reflect a difference in the metabolic potential of this cell, or a toxic metabolite formed in an adjacent cell may diffuse to the endothelial cell where it manifests its toxicity.

With nitrofurantoin and CCl_4 there have been no direct studies to investigate the cellular disposition in the lung. However, the histological effects produced by both compounds seem to indicate that they are localized to some extent in the alveolar type II cells and Clara cells of the lung.

MECHANISM OF TOXICITY

Paraquat

Paraquat has the ability to undergo a single electron reduction from the cation to form a stable free radical in the absence of oxygen. However, the radical reacts avidly with molecular oxygen to reform the cation and concomitantly produce superoxide anion (O_2^-) (13). Provided there is a continuous supply of electrons to paraquat, and oxygen is available, paraquat will cycle from the oxidized to reduced form with the continuous production of O_2^-. Gage (19) first reported that under anaerobic conditions NADPH together with a flavoprotein could reduce paraquat cation to its radical. Under aerobic conditions the radical is reoxidized and the redox cycling continues until the available NADPH is consumed. Baldwin et al (2) demonstrated that microsomal preparations from lung, liver, and kidney were all able to generate radicals of paraquat, and eventually produced hydrogen peroxide. Thus the cycling of paraquat from its reduced to reoxidized form provides a plausible hypothesis for its primary mechanism of toxicity.

However, the mechanism by which the redox cycling of paraquat leads to lung damage is still subject to considerable speculation. Since O_2^- and subsequently H_2O_2 are the products of the redox cycling of paraquat, it has been suggested that in the presence of certain transition metals the hydroxyl radical (OH·) is formed (34). Because of the possibility of this reaction occurring, emphasis has been placed upon the hypothesis that paraquat initiates membrane damage by causing lipid peroxidation (5). Despite results to the contrary (46, 53), the balance of evidence indicates that there is considerable stimulation of lipid peroxidation by paraquat in vitro using rat lung microsomes (54). Bus et al (5) have provided evidence that lipid peroxidation is the mechanism of paraquat toxicity in vivo. However, much of this evidence is indirect and does not provide definitive evidence that lipid peroxidation is the mechanism of toxicity in the lung.

In addition to producing O_2^-, the redox cycling of paraquat also consumes reducing equivalents, leading to the oxidation of NADPH (19). It has been suggested that if the oxidation of NADPH is both extensive and prolonged the lung cells are unable to carry out essential physiological and biochemical functions, which in turn leads to cell death (14). Several authors have provided both direct and indirect evidence for the rapid and extensive oxidation of NADPH in lungs exposed to paraquat (14, 27, 58). It has been found that the pathway responsible for the reduction of $NADP^+$ to NADPH (the hexose monophosphate shunt) is stimulated in the lung in direct proportion to the level of paraquat present (28). In addition, fatty acid synthesis, a system highly dependent on NADPH, is inhibited in a dose-dependent manner in the lungs of paraquat-treated rats. These data indicate that the oxidation of NADPH in the lung leads to compensatory changes in intermediary metabolism in an attempt to maintain the redox status of the cell (28).

It seems clear that the primary reaction involved in the mechanism of paraquat toxicity in the lung is the cycling of paraquat from its oxidised to reduced form, with the consumption of reducing equivalents and the production of O_2^-. The evidence in vitro demonstrates that this process leads to the formation of lipid peroxides, although the evidence for this from in vivo studies is more tenuous. Possibly the continuous oxidation of NADPH is in itself a sufficient perturbation of the biochemistry of the cell to lead to cell damage and death. In any event, it seems likely that the depletion of NADPH would render the cell more susceptible to lipid peroxidation, as the cell would be unable to detoxify hydrogen peroxide or lipid hydroperoxides by the glutathione peroxidase and reductase system. Therefore these hypotheses need not be mutually exclusive.

Other Free Radical Generators

The evidence for the mechanism of toxicity of the gaseous pollutants ozone and NO_2 comes largely from in vitro studies. It is possible that ozone can oxidize cell components directly. However, since it contains two unpaired electrons it seems probably that free radicals are formed when ozone reacts in biological systems. In support of this several authors have provided evidence that ozone produces lipid peroxidation in vitro (10, 38). Similarly, there is evidence that NO_2 can cause lipid peroxidation in vitro (43). However, there is little evidence to support lipid peroxidation in vivo with either ozone or NO_2.

With bleomycin, the current evidence suggests that its toxicity is attributable to its ability to damage DNA via the generation of free radicals of oxygen. Unlike paraquat, which redox cycles in the cytosol, it appears that bleomycin has a high affinity for DNA, and that in the presence of Fe^{2+} it forms a DNA-bleomycin-Fe^{2+} complex (40). The Fe^{3+} in this complex can be reduced from Fe^{3+} to Fe^{2+} by endogenous reducing systems (6). The Fe^{2+}-bleomycin complex may then react with molecular oxygen to form O_2^- (6), or possibly with hydrogen peroxide, leading to the generation of OH· in close proximity to the DNA. Therefore, bleomycin exposure is likely to result in a targeted direct attack by radicals of oxygen on the DNA of the cell.

The mechanism of ANTU toxicity to the lung is not well understood. However, it appears that the metabolism of ANTU in the lung is important. Thiourea, a structural analogue of ANTU, is known to be metabolized by rat lung tissue (23). The lung edema produced by thiourea can be reduced if the rats are treated with OH· scavengers. By analogy with thiourea, it is possible that ANTU toxicity is also mediated via the generation of species of oxygen radical.

Nitrofurantoin is capable of redox cycling in a manner similar to paraquat by virtue of its ability to form an ion-free radical with lung microsomes in anaerobic conditions (32). It has been suggested that this radical reacts with molecular oxygen to regenerate the parent compound and concomitantly produce O_2^- (32). Using lung parenchyma cells in vitro, Martin (31) has provided evidence that the mechanism of nitrofurantoin toxicity is associated with oxidant attack. Although the biochemical perturbations caused by nitrofurantoin in the lung have not been as extensively described as those induced by paraquat, it seems reasonable to speculate that nitrofurantoin is capable of oxidizing NADPH and producing large amounts of oxygen radicals. However, as mentioned earlier, unlike paraquat there is no evidence of selective uptake of nitrofurantoin into individual lung cell types. This may in part explain why nitrofurantoin is less toxic to the lung than paraquat.

It has been shown that the lung microsomal cytochromes are capable of metabolizing CCl_4 in a manner similar to that which has previously been described with hepatic microsomes (3). Extensive investigation of the ability of CCl_4 to cause hepatic necrosis, and the generally held view that this process involves activation of carbon tetrachloride to a highly reactive free radical (CCl_3), make plausible the suggestion that this is the mechanism of toxicity in the lung.

GENERAL PERSPECTIVE

From the preceding discussion of the pathology, disposition, and mechanism of toxicity of paraquat and other chemicals considered to exert free radical toxicity in the lung it is clear that there are differences in the individual cell types that are damaged. Certain chemicals are selectively toxic. For example, after exposure to paraquat the initial lesions are found in the alveolar type I and type II cells, whereas ANTU selectively damages the capillary endothelium, and CCl_4 destroys the type II epithelial cells and Clara cells. However, other agents, such as bleomycin and nitrofurantoin, cause more widespread cell damage. In several cases the initial lung damage is compounded by the infiltration of inflammatory cells, such as neutrophils. These cells may contribute to the pulmonary lesion by disrupting the normal architecture of the alveoli. They may also contribute to cell damage by producing reactive oxygen species (17, 25). In many cases the pulmonary lesion that ultimately develops following chemical insult is similar irrespective of the sequence or selectivity of cell damage. It is important for a proper appreciation of the mechanism of chemical toxicity to determine the initial cellular toxicity in the lung, and separate this from the consequential lesions that develop.

Obviously, the cellular localization of xenobiotics or their active metabolites help determine the site of damage. Paraquat is taken up by a process that allows diamines and polyamines to accumulate in the alveolar type I and type II cells, and these cells are the first and most severely damaged. In contrast, nitrofurantoin, which has a similar mechanism of toxicity, is not selectively localized in specific lung cells. The concentration in the atmosphere, solubility, and reactivity of the pollutants NO_2 and ozone determine their cellular localization. Bleomycin, although not selectively accumulated into lung cells, has a high affinity for DNA. It is internalized and targeted to this critical area of the cell. As with nitrofurantoin, CCl_4 and ANTU do not appear to be selectively accumulated, although the conversion of these compounds to an active metabolite in specific cell types may lead to the covalent retention of a metabolite in these cells. In this case, even if the covalent binding does not per se cause cell damage, its occurrence may indicate the site of production of the toxic radical species.

A striking feature of the mechanism of toxicity of xenobiotics that form free radicals in the lung is the involvement of radical species of oxygen. With the exception of NO_2, CCl_4, and possibly ANTU (in which the radical species of the parent molecule may directly attack cellular constituents), the chemicals discussed all involve the generation of oxygen radicals. Indeed, paraquat, nitrofurantoin, and to some extent bleomycin, may be considered chemical forms of oxygen toxicity. However, there are at least two qualifications to that statement:

First, the cellular compartment or the intracellular site responsible for oxygen radical formation is likely to differ between molecular oxygen and these free radical generators. For example, exposure to high concentrations of oxygen may raise the oxygen concentration in numerous cell types, whereas radicals derived from paraquat will predominantly form in the alveolar type I and type II cells. Also, in exposure to high concentrations of oxygen the major site of the one electron addition is the mitochondria, whereas with bleomycin this takes place in the nucleus.

Second, the high concentration of paraquat in the cytosol of specific cell types may cause a more rapid and severe drain on cellular reducing equivalents than would a prolonged but less severe exposure to high concentrations of oxygen. Alternatively, the rapid and concentrated flux of O_2^- that results from the redox cycling of paraquat may lead to an attack on cytosol constituents by $OH^.$ radical, whereas the redox cycling of bleomycin Fe^{2+} complex in the nucleus may damage the DNA and spare the cytosol.

Nevertheless, there appears to be a strong relationship between the mechanism of toxicity of some of these free radical generators and that of oxygen toxicity. This is perhaps seen most strikingly with paraquat: its toxicity in rats can be increased tenfold by placing paraquat-treated rats in an atmosphere of 85% oxygen (26).

Considerable emphasis in the literature has been placed on the likelihood that xenobiotics that form free radicals cause damage by lipid peroxidation. Certainly in the case of the hepatotoxicity of CCl_4, lipid peroxidation as a mechanism of toxicity is well supported (33, 41). However, as stated earlier, the evidence in the lung is less certain. In a recent review Halliwell & Gutteridge (22) recalled that it was established many years ago that disrupted tissues undergo peroxidation more quickly than healthy ones. Reasons for this include the inactivation of antioxidants and the release of metal ions (especially the transition metals) from metalloenzymes. It is therefore possible that in the case of some xenobiotics capable of producing free radicals, the demonstration of lipid peroxidation in vitro leads to a self-fulfilling hypothesis. The absence of convincing evidence of lipid peroxidation in the lung in vivo is explained by the difficulty of detecting a small but critical biochemical change in a subpopulation of cells in a heterocellular organ. Certainly it remains one of the challenges of those interested in the mechanisms of toxicity to separate the biochemical events that cause cell damage from those that occur in the biochemical cascade associated with dead and dying cells.

In conclusion, studies with several disparate chemicals have shown that when the lung is damaged by xenobiotic compounds capable of forming radical species, the initial lesions that develop are varied, and are heavily influenced by the disposition and localization of the individual chemical. Several of these chemicals are known to produce radical species of oxygen, and it is often suggested that these in turn cause lipid peroxidation as the primary mechanism of toxicity. It is possible in some cases that the primary mechanism of cell damage involves the prolonged oxidation, and subsequent depletion of reducing equivalents in the lung, and that lipid peroxidation is a consequence of cell damage, rather than its cause.

Literature Cited

1. Adamson, I. Y. R., Bowden, D. H. 1974. The pathogenesis of bleomycin-induced pulmonary fibrosis in mice. *Am. J. Pathol.* 77:185–98

2. Baldwin, R. C., Pasi, A., MacGregor, J. T., Hine, G. H. 1975. The rates of radical formation from the dipyridilium herbicides, paraquat, diquat and morfamquat in homogenates of lung, kidney and liver: an inhibitory effect of carbon monoxide. *Toxicol. Appl. Pharmacol.* 32:298–304

3. Boyd, M. 1980. Biochemical mechanisms in chemical-induced lung injury: Roles of metabolic activation. *CRC Crit. Rev. Toxicol.* 7:103–76

4. Boyd, M., Statham, C., Longo, N. 1980. The pulmonary Clara cell as a target for toxic chemicals requiring metabolic activation: studies with carbon tetrachloride. *J. Pharmacol. Exp. Ther.* 212:109–14

5. Bus, J. S., Cagen, S. Z., Olgaard, M., Gibson, J. E. 1976. A mechanism of paraquat toxicity in mice and rats. *Toxicol. Appl. Pharmacol.* 35:501–13

6. Caspary, W. J., Lanzo, D. A., Niziak, C. 1981. Intermediates in the ferrous oxidase cycle of bleomycin. *Biochemistry* 20:3868–75

7. Conning, D. M., Fletcher, K., Swan, A. A. B. 1969. Paraquat and related bipyridyls. *Br. Med. Bull.* 25:245–49

8. Cunningham, A. L., Harley, J. V. 1972. Alphanaphthylthiourea-induced pulmonary edema in the rat: a topographical and electron-microscope study. *J. Pathol.* 106:25–35

9. DeLena, M., Guzzon, A., Monfardini, S., Bonadonna, G. 1972. Clinical ra-diologic and histopathologic studies on pulmonary toxicity induced by treatment with bleomycin. *Cancer Chemother. Rep.* 56:343–56

10. DeLucia, A. J., Hoque, P. M., Mustafa, M. G., Cross, C. E. 1972. Ozone interaction with rodent lung. I. Effect of sulfhydryls and sulfhydryl-containing enzyme activities. *J. Lab. Clin. Med.* 80:559–66

11. Etherton, J. E., Gresham, G. A. 1979. Early bronchiolar damage following paraquat poisoning in mice. *J. Pathol.* 128:21–27

12. Evans, M. J., Cabral, L. J., Stephens, R. J., Freeman, G. 1973. Renewal of alveolar epithelium in the rat following exposure to nitrogen dioxide. *Am. J. Pathol.* 70:175–98

13. Farrington, J. A., Ebert, M., Land, E. J., Fletcher, K. 1973. Bipyridilium quaternary salts and related compounds. V. Pulse radiolysis studies of the reaction of paraquat radical with oxygen. *Biochim. Biophys. Acta* 314:372–81

14. Fisher, H. K., Clements, J. A., Tierney, D. F., Wright, R. R. 1975. Pulmonary effects of paraquat in the first day after injection. *Am. J. Physiol.* 228:1217–23

15. Fleischman, R. W., Baker, J. R., Thompson, G. R., Schaeppi, U. H., Illievski, V. R., et al. 1971. Bleomycin-induced interstitial pneumonia in dogs. *Thorax* 26:675–82

16. Fletcher, K. 1974. Paraquat poisoning. In *Forensic Toxicology,* ed. B. Ballantyne, pp. 86–98. Birmingham: Wright & Sons

17. Flick, M. R., Perel, A., Staub, N. C.

1981. Leukocytes are required for increased lung microvascular permeability after microembolization in sheep. *Circ. Res.* 48:344–51

18. Fox, R. B., Harada, R. N., Tate, R. M., Repine, J. E. 1983. Prevention of thiourea induced pulmonary edema by hydroxyl-radical scavengers. *J. Appl. Physiol.* 55:1456–59

19. Gage, J. C. 1968. The action of paraquat and diquat on the respiration of liver cell fractions. *Biochem. J.* 109:757–61

20. Gould, V. E., Smuckler, E. A. 1971. Alveolar injury in acute carbon tetrachloride intoxication. *Arch. Intern. Med.* 128:109–17

21. Gordonsmith, R. H., Brooke-Taylor, S., Smith, L. L., Cohen, G. M. 1983. Structural requirements of compounds to inhibit pulmonary diamine accumulation. *Biochem. Pharmacol.* 32:3701–9

22. Halliwell, B., Gutteridge, J. M. C. 1984. Lipid peroxidation, oxygen radicals, cell damage and antioxidant therapy. *Lancet* 23:1396–97

23. Hollinger, M. A., Giri, S. N., Alley, M., Budd, E., Hwang, F. 1974. Tissue distribution and binding of radioactivity from ^{14}C-thiourea in the rat. *Drug Metab. Dispos.* 2:521–25

24. Hollinger, M. A., Giri, S. N., Budd, E. 1976. A pharmacodynamic study of [^{14}C]-thiourea toxicity in immature, tolerant and nontolerant rats. *Toxicol. Appl. Pharmacol.* 37:545–56

25. Johnson, A., Malik, A. B. 1982. Pulmonary edema after glass bead microembolization: protective effect of granulocytopenia. *J. Appl. Physiol.* 52:155–61

26. Keeling, P. L., Pratt, I. S., Aldridge, W. N., Smith, L. L. 1981. The enhancement of paraquat toxicity in rats by 85% oxygen: lethality and cell-specific lung damage. *Br. J. Exp. Path.* 62:643–54

27. Keeling, P. L., Smith, L. L. 1982. Relevance of NADPH depletion and mixed disulphide formation in rat lung to the mechanism of cell damage following paraquat administration. *Biochem. Pharmacol.* 31:3243–49

28. Keeling, P. L., Smith, L. L., Aldridge, W. N. 1982. The formation of mixed disulphides in the rat lung following paraquat administration. Correlation with changes in intermediary metabolism. *Biochim. Biophys. Acta* 716:249–57

29. Longo, N., Statham, C., Sasame, H., Boyd, M. 1978. Pulmonary Clara cell damage by carbon tetrachloride. *Fed. Proc.* 37:505

30. Martin, W. J. 1983. Nitrofurantoin.

Potential direct and indirect mechanisms of lung injury. *Chest* 83:51S–52S

31. Martin, W. J. 1983. Nitrofurantoin: evidence for the oxidant injury of lung parenchyma cells. *Am. Rev. Respir. Dis.* 127:482–86

32. Mason, R. P., Holtzman, J. L. 1975. The role of catalytic superoxide formation in the O_2 inhibition of nitroreductase. *Biochem. Biophys. Res. Commun.* 67:1267–74

33. McBrien, D. C. H., Slater, T. F. 1982. *Free Radicals, Lipid Peroxidation and Cancer*, pp. 243–74. London: Academic

34. McCord, J. M., Day, E. D. Jr. 1978. Superoxide dependent production of hydroxyl radical catalysed by iron-EDTA complex. *FEBS Lett.* 86:139–42

35. Meyrick, B., Miller, J., Reid, L. 1972. Pulmonary oedema induced by ANTU, or by high or low oxygen concentrations in the rat—an electronmicroscope study. *Br. J. Exp. Pathol.* 53:347–58

36. Mimnaugh, E. G., Gram, T. E., Trush, M. A. 1983. Stimulation of mouse heart and liver microsomal lipid peroxidation by anthracycline anticancer drugs: characterization and effects of reactive oxygen scavengers. *J. Pharmacol. Exp. Ther.* 226:806–16

37. Murray, R. E., Gibson, J. E. 1972. A comparative study of paraquat intoxication in rats, guinea pigs and monkeys. *Exp. Mol. Pathol.* 17:317–25

38. Mustafa, M. G., Cross, C. E. 1974. Effects of short-term ozone exposure on lung mitochondrial oxidative and energy metabolism. *Arch. Biochem. Biophys.* 162:585–94

39. Mustafa, M. G., Tierney, D. F. 1978. Biochemical and metabolic changes in the lung with oxygen, ozone and nitrogen dioxide toxicity. *Am. Rev. Resp. Dis.* 118:1061–88

40. Oberley, L. W., Buettner, G. R. 1979. The production of hydroxyl radical by bleomycin and iron (II). *FEBS Lett.* 97:47–49

41. Reddrop, C. J., Cheesman, K. H., Slater, T. F. 1983. Correlations between common tests for assessment of liver damage: indices of the hepato-protective activity of promethazine in carbon tetrachloride hepatotoxicity. *Cell Biochem. Funct.* 1:55–63

42. Richter, C. P. 1945. The development and use of alphanaphthyl-thiourea (ANTU) as a rat poison. *J. Am. Med. Assoc.* 129:927–31

43. Roehm, J. N., Hadley, J. C., Menzel, D. B. 1971. Oxidation of unsaturated fatty acids by ozone and nitrogen dioxide. *Arch. Environ. Health* 23:142–53

44. Rose, M. S., Lock, E. A., Smith, L. L., Wyatt, I. 1976. Paraquat accumulation and species specificity. *Biochem. Pharmacol.* 25:419–23

45. Rose, M. S., Smith, L. L., Wyatt, I. 1974. Evidence for energy-dependent accumulation of paraquat into rat lung. *Nature* 252:314–15

46. Shu, H., Talcott, R. E., Rice, S. A., Wei, E. T. 1979. Lipid peroxidation and paraquat toxicity. *Biochem. Pharmacol.* 28:327–31

47. Smith, L. L. 1982. The identification of an accumulation system for diamines and polyamines into the lung and its relevance to paraquat toxicity. *Arch. Toxicol. Suppl.* 5:1–14

48. Smith, L. L., Wyatt, I. 1981. The accumulation of putrescine into slices of rat lung and brain and its relationship to the accumulation of paraquat. *Biochem. Pharmacol.* 30:1053–58

49. Smith, L. L., Wyatt, I., Cohen, G. M. 1982. The accumulation of diamines and polyamines into rat lung slices. *Biochem. Pharmacol.* 31:3029–33

50. Smith, P., Heath, D. 1976. Paraquat. *CRC Crit. Rev. Toxicol.* 4:411–45

51. Snider, G. L., Hayes, J. A., Korthy, A. L. 1978. Chronic interstitial pulmonary fibrosis produced in hamsters by endotracheal bleomycin. *Am. Rev. Respir. Dis.* 117:1099–1108

52. Sorokin, S. P. 1970. The cells of the lungs. In *Conference on Morphology of Experimental Respiratory Carcinogenesis*, ed. P. Nettesheim, M. G. Hanna, J. W. Deatherage, pp. 3–43. Gatlinburg, Tenn.: US Atomic Energy Commission

53. Steffen, C., Netter, K. J. 1979. On the mechanism of paraquat action on microsomal oxygen reduction and its relation to lipid peroxidation. *Toxicol. Appl. Pharmacol.* 47:593–602

54. Trush, M. A., Mimnaugh, E. G., Ginsberg, E., Gram, T. E. 1981. *In vitro* stimulation by paraquat of reactive oxygen-mediated lipid peroxidation in rat lung microsomes. *Toxicol. Appl. Pharmacol.* 60:279–86

55. Umezawa, H. 1974. Chemistry and mechanism of action of bleomycin. *Fed. Proc.* 33:2296–302

56. Vijeyaratnam, G. S., Corrin, B. 1971. Experimental paraquat poisoning: a histological and electron-optical study of the changes in the lung. *J. Pathol.* 103:123–29

57. Waddell, W. J., Marlowe, C. 1980. Tissue and cellular disposition of paraquat in mice. *Toxicol. Appl. Pharmacol.* 56:127–40

58. Witschi, H., Kacew, S., Hirai, K., Cote, M. 1977. *In vivo* oxidation of reduced nicotinamide-adenine dinucleotide phosphate by paraquat and diquat in rat lung. *Chem. Biol. Interact.* 19:143–60

59. Zsoldos, T., Tigyi, A., Montsko, T., Puppi, A. 1983. Lipid peroxidation in the membrane damaging effect of silica-containing dust on rat lungs. *Exp. Pathol.* 23:73–77

Ann. Rev. Physiol. 1986. 48:693–702

ANTIOXIDANT DEFENSES IN THE LUNG

Irwin Fridovich

Department of Biochemistry, Duke University Medical Center, Durham, North Carolina 27710

Bruce Freeman

Departments of Anesthesiology and Biochemistry, University of Alabama in Birmingham, Birmingham, Alabama 32507

The electronic structure of ground state molecular oxygen, or dioxygen, predisposes it to a univalent pathway of reduction (61). This facile free-radical pathway of dioxygen reduction predominates in autoxidation reactions and is also seen in a number of enzymic oxidations (32). The intermediates encountered during successive univalent reductions of dioxygens are the superoxide radical (O_2^-), hydrogen peroxide (H_2O_2), and the hydroxyl radical ($HO\cdot$). These reactive intermediates can be generated within oxygenated living cells, and they pose a threat to the integrity of such cells. A multilayered system of defense has evolved to counter this threat, and possession of these defenses is a prerequisite for aerobic life.

The first defense is simply avoidance of the univalent pathway. This is achieved by enzymes with multiple electron-carrying components, which can accomplish the tetravalent reduction of dioxygen to water without the release of intermediates. Cytochrome oxidase is such an enzyme (70), and in actively respiring cells it is responsible for more than 90% of the observed dioxygen reduction. This strategy of avoidance of the univalent pathway reduces the burden of reactive intermediates the cell must face.

The second layer of defense is provided by metalloenzymes, called superoxide dismutases, which catalyze the reaction:

0066-4278/86/0315-0693$02.00

$$O_2^- + O_2^- + 2H^+ \rightarrow H_2O_2 + O_2, \qquad\qquad 1.$$

and do so with an efficiency that approaches the theoretical diffusion limit (32). The superoxide dismutase found in the cytosol of mammalian cells is a homo-dimer whose molecular weight is 32,500, and which contains both Cu(II) and Zn(II) at its active sites. X-ray crystallography has provided a detailed view of the structure of this enzyme, and has shown that the copper and zinc are close together and are bridged by the imidazolate of histidine 61 (58). During the catalytic cycle the Cu(II) is alternately reduced to Cu(I) and then reoxidized, whereas the Zn(II) does not change valence and plays a secondary role which has not yet been fully elucidated (3). It is clear, however, that the Zn(II) contributes to the structural stability of the enzyme (8, 22).

Eukaryotic cells contain another superoxide dismutase, which has manganese at its active sites (68). This enzyme, a homotetramer of molecular weight $\sim$95,000, is found in the matrix of the mitochondria. In accord with the symbiotic theory of the origin of these organelles, a very similar manganese-containing superoxide dismutase is found in bacteria. The mechanism of the manganese superoxide dismutases involves alternate reduction and reoxidation of the active site Mn(III) during successive encounters with O_2^- (50).

The third layer of antioxidant defense is provided by enzymes that eliminate the H_2O_2 produced either by the dismutation of O_2^-, or directly by the reoxidation of reduced flavoenzymes. Catalase, which in mammals is always a heme protein, dismutes H_2O_2 into H_2O and O_2 by catalyzing the reaction:

$$H_2O_2 + H_2O_2 \rightarrow 2\ H_2O + O_2. \qquad\qquad 2.$$

Mammalian catalase is a homotetrameric enzyme whose molecular weight is 240,000 (15). During the catalytic cycle the active site heme undergoes alternate divalent oxidation and reduction during successive encounters with H_2O_2. The oxidized state of the enzyme, which is often called compound I, is an Fe(IV) porphyrin π cation radical (18). This implies that during the divalent oxidation of the ferriheme at the active site by H_2O_2, one electron is taken from the central iron atom and the second from the porphyrin, which provides its ligand field. Compound I is a powerful oxidant and could be reduced by substances other than H_2O_2. In the case of catalase the heme fits deeply and snugly into a crevice in the protein structure, and only small molecules can gain access to the heme iron (52). It is thus not surprising that catalase compound I can be reduced easily only by small molecules, such as methanol, ethanol, formate, and nitrite, and therefore that native catalase effectively acts as a peroxidase only towards such small molecules (9, 44).

H_2O_2 can also be eliminated by peroxidases that catalyze the reduction of H_2O_2 by a variety of electron donors. In mammalian tissues the most important of these is the seleno enzyme, glutathione peroxidase (1, 11), which catalyzes the reactions:

$$2 \, GSH + H_2O_2 \rightarrow G\text{-}S\text{-}S\text{-}G + 2H_2O \qquad\qquad 3.$$

This reaction accomplishes the reduction of H_2O_2 to water at the expense of the oxidation of glutathione thiol (GSH) to the corresponding disulfide. Glutathione reductase, which catalyzes the reduction of the glutathione disulfide (G-S-S-G) by NADPH (48), prevents depletion of cellular glutathione thiol. Although quite specific with respect to glutathione, the glutathione peroxidase is less finicky regarding the hydroperoxide: It can catalyze the reduction of fatty acid hydroperoxides (23) produced during the peroxidation of polyunsaturated fatty acids. Catalase is located in peroxisomes, while glutathione peroxidase is distributed throughout the cytosol. This compartmentation, coupled with the lower Km of glutathione peroxidase for H_2O_2 (42), suggests that catalase is less important than glutathione peroxidase in cellular H_2O_2 decomposition. As intracellular rates of H_2O_2 generation are increased, however, catalase becomes more important because the catalatic reaction, which has a greater rate constant, predominates over the peroxidatic reaction.

Excepting the action of ionizing radiation, the very reactive HO· can only be generated by the univalent reduction of hydroperoxides. This can be accomplished by organic radicals, such as the paraquat monocation radical (72, 73), or by certain reduced metal cations, such as Cu(I) or Fe(II) (66). Iron deserves special mention since a variety of ferric complexes can be reduced by O_2^-. This enables these complexes to catalyze the reduction of H_2O_2 by O_2^- in a process called the metal-catalyzed Haber-Weiss reaction (5, 16, 21, 35, 36, 46). It follows that complete elimination of O_2^- and H_2O_2 would prevent production of HO·. However, no defense can be entirely perfect and some HO· will be produced. HO· is an extremely potent oxidant and will convert virtually any organic molecule to the corresponding free radical (53), by hydrogen atom abstraction. This can be particularly damaging in cell membranes, which are rich in polyunsaturated fatty acids, because abstraction of the allylic hydrogen initiates a free radical chain reaction. This results in the oxidation of many molecules of the polyunsaturated fatty acid per initiation event (2, 43, 51, 60), and thus greatly amplifies the damage.

α-Tocopherol interrupts this chain reaction because it reacts rapidly with the chain-propagating fatty acid radicals to yield α-tocopherol radical, which is unable to further propagate the chain reaction (6, 7). This markedly reduces the damage sustained by the membrane, and α-tocopherol thus constitutes a fourth layer of defense. It is particularly effective in this regard because it is an excellent antioxidant and because its hydrophobic properties cause it to partition into biological membranes, thus positioning it for maximum effectiveness.

To the extent that this multilayered defensive system falls short of perfection, some damage will occur and must be repaired. Repair processes may be considered the fifth and the final line of defense. For most of the molecules in the cell, repair is easily accomplished by replacement, which is part of the turnover process. In the case of DNA, repair must be accomplished without loss of the genetic information inherent in the sequence of bases, and numerous mechanisms have been evolved to accomplish this end (65). In what follows, the production and scavenging of O_2^- and H_2O_2 in lung will be examined.

The intracellular production of O_2^- and H_2O_2 by lung cells has been inferred from indirect measurements and in vitro studies of isolated organelles and cells. A number of factors can modify the rate of O_2^- and H_2O_2 production by lung tissue. Xenobiotics, such as paraquat (20) and nitrofurantoin (40), are metabolically activated by cellular reductases and then exert cell damage via reduction of dioxygen to O_2^-. Cytochrome P450-dependent monooxygenase and prostaglandin synthetase can cooxidize aromatic hydrocarbons (34) and 4-ipomeanol (56) to highly reactive electrophiles. Exposure to hyperoxic conditions used to treat respiratory insufficiency also increases the rate of pulmonary O_2^- and H_2O_2 generation (26, 29, 63, 64, 75). Infiltration of activated inflammatory cells or activation of resident alveolar and interstitial inflammatory cells will also increase the organ's rate of production of reactive oxygen species. This often occurs as a secondary response to primary free-radical injury, and can involve complex signalling processes via messenger proteins or oxidized lipids derived from injured target cells (37, 47). The extent of oxidant-induced lung injury will depend on the effectiveness of antioxidant defenses in scavenging elevated concentrations of O_2^- and H_2O_2 and the ability of repair processes to restore normal cellular function.

The reactivity of O_2^- and H_2O_2 and the high rate constants of scavenging systems effectively prevent quantitative studies of oxygen metabolite concentrations in intact cell and organ systems. Inhibition of lung homogenate and tissue slice mitochondrial oxygen consumption with CN^-, azide, or antimycin A provides an indirect measure of maximum rates of partial reduction of oxygen to O_2^- and H_2O_2 by other cellular sources. Mitochondrial cytochrome oxidase accounts for greater than 90% of lung cell oxygen consumption, yielding water without releasing O_2^- or H_2O_2 as intermediates. Rat lung CN^--resistant oxygen consumption is 8% of the total under normoxic conditions, while rat lung mitochondrial non-cytochrome oxidase–dependent oxygen uptake is 5% of state 3 respiration (26, 29). Lung superoxide production accounted for by mitochondria is estimated to be 19 nmol $\cdot min^{-1} \cdot g$ lung^{-1}. There is ~ 5 mg mitochondrial protein per gram lung. Extraorganelle O_2^- release by lung mitochondria has not been observed, but the dismutation product H_2O_2 is released from succinate-supplemented mitochondria at a rate of between 2 and 3 nmol$\cdot min^{-1} \cdot g$ lung^{-1} (63, 64). This suggests that mitochondrial O_2^- spontaneously dismutes or is efficiently scavenged, while H_2O_2 can escape mitochondrial peroxidases to react in the cytosol. In vitro studies also permit estimation that lung endoplasmic reticulum can yield 20–30 nmol $H_2O_2 \cdot min^{-1} \cdot g$ lung^{-1}, depending on whether NADH or NADPH was oxidized (63). Dismutation of microsomal O_2^- could account for a significant proportion of this H_2O_2. Intact nuclei isolated from lung show an NADH-dependent O_2^- generation of 3.5 nmol$\cdot min^{-1} \cdot g$ lung^{-1} (75). Lung organelle-derived O_2^- and H_2O_2 is primarily formed by autoxidation of cytochromes, quinones, and flavoprotein dehydrogenases associated with electron transport processes (27).

Other important intracellular sources of reactive oxygen species have recently been reviewed (27, 31) and include the oxidases and flavoproteins of peroxisomes, xanthine oxidase, aldehyde oxidase, tryptophan dioxygenase, and dihydroorotate dehydrogenase. Autoxidation of low molecular weight cystolic components is also a quantitatively important source of O_2^- and H_2O_2. This includes thiols, hydroquinones, catecholamines, flavins, and tetrahydropterins.

Activated phagocytic cells, including alveolar macrophages and neutrophils, produce O_2^-, H_2O_2, OH·, hypochlorite, and N-chloroamines (27). These species, released during the response of inflammatory cells to lung injury, can be hazardous to adjacent lung cells such as the capillary endothelium and alveolar epithelium. Red cells, serum proteins, or lipoproteins and low molecular weight components of the alveolar lining layer, such as ascorbate, can scavenge some phagocyte-derived reactive oxygen species present in extracellular spaces (57, 71). An extracellular superoxide dismutase has been described that is an ~ 135,000-dalton homotetramer containing four copper and possibly four zinc atoms. This glycoprotein exhibits some hydrophobic properties, may be associated with cellular membranes and is found associated with lung tissue. This enzyme accounts for ~ 5% of lung superoxide dismutase activity, and has a potentially significant but still obscure physiologic role (45).

The complex cell composition and architecture of the lung must be recognized when considering rates of O_2^- or H_2O_2 production, mechanisms of oxidant injury, and adaptive responses of antioxidant defenses. For example, specific lung cells could be more or less susceptible to oxidant toxicity because of (a) unique cellular transport mechanisms, (b) unique enzymatic activating systems, (c) a rich complement of autoxidizable components, (d) particularly oxidant-sensitive structural elements or metabolic processes, (e) proximity to activated inflammatory cells, or (f) content or activities of antioxidants. For these reasons the pathology of oxidant injury to lung will differ with the dose and source of oxidant stress, and with the metabolic state of the lung. Subsequent analysis of pulmonary antioxidant and general metabolic responses to oxidant stress must also take into account shifts in lung cell populations in response to injury. Site-specific toxicity often occurs, followed by proliferation or hypertrophy of resident cells. Infiltration of inflammatory cells, hemorrhage, edema, increased collagen deposition, and shifts in endogenous cell populations often complicate interpretation of the relevance of observed biochemical changes.

In spite of these complications, superoxide dismutases are clearly an important participant in pulmonary antioxidant defense. The specific activity (12) and immunoassayable superoxide dismutase content (14) of rat lungs increased following exposure to sublethal hyperoxia (24). The subsequent survival of rats in normally lethal 100% oxygen is directly related to lung superoxide dismutase activity (14). Isolation of type II alveolar epithelial cells from "oxygen-adapted" rats showed elevated Cu, Zn, and Mn superoxide dismutase activity when expressed either as a function of cell number or unit cell volume (24, 28). Finally, specific augmentation of cultured lung vascular endothelial cell Cu-Zn superoxide dismutase activity by liposome-mediated intracellular transfer of enzyme rendered cells more resistant to toxic effects of 95% oxygen (30). These observations all support concepts established from bacterial studies thirteen years ago (33).

Pulmonary H_2O_2 scavenging by catalase and glutathione peroxidase also plays a key role in lung oxidant metabolism. While catalase and glutathione peroxidase activities increase in response to hyperoxic exposure of rodents (12, 41), it is unclear whether these responses represent enzyme induction or are a consequence of peroxisomal proliferation or cell population changes. A direct correlation between the activities of these enzymes and oxidant resistance has not been established as it has for superoxide dismutase. Animal studies have shown, however, that resistance to hyperoxia rendered by liposome-mediated delivery of superoxide dismutase and catalase to the lung requires augmentation of both enzymes (62). This suggests that defense against oxygen toxicity require that O_2^- be fully reduced to H_2O. In vivo studies of lung antioxidant enzyme responses during pulmonary oxygen toxicity also suggest that the ability of lung cells to respond rapidly to hyperoxic challenge with increases of antioxidant enzyme activities over basal enzyme activities is more important than endogenous antioxidant enzyme specific activities (25).

Cellular GSSG efflux is a marker of glutathione peroxidase-mediated reduction of hydroperoxides (54) and can be considered an antioxidant defense because formation of mixed disulfides by protein sulfhydryl-GSSG exchange can detrimentally alter protein function. In vivo and in vitro models using an inhibitor of glutathione reductase, 1,3-bis(2-chloroethyl)-1-nitrosourea, also suggest the importance of maintaining low intracellular GSSG concentrations (55). Isolated and perfused lungs exhibit increased GSSG efflux into the vascular perfusate following perfusion with nitrofurantoin or paraquat-containing medium (19) and exposure of lungs to hyperbaric hyperoxia (49). Pyridine nucleotides become more oxidized in concert with GSSG efflux from t-butyl hydroperoxide perfused lungs, which suggests increased NADPH utilization during glutathione reductase metabolism of intracellular GSSG (10). Depletion of cultured endothelial cell GSH with thiol-specific reagents or by inhibition of glutathione synthesis using buthionine sulfoximine potentiates the cytotoxicity of H_2O_2 (38).

There is a gestational age–dependant increase in specific activities of Cu, Zn, and Mn superoxide dismutases, glutathione peroxidase, catalase, and glucose-6-phosphate dehydrogenase in fetal lungs before the onset of air breathing that exceeds specific activities measured in adult lungs (74). The increased enzyme activities may reflect increased metabolic activity of the lung in late gestation (59), contribute to the resistance to hyperoxia evident in the young of many species (67), and serve as adaptive preparation for the relative hyperoxic stress of birth. It follows that the greater susceptibility of preterm infants to oxygen toxicity can be in part ascribed to deficiencies in antioxidant defense mechanisms.

The premature human is deficient in α-tocopherol relative to full term infants (39). While α-tocopherol clearly reduces the severity of pulmonary oxygen toxicity in rodents (4, 69), its efficacy in clinical trials has been disappointing. Studies of rodents exposed to ozone show that supplements of α-tocopherol did not provide additional protection, while α-tocopherol-deficient animals suffered increased oxidant lung injury, as reflected by lipid peroxidation (17). This suggests that α-tocopherol is usually sufficient and becomes a critical modulator of pulmonary antioxidant defenses during malnutrition or extended periods of parenteral nutrition.

The lung is an important target of injury from inhaled xenobiotics and toxic processes mediated by reactive oxygen species because of its greater than 50 m^2 surface area exposed to inhaled gases, and its relatively hyperoxic state compared with cells of other organs. The structural and biochemical heterogeneity of the lung often contributes to localized pathologic responses from toxic phenomena. Advances in lung cell biology that permit isolation of specific lung cell types and in situ cytochemical detection of enzyme systems involved in metabolic activation of xenobiotics and antioxidant defenses will provide insight into biochemical mechanisms of pulmonary oxidant injury.

Literature Cited

1. Arias, I. M., Jakoby, N. B., eds. 1976. Glutathione Peroxidase: Metabolic Functions. New York: Raven
2. Barber, A. A., Bernheim, F. 1967. Lipid peroxidation. Adv. Gerontol. Res. 2: 355–403
3. Blackburn, N. J., Hasnain, S. S., Binstead, N., Diakun, G. P., Garner, G. D., Knowles, P. F., 1984. An extended X-ray absorption fine structure study of bovine erythrocyte superoxide dimustase in aqueous solution. Direct evidence for three co-ordinate Cu(I) in reduced enzyme. Biochem. J. 219:985–90
4. Bucher, J. R., Roberts, R. J. 1982.

Effects of α-tocopherol treatment on newborn rat lung development and injury in hyperoxia. Ped. Pharmacol. 2:1–9
5. Buettner, G. R., Oberley, L. W., Chan-Leuthauser, S. W. H. 1978. The effect of iron on the distribution of superoxide and hydroxyl radicals as seen by spin trapping and on the superoxide dismutase assay. Photochem. Photobiol. 28:693–95
6. Burton, G. W., Ingold, K. U. 1981. Autoxidation of biological molecules. 1. The antioxidant activity of vitamin E and related chain-breaking phenolic antioxidants in vitro. J. Am. Chem. Soc. 103:6472–77

7. Burton, G. W., Joyce, A., Ingold, K. U. 1983. Is vitamin E the only lipid-double, chain-breaking antioxidant in human blood plasma and erythrocyte membranes? *Arch. Biochem. Biophys.* 221: 281–90

8. Cass, A. E., Hill, H. A., Bannister, J. V., Bannister, W. H. 1979. Zinc(II) binding to apo-bovine superoxide dismutase. *Biochem. J.* 177:477–86

9. Chance, B. 1949. The properties of the enzyme-substrate compounds of horseradish and lacto-peroxidase. *Science* 109:204–8

10. Chance, B., Boveris, A. 1978. Hyperoxia and hydroperoxide metabolism. In *Extrapulmonary Manifestations of Respiratory Disease*. ed. E. D. Robin, pp. 185–236. New York: Dekker

11. Chaudiere, J., Tappel, A. L. 1983. Purification and characterization of selenium-glutathione peroxidase from hamster liver. *Arch. Biochem. Biophys.* 226:448–57

12. Crapo, J. D., Barry, B. E., Foscue, H. A., Shelburne, J. 1980. Structural and biochemical changes in rat lungs occurring during exposures to lethal and adaptive doses of oxygen. *Am. Rev. Respir. Dis.* 122:123–37

13. Crapo, J. D., McCord, J. M. 1976. Oxygen-induced changes in pulmonary superoxide dismutase assayed by antibody titration. *Am. J. Physiol.* 231:1196–1203

14. Crapo, J. D., Tierney, D. F. 1974. Superoxide dismutase and pulmonary oxygen toxicity. *Am. J. Physiol.* 226:1401–7

15. Deisseroth, A., Dounce, A. L. 1970. Catalase: physical and chemical properties, mechanism of catalysis, and physiological role. *Physiol. Rev.* 50:319–75

16. DiGiuseppi, J., Fridovich, I. 1980. Ethylene from 2-keto-4-thiomethyl butyric acid: the Haber-Weiss reaction. *Arch. Biochem. Biophys.* 205:323–29

17. Dillard, C. J., Litov, R. E., Savin, W. M., Dumelin, E. E., Tappel, A. L. 1978. Effects of exercise, vitamin E, and ozone on pulmonary function and lipid peroxidation. *J. Appl. Physiol. Respir. Environ. Exercise Physiol.* 45:927–32

18. Dolphin, D., Forman, A., Berg, D. C., Fajer, J., Felton, R. H. 1971. Compounds I of catalase and horseradish peroxidase. π-cation radicals. *Proc. Natl. Acad. Sci. USA* 68:614–18

19. Dunbar, J. R., DeLucia, A. J., Bryant, L. R. 1984. Glutathione status of isolated rabbit lungs: effects of nitrofurantoin and paraquat perfusion with normoxic and hyperoxic ventilation. *Biochem. Pharmacol.* 33:1343–52

20. Fisher, H. K., Clements, J. A., Wright, R. R. 1973. Enhancement of oxygen toxicity by the herbicide paraquat. *Am. Rev. Respir. Dis.* 107:246–52

21. Fong, K.-L., McCay, P. B., Pouer, J. L., Misra, H. P., Keele, B. B. Jr. 1976. Evidence for superoxide-dependent reduction of Fe^{3+} and its role in enzyme-generated hydroxyl radical formation. *Chem.-Biol. Interact.* 15:77–89

22. Forman, H. J., Fisher, A. B. 1981. Antioxidant enzymes of rat granular pneumocytes: constitutive levels and effect of hyperoxia. *Lab. Invest.* 45:1–8

23. Forman, H. J., Fridovich, I., 1973. On the stability of bovine superoxide dismutase: the effects of metals. *J. Biol. Chem.* 248:2645–49

24. Forstrom, J. W., Stutts, F. H., Tappel, A. L. 1979. Rat liver cytosolic glutathione peroxidase: reactivity with linoleic acid hydroperoxide and cumene hydroperoxide. *Arch. Biochem. Biophys.* 193:51–56

25. Frank, L., Bucher, J., Roberts, R. J. 1979. Oxygen toxicity in neonatal and adult animals of various species. *J. Appl. Phys.* 45:699–704

26. Freeman, B. A., Crapo, J. D. 1981. Hyperoxia increases oxygen radical production in rat lungs and lung mitochondria. *J. Biol. Chem.* 256:10986–92

27. Freeman, B. A., Crapo, J. D. 1982. Biology of disease: Free radicals and tissue injury. *Lab. Invest.* 47:412–26

28. Freeman, B. A., Mason, R. J., Williams, M. C., Crapo, J. D. 1985. Antioxidant enzyme activity in alveolar type II cells after exposure of rats to hyperoxia. *Exp. Lung Res.* In press

29. Freeman, B. A., Toplosky, M. K., Crapo, J. D. 1982. Hyperoxia increases oxygen radical production in rat lung homogenates. *Arch. Biochem. Biophys.* 216:477–85

30. Freeman, B. A., Young, S. L., Crapo, J. D. 1983. Liposome-mediated augmentation of superoxide dismutase in endothelial cells prevents oxygen injury. *J. Biol. Chem.* 258:12534–41

31. Fridovich, I. 1982. Superoxide radical and superoxide dismutases. In *Oxygen and Living Processes. An Interdisciplinary Approach*, ed. D. L. Gilbert, p. 251. New York: Springer-Verlag

32. Fridovich, I. 1983. Superoxide radical: an endogenous toxicant. *Ann. Rev. Pharmacol. Toxicol.* 23:239–57

33. Gregory, E. M., Fridovich, I. 1973. Oxygen toxicity and the superoxide dismutase. *J. Bacteriol.* 114:1193–97

34. Griffin, K. A., Johnson, C. B., Breger,

R. K., Franklin, R. B. 1981. Pulmonary toxicity, hepatic and extrahepatic metabolism of 2-methylnaphthalene in mice. *Toxicol. Appl. Pharmacol.* 61:185–96

35. Gutteridge, J. M. C., Richmond, R., Halliwell, B. 1979. Inhibition of the iron-catalysed formation of hydroxyl radicals from superoxide and lipid peroxidation by desferrioxamine. *Biochem. J.* 184: 469–72

36. Halliwell, B. 1978. Superoxide-dependent formation of hydroxyl radicals in the presence of iron salts. *FEBS Lett.* 96:238–42

37. Harada, R. N., Vatter, A. E., Repine, J. E. 1984. Macrophage effector function in pulmonary oxygen toxicity: hyperoxia damages and stimulates alveolar macrophages to make and release chemotaxins for polymorphonuclear leukocytes. *J. Leuk. Biol.* 35:373–83

38. Harlan, J. M., Levine, J. D., Callahan, K. S., Schwartz, B. R. 1984. Glutathione redox cycle protects cultured endothelial cells against lysis by extracellularly generated hydrogen peroxide. *J. Clin. Invest.* 73:706–13

39. Hodson, W. A., Truog, W. E., Mayock, D. E., Lyrene, R., Woodrum, D. E. 1979. Bronchopulmonary dysplasia: The need of epidemiologic studies. *J. Pediatr.* 95:848–53

40. Holtzman, J. L., Crankshaw, D. L., Peterson, F. J., Polnaszek, C. F. 1981. The kinetics of the aerobic reduction of nitrofurantoin by NADPH-cytochrome P-450 reductase. *Mol. Pharmacol.* 20: 669–73

41. Jenkinson, S. G., Lawrence, R. A., Burk, R. F., Gregory, P. E. 1983. Non-selenium-dependent glutathione peroxidase activity in rat lung: association with lung glutathione S-transferase activity and the effects of hyperoxia. *Toxicol. Appl. Pharmacol.* 68:399–404

42. Jones, D. P., Eklow, L., Thor, H., Orrenius, S. 1981. Metabolism of hydrogen peroxide in isolated hepatocytes: relative contributions of catalase and glutathione peroxidase in decomposition of endogenously generated H_2O_2. *Arch. Biochem. Biophys.* 210:505–16

43. Kappus, H., Sies, H. 1981. Toxic drug effects associated with oxygen metabolism: redox cycling and lipid peroxidation. *Experientia* 37:1233–41

44. Keilin, D., Hartree, E. F. 1955. Catalase, peroxidase and metmyoglobin as catalysts of coupled peroxidatic reactions. *Biochem. J.* 60:310–25

45. Marklund, S. L. 1984. Extracellular superoxide dismutase in human tissues and human cell lines. *J. Clin. Invest.* 74: 1398–1403

46. McCord, J. M., Day, E. D. Jr. 1978. Superoxide-dependent production of hydroxyl radical catalyzed by iron-EDTA complex. *FEBS Lett.* 86:139–42

47. McCord, J. M., Wong, K. 1979. Phagocyte-produced free radicals: roles in cytotoxicity and inflammation. In *Oxygen Free Radicals and Tissue Damage. Ciba Symp.* 65:343–60

48. Mize, C. E., Langdon, R. G. 1962. Hepatic glutathione reductase. I. Purification and general kinetic properties; II. Physical properties and mechanism of action. *J. Biol. Chem.* 237: 1589–1600

49. Nishiki, K., Jamieson, D., Chance, B. 1976. Oxygen toxicity in the perfused rat liver and lung under hyperbaric conditions. *Biochem. J.* 160:343–55

50. Pick, M., Rabani, J., Yost, F., Fridovich, I. 1974. The catalytic mechanism of the manganese-containing superoxide dismutase of *Escherichia coli* studied by pulse radiolysis. *J. Am. Chem. Soc.* 7329–33

51. Pryor, W. A. 1978. The formation of free-radicals and the consequences of their reactions in vivo. *Photochem. Photobiol.* 28:787–801

52. Reid, T. J. III, Murthy, M. R. N., Sicignano, A., Tanaka, N., Musick, W. D. L., Rossman, M. G. 1981. Structure and heme environment of beef liver catalase at 2.5 Å resolution. *Proc. Natl. Acad. Sci. USA* 78:4767–71

53. Ross, F., Ross, A. B. 1977. *Selected Specific Rates of Reactions of Transients from Water in Aqueous Solution. III. Hydroxyl Radical and Perhydroxyl Radical and Their Radical Ions.* Natl. Bureau Standards No. 59

54. Sies, H., Akerboom, T. P. M. 1984. [59]Glutathione disulfide (GSSG) efflux from cells and tissues. *Methods Enzymol.* 105:445–51

55. Smith, A. C., Boyd, M. R. 1984. Preferential effects of 1,3-bis(2-chloroethyl)-1-nitrosourea (BCNU) on pulmonary glutathione reductase and glutathione/glutathione disulfide ratios: possible implications for lung toxicity. *J. Pharmacol. Exp. Ther.* 229:658–63

56. Statham, C. N., Boyd, M. R. 1982. Distribution and metabolism of the pulmonary alkylating agent and cytotoxin, 4-ipomeanol, in control and diethylmaleate-treated rats. *Biochem. Pharmacol.* 31:1584–89

57. Sweder, V. A., Hoidal, J., Vercellotti, G. M., Schwartz, B. A., Moldow, C. F., Jacob, H. S. 1985. Protection against

lethal hyperoxia by tracheal insufflation of erythrocytes: role of red cell glutathione. *Science* 227:756–58

58. Tainer, J. A., Getzoff, E. D., Beem, K. D., Richardson, J. S., Richardson, D. C. 1982. Determination and analysis of the 2Å structure of copper, zinc superoxide dismutase. *J. Mol. Biol.* 160:181–217

59. Tanswell, A. K., Freeman, B. A. 1984. Pulmonary antioxidant enzyme maturation in the fetal and neonatal rat. I. Developmental profiles. *Pediatr. Res.* 18:584–87

60. Tappel, A. L. 1972. Vitamin E and free radical peroxidation of lipids. *Ann. NY Acad. Sci.* 203:12–28

61. Taube, H. 1965. Mechanisms of oxidation with oxygen. In *Oxygen. Proc. Symp. NY Heart Assoc.,* pp. 29–50. New York: Little Brown

62. Turrens, J. F., Crapo, J. D., Freeman, B. A. 1984. Protection against oxygen toxicity by intravenous injection of liposome-entrapped catalase and superoxide dismutase. *J. Clin. Invest.* 73:87–97

63. Turrens, J. F., Freeman, B. A., Crapo, J. D. 1982. Hyperoxia increases H_2O_2 release by lung mitochondria and microsomes. *Arch. Biochem. Biophys.* 217:411–19

64. Turrens, J. F., Freeman, B. A., Levitt, J. G., Crapo, J. D. 1982. The effect of hyperoxia on superoxide production by lung submitochondrial particles. *Arch. Biochem. Biophys.* 217:401–10

65. Walker, G. C. 1984. Mutagenesis and inducible responses to deoxyribonucleic acid damage in *E. coli. Microbiol. Rev.* 48:60–93

66. Walling, C. 1975. Fenton's reagent revisited. *Acc. Chem. Res.* 8:125–31

67. Warshaw, J. B., Terry, M. L., Ranis, M. B. 1980. Metabolic adaptation in developing lung. *Pediatr. Res.* 14:296–300

68. Weisiger, R. A., Fridovich, I. 1973. Superoxide dismutase: organelle specificity. *J. Biol. Chem.* 248:3582–92

69. Wender, D. F., Thulin, G. E., Smith, G. J. W., Warshaw, J. B. 1981. Vitamin E affects lung biochemical and morphologic response to hyperoxia in the newborn rabbit. *Pediatr. Res.* 15:262–68

70. Wharton, D. C., Gibson, Q. H. 1968. Studies of the oxygenated compound of cytochrome oxidase. *J. Biol. Chem.* 243:702–6

71. Willis, R. J., Kratzing, C. C. 1974. Ascorbic acid in rat lung. *Biochem. Biophys. Res. Commun.* 59:1250–53

72. Winterbourne, C. C. 1981. Production of hydroxyl radical from paraquat radical and H_2O_2. *FEBS Lett.* 128:339–42

73. Winterbourne, C. C., Sutton, H. C. 1984. Hydroxyl radical production from hydrogen peroxide and enzymatically generated paraquat radicals: catalytic requirements and oxygen dependence. *Arch. Biochem. Biophys.* 235:116–26

74. Yam, J., Frank, L., Roberts, R. J. 1978. Age-related development of pulmonary antioxidant enzymes in the rat. *Proc. Soc. Exp. Biol. Med.* 157:293–97

75. Yusa, T., Crapo, J. D., Freeman, B. A. 1984. Hyperoxia enhances lung and liver nuclear superoxide generation. *Biochim. Biophys. Acta.* 798:167–73

Ann. Rev. Physiol. 1986. 48:703–19

THE RELATION OF FREE RADICAL PRODUCTION TO HYPEROXIA

Dana Jamieson

School of Physiology and Pharmacology, University of New South Wales, New South Wales, Australia

Britton Chance

Department of Biochemistry and Biophysics, University of Pennsylvania, Philadelphia, Pennsylvania 19104

Enrique Cadenas

Institute of Physiological Chemistry, University of Düsseldorf, Düsseldorf, Federal Republic of Germany

Alberto Boveris

Department of Chemical Biology, University of Buenos Aires, Buenos Aires, Argentina

INTRODUCTION

Exposure to a hyperoxic environment leads to toxic effects, the severity of which depends upon the degree of hyperoxia and the duration of the exposure. In mammals, inspired oxygen at partial pressure above about 500 torr leads to lung damage (5) characterized by such changes as: edema formation, atelectasis, consolidation, fibrin deposits, congestion, inflammation, arteriolar thickening and hyalinization, hypertrophy of alveolar cells, and hyperplasia. Convulsions, pulmonary edema, and alveolar hemorrhage are the most obvious macroscopic changes. Edema formation in pulmonary oxygen poisoning is due to the increased permeability of the pulmonary capillaries (24), which is now thought to be caused by reactive oxygen species forming at a rate that over-

0066-4278/86/0315-0703$02.00

whelms the capability of the cells to maintain their ionic equilibria under oxidative stress (28, 38, 45, 48, 71, 80).

While convulsions are the first overt manifestation of hyperbaric oxygen toxicity at pressures lower than 2 ATA, central nervous system (CNS) symptoms are rare, and it can be assumed that pulmonary damage is the cause of death. Thus, when discussing tolerance and prolongation of survival under various conditions of hyperoxia, it will be generally assumed that the survival time correlates with pulmonary pathology (52).

Additionally, hyperoxia must be defined in the context of this review. The term "hyperoxic environment" implies one in which the partial pressure of oxygen is above that normally seen by the particular animal organ or organelle. If subcellular particles or cell suspensions from mammalian tissue are gassed with 20% oxygen in vitro their environment is hyperoxic compared to their physiological environment. The exception to this is lung tissue, in which cells are normally exposed to oxygen tensions averaging 100 torr. By comparison, cerebral pO_2 is about 30 torr in air-breathing rats, and only reachs 150 torr (47) (measured fluorometrically) to 600 torr (54) (measured polarographically) when exposed to about 4 ATA pure O_2. Other organs gave pO_2 values fairly similar to those found for brain (55). Mitochondria, the site of O_2 consumption, may be expected to operate under even lower oxygen tensions than these average values in tissues because of O_2 diffusion gradients. Such considerations make comparisons of hyperoxic effects in vitro and in vivo difficult, especially if quantitative conclusions are to be drawn. Thus, while the lung is usually the target organ for lethality in mammals breathing elevated oxygen tensions, this in no way implies that lung tissue per se is more sensitive to raised oxygen tensions than other tissues.

Most investigators today believe that hyperoxic toxicity is due to the production of reactive oxygen species at a rate in excess of the capacity of the cellular defense mechanisms to inactivate such toxic species, and thus the sensitivity to oxygen toxicity could be expected to vary depending on the cells defense mechanisms. Gerschmann et al (41) proposed that hyperoxic toxicity may be due to excessive production of oxygen radicals. They drew attention to certain similarities in X-irradiation and oxygen poisoning and hypothesized a common mechanism. However, there are also many dissimilarities in the damage produced by these treatments (51). Investigations over the last fifteen years have clarified some of the mechanisms these processes have in common and some of the reasons for the different end effects in cells. In this review we present largely circumstantial and some direct evidence for the increased formation of superoxide (O_2^-), singlet oxygen ($^1O_2$), hydrogen peroxide (H_2O_2), and lipid peroxides, and their role in the toxicology of hyperoxia. As combinations of these substances, particularly in the presence of Fe^{2+} ions, can produce the very highly reactive and damaging hydroxyl (OH) radical, it is generally assumed that the latter is important in causing molecular damage (23, 28, 32, 35, 38, 45, 46, 71).

REACTIONS

The various O_2 species are formed in different amounts in different parts of the cell by various mechanisms (see review by F. Pryor, this volume). Their steady-state levels depend on the degree of hyperoxia, the availability of substrates, availability of Fe^{2+}, the ratio of different organelles in the cells, and the activity of antioxidant enzymes, such as superoxide dismutase (SOD), catalase, glutathione peroxidase, and all the components necessary for their activities. The level of antioxidants, such as alpha-tocopherol (Vitamin E), and ascorbic acid is also critical. Thus, different cell types or even similar cells under dissimilar conditions may be expected to vary in the type and intensity of their response to raised oxygen tensions or other free-radical producing procedures, such as ionizing radiation or the presence of radical-generating chemicals such as paraquat. In the case of ionizing radiation, for example, the usual target molecule for biological damage is the DNA molecule, whereas in hyperoxia the plasma membrane appears to be the principal site of damage, with lipid peroxidation resulting in a nonselective increase in membrane permeability. This peroxidation may be initiated by other species of active oxygen, notably $OH\cdot$, which in turn can be produced from $O^{\cdot-}{}_2$ and H_2O_2.

The direct evidence for the formation of oxygen radicals comes from experiments done in vitro. The in vitro experiments were usually done under normobaric conditions, but as pointed out earlier, even air-saturated medium would be a very hyperoxic environment for most cells and subcellular particles, except those of lung tissues. Some of the most convincing indirect evidence of the involvement of reactive oxygen in oxygen toxicity comes from in vivo studies of animals made tolerant to hyperoxia; most of these experiments were done in normobaric conditions. Other indirect evidence comes from studies that involved the administration of agents that protect against (or potentiate) oxygen toxicity. Under normobaric conditions multiple dosing is required, with its attendant technical difficulties, thus the latter experiments have usually been carried out using hyperbaric 100% O_2.

Due to the transient nature of various forms of reactive oxygen, it is difficult to obtain accurate measurements of levels of such components in tissues and, virtually by definition, the more reactive the radical the more difficult it is to measure since its half-life is so short. However, several studies over the past fifteen years have succeeded in demonstrating that hyperoxia can indeed increase the rate of formation of superoxide, hydrogen peroxide, and lipid peroxides and, by inference, the hydroxyl radical and probably singlet oxygen.

DIRECT EVIDENCE FOR THE INCREASED FORMATION OF REACTIVE O_2 SPECIES IN HYPEROXIA

Superoxide Formation in Hyperoxia

Recently, Crapo and coworkers (34, 36) tested the hypothesis that hyperoxia increases free-radical production in the lung and that tissue injury represented by lipid peroxidation was a consequence of increased O_2^- and H_2O_2 production. Superoxide production was tested for initially by the measurement of CN^--insensitive respiration in lung homogenates and slices exposed to air or 100% O_2 (34, 36). An increase in CN^--insensitive respiration, which is an indirect measurement of oxygen radical formation, was recorded in hyperoxia. This indicated that increased oxygen utilization occurred through the "leak" in the respiratory chain, allowing one electron to be transferred to oxygen from NADH or ubiquinone, which results in superoxide formation. From their data these authors calculated the contribution of the mitochondria to the whole-lung CN^--resistant respiration. They showed that while the mitochondrial contribution was negligible in normoxic conditions (21% oxygenation), it accounted for 15% of the CN^--resistant respiration at 100% oxygenation. However, CN^- inhibits the ubiquinone site of O_2^- production (8, 74). Although this underestimates O_2^- production, the use of CN^- poises the respiratory chain carriers in the reduced state, which augments superoxide production (8, 11, 35, 77). Thus, quantitative results and comparisons with in vivo situations must be treated with caution. However, the results do show that superoxide formation increases with increased oxygen tensions.

These workers later extended their experiments to superoxide production in submitochondrial particles (77). Several methods were used to estimate superoxide production in these later experiments, vis-à-vis CN^--resistant respiration, epinephrine oxidation, and cytochrome C reduction. Since CN^- somewhat inhibits superoxide production at the ubiquinone site, the measurement of CN^--resistant respiration of mitochondrial or submitochondrial particles should measure superoxide formation predominantly at the NADH site. In nonsupplemented submitochondrial particles, the respiratory chain is oxidized, thus addition of either NADH or succinate in the presence of rotenone, antimycin, or CN^- should distinguish O_2^- production by individual components of the respiratory chain. This type of experiment was carried out using porcine lung submitochondrial particles, and overall the results showed a marked increase in superoxide production when the oxygen tension of the medium was increased from 0 to 100% O_2. In porcine lung the mitochondrial NADH site appeared to produce relatively more O_2^- than the ubiquinone site, in contrast to heart (74) or liver mitochondria (10). This result is not surprising since lung mitochondria have a low ubiquinone content compared with that of other tissues (76).

H_2O_2 Formation in Hyperoxia

H_2O_2 release by lung mitochondria and microsomes in hyperoxic conditions (up to normobaric 100% O_2) has recently been measured (76). Mitochondria (12, 61), microsomes (13, 42), nuclear membranes (3), and soluble enzymes are recognized sources of intracellular H_2O_2. An increase in oxygen tension of the medium from 0 to 60% O_2 saturation caused a linear increase in detectable H_2O_2 from 0 to 0.05 nmol/min/mg protein. Above 60% O_2 there was a dramatic increase in the rate of H_2O_2 release to 0.19 nmol/min/mg protein at 100% O_2 saturation. H_2O_2 production was also measured at the NADH dehydrogenase site. Again a biphasic increase in H_2O_2 production occurred as oxygen tension was increased from 0 to 100%, with a much steeper increase after 60%. The biphasic increase in CN^--resistant respiration that was found earlier by these authors (36) in lung homogenates during hypoxia was presumably due to this mitochondrial effect. Lung microsomal H_2O_2 generation was also studied in NADH- or NADPH-supplemented microsomes, and H_2O_2 generation from microsomes was also found to increase linearly with oxygen concentration. The calculation of the relative contribution of mitochondria and microsomes to the total production of H_2O_2 by whole lung indicated that microsomes accounted for about 85% of the total H_2O_2 produced in 100% oxygen, under optimal conditions for H_2O_2 production at each site. However, as pointed out by these authors, it is difficult to extrapolate such in vitro data to the in vivo situation because of the variation in the substrate supply for the various systems and the oxidation reduction state of the carriers producing H_2O_2.

The actual amount of H_2O_2 generated by the lung mitochondria is low compared to the quantities found by Boveris & Chance (12) under similar conditions for rat liver mitochondria (namely 0.04 in lung as compared to 0.42 nM/min/mg protein in liver in air-saturated medium, and 0.19 in lung as compared to 0.65 nmol/min/mg protein in liver in 100% O_2). This probably reflects the low ubiquinone content of the lung tissue, and the consequent lower level of superoxide formation due to the fact that H_2O_2 in mitochondria is generated stoichiometrically from O_2^- (23, 29).

Lipid Peroxidation in Hyperoxia

The formation and breakdown of lipid peroxides has been extensively studied in relation to oxygen toxicity because lipid peroxidation of the plasma membrane could provide a likely explanation of the increased membrane permeability in the lungs of mammals exposed to hyperoxia. Again, much of the evidence is indirect and is derived from studies on O_2-tolerant animals or from studies involving agents that affect the generation or breakdown of peroxides (Figure 1). The formation and consequences of lipid peroxidation and the detoxifying mechanisms for prevention of lipid peroxide formation are discussed in detail by Pryor (this volume).

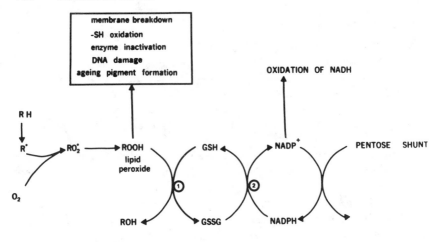

Figure 1   Summary of some of the events leading to the production and breakdown of lipid peroxides.

The most common way to measure lipid peroxides is to estimate malondial-dehyde (MDA) content; MDA is formed during lipid peroxidation after rupture of the carbon chain of unsaturated fatty acids (6, 67). The amount of malondial-dehyde is then determined colorometrically after reaction with thiobarbituric acid (6, 67). The efflux of glutathione disulfide (GSSG) from cells has also been used as an indicator of lipid peroxidation (15, 66, 70). Oxidized glu-tathione efflux is proportional to intracellular oxidized glutathione levels (66, 70), and this efflux can be correlated with the turnover of intracellular peroxides (lipid peroxides and hydrogen peroxides act as substrates for glutathione peroxidase). However, glutathione peroxidase activity has not yet been demon-strated for membrane-bound lipid hydroperoxides, and probably only those lipid hydroperoxides released from the membrane phospholipids by phospholi-pases serve as substrate for the peroxidase (44). Spin trapping of radicals during peroxidation has also been measured (69), and chemiluminescence correlates well with lipid peroxidation (10, 17).

The efflux of oxidized glutathione (GSSG) has been used in the isolated perfused lung preparation as a measure of cellular oxidative conditions (65). On the basis of titration curves of GSSG release with infusions of t-butylhydroperoxide Nishiki et al (65) were able to give quantitative data for lipid peroxide formation. In isolated perfused rat lungs, control values were 92 nM peroxide/min/g wet weight, and this increased by about 50% at 4.1 ATA of O_2. The organs from tocopherol deficient rats were much more sensitive to peroxidation: about 500–600 nM peroxide/min/g were formed at 4.1 ATA, and GSSG release began to increase immediately upon pressurization.

Chance et al (23) have pointed out that the immediate release of GSSG (glutathione disulfide) as oxygen tension is raised may indicate that lipid peroxidation is a primary metabolic change, and that this may help to explain the immediate oxidation of NADPH and NADH, which occurs in a wide variety of tissues and organs exposed to hyperbaric oxygen (21, 22).

The most recent measurements of lipid peroxidation in hyperoxic lung tissue were made by Freeman et al (36) using normobaric oxygen; details of these experiments are discussed in the section on superoxide. These authors found a 2.5-fold increase in MDA levels produced in lung tissue of rats exposed to 85% normobaric oxygen for 7 days. Lung homogenates incubated in 80% O_2 for 75 min formed more malondialdehyde than homogenates incubated in air, and this increase was inhibited by addition of SOD or catalase to the medium. Brain and liver homogenates under hyperoxic conditions showed low-level chemiluminescence, which correlated with lipid peroxide formation. Brain homogenates were more sensitive to hyperoxia than liver homogenates, and chemiluminescence and malondialdehyde formation by the former were twentyfold higher than by the latter. Moreover, the rise in the chemiluminescence of liver homogenates was preceded by a lag phase, which is indicative of antioxidant defenses that must be overcome. This lag phase was absent in brain homogenates. The higher sensitivity of brain homogenates can be explained by their lower glutathione peroxidase level, low ratio of vitamin E to polyunsaturated fatty acids, and lack of catalase. These factors may account for the early toxic manifestations of hyperoxia in the brain (20). However, as was found in the perfused, isolated lung (65), the increases in lipid peroxidation are relatively small in the in vivo experiments on tissues from normally fed rats. It would be of great benefit to have more direct in vivo data on lipid peroxide formation in lungs both in normobaric and hyperbaric oxygen, but the influx of varying amounts of various cell types during the development of pulmonary pathology presents obvious difficulties.

INDIRECT EVIDENCE FOR THE IMPORTANCE OF REACTIVE OXYGEN SPECIES IN OXYGEN TOXICITY

There is a convincing and extensive body of circumstantial evidence for the involvement of oxygen radicals in the sequelae of events that lead to the overt manifestations of hyperoxic damage. This indirect evidence is composed of data derived from animals made tolerant to hyperoxia, comparisons of animals and lower organisms in more or less aerobic environments, administration of the enzymes involved in metabolizing reactive oxygen, and administration of other compounds that may potentiate or inhibit the activity of the natural antioxidant systems or substitute for them. The various species of reactive oxygen and the indirect evidence for their involvement in hyperoxia will be considered individually.

Superoxide

IS SUPEROXIDE INVOLVED IN TOLERANCE TO HYPEROXIA? The importance of SOD in mediating oxygen tolerance was first studied by Fridovich and coworkers, who demonstrated the presence of SOD in a large variety of aerobic bacteria, and its absence in anaerobes for which oxygen exposure is rapidly toxic (62). These investigations also demonstrated that SOD could be induced in prokaryotes by exposure to hyperoxia and that these organisms with raised levels of SOD could resist subsequent exposure to normally lethal hyperbaric oxygen treatment (43). Recently a correlation between SOD activity and adaptation to a hyperoxic environment has been found in amphibia. A predominantly aquatic frog, *Rana ridibunda,* was shown to have considerably lower SOD activity and to be much less resistant to hyperoxia than a predominantly terrestial frog, *Discoglossus pictus.* SOD activity could be readily induced in *D. pictus* by hyperoxia, and this activity correlated with an increased tolerance to hyperoxia (1, 2).

The correlation between SOD activity and tolerance to hyperoxia in mammals was first demonstrated by showing that previous exposures to sublethal (85%) hyperoxic oxygen levels protected against subsequent, normally lethal (100%) oxygen concentrations, and that this correlated with raised SOD activity in lung (26, 30, 60). It was later shown (72) that SOD was very rapidly induced in the lungs of neonate rats exposed to 95–100% O_2. Although these neonate rats were resistant to this level of hyperoxia, it was lethal to adult rats, who failed to show induction of antioxidant enzymes within the experimental time period. In other experiments, mice, guinea pigs, and hamsters showed little or no increase in SOD activity when exposed to 85% O_2, and did not become tolerant to subsequent hyperoxia (30).

Recently, Brousolle et al (14) adapted rats to hyperoxia and measured changes in their lung surfactants, and changes in CuSOD and MnSOD levels. Surfactant quality remained virtually normal in adapted rats, while both CuSOD and MnSOD levels increased (by 152 and 101%, respectively). Such adapted rats were more tolerant to subsequent normobaric hyperoxia.

Some very interesting results were obtained by Frank et al (33), who accidentally discovered that bacterial endotoxin had a very marked protective effect against lethality in adult rats exposed to normobaric 96–98% O_2. On investigation of this protective action, these authors found that SOD, catalase, and glutathione peroxidase activity were increased in the lungs of rats pretreated with endotoxin. A later extension of this study (32) showed that endotoxin was an effective protection against hyperoxia in rats, and concomitantly increased SOD and other antioxidant enzyme levels, even when given at 24 or 36 hr after commencement of 98% O_2 administration. However, endotoxin did not prevent lung damage in mice, nor did it raise their levels of any of the antioxidant enzymes. Apparently, SOD is more easily induced in rats than in other animals. The overall results certainly provide strong evidence that SOD activity correlates with susceptibility to oxygen poisoning.

DOES ADMINISTRATION OF SOD CONFER PROTECTION AGAINST OXYGEN TOXICITY?   There have been several attempts to raise SOD activity in animals by administering it in various ways. Block (7) injected SOD intraperitoneally or intrathecally, but could not obtain protection against hyperbaric oxygen–induced convulsions. Similarly, Hilton et al (48) administered SOD subcutaneously to mice and measured preconvulsive times at 3 or 6 ATA O_2. This treatment was ineffective. Gerasimov et al (39) injected SOD intravenously before pressurization to 5 ATA O_2, but this also did not prolong the preconvulsive time in mice, nor did it increase survival time. Aerosol administration of SOD failed to protect rats against lung damage produced by 100% normobaric O_2. However, such negative results are hardly surprising since the penetration of SOD into cells is negligible (50). More pertinent in view of this fact is that several workers have been able to show a protective effect of SOD in hyperoxia. McLennan & Autor (63) used a continuous delivery of intraperitoneal SOD in rats maintained in 95% O_2 for 72 hr and recorded a decreased death rate, from 42% dead in controls to 20% in SOD-treated rats. Postmortem examination of the lungs of those animals that died during the oxygen exposure showed evidence of hemorrhage and pleural effusions in both groups, with no obvious differences between controls and SOD-treated rats. Examination of the lungs of surviving rats did, however, show considerably less oxygen-induced damage, as evidenced by severe perivascular edema, alveolar wall thickening and alveolar infiltrate, hemorrhage, and hyaline membrane formation, in the SOD-treated rats. During discussion of uptake of exogenously administered SOD into cells, these authors made the point that "cells may develop a compromised permeability barrier when exposed to prolonged hyperoxia in situ." More recently SOD has been incorporated into liposomes (37, 75) in an attempt to introduce the enzyme intracellularly. Initially, aortic endothelial cells were used as a model, and cytotoxicity was assessed by the release of $^{51}Cr-$ or lactic dehydrogenase into the culture medium. SOD activity proved to be six- to twelvefold higher in treated cells, and these cells were more resistant to damage by oxygen. This work was extended to the intact rat (75) injected with liposomes containing SOD or catalase, or both; the survival times of these animals when maintained at 100% O_2 were recorded. Rats treated with liposomes containing SOD and catalase had a mean survival time of 118 hr compared to 69.5 hr in controls. However, there was no increase in survival time in rats treated with liposomes containing either SOD or catalase alone.

Perhaps the lack of protection by SOD administration in hyperbaric O_2 and the positive results found in much longer term exposures to normobaric O_2 may be due not only to the capacity to raise intracellular SOD but to an extracellular component of superoxide damage during normobaric hyperoxia. For example, during the several days of exposure to 95–100% O_2 the lung cell population changes, and macrophages, polymorphonuclear leucocytes, and other inflammatory cells enter the lung. These cells are capable of producing large quantities of superoxide, which appears to be membrane generated. Other highly reactive species, such as OCl^- and $^1O_2$, may be produced by the infiltrating inflammatory cells via their myeloperoxidase activity (80). The leucocytes are themselves damaged by oxidants and may then release lysosomal enzymes (33). Thus release of cytotoxic agents from macrophages and leucocytes may be responsible for exacerbating oxygen injury to the lung. Administration of SOD could affect lung tissue directly or indirectly by an effect on white blood cells. However, in a recent review (71) Small concluded that the experimental evidence was weak in support of an important role for inflammatory cells in the development of hyperoxic pulmonary toxicity.

Hydrogen Peroxide

IS HYDROGEN PEROXIDE INVOLVED IN TOLERANCE TO HYPEROXIA?   Hydrogen peroxide formed intracellularly may be broken down by glutathione peroxidase or catalase; we will first consider catalase induction in tolerance. The induction of catalase and its relation to oxygen poisoning are not as well documented as those of SOD or glutathione peroxidase. A recent study (25) showed that catalase activity was increased by 176% in the lungs of rats made tolerant to hyperoxia by previous exposure to 85% O_2. Stevens & Autor (72) found that catalase and SOD production were rapidly induced in lungs of neonate rats exposed to 95% O_2. Other workers (32) also found that lung catalase levels were increased by endotoxin pretreatment in rats, and that this procedure protected the rats against hyperoxia.

DOES ADMINISTRATION OF CATALASE CONFER PROTECTION AGAINST OXYGEN TOXICITY?   There is some evidence that catalase administration may have a protective effect in pulmonary oxygen toxicity. An increase in preconvulsive time in mice exposed to 3 or 6 ATA of O_2 was found in catalase-treated animals (48), and Turrens et al (75) recently obtained interesting results with catalase-containing liposomes. As described in the section on superoxide, liposomes containing both superoxide and catalase increased survival time in rats exposed to 100% O_2. Administration of catalase-containing liposomes did not affect survival time, but some interesting effects of catalase were seen. Regardless of whether catalase was actually incorporated in the liposome or was administered concurrently with empty liposomes, the degree of pleural effusion (fluid surrounding the lungs) was very markedly reduced and lung wet weight (intra-alveolar edema) was increased. This indicates that the combined effect of edema in the alveoli and surrounding the lung contributes to cessation of respiration, and that in the presence of liposomes (saturated fatty acid?) catalase changes the response of the lung to hyperoxia. This effect of catalase may result from the cells that infiltrate the lung during exposure to high concentrations of O_2 under normobaric conditions. However, until further studies and morphological examinations are performed under such conditions the accuracy of this hypothesis will remain unknown.

Lipid Peroxides

IS LIPID PEROXIDATION INVOLVED IN TOLERANCE TO O_2?   Lipid peroxidation has been implicated by several authors as the event most likely to be responsible for the increased permeability of and damage to the plasma membrane in oxygen toxicity (28, 46, 49, 64, 65, 71).

The interactions of some of the cellular antioxidant mechanisms involved in lipid peroxidation are discussed in detail elsewhere in this volume (see review by Pryor). Very briefly, glutathione peroxidase is able to convert lipid peroxides formed through free-radical attack on unsaturated lipid in the cell into nontoxic products (28, 31, 65). Reduced glutathione (GSH) provides the reducing equivalent for this reaction, and glutathione reductase transfers reducing equivalents from NADPH to regenerate GSH, and NADPH must in turn be regenerated by the pentose phosphate shunt. These components have been examined in various combinations in animals made tolerant to oxygen.

Tierney and coworkers (73) showed that rats exposed to 85% O_2 for 7 days doubled their lung glucose-6-phosphate dehydrogenase activity, which indicates increased activity of the pentose phosphate pathway. Such rats were protected against subsequent exposure to 99% oxygen. Several similar studies are consistent with the induction of peroxidase, glutathione reductase, and glucose-6-phosphate dehydrogenase in lungs of rats exposed to 85–90% oxygen for several days (25, 60). Stevens & Autor (72) also found rapid induction of glutathione peroxidase, along with SOD and catalase, in their study of tolerance in neonate rats. Thus there is ample evidence that enzymes involved in antioxidant defenses against lipid peroxidation are raised in animals made tolerant to hyperoxia.

Levels of reduced glutathione and total nonprotein sulfhydryl compounds were also elevated in rats exposed to sublethal amounts of oxygen (30).

DOES ADMINISTRATION OF SUBSTANCES INVOLVED IN DEFENSES AGAINST LIPID PEROXIDATION PROTECT AGAINST O_2 TOXICITY?   Alpha-tocopherol (Vitamin E), a natural antioxidant, diminishes the rate of lipid peroxidation in membranes (see review by Fridovich, this volume). While there is ample evidence that depletion of alpha-tocopherol potentiates the effects of hyperoxia (56, 58, 59, 65, 72), there is little to suggest that administration of α-tocopherol has a protective effect. However, Jerret et al (56) reported decreased H_2O_2 and lipid peroxidation and decreased convulsions in mice exposed to 5 ATA O_2 after administration of α-tocopherol. It is generally thought that the level of Vitamin E is optimal in animals fed a normal diet. Oxygen/iron-initiated chemiluminescence (an index of lipid peroxidation) of microsomal fractions shows the presence of a lag phase. When this lag phase is overcome, the intensity of chemiluminescence rises. A recent report showed that α-tocopherol present in the microsomal membranes may be responsible for the temporary protection against lipid peroxidation indicated by the presence of a lag phase. Moreover, microsomes from rats deficient in vitamin E showed no lag phase preceding the rise in chemiluminescence (19).

Treatment with substances that enhance GSH levels is effective in reducing normobaric or hyperbaric oxygen-induced lung toxicity. For example, pro-pylthiouracil, which raises pulmonary GSH levels, decreased pulmonary toxic-ity in rats maintained in 98% O_2 (79). Several sulfhydryl compounds, including GSH itself, have been shown to increase survival times in mice exposed to hyperbaric oxygen (40, 41, 53, 78); they may act by maintaining GSH levels in tissues. However, sulfhydryl agents may also act more directly as radical scavengers (80). It was recently shown that glutathione and other low–molecular weight thiols can exert a temporary protection against O_2/Fe-induced lipid peroxidation and chemiluminescence of microsomal fractions. This pro-tection was expressed as a prolongation of the lag phase that precedes the rise in chemiluminescent intensity. The protective effect of GSH may result from a direct free radical/thiol interaction or indirectly by participating in the recovery of vitamin E (4). Treatment with dexamethasone or levothyroxine lowered GSH levels in rat lungs, and these rats showed accelerated development of pulmonary oxygen toxicity (79). Decreased survival times in rats maintained in approximately 100% oxygen after treatment with diethylmaleate, which lowers GSSH in lungs, was recently reported (28a). Similarly, a diet deficient in Se, which is necessary for glutathione peroxidase function, enhanced pulmonary oxygen toxicity in rats (27).

The Hydroxyl Radical

We have considered the evidence for the enhanced formation of superoxide, hydrogen peroxide, and lipid peroxidation during hyperoxic toxicity. This evidence is largely indirect, but the evidence for increased OH· radical forma-tion, and its possible role, is even more circumstantial. In spite of the lack of direct measurement of OH· formation (spin trapping is probably the only method available), many investigators believe that OH· formation is the most critical event in the etiology of O_2 toxicity. Halliwell & Gutteridge (46) wrote an excellent discussion of the available sources of iron salts for this reaction. The overall conclusion was that superoxide and H_2O_2 are probably formed in excess in hyperoxia, react together in the presence of trace amounts of iron, and generate the OH· radical. The latter species is extremely reactive and, once formed, will react with molecules in the immediate surroundings. Superoxide and H_2O_2 are less reactive and can diffuse away from their site of formation, which can lead to OH· generation in different parts of the cell, wherever they encounter a transition metal ion. The principal reason for the popularity of the OH⁻ radical theory is that OH· is able to initiate lipid peroxidation by hydrogen abstraction. Once the process is begun, molecular O_2 reacts with the lipid radical, and the process continues in a chain reaction (see Fridovich, this volume). It now seems fairly certain that neither superoxide nor H_2O_2 alone are able to initiate lipid peroxidation (46).

Singlet O_2

The evidence supporting singlet O_2 as the initiating toxic O_2 species in hyperoxia is similar to that discussed for the hydroxyl radical. Singlet O_2 is able to initiate peroxidation of unsaturated fats, and singlet O_2-generating systems stimulate the peroxidation of fatty acids and membranes (46, 68).

A considerable portion of the low-level chemiluminescence observed in biological material can be attributed to singlet oxygen (16, 17). Measurement of chemiluminescence has been carried out in several intact organs, including the perfused lung (17), and an excellent correlation was found between chemiluminescence levels and oxidative stress induced by H_2O_2 or t-butylhydroperoxide. It has been speculated that the low levels of spontaneous light emission may be enhanced by hyperoxic stress (10), and recent investigations (18) have proved this to be true. For example, chemiluminescence from rat liver and brain increased considerably and quickly when rats were pressurized to approximately 6 ATA oxygen. Experiments showed that a rapid increase in the chemiluminescence of the rat cortex occurred when the animal was exposed to hyperbaric oxygen (E. Cadanes, personal communication) (Figure 2). However, it is unclear whether the chemiluminescence due to excited states precedes, or is a result of, lipid peroxidation. Singlet oxygen may form following superoxide and H_2O_2 generation, as described earlier, and initiate lipid peroxidation. Alternatively, as suggested by Boveris et al (8, 9), singlet oxygen may be generated as a result of lipid peroxidation. Certainly it appears that chemiluminescence correlates well with formation of lipid peroxides, and thus it should provide an elegant, noninvasive approach to further study of the role of excited states in hyperoxic toxicity.

Experiments in rats have shown that intrapulmonary installation of enzymes and substrates that generate oxygen metabolites produces severe lung damage (57). Lung damage was assessed by a permeability index, using infusion of

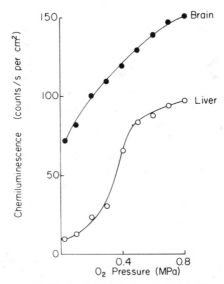

Figure 2   Chemiluminescence of exposed liver and brain under hyperbaric oxygen conditions. Chemiluminescence dependence on oxygen pressure.

[125]I-rat albumin. Administration of xanthine plus xanthine oxidase, which generates O_2^-, produced lung damage; this effect was largely inhibited by CO-administration of SOD. Glucose plus glucose oxidase, which generates H_2O_2, also increased lung permeability; this effect was inhibited by catalase. The lung injury was greatly increased when lactoperoxidase or myeloperoxidase was added to the glucose plus glucose oxidase. This finding strongly suggests that other more reactive species, such as HOCl and $^1O_2$, may be involved in oxidative lung damage (57).

ACKNOWLEDGMENT

This work has been supported in part by NIH Grants HL-31909 and HL-18708.

Literature Cited

1. Barja de Quiroga, G., Gutierrez, P. 1984. Superoxide dismutase during the development of two amphibian species and its role in hyperoxia tolerance. *Molecular Physiol.* 6:221–32
2. Barja de Quiroga, G., Gutierrez, P., Rojo, S., Alonso-Bedate, M. 1984. A comparative study of superoxide dismutase in amphibian tissues. *Comp. Biochem. Physiol.* 77B:589–93
3. Bartoli, G. M., Galeotti, T., Azzi, A. 1977. Production of superoxide anions

and hydrogen peroxide in Ehrlich ascites tumor cell nuclei. *Biochim. Biophys. Acta* 497:622–26
4. Bartoli, G. M., Muller, A., Cadenas, E., Sies, H. 1983. Antioxidant effect of diethyldithiocarbonate on microsomal lipid peroxidation assessed by low-level chemiluminescence and alkane production. *FEBS Lett.* 164:371–74
5. Bean, J. W. 1945. Effects of oxygen at increased pressure. *Physiol. Rev.* 25:1–47

6. Bernheim, F., Bernheim, M. L. C., Wilbur, K. M. 1948. The reaction between thiobarbituric acid and the oxidation products of certain lipids. *J. Biol. Chem.* 174:257–64

7. Block, E. 1977. Effect of superoxide dismutase and succinate on the development of hyperbaric oxygen toxicity. *Aviat. Space. Environ. Med.* 48:645–48

8. Boveris, A. 1977. Mitochondrial production of superoxide radical and hydrogen peroxide. *Adv. Exp. Med. Biol.* 78:67–82

9. Boveris, A., Cadenas, E., Chance, B. 1981. Ultraweak chemiluminescence: A sensitive assay for oxidative radical reactions. *Fed. Proc.* 40:195–98

10. Boveris, A., Cadenas, E., Reiter, R., Filipkowski, M., Nakase, Y., Chance, B. 1980. Organ chemiluminescence: Noninvasive assay for oxidative radical reactions. *Proc. Natl. Acad. Sci. USA* 77:347–51

11. Boveris, A., Cadenas, E., Stoppani, A. O. M. 1976. Role of ubiquinone in the mitochondrial generation of hydrogen peroxide. *Biochem. J.* 156:435–44

12. Boveris, A., Chance, B. 1973. The mitochondrial generation of hydrogen peroxide. General properties and effect of hyperbaric oxygen. *Biochem. J.* 134:707–16

13. Boveris, A., Oshino, N., Chance, B. 1972. The cellular production of hydrogen peroxide. *Biochem. J.* 128:617–30

14. Broussole, B., Burnet, H., Baret, A., Foliguet, B., Michel, P., Marchal, L. 1978. Adaptation to pulmonary chronic hyperoxia in rats: Demonstration by a study of pulmonary surfactant, tissue superoxide dismutase and histology, ed. Ph. H. Quanjer, J. G. Widdicombe. *Bull. Eur. Physiopathol. Respir.* 133p–35p

15. Burk, R. F. Jr., Nishiki, K., Lawrence, R. A., Chance, B. 1978. Peroxide removal by selenium-dependent and selenium-independent glutathione peroxidases in hemoglobin-free perfused rat liver. *J. Biol. Chem.* 253:43–46

16. Cadenas, E., Arad, I. D., Boveris, A., Fisher, A. B., Chance, B. 1980. Partial spectral analysis of the hydroperoxide-induced chemiluminescence of the perfused lung. *FEBS Lett.* 111:413–18

17. Cadenas, E., Boveris, A., Chance, B. 1980. Low-level chemiluminescence of bovine heart submitochondrial particles. *Biochem. J.* 186:659–67

18. Cadenas, E., Boveris, A., Chance, B. 1984. Low-level chemiluminescence of biological systems. In *Free Radicals in Biology*, VI:211–42, ed. W. A. Pryor. New York: Academic

19. Cadenas, E., Ginsberg, M., Rabe, U.,

Sies, H. 1983. Evaluation of alpha-tocotherol antioxidant activity against microsomal lipid peroxidation as detected by low-level chemiluminescence. *Biochem. J.* 223:755–59

20. Cadenas, E., Varsavsky, A. I., Boveris, A., Chance, B. 1981. Oxygen- and organic hydroperoxide-induced chemiluminescence of brain and liver homogenates. *Biochem. J.* 198:645–54

21. Chance, B., Jamieson, D., Coles, H. 1965. Energy-linked pyridine nucleotide reduction: Inhibitory effects of hyperbaric oxygen in vitro and in vivo. *Nature* 206:257–63

22. Chance, B., Jamieson, D., Williamson, J. R. 1966. Control of the oxidation-reduction state of reduced pyridine nucleotides in vivo and in vitro. In *Proc. 3rd Int. Conf. Hyperbaric Med.*, ed. I. W. Brown, B. G. Cox, pp. 15–41. Washington, DC: Natl. Acad. Sci.

23. Chance, B., Sies, H., Boveris, A. 1979. Hydroperoxide metabolism in mammalian organs. *Physiol. Rev.* 59:527–605

24. Clark, J. M., Lambertsen, C. J. 1971. Pulmonary oxygen toxicity: a review. *Pharmacol. Rev.* 23:37–133

25. Crapo, J. D., Sjostrom, K., Drew, R. T. 1978. Tolerance and cross-tolerance using NO$_2$ and O$_2$. 1. Toxicology and biochemistry. *J. Appl. Physiol.* 44:364–69

26. Crapo, J. D., Tierney, D. F. 1974. Superoxide dismutase and pulmonary oxygen toxicity. *Am. J. Physiol.* 226:1401–7

27. Cross, C. E., Hasegawa, G. 1977. Enhanced lung toxicity of O$_2$ in selenium-deficient rats. *Res. Commun. Chem. Pathol. Pharmacol.* 16:695–706

28. Deneke, S. M., Barry, L. F. 1980. Normobaric oxygen toxicity of the lung. *N. Engl. J. Med.* 303:76–86

28a. Deneke, S. M., Lynch, B. A., Sanberg, B. L. 1985. Transient depletion of lung glutathiomine by diethylmaleate enhances oxygen toxicity. *J. Appl. Physiol.* 85:571–74

29. Dionisi, O., Galeotti, T., Terranova, T., Azzi, A. 1975. Superoxide radicals and hydrogen peroxide formation in mitochondria from normal and neoplastic tissues. *Biochim. Biophys. Acta* 403:292–301

30. Forman, H. J., Fisher, A. B. 1981. Antioxidant defenses. In *Oxygen and Living Processes, An Interdisciplinary Approach*, Ch. 12, pp. 235–49, ed. D. L. Gilbert. New York: Springer-Verlag

31. Frank, L., Massaro, D. 1980. Oxygen Toxicity. *Am. J. Med.* 69:117–26

32. Frank, L., Summerville, J., Massaro, D.

718   JAMIESON ET AL

1980. Protection from oxygen toxicity with endotoxin. *J. Clin. Invest.* 65:1104–10
33. Frank, L., Yam, J., Roberts, R. J. 1978. The role of endotoxin in protection of adult rats from oxygen-induced lung toxicity. *J. Clin. Invest.* 61:269–75
34. Freeman, B. A., Crapo, J. D. 1981. Hyperoxia increases oxygen radical production in rat lungs and lung mitochondria. *J. Biol. Chem.* 256:10986–92
35. Freeman, B. A., Crapo, J. D. 1982. Biology of disease. Free radicals and tissue injury. *Lab. Invest.* 47:412–26
36. Freeman, B. A., Topolsky, M. K., Crapo, J. D. 1982. Hyperoxia increases oxygen radical production in rat lung homogenates. *Arch. Biochem. Biophys.* 216:477–84
37. Freeman, B. A., Young, S. L., Crapo, J. D. 1983. Liposome-mediated agumentation of superoxide dismutase in endothelial cells prevents oxygen injury. *J. Biol. Chem.* 258:12534–42
38. Fridovich, I. 1981. Superoxide radical and superoxide dismutases. See Ref. 30, Ch. 13, pp. 250–72
39. Gerasimov, A. M., Gusev, V. A., Brusov, O. S. 1977. Effect of exogenous superoxide dismutase and 1,4-diazobicyclo-[2,2.2] octane on the resistance of mice to acute oxygen poisoning. *Bull. Exp. Biol. Med.* 83:140–45
40. Gerschman, R., Gilbert, D. L., Caccamise, D. 1958. Effects of various substances on survival times of mice exposed to different high oxygen tensions. *Am. J. Physiol.* 192:563–71
41. Gerschman, R., Gilbert, D. L., Nye, S. W., Dwyer, P., Fenn, W. O. 1954. Oxygen poisoning and x-irradiation: A mechanism in common. *Science* 119:623–26
42. Gillette, J. R., Brodie, B. B., La Du, B. N. 1957. The oxidation of drugs by liver microsomes: on the role of TPNH and oxygen. *J. Pharmacol. Exp. Ther.* 119:532–43
43. Gregory, E. M., Fridovich, I. 1973. Induction of superoxide dismutase by molecular oxygen. *J. Bacteriol.* 114:543–48
44. Grossman, A., Wendel, A. 1984. Nonreactivity of the seleno-enzyme glutathione peroxidase with enzyme-generated hydroperoxide phospholipids. *Eur. J. Biochem.* 135:549–52
45. Halliwell, B. 1978. Biochemical mechanisms accounting for the toxic action of oxygen in living organisms: The key role of superoxide dismutase. *Cell. Biol. Int. Rep.* 2:113–28
46. Halliwell, B., Gutteridge, J. M. C. 1984.

Oxygen toxicity, oxygen radicals, transition metals and disease. *Biochem. J.* 219:1–14
47. Hempel, F. G. 1979. Oxygen tensions measured in cat cerebral cortex under hyperbaric conditions. *J. Appl. Physiol.* 46:53–60
48. Hilton, J. G., Brown, G. L., Proctor, P. H. 1980. Effects of superoxide dismutase and catalase on central nervous system toxicity of hyperbaric oxygen. *Toxicol. Appl. Pharmacol.* 53:50–53
49. Huber, G. L., Drath, D. B. 1981. Pulmonary oxygen toxicity. See Ref. 30, Ch. 14, pp. 273–342
50. Huber, W., Saifer, M. G. P. 1977. Orgotein, the drug version of bovine Cu-Zn superoxide dismutase. 1. A summary account of safety and pharmacology in laboratory animals. In *Superoxide and Superoxide Dismutases*, ed. A. M. Michelson, J. M. McCord, I. Fridovich, pp. 517–36. New York: Academic
51. Jamieson, D. 1966. Ionizing radiation and the intracellular oxidation-reduction state. *Nature* 209:361–65
52. Jamieson, D., Cass, N. 1967. CNS and pulmonary damage in anesthetized rats exposed to hyperbaric oxygen. *J. Appl. Physiol.* 23:235–42
53. Jamieson, D., van den Brenk, H. A. S. 1962. Pulmonary damage due to high pressure oxygen breathing in rats. 2. Changes in dehydrogenase activity or rat lung. *Aust. J. Exp. Biol. Med. Sci.* 40:51–56
54. Jamieson, D., van den Brenk, H. A. S. 1963. Measurement of oxygen tensions in cerebral tissues of rats exposed to high pressures of oxygen. *J. Appl. Physiol.* 18:869–76
55. Jamieson, D., van den Brenk, H. A. S. 1965. Electrode size and tissue pO_2 measurement in rats exposed to air or high pressure oxygen. *J. Appl. Physiol.* 20:514–18
56. Jarrett, S. A., Jefferson, D., Mengel, C. E. 1973. Seizures, H_2O_2 formation and lipid peroxides in brain during exposure to oxygen under high pressure. *Aerosp. Med.* 44:40–44
57. Johnson, K. J., Fantone, J. C., Kaplan, J., Ward, P. A. 1981. In vivo damage of rat lungs by oxygen metabolites. *J. Clin. Invest.* 67:983–93
58. Johnson, W. P., Jefferson, D., Mengel, C. E. 1972. In vivo formation of H_2O_2 in red cells during exposure to hyperoxia. *J. Clin. Invest.* 51:2211–13
59. Kann, N. E. Jr., Mengel, C. E., Smith, W., Horton, B. 1964. Oxygen toxicity and vitamin E. *Aerosp. Med.* 35:840–44
60. Kimball, R. E., Reddy, K., Pierce, T.

H., Schwartz, L. W., Mustafa, M. G., Cross, C. E. 1976. Oxygen toxicity: Augmentation of antioxidant defense mechanisms in rat lung. *Am. J. Physiol.* 230:1425–31

61. Loschen, G., Flohe, L., Chance, B. 1971. Respiratory chain linked H_2O_2 production in pigeon heart mitochondria. *FEBS Lett.* 18:261–64

62. McCord, J. M., Fridovich, I. 1969. Superoxide dismutase: An enzymic function for erythrocuprein (hemocuprein). *J. Biol. Chem.* 244:6049–55

63. McLennan, G., Autor, A. P. 1982. Effect of intraperitoneally administered superoxide dismutase on pulmonary damage resulting from hyperoxia. In *Pathology of Oxygen*, ed. A. P. Autor, Ch. 6, pp. 85–97. New York: Academic

64. Mustafa, M. G., Tierney, D. F. 1978. Biochemical and metabolic changes in the lung on oxygen, ozone and nitrogen dioxide toxicity. *Am. Rev. Respir. Dis.* 118:1061–90

65. Nishiki, K., Jamieson, D., Oshino, N., Chance, B. 1976. Oxygen toxicity in the perfused rat liver and lung under hyperbaric conditions. *Biochem. J.* 160: 343–55

66. Oshino, N., Chance, B. 1977. Properties of glutathione release observed during reduction of organic hydroperoxide, demethylation of aminopyrine and oxidation of some substances in perfused rat liver and their implications for the physiological function of catalase. *Biochem. J.* 162:509–25

67. Ottolenghi, A. 1959. Interaction of ascorbic acid and mitochondrial lipids. *Arch. Biochem. Biophys.* 79:355–63

68. Politzer, I. R., Griffin, G. W., Laseter, J. L. 1971. Singlet oxygen and biological systems. *Chem.-Biol. Interactions* 3:73–93

69. Rosen, G. M., Rauckman, E. J. 1981. Spin trapping of free radicals during hepatic microsomal lipid peroxidation. *Proc. Natl. Acad. Sci. USA* 78:7346–49

70. Sies, H., Gerstenecker, C., Menzel, H., Flohe, L. 1972. Oxidation in the NADP

system and the release of GSSG from hemoglobin-free perfused rat liver during peroxidatic oxidation of glutathione by hydroperoxides. *FEBS Lett.* 27:171–75

71. Small, A. 1984. New perspectives on hyperoxic pulmonary toxicity—a review. *Undersea Biomed. Res.* 11:1–23

72. Stevens, J. B., Autor, A. P. 1980. Proposed mechanism for neonatal rat tolerance to normobaric hyperoxia. *Fed. Proc.* 39:3138–43

73. Tierney, D. F., Ayers, L., Herzog, S., Yang, J. 1973. Pentose pathway and production of reduced nicotinamide adenine dinucleotide phosphate. *Am. Rev. Respir. Dis.* 108:1348–51

74. Turrens, J. F., Boveris, A. 1980. Generation of superoxide anion by the NADH dehydrogenase of bovine heart mitochondria. *Biochem. J.* 191:421–27

75. Turrens, J. F., Crapo, J. D., Freeman, B. A. 1984. Protection against oxygen toxicity by intravenous injection of liposome-entrapped catalase and superoxide dismutase. *J. Clin. Invest.* 73:87–95

76. Turrens, J. F., Freeman, B. A., Crapo, J. D. 1982. Hyperoxia increases in H_2O_2 release by lung mitochondria and microsomes. *Arch. Biochem. Biophys.* 217: 411–21

77. Turrens, J. F., Freeman, B. A., Levitt, J. G., Crapo, J. D. 1982. The effect of hyperoxia on superoxide production by lung submitochondrial particles. *Arch. Biochem. Biophys.* 217:401–10

78. van den Brenk, H. A. S., Jamieson, D. 1962. Studies of mechanisms of chemical radiation protection in vivo. II. Effect of high pressure oxygen on radioprotection in vivo and its relationship to "oxygen poisoning." *Int. J. Radiat. Biol.* 4:379–402

79. Yam, J., Roberts, R. J. 1979. Pharmacological alteration of oxygen-induced lung toxicity. *Toxicol. Appl. Pharmacol.* 47: 367–75

80. Youngman, R. J. 1984. Oxygen activation: Is the hydroxyl radical always biologically relevant? *TIBS* 9:280–83

Ann. Rev. Physiol. 1986. 48:721–31

MORPHOLOGIC CHANGES IN PULMONARY OXYGEN TOXICITY

James D. Crapo

Department of Medicine, Duke University, Durham, North Carolina 27710

INTRODUCTION

Exposure to high concentrations of oxygen has been demonstrated to cause alterations throughout the respiratory tract in humans and other animals. Changes occur in the airway epithelium, the arterial vascular bed, the alveolar septa, and in the pleural space. Atelectasis, interstitial and alveolar edema, pleural effusions, and changes in cell function and structure occur. The morphologic changes that occur in the lung in response to inhalation of high concentrations of oxygen were first described in 1897–1899 by J. Lorraine Smith (24, 25) who characterized the acute histologic features as including atelectasis, inflammation, and vascular congestion, with death due to consolidation of the lungs from congestion and exudation into the alveoli. This has subsequently been defined as the early or exudative phase of severe pulmonary oxygen toxicity. Multiple investigators have confirmed similar morphologic patterns in a wide variety of animal species (6), including primates (19) and man (14, 18, 22).

   Among the most dramatic effects are those involving the cells of the alveolar septum. Kistler et al (20) used electron microscopy to identify qualitatively and quantitatively many of the changes occurring in rat lungs. The earliest change was a twofold increase in the width of the interstitial space caused initially by edema. Subsequently the number of interstitial cells and interstitial matrix elements increased. The capillary endothelial cell was identified as one of the primary targets of oxygen-mediated cell injury; cytoplasmic changes in these endothelial cells were followed by fragmentation and cell destruction. These changes in the lung microvasculature are those most closely associated with events leading to death of animals given lethal doses of hyperoxia.

721

0066-4278/86/0315-0721$02.00

Investigators working with sublethal but toxic doses of oxygen have identified a second phase of morphologic response, which has been characterized as the proliferative phase (6, 19). It involves proliferation of epithelial (1, 7, 19), interstitial (7, 19), and endothelial (4, 22) cells within the alveolar septum. The recent application of morphometric techniques to the task of quantifying changes in cell structure and ultrastructure now permits a more precise definition of the stages and timing of the morphologic changes that occur in response to pulmonary oxygen toxicity, as outlined below.

STAGES IN THE PROGRESSION OF PULMONARY OXYGEN TOXICITY

The sequence of morphologic changes that occurs in the lungs in response to pulmonary oxygen toxicity is very similar in different animal species (6, 7, 18, 19). However, the duration and relative severity of each portion of the process shows species variability. Exposure to a lethal dose of hyperoxia (e.g. 100% O_2 at 1 ATA) is associated with an initiation phase of injury during which no significant evidence of morphologic injury is apparent. This is soon followed by an inflammatory phase and then by a destructive phase in which the extent of injury to lung parenchymal cells is sufficient to lead to the death of the animal. The response to exposure to sublethal doses of hyperoxia differs substantially in that the onset of each of the various phases of morphologic injury is delayed. A proliferative response significantly blunts the lung cell destructive reaction; this response may progress to a final fibrotic stage if the reaction is sufficient. Figure 1 illustrates the sequence of these events and the proportional change in

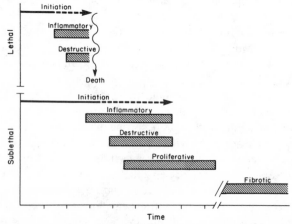

Figure 1   Relative time course of each phase of lung injury caused by lethal and sublethal exposure to hyperoxia. The metabolic events associated with initiation of the injury do not cause morphologic changes during the first phase. These metabolic events continue throughout most or all of the duration of exposure to hyperoxia.

the timing of each stage of lung morphologic responses to lethal and sublethal doses of hyperoxia.

Stages in Lethal Pulmonary Oxygen Toxicity

INITIATION PHASE   Since the production of oxygen free radicals occurs as a normal part of cell metabolism (12), some degree of free radical–mediated cell injury must occur under normal conditions. Thus the cell repair process must be effective enough to maintain homeostasis under such conditions. The initiation phase of pulmonary oxygen toxicity is characterized by an augmentation in the production rates of partially reduced species of oxygen; this increase eventually overwhelms the cell repair processes and thereby causes net cell injury.

During the first 24 to 72 hr after exposure to 100% oxygen, most animal species do not demonstrate significant morphologic changes in the alveolar septa. Biochemical studies demonstrate that the intracellular metabolism of oxygen is altered rapidly upon exposure to high partial pressures of oxygen (12). Total oxygen consumption by lung cells increases as a function of PO$_2$ (11, 13), and the fraction of oxygen metabolism that produces partially reduced oxygen species (superoxide, O$_2^-$; hydrogen peroxide, H$_2$O$_2$; and hydroxyl radical, OH·) increases. Enhanced rates of production of these partially reduced species of oxygen have been demonstrated in lung mitochondria (26, 27), lung microsomes (26), and nuclear membranes (30). As illustrated in Figure 2, these free radicals are associated with alterations in cell metabolism which initially

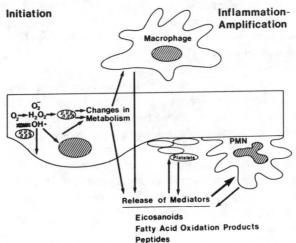

Figure 2   Early events in the pathogenesis of pulmonary oxygen toxicity. The initiation phase is associated with production of partially reduced species of oxygen and alteration of cell metabolic functions. The inflammatory phase amplifies endothelial cell injury by releasing mediators of the inflammation and attracting inflammatory cell elements into the lung microvasculature and interstitium.

are not manifested by changes in lung structure or ultrastructure. The initiation phase of lung cell injury begins at the initiation of the hyperoxic exposure (Figure 1). The toxic processes caused by free radical–mediated intracellular injury are likely to continue throughout the duration of the hyperoxic exposure.

INFLAMMATORY PHASE   The earliest morphologic changes seen in the lung in response to hyperoxic stress probably involve subtle changes in endothelial cell ultrastructure, which result in pericapillary accumulation of fluid (7, 17, 18). This stage of lung cell injury is associated with, or rapidly followed by, accumulation of inflammatory blood cell elements in the lung and the release of soluble mediators of inflammation (2). Direct injury to the capillary endothelium and/or other lung cells can lead to a release of inflammatory mediators and/or stimulation of alveolar macrophages to release similar classes of mediators (Figure 2). The timing of the major sequence of events in the inflammatory phase in rat lungs is illustrated in Figure 3a. After exposure to 100% oxygen for 48 hr, the volume of platelets retained in the pulmonary capillary bed almost doubles (2). This change in platelets in the pulmonary microvasculature precedes any influx of neutrophils into the lung microvasculature or interstitial and alveolar spaces. Following platelet accumulation, neutrophils are rapidly recruited to the lung. Neutrophils accumulate within the intravascular space, frequently adhering to the pulmonary capillary endothelial cells, and at the same time increase in number within the lung interstitium (2, 7). The appearance of neutrophils in the lung is associated with a rapid amplification of the extent of morphologic lung injury. The neutrophil probably initiates the final stage of lethal pulmonary oxygen toxicity by releasing further mediators of inflammation and, once activated, by producing toxic oxygen species via oxidases on their plasma membranes (9, 12). Depletion of neutrophils in animals has been shown to substantially decrease the toxic effects of exposure to hyperoxia (10). Neutrophils have been shown to be important mediators in a variety of experimentally induced forms of acute lung injury. Their role as a primary mediator of hyperoxic lung injury is controversial. Under some experimental conditions, depletion of neutrophils has been found to decrease the toxic effects of exposure to hyperoxia (10, 23a). However, other studies have shown that neutropenia induced in rabbits and lambs by administration of nitrogen mustard does not prevent development of lung microvascular injury and pulmonary edema caused by exposure to hyperoxia (22a). These observations suggest that the neutrophil may contribute to, but is not essential to, the development of pulmonary oxygen toxicity.

Since the inflammatory phase of hyperoxic-induced lung injury is associated with the earliest morphologic evidence of the onset of injury, attempts have been made to evaluate the severity of lung injury in response to a dose of oxygen by evaluating the recovery of neutrophils from lung lavage fluid. Studies have

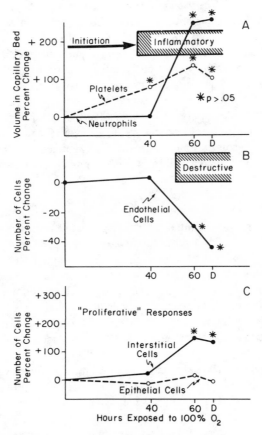

Figure 3 Major morphologic changes in the lungs of rats associated with each major phase of injury during exposure to a lethal level of hyperoxia. Panel *A* shows the changes in the total volume of platelets and neutrophils found in the alveolar capillary bed. Panels *B* and *C* correlate the timing of changes in the numbers of endothelial, interstitial, and epithelial cells.

demonstrated a correlation of the number of neutrophils obtained by lung lavage and the magnitude of injury (9, 10). The source of neutrophils found in lung lavage fluid from experimental animals exposed to hyperoxia is not clear. Crapo et al (7, 8) found increased numbers of alveolar macrophages during the progression of both lethal and sublethal doses of hyperoxia; however, neutrophils were rare on the alveolar surface, and significant increases in their number occurred only within the alveolar septa during exposure to hyperoxia (2). Bowden et al (5) found no change in free alveolar cells in mice exposed to 90% oxygen for 7 days, although increased numbers of leukocytes were found in alveolar lavage fluid. Pratt (22) evaluated the lungs of humans exposed to significant degrees of hyperoxia and found that leukocytes were absent from the alveolar space, except in the few individuals who had pneumonic consolidation or congestive failure. Thus, morphologic studies of pure pulmonary oxygen toxicity suggest that neutrophils accumulate in the pulmonary microvasculature and in the lung interstitium as part of the inflammatory response, but do not accumulate to a significant degree within the alveolar spaces. The recovery of neutrophils from broncho-alveolar lavage fluid from hyperoxic-exposed animals may be due to rapid movement of interstitial neutrophils across an injured alveolar epithelium in direct response to the alveolar lavage procedure, or it may be due to lavage of neutrophils from the airway epithelium, which has been described as having scattered infiltrates of neutrophils after injury by exposure to hyperoxia (3).

DESTRUCTIVE PHASE   Overt destruction of the pulmonary capillary endothelium begins shortly after the inflammatory stage. In rats approximately 50% of capillary endothelial cells are destroyed in the few hours preceding the death of the animal (Figure 3b). The total mass of endothelial cells and the total capillary surface area decrease in direct proportion to the loss of endothelial cells, which suggests that major portions of the pulmonary capillary bed are completely destroyed (7). The capillary endothelial cells that remain at the time of death show cell membrane injury, margination and clumping of nuclear chromatin, dilatation of perinuclear cisternae and cisternae of endoplasmic reticulum, intracellular edema, swelling, and frank necrosis (7, 20).

In rats exposed to 100% oxygen, 1 ATA, no significant reparative or proliferative morphologic response occurs. An apparent "proliferation" of interstitial cells occurs (Figure 3c); however, evaluation of the cell composition of the lung interstitium in these animals reveals no significant proliferation of fibroblasts (7). The interstitial cells whose numbers are increased are predominantly inflammatory cells, including polymorphonuclear leukocytes, macrophages, monocytes, and probably lymphocytes (Table 1).

At the time of death in rats exposed to a lethal dose of oxygen there is no significant change in the number of type I or type II epithelial cells. Some ultrastructural changes in these cells occur, including ruffling of the membranes of alveolar type I epithelial cells and blunting of the microvilli on alveolar type II epithelial cells (7). A significant epithelial cell proliferative response (1, 7) or frank epithelial cell destruction (7, 20) has not yet been documented.

In primates, including man, there appears to be proportionally more injury to the alveolar epithelium during the destructive phase of oxygen toxicity. Although *Macaca mulatta* monkeys can survive up to 13 days in 100% oxygen at 1 ATA, most die during this time (19). Kapanci et al (19) found that the alveolar type I epithelium was almost completely destroyed after 4 days in 100% oxygen. Hyperplasia of type II epithelial cells led to almost total replace-

Table 1 Number of interstitial cells in relation to level of oxygen exposure[a]

| | Number of Cells ($\times$ 10^6) | | |
| | Exposure Level | | |
Interstitial cell type	Control (21% O_2)	Lethal (100% O_2 $\times$ 60 hr)	Sublethal (85% O_2 $\times$ 7 days)
Fibroblasts	~165	~208	~479
Monocytes	0	~6	~129
Plasma Cells	~5	~2	~18
Macrophages	~5	~6	~18
Polymorphonuclear leukocytes	0	~67	~9
Pericytes	~5	~24	~4
Indeterminant[b]	~67	~300	~258
Total	247 ± 20	612 ± 64	922 ± 116

[a] This distribution of cells is approximate since it is based on the distribution of random nuclear profiles for each of the various cells. The mean size of cell nuclei can affect the results; however, this parameter shows relatively little variation between most classes of cells. (Data from Reference 7)

[b] Indeterminant cells are usually small round cells with no distinguishing organelles. They are probably a mixture of lymphocytes, immature macrophages or monocytes, and fibroblasts.

ment of the alveolar epithelial lining with type II cells by the seventh day of exposure. In these monkeys subtle endothelial cell injury began after 2 days of exposure to hyperoxia and progressed by the seventh day of exposure to a 50% loss of capillary endothelial cell volume (19). This loss is similar to that of endothelial cells in rats (Figure 3b), but occurs later. Humans exposed to hyperoxia demonstrate similar general patterns of acute injury to the alveolar epithelium (14) and to the capillary endothelium (18).

Stages in Sublethal Pulmonary Oxygen Toxicity

INITIATION PHASE   As with lethal doses of hyperoxia, lower levels of exposure are associated with an early period in which no morphologic injury occurs. The length of the initiation phase of injury varies inversely with the dose of oxygen. The dose/response curve is steep: In rats a drop in the level of hyperoxic exposure from 100% to 85% oxygen at 1 ATA prolongs the initiation phase such that only early evidence of the beginning of the inflammatory phase can be seen at 72 hr (2, 7), whereas almost all the rats exposed to 100% oxygen for that period will have died (Figure 1). Exposure to 60% oxygen for up to 7 days results in almost no detectable morphological lung injury in otherwise normal animals (17). Biochemical and physiologic evidence of early lung injury after exposure to 60% oxygen can be found (6, 17), which suggests that the metabolic changes associated with the initiation of hyperoxic lung injury are present. In addition, an interstitial fibrotic response has been identified in primates 8 weeks after a 2 week exposure to 60% oxygen (16). Thus, although the initiation phase is not associated with substantial overt morphologic changes, significant biochemical and functional alterations involving the lung may occur, and long-term effects on lung structure may be initiated.

INFLAMMATORY PHASE   Rats exposed to 85% oxygen show an increase in platelets in the lung microvasculature after 72 hr (Figure 4a). This is the first evidence of accumulation of inflammatory, blood-borne elements in the lung (2). Neutrophils are transiently found in increased numbers in the lung microvasculature after about 5 days of exposure (Figure 4a). The number of neutrophils found in the lung interstitium parallels the changes in the lung microvasculature with a transient increase in interstitial neutrophils occurring on the fifth day of exposure to 85% oxygen (2). By the seventh day of exposure the number of neutrophils in the lung interstitium falls to almost negligible levels (Table 1). Exposure to sublethal doses of oxygen not only delays the onset of the inflammatory stage relative to that induced by a lethal dose, but substantially

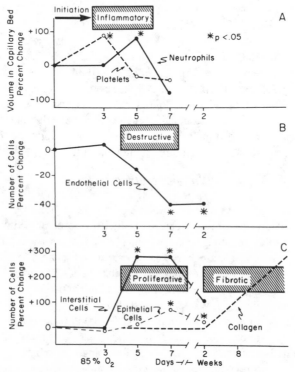

Figure 4   Major morphologic changes in the lung associated with each major phase of injury during exposure to a sublethal level of hyperoxia.

blunts the magnitude and duration of the inflammatory response as indicated by the numbers of inflammatory cells found in various compartments of the alveolar septum (2, 7).

DESTRUCTIVE PHASE   Sublethal exposure to oxygen, associated with a sufficient inflammatory response, results in the onset of a destructive phase, which can be identified by the loss of capillary endothelial cells in the lung microvasculature (4, 7, 8). Under such conditions the rate of destruction of capillary endothelium is substantially slower than that resulting from exposure to 100% oxygen. In rats exposed to 85% oxygen, 40–50% of the endothelial cells are destroyed by the seventh day, but further net destruction does not occur (7), and the remaining endothelial cells show hypertrophy of subcellular organelles and cytoplasmic components (8). In rats allowed to recover in air the capillary endothelium gradually returns toward relatively normal ultrastructure, although the size of the alveolar capillary bed may be substantially reduced (7).

PROLIFERATIVE PHASE   Under conditions of sublethal exposure to oxygen, a proliferative response that involves all major compartments in the alveolar septum begins near the time of the onset of destruction of the pulmonary capillary endothelium (7). The cell proliferative response blunts the destructive phase and is probably responsible for survival of the animals. Exposure of rats to 85% oxygen is associated with an almost fourfold increase in the number of interstitial cells. This is predominantly a fibroblast and monocyte response (Table 1). The relative absence of polymorphonuclear leukocytes and a high concentration of monocytes in the lung interstitium are important characteristics in differentiating the morphologic changes associated with sublethal and lethal pulmonary oxygen toxicity. The specific role of the monocyte response and mechanism for its augmentation are not well defined.

An epithelial cell response occurs, which is predominantly characterized by an increase in the number of type II epithelial cells (7, 8). Evidence of type I cell injury is suggested by the fact that the average size of type I cells decreases after 7 or 14 days in 85% oxygen (7). This finding suggests that the later cell population is younger and more recently differentiated. Type II cells subject to these conditions become larger in mean size and their ultrastructure is substantially altered. These alterations include changes in the number and size of mitochondria as well as in the mitochondrial structure, which can take on bizarre shapes (7, 21, 23). The number and size of lamellar bodies in the average type II cell were unchanged after exposure to 85% oxygen for 7 days, but because of type II cell hyperplasia the total amount of lamellar bodies per lung more than doubled (29).

FIBROTIC PHASE   Long-term exposures to hyperoxia and/or acute, intense exposures to hyperoxia followed by recovery periods in air have been shown by a variety of investigators to be associated with a fibrotic reaction that involves the lung interstitium. Increased levels of hydroxyproline following such exposure have been documented by biochemical analysis (28). Ultrastructural studies have demonstrated that long-term or acute hyperoxia increases deposition of collagen in the lung interstitium (3), increases the thickness of the alveolar interstitial space (3, 7, 18), and increases the number of interstitial cells (7, 15, 18). Enlargement of airspaces and destruction of large segments of the alveolar septal wall may be part of this chronic reaction (3, 15). Although this is termed an emphysematous response by some investigators, the presence of substantial fibrosis separates it from the lung morphology usually identified as emphysema. The timing of the events leading to the fibrotic response and the extent and physiologic impact of this response have not yet been adequately defined.

Literature Cited

1. Adamson, I. Y. R., Bowden, D. H. 1974. The type 2 cell as progenitor of alveolar epithelial regeneration: A cytodynamic study in mice after exposure to oxygen. *Lab. Invest.* 30:35–42
2. Barry, B. E., Crapo, J. D. 1985. Patterns of accumulation of platelets and neutrophils in rat lungs during exposure to 100% and 85% oxygen. *Am. Rev. Respir. Dis.* In press
3. Bonikos, D. S., Bensch, K. G., Northway, W. H. 1976. Oxygen toxicity in the newborn. *Am. J. Pathol.* 85:623–50
4. Bowden, D. H., Adamson, I. Y. R. 1974. Endothelial regeneration as a marker of the differential vascular responses in oxygen-induced pulmonary edema. *Lab. Invest.* 30:350–57
5. Bowden, D. H., Adamson, I. Y. R., Wyatt, J. P. 1968. Reaction of the lung cells to a high concentration of oxygen. *Arch. Pathol.* 86:671–75
6. Clark, J. M., Lambertsen, C. J. 1971. Pulmonary oxygen toxicity: A review. *Pharmacol. Rev.* 23:37–133
7. Crapo, J. D., Barry, B. E., Foscue, H. A., Shelburne, J. 1980. Structural and biochemical changes in rat lungs occurring during exposures to lethal and adaptive doses of oxygen. *Am. Rev. Respir. Dis.* 122:123–43
8. Crapo, J. D., Peters-Golden, M., Marsh-Salin, J., Shelburne, J. S. 1978. Pathologic changes in the lungs of oxygen-adapted rats. *Lab. Invest.* 39:640–53
9. Fox, R. B., Hoidal, J. R., Brown, D. M., Repine, J. E. 1981. Pulmonary inflammation due to oxygen toxicity: Involvement of chemotactic factors and polymorphonuclear leukocytes. *Am. Rev. Respir. Dis.* 123:521–23
10. Fox, R. B., Shasby, M., Harada, R. N., Repine, J. E. 1981. A novel mechanism for pulmonary oxygen toxicity: Phagocyte mediated lung injury. *Chest* 80:3S–4S
11. Freeman, B. A., Crapo, J. D. 1981. Hyperoxia increases oxygen radical production in rat lungs and lung mitochondria. *J. Biol. Chem.* 256:10986–92
12. Freeman, B. A., Crapo, J. D. 1982. Biology of disease: Free radicals and tissue injury. *Lab. Invest.* 47:412–26
13. Freeman, B. A., Topolosky, M. K., Crapo, J. D. 1982. Hyperoxia increases oxygen radical production in rat lung homogenates. *Arch. Biochem. Biophys.* 216:477–84
14. Gould, V. E., Tosco, R., Wheelis, R. G., Gould, N. S., Kapanci, Y. 1972. Oxygen pneumonitis in man: Ultrastructural observations on the development of alveolar lesions. *Lab. Invest.* 26:499–508
15. Harrison, G. A. 1971. Ultrastructural changes in rat lung during long-term exposure to oxygen. *Exp. Med. Surg.* 29:96–107
16. Hayatdavoudi, G., Crapo, J. D., Wolfe, W., Pratt, P. C., Hutchinson, L. 1979.

Lung injury in baboons exposed to 60% oxygen. *Clin. Res.* 27:493A

17. Hayatdavoudi, G., O'Neil, J. J., Barry, B. E., Freeman, B. A., Crapo, J. D. 1981. Pulmonary injury in rats following continuous exposure to 60% O₂ for 7 days. *J. Appl. Physiol: Respir. Environ. Exercise Physiol.* 51:1220–31

18. Kapanci, Y., Tosco, R., Eggermann, J., Gould, V. E. 1972. Oxygen pneumonitis in man: Light- and electron-microscopic morphometric studies. *Chest* 62:162–69

19. Kapanci, Y., Weibel, E. R., Kaplan, H. P., Robinson, F. R. 1969. Pathogenesis and reversibility of the pulmonary lesions of oxygen toxicity in monkeys. II. Ultrastructural and morphometric studies. *Lab. Invest.* 20:101–17

20. Kistler, G. S., Caldwell, P. R. B., Weibel, E. R. 1967. Development of fine structural damage to alveolar and capillary lining cells in oxygen-poisoned rat lungs. *J. Cell Biol.* 32:605–28

21. Massaro, G. D., Massaro, D. 1973. Pulmonary granular pneumocytes: Loss of mitochondrial granules during hyperoxia. *J. Cell Biol.* 59:246–49

22. Pratt, P. C. 1958. Pulmonary capillary proliferation induced by oxygen inhalation. *Am. J. Pathol.* 34:1033–49

22a. Raj, J. U., Hazinski, T. A., Bland, R. D. 1985. Oxygen-induced lung microvascular injury in neutropenic rabbits and lambs. *J. Appl. Physiol.* 58:921–27

23. Rosenbaum, R. M., Whittner, M., Lenger, M. 1969. Mitochondrial and other ultrastructural changes in great alveolar cells of oxygen-adapted and poisoned rats. *Lab. Invest.* 20:516–28

23a. Shasby, D. M., Fox, R. B., Harada, R. N., Repine, J. E. 1982. Reduction of the edema of acute hyperoxic lung injury by granulocyte depletion. *J. Appl. Physiol.* 52:1237–44

24. Smith, J. L. 1897. The influence of pathological conditions on active absorption of oxygen by the lungs. *J. Physiol.* 22:307–8

25. Smith, J. L. 1899. The pathological effects due to increase of oxygen tension in the air breathed. *J. Physiol.* 24:19–35

26. Turrens, J. F., Freeman, B. A., Crapo, J. D. 1982. Hyperoxia increases H₂O₂ release by lung mitochondria and microsomes. *Arch. Biochem. Biophys.* 217:411–21

27. Turrens, J. F., Freeman, B. A., Levitt, J. G., Crapo, J. D. 1982. The effect of hyperoxia on superoxide production by lung submitochondrial particles. *Arch. Biochem. Biophys.* 217:401–10

28. Valimaki, M., Juva, K., Rantanen, J., Ekfors, T., Niinikoski, J. 1975. Collagen metabolism in rat lungs during chronic intermittent exposure to oxygen. *Aviat. Space Environ. Med.* 46:684–90

29. Young, S. L., Crapo, J. D., Kremers, S. A., Brumley, G. W. 1982. Pulmonary surfactant lipid production in oxygen-exposed rat lungs. *Lab. Invest.* 46:570–76

30. Yusa, T., Crapo, J. D., Freeman, B. A. 1984. Hyperoxia enhances lung and liver nuclear superoxide generation. *Biochim. Biophys. Acta* 798:167–74

SUBJECT INDEX

733

damage
  and free radical toxicity in
    lung, 689
degeneration of
  and free radical biology,
    664
double helices
  modeling neuroendocrine
    peptide genes, 431
  and irreversible injury follow-
    ing ischemia, 38
  recombinant
    and neuroendocrine peptide
      genes, 431
  synthesis
    growth factors and pH, 372
    and intracellular pH regula-
      tion, 363-72
DOPA-decarboxylase activity
  and receptors regulating acid
    secretion, 90
Dopamine
  in brain capillaries, 245
  in central control of tempera-
    ture, 618
  and endothelial biogenic
    amines, 336
  and somatostatin in anterior
    pituitary function, 554
  synthesis
    and neural grafting, 456
Dopamine agonists
  hypothermic response
    and neurotensin, 616
Dopamine-B-hydroxylase
  and osmotic forces in ex-
    ocytosis, 176
Dorsal horn neurons (DHNs)
  and temperature regulation,
    596-97
Down regulation
  and the gonadotropin releasing
    hormone (GnRH), 510
Drug receptors
  endogenous neurotransmitter
    ligands for, 461
Dynorphin
  and neuronal receptors, 463

E

Ectotherms
  thermoreceptors in, 641
Edema formation
  and free radical production,
    703
EDTA
  decomposing hydrogen per-
    oxides, 663
  and receptors regulating acid
    secretion, 90
Effector coupling

and gonadotropin releasing
    hormone, 500-2
Effector mechanisms
  and secretory exocytosis, 230-
    34
Efrapeptin
  and organelle acidification,
    406
Eicosanoid biochemistry
  in endothelium, 251
Electrical regulation
  of sperm-egg fusion, 191-98
Electrogenic pump
  and the K:Na permeability
    ratio, 649
Electrolyte transport
  intestinal
    and calcium uptake, 135
  regulation of
    by intracellular mediators,
      138
Electrophiles
  and antioxidant defenses in the
    lung, 696
Electrophysiology
  of thermosensitive neurons,
    642-45
Electrostatic sorting
  and endothelial cell surface,
    287
Embryogenesis
  and cell adhesion molecules,
    420
Endocrine function
  GnRH receptor in, 498-99
Endocrine pathway
  and regulation of acid secre-
    tion, 89
Endocytic organelles
  lipoprotein-filled
    isolation and characteriza-
      tion of, 126
Endocytosis
  and organelle acidification,
    404
  receptor-mediated, 409
Endogenous lectins
  and the endothelial cell sur-
    face, 282
Endogenous opioid peptides
  and hypothalamo-pituitary
    function
    anterior pituitary hormones,
      528-30
    opioid peptides, 527-28
    posterior pituitary, 531-32
Endoneurial O$_2$ consumption
  and inositol transferase, 63
Endoperoxides-hydroperoxides
  and bactericidal oxidant pro-
    duction, 675
ß-Endorphin
  and substance P, 541

and temperature control,
    616
Endosomes
  and organelle acidification,
    404
Endothelial cells
  activation
    and phagocytosis, 272
  chemical mapping, 280-85
    in studies of subtle injuries,
      271
  location of PGH synthase in,
    256
  metabolism of biogenic
    amines
    metabolism, 338-41
    receptor mediation, 340-
      41
  relationship between
    astrocytes, 243-45
  surface antithrombogenicity,
    289
    see also Vascular pros-
      taglandin metabolism
  surface- and membrane-
    associated activities, 287-
    90
  surface-associated plasma pro-
    teins, 286
  surface charge-differentiated
    microdomains, 285-86
Endothelial denudation
  in arterial cell interactions,
    296-97
Endothelial transport
  see Capillary endothelial trans-
    port
Endothelial-derived growth factor (EDGF)
  and arterial cell interactions,
    299
Endothelium
  brain capillary
    epithelial properties of, 242-
      43
  see also Endothelial cells
Endotoxin
  and activities of pulmonary
    endothelium, 265
Energy resonance transfer
  modeling membrane fusion,
    203
Enkephalins
  analogues
    and opiod peptides, 530
  and homology with GHRH,
    572
  thermoregulatory actions of,
    617
Enzyme secretion
  and salivary activation mech-
    anisms, 85
Enzymes

CUMULATIVE INDEXES

CONTRIBUTING AUTHORS, VOLUMES 44–48

CHAPTER TITLES, VOLUMES 44-48

Annual Reviews Inc. ORDER FORM

A NONPROFIT SCIENTIFIC PUBLISHER

4139 El Camino Way, Palo Alto, CA 94306-9981, USA • (415) 493-4400

Annual Reviews Inc. publications are available directly from our office by mail or telephone (paid by credit card or purchase order), through booksellers and subscription agents, worldwide, and through participating professional societies. Prices subject to change without notice.

- **Individuals:** Prepayment required on new accounts by check or money order (in U.S. dollars, check drawn on U.S. bank) or charge to credit card — American Express, VISA, MasterCard.
- **Institutional buyers:** Please include purchase order number.
- **Students:** $10.00 discount from retail price, per volume. Prepayment required. Proof of student status must be provided (photocopy of student I.D. or signature of department secretary is acceptable). Students must send orders direct to Annual Reviews. Orders received through bookstores and institutions requesting student rates will be returned.
- **Professional Society Members:** Members of professional societies that have a contractual arrangement with Annual Reviews may order books through their society at a reduced rate. Check with your society for information.

Regular orders: Please list the volumes you wish to order by volume number.
Standing orders: New volume in the series will be sent to you automatically each year upon publication. Cancellation may be made at any time. Please indicate volume number to begin standing order.
Prepublication orders: Volumes not yet published will be shipped in month and year indicated.
California orders: Add applicable sales tax.
Postage paid (4th class bookrate/surface mail) **by Annual Reviews Inc.** Airmail postage extra.

ANNUAL REVIEWS SERIES		Prices Postpaid per volume USA/elsewhere	Regular Order Please send:	Standing Order Begin with:
			Vol. number	Vol. number
Annual Review of ANTHROPOLOGY (Prices of Volumes in brackets effective until 12/31/85)				
[Vols. 1-10	(1972-1981)	$20.00/$21.00]		
[Vol. 11	(1982)	$22.00/$25.00]		
[Vols. 12-14	(1983-1985)	$27.00/$30.00]		
Vols. 1-14	(1972-1985)	$27.00/$30.00		
Vol. 15	(avail. Oct. 1986)	$31.00/$34.00	Vol(s). _____	Vol. _____
Annual Review of ASTRONOMY AND ASTROPHYSICS (Prices of Volumes in brackets effective until 12/31/85)				
[Vols. 1-2, 4-19	(1963-1964; 1966-1981)	$20.00/$21.00]		
[Vol. 20	(1982)	$22.00/$25.00]		
[Vols. 21-23	(1983-1985)	$44.00/$47.00]		
Vols. 1-2, 4-20	(1963-1964; 1966-1982)	$27.00/$30.00		
Vols. 21-23	(1983-1985)	$44.00/$47.00		
Vol. 24	(avail. Sept. 1986)	$44.00/$47.00	Vol(s). _____	Vol. _____
Annual Review of BIOCHEMISTRY (Prices of Volumes in brackets effective until 12/31/85)				
[Vols. 30-34, 36-50	(1961-1965; 1967-1981)	$21.00/$22.00]		
[Vol. 51	(1982)	$23.00/$26.00]		
[Vols. 52-54	(1983-1985)	$29.00/$32.00]		
Vols. 30-34, 36-54	(1961-1965; 1967-1985)	$29.00/$32.00		
Vol. 55	(avail. July 1986)	$33.00/$36.00	Vol(s). _____	Vol. _____
Annual Review of BIOPHYSICS AND BIOPHYSICAL CHEMISTRY (Prices of Vols. in brackets effective until 12/31/85) *(Formerly Annual Review of Biophysics and Bioengineering)*				
[Vols. 1-10	(1972-1981)	$20.00/$21.00]		
[Vol. 11	(1982)	$22.00/$25.00]		
[Vols. 12-14	(1983-1985)	$47.00/$50.00]		
Vols. 1-11	(1972-1982)	$27.00/$30.00		
Vols. 12-14	(1983-1985)	$47.00/$50.00		
Vol. 15	(avail. June 1986)	$47.00/$50.00	Vol(s). _____	Vol. _____
Annual Review of CELL BIOLOGY				
Vol. 1	(1985)	$27.00/$30.00		
Vol. 2	(avail. Nov. 1986)	$31.00/$34.00	Vol(s). _____	Vol. _____
Annual Review of COMPUTER SCIENCE				
Vol. 1	(avail. late 1986)	**Price not yet established**	Vol. _____	Vol. _____
Annual Review of EARTH AND PLANETARY SCIENCES (Prices of Volumes in brackets effective until 12/31/85)				
[Vols. 1-9	(1973-1981)	$20.00/$21.00]		
[Vol. 10	(1982)	$22.00/$25.00]		
[Vols. 11-13	(1983-1985)	$44.00/$47.00]		
Vols. 1-10	(1973-1982)	$27.00/$30.00		
Vols. 11-13	(1983-1985)	$44.00/$47.00		
Vol. 14	(avail. May 1986)	$44.00/$47.00	Vol(s). _____	Vol. _____

ANNUAL REVIEWS SERIES	Prices Postpaid per volume USA/elsewhere	Regular Order Please send:	Standing Order Begin with:

Annual Review of **ECOLOGY AND SYSTEMATICS** (Prices of Volumes in brackets effective until 12/31/85)

[Vols. 1-12	(1970-1981) . . . . $20.00/$21.00]		
[Vol. 13	(1982) . . . . $22.00/$25.00]		
[Vols. 14-16	(1983-1985) . . . . $27.00/$30.00]		
Vols. 1-16	(1970-1985) . . . . $27.00/$30.00		
Vol. 17	(avail. Nov. 1986) . . . . $31.00/$34.00	Vol(s). _____	Vol. _____

Annual Review of **ENERGY** (Prices of Volumes in brackets effective until 12/31/85)

[Vols. 1-6	(1976-1981) . . . . $20.00/$21.00]		
[Vol. 7	(1982) . . . . $22.00/$25.00]		
[Vols. 8-10	(1983-1985) . . . . $56.00/$59.00]		
Vols. 1-7	(1976-1982) . . . . $27.00/$30.00		
Vols. 8-10	(1983-1985) . . . . $56.00/$59.00		
Vol. 11	(avail. Oct. 1986) . . . . $56.00/$59.00	Vol(s). _____	Vol. _____

Annual Review of **ENTOMOLOGY** (Prices of Volumes in brackets effective until 12/31/85)

[Vols. 9-16, 18-26	(1964-1971; 1973-1981) . . . . $20.00/$21.00]		
[Vol. 27	(1982) . . . . $22.00/$25.00]		
[Vols. 28-30	(1983-1985) . . . . $27.00/$30.00]		
Vols. 9-16, 18-30	(1964-1971; 1973-1985) . . . . $27.00/$30.00		
Vol. 31	(avail. Jan. 1986) . . . . $31.00/$34.00	Vol(s). _____	Vol. _____

Annual Review of **FLUID MECHANICS** (Prices of Volumes in brackets effective until 12/31/85)

[Vols. 1-5, 7-13	(1969-1973; 1975-1981) . . . . $20.00/$21.00]		
[Vol. 14	(1982) . . . . $22.00/$25.00]		
[Vols. 15-17	(1983-1985) . . . . $28.00/$31.00]		
Vols. 1-5, 7-17	(1969-1973; 1975-1985) . . . . $28.00/$31.00		
Vol. 18	(avail. Jan. 1986) . . . . $32.00/$35.00	Vol(s). _____	Vol. _____

Annual Review of **GENETICS** (Prices of Volumes in brackets effective until 12/31/85)

[Vols. 1-15	(1967-1981) . . . . $20.00/$21.00]		
[Vol. 16	(1982) . . . . $22.00/$25.00]		
[Vols. 17-19	(1983-1985) . . . . $27.00/$30.00]		
Vols. 1-19	(1967-1985) . . . . $27.00/$30.00		
Vol. 20	(avail. Dec. 1986) . . . . $31.00/$34.00	Vol(s). _____	Vol. _____

Annual Review of **IMMUNOLOGY**

Vols. 1-3	(1983-1985) . . . . $27.00/$30.00		
Vol. 4	(avail. April 1986) . . . . $31.00/$34.00	Vol(s). _____	Vol. _____

Annual Review of **MATERIALS SCIENCE** (Prices of Volumes in brackets effective until 12/31/85)

[Vols. 1-11	(1971-1981) . . . . $20.00/$21.00]		
[Vol. 12	(1982) . . . . $22.00/$25.00]		
[Vols. 13-15	(1983-1985) . . . . $64.00/$67.00]		
Vols. 1-12	(1971-1982) . . . . $27.00/$30.00		
Vols. 13-15	(1983-1985) . . . . $64.00/$67.00		
Vol. 16	(avail. August 1986) . . . . $64.00/$67.00	Vol(s). _____	Vol. _____

Annual Review of **MEDICINE** (Prices of Volumes in brackets effective until 12/31/85)

[Vols. 1-3, 5-15, 17-32	(1950-52; 1954-64; 1966-81) . . . . . $20.00/$21.00]		
[Vol. 33	(1982) . . . . $22.00/$25.00]		
[Vols. 34-36	(1983-1985) . . . . $27.00/$30.00]		
Vols. 1-3, 5-15, 17-36	(1950-52; 1954-64; 1966-85) . . . . . $27.00/$30.00		
Vol. 37	(avail. April 1986) . . . . $31.00/$34.00	Vol(s). _____	Vol. _____

Annual Review of **MICROBIOLOGY** (Prices of Volumes in brackets effective until 12/31/85)

[Vols. 18-35	(1964-1981) . . . . $20.00/$21.00]		
[Vol. 36	(1982) . . . . $22.00/$25.00]		
[Vols. 37-39	(1983-1985) . . . . $27.00/$30.00]		
Vols. 18-39	(1964-1985) . . . . $27.00/$30.00		
Vol. 40	(avail. Oct. 1986) . . . . $31.00/$34.00	Vol(s). _____	Vol. _____

Annual Review of **NEUROSCIENCE** (Prices of Volumes in brackets effective until 12/31/85)

[Vols. 1-4	(1978-1981) . . . . $20.00/$21.00]		
[Vol. 5	(1982) . . . . $22.00/$25.00]		
[Vols. 6-8	(1983-1985) . . . . $27.00/$30.00]		
Vols. 1-8	(1978-1985) . . . . $27.00/$30.00		
Vol. 9	(avail. March 1986) . . . . $31.00/$34.00	Vol(s). _____	Vol. _____